Instructor's Solutions Manual
for Swokowski and Cole's
PRECALCULUS
Functions and Graphs

Eighth Edition

JEFFERY A. COLE
Anoka-Ramsey Community College

Brooks/Cole Publishing Company

I(T)P® *An International Thomson Publishing Company*

Pacific Grove • Albany • Belmont • Bonn • Boston • Cincinnati • Detroit
Johannesburg • London • Madrid • Melbourne • Mexico City • New York
Paris • Singapore • Tokyo • Toronto • Washington

For more information, contact:

BROOKS/COLE PUBLISHING COMPANY
511 Forest Lodge Road
Pacific Grove, CA 93950
USA

International Thomson Editores
Seneca 53
Col. Polanco
11560 México, D. F., México

International Thomson Publishing Europe
Berkshire House 168-173
High Holborn
London WC1V 7AA
England

International Thomson Publishing GmbH
Königswinterer Strasse 418
53227 Bonn
Germany

Thomas Nelson Australia
102 Dodds Street
South Melbourne, 3205
Victoria, Australia

International Thomson Publishing Asia
221 Henderson Road
#05-10 Henderson Building
Singapore 0315

Nelson Canada
1120 Birchmount Road
Scarborough, Ontario
Canada M1K 5G4

International Thomson Publishing Japan
Hirakawacho Kyowa Building, 3F
2-2-1 Hirakawacho
Chiyoda-ku, Tokyo 102
Japan

Printed in the United States of America

5   4   3   2   1

ISBN 0-534-35265-0

Preface

This Instructor's Solutions Manual contains answers to all exercises in the text, *Precalculus: Functions and Graphs, Eighth Edition*, by Earl W. Swokowski and Jeffery A. Cole. For most problems, a reasonably detailed solution is included. I have tried to correlate the length of the solutions with their difficulty. It is my hope that by merely browsing through the solutions, instructors will save time in determining appropriate assignments for their particular class.

I truly appreciate feedback concerning errors, solution correctness, solution style, or manual style—comments from professors using previous editions have greatly strengthened the ancillary package as well as the text. Any comments may be sent directly to me or in care of the publisher (there is a comment card in the back of this manual or you can use the internet address: coleje@an.cc.mn.us).

In each section of Chapters 2 through 5 of this manual, there are some additional questions and answers under the heading *Concept Check*. These are suitable for reading quizzes, short answer exam items, or stimulating classroom discussion. Let me know if you would like the *Concept Check* to become a feature of future editions of the text.

I would like to thank: Gary Rockswold, of Mankato State University, for supplying solutions for many of the new applied problems and calculator exercises; Joan Cole, my wife, for proofing various features of the manual; George Morris, of Scientific Illustrators, for creating the mathematically precise art package; and Sally Lifland and Gail Magin, of Lifland et al., Bookmakers, for assembling the final manuscript. I dedicate this book to my children, Becky and Brad.

Jeffery A. Cole

Anoka-Ramsey Community College

11200 Mississippi Blvd. NW

Coon Rapids, MN 55433

Table of Contents

Table of Contents

Table of Contents

To the Instructor

In the chapter review sections, the solutions are abbreviated since more detailed solutions were given in chapter sections. In easier groups of exercises, representative solutions are shown. When appropriate, only the answer is listed.

The accompanying *Student's Solutions Manual* contains solutions to a subset of the odd-numbered exercises in the chapter sections and for the discussion exercises, and a subset of all exercises in the chapter review sections. There are additional explanations in that manual and an emphasis on the applied problems.

All figures have been plotted using computer software, offering a high degree of precision. The calculator graphs are from the TI-82 screen. When possible, we tried to make each piece of art with the same scale to show a realistic and consistent graph.

This manual was done using EXP: *The Scientific Word Processor.*

The following <u>notations</u> are used in the manual.

Note: Notes to the instructor pertaining to hints on instruction or conventions to follow.

{ }	{ comments to the reader are in braces }
LS	{ Left Side of an equation }
RS	{ Right Side of an equation }
$\Rightarrow$	{ implies, next equation, logically follows }
$\Leftrightarrow$	{ if and only if, is equivalent to }
•	{ bullet, used to separate problem statement from solution or explanation }
★	{ used to identify the answer to the problem }
§	{ *section* references }
$\forall$	{ For all, i.e., $\forall x$ means "for all x". }
$\mathbb{R} - \{a\}$	{ The set of all real numbers except a. }
$\therefore$	{ therefore }
QI–QIV	{ quadrants I, II, III, IV }

Chapter 1: Topics From Algebra

1. (a) Since x and y have opposite signs, the product xy is negative.

   (b) Since $x^2 > 0$ and $y > 0$, $x^2y > 0$.

   (c) Since $x < 0$ and $y > 0$, $\frac{x}{y} < 0$, and $\frac{x}{y} + x < 0$.

   (d) Since $y > 0$ and $x < 0$, $y - x > 0$.

2. (a) Since x and y have opposite signs, the quotient $\frac{x}{y}$ is negative.

   (b) Since $x < 0$ and $y^2 > 0$, $xy^2 < 0$.

   (c) Since $x - y < 0$ and $xy < 0$, $\frac{x-y}{xy} > 0$.

   (d) Since $y > 0$ and $y - x > 0$, $y(y - x) > 0$.

3. (a) Since -7 is to the left of -4 on a coordinate line, $-7 \boxed{<} -4$.

   (b) Using a calculator, we see that $\frac{\pi}{2} \approx 1.5708$. Hence, $\frac{\pi}{2} \boxed{>} 1.57$.

   (c) $\sqrt{225} \boxed{=} 15$

4. (a) Since -3 is to the right of -5 on a coordinate line, $-3 \boxed{>} -5$.

   (b) Using a calculator, we see that $\frac{\pi}{4} \approx 0.7854$. Hence, $\frac{\pi}{4} \boxed{<} 0.8$.

   (c) $\sqrt{289} \boxed{=} 17$

5. (a) Since $\frac{1}{11} = 0.\overline{09}$, $\frac{1}{11} \boxed{>} 0.09$.   (b) Since $\frac{2}{3} = 0.\overline{6}$, $\frac{2}{3} \boxed{>} 0.6666$.

   (c) Since $\frac{22}{7} = 3.\overline{142857}$ and $\pi \approx 3.141593$, $\frac{22}{7} \boxed{>} \pi$.

6. (a) Since $\frac{1}{7} = 0.\overline{142857}$, $\frac{1}{7} \boxed{<} 0.143$.   (b) Since $\frac{5}{6} = 0.8\overline{3}$, $\frac{5}{6} \boxed{>} 0.833$.

   (c) Since $\sqrt{2} \approx 1.4142$, $\sqrt{2} \boxed{>} 1.4$.

7. (a) x is negative $\Leftrightarrow x < 0$ (b) y is nonnegative $\Leftrightarrow y \geq 0$

   (c) q is less than or equal to $\pi \Leftrightarrow q \leq \pi$ (d) d is between 4 and 2 $\Leftrightarrow 2 < d < 4$

   (e) t is not less than 5 $\Leftrightarrow t \geq 5$

   (f) The negative of z is not greater than 3 $\Leftrightarrow -z \leq 3$

   (g) The quotient of p and q is at most 7 $\Leftrightarrow \frac{p}{q} \leq 7$

   (h) The reciprocal of w is at least 9 $\Leftrightarrow \frac{1}{w} \geq 9$

   (i) The absolute value of x is greater than 7 $\Leftrightarrow |x| > 7$

8. (a) b is positive $\Leftrightarrow b > 0$ (b) s is nonpositive $\Leftrightarrow s \leq 0$

   (c) w is greater than or equal to $-4 \Leftrightarrow w \geq -4$

   (d) c is between $\frac{1}{5}$ and $\frac{1}{3} \Leftrightarrow \frac{1}{5} < c < \frac{1}{3}$ (e) p is not greater than $-2 \Leftrightarrow p \leq -2$

   (f) The negative of m is not less than $-2 \Leftrightarrow -m \geq -2$

   (g) The quotient of r and s is at least $\frac{1}{5} \Leftrightarrow \frac{r}{s} \geq \frac{1}{5}$

   (h) The reciprocal of f is at most 14 $\Leftrightarrow \frac{1}{f} \leq 14$

   (i) The absolute value of x is less than 4 $\Leftrightarrow |x| < 4$

$\boxed{9}$ (a) $|-3-2| = |-5| = -(-5)$ {since $-5 < 0$} $= 5$

    (b) $|-5| - |2| = -(-5) - 2 = 5 - 2 = 3$

    (c) $|7| + |-4| = 7 + [-(-4)] = 7 + 4 = 11$

$\boxed{10}$ (a) $|-11+1| = |-10| = -(-10)$ {since $-10 < 0$} $= 10$

    (b) $|6| - |-3| = 6 - [-(-3)] = 6 - 3 = 3$

    (c) $|8| + |-9| = 8 + [-(-9)] = 8 + 9 = 17$

$\boxed{11}$ (a) $(-5)|3-6| = (-5)|-3| = (-5)[-(-3)] = (-5)(3) = -15$

    (b) $|-6|/(-2) = -(-6)/(-2) = 6/(-2) = -3$

    (c) $|-7| + |4| = -(-7) + 4 = 7 + 4 = 11$

$\boxed{12}$ (a) $(4)|6-7| = (4)|-1| = (4)[-(-1)] = (4)(1) = 4$

    (b) $5/|-2| = 5/[-(-2)] = 5/2$

    (c) $|-1| + |-9| = -(-1) + [-(-9)] = 1 + 9 = 10$

$\boxed{13}$ (a) Since $(4 - \pi)$ is positive, $|4 - \pi| = 4 - \pi$.

    (b) Since $(\pi - 4)$ is negative, $|\pi - 4| = -(\pi - 4) = 4 - \pi$.

    (c) Since $(\sqrt{2} - 1.5)$ is negative, $|\sqrt{2} - 1.5| = -(\sqrt{2} - 1.5) = 1.5 - \sqrt{2}$.

$\boxed{14}$ (a) Since $(\sqrt{3} - 1.7)$ is positive, $|\sqrt{3} - 1.7| = \sqrt{3} - 1.7$.

    (b) Since $(1.7 - \sqrt{3})$ is negative, $|1.7 - \sqrt{3}| = -(1.7 - \sqrt{3}) = \sqrt{3} - 1.7$.

    (c) $|\frac{1}{5} - \frac{1}{3}| = |\frac{3}{15} - \frac{5}{15}| = |-\frac{2}{15}| = -(-\frac{2}{15}) = \frac{2}{15}$

$\boxed{15}$ (a) $d(A, B) = |7 - 3| = |4| = 4$ (b) $d(B, C) = |-5 - 7| = |-12| = 12$

    (c) $d(C, B) = d(B, C) = 12$ (d) $d(A, C) = |-5 - 3| = |-8| = 8$

$\boxed{16}$ (a) $d(A, B) = |-2 - (-6)| = |4| = 4$ (b) $d(B, C) = |4 - (-2)| = |6| = 6$

    (c) $d(C, B) = d(B, C) = 6$ (d) $d(A, C) = |4 - (-6)| = |10| = 10$

$\boxed{17}$ (a) $d(A, B) = |1 - (-9)| = |10| = 10$ (b) $d(B, C) = |10 - 1| = |9| = 9$

    (c) $d(C, B) = d(B, C) = 9$ (d) $d(A, C) = |10 - (-9)| = |19| = 19$

$\boxed{18}$ (a) $d(A, B) = |-4 - 8| = |-12| = 12$ (b) $d(B, C) = |-1 - (-4)| = |3| = 3$

    (c) $d(C, B) = d(B, C) = 3$ (d) $d(A, C) = |-1 - 8| = |-9| = 9$

Note: Exer. 19–24: Since $|a| = |-a|$, the answers could have a different form.

    For example, $|-3 - x| \geq 8$ is equivalent to $|x + 3| \geq 8$.

$\boxed{19}$ $d(A, B) = |7 - x| \Rightarrow |7 - x| < 5$

$\boxed{20}$ $d(A, B) = |-\sqrt{2} - x| \Rightarrow |-\sqrt{2} - x| > 1$

$\boxed{21}$ $d(A, B) = |-3 - x| \Rightarrow |-3 - x| \geq 8$ $\boxed{22}$ $d(A, B) = |4 - x| \Rightarrow |4 - x| \leq 2$

$\boxed{23}$ $d(A, B) = |x - 4| \Rightarrow |x - 4| \leq 3$

$\boxed{24}$ $d(A, B) = |x - (-2)| = |x + 2| \Rightarrow |x + 2| \geq 2$

Note: Exer. 25–32: Have students substitute a permissible value for the letter to first test

if the expression inside the absolute value symbol is positive or negative.

$\boxed{25}$ Pick an arbitrary value for x that is less than -3, say -5.

Since $3 + (-5) = -2$ is negative, we conclude that if $x < -3$, then $3 + x$ is negative.

Hence, $|3 + x| = -(3 + x) = -x - 3$.

$\boxed{26}$ If $x > 5$, then $5 - x < 0$, and $|5 - x| = -(5 - x) = x - 5$.

$\boxed{27}$ If $x < 2$, then $2 - x > 0$, and $|2 - x| = 2 - x$.

$\boxed{28}$ If $x \geq -7$, then $7 + x \geq 0$, and $|7 + x| = 7 + x$.

$\boxed{29}$ If $a < b$, then $a - b < 0$, and $|a - b| = -(a - b) = b - a$.

$\boxed{30}$ If $a > b$, then $a - b > 0$, and $|a - b| = a - b$.

$\boxed{31}$ Since $x^2 + 4 > 0$ for every x, $|x^2 + 4| = x^2 + 4$.

$\boxed{32}$ Since $-x^2 - 1 < 0$ for every x, $|-x^2 - 1| = -(-x^2 - 1) = x^2 + 1$.

$\boxed{33}$ LS $= \frac{ab + ac}{a} = \frac{ab}{a} + \frac{ac}{a} = b + c \boxed{\neq}$ RS $(b + ac)$.

$\boxed{34}$ From Exercise 33, LS $\boxed{=}$ RS. $\qquad$ $\boxed{35}$ LS $= \frac{b + c}{a} = \frac{b}{a} + \frac{c}{a} \boxed{=}$ RS.

$\boxed{36}$ LS $= \frac{a + c}{b + d} = \frac{a}{b + d} + \frac{c}{b + d} \boxed{\neq}$ RS $\left(\frac{a}{b} + \frac{c}{d}\right)$.

$\boxed{37}$ LS $= (a \div b) \div c = \frac{a}{b} \cdot \frac{1}{c} = \frac{a}{bc}$. RS $= a \div (b \div c) = a \div \frac{b}{c} = a \cdot \frac{c}{b} = \frac{ac}{b}$. LS $\boxed{\neq}$ RS

$\boxed{38}$ LS $= (a - b) - c = a - b - c$. RS $= a - (b - c) = a - b + c$. LS $\boxed{\neq}$ RS

$\boxed{39}$ LS $= \frac{a - b}{b - a} = \frac{-(b - a)}{b - a} = -1 \boxed{=}$ RS. $\qquad$ $\boxed{40}$ LS $= -(a + b) = -a - b \boxed{\neq}$ RS $(-a + b)$.

$\boxed{41}$ (a) $|3.2^2 - \sqrt{3.15}| \approx 8.4652$ $\qquad$ (b) $\sqrt{(15.6 - 1.5)^2 + (4.3 - 5.4)^2} \approx 14.1428$

$\boxed{42}$ (a) $\frac{3.42 - 1.29}{5.83 + 2.64} \approx 0.2515$ $\qquad$ (b) $\pi^3 \approx 31.0063$

$\boxed{43}$ (a) $\frac{1.2 \times 10^3}{3.1 \times 10^2 + 1.52 \times 10^3} \approx 0.6557 = 6.557 \times 10^{-1}$ *Note:* For the TI-82/83,

use 1.2E3/(3.1E2 + 1.52E3), where E is obtained by pressing $\boxed{\text{2nd}}$ $\boxed{\text{EE}}$.

(b) $(1.23 \times 10^{-4}) + \sqrt{4.5 \times 10^3} \approx 67.08 = 6.708 \times 10^1$

$\boxed{44}$ (a) $\sqrt{|3.45 - 1.2 \times 10^4| + 10^5} \approx 334.7 = 3.347 \times 10^2$

(b) $(1.791 \times 10^2) \times (9.84 \times 10^3) = 1{,}762{,}344 \approx 1.762 \times 10^6$

$\boxed{45}$ Construct a right triangle with sides of lengths $\sqrt{2}$ and 1. The hypotenuse will have

length $\sqrt{3}$. Next construct a right triangle with sides of lengths $\sqrt{3}$ and $\sqrt{2}$.

The hypotenuse will have length $\sqrt{5}$.

$\boxed{46}$ Use $C = 2\pi r$ with $r = 1, 2, 10$. (a) 2π (b) 4π (c) 20π

$\boxed{47}$ The large rectangle has area $a(b + c)$.

The sum of the areas of the two small rectangles is $ab + ac$.

48 $x_1 = \frac{3}{2}$ and $n = 2 \Rightarrow x_2 = \frac{1}{2}\left(x_1 + \frac{n}{x_1}\right) = \frac{1}{2}\left(\frac{3}{2} + \frac{2}{\frac{3}{2}}\right) = \frac{1}{2}(\frac{3}{2} + \frac{4}{3}) = \frac{1}{2}(\frac{17}{6}) = \frac{17}{12}.$

$$x_3 = \frac{1}{2}\left(x_2 + \frac{2}{x_2}\right) = \frac{1}{2}\left(\frac{17}{12} + \frac{2}{\frac{17}{12}}\right) = \frac{1}{2}(\frac{17}{12} + \frac{24}{17}) = \frac{1}{2}(\frac{577}{204}) = \frac{577}{408}$$

49 (a) $427,000 = 4.27 \times 10^5$ (b) $0.000\ 000\ 098 = 9.8 \times 10^{-8}$

(c) $810,000,000 = 8.1 \times 10^8$

50 (a) $85,200 = 8.52 \times 10^4$ (b) $0.000\ 005\ 5 = 5.5 \times 10^{-6}$

(c) $24,900,000 = 2.49 \times 10^7$

51 (a) $8.3 \times 10^5 = 830,000$ (b) $2.9 \times 10^{-12} = 0.000\ 000\ 000\ 002\ 9$

(c) $5.63 \times 10^8 = 563,000,000$

52 (a) $2.3 \times 10^7 = 23,000,000$ (b) $7.01 \times 10^{-9} = 0.000\ 000\ 007\ 01$

(c) $1.23 \times 10^{10} = 12,300,000,000$

53 $0.000\ 000\ 000\ 000\ 000\ 000\ 000\ 001\ 7 = 1.7 \times 10^{-24}$

54 $9.1 \times 10^{-31} = 0.000\ 000\ 000\ 000\ 000\ 000\ 000\ 000\ 000\ 000\ 91$

55 $\dfrac{186,000 \text{ miles}}{\text{second}} \cdot \dfrac{60 \text{ seconds}}{1 \text{ minute}} \cdot \dfrac{60 \text{ minutes}}{1 \text{ hour}} \cdot \dfrac{24 \text{ hours}}{1 \text{ day}} \cdot \dfrac{365 \text{ days}}{1 \text{ year}} \cdot 1 \text{ year} \approx 5.87 \times 10^{12} \text{ mi}$

56 (a) $100 \text{ billion} = 100,000,000,000 = 1 \times 10^{11}$

(b) $d \approx (100,000 \text{ yr})\left(5.87 \times 10^{12} \frac{\text{mi}}{\text{yr}}\right) = 5.87 \times 10^{17} \text{ mi}$

57 $\dfrac{\dfrac{1.01 \text{ grams}}{\text{mole}}}{\dfrac{6.02 \times 10^{23} \text{ atoms}}{\text{mole}}} \cdot 1 \text{ atom} = \dfrac{1.01 \text{ grams}}{6.02 \times 10^{23}} \approx 0.1678 \times 10^{-23} \text{ g} = 1.678 \times 10^{-24} \text{ g}$

58 $(2.5 \text{ million})(0.00035\%) = (2.5 \times 10^6)(3.5 \times 10^{-6}) = 8.75 \approx 9 \text{ halibut}$

59 $\dfrac{24 \text{ frames}}{\text{second}} \cdot \dfrac{60 \text{ seconds}}{1 \text{ minute}} \cdot \dfrac{60 \text{ minutes}}{1 \text{ hour}} \cdot 48 \text{ hours} = 4.1472 \times 10^6 \text{ frames}$

60 $\dfrac{2 \times 10^{11} \text{ calculations}}{\text{second}} \cdot \dfrac{60 \text{ seconds}}{1 \text{ minute}} \cdot \dfrac{60 \text{ minutes}}{1 \text{ hour}} \cdot \dfrac{24 \text{ hours}}{1 \text{ day}} \cdot 60 \text{ days} =$

$1.0368 \times 10^{18} \text{ calculations}$

61 (a) $\text{IQ} = \dfrac{\text{mental age (MA)}}{\text{chronological age (CA)}} \times 100 = \frac{15}{12} \times 100 = 125.$

(b) $\text{CA} = 15$ and $\text{IQ} = 140 \Rightarrow 140 = \text{MA}/15 \times 100 \Rightarrow \text{MA} = 21.$

62 Let S denote the surface area of the earth.

Then, $0.708S = 361 \times 10^6 \Rightarrow S \approx 510 \times 10^6 \text{ km}^2.$

63 (a) $1 \text{ ft}^2 = 144 \text{ in}^2 \Rightarrow 144 \text{ in}^2 \times 1.4 \text{ lb/in}^2 = 201.6 \text{ lb}.$

(b) $40 \times 8 = 320 \text{ ft}^2 = 46,080 \text{ in}^2;\ 46,080 \times 1.4 = 64,512 \text{ lb};$

$64,512 \text{ lb}/(2000 \text{ lb/ton}) = 32.256 \text{ tons}$

> ### 1.2 Exercises

1 $(-\frac{2}{3})^4 = \frac{16}{81}$

2 $(-3)^3 = -27 = \frac{-27}{1}$

3 $\frac{2^{-3}}{3^{-2}} = \frac{3^2}{2^3} = \frac{9}{8}$

4 $\frac{2^0 + 0^2}{2 + 0} = \frac{1+0}{2} = \frac{1}{2}$

5 $-2^4 + 3^{-1} = -16 + \frac{1}{3} = -\frac{48}{3} + \frac{1}{3} = \frac{-47}{3}$

6 $(-\frac{3}{2})^4 - 2^{-4} = \frac{81}{16} - \frac{1}{16} = \frac{80}{16} = \frac{5}{1}$

7 $16^{-3/4} = 1/16^{3/4} = 1/(\sqrt[4]{16})^3 = 1/2^3 = \frac{1}{8}$

8 $9^{5/2} = (\sqrt{9})^5 = 3^5 = \frac{243}{1}$

9 $(-0.008)^{2/3} = (\sqrt[3]{-0.008})^2 = (-0.2)^2 = 0.04 = \frac{4}{100} = \frac{1}{25}$

10 $(0.008)^{-2/3} = 1/(0.008)^{2/3} = 1/(\sqrt[3]{0.008})^2 = 1/(0.2)^2 = 1/(0.04) = \frac{25}{1}$

11 $(\frac{1}{2}x^4)(16x^5) = (\frac{1}{2} \cdot 16)x^{4+5} = 8x^9$

12 $(-3x^{-2})(4x^4) = (-3 \cdot 4)x^{-2+4} = -12x^2$

13 $\frac{(2x^3)(3x^2)}{(x^2)^3} = \frac{6x^5}{x^6} = \frac{6}{x}$

14 $\frac{(2x^2)^3}{4x^4} = \frac{8x^6}{4x^4} = 2x^2$

15 $(\frac{1}{6}a^5)(-3a^2)(4a^7) = -2a^{14}$

16 $(-4b^3)(\frac{1}{6}b^2)(-9b^4) = 6b^9$

17 $\frac{(6x^3)^2}{(2x^2)^3} = \frac{36x^6}{8x^6} = \frac{9}{2}$

18 $\frac{(3y^3)(2y^2)^2}{(y^4)^3} = \frac{(3y^3)(4y^4)}{y^{12}} = \frac{12}{y^5} = \frac{12y^7}{y^{12}}$

19 $(3u^7v^3)(4u^4v^{-5}) = 12u^{11}v^{-2} = \frac{12u^{11}}{v^2}$

20 $(x^2yz^3)(-2xz^2)(x^3y^{-2}) = -2x^6y^{-1}z^5 = \frac{-2x^6z^5}{y}$

21 $(8x^4y^{-3})(\frac{1}{2}x^{-5}y^2) = 4x^{-1}y^{-1} = \frac{4}{xy}$

22 $\left(\frac{4a^2b}{a^3b^2}\right)\left(\frac{5a^2b}{2b^4}\right) = \frac{20a^4b^2}{2a^3b^6} = \frac{10a}{b^4}$

23 $(\frac{1}{3}x^4y^{-3})^{-2} = (\frac{1}{3})^{-2}x^{-8}y^6 = 3^2x^{-8}y^6 = \frac{9y^6}{x^8}$

24 $(-2xy^2)^5\left(\frac{x^7}{8y^3}\right) = (-32x^5y^{10})\left(\frac{x^7}{8y^3}\right) = -4x^{12}y^7$

25 $(3y^3)^4(4y^2)^{-3} = 81y^{12} \cdot 4^{-3}y^{-6} = 81y^6 \cdot \frac{1}{64} = \frac{81}{64}y^6$

26 $(-3a^2b^{-5})^3 = -27a^6b^{-15} = -\frac{27a^6}{b^{15}}$

27 $(-2r^4s^{-3})^{-2} = (-2)^{-2}r^{-8}s^6 = \frac{s^6}{(-2)^2r^8} = \frac{s^6}{4r^8}$

28 $(2x^2y^{-5})(6x^{-3}y)(\frac{1}{3}x^{-1}y^3) = 4x^{-2}y^{-1} = \frac{4}{x^2y}$

29 $(5x^2y^{-3})(4x^{-5}y^4) = 20x^{-3}y = \frac{20y}{x^3}$

30 $(-2r^2s)^5(3r^{-1}s^3)^2 = (-32r^{10}s^5)(9r^{-2}s^6) = -288r^8s^{11}$

31 $\left(\frac{3x^5y^4}{x^0y^{-3}}\right)^2 = \frac{9x^{10}y^8}{y^{-6}} = 9x^{10}y^{14}$

32 $(4a^2b)^4\left(\frac{-a^3}{2b}\right)^2 = (256a^8b^4)\left(\frac{a^6}{4b^2}\right) = 64a^{14}b^2$

33 $(4a^{3/2})(2a^{1/2}) = 8a^{4/2} = 8a^2$

34 $(-6x^{7/5})(2x^{8/5}) = -12x^{15/5} = -12x^3$

35 $(3x^{5/6})(8x^{2/3}) = 24x^{(5/6)+(4/6)} = 24x^{9/6} = 24x^{3/2}$

36. $(8r)^{1/3}(2r^{1/2}) = (2r^{1/3})(2r^{1/2}) = 4r^{(2/6)+(3/6)} = 4r^{5/6}$

37. $(27a^6)^{-2/3} = 27^{-2/3}a^{-12/3} = \dfrac{1}{(\sqrt[3]{27})^2 a^4} = \dfrac{1}{9a^4}$

38. $(25z^4)^{-3/2} = 25^{-3/2}z^{-12/2} = \dfrac{1}{(\sqrt{25})^3 z^6} = \dfrac{1}{125z^6}$

39. $(8x^{-2/3})x^{1/6} = 8x^{(-4/6)+(1/6)} = 8x^{-3/6} = \dfrac{8}{x^{1/2}}$

40. $(3x^{1/2})(-2x^{5/2}) = -6x^3$

41. $\left(\dfrac{-8x^3}{y^{-6}}\right)^{2/3} = \dfrac{(-2)^2 x^2}{(y^{-2})^2} = \dfrac{4x^2}{y^{-4}} = 4x^2 y^4$ 42. $\left(\dfrac{-y^{3/2}}{y^{-1/3}}\right)^3 = \dfrac{-y^{9/2}}{y^{-1}} = -y^{11/2}$

43. $\left(\dfrac{x^6}{9y^{-4}}\right)^{-1/2} = \dfrac{x^{-3}}{9^{-1/2}y^2} = \dfrac{9^{1/2}x^{-3}}{y^2} = \dfrac{3}{x^3 y^2}$

44. $\left(\dfrac{c^{-4}}{16d^8}\right)^{3/4} = \dfrac{c^{-3}}{(\sqrt[4]{16})^3 d^6} = \dfrac{c^{-3}}{8d^6} = \dfrac{1}{8c^3 d^6}$ 45. $\dfrac{(x^6 y^3)^{-1/3}}{(x^4 y^2)^{-1/2}} = \dfrac{x^{-2}y^{-1}}{x^{-2}y^{-1}} = 1$

46. $a^{4/3}a^{-3/2}a^{1/6} = a^{(8/6)-(9/6)+(1/6)} = a^{0/6} = a^0 = 1$

47. $\sqrt[4]{x^3} = (x^3)^{1/4} = x^{3/4}$ 48. $\sqrt[3]{x^5} = (x^5)^{1/3} = x^{5/3}$

49. $\sqrt[3]{(a+b)^2} = [(a+b)^2]^{1/3} = (a+b)^{2/3}$ 50. $\sqrt{a + \sqrt{b}} = (a + b^{1/2})^{1/2}$

51. $\sqrt{x^2 + y^2} = (x^2 + y^2)^{1/2}$ 52. $\sqrt[3]{r^3 - s^3} = (r^3 - s^3)^{1/3}$

53. (a) $4x^{3/2} = 4x^1 x^{1/2} = 4x\sqrt{x}$ (b) $(4x)^{3/2} = (4x)^1 4^{1/2} x^{1/2} = 8x\sqrt{x}$

54. (a) $4 + x^{3/2} = 4 + x^1 x^{1/2} = 4 + x\sqrt{x}$

    (b) $(4+x)^{3/2} = (4+x)^1 (4+x)^{1/2} = (4+x)\sqrt{4+x}$

55. (a) $8 - y^{1/3} = 8 - \sqrt[3]{y}$ (b) $(8y)^{1/3} = \sqrt[3]{8-y}$

56. (a) $8y^{1/3} = 8\sqrt[3]{y}$ (b) $(8y)^{1/3} = 8^{1/3}y^{1/3} = 2\sqrt[3]{y}$

57. $\sqrt{81} = \sqrt{9^2} = 9$ 58. $\sqrt[3]{-125} = \sqrt[3]{(-5)^3} = -5$

59. $\sqrt[5]{-64} = \sqrt[5]{-32}\sqrt[5]{2} = \sqrt[5]{(-2)^5}\sqrt[5]{2} = -2\sqrt[5]{2}$

60. $\sqrt[4]{256} = \sqrt[4]{4^4} = 4$

61. $\dfrac{1}{\sqrt[3]{2}} = \dfrac{1}{\sqrt[3]{2}} \cdot \dfrac{\sqrt[3]{4}}{\sqrt[3]{4}} = \frac{1}{2}\sqrt[3]{4}$ 62. $\sqrt{\frac{1}{7}} = \sqrt{\frac{1}{7}} \cdot \dfrac{\sqrt{7}}{\sqrt{7}} = \frac{1}{7}\sqrt{7}$

63. $\sqrt{9x^{-4}y^6} = 3x^{-2}y^3 = \dfrac{3y^3}{x^2}$ 64. $\sqrt{16a^8 b^{-2}} = 4a^4 b^{-1} = \dfrac{4a^4}{b}$

65. $\sqrt[3]{8a^6 b^{-3}} = 2a^2 b^{-1} = \dfrac{2a^2}{b}$ 66. $\sqrt[4]{81r^5 s^8} = \sqrt[4]{3^4 r^4 s^8}\sqrt[4]{r} = 3rs^2\sqrt[4]{r}$

67. $\sqrt{\dfrac{3x}{2y^3}} = \sqrt{\dfrac{3x}{2y^3}} \cdot \dfrac{\sqrt{2y}}{\sqrt{2y}} = \dfrac{1}{2y^2}\sqrt{6xy}$ 68. $\sqrt{\dfrac{1}{3x^3 y}} = \sqrt{\dfrac{1}{3x^3 y}} \cdot \dfrac{\sqrt{3xy}}{\sqrt{3xy}} = \dfrac{1}{3x^2 y}\sqrt{3xy}$

69. $\sqrt[3]{\dfrac{2x^4 y^4}{9x}} = \sqrt[3]{\dfrac{2x^4 y^4}{9x}} \cdot \dfrac{\sqrt[3]{3x^2}}{\sqrt[3]{3x^2}} = \dfrac{\sqrt[3]{x^6 y^3}\sqrt[3]{6y}}{3x} = \dfrac{x^2 y\sqrt[3]{6y}}{3x} = \dfrac{xy}{3}\sqrt[3]{6y}$

70 $\sqrt[3]{\dfrac{3x^2y^5}{4x}} = \sqrt[3]{\dfrac{3x^2y^5}{4x}} \cdot \dfrac{\sqrt[3]{2x^2}}{\sqrt[3]{2x^2}} = \dfrac{\sqrt[3]{x^3y^3}\,\sqrt[3]{6xy^2}}{2x} = \dfrac{xy\,\sqrt[3]{6xy^2}}{2x} = \dfrac{y}{2}\sqrt[3]{6xy^2}$

71 $\sqrt[4]{\dfrac{5x^8y^3}{27x^2}} = \sqrt[4]{\dfrac{5x^8y^3}{27x^2}} \cdot \dfrac{\sqrt[4]{3x^2}}{\sqrt[4]{3x^2}} = \dfrac{\sqrt[4]{x^8}\,\sqrt[4]{15x^2y^3}}{3x} = \dfrac{x^2\,\sqrt[4]{15x^2y^3}}{3x} = \dfrac{x}{3}\sqrt[4]{15x^2y^3}$

72 $\sqrt[4]{\dfrac{x^7y^{12}}{125x}} = \sqrt[4]{\dfrac{x^7y^{12}}{125x}} \cdot \dfrac{\sqrt[4]{5x^3}}{\sqrt[4]{5x^3}} = \dfrac{\sqrt[4]{x^8y^{12}}\,\sqrt[4]{5x^2}}{5x} = \dfrac{x^2y^3\,\sqrt[4]{5x^2}}{5x} = \dfrac{xy^3}{5}\sqrt[4]{5x^2}$

73 $\sqrt[5]{\dfrac{5x^7y^2}{8x^3}} = \sqrt[5]{\dfrac{5x^7y^2}{8x^3}} \cdot \dfrac{\sqrt[5]{4x^2}}{\sqrt[5]{4x^2}} = \dfrac{\sqrt[5]{x^5}\,\sqrt[5]{20x^4y^2}}{2x} = \dfrac{x\,\sqrt[5]{20x^4y^2}}{2x} = \dfrac{1}{2}\sqrt[5]{20x^4y^2}$

74 $\sqrt[5]{\dfrac{3x^{11}y^3}{9x^2}} = \sqrt[5]{\dfrac{3x^{11}y^3}{9x^2}} \cdot \dfrac{\sqrt[5]{27x^3}}{\sqrt[5]{27x^3}} = \dfrac{\sqrt[5]{x^{10}}\,\sqrt[5]{81x^4y^3}}{3x} = \dfrac{x^2\,\sqrt[5]{81x^4y^3}}{3x} = \dfrac{x}{3}\sqrt[5]{81x^4y^3}$

75 $\sqrt[4]{(3x^5y^{-2})^4} = 3x^5y^{-2} = \dfrac{3x^5}{y^2}$ **76** $\sqrt[6]{(2u^{-3}v^4)^6} = 2u^{-3}v^4 = \dfrac{2v^4}{u^3}$

77 $\sqrt[5]{\dfrac{8x^3}{y^4}}\,\sqrt[5]{\dfrac{4x^4}{y^2}} = \sqrt[5]{\dfrac{8x^3}{y^4}}\,\sqrt[5]{\dfrac{4x^4}{y^2}} \cdot \dfrac{\sqrt[5]{y^4}}{\sqrt[5]{y^4}} = \dfrac{\sqrt[5]{32x^5}\,\sqrt[5]{x^2y^4}}{y^2} = \dfrac{2x}{y^2}\sqrt[5]{x^2y^4}$

78 $\sqrt{5xy^7}\,\sqrt{10x^3y^3} = \sqrt{25x^4y^{10}}\,\sqrt{2} = 5x^2y^5\sqrt{2}$

79 $\sqrt[3]{3t^4v^2}\,\sqrt[3]{-9t^{-1}v^4} = \sqrt[3]{-27t^3v^6} = -3tv^2$

80 $\sqrt[3]{(2r-s)^3} = 2r - s$

81 $\sqrt{x^6y^4} = \sqrt{(x^3)^2(y^2)^2} = |\,x^3\,|\,|\,y^2\,| = |\,x^3\,|\,y^2, \text{ or } x^2y^2\,|\,x\,|$

82 $\sqrt{x^4y^{10}} = \sqrt{(x^2)^2(y^5)^2} = |\,x^2\,|\,|\,y^5\,| = x^2\,|\,y^5\,|, \text{ or } x^2y^4\,|\,y\,|$

83 $\sqrt[4]{x^8(y-1)^{12}} = \sqrt[4]{(x^2)^4((y-1)^3)^4} = |\,x^2\,|\,|\,(y-1)^3\,| = x^2\,|\,(y-1)^3\,|,$

                                      or $x^2(y-1)^2\,|\,(y-1)\,|$

84 $\sqrt[4]{(x+2)^{12}y^4} = \sqrt[4]{((x+2)^3)^4y^4} = |\,(x+2)^3\,|\,|\,y\,|, \text{ or } (x+2)^2\,|\,(x+2)y\,|$

85 $(a^r)^2 = a^{2r}\,\boxed{\neq}\,a^{(r^2)}$ since $2r \neq r^2$ for every r.

86 Squaring the right side gives us $(a+1)^2 = a^2 + 2a + 1$.

    Squaring the left side gives us $a^2 + 1$. $a^2 + 2a + 1\,\boxed{\neq}\,a^2 + 1$ for every a.

87 $(ab)^{xy} = a^{xy}b^{xy}\,\boxed{\neq}\,a^xb^y$ for every x and y.

88 $\sqrt{a^r} = (a^r)^{1/2} = (a^{1/2})^r\,\boxed{\equiv}\,(\sqrt{a})^r$

89 $\sqrt[n]{\dfrac{1}{c}} = \left(\dfrac{1}{c}\right)^{1/n} = \dfrac{1^{1/n}}{c^{1/n}}\,\boxed{\equiv}\,\dfrac{1}{\sqrt[n]{c}}$ **90** $\dfrac{1}{a^k} = a^{-k}\,\boxed{\neq}\,a^{1/k}$

91   (a) $(-3)^{2/5} = [(-3)^2]^{1/5} = 9^{1/5} \approx 1.5518$

     (b) $(-5)^{4/3} = [(-5)^4]^{1/3} = 625^{1/3} \approx 8.5499$

92   (a) $(-1.2)^{3/7} = [(-1.2)^3]^{1/7} = (-1.728)^{1/7} \approx -1.0813$

     (b) $(-5.08)^{7/3} = [(-5.08)^7]^{1/3} \approx (-87{,}306.38)^{1/3} \approx -44.3624$

93 (a) $\sqrt{\pi + 1} \approx 2.0351$ (b) $\sqrt[3]{15.1} + 5^{1/4} \approx 3.9670$

94 (a) $(2.6 - 1.9)^{-2} \approx 2.0408$ (b) $5^{\sqrt{7}} \approx 70.6807$

95 $\$200(1.04)^{180} \approx \$232{,}825.78$

96 $h = 1454 \text{ ft} \Rightarrow d = 1.2\sqrt{h} = 1.2\sqrt{1454} \approx 45.8 \text{ mi}$

97 $W = 230 \text{ kg} \Rightarrow L = 0.46\sqrt[3]{W} = 0.46\sqrt[3]{230} \approx 2.82 \text{ m}$

98 $L = 25 \text{ ft} \Rightarrow W = 0.0016L^{2.43} = 0.0016(25)^{2.43} \approx 3.99 \text{ tons}$

99 $b = 75 \text{ and } w = 180 \Rightarrow W = \dfrac{w}{\sqrt[3]{b - 35}} = \dfrac{180}{\sqrt[3]{75 - 35}} \approx 52.6.$

     $b = 120 \text{ and } w = 250 \Rightarrow W = \dfrac{w}{\sqrt[3]{b - 35}} = \dfrac{250}{\sqrt[3]{120 - 35}} \approx 56.9.$

It is interesting to note that the 75-kg lifter can lift 2.4 times his/her body weight and the 120-kg lifter can lift approximately 2.08 times his/her body weight, but

the formula ranks the 120-kg lifter as the superior lifter.

100 (a) $h = 72 \text{ in and } w = 175 \text{ lb} \Rightarrow$

$$S = (0.1091)w^{0.425}h^{0.725} = (0.1091)(175)^{0.425}(72)^{0.725} \approx 21.76 \text{ ft}^2.$$

(b) $h = 66 \text{ in} \Rightarrow S_1 = (0.1091)w^{0.425}(66)^{0.725}$. A 10% increase in weight would be represented by $1.1w$ and thus $S_2 = (0.1091)(1.1w)^{0.425}(66)^{0.725}$.

$$S_2/S_1 = (1.1)^{0.425} \approx 1.04, \text{ which represents a } 4\% \text{ increase in } S.$$

101 $W = 0.1166h^{1.7}$

Height	64	65	66	67	68	69	70	71
Weight	137	141	145	148	152	156	160	164
Height	72	73	74	75	76	77	78	79
Weight	168	172	176	180	184	188	192	196

102 $W = 0.1049h^{1.7}$

Height	60	61	62	63	64	65	66	67
Weight	111	114	117	120	123	127	130	133
Height	68	69	70	71	72	73	74	75
Weight	137	140	144	147	151	154	158	162

1.3 Exercises

1 $(2u + 3)(u - 4) + 4u(u - 2) = (2u^2 - 5u - 12) + (4u^2 - 8u) = 6u^2 - 13u - 12$

2 $(3u - 1)(u + 2) + 7u(u + 1) = (3u^2 + 5u - 2) + (7u^2 + 7u) = 10u^2 + 12u - 2$

3 $\dfrac{8x^2y^3 - 10x^3y}{2x^2y} = \dfrac{8x^2y^3}{2x^2y} - \dfrac{10x^3y}{2x^2y} = 4y^2 - 5x$

4 $\dfrac{6x^2yz^3 - xy^2z}{xyz} = \dfrac{6x^2yz^3}{xyz} - \dfrac{xy^2z}{xyz} = 6xz^2 - y$

$\boxed{5}$ $(2x + 3y)(2x - 3y) = (2x)^2 - (3y)^2 = 4x^2 - 9y^2$

$\boxed{6}$ $(5x + 4y)(5x - 4y) = (5x)^2 - (4y)^2 = 25x^2 - 16y^2$

$\boxed{7}$ $(3x + 2y)^2 = (3x)^2 + 2(3x)(2y) + (2y)^2 = 9x^2 + 12xy + 4y^2$

$\boxed{8}$ $(5x - 4y)^2 = (5x)^2 - 2(5x)(4y) + (4y)^2 = 25x^2 - 40xy + 16y^2$

$\boxed{9}$ $(\sqrt{x} + \sqrt{y})(\sqrt{x} - \sqrt{y}) = (\sqrt{x})^2 - (\sqrt{y})^2 = x - y$

$\boxed{10}$ $(\sqrt{x} + \sqrt{y})^2(\sqrt{x} - \sqrt{y})^2 = [(\sqrt{x} + \sqrt{y})(\sqrt{x} - \sqrt{y})]^2 = (x - y)^2 = x^2 - 2xy + y^2$

$\boxed{11}$ $(x - 2y)^3 = (x)^3 - 3(x)^2(2y) + 3(x)(2y)^2 - (2y)^3 = x^3 - 6x^2y + 12xy^2 - 8y^3$

$\boxed{12}$ $(x + 3y)^3 = (x)^3 + 3(x)^2(3y) + 3(x)(3y)^2 + (3y)^3 = x^3 + 9x^2y + 27xy^2 + 27y^3$

$\boxed{13}$ $8x^2 - 53x - 21 = (8x + 3)(x - 7)$ $\boxed{14}$ $7x^2 + 10x - 8 = (7x - 4)(x + 2)$

$\boxed{15}$ $x^2 + 3x + 4$ is irreducible $\boxed{16}$ $3x^2 - 4x + 2$ is irreducible

$\boxed{17}$ $4x^2 - 20x + 25 = (2x - 5)(2x - 5) = (2x - 5)^2$

$\boxed{18}$ $9x^2 + 24x + 16 = (3x + 4)(3x + 4) = (3x + 4)^2$

$\boxed{19}$ $x^4 - 4x^2 = x^2(x^2 - 4) = x^2(x^2 - 2^2) = x^2(x + 2)(x - 2)$

$\boxed{20}$ $x^3 - 25x = x(x^2 - 25) = x(x^2 - 5^2) = x(x + 5)(x - 5)$

$\boxed{21}$ $64x^3 - y^6 = (4x)^3 - (y^2)^3 = (4x - y^2)\left[(4x)^2 + (4x)(y^2) + (y^2)^2\right] =$
$$(4x - y^2)(16x^2 + 4xy^2 + y^4)$$

$\boxed{22}$ $x^6 - 27y^3 = (x^2)^3 - (3y)^3 = (x^2 - 3y)\left[(x^2)^2 + (x^2)(3y) + (3y)^2\right] =$
$$(x^2 - 3y)(x^4 + 3x^2y + 9y^2)$$

$\boxed{23}$ $64x^3 + 27 = (4x)^3 + (3)^3 = (4x + 3)\left[(4x)^2 - (4x)(3) + (3)^2\right] = (4x + 3)(16x^2 - 12x + 9)$

$\boxed{24}$ $125x^3 + 8 = (5x)^3 + (2)^3 = (5x + 2)\left[(5x)^2 - (5x)(2) + (2)^2\right] = (5x + 2)(25x^2 - 10x + 4)$

$\boxed{25}$ $3x^3 + 3x^2 - 27x - 27 = 3(x^3 + x^2 - 9x - 9) =$
$$3[x^2(x + 1) - 9(x + 1)] = 3(x^2 - 9)(x + 1) = 3(x + 3)(x - 3)(x + 1)$$

$\boxed{26}$ $5x^3 + 10x^2 - 20x - 40 = 5(x^3 + 2x^2 - 4x - 8) = 5[x^2(x + 2) - 4(x + 2)] =$
$$5(x^2 - 4)(x + 2) = 5(x + 2)(x - 2)(x + 2) = 5(x + 2)^2(x - 2)$$

$\boxed{27}$ $a^6 - b^6 = (a^3)^2 - (b^3)^2 = (a^3 + b^3)(a^3 - b^3) = (a + b)(a - b)(a^2 - ab + b^2)(a^2 + ab + b^2)$

$\boxed{28}$ $x^8 - 16 = (x^4)^2 - 4^2 = (x^4 + 4)(x^4 - 4) = (x^4 + 4)(x^2 + 2)(x^2 - 2)$

$\boxed{29}$ $x^2 + 4x + 4 - 9y^2 = (x + 2)^2 - (3y)^2 = (x + 2 + 3y)(x + 2 - 3y)$

$\boxed{30}$ $x^2 - 4y^2 - 6x + 9 = (x^2 - 6x + 9) - 4y^2 = (x - 3)^2 - (2y)^2 = (x - 3 + 2y)(x - 3 - 2y)$

$\boxed{31}$ $\dfrac{y^2 - 25}{y^3 - 125} = \dfrac{(y + 5)(y - 5)}{(y - 5)(y^2 + 5y + 25)} = \dfrac{y + 5}{y^2 + 5y + 25}$

$\boxed{32}$ $\dfrac{12 + r - r^2}{r^3 + 3r^2} = \dfrac{(3 + r)(4 - r)}{r^2(r + 3)} = \dfrac{4 - r}{r^2}$

$\boxed{33}$ $\dfrac{9x^2 - 4}{3x^2 - 5x + 2} \cdot \dfrac{9x^4 - 6x^3 + 4x^2}{27x^4 + 8x} = \dfrac{(3x + 2)(3x - 2)}{(3x - 2)(x - 1)} \cdot \dfrac{x^2(9x^2 - 6x + 4)}{x(3x + 2)(9x^2 - 6x + 4)} = \dfrac{x}{x - 1}$

34 $\dfrac{5a^2+12a+4}{a^4-16} \div \dfrac{25a^2+20a+4}{a^2-2a} = \dfrac{(5a+2)(a+2)}{(a^2+4)(a+2)(a-2)} \cdot \dfrac{a(a-2)}{(5a+2)(5a+2)} = $

$$\dfrac{a}{(a^2+4)(5a+2)}$$

35 $\dfrac{2}{3s+1} - \dfrac{9}{(3s+1)^2} = \dfrac{2(3s+1)-9}{(3s+1)^2} = \dfrac{6s-7}{(3s+1)^2}$

36 $\dfrac{4}{(5s-2)^2} + \dfrac{s}{5s-2} = \dfrac{4+s(5s-2)}{(5s-2)^2} = \dfrac{5s^2-2s+4}{(5s-2)^2}$

37 $\dfrac{2}{x} + \dfrac{3x+1}{x^2} - \dfrac{x-2}{x^3} = \dfrac{2x^2+(3x+1)x-x+2}{x^3} = \dfrac{5x^2+2}{x^3}$

38 $\dfrac{5}{x} - \dfrac{2x-1}{x^2} + \dfrac{x+5}{x^3} = \dfrac{5x^2-x(2x-1)+x+5}{x^3} = \dfrac{3x^2+2x+5}{x^3}$

39 $\dfrac{3t}{t+2} + \dfrac{5t}{t-2} - \dfrac{40}{t^2-4} = \dfrac{3t(t-2)+5t(t+2)-40}{t^2-4} = \dfrac{8t^2+4t-40}{t^2-4} = \dfrac{4(2t+5)(t-2)}{(t+2)(t-2)} = $

$$\dfrac{4(2t+5)}{t+2}$$

40 $\dfrac{t}{t+3} + \dfrac{4t}{t-3} - \dfrac{18}{t^2-9} = \dfrac{t(t-3)+4t(t+3)-18}{t^2-9} = \dfrac{5t^2+9t-18}{t^2-9} = \dfrac{(5t-6)(t+3)}{(t+3)(t-3)} = $

$$\dfrac{5t-6}{t-3}$$

41 $\dfrac{4x}{3x-4} + \dfrac{8}{3x^2-4x} + \dfrac{2}{x} = \dfrac{4x(x)+8+2(3x-4)}{x(3x-4)} = \dfrac{4x^2+6x}{x(3x-4)} = \dfrac{2x(2x+3)}{x(3x-4)} = \dfrac{2(2x+3)}{3x-4}$

42 $\dfrac{12x}{2x+1} - \dfrac{3}{2x^2+x} + \dfrac{5}{x} = \dfrac{12x(x)-3+5(2x+1)}{x(2x+1)} = \dfrac{12x^2+10x+2}{x(2x+1)} = \dfrac{2(6x^2+5x+1)}{x(2x+1)} = $

$$\dfrac{2(2x+1)(3x+1)}{x(2x+1)} = \dfrac{2(3x+1)}{x}$$

43 $\dfrac{2x}{x+2} - \dfrac{8}{x^2+2x} + \dfrac{3}{x} = \dfrac{2x(x)-8+3(x+2)}{x(x+2)} = \dfrac{2x^2+3x-2}{x(x+2)} = \dfrac{(2x-1)(x+2)}{x(x+2)} = \dfrac{2x-1}{x}$

44 $\dfrac{5x}{2x+3} - \dfrac{6}{2x^2+3x} + \dfrac{2}{x} = \dfrac{5x(x)-6+2(2x+3)}{x(2x+3)} = \dfrac{5x^2+4x}{x(2x+3)} = \dfrac{x(5x+4)}{x(2x+3)} = \dfrac{5x+4}{2x+3}$

45 $3 + \dfrac{5}{u} + \dfrac{2u}{3u+1} = \dfrac{3u(3u+1)+5(3u+1)+2u(u)}{u(3u+1)} = \dfrac{11u^2+18u+5}{u(3u+1)}$

46 $4 + \dfrac{2}{u} - \dfrac{3u}{u+5} = \dfrac{4u(u+5)+2(u+5)-3u(u)}{u(u+5)} = \dfrac{u^2+22u+10}{u(u+5)}$

47 $\dfrac{2x+1}{x^2+4x+4} - \dfrac{6x}{x^2-4} + \dfrac{3}{x-2} = \dfrac{(2x+1)(x-2)-6x(x+2)+3(x^2+4x+4)}{(x+2)^2(x-2)} = $

$$\dfrac{-x^2-3x+10}{(x+2)^2(x-2)} = -\dfrac{x^2+3x-10}{(x+2)^2(x-2)} = -\dfrac{(x+5)(x-2)}{(x+2)^2(x-2)} = -\dfrac{x+5}{(x+2)^2}$$

48 $\dfrac{2x+6}{x^2+6x+9} + \dfrac{5x}{x^2-9} + \dfrac{7}{x-3} = \dfrac{2}{x+3} + \dfrac{5x}{x^2-9} + \dfrac{7}{x-3} = \dfrac{2(x-3)+5x+7(x+3)}{x^2-9} = $

$$\dfrac{14x+15}{x^2-9}$$

49 $\dfrac{\frac{b}{a}-\frac{a}{b}}{\frac{1}{a}-\frac{1}{b}}=\dfrac{\left(\frac{b}{a}-\frac{a}{b}\right)\cdot ab}{\left(\frac{1}{a}-\frac{1}{b}\right)\cdot ab}=\dfrac{b^2-a^2}{b-a}=\dfrac{(b+a)(b-a)}{b-a}=a+b$

50 $\dfrac{\frac{x}{y^2}-\frac{y}{x^2}}{\frac{1}{y^2}-\frac{1}{x^2}}=\dfrac{\left(\frac{x}{y^2}-\frac{y}{x^2}\right)\cdot x^2y^2}{\left(\frac{1}{y^2}-\frac{1}{x^2}\right)\cdot x^2y^2}=\dfrac{x^3-y^3}{x^2-y^2}=\dfrac{(x-y)(x^2+xy+y^2)}{(x+y)(x-y)}=\dfrac{x^2+xy+y^2}{x+y}$

51 $\dfrac{y^{-1}+x^{-1}}{(xy)^{-1}}=\dfrac{\frac{1}{y}+\frac{1}{x}}{\frac{1}{xy}}=\dfrac{\left(\frac{1}{y}+\frac{1}{x}\right)\cdot xy}{\left(\frac{1}{xy}\right)\cdot xy}=\dfrac{x+y}{1}=x+y$

52 $\dfrac{y^{-2}-x^{-2}}{y^{-2}+x^{-2}}=\dfrac{\frac{1}{y^2}-\frac{1}{x^2}}{\frac{1}{y^2}+\frac{1}{x^2}}=\dfrac{\left(\frac{1}{y^2}-\frac{1}{x^2}\right)\cdot x^2y^2}{\left(\frac{1}{y^2}+\frac{1}{x^2}\right)\cdot x^2y^2}=\dfrac{x^2-y^2}{x^2+y^2}$

53 $\dfrac{\frac{r}{s}+\frac{s}{r}}{\frac{r^2}{s^2}-\frac{s^2}{r^2}}=\dfrac{\left(\frac{r}{s}+\frac{s}{r}\right)\cdot r^2s^2}{\left(\frac{r^2}{s^2}-\frac{s^2}{r^2}\right)\cdot r^2s^2}=\dfrac{r^3s+rs^3}{r^4-s^4}=\dfrac{rs(r^2+s^2)}{(r^2+s^2)(r^2-s^2)}=\dfrac{rs}{r^2-s^2}$

54 $\dfrac{\frac{3}{w}-\frac{6}{2w+1}}{\frac{5}{w}+\frac{8}{2w+1}}=\dfrac{\dfrac{3(2w+1)-6w}{w(2w+1)}}{\dfrac{5(2w+1)+8w}{w(2w+1)}}=\dfrac{6w+3-6w}{10w+5+8w}=\dfrac{3}{18w+5}$

55 $\dfrac{(x+h)^2-3(x+h)-(x^2-3x)}{h}=\dfrac{2xh+h^2-3h}{h}=\dfrac{h(2x+h-3)}{h}=2x+h-3$

56 $\dfrac{(x+h)^3+5(x+h)-(x^3+5x)}{h}=\dfrac{3x^2h+3xh^2+h^3+5h}{h}=\dfrac{h(3x^2+3xh+h^2+5)}{h}=$

$$3x^2+3xh+h^2+5$$

57 $\dfrac{\frac{3}{x-1}-\frac{3}{a-1}}{x-a}=\dfrac{\dfrac{3(a-1)-3(x-1)}{(x-1)(a-1)}}{x-a}=\dfrac{3a-3x}{(x-1)(a-1)(x-a)}=\dfrac{3(a-x)}{(x-1)(a-1)(x-a)}=$

$$-\dfrac{3}{(x-1)(a-1)}$$

58 $\dfrac{\frac{x+2}{x}-\frac{a+2}{a}}{x-a}=\dfrac{\dfrac{a(x+2)-x(a+2)}{ax}}{x-a}=\dfrac{2a-2x}{ax(x-a)}=\dfrac{2(a-x)}{ax(x-a)}=-\dfrac{2}{ax}$

59 $\dfrac{\frac{1}{(x+h)^3}-\frac{1}{x^3}}{h}=\dfrac{\dfrac{x^3-(x+h)^3}{(x+h)^3x^3}}{h}=\dfrac{x^3-(x+h)^3}{hx^3(x+h)^3}=$

$$\dfrac{[x-(x+h)][x^2+x(x+h)+(x+h)^2]}{hx^3(x+h)^3}=\dfrac{-h(3x^2+3xh+h^2)}{hx^3(x+h)^3}=-\dfrac{3x^2+3xh+h^2}{x^3(x+h)^3}$$

60 $\dfrac{\frac{1}{x+h}-\frac{1}{x}}{h}=\dfrac{\dfrac{x-(x+h)}{(x+h)x}}{h}=\dfrac{-h}{hx(x+h)}=\dfrac{-1}{x(x+h)}$

61 $\dfrac{\sqrt{t}+5}{\sqrt{t}-5} = \dfrac{\sqrt{t}+5}{\sqrt{t}-5} \cdot \dfrac{\sqrt{t}+5}{\sqrt{t}+5} = \dfrac{t+10\sqrt{t}+25}{t-25}$

62 $\dfrac{16x^2-y^2}{2\sqrt{x}-\sqrt{y}} = \dfrac{16x^2-y^2}{2\sqrt{x}-\sqrt{y}} \cdot \dfrac{2\sqrt{x}+\sqrt{y}}{2\sqrt{x}+\sqrt{y}} = \dfrac{(4x+y)(4x-y)(2\sqrt{x}+\sqrt{y})}{4x-y} =$

$$(4x+y)(2\sqrt{x}+\sqrt{y})$$

63 $\dfrac{1}{\sqrt[3]{a}-\sqrt[3]{b}} = \dfrac{1}{\sqrt[3]{a}-\sqrt[3]{b}} \cdot \dfrac{\sqrt[3]{a^2}+\sqrt[3]{ab}+\sqrt[3]{b^2}}{\sqrt[3]{a^2}+\sqrt[3]{ab}+\sqrt[3]{b^2}} = \dfrac{\sqrt[3]{a^2}+\sqrt[3]{ab}+\sqrt[3]{b^2}}{a-b}$

64 $\dfrac{1}{\sqrt[3]{x}+\sqrt[3]{y}} = \dfrac{1}{\sqrt[3]{x}+\sqrt[3]{y}} \cdot \dfrac{\sqrt[3]{x^2}-\sqrt[3]{xy}+\sqrt[3]{y^2}}{\sqrt[3]{x^2}-\sqrt[3]{xy}+\sqrt[3]{y^2}} = \dfrac{\sqrt[3]{x^2}-\sqrt[3]{xy}+\sqrt[3]{y^2}}{x+y}$

65 $\dfrac{\sqrt{a}-\sqrt{b}}{a^2-b^2} = \dfrac{\sqrt{a}-\sqrt{b}}{a^2-b^2} \cdot \dfrac{\sqrt{a}+\sqrt{b}}{\sqrt{a}+\sqrt{b}} = \dfrac{a-b}{(a+b)(a-b)(\sqrt{a}+\sqrt{b})} = \dfrac{1}{(a+b)(\sqrt{a}+\sqrt{b})}$

66 $\dfrac{\sqrt{b}+\sqrt{c}}{b^2-c^2} = \dfrac{\sqrt{b}+\sqrt{c}}{b^2-c^2} \cdot \dfrac{\sqrt{b}-\sqrt{c}}{\sqrt{b}-\sqrt{c}} = \dfrac{b-c}{(b+c)(b-c)(\sqrt{b}-\sqrt{c})} = \dfrac{1}{(b+c)(\sqrt{b}-\sqrt{c})}$

67 $\dfrac{\sqrt{2(x+h)+1}-\sqrt{2x+1}}{h} = \dfrac{\sqrt{2(x+h)+1}-\sqrt{2x+1}}{h} \cdot \dfrac{\sqrt{2(x+h)+1}+\sqrt{2x+1}}{\sqrt{2(x+h)+1}+\sqrt{2x+1}} =$

$$\dfrac{(2x+2h+1)-(2x+1)}{h(\sqrt{2(x+h)+1}+\sqrt{2x+1})} = \dfrac{2}{\sqrt{2(x+h)+1}+\sqrt{2x+1}}$$

68 $\dfrac{\sqrt{x}-\sqrt{x+h}}{h\sqrt{x}\sqrt{x+h}} = \dfrac{\sqrt{x}-\sqrt{x+h}}{h\sqrt{x}\sqrt{x+h}} \cdot \dfrac{\sqrt{x}+\sqrt{x+h}}{\sqrt{x}+\sqrt{x+h}} = \dfrac{x-(x+h)}{h\sqrt{x}\sqrt{x+h}(\sqrt{x}+\sqrt{x+h})} =$

$$\dfrac{-1}{\sqrt{x}\sqrt{x+h}(\sqrt{x}+\sqrt{x+h})}$$

69 $\dfrac{4x^2-x+5}{x^{2/3}} = \dfrac{4x^2}{x^{2/3}} - \dfrac{x}{x^{2/3}} + \dfrac{5}{x^{2/3}} = 4x^{4/3} - x^{1/3} + 5x^{-2/3}$

70 $\dfrac{x^2+4x-6}{\sqrt{x}} = \dfrac{x^2}{\sqrt{x}} + \dfrac{4x}{\sqrt{x}} - \dfrac{6}{\sqrt{x}} = x^{3/2} + 4x^{1/2} - 6x^{-1/2}$

71 $\dfrac{(x^2+2)^2}{x^5} = \dfrac{x^4+4x^2+4}{x^5} = \dfrac{x^4}{x^5} + \dfrac{4x^2}{x^5} + \dfrac{4}{x^5} = x^{-1} + 4x^{-3} + 4x^{-5}$

72 $\dfrac{(\sqrt{x}-3)^2}{x^3} = \dfrac{x-6\sqrt{x}+9}{x^3} = \dfrac{x}{x^3} - \dfrac{6\sqrt{x}}{x^3} + \dfrac{9}{x^3} = x^{-2} - 6x^{-5/2} + 9x^{-3}$

Note: You may wish to demonstrate the 3 techniques shown in Example 7 with one of these simpler expressions in 73–76. Exercises 77–90 are worked using the factoring concept given as the third method of simplification in Example 7.

73 $x^{-3} + x^2 = x^{-3}(1+x^5) = \dfrac{1+x^5}{x^3}$ **74** $x^{-4} - x = x^{-4}(1-x^5) = \dfrac{1-x^5}{x^4}$

75 $x^{-1/2} - x^{3/2} = x^{-1/2}(1-x^2) = \dfrac{1-x^2}{x^{1/2}}$ **76** $x^{-2/3} + x^{7/3} = x^{-2/3}(1+x^3) = \dfrac{1+x^3}{x^{2/3}}$

77 $(2x^2 - 3x + 1)(4)(3x + 2)^3(3) + (3x + 2)^4(4x - 3) =$

$$(3x + 2)^3[12(2x^2 - 3x + 1) + (3x + 2)(4x - 3)] = (3x + 2)^3(36x^2 - 37x + 6)$$

78 $(6x - 5)^3(2)(x^2 + 4)(2x) + (x^2 + 4)^2(3)(6x - 5)^2(6) =$

$$2(6x - 5)^2(x^2 + 4)[2x(6x - 5) + 9(x^2 + 4)] = 2(x^2 + 4)(6x - 5)^2(21x^2 - 10x + 36)$$

79 $(x^2 - 4)^{1/2}(3)(2x + 1)^2(2) + (2x + 1)^3(\frac{1}{2})(x^2 - 4)^{-1/2}(2x) =$

$$(x^2 - 4)^{-1/2}(2x + 1)^2[6(x^2 - 4) + x(2x + 1)] = \frac{(2x + 1)^2(8x^2 + x - 24)}{(x^2 - 4)^{1/2}}$$

80 $(3x + 2)^{1/3}(2)(4x - 5)(4) + (4x - 5)^2(\frac{1}{3})(3x + 2)^{-2/3}(3) =$

$$(3x + 2)^{-2/3}(4x - 5)[8(3x + 2) + (4x - 5)] = \frac{(4x - 5)(28x + 11)}{(3x + 2)^{2/3}}$$

81 $(3x + 1)^6(\frac{1}{2})(2x - 5)^{-1/2}(2) + (2x - 5)^{1/2}(6)(3x + 1)^5(3) =$

$$(3x + 1)^5(2x - 5)^{-1/2}[(3x + 1) + 18(2x - 5)] = \frac{(3x + 1)^5(39x - 89)}{(2x - 5)^{1/2}}$$

82 $(x^2 + 9)^4(-\frac{1}{3})(x + 6)^{-4/3} + (x + 6)^{-1/3}(4)(x^2 + 9)^3(2x) =$

$$(\frac{1}{3})(x^2 + 9)^3(x + 6)^{-4/3}[-(x^2 + 9) + 24x(x + 6)] = \frac{(x^2 + 9)^3(23x^2 + 144x - 9)}{3(x + 6)^{4/3}}$$

83 $\dfrac{(6x + 1)^3(27x^2 + 2) - (9x^3 + 2x)(3)(6x + 1)^2(6)}{(6x + 1)^6} =$

$$\frac{(6x + 1)^2[(6x + 1)(27x^2 + 2) - 18(9x^3 + 2x)]}{(6x + 1)^6} = \frac{27x^2 - 24x + 2}{(6x + 1)^4}$$

84 $\dfrac{(x^2 - 1)^4(2x) - x^2(4)(x^2 - 1)^3(2x)}{(x^2 - 1)^8} = \dfrac{(2x)(x^2 - 1)^3[(x^2 - 1) - 4x^2]}{(x^2 - 1)^8} = \dfrac{-2x(3x^2 + 1)}{(x^2 - 1)^5}$

85 $\dfrac{(x^2 + 2)^3(2x) - x^2(3)(x^2 + 2)^2(2x)}{[(x^2 + 2)^3]^2} = \dfrac{(x^2 + 2)^2(2x)\left[(x^2 + 2)^1 - x^2(3)\right]}{(x^2 + 2)^6} =$

$$\frac{2x(x^2 + 2 - 3x^2)}{(x^2 + 2)^4} = \frac{2x(2 - 2x^2)}{(x^2 + 2)^4} = \frac{4x(1 - x^2)}{(x^2 + 2)^4}$$

86 $\dfrac{(x^2 - 5)^4(3x^2) - x^3(4)(x^2 - 5)^3(2x)}{[(x^2 - 5)^4]^2} = \dfrac{(x^2 - 5)^3(x^2)\left[(x^2 - 5)^1(3) - (x)(4)(2x)\right]}{(x^2 - 5)^8} =$

$$\frac{x^2(3x^2 - 15 - 8x^2)}{(x^2 - 5)^5} = \frac{x^2(-5x^2 - 15)}{(x^2 - 5)^5} = -\frac{5x^2(x^2 + 3)}{(x^2 - 5)^5}$$

87 $\dfrac{(x^2 + 4)^{1/3}(3) - (3x)(\frac{1}{3})(x^2 + 4)^{-2/3}(2x)}{[(x^2 + 4)^{1/3}]^2} = \dfrac{(x^2 + 4)^{-2/3}[3(x^2 + 4) - 2x^2]}{(x^2 + 4)^{2/3}} = \dfrac{x^2 + 12}{(x^2 + 4)^{4/3}}$

88 $\dfrac{(1 - x^2)^{1/2}(2x) - x^2(\frac{1}{2})(1 - x^2)^{-1/2}(-2x)}{[(1 - x^2)^{1/2}]^2} = \dfrac{x(1 - x^2)^{-1/2}[2(1 - x^2) + x^2]}{(1 - x^2)} = \dfrac{x(2 - x^2)}{(1 - x^2)^{3/2}}$

89
$$\frac{(4x^2+9)^{1/2}(2)-(2x+3)(\frac{1}{2})(4x^2+9)^{-1/2}(8x)}{[(4x^2+9)^{1/2}]^2}=$$

$$\frac{(4x^2+9)^{-1/2}[2(4x^2+9)-4x(2x+3)]}{(4x^2+9)}=\frac{18-12x}{(4x^2+9)^{3/2}}=\frac{6(3-2x)}{(4x^2+9)^{3/2}}$$

90
$$\frac{(3x+2)^{1/2}(\frac{1}{3})(2x+3)^{-2/3}(2)-(2x+3)^{1/3}(\frac{1}{2})(3x+2)^{-1/2}(3)}{[(3x+2)^{1/2}]^2}=$$

$$\frac{(\frac{1}{3})(\frac{1}{2})(3x+2)^{-1/2}(2x+3)^{-2/3}[4(3x+2)-9(2x+3)]}{3x+2}=-\frac{6x+19}{6(3x+2)^{3/2}(2x+3)^{2/3}}$$

91 Table $Y_1=\dfrac{113x^3+280x^2-150x}{22x^3+77x^2-100x-350}$ and $Y_2=\dfrac{3x}{2x+7}+\dfrac{4x^2}{1.1x^2-5}$.

x	Y_1	Y_2
1	-0.6923	-0.6923
2	-26.12	-26.12
3	8.0392	8.0392
4	5.8794	5.8794
5	5.3268	5.3268

The values for Y_1 and Y_2 agree. Therefore, the two expressions might be equal.

92 Table $Y_1=\dfrac{20x^2+41x+31}{10x^3+10x^2}$ and $Y_2=\dfrac{1}{x}+\dfrac{1}{x+1}+\dfrac{3.2}{x^2}$.

x	Y_1	Y_2
1	4.6	4.7
2	1.6083	1.6333
3	0.92778	0.93889
4	0.64375	0.65
5	0.49067	0.49467

The values for Y_1 and Y_2 do not agree. Therefore, the two expressions are not equal.

93 Area of I is $(x-y)x$, area of II is $(x-y)y$,

$$\text{and } A=x^2-y^2=(x-y)x+(x-y)y=(x-y)(x+y).$$

94 Volume of I is $x^2(x-y)$, volume of II is $xy(x-y)$, and volume of III is $y^2(x-y)$.

$$V=x^3-y^3=x^2(x-y)+xy(x-y)+y^2(x-y)=(x-y)(x^2+xy+y^2).$$

95 (a) $C_f=66.5+13.8(59)+5(163)-6.8(25)=1525.7$ calories

$C_m=655+9.6(75)+1.9(178)-4.7(55)=1454.7$ calories

(b) As people age they require fewer calories. The coefficients of w and h are positive because large people require more calories.

1.4 Exercises

$\boxed{1}$ $4x - 3 = -5x + 6 \Rightarrow 4x + 5x = 6 + 3 \Rightarrow 9x = 9 \Rightarrow x = 1$

$\boxed{2}$ $5x - 4 = 2(x - 2) \Rightarrow 5x - 4 = 2x - 4 \Rightarrow 3x = 0 \Rightarrow x = 0$

$\boxed{3}$ $(3x - 2)^2 = (x - 5)(9x + 4) \Rightarrow 9x^2 - 12x + 4 = 9x^2 - 41x - 20 \Rightarrow 29x = -24 \Rightarrow$

$$x = -\tfrac{24}{29}$$

$\boxed{4}$ $(x + 5)^2 + 3 = (x - 2)^2 \Rightarrow x^2 + 10x + 25 + 3 = x^2 - 4x + 4 \Rightarrow 14x = -24 \Rightarrow x = -\tfrac{12}{7}$

$\boxed{5}$ $\left[\dfrac{3x + 1}{6x - 2} = \dfrac{2x + 5}{4x - 13}\right] \cdot (6x - 2)(4x - 13) \Rightarrow 12x^2 - 35x - 13 = 12x^2 + 26x - 10 \Rightarrow$

$$-3 = 61x \Rightarrow x = -\tfrac{3}{61}$$

$\boxed{6}$ $\left[\dfrac{5x + 2}{10x - 3} = \dfrac{x - 8}{2x + 3}\right] \cdot (10x - 3)(2x + 3) \Rightarrow 10x^2 + 19x + 6 = 10x^2 - 83x + 24 \Rightarrow$

$$102x = 18 \Rightarrow x = \tfrac{3}{17}$$

$\boxed{7}$ $\left[\dfrac{4}{x + 2} + \dfrac{1}{x - 2} = \dfrac{5x - 6}{x^2 - 4}\right] \cdot (x + 2)(x - 2) \Rightarrow 4(x - 2) + x + 2 = 5x - 6 \Rightarrow 0 = 0,$

indicating an identity. $\mathbb{R} - \{\pm 2\}$

$\boxed{8}$ $\left[\dfrac{2}{2x + 5} + \dfrac{3}{2x - 5} = \dfrac{10x + 5}{4x^2 - 25}\right] \cdot (2x + 5)(2x - 5) \Rightarrow 2(2x - 5) + 3(2x + 5) = 10x + 5 \Rightarrow$

$$10x + 5 = 10x + 5, \text{ indicating an identity. } \mathbb{R} - \{\pm \tfrac{5}{2}\}$$

$\boxed{9}$ $\left[\dfrac{5}{2x + 3} + \dfrac{4}{2x - 3} = \dfrac{14x + 3}{4x^2 - 9}\right] \cdot (2x + 3)(2x - 3) \Rightarrow 5(2x - 3) + 4(2x + 3) = 14x + 3 \Rightarrow$

$$18x - 3 = 14x + 3 \Rightarrow 4x = 6 \Rightarrow x = \tfrac{3}{2},$$

which is not in the domain of the given expressions. No solution

$\boxed{10}$ $\left[\dfrac{-3}{x + 4} + \dfrac{7}{x - 4} = \dfrac{-5x + 4}{x^2 - 16}\right] \cdot (x + 4)(x - 4) \Rightarrow -3(x - 4) + 7(x + 4) = -5x + 4 \Rightarrow$

$$4x + 40 = -5x + 4 \Rightarrow 9x = -36 \Rightarrow x = -4,$$

which is not in the domain of the given expressions. No solution

$\boxed{11}$ $75x^2 + 35x - 10 = 0 \Rightarrow 15x^2 + 7x - 2 = 0 \Rightarrow (3x + 2)(5x - 1) = 0 \Rightarrow x = -\tfrac{2}{3}, \tfrac{1}{5}$

$\boxed{12}$ $48x^2 + 12x - 90 = 0 \Rightarrow 8x^2 + 2x - 15 = 0 \Rightarrow (2x + 3)(4x - 5) = 0 \Rightarrow x = -\tfrac{3}{2}, \tfrac{5}{4}$

$\boxed{13}$ $\left[\dfrac{2x}{x + 3} + \dfrac{5}{x} - 4 = \dfrac{18}{x^2 + 3x}\right] \cdot x(x + 3) \Rightarrow 2x(x) + 5(x + 3) - 4(x^2 + 3x) = 18 \Rightarrow$

$$0 = 2x^2 + 7x + 3 \Rightarrow (2x + 1)(x + 3) = 0 \Rightarrow$$

$$x = -\tfrac{1}{2} \{-3 \text{ is not in the domain of the given expressions}\}$$

$\boxed{14}$ $\left[\dfrac{3x}{x - 2} + \dfrac{1}{x + 2} = \dfrac{-4}{x^2 - 4}\right] \cdot (x + 2)(x - 2) \Rightarrow 3x(x + 2) + 1(x - 2) = -4 \Rightarrow$

$$3x^2 + 7x + 2 = 0 \Rightarrow (3x + 1)(x + 2) = 0 \Rightarrow$$

$$x = -\tfrac{1}{3} \{-2 \text{ is not in the domain of the given expressions}\}$$

$\boxed{15}$ $25x^2 = 9 \Rightarrow x^2 = \tfrac{9}{25} \Rightarrow x = \pm\sqrt{\tfrac{9}{25}} = \pm\tfrac{3}{5}$

$\boxed{16}$ $16x^2 = 49 \Rightarrow x^2 = \tfrac{49}{16} \Rightarrow x = \pm\sqrt{\tfrac{49}{16}} = \pm\tfrac{7}{4}$

$\boxed{17}$ $(x - 3)^2 = 17 \Rightarrow x - 3 = \pm\sqrt{17} \Rightarrow x = 3 \pm \sqrt{17}$

18   $(x+4)^2 = 31 \Rightarrow x + 4 = \pm\sqrt{31} \Rightarrow x = -4 \pm \sqrt{31}$

19   $x^2 + 4x + 2 = 0 \Rightarrow x = \dfrac{-4 \pm \sqrt{16 - 8}}{2} = \dfrac{-4 \pm 2\sqrt{2}}{2} = -2 \pm \sqrt{2}$

20   $x^2 - 6x - 3 = 0 \Rightarrow x = \dfrac{6 \pm \sqrt{36 + 12}}{2} = \dfrac{6 \pm 4\sqrt{3}}{2} = 3 \pm 2\sqrt{3}$

21   $|3x - 2| + 3 = 7 \Rightarrow |3x - 2| = 4 \Rightarrow 3x - 2 = 4$ or $3x - 2 = -4 \Rightarrow$

$$3x = 6 \text{ or } 3x = -2 \Rightarrow x = 2 \text{ or } x = -\tfrac{2}{3}$$

22   $2|5x + 2| - 1 = 5 \Rightarrow 2|5x + 2| = 6 \Rightarrow |5x + 2| = 3 \Rightarrow$

$$5x + 2 = 3 \text{ or } 5x + 2 = -3 \Rightarrow 5x = 1 \text{ or } 5x = -5 \Rightarrow x = \tfrac{1}{5} \text{ or } x = -1$$

23   $3|x + 1| - 2 = -11 \Rightarrow 3|x + 1| = -9 \Rightarrow |x + 1| = -3$. Since the absolute value of
an expression is nonnegative, $|x + 1| = -3$ has no solution.

24   $|x - 2| + 5 = 5 \Rightarrow |x - 2| = 0$. Since the absolute value of an expression can only

equal 0 if the expression itself is 0, $|x - 2| = 0 \Rightarrow x - 2 = 0 \Rightarrow x = 2$.

25   $9x^3 - 18x^2 - 4x + 8 = 0 \Rightarrow 9x^2(x - 2) - 4(x - 2) = 0 \Rightarrow (9x^2 - 4)(x - 2) = 0 \Rightarrow$

$$x = \pm\tfrac{2}{3}, \, 2$$

26   $4x^4 + 10x^3 = 6x^2 + 15x \Rightarrow x(4x^3 + 10x^2 - 6x - 15) = 0 \Rightarrow$

$$x\left[2x^2(2x + 5) - 3(2x + 5)\right] = 0 \Rightarrow x(2x^2 - 3)(2x + 5) = 0 \Rightarrow x = 0, \, \pm\tfrac{1}{2}\sqrt{6}, \, -\tfrac{5}{2}$$

27   $y^{3/2} = 5y \Rightarrow y^{3/2} - 5y = 0 \Rightarrow y(y^{1/2} - 5) = 0 \Rightarrow y = 0$ or $y^{1/2} = 5$.

$$y^{1/2} = 5 \Rightarrow (y^{1/2})^2 = 5^2 \Rightarrow y = 25. \;\; y = 0, \, 25$$

28   $y^{4/3} = -3y \Rightarrow y^{4/3} + 3y = 0 \Rightarrow y(y^{1/3} + 3) = 0 \Rightarrow y = 0$ or $y^{1/3} = -3$.

$$y^{1/3} = -3 \Rightarrow (y^{1/3})^3 = (-3)^3 \Rightarrow y = -27. \;\; y = 0, \, -27$$

29   $\sqrt{7 - x} = x - 5 \Rightarrow 7 - x = x^2 - 10x + 25 \Rightarrow x^2 - 9x + 18 = 0 \Rightarrow$

$$(x - 3)(x - 6) = 0 \Rightarrow x = 6 \text{ and } 3 \text{ is an extraneous solution.}$$

30   $\sqrt{3 - x} - x = 3 \Rightarrow (\sqrt{3 - x})^2 = (x + 3)^2 \Rightarrow 3 - x = x^2 + 6x + 9 \Rightarrow x^2 + 7x + 6 = 0 \Rightarrow$

$$(x + 1)(x + 6) = 0 \Rightarrow x = -1 \text{ and } -6 \text{ is an extraneous solution.}$$

31   $x = 3 + \sqrt{5x - 9} \Rightarrow x - 3 = \sqrt{5x - 9} \Rightarrow x^2 - 6x + 9 = 5x - 9 \Rightarrow$

$$x^2 - 11x + 18 = 0 \Rightarrow (x - 2)(x - 9) = 0 \Rightarrow x = 9 \text{ and } 2 \text{ is an extraneous solution.}$$

32   $x + \sqrt{5x + 19} = -1 \Rightarrow \sqrt{5x + 19} = -x - 1 \Rightarrow 5x + 19 = x^2 + 2x + 1 \Rightarrow$

$$x^2 - 3x - 18 = 0 \Rightarrow (x - 6)(x + 3) = 0 \Rightarrow x = -3 \text{ and } 6 \text{ is an extraneous solution.}$$

33   $5y^4 - 7y^2 + 1 = 0 \Rightarrow y^2 = \dfrac{7 \pm \sqrt{29}}{10} \cdot \dfrac{10}{10} = \dfrac{70 \pm 10\sqrt{29}}{100} \Rightarrow y = \pm\tfrac{1}{10}\sqrt{70 \pm 10\sqrt{29}}$

34   $3y^4 - 5y^2 + 1 = 0 \Rightarrow y^2 = \dfrac{5 \pm \sqrt{13}}{6} \cdot \dfrac{6}{6} = \dfrac{30 \pm 6\sqrt{13}}{36} \Rightarrow y = \pm\tfrac{1}{6}\sqrt{30 \pm 6\sqrt{13}}$

Note: Substitution could be used instead of factoring for the following exercises.

35   $36x^{-4} - 13x^{-2} + 1 = 0 \Rightarrow (4x^{-2} - 1)(9x^{-2} - 1) = 0 \Rightarrow x^{-2} = \tfrac{1}{4}, \, \tfrac{1}{9} \Rightarrow x^2 = 4, \, 9 \Rightarrow$

$$x = \pm 2, \, \pm 3$$

36 $x^{-2} - 2x^{-1} - 35 = 0 \Rightarrow (x^{-1} - 7)(x^{-1} + 5) = 0 \Rightarrow x^{-1} = 7, -5 \Rightarrow x = \frac{1}{7}, -\frac{1}{5}$

37 $3x^{2/3} + 4x^{1/3} - 4 = 0 \Rightarrow (3x^{1/3} - 2)(x^{1/3} + 2) = 0 \Rightarrow \sqrt[3]{x} = \frac{2}{3}, -2 \Rightarrow x = \frac{8}{27}, -8$

38 $2y^{1/3} - 3y^{1/6} + 1 = 0 \Rightarrow (2y^{1/6} - 1)(y^{1/6} - 1) = 0 \Rightarrow \sqrt[6]{y} = \frac{1}{2}, 1 \Rightarrow y = \frac{1}{64}, 1$

39 (a) $x^{5/3} = 32 \Rightarrow (x^{5/3})^{3/5} = (32)^{3/5} \Rightarrow x = (\sqrt[5]{32})^3 = 2^3 = 8$

  (b) $x^{4/3} = 16 \Rightarrow (x^{4/3})^{3/4} = \pm(16)^{3/4} \Rightarrow x = \pm(\sqrt[4]{16})^3 = \pm 2^3 = \pm 8$

  (c) $x^{2/3} = -36 \Rightarrow (x^{2/3})^{3/2} = \pm(-36)^{3/2} \Rightarrow x = \pm(\sqrt{-36})^3,$

which are not real numbers. No real solutions

  (d) $x^{3/4} = 125 \Rightarrow (x^{3/4})^{4/3} = (125)^{4/3} \Rightarrow x = (\sqrt[3]{125})^4 = 5^4 = 625$

  (e) $x^{3/2} = -27 \Rightarrow (x^{3/2})^{2/3} = (-27)^{2/3} \Rightarrow x = (\sqrt[3]{-27})^2 = (-3)^2 = 9,$

which is an extraneous solution. No real solutions

40 (a) $x^{3/5} = -27 \Rightarrow (x^{3/5})^{5/3} = (-27)^{5/3} \Rightarrow x = (\sqrt[3]{-27})^5 = (-3)^5 = -243$

  (b) $x^{2/3} = 25 \Rightarrow (x^{2/3})^{3/2} = \pm(25)^{3/2} \Rightarrow x = \pm(\sqrt{25})^3 = \pm 5^3 = \pm 125$

  (c) $x^{4/3} = -49 \Rightarrow (x^{4/3})^{3/4} = \pm(-49)^{3/4} \Rightarrow x = \pm(\sqrt[4]{-49})^3,$

which are not real numbers. No real solutions

  (d) $x^{3/2} = 27 \Rightarrow (x^{3/2})^{2/3} = (27)^{2/3} \Rightarrow x = (\sqrt[3]{27})^2 = 3^2 = 9$

  (e) $x^{3/4} = -8 \Rightarrow (x^{3/4})^{4/3} = (-8)^{4/3} \Rightarrow x = (\sqrt[3]{-8})^4 = (-2)^4 = 16,$

which is an extraneous solution. No real solutions

41 (a) $4x^2 - 4xy + 1 - y^2 = 0 \Rightarrow (4)x^2 + (-4y)x + (1 - y^2) = 0 \Rightarrow$

$$x = \frac{4y \pm \sqrt{16y^2 - 16(1 - y^2)}}{8} = \frac{4y \pm 4\sqrt{2y^2 - 1}}{8} = \frac{y \pm \sqrt{2y^2 - 1}}{2}$$

  (b) $4x^2 - 4xy + 1 - y^2 = 0 \Rightarrow (-1)y^2 + (-4x)y + (4x^2 + 1) = 0 \Rightarrow$

$$y = \frac{4x \pm \sqrt{16x^2 + 4(4x^2 + 1)}}{-2} = \frac{4x \pm 2\sqrt{8x^2 + 1}}{-2} = -2x \pm \sqrt{8x^2 + 1}$$

42 (a) $2x^2 - xy = 3y^2 + 1 \Rightarrow (2)x^2 + (-y)x + (-3y^2 - 1) = 0 \Rightarrow$

$$x = \frac{y \pm \sqrt{y^2 - 8(-3y^2 - 1)}}{4} = \frac{y \pm \sqrt{25y^2 + 8}}{4}$$

  (b) $2x^2 - xy = 3y^2 + 1 \Rightarrow (-3)y^2 + (-x)y + (2x^2 - 1) = 0 \Rightarrow$

$$y = \frac{x \pm \sqrt{x^2 + 12(2x^2 - 1)}}{-6} = \frac{x \pm \sqrt{25x^2 - 12}}{-6}$$

43 (a) $x = \dfrac{-4{,}500{,}000 \pm \sqrt{4{,}500{,}000^2 - 4(1)(-0.96)}}{2} \approx 0$ and $-4{,}500{,}000$

(b) $x = \dfrac{-b \pm \sqrt{b^2 - 4ac}}{2a} \cdot \dfrac{-b \mp \sqrt{b^2 - 4ac}}{-b \mp \sqrt{b^2 - 4ac}} = \dfrac{b^2 - (b^2 - 4ac)}{2a(-b \mp \sqrt{b^2 - 4ac})} =$

$\dfrac{4ac}{2a(-b \mp \sqrt{b^2 - 4ac})} = \dfrac{2c}{-b \mp \sqrt{b^2 - 4ac}}$. The root near zero was obtained in part

(a) using the plus sign, In the second formula, it corresponds to the minus sign.

$$x = \dfrac{2(-0.96)}{-4{,}500{,}000 - \sqrt{4{,}500{,}000^2 - 4(1)(-0.96)}} \approx 2.13 \times 10^{-7}$$

44 (a) $x = \dfrac{73{,}000{,}000 \pm \sqrt{(-73{,}000{,}000)^2 - 4(1)(2.01)}}{2} \approx 73{,}000{,}000$ and 0

(b) The root near zero was obtained in part (a) using the minus sign,

In the second formula, it corresponds to the plus sign.

$$x = \dfrac{2(2.01)}{73{,}000{,}000 + \sqrt{(-73{,}000{,}000)^2 - 4(1)(2.01)}} \approx 2.75 \times 10^{-8}$$

45 $A = P + Prt \Rightarrow A - P = Prt \Rightarrow r = \dfrac{A - P}{Pt}$

46 $s = \frac{1}{2}gt^2 + v_0 t \Rightarrow 2s = gt^2 + 2v_0 t \Rightarrow 2s - gt^2 = 2v_0 t \Rightarrow v_0 = \dfrac{2s - gt^2}{2t}$

47 $S = \dfrac{p}{q + p(1 - q)} \Rightarrow Sq + Sp(1 - q) = p \Rightarrow Sq + Sp - Spq = p \Rightarrow$

$$Sq - Spq = p - Sp \Rightarrow Sq(1 - p) = p(1 - S) \Rightarrow q = \dfrac{p(1 - S)}{S(1 - p)}$$

48 $S = 2(lw + hw + hl) \Rightarrow S = 2lw + 2hw + 2hl \Rightarrow S - 2lw = 2h(w + l) \Rightarrow h = \dfrac{S - 2lw}{2(w + l)}$

49 $\frac{1}{f} = \frac{1}{p} + \frac{1}{q}$ { multiply by fpq } $\Rightarrow pq = fq + fp \Rightarrow pq - fq = fp \Rightarrow q(p - f) = fp \Rightarrow$

$$q = \dfrac{fp}{p - f}$$

50 $\frac{1}{R} = \frac{1}{R_1} + \frac{1}{R_2} + \frac{1}{R_3}$ { multiply by $RR_1 R_2 R_3$ } $\Rightarrow$

$R_1 R_2 R_3 = RR_2 R_3 + RR_1 R_3 + RR_1 R_2 \Rightarrow R_1 R_2 R_3 - RR_2 R_3 - RR_1 R_2 = RR_1 R_3 \Rightarrow$

$$R_2(R_1 R_3 - RR_3 - RR_1) = RR_1 R_3 \Rightarrow R_2 = \dfrac{RR_1 R_3}{R_1 R_3 - RR_3 - RR_1}$$

51 $K = \frac{1}{2}mv^2 \Rightarrow v^2 = \dfrac{2K}{m} \Rightarrow v = \pm\sqrt{\dfrac{2K}{m}} \Rightarrow v = \sqrt{\dfrac{2K}{m}}$ since $v > 0$.

52 $F = g\dfrac{mM}{d^2} \Rightarrow d^2 = \dfrac{gmM}{F} \Rightarrow d = \pm\sqrt{\dfrac{gmM}{F}} \Rightarrow d = \sqrt{\dfrac{gmM}{F}}$ since $d > 0$.

53 $A = 2\pi r(r + h) \Rightarrow A = 2\pi r^2 + 2\pi rh \Rightarrow (2\pi)r^2 + (2\pi h)r - A = 0 \Rightarrow$

$$r = \dfrac{-2\pi h \pm \sqrt{4\pi^2 h^2 + 8\pi A}}{4\pi} = \dfrac{-\pi h \pm \sqrt{\pi^2 h^2 + 2\pi A}}{2\pi}.$$

Since $r > 0$, we must use the plus sign, and $r = \dfrac{-\pi h + \sqrt{\pi^2 h^2 + 2\pi A}}{2\pi}$.

54 $s = \frac{1}{2}gt^2 + v_0t \Rightarrow (\frac{1}{2}g)t^2 + (v_0)t - s = 0 \Rightarrow t = \dfrac{-v_0 \pm \sqrt{v_0^2 + 2gs}}{g}.$

Since $t > 0$, we must use the plus sign, and $t = \dfrac{-v_0 + \sqrt{v_0^2 + 2gs}}{g}.$

55 $d = \frac{1}{2}\sqrt{4R^2 - C^2} \Rightarrow 2d = \sqrt{4R^2 - C^2} \Rightarrow 4d^2 = 4R^2 - C^2 \Rightarrow C^2 = 4(R^2 - d^2) \Rightarrow$

$C = \pm 2\sqrt{R^2 - d^2} \Rightarrow C = 2\sqrt{R^2 - d^2}$ since $C > 0$

56 $S = \pi r\sqrt{r^2 + h^2} \Rightarrow \frac{S}{\pi r} = \sqrt{r^2 + h^2} \Rightarrow \frac{S^2}{\pi^2 r^2} = h^2 + r^2 \Rightarrow \frac{S^2}{\pi^2 r^2} - r^2 = h^2 \Rightarrow$

$h^2 = \frac{1}{\pi^2 r^2}(S^2 - \pi^2 r^4) \Rightarrow h = \pm\frac{1}{\pi r}\sqrt{S^2 - \pi^2 r^4} \Rightarrow h = \frac{1}{\pi r}\sqrt{S^2 - \pi^2 r^4}$ since $h > 0$

57 Let x denote the number of months needed to recover the cost of the insulation. The

savings in one month is 10% of $60 = \$6$. $6x = 1080 \Rightarrow x = 180$ months (or 15 yr).

58 Let x denote the amount (in millions) invested in bonds.

$x(0.12) + (50 - x)(0.10) = 5.2 \Rightarrow 0.02x = 0.2 \Rightarrow x = 10$. The arena should be

financed by selling $10 million in bonds and borrowing $40 million.

59 (a) Let t denote the desired number of seconds. $1.5t + 2t = 224 \Rightarrow t = 64$ sec

(b) $64(1.5) = 96$ m and $64(2) = 128$ m, respectively

60 Let l denote the length of the side parallel to the river bank. $P = 2w + l$

(a) $P = 2w + 2w = 4w; 4w = 180 \Rightarrow w = 45$ ft and $A = (45)(90) = 4050$ ft^2.

(b) $P = 2w + \frac{1}{2}w = \frac{5}{2}w; \frac{5}{2}w = 180 \Rightarrow w = 72$ ft and $A = (72)(36) = 2592$ ft^2.

(c) $P = 2w + w = 3w; 3w = 180 \Rightarrow w = 60$ ft and $A = (60)(60) = 3600$ ft^2.

61 Let x denote the distance to the target.

$\text{Time}_{\text{to target}} + \text{Time}_{\text{from target}} = \text{Time}_{\text{total}} \Rightarrow \frac{x}{3300} + \frac{x}{1100} = 1.5 \Rightarrow$

$x + 3x = 1.5(3300) \Rightarrow 4x = 4950 \Rightarrow x = 1237.5$ ft.

62 Let x denote the miles in one direction. A 6-minute-mile pace is equivalent to a rate

of $\frac{1}{6}$ mile/min. $\text{Minutes}_{\text{north}} + \text{Minutes}_{\text{south}} = \text{Minutes}_{\text{total}} \Rightarrow \frac{x}{1/6} + \frac{x}{1/7} = 45 \Rightarrow$

$6x + 7x = 45 \Rightarrow x = \frac{45}{13}$. The total distance is $2 \cdot \frac{45}{13} = \frac{90}{13}$, or $6\frac{12}{13}$ mi.

63 $A = \frac{1}{2}(b_1 + b_2)h \Rightarrow 5 = \frac{1}{2}(3 + b_2)(1) \Rightarrow b_2 = 7$ ft.

64 Let h_1 denote the height of the cylinder. $V = \frac{2}{3}\pi r^3 + \pi r^2 h_1 = 11{,}250\pi$ and $r = 15 \Rightarrow$

$2250\pi + 225\pi h_1 = 11{,}250\pi \Rightarrow h_1 = 40$. The total height is 40 ft + 15 ft = 55 ft.

65 (a) $h = 5280$ and $T_0 = 70 \Rightarrow T = 70 - \left(\frac{5.5}{1000}\right)5280 = 40.96°$ F.

(b) $T = 32 \Rightarrow 32 = 70 - \left(\frac{5.5}{1000}\right)h \Rightarrow h = (70 - 32)\left(\frac{1000}{5.5}\right) \approx 6909$ ft.

66 (a) $T = 70$ and $D = 55 \Rightarrow h = 227(70 - 55) = 3405$ ft.

(b) $h = 3500$ and $D = 65 \Rightarrow 3500 = 227(T - 65) \Rightarrow T = \frac{3500}{227} + 65 \approx 80.4°$ F

$\boxed{67}$ $B = 55$ and $h = 10,000 - 4000 = 6000 \Rightarrow T = 55 - \left(\frac{3}{1000}\right)(6000) = 37°$F.

$\boxed{68}$ (a) $x = 30 \Rightarrow h = 65 + 3.14(30) = 159.2$ cm.

(b) $x = 34 \Rightarrow h = 73.6 + 3(34) = 175.6$ cm. The height of the skeleton has decreased by $175.6 - 174 = 1.6$ cm due to aging after age 30. $\frac{1.6}{0.06} \approx 27$ years. The male was approximately $30 + 27 = 57$ years old at death.

$\boxed{69}$ (a) $v = 55 \Rightarrow d = v + (v^2/20) = 55 + (55^2/20) = 206.25$ ft

(b) $d = 120 \Rightarrow 120 = v + (v^2/20) \Rightarrow 2400 = 20v + v^2 \Rightarrow (v + 60)(v - 40) = 0 \Rightarrow$

$$v = 40 \text{ mi/hr}$$

$\boxed{70}$ (a) $T = 98 \Rightarrow h = 1000(100 - T) + 580(100 - T)^2 = 1000(2) + 580(2)^2 = 4320$ m.

(b) If $x = 100 - T$ and $h = 8840$, then $8840 = 1000x + 580x^2 \Rightarrow$

$$29x^2 + 50x - 442 = 0 \Rightarrow x = \frac{-25 \pm \sqrt{13,443}}{29} \approx -4.86, 3.14.$$

$$T = 100 - x \Rightarrow x = 3.14 \text{ and } T = 96.86°\text{C for } 95 \le T \le 100.$$

$\boxed{71}$ (a) The distances of the northbound and eastbound planes are $100 + 200t$ and $400t$, respectively. Using the Pythagorean theorem,

$$d = \sqrt{(100 + 200t)^2 + (400t)^2} = \sqrt{100^2(1 + 2t)^2 + 100^2(4t)^2} = 100\sqrt{20t^2 + 4t + 1}.$$

(b) $d = 500 \Rightarrow 500 = 100\sqrt{20t^2 + 4t + 1} \Rightarrow 5^2 = 20t^2 + 4t + 1 \Rightarrow 5t^2 + t - 6 = 0 \Rightarrow$

$$(5t + 6)(t - 1) = 0 \Rightarrow t = 1 \text{ hour after 2:30 P.M., or 3:30 P.M.}$$

$\boxed{72}$ Let t denote the number of seconds the rock falls. Distance$_{\text{down}}$ = Distance$_{\text{up}}$ $\Rightarrow$

$$16t^2 = 1100(4 - t) \ \{d = rt\} \Rightarrow 4t^2 + 275t - 1100 = 0 \Rightarrow t = \frac{-275 + 5\sqrt{3729}}{8} \approx 3.79.$$

$$\text{The height is } 16t^2 \approx 229.94, \text{ or } 230 \text{ ft.}$$

$\boxed{73}$ Let x denote the number of \$10 reductions in price.

Revenue = (unit price) $\times$ (# of units) $\Rightarrow 7000 = (300 - 10x)(15 + 2x) \Rightarrow$

$700 = -2x^2 + 45x + 450 \Rightarrow 2x^2 - 45x + 250 = 0 \Rightarrow (2x - 25)(x - 10) = 0 \Rightarrow x = 10$ or

12.5. The selling price is $\$300 - \$10(10) = \$200$, or $\$300 - \$10(12.5) = \$175$.

$\boxed{74}$ The total surface area is the sum of the surface area of the cylinder and that of the top and bottom. $S = 2\pi rh + 2\pi r^2 \Rightarrow 10\pi = 8\pi r + 2\pi r^2 \Rightarrow$

$$r^2 + 4r - 5 = 0 \Rightarrow (r + 5)(r - 1) = 0 \Rightarrow r = 1, \text{ and the diameter is 2 ft.}$$

$\boxed{75}$ (a) Area$_{\text{capsule}}$ = Area$_{\text{sphere}}$ $\{$ the two ends are hemispheres $\}$ + Area$_{\text{cylinder}}$ =

$$4\pi r^2 + 2\pi rh = 4\pi(\tfrac{1}{4})^2 + 2\pi(\tfrac{1}{4})(2 - \tfrac{1}{2}) = \tfrac{\pi}{4} + \tfrac{3\pi}{4} = \pi \text{ cm}^2.$$

Area$_{\text{tablet}}$ = Area$_{\text{top and bottom}}$ + Area$_{\text{cylinder}}$ = $2\pi r^2 + 2\pi r(\tfrac{1}{2}) = 2\pi r^2 + \pi r.$

Equating the two surface areas yields $2\pi r^2 + \pi r = \pi \Rightarrow$

$$2r^2 + r - 1 = 0 \Rightarrow (2r - 1)(r + 1) = 0 \Rightarrow r = \tfrac{1}{2}, \text{ and the diameter is 1 cm.}$$

(b) $\text{Volume}_{\text{capsule}} = \text{Volume}_{\text{sphere}} + \text{Volume}_{\text{cylinder}} =$

$$\tfrac{4}{3}\pi r^3 + \pi r^2 h = \tfrac{4}{3}\pi\left(\tfrac{1}{4}\right)^3 + \pi\left(\tfrac{1}{4}\right)^2\tfrac{3}{2} = \tfrac{\pi}{48} + \tfrac{3\pi}{32} = \tfrac{11\pi}{96} \approx 0.360 \text{ cm}^3.$$

$\text{Volume}_{\text{tablet}} = \text{Volume}_{\text{cylinder}} = \pi r^2 h = \pi\left(\tfrac{1}{2}\right)^2\tfrac{1}{2} = \tfrac{\pi}{8} \approx 0.393 \text{ cm}^3.$

76 $P = 15{,}700S^{5/2}RD \Rightarrow S = \left(\dfrac{P}{15{,}700RD}\right)^{2/5} = \left(\dfrac{380}{(15{,}700)(0.113/2)(2)}\right)^{2/5} \approx 0.54$

77 $Q = kP^{-c} = 10^5 P^{-1/2} \Rightarrow$

$$\sqrt{P} = \frac{10^5}{Q} \Rightarrow P = \left(\frac{10^5}{Q}\right)^2 = \left(\frac{100{,}000}{5000}\right)^2 = (20)^2 = 400 \text{ cents, or, } \$4.00.$$

78 $T = 0.25P^{1/4}/\sqrt{v} \Rightarrow P^{1/4} = 4T\sqrt{v} \Rightarrow P = (4T)^4 v^2 = 4^4 3^4 5^2 = 518{,}400$

79 $\text{Cost}_{\text{underwater}} + \text{Cost}_{\text{overland}} = \text{Cost}_{\text{total}} \Rightarrow$

$7500\sqrt{x^2+1} + 6000(5-x) = 35{,}000 \Rightarrow 15\sqrt{x^2+1} = 12x + 10 \Rightarrow$

$225(x^2+1) = 144x^2 + 240x + 100 \Rightarrow 81x^2 - 240x + 125 = 0 \Rightarrow$

$x = \dfrac{240 \pm \sqrt{17{,}100}}{162} = \dfrac{40 \pm 5\sqrt{19}}{27} \approx 2.2887,\ 0.6743$ mi. There are two possible routes.

80 The y-value decreases 1.2 units for each 1 unit increase in the x-value. The data is best described by equation (1), $y = -1.2x + 2$.

81 The y-values are increasing rapidly and can best be described by equation (4), $y = x^3 - x^2 + x - 10$.

82 (a) Let $Y_1 = T_1 = -1.09L + 96.01$ and $Y_2 = T_2 = -0.011L^2 - 0.126L + 81.45$.

Table each equation and compare them to the actual temperatures.

$x\ (L)$	Y_1	Y_2	S. Hem.
85	3.36	-8.74	-5
75	14.26	10.13	10
65	25.16	26.79	27
55	36.06	41.25	42
45	46.96	53.51	53
35	57.86	63.57	65
25	68.76	71.43	75
15	79.66	77.09	78
5	90.56	80.55	79

Comparing Y_1 (T_1) with Y_2 (T_2), we can see that the linear equation T_1 is not as accurate as the quadratic equation T_2.

(b) $L = 50 \Rightarrow T_2 = -0.011(50)^2 - 0.126(50) + 81.45 = 47.65°\text{F}.$

83 (a) Let $Y_1 = D_1 = 6.096L + 685.7$ and

       $Y_2 = D_2 = 0.00178L^3 - 0.072L^2 + 4.37L + 719$.

Table each equation and compare them to the actual values.

x (L)	Y_1	Y_2	Summer
0	686	719	720
10	747	757	755
20	808	792	792
30	869	833	836
40	930	893	892
50	991	980	978
60	1051	1106	1107

Comparing Y_1 (D_1) with Y_2 (D_2) we can see that the linear equation D_1 is not as accurate as the cubic equation D_2.

(b) $L = 35 \Rightarrow D_2 = 0.00178(35)^3 - 0.072(35)^2 + 4.37(35) + 719 \approx 860$ min.

84 (a) The volume of the box is given by $V = x(24 - 2x)(36 - 2x)$.

(b) Let $Y_1 = x(24 - 2x)(36 - 2x)$.

                      The maximum V is $1825.292 \approx 1825.3$ in^2 when $x = 4.7$ in.

x	V	x	V
4.5	1822.5	4.8	1824.8
4.6	1824.5	4.9	1823.0
4.7	1825.3	5.0	1820.0

85 The volume of the box is $V = hw^2 = 25$, where h is the height and w is the length of a side of the square base. The amount of cardboard will be minimized when the surface area of the box is a minimum. The surface area is given by $S = w^2 + 4wh$. Since $h = 25/w^2$, we have $S = w^2 + 100/w$. Form a table for w and S.

w	S	w	S
3.4	40.972	3.7	40.717
3.5	40.821	3.8	40.756
3.6	40.738	3.9	40.851

The minimum surface area is $S \approx 40.717$ when $w \approx 3.7$ and $h = 25/w^2 \approx 1.8$.

1.5 Exercises

1   $(5 - 2i) + (-3 + 6i) = [5 + (-3)] + (-2 + 6)i = 2 + 4i$

2   $(-5 + 7i) + (4 + 9i) = (-5 + 4) + (7 + 9)i = -1 + 16i$

$\boxed{3}$ $(7-6i)-(-11-3i)=(7+11)+(-6+3)i=18-3i$

$\boxed{4}$ $(-3+8i)-(2+3i)=(-3-2)+(8-3)i=-5+5i$

$\boxed{5}$ $(3+5i)(2-7i)=(6-35i^2)+(10-21)i=(6+35)-11i=41-11i$

$\boxed{6}$ $(-2+6i)(8-i)=(-16-6i^2)+(2+48)i=(-16+6)+50i=-10+50i$

$\boxed{7}$ $(1-3i)(2+5i)=(2-15i^2)+(5-6)i=(2+15)-i=17-i$

$\boxed{8}$ $(8+2i)(7-3i)=(56-6i^2)+(-24+14)i=(56+6)-10i=62-10i$

$\boxed{9}$ $(5-2i)^2=5^2-2(5)(2i)+(2i)^2=(25-4)-20i=21-20i$

$\boxed{10}$ $(6+7i)^2=6^2+2(6)(7i)+(7i)^2=(36-49)+84i=-13+84i$

$\boxed{11}$ $i(3+4i)^2=i\big[(9-16)+2(3)(4i)\big]=i(-7+24i)=-24-7i$

$\boxed{12}$ $i(2-7i)^2=i\big[(4-49)-2(2)(7i)\big]=i(-45-28i)=28-45i$

$\boxed{13}$ $(3+4i)(3-4i)=3^2-(4i)^2=9-(-16)=9+16=25$

$\boxed{14}$ $(4+9i)(4-9i)=4^2-(9i)^2=16-(-81)=16+81=97$

$\boxed{15}$ $i^{43}=i^{40}i^3=(i^4)^{10}(-i)=1^{10}(-i)=-i$ $\boxed{16}$ $i^{92}=(i^4)^{23}=1^{23}=1$

$\boxed{17}$ $i^{73}=i^{72}i=(i^4)^{18}i=1^{18}i=i$ $\boxed{18}$ $i^{66}=i^{64}i^2=(i^4)^{16}(-1)=1^{16}(-1)=-1$

$\boxed{19}$ $\dfrac{3}{2+4i}\cdot\dfrac{2-4i}{2-4i}=\dfrac{6-12i}{4-(-16)}=\dfrac{6-12i}{20}=\dfrac{3}{10}-\dfrac{3}{5}i$

$\boxed{20}$ $\dfrac{5}{2-7i}\cdot\dfrac{2+7i}{2+7i}=\dfrac{10+35i}{4-(-49)}=\dfrac{10+35i}{53}=\dfrac{10}{53}+\dfrac{35}{53}i$

$\boxed{21}$ $\dfrac{1-7i}{6-2i}\cdot\dfrac{6+2i}{6+2i}=\dfrac{(6+14)+(2-42)i}{36-(-4)}=\dfrac{20-40i}{40}=\dfrac{1}{2}-i$

$\boxed{22}$ $\dfrac{2+9i}{-3-i}\cdot\dfrac{-3+i}{-3+i}=\dfrac{(-6-9)+(2-27)i}{9-(-1)}=\dfrac{-15-25i}{10}=-\dfrac{3}{2}-\dfrac{5}{2}i$

$\boxed{23}$ $\dfrac{-4+6i}{2+7i}\cdot\dfrac{2-7i}{2-7i}=\dfrac{(-8+42)+(28+12)i}{4-(-49)}=\dfrac{34+40i}{53}=\dfrac{34}{53}+\dfrac{40}{53}i$

$\boxed{24}$ $\dfrac{-3-2i}{5+2i}\cdot\dfrac{5-2i}{5-2i}=\dfrac{(-15-4)+(6-10)i}{25-(-4)}=\dfrac{-19-4i}{29}=-\dfrac{19}{29}-\dfrac{4}{29}i$

$\boxed{25}$ $\dfrac{4-2i}{-5i}=\dfrac{4-2i}{-5i}\cdot\dfrac{i}{i}=\dfrac{4i-2i^2}{-5i^2}=\dfrac{2+4i}{5}=\dfrac{2}{5}+\dfrac{4}{5}i$

$\boxed{26}$ $\dfrac{-2+6i}{3i}=\dfrac{-2+6i}{3i}\cdot\dfrac{-i}{-i}=\dfrac{2i-6i^2}{-3i^2}=\dfrac{6+2i}{3}=2+\dfrac{2}{3}i$

$\boxed{27}$ $(2+5i)^3=(2)^3+3(2)^2(5i)+3(2)(5i)^2+(5i)^3=(8+150i^2)+(60i+125i^3)=$
$$(8-150)+(60-125)i=-142-65i$$

$\boxed{28}$ $(3-2i)^3=(3)^3+3(3)^2(-2i)+3(3)(-2i)^2+(-2i)^3=(27+36i^2)+(-54i-8i^3)=$
$$(27-36)+(-54+8)i=-9-46i$$

$\boxed{29}$ $(2-\sqrt{-4})(3-\sqrt{-16})=(2-2i)(3-4i)=-2-14i$

$\boxed{30}$ $(-3+\sqrt{-25})(8-\sqrt{-36})=(-3+5i)(8-6i)=6+58i$

31 $\dfrac{4+\sqrt{-81}}{7-\sqrt{-64}} = \dfrac{4+9i}{7-8i} \cdot \dfrac{7+8i}{7+8i} = \dfrac{(28-72)+(32+63)i}{49-(-64)} = \dfrac{-44+95i}{113} = -\dfrac{44}{113} + \dfrac{95}{113}i$

32 $\dfrac{5-\sqrt{-121}}{1+\sqrt{-25}} = \dfrac{5-11i}{1+5i} \cdot \dfrac{1-5i}{1-5i} = \dfrac{(5-55)+(-25-11)i}{1-(-25)} = \dfrac{-50-36i}{26} = -\dfrac{25}{13} - \dfrac{18}{13}i$

33 $\dfrac{\sqrt{-36}\,\sqrt{-49}}{\sqrt{-16}} = \dfrac{(6i)(7i)}{4i} \cdot \dfrac{-i}{-i} = \dfrac{(-42)(-i)}{-4i^2} = \dfrac{42i}{4} = \dfrac{21}{2}i$

34 $\dfrac{\sqrt{-25}}{\sqrt{-16}\,\sqrt{-81}} = \dfrac{5i}{(4i)(9i)} = \dfrac{5i}{36i^2} = \dfrac{5i}{-36} = -\dfrac{5}{36}i$

35 $8 + (3x+y)i = 2x - 4i \Rightarrow 2x = 8$ and $3x + y = -4 \Rightarrow x = 4,\ y = -16$

36 $(x-y) + 3i = 7 + yi \Rightarrow 3 = y$ and $x - y = 7 \Rightarrow x = 10,\ y = 3$

37 $(3x+2y) - y^3 i = 9 - 27i \Rightarrow y^3 = 27\ \{y = 3\}$ and $3x + 2y = 9 \Rightarrow x = 1,\ y = 3$

38 $x^3 + (2x-y)i = -8 - 3i \Rightarrow x^3 = -8$ and $2x - y = -3 \Rightarrow x = -2,\ y = -1$

39 $x^2 - 6x + 13 = 0 \Rightarrow x = \dfrac{6 \pm \sqrt{36-52}}{2} = \dfrac{6 \pm 4i}{2} = 3 \pm 2i$

40 $x^2 - 2x + 26 = 0 \Rightarrow x = \dfrac{2 \pm \sqrt{4-104}}{2} = \dfrac{2 \pm 10i}{2} = 1 \pm 5i$

41 $x^2 + 4x + 13 = 0 \Rightarrow x = \dfrac{-4 \pm \sqrt{16-52}}{2} = \dfrac{-4 \pm 6i}{2} = -2 \pm 3i$

42 $x^2 + 8x + 17 = 0 \Rightarrow x = \dfrac{-8 \pm \sqrt{64-68}}{2} = \dfrac{-8 \pm 2i}{2} = -4 \pm i$

43 $x^2 - 5x + 20 = 0 \Rightarrow x = \dfrac{5 \pm \sqrt{25-80}}{2} = \dfrac{5}{2} \pm \dfrac{1}{2}\sqrt{55}\,i$

44 $x^2 + 3x + 6 = 0 \Rightarrow x = \dfrac{-3 \pm \sqrt{9-24}}{2} = -\dfrac{3}{2} \pm \dfrac{1}{2}\sqrt{15}\,i$

45 $4x^2 + x + 3 = 0 \Rightarrow x = \dfrac{-1 \pm \sqrt{1-48}}{8} = -\dfrac{1}{8} \pm \dfrac{1}{8}\sqrt{47}\,i$

46 $-3x^2 + x - 5 = 0 \Rightarrow x = \dfrac{-1 \pm \sqrt{1-60}}{-6} = \dfrac{1}{6} \pm \dfrac{1}{6}\sqrt{59}\,i$

47 $x^3 + 125 = 0 \Rightarrow (x+5)(x^2 - 5x + 25) = 0 \Rightarrow$

$x = -5$ or $x = \dfrac{5 \pm \sqrt{25-100}}{2} = \dfrac{5 \pm 5\sqrt{3}\,i}{2}$. The three solutions are $-5,\ \dfrac{5}{2} \pm \dfrac{5}{2}\sqrt{3}\,i$.

48 $x^3 - 27 = 0 \Rightarrow (x-3)(x^2 + 3x + 9) = 0 \Rightarrow$

$x = 3$ or $x = \dfrac{-3 \pm \sqrt{9-36}}{2} = \dfrac{-3 \pm 3\sqrt{3}\,i}{2}$. The three solutions are $3,\ -\dfrac{3}{2} \pm \dfrac{3}{2}\sqrt{3}\,i$.

49 $x^4 = 256 \Rightarrow x^4 - 256 = 0 \Rightarrow (x^2 - 16)(x^2 + 16) = 0 \Rightarrow x = \pm 4,\ \pm 4i$

50 $x^4 = 81 \Rightarrow x^4 - 81 = 0 \Rightarrow (x^2 - 9)(x^2 + 9) = 0 \Rightarrow x = \pm 3,\ \pm 3i$

51 $4x^4 + 25x^2 + 36 = 0 \Rightarrow (x^2 + 4)(4x^2 + 9) = 0 \Rightarrow x = \pm 2i,\ \pm\dfrac{3}{2}i$

52 $27x^4 + 21x^2 + 4 = 0 \Rightarrow (9x^2 + 4)(3x^2 + 1) = 0 \Rightarrow x = \pm\dfrac{2}{3}i,\ \pm\dfrac{1}{3}\sqrt{3}\,i$

53 $x^3 + 3x^2 + 4x = 0 \Rightarrow x(x^2 + 3x + 4) = 0 \Rightarrow x = 0,\ -\dfrac{3}{2} \pm \dfrac{1}{2}\sqrt{7}\,i$

$\boxed{54}$ $8x^3 - 12x^2 + 2x - 3 = 0 \Rightarrow 4x^2(2x - 3) + 1(2x - 3) = 0 \Rightarrow (4x^2 + 1)(2x - 3) = 0 \Rightarrow$

$$x = \tfrac{3}{2}, \ \pm\tfrac{1}{2}i$$

Note: Exer. 55–58: Let $z = a + bi$ and $w = c + di$.

$\boxed{55}$ $\overline{z + w} = \overline{(a + bi) + (c + di)}$

$\qquad = \overline{(a + c) + (b + d)i} = (a + c) - (b + d)i = (a - bi) + (c - di) = \overline{z} + \overline{w}.$

$\boxed{56}$ $\overline{z - w} = \overline{(a + bi) - (c + di)}$

$\qquad = \overline{(a - c) + (b - d)i} = (a - c) - (b - d)i = (a - bi) - (c - di) = \overline{z} - \overline{w}.$

$\boxed{57}$ $\overline{z \cdot w} = \overline{(a + bi) \cdot (c + di)} = \overline{(ac - bd) + (ad + bc)i} =$

$\qquad (ac - bd) - (ad + bc)i = ac - adi - bd - bci = a(c - di) - bi(c - di) =$

$$(a - bi) \cdot (c - di) = \overline{z} \cdot \overline{w}$$

$\boxed{58}$ $\overline{\left(\dfrac{z}{w}\right)} = \overline{\left(\dfrac{a + bi}{c + di}\right)} = \overline{\left(\dfrac{a + bi}{c + di} \cdot \dfrac{c - di}{c - di}\right)} = \overline{\left(\dfrac{(ac + bd) + (bc - ad)i}{c^2 + d^2}\right)} =$

$\overline{\left(\dfrac{ac + bd}{c^2 + d^2} + \dfrac{bc - ad}{c^2 + d^2}i\right)} = \dfrac{ac + bd}{c^2 + d^2} - \dfrac{bc - ad}{c^2 + d^2}i = \dfrac{(ac + bd) + (ad - bc)i}{c^2 + d^2} =$

$$\dfrac{a - bi}{c - di} \cdot \dfrac{c + di}{c + di} = \dfrac{a - bi}{c - di} = \dfrac{\overline{(a + bi)}}{\overline{(c + di)}} = \dfrac{\overline{z}}{\overline{w}}$$

$\boxed{59}$ If $\overline{z} = z$, then $a - bi = a + bi$ and hence $-bi = bi$, or $2bi = 0$.

Thus, $b = 0$ and $z = a$ is real. Conversely, if z is real, then $b = 0$ and hence

$$\overline{z} = \overline{a + 0i} = a - 0i = a + 0i = z.$$

$\boxed{60}$ $\overline{z^2} = \overline{(a + bi)^2} = \overline{a^2 + 2abi - b^2} = \overline{(a^2 - b^2) + 2abi} =$

$$(a^2 - b^2) - 2abi = a^2 - 2abi - b^2 = (a - bi)^2 = (\overline{z})^2$$

1.6 Exercises

$\boxed{1}$ $x < -2 \Leftrightarrow (-\infty, -2)$ $\qquad\qquad$ $\boxed{2}$ $x \geq 4 \Leftrightarrow [4, \infty)$

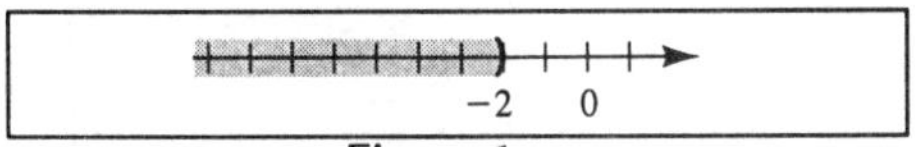

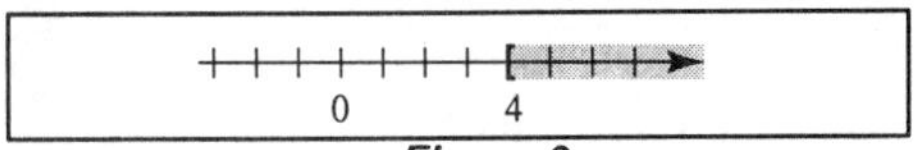

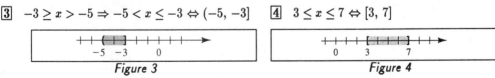

Figure 1 $\qquad\qquad\qquad\qquad\qquad$ Figure 2

$\boxed{3}$ $-3 \geq x > -5 \Rightarrow -5 < x \leq -3 \Leftrightarrow (-5, -3]$ $\qquad$ $\boxed{4}$ $3 \leq x \leq 7 \Leftrightarrow [3, 7]$

Figure 3 $\qquad\qquad\qquad\qquad\qquad$ Figure 4

$\boxed{5}$ $(-5, 8] \Leftrightarrow -5 < x \leq 8$ $\qquad\qquad$ $\boxed{6}$ $(-3, \infty) \Leftrightarrow x > -3$

$\boxed{7}$ $2x + 5 < 3x - 7 \Rightarrow -x < -12 \Rightarrow x > 12 \Leftrightarrow (12, \infty)$

$\boxed{8}$ $x - 8 > 5x + 3 \Rightarrow -4x > 11 \Rightarrow x < -\tfrac{11}{4} \Leftrightarrow (-\infty, -\tfrac{11}{4})$

$\boxed{9}$ $\left[3 \leq \dfrac{2x - 3}{5} < 7\right] \cdot 5 \Rightarrow 15 \leq 2x - 3 < 35 \Rightarrow 18 \leq 2x < 38 \Rightarrow 9 \leq x < 19 \Leftrightarrow [9, 19)$

$\boxed{10}$ $\left[-2 < \dfrac{4x + 1}{3} \leq 0\right] \cdot 3 \Rightarrow -6 < 4x + 1 \leq 0 \Rightarrow -7 < 4x \leq -1 \Rightarrow -\tfrac{7}{4} < x \leq -\tfrac{1}{4} \Leftrightarrow$

$$(-\tfrac{7}{4}, -\tfrac{1}{4}]$$

$\boxed{11}$ By the law of signs, a quotient is positive if the sign of the numerator and the sign of the denominator are the same. Since the numerator is positive, $\dfrac{4}{3x+2} > 0 \Rightarrow$

$3x + 2 > 0 \Rightarrow x > -\frac{2}{3} \Leftrightarrow (-\frac{2}{3}, \infty)$. The expression is never equal to 0 since the numerator is never 0. Thus, the solution of $\dfrac{4}{3x+2} \geq 0$ is $(-\frac{2}{3}, \infty)$.

$\boxed{12}$ $\dfrac{3}{2x+5} \leq 0 \Rightarrow 2x + 5 < 0 \Rightarrow x < -\frac{5}{2} \Leftrightarrow (-\infty, -\frac{5}{2})$

$\boxed{13}$ $\dfrac{-2}{4-3x} > 0 \Rightarrow 4 - 3x < 0 \,\{\text{denominator must also be negative}\} \Rightarrow x > \frac{4}{3} \Leftrightarrow (\frac{4}{3}, \infty)$

$\boxed{14}$ $\dfrac{-3}{2-x} < 0 \Rightarrow 2 - x > 0 \Rightarrow x < 2 \Leftrightarrow (-\infty, 2)$

$\boxed{15}$ $(1-x)^2 > 0 \; \forall x$ except 1. Thus, $\dfrac{2}{(1-x)^2} > 0$ has solution $\mathbb{R} - \{1\}$.

$\boxed{16}$ $x^2 + 4 > 0 \; \forall x$. Hence, $\dfrac{4}{x^2+4} > 0 \; \forall x$, and $\dfrac{4}{x^2+4} < 0$ has no solution.

$\boxed{17}$ $|x+3| < 0.01 \Rightarrow -0.01 < x + 3 < 0.01 \Rightarrow -3.01 < x < -2.99 \Leftrightarrow (-3.01, -2.99)$

$\boxed{18}$ $|x-4| \leq 0.03 \Rightarrow -0.03 \leq x - 4 \leq 0.03 \Rightarrow 3.97 \leq x \leq 4.03 \Leftrightarrow [3.97, 4.03]$

$\boxed{19}$ $|3x-7| \geq 5 \Rightarrow 3x - 7 \geq 5$ or $3x - 7 \leq -5 \Rightarrow x \geq 4$ or $x \leq \frac{2}{3} \Leftrightarrow (-\infty, \frac{2}{3}] \cup [4, \infty)$

$\boxed{20}$ $-\frac{1}{3}|6-5x| + 2 \leq 1 \Rightarrow -\frac{1}{3}|6-5x| \leq -1 \Rightarrow |6-5x| \geq 3 \Rightarrow$

$6 - 5x \geq 3$ or $6 - 5x \leq -3 \Rightarrow 5x \leq 3$ or $5x \geq 9 \Rightarrow x \leq \frac{3}{5}$ or $x \geq \frac{9}{5} \Leftrightarrow (-\infty, \frac{3}{5}] \cup [\frac{9}{5}, \infty)$

$\boxed{21}$ Since $|7x+2| \geq 0 \; \forall x$, $|7x+2| > -2$ has solution $(-\infty, \infty)$.

$\boxed{22}$ Since $|6x-5| \geq 0 \; \forall x$, $|6x-5| \leq -2$ has no solution.

$\boxed{23}$ $|3x-9| > 0 \; \forall x$ except when $3x - 9 = 0$, or $x = 3$. The solution is $(-\infty, 3) \cup (3, \infty)$.

$\boxed{24}$ $|5x+2| = 0$ if $x = -\frac{2}{5}$, but is never less than 0.

Thus, $|5x+2| \leq 0$ has solution $x = -\frac{2}{5}$.

$\boxed{25}$ $-2 < |x| < 4 \Rightarrow |x| > -2$ and $|x| < 4 \Rightarrow$

$|x| < 4 \,\{\text{since } |x| \text{ is always greater than } -2\} \Rightarrow -4 < x < 4 \Leftrightarrow (-4, 4)$

$\boxed{26}$ $1 < |x| < 5 \Rightarrow 1 < x < 5$ or $1 < -x < 5 \Rightarrow 1 < x < 5$ or $-1 > x > -5 \Rightarrow$

$1 < x < 5$ or $-5 < x < -1 \Leftrightarrow (-5, -1) \cup (1, 5)$

$\boxed{27}$ $(3x+1)(5-10x) > 0$ has solutions in the interval $(-\frac{1}{3}, \frac{1}{2})$. See *Diagram 27* for details concerning the signs of the individual factors and the resulting sign.

Resulting sign:	$\ominus$	$\oplus$	$\ominus$
Sign of $5 - 10x$:	$+$	$+$	$-$
Sign of $3x + 1$:	$-$	$+$	$+$
x values:	$-1/3$		$1/2$

Diagram 27

Resulting sign:	$\oplus$	$\ominus$	$\oplus$	$\ominus$
Sign of $4 - x$:	$+$	$+$	$+$	$-$
Sign of $x - 1$:	$-$	$-$	$+$	$+$
Sign of $x + 2$:	$-$	$+$	$+$	$+$
x values:		-2	1	4

Diagram 28

$\boxed{28}$ $(x+2)(x-1)(4-x) \leq 0$; $[-2, 1] \cup [4, \infty)$

29 $x^2 - x - 6 < 0 \Rightarrow (x-3)(x+2) < 0;\ (-2, 3)$

Resulting sign:	$\oplus$	$\ominus$	$\oplus$
Sign of $x - 3$:	$-$	$-$	$+$
Sign of $x + 2$:	$-$	$+$	$+$
x values:	-2		3

Diagram 29

Resulting sign:	$\oplus$	$\ominus$	$\oplus$
Sign of $x + 1$:	$-$	$-$	$+$
Sign of $x + 3$:	$-$	$+$	$+$
x values:	-3		-1

Diagram 30

30 $x^2 + 4x + 3 \geq 0 \Rightarrow (x+1)(x+3) \geq 0;\ (-\infty, -3] \cup [-1, \infty)$

31 $x(2x+3) \geq 5 \Rightarrow 2x^2 + 3x - 5 \geq 0 \Rightarrow (2x+5)(x-1) \geq 0;\ (-\infty, -\frac{5}{2}] \cup [1, \infty)$

Resulting sign:	$\oplus$	$\ominus$	$\oplus$
Sign of $x - 1$:	$-$	$-$	$+$
Sign of $2x + 5$:	$-$	$+$	$+$
x values:	$-5/2$		1

Diagram 31

Resulting sign:	$\oplus$	$\ominus$	$\oplus$
Sign of $x - 4$:	$-$	$-$	$+$
Sign of $x - 2$:	$-$	$+$	$+$
x values:	2		4

Diagram 32

32 $6x - 8 > x^2 \Rightarrow x^2 - 6x + 8 < 0 \Rightarrow (x-2)(x-4) < 0;\ (2, 4)$

Note: Solving $x^2 < $ (or $>$) a^2 for $a > 0$ may be solved using factoring, that is,

$$x^2 - a^2 < 0 \Rightarrow (x+a)(x-a) < 0 \Rightarrow -a < x < a;\ \text{or by taking the square}$$

root of each side, that is, $\sqrt{x^2} < \sqrt{a^2} \Rightarrow |x| < a \Rightarrow -a < x < a$.

33 $25x^2 - 9 < 0 \Rightarrow x^2 < \frac{9}{25} \Rightarrow |x| < \frac{3}{5} \Rightarrow -\frac{3}{5} < x < \frac{3}{5} \Leftrightarrow (-\frac{3}{5}, \frac{3}{5})$

34 $25x^2 - 9x < 0 \Rightarrow x(25x - 9) < 0;\ (0, \frac{9}{25})$

Resulting sign:	$\oplus$	$\ominus$	$\oplus$
Sign of $25x - 9$:	$-$	$-$	$+$
Sign of x:	$-$	$+$	$+$
x values:	0		$9/25$

Diagram 34

35 $\dfrac{x^2(x+2)}{(x+2)(x+1)} \leq 0 \Rightarrow \dfrac{x^2}{x+1} \leq 0\ \{\text{exclude } -2\} \Rightarrow \dfrac{1}{x+1} \leq 0\ \{\text{include } 0\} \Rightarrow$

$$x + 1 < 0 \Rightarrow x < -1;\ (-\infty, -2) \cup (-2, -1) \cup \{0\}$$

36 $\dfrac{(x^2+1)(x-3)}{x^2 - 9} \geq 0 \Rightarrow \dfrac{x-3}{(x+3)(x-3)} \geq 0\ \{x^2 + 1 > 0\} \Rightarrow \dfrac{1}{x+3} \geq 0\ \{\text{exclude } 3\} \Rightarrow$

$$x + 3 > 0\ \{\text{exclude } -3\} \Rightarrow x > -3;\ (-3, 3) \cup (3, \infty)$$

37 $\dfrac{x^2 - x}{x^2 + 2x} \leq 0 \Rightarrow \dfrac{x(x-1)}{x(x+2)} \leq 0 \Rightarrow \dfrac{x-1}{x+2} \leq 0\ \{\text{exclude } 0\};\ (-2, 0) \cup (0, 1]$

Resulting sign:	$\oplus$	$\ominus$	$\oplus$
Sign of $x - 1$:	$-$	$-$	$+$
Sign of $x + 2$:	$-$	$+$	$+$
x values:	-2		1

Diagram 37

Resulting sign:	$\oplus$	$\ominus$	$\oplus$
Sign of $x + 2$:	$-$	$-$	$+$
Sign of $x + 4$:	$-$	$+$	$+$
x values:	-4		-2

Diagram 38

38 $\dfrac{(x+3)^2(2-x)}{(x+4)(x^2-4)} \leq 0 \Rightarrow \dfrac{2-x}{(x+4)(x+2)(x-2)} \leq 0\ \{\text{include } -3\} \Rightarrow \dfrac{1}{(x+4)(x+2)} \geq 0$

$\{\text{cancel, change inequality, exclude } 2\};\ (-\infty, -4) \cup \{-3\} \cup (-2, 2) \cup (2, \infty)$

39 $\dfrac{x-2}{x^2-3x-10} \geq 0 \Rightarrow \dfrac{x-2}{(x-5)(x+2)} \geq 0$; $(-2, 2] \cup (5, \infty)$

Resulting sign:	$\ominus$	$\oplus$	$\ominus$	$\oplus$ ·
Sign of $x-5$:	$-$	$-$	$-$	$+$
Sign of $x-2$:	$-$	$-$	$+$	$+$
Sign of $x+2$:	$-$	$+$	$+$	$+$
x values:		-2	2	5

Diagram 39

Resulting sign:	$\ominus$	$\oplus$	$\ominus$	$\oplus$
Sign of $x-4$:	$-$	$-$	$-$	$+$
Sign of $x-3$:	$-$	$-$	$+$	$+$
Sign of $x+5$:	$-$	$+$	$+$	$+$
x values:		-5	3	4

Diagram 40

40 $\dfrac{x+5}{x^2-7x+12} \leq 0 \Rightarrow \dfrac{x+5}{(x-3)(x-4)} \leq 0$; $(-\infty, -5] \cup (3, 4)$

41 $\dfrac{-3x}{x^2-9} > 0 \Rightarrow \dfrac{x}{(x+3)(x-3)} < 0$ { divide by -3 }; $(-\infty, -3) \cup (0, 3)$

Resulting sign:	$\ominus$	$\oplus$	$\ominus$	$\oplus$
Sign of $x-3$:	$-$	$-$	$-$	$+$
Sign of x:	$-$	$-$	$+$	$+$
Sign of $x+3$:	$-$	$+$	$+$	$+$
x values:		-3	0	3

Diagram 41

Resulting sign:	$\oplus$	$\ominus$	$\oplus$	$\ominus$
Sign of $4-x$:	$+$	$+$	$+$	$-$
Sign of x:	$-$	$-$	$+$	$+$
Sign of $4+x$:	$-$	$+$	$+$	$+$
x values:		-4	0	4

Diagram 42

42 $\dfrac{2x}{16-x^2} < 0 \Rightarrow \dfrac{x}{(4+x)(4-x)} < 0$ { divide by 2 }; $(-4, 0) \cup (4, \infty)$

43 $\dfrac{x+1}{2x-3} > 2 \Rightarrow \dfrac{x+1-2(2x-3)}{2x-3} > 0 \Rightarrow \dfrac{-3x+7}{2x-3} > 0$; $(\frac{3}{2}, \frac{7}{3})$

Resulting sign:	$\ominus$	$\oplus$	$\ominus$
Sign of $-3x+7$:	$+$	$+$	$-$
Sign of $2x-3$:	$-$	$+$	$+$
x values:		$3/2$	$7/3$

Diagram 43

Resulting sign:	$\ominus$	$\oplus$	$\ominus$
Sign of $3x+5$:	$-$	$-$	$+$
Sign of $-11x-22$:	$+$	$-$	$-$
x values:		-2	$-5/3$

Diagram 44

44 $\dfrac{x-2}{3x+5} \leq 4 \Rightarrow \dfrac{x-2-4(3x+5)}{3x+5} \leq 0 \Rightarrow \dfrac{-11x-22}{3x+5} \leq 0$; $(-\infty, -2] \cup (-\frac{5}{3}, \infty)$

45 $\dfrac{1}{x-2} \geq \dfrac{3}{x+1} \Rightarrow \dfrac{1(x+1)-3(x-2)}{(x-2)(x+1)} \geq 0 \Rightarrow \dfrac{-2x+7}{(x-2)(x+1)} \geq 0$; $(-\infty, -1) \cup (2, \frac{7}{2}]$

Resulting sign:	$\oplus$	$\ominus$	$\oplus$	$\ominus$
Sign of $-2x+7$:	$+$	$+$	$+$	$-$
Sign of $x-2$:	$-$	$-$	$+$	$+$
Sign of $x+1$:	$-$	$+$	$+$	$+$
x values:		-1	2	$7/2$

Diagram 45

Resulting sign:	$\oplus$	$\ominus$	$\oplus$	$\ominus$
$x-5$:	$-$	$-$	$-$	$+$
$2x+3$:	$-$	$-$	$+$	$+$
$-2x-16$:	$+$	$-$	$-$	$-$
x values:		-8	$-3/2$	5

Diagram 46

46 $\dfrac{2}{2x+3} \leq \dfrac{2}{x-5} \Rightarrow \dfrac{2(x-5)-2(2x+3)}{(2x+3)(x-5)} \leq 0 \Rightarrow \dfrac{-2x-16}{(2x+3)(x-5)} \leq 0$; $[-8, -\frac{3}{2}) \cup (5, \infty)$

47 $\dfrac{x}{3x-5} \le \dfrac{2}{x-1} \Rightarrow \dfrac{x(x-1)-2(3x-5)}{(3x-5)(x-1)} \le 0 \Rightarrow \dfrac{(x-2)(x-5)}{(3x-5)(x-1)} \le 0;\ (1,\tfrac{5}{3}) \cup [2,\,5]$

Res. sign:	⊕	⊖	⊕	⊖	⊕
$x-5$:	−	−	−	−	+
$x-2$:	−	−	−	+	+
$3x-5$:	−	−	+	+	+
$x-1$:	−	+	+	+	+
x values:	1	5/3	2	5	

Res. sign:	⊕	⊖	⊕	⊖	⊕
$x-3$:	−	−	−	−	+
$x-1$:	−	−	−	+	+
$2x-1$:	−	−	+	+	+
$x+2$:	−	+	+	+	+
x values:	−2	1/2	1	3	

Diagram 47   Diagram 48

48 $\dfrac{x}{2x-1} \ge \dfrac{3}{x+2} \Rightarrow \dfrac{x(x+2)-3(2x-1)}{(2x-1)(x+2)} \ge 0 \Rightarrow \dfrac{(x-1)(x-3)}{(2x-1)(x+2)} \ge 0;$

$$(-\infty,\,-2) \cup (\tfrac{1}{2},\,1] \cup [3,\,\infty)$$

49 $x^3 > x \Rightarrow x^3 - x > 0 \Rightarrow x(x^2-1) > 0 \Rightarrow x(x+1)(x-1) > 0;\ (-1,\,0) \cup (1,\,\infty)$

Resulting sign:	⊖	⊕	⊖	⊕
Sign of $x-1$:	−	−	−	+
Sign of x:	−	−	+	+
Sign of $x+1$:	−	+	+	+
x values:	−1	0	1	

Resulting sign:	⊕	⊖	⊕
Sign of $x-1$:	−	−	+
Sign of $x+1$:	−	+	+
x values:	−1	1	

Diagram 49   Diagram 50

50 $x^4 \ge x^2 \Rightarrow x^4 - x^2 \ge 0 \Rightarrow x^2(x+1)(x-1) \ge 0.$

Since $x^2 \ge 0$, x^2 does not need to be included in the sign diagram, but 0 must be

included in the answer because of the equality.   ★ $(-\infty,\,-1] \cup \{0\} \cup [1,\,\infty)$

51 (a) $|x+5| = 3 \Rightarrow x+5 = 3$ or $x+5 = -3 \Rightarrow x = -2$ or $x = -8.$

(b) $|x+5| < 3$ has solutions between the values found in part (a), that is, $(-8,\,-2).$

(c) The solutions of $|x+5| > 3$ are the portions of the real line that are not in

parts (a) and (b), that is, $(-\infty,\,-8) \cup (-2,\,\infty).$

52 (a) $|x-3| < 2 \Rightarrow -2 < x-3 < 2 \Rightarrow 1 < x < 5 \Leftrightarrow (1,\,5).$

(b) $|x-3| = 2$ has solutions at the endpoints of the interval in part (a).

(c) As in Exercise 51(c), $|x-3| > 2$ has solutions in $(-\infty,\,1) \cup (5,\,\infty).$

53 $|w - 148| \le 2$ **54** $|r-1| \le 0.01$

55 $M \ge 3 \Rightarrow \dfrac{6}{6-p} \ge 3 \Rightarrow 6 \ge 18 - 3p\ \{6-p > 0\} \Rightarrow p \ge 4,$ but $p < 6$ since $p < f.$

Thus, $4 \le p < 6.$

56 $c > 1.5 \Rightarrow \dfrac{3.5t}{t+1} > 1.5 \Rightarrow \{t+1 > 0\}\ 3.5t > 1.5t + 1.5 \Rightarrow t > \tfrac{3}{4}$ hr

57 $\text{Cost}_A < \text{Cost}_B \Rightarrow 50{,}000 + 4000x < 40{,}000 + 5500x \Rightarrow 10{,}000 < 1500x \Rightarrow$

$$x > \tfrac{20}{3}, \text{ or } 6\tfrac{2}{3} \text{ yr}$$

58 Let t denote the time in years from the present. $\text{Cost}_B < \text{Cost}_A \Rightarrow$

$\text{Purchase}_B + \text{Insurance}_B + \text{Gas}_B < \text{Purchase}_A + \text{Insurance}_A + \text{Gas}_A \Rightarrow$

$12{,}000 + 600t + \dfrac{15{,}000}{50} \cdot 1.25t < 10{,}000 + 550t + \dfrac{15{,}000}{30} \cdot 1.25t \Rightarrow$

$$12{,}000 + 975t < 10{,}000 + 1175t \Rightarrow 2000 < 200t \Rightarrow t > 10 \text{ yr.}$$

$\boxed{59}$ $s > 9 \Rightarrow -16t^2 + 24t + 1 > 9 \Rightarrow -16t^2 + 24t - 8 > 0 \Rightarrow$

$2t^2 - 3t + 1 < 0$ { divide by -8 } $\Rightarrow (2t - 1)(t - 1) < 0 \Rightarrow \frac{1}{2} < t < 1$.

The dog is more than 9 ft off the ground for $1 - \frac{1}{2} = \frac{1}{2}$ sec.

$\boxed{60}$ $s \geq 1536 \Rightarrow -16t^2 + 320t \geq 1536 \Rightarrow -16t^2 + 320t - 1536 \geq 0 \Rightarrow t^2 - 20t + 96 \leq 0 \Rightarrow$

$(t - 8)(t - 12) \leq 0 \Leftrightarrow 8 \leq t \leq 12$

$\boxed{61}$ $d < 75 \Rightarrow v + \frac{1}{20}v^2 < 75 \Rightarrow v^2 + 20v - 1500 < 0 \Rightarrow (v + 50)(v - 30) < 0 \Rightarrow$

$-50 < v < 30 \Rightarrow 0 \leq v < 30 \; \{ v \geq 0 \}$

$\boxed{62}$ $M \geq 45 \Rightarrow -\frac{1}{30}v^2 + \frac{5}{2}v \geq 45 \Rightarrow -\frac{1}{30}v^2 + \frac{5}{2}v - 45 \geq 0 \Rightarrow v^2 - 75v + 1350 \leq 0 \Rightarrow$

$(v - 30)(v - 45) \leq 0 \Leftrightarrow 30 \leq v \leq 45$

$\boxed{63}$ (a) 5 ft 9 in $= 69$ in. In a 40 year period, a person's height will decrease by

$40 \times 0.024 = 0.96$ in ≈ 1 in. The person will be approximately one inch shorter,

or 5 ft 8 in at age 70.

(b) 5 ft 6 in $= 66$ in. In 20 years, a person's height $(h = 66)$ will change by

$0.024 \times 20 = 0.48$ in. Thus, $66 - 0.48 \leq h \leq 66 + 0.48 \Rightarrow 65.52 \leq h \leq 66.48$.

$\boxed{64}$ $7500 \leq 0.00334V^2 S \leq 10,000 \Rightarrow 7500 \leq 0.00334(210)V^2 \leq 10,000 \Rightarrow$

$\dfrac{7500}{0.7014} \leq V^2 \leq \dfrac{10,000}{0.7014} \Rightarrow \sqrt{\dfrac{7500}{0.7014}} \leq V \leq \sqrt{\dfrac{10,000}{0.7014}} \Rightarrow$

$103.4 \leq V \leq 119.4$ ft/sec $\Rightarrow$ { multiply by $\frac{60}{88}$ to convert } $70.5 \leq V \leq 81.4$ mi/hr.

$\boxed{65}$ The numerator is equal to zero when $x = 2, 3$ and the denominator is equal to zero

when $x = \pm 1$. From the table, the expression $Y_1 = \dfrac{(2 - x)(3x - 9)}{(1 - x)(x + 1)}$ is positive when

$x \in [-2, -1) \cup (1, 2) \cup (3, 3.5]$.

x	Y_1	x	Y_1
-2.0	20	1.0	ERROR
-1.5	37.8	1.5	1.8
-1.0	ERROR	2.0	0
-0.5	-35	2.5	-0.1429
0.0	-18	3.0	0
0.5	-15	3.5	0.2

66 By using a table it can be shown that the expression is equal to zero when $x = -3$, -2, 2, 4. The expression $Y_1 = x^4 - x^3 - 16x^2 + 4x + 48$ is negative when $x \in (-3, -2) \cup (2, 4)$.

x	Y_1	x	Y_1
-3.5	30.938	1.0	36
-3.0	0	1.5	19.688
-2.5	-7.313	2.0	0
-2.0	0	2.5	-18.56
-1.5	14.438	3.0	-30
-1.0	30	3.5	-26.81
-0.5	42.188	4.0	0
0.0	48	4.5	60.938
0.5	45.938	5.0	168

1.7 Exercises

1. (a) $x = -2$ is the line parallel to the y-axis that intersects the x-axis at $(-2, 0)$.

  (b) $y = 3$ is the line parallel to the x-axis that intersects the y-axis at $(0, 3)$.

  (c) $x \geq 0$ is the set of all points to the right of and on the y-axis.

  (d) $xy > 0$ is the set of all points in quadrants I and III

  { x and y have the same sign }.

  (e) $y < 0$ is the set of all points below the x-axis.

  (f) $x = 0$ is the set of all points on the y-axis.

2. (a) $y = -2$ is the line parallel to the x-axis that intersects the y-axis at $(0, -2)$.

  (b) $x = -4$ is the line parallel to the y-axis that intersects the x-axis at $(-4, 0)$.

  (c) $x/y < 0$ is the set of all points in quadrants II and IV.

  { x and y have opposite signs }.

  (d) $xy = 0$ is the set of all points on the x-axis or y-axis.

  (e) $y > 1$ is the set of all points

  above the line parallel to the x-axis which intersects the y-axis at $(0, 1)$.

  (f) $y = 0$ is the set of all points on the x-axis.

3. (a) $A(4, -3)$, $B(6, 2) \Rightarrow d(A, B) = \sqrt{(6-4)^2 + [2-(-3)]^2} = \sqrt{4 + 25} = \sqrt{29}$

  (b) $M_{AB} = \left(\frac{4+6}{2}, \frac{-3+2}{2} \right) = (5, -\frac{1}{2})$

4.   (a) $A(-2, -5)$, $B(4, 6)$ $\Rightarrow$

$$d(A, B) = \sqrt{[4-(-2)]^2 + [6-(-5)]^2} = \sqrt{36 + 121} = \sqrt{157}$$

    (b) $M_{AB} = \left(\dfrac{-2+4}{2}, \dfrac{-5+6}{2}\right) = (1, \tfrac{1}{2})$

5.   Show that $d(A, C)^2 = d(A, B)^2 + d(B, C)^2$, that is, $(\sqrt{130})^2 = (\sqrt{98})^2 + (\sqrt{32})^2$.

$$\text{Area} = \tfrac{1}{2}bh = \tfrac{1}{2}(\sqrt{32})(\sqrt{98}) = \tfrac{1}{2}(4\sqrt{2})(7\sqrt{2}) = 28.$$

6.   Show that $d(A, B)^2 = d(A, C)^2 + d(B, C)^2$, that is, $(\sqrt{145})^2 = (\sqrt{29})^2 + (\sqrt{116})^2$.

$$\text{Area} = \tfrac{1}{2}bh = \tfrac{1}{2}(\sqrt{29})(\sqrt{116}) = \tfrac{1}{2}(\sqrt{29})(2\sqrt{29}) = 29.$$

7.   Show that $d(A, B) = d(B, C) = d(C, D) = d(D, A)$ {each is $\sqrt{29}$} and

$$d(A, C)^2 = d(A, B)^2 + d(B, C)^2 \ \{d(A, C) = \sqrt{58}\}$$

8.   Show that $d(A, D) = d(B, C)$ {each is $\sqrt{45}$} and $d(A, B) = d(C, D)$ {each is $\sqrt{17}$}

9.   Let $B = (x, y)$. $A(-3, 8) \Rightarrow M_{AB} = \left(\dfrac{-3+x}{2}, \dfrac{8+y}{2}\right)$. $M_{AB} = C(5, -10) \Rightarrow$

$$-3 + x = 2(5) \text{ and } 8 + y = 2(-10) \Rightarrow x = 13 \text{ and } y = -28. \ \ B = (13, -28).$$

10.   If Q is the midpoint of segment AB, then the midpoint of QB is the point that is three-fourths of the way from $A(5, -8)$ to $B(-6, 2)$.

$$Q = M_{AB} = \left(\dfrac{5+(-6)}{2}, \dfrac{-8+2}{2}\right) = (-\tfrac{1}{2}, -3).$$

$$M_{QB} = \left(\dfrac{(-1/2)+(-6)}{2}, \dfrac{-3+2}{2}\right) = (-\tfrac{13}{4}, -\tfrac{1}{2}).$$

11.   Similar to Example 1, we must show that $d(A, C) = d(B, C) = \sqrt{145}$.

12.   Show that $d(A, C) = d(B, C) = \sqrt{125}$.

13.   Let $Q(0, y)$ be an arbitrary point on the y-axis.

$$6 = d(P, Q) \Rightarrow 6 = \sqrt{(0-5)^2 + (y-3)^2} \Rightarrow 36 = 25 + y^2 - 6y + 9 \Rightarrow$$

$$y^2 - 6y - 2 = 0 \Rightarrow y = 3 \pm \sqrt{11}. \text{ The points are } (0, 3+\sqrt{11}) \text{ and } (0, 3-\sqrt{11}).$$

14.   Let $Q(x, 0)$ be an arbitrary point on the x-axis.

$$5 = d(P, Q) \Rightarrow 5 \Rightarrow \sqrt{(x+2)^2 + (0-4)^2} \Rightarrow 25 = x^2 + 4x + 4 + 16 \Rightarrow$$

$$x^2 + 4x - 5 = 0 \Rightarrow (x+5)(x-1) = 0 \Rightarrow x = -5, 1. \text{ The points are } (1, 0) \text{ and } (-5, 0).$$

15. $d(P, Q) > \sqrt{26} \Rightarrow \sqrt{(5-a)^2 + (2a-3)^2} > \sqrt{26} \Rightarrow$

$$25 - 10a + a^2 + 4a^2 - 12a + 9 > 26 \Rightarrow 5a^2 - 22a + 8 > 0 \Rightarrow (5a-2)(a-4) > 0 \Rightarrow$$

$$a < \tfrac{2}{5} \text{ or } a > 4. \text{ Use a sign diagram to establish the final answer.}$$

16. $3 = \sqrt{(a+2)^2 + (a-1)^2} \Rightarrow 9 = a^2 + 4a + 4 + a^2 - 2a + 1 \Rightarrow 0 = 2a^2 + 2a - 4 \Rightarrow$

$$a^2 + a - 2 = 0 \Rightarrow (a+2)(a-1) = 0 \Rightarrow a = -2, 1. \text{ The points are } (-2, -2) \text{ and } (1, 1).$$

[17] To find the x-intercept, let $y = 0$ in $y = 2x - 3$, and solve for x. (1.5, 0)

To find the y-intercept, let $x = 0$ in $y = 2x - 3$, and solve for y. (0, −3)

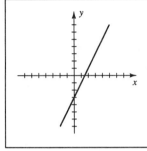

Figure 17

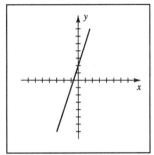

Figure 18

[18] $y = 3x + 2$ • x-intercept: $\left(-\frac{2}{3}, 0\right)$ y-intercept: (0, 2)

[19] $y = -x + 1$ • x-intercept: (1, 0) y-intercept: (0, 1)

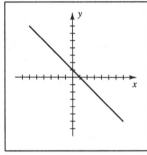

Figure 19

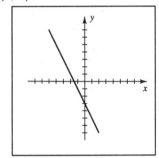

Figure 20

[20] $y = -2x - 3$ • x-intercept: (−1.5, 0) y-intercept: (0, −3)

[21] $y = -4x^2$ • x-intercept: (0, 0) y-intercept: (0, 0)

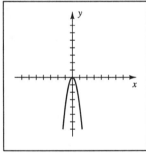

Figure 21

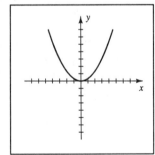

Figure 22

[22] $y = \frac{1}{3}x^2$ • x-intercept: (0, 0) y-intercept: (0, 0)

$\boxed{23}$ $y = 2x^2 - 1$ • x-intercepts: $(\pm\frac{1}{2}\sqrt{2},\ 0)$ y-intercept: $(0,\ -1)$

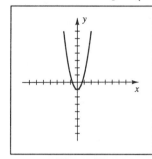

Figure 23

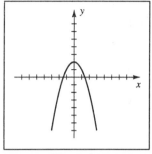

Figure 24

$\boxed{24}$ $y = -x^2 + 2$ • x-intercepts: $(\pm\sqrt{2},\ 0)$ y-intercept: $(0,\ 2)$

$\boxed{25}$ $x = \frac{1}{4}y^2$ • x-intercept: $(0,\ 0)$ y-intercept: $(0,\ 0)$

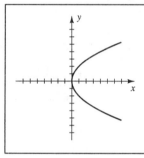

Figure 25

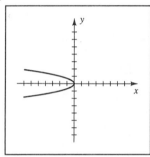

Figure 26

$\boxed{26}$ $x = -2y^2$ • x-intercept: $(0,\ 0)$ y-intercept: $(0,\ 0)$

$\boxed{27}$ $x = -y^2 + 3$ • x-intercept: $(3,\ 0)$ y-intercepts: $(0,\ \pm\sqrt{3})$

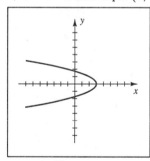

Figure 27

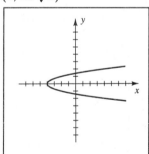

Figure 28

$\boxed{28}$ $x = 2y^2 - 4$ • x-intercept: $(-4,\ 0)$ y-intercepts: $(0,\ \pm\sqrt{2})$

$\boxed{29}$ $y = -\frac{1}{2}x^3$ • x-intercept: $(0, 0)$ y-intercept: $(0, 0)$

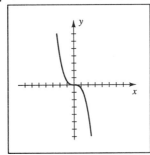

Figure 29

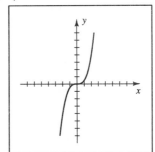

Figure 30

$\boxed{30}$ $y = \frac{1}{2}x^3$ • x-intercept: $(0, 0)$ y-intercept: $(0, 0)$

$\boxed{31}$ $y = x^3 - 8$ • x-intercept: $(2, 0)$ y-intercept: $(0, -8)$

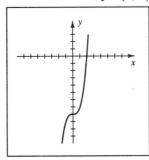

Figure 31

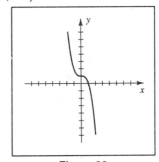

Figure 32

$\boxed{32}$ $y = -x^3 + 1$ • x-intercept: $(1, 0)$ y-intercept: $(0, 1)$

$\boxed{33}$ $y = \sqrt{x}$ • x-intercept: $(0, 0)$ y-intercept: $(0, 0)$

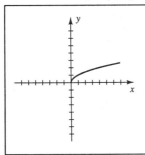

Figure 33

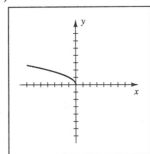

Figure 34

$\boxed{34}$ $y = \sqrt{-x}$ • x-intercept: $(0, 0)$ y-intercept: $(0, 0)$

35 $y = \sqrt{x} - 4$ • x-intercept: $(16, 0)$ y-intercept: $(0, -4)$

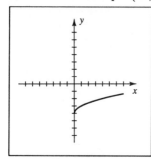

Figure 35

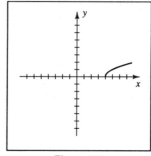

Figure 36

36 $y = \sqrt{x - 4}$ • x-intercept: $(4, 0)$ y-intercept: None

37 (a) 21, 23   (b) 25, 27   (c) 29

38 (a) 22, 24   (b) 26, 28   (c) 30

39 $x^2 + y^2 = 11$ is a circle of radius $\sqrt{11}$ with center at the origin.

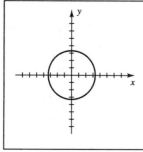

Figure 39

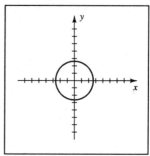

Figure 40

40 $x^2 + y^2 = 7$ is a circle of radius $\sqrt{7}$ with center at the origin.

41 $(x + 3)^2 + (y - 2)^2 = 9$ is a circle of radius $r = \sqrt{9} = 3$ with center $C(-3, 2)$.

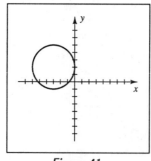

Figure 41

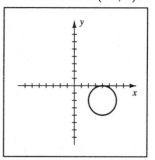

Figure 42

42 $(x - 4)^2 + (y + 2)^2 = 4$ is a circle of radius $r = \sqrt{4} = 2$ with center $C(4, -2)$.

⓸⓷ $(x+3)^2 + y^2 = 16$ is a circle of radius $r = \sqrt{16} = 4$ with center $C(-3, 0)$.

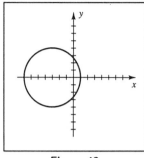

Figure 43

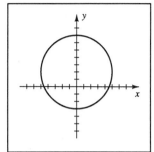

Figure 44

⓸⓸ $x^2 + (y-2)^2 = 25$ is a circle of radius $r = \sqrt{25} = 5$ with center $C(0, 2)$.

⓸⓹ $4x^2 + 4y^2 = 25 \Rightarrow x^2 + y^2 = \frac{25}{4}$ is a circle of radius $r = \sqrt{\frac{25}{4}} = \frac{5}{2}$ with center $C(0, 0)$.

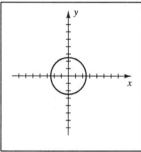

Figure 45

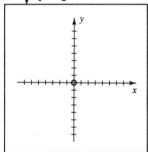

Figure 46

⓸⓺ $9x^2 + 9y^2 = 1 \Rightarrow x^2 + y^2 = \frac{1}{9}$ is a circle of radius $r = \sqrt{\frac{1}{9}} = \frac{1}{3}$ with center $C(0, 0)$.

⓸⓻ As in Example 9, $y = -\sqrt{16 - x^2}$ is the lower half of the circle $x^2 + y^2 = 16$.

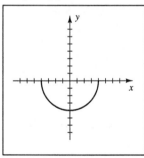

Figure 47

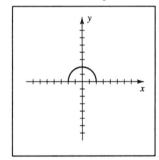

Figure 48

⓸⓼ $y = \sqrt{4 - x^2}$ is the upper half of the circle $x^2 + y^2 = 4$.

$\boxed{49}$ $x = \sqrt{9 - y^2}$ is the right half of the circle $x^2 + y^2 = 9$.

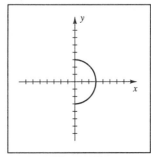

Figure 49

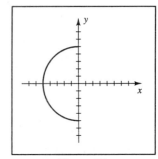

Figure 50

$\boxed{50}$ $x = -\sqrt{25 - y^2}$ is the left half of the circle $x^2 + y^2 = 25$.

$\boxed{51}$ Center $C(2, -3)$, radius 5 • $(x - 2)^2 + (y + 3)^2 = 5^2 = 25$

$\boxed{52}$ Center $C(-4, 1)$, radius 3 • $(x + 4)^2 + (y - 1)^2 = 3^2 = 9$

$\boxed{53}$ Center $C(\frac{1}{4}, 0)$, radius $\sqrt{5}$ • $(x - \frac{1}{4})^2 + y^2 = (\sqrt{5})^2 = 5$

$\boxed{54}$ Center $C(\frac{3}{4}, -\frac{2}{3})$, radius $3\sqrt{2}$ • $(x - \frac{3}{4})^2 + (y + \frac{2}{3})^2 = (3\sqrt{2})^2 = 18$

$\boxed{55}$ An equation of a circle with center $C(-4, 6)$ is $(x + 4)^2 + (y - 6)^2 = r^2$.

Letting $x = 1$ and $y = 2$ yields $5^2 + (-4)^2 = r^2 \Rightarrow r^2 = 41$. $(x + 4)^2 + (y - 6)^2 = 41$

$\boxed{56}$ An equation of a circle with center at the origin is $x^2 + y^2 = r^2$.

Letting $x = 4$ and $y = -7$ yields $4^2 + (-7)^2 = r^2 \Rightarrow r^2 = 65$. $x^2 + y^2 = 65$

$\boxed{57}$ The circle is tangent to the y-axis and has center $C(-3, 6)$.

Its radius, 3, is the distance from the y-axis to the x-value of the center.

An equation is $(x + 3)^2 + (y - 6)^2 = 9$.

$\boxed{58}$ The circle is tangent to the x-axis and has center $C(4, -1)$.

Its radius, 1, is the distance from the x-axis to the y-value of the center.

An equation is $(x - 4)^2 + (y + 1)^2 = 1$.

$\boxed{59}$ Since the radius is 4 and $C(h, k)$ is in QII, $h = -4$ and $k = 4$.

An equation is $(x + 4)^2 + (y - 4)^2 = 16$.

$\boxed{60}$ Since the radius is 3 and $C(h, k)$ is in QIV, $h = 3$ and $k = -3$.

An equation is $(x - 3)^2 + (y + 3)^2 = 9$.

$\boxed{61}$ The center of the circle is the midpoint M of $A(4, -3)$ and $B(-2, 7)$. $M = (1, 2)$.

The radius of the circle is $\frac{1}{2} \cdot d(A, B) = \frac{1}{2}\sqrt{136} = \sqrt{34}$.

An equation is $(x - 1)^2 + (y - 2)^2 = 34$.

$\boxed{62}$ As in the solution to Exercise 61, $M_{AB} = (-1, 4)$ and

$r = \frac{1}{2} \cdot d(A, B) = \frac{1}{2}\sqrt{80} = \sqrt{20}$. An equation is $(x + 1)^2 + (y - 4)^2 = 20$.

$\boxed{63}$ $x^2 + y^2 - 4x + 6y - 36 = 0 \Rightarrow x^2 - 4x + \underline{4} + y^2 + 6y + \underline{9} = 36 + \underline{4} + \underline{9} \Rightarrow$

$(x - 2)^2 + (y + 3)^2 = 49$. $C(2, -3)$; $r = 7$

$\boxed{64}$ $x^2 + y^2 + 8x - 10y + 37 = 0 \Rightarrow x^2 + 8x + \underline{\ 16\ } + y^2 - 10y + \underline{\ 25\ } = -37 + \underline{\ 16\ } + \underline{\ 25\ } \Rightarrow$
$$(x+4)^2 + (y-5)^2 = 4. \quad C(-4,\ 5);\ r = 2$$

$\boxed{65}$ $x^2 + y^2 + 4y - 117 = 0 \Rightarrow x^2 + y^2 + 4y + \underline{\ 4\ } = 117 + \underline{\ 4\ } \Rightarrow x^2 + (y+2)^2 = 121.$
$$C(0,\ -2);\ r = 11$$

$\boxed{66}$ $x^2 + y^2 - 10x + 18 = 0 \Rightarrow x^2 - 10x + \underline{\ 25\ } + y^2 = -18 + \underline{\ 25\ } \Rightarrow (x-5)^2 + y^2 = 7.$
$$C(5,\ 0);\ r = \sqrt{7}$$

$\boxed{67}$ $2x^2 + 2y^2 - 12x + 4y - 15 = 0 \Rightarrow x^2 - 6x + \underline{\ 9\ } + y^2 + 2y + \underline{\ 1\ } = \frac{15}{2} + \underline{\ 9\ } + \underline{\ 1\ } \Rightarrow$
$$(x-3)^2 + (y+1)^2 = \tfrac{35}{2}. \quad C(3,\ -1);\ r = \tfrac{1}{2}\sqrt{70}$$

$\boxed{68}$ $9x^2 + 9y^2 + 12x - 6y + 4 = 0 \Rightarrow x^2 + \frac{4}{3}x + \frac{4}{9} + y^2 - \frac{2}{3}y + \frac{1}{9} = -\frac{4}{9} + \frac{4}{9} + \frac{1}{9} \Rightarrow$
$$(x+\tfrac{2}{3})^2 + (y-\tfrac{1}{3})^2 = \tfrac{1}{9}. \quad C(-\tfrac{2}{3},\ \tfrac{1}{3});\ r = \tfrac{1}{3}$$

$\boxed{69}$ $x^2 + y^2 + 4x - 2y + 5 = 0 \Rightarrow x^2 + 4x + \underline{\ 4\ } + y^2 - 2y + \underline{\ 1\ } = -5 + \underline{\ 4\ } + \underline{\ 1\ } \Rightarrow$
$$(x+2)^2 + (y-1)^2 = 0. \quad C(-2,\ 1);\ r = 0 \text{ (a point)}$$

$\boxed{70}$ $x^2 + y^2 - 6x + 4y + 13 = 0 \Rightarrow x^2 - 6x + \underline{\ 9\ } + y^2 + 4y + \underline{\ 4\ } = -13 + \underline{\ 9\ } + \underline{\ 4\ } \Rightarrow$
$$(x-3)^2 + (y+2)^2 = 0. \quad C(3,\ -2);\ r = 0 \text{ (a point)}$$

$\boxed{71}$ $x^2 + y^2 - 2x - 8y + 19 = 0 \Rightarrow x^2 - 2x + \underline{\ 1\ } + y^2 - 8y + \underline{\ 16\ } = -19 + \underline{\ 1\ } + \underline{\ 16\ } \Rightarrow$
$$(x-1)^2 + (y-4)^2 = -2. \text{ This is not a circle since } r^2 \text{ cannot equal } -2.$$

$\boxed{72}$ $x^2 + y^2 + 4x + 6y + 16 = 0 \Rightarrow x^2 + 4x + \underline{\ 4\ } + y^2 + 6y + \underline{\ 9\ } = -16 + \underline{\ 4\ } + \underline{\ 9\ } \Rightarrow$
$$(x+2)^2 + (y+3)^2 = -3. \text{ This is not a circle since } r^2 \text{ cannot equal } -3.$$

$\boxed{73}$ To obtain equations for the upper and lower halves, we solve the given equation for y in terms of x. $x^2 + y^2 = 36 \Rightarrow y^2 = 36 - x^2 \Rightarrow y = \pm\sqrt{36 - x^2}$. The upper half is $y = \sqrt{36 - x^2}$ and the lower half is $y = -\sqrt{36 - x^2}$. To obtain equations for the right and left halves, we solve for x in terms of y. $x^2 + y^2 = 36 \Rightarrow x^2 = 36 - y^2 \Rightarrow$ $x = \pm\sqrt{36 - y^2}$. The right half is $x = \sqrt{36 - y^2}$ and the left half is $x = -\sqrt{36 - y^2}$.

$\boxed{74}$ $(x+3)^2 + y^2 = 64 \Rightarrow y^2 = 64 - (x+3)^2 \Rightarrow y = \pm\sqrt{64 - (x+3)^2}.$
$(x+3)^2 + y^2 = 64 \Rightarrow (x+3)^2 = 64 - y^2 \Rightarrow$
$$x + 3 = \pm\sqrt{64 - y^2} \Rightarrow x = -3 \pm\sqrt{64 - y^2}.$$

$\boxed{75}$ $(x-2)^2 + (y+1)^2 = 49 \Rightarrow (y+1)^2 = 49 - (x-2)^2 \Rightarrow$
$$y + 1 = \pm\sqrt{49 - (x-2)^2} \Rightarrow y = -1 \pm\sqrt{49 - (x-2)^2}.$$
$(x-2)^2 + (y+1)^2 = 49 \Rightarrow (x-2)^2 = 49 - (y+1)^2 \Rightarrow$
$$x - 2 = \pm\sqrt{49 - (y+1)^2} \Rightarrow x = 2 \pm\sqrt{49 - (y+1)^2}.$$

$\boxed{76}$ $(x-3)^2 + (y-5)^2 = 4 \Rightarrow (y-5)^2 = 4 - (x-3)^2 \Rightarrow$
$$y - 5 = \pm\sqrt{4 - (x-3)^2} \Rightarrow y = 5 \pm\sqrt{4 - (x-3)^2}.$$
$(x-3)^2 + (y-5)^2 = 4 \Rightarrow (x-3)^2 = 4 - (y-5)^2 \Rightarrow$
$$x - 3 = \pm\sqrt{4 - (y-5)^2} \Rightarrow x = 3 \pm\sqrt{4 - (y-5)^2}.$$

$\boxed{77}$ We need to determine if the distance from P to C is *less than* r, *greater than* r, or *equal to* r and hence, P will be *inside* the circle, *outside* the circle, or *on* the circle, respectively.

(a) $P(2, 3)$, $C(4, 6) \Rightarrow d(P, C) = \sqrt{4+9} = \sqrt{13} < r \ \{r = 4\} \Rightarrow P$ is *inside* C.

(b) $P(4, 2)$, $C(1, -2) \Rightarrow d(P, C) = \sqrt{9+16} = 5 = r \ \{r = 5\} \Rightarrow P$ is *on* C.

(c) $P(-3, 5)$, $C(2, 1) \Rightarrow d(P, C) = \sqrt{25+16} = \sqrt{41} > r \ \{r = 6\} \Rightarrow P$ is *outside* C.

$\boxed{78}$ (a) $P(3, 8)$, $C(-2, -4) \Rightarrow d(P, C) = \sqrt{25+144} = 13 = r \ \{r = 13\} \Rightarrow P$ is *on* C.

(b) $P(-2, 5)$, $C(3, 7) \Rightarrow d(P, C) = \sqrt{25+4} = \sqrt{29} < r \ \{r = 6\} \Rightarrow P$ is *inside* C.

(c) $P(1, -2)$, $C(6, -7) \Rightarrow d(P, C) = \sqrt{25+25} = \sqrt{50} > r \ \{r = 7\} \Rightarrow$
$$P \text{ is } outside \ C.$$

$\boxed{79}$ (a) To find the x-intercepts, let $y = 0$ and solve the resulting equation for x.
$$x^2 - 4x + 4 = 0 \Rightarrow (x - 2)^2 = 0 \Rightarrow x = 2$$

(b) To find the y-intercepts, let $x = 0$ and solve the resulting equation for y.
$$y^2 - 6y + 4 = 0 \Rightarrow y = \frac{6 \pm \sqrt{36 - 16}}{2} = 3 \pm \sqrt{5}.$$

$\boxed{80}$ (a) $y = 0 \Rightarrow x^2 - 10x + 13 = 0 \Rightarrow x = \dfrac{10 \pm \sqrt{100 - 52}}{2} = 5 \pm 2\sqrt{3}$

(b) $x = 0 \Rightarrow y^2 + 4y + 13 = 0 \Rightarrow y = \dfrac{-4 \pm \sqrt{16 - 52}}{2}$.

The negative discriminant implies that there are no real solutions to the equation and hence, no y-intercepts.

$\boxed{81}$ $x^2 + y^2 + 4x - 6y + 4 = 0 \Leftrightarrow (x + 2)^2 + (y - 3)^2 = 9$. This is a circle with center $C(-2, 3)$ and radius 3. The circle we want has the same center, $C(-2, 3)$, and radius that is equal to the distance from C to $P(2, 6)$.
$$d(P, C) = \sqrt{16 + 9} = 5 \text{ and an equation is } (x + 2)^2 + (y - 3)^2 = 25.$$

$\boxed{82}$ By the Pythagorean theorem, the two stations are $d = \sqrt{100^2 + 80^2} \approx 128.06$ miles apart. The sum of their radii, $80 + 50 = 130$, is greater than d,

indicating that the circles representing their broadcast ranges do overlap.

$\boxed{83}$ The equation of circle C_2 is $(x - h)^2 + (y - 2)^2 = 2^2$. If we draw a line from the origin to the center of C_2, we form a right triangle with hypotenuse $5 - 2$ $\{C_2$ radius $- C_1$ radius$\} = 3$ and sides of length 2 and h. Thus, $h^2 + 2^2 = 3^2 \Rightarrow h = \sqrt{5}$.

$\boxed{84}$ The equation of circle C_2 is $(x - h)^2 + (y - 3)^2 = 2^2$. If we draw a line from the origin to the center of C_2, we form a right triangle with hypotenuse $5 + 2$ $\{C_2$ radius $+ C_1$ radius$\} = 7$ and sides of length 3 and h. Thus, $h^2 + 3^2 = 7^2 \Rightarrow h = \sqrt{40}$.

$\boxed{85}$ The y-value assignments are $Y_1 = -x^2 + 4$ and $Y_2 = x - 2$. Assuming that the x- and y-values of each point of intersection are integers, and that the tics each represent one unit, we see that the intersection points are $(-3, -5)$ and $(2, 0)$. The viewing rectangle (VR) is $[-15, 15]$ by $[-10, 10]$. $Y_1 < Y_2$ on $[-15, -3) \cup (2, 15]$.

86. $Y_1 = \sqrt{100 - x^2}$, $Y_2 = 6$, VR: $[-10, 10]$ by $[-2, 12]$.

The intersection points are $(-8, 6)$ and $(8, 6)$. $Y_1 < Y_2$ on $[-10, -8) \cup (8, 10]$.

87. $Y_1 = x^2$, $Y_2 = x^{2/3}$, VR: $[-5, 5]$ by $[-1, 5]$.

The intersection points are $(-1, 1)$, $(0, 0)$, and $(1, 1)$. $Y_1 < Y_2$ on $(-1, 0) \cup (0, 1)$.

88. $Y_1 = -\frac{1}{21}x^2 + \frac{1}{21}$, $Y_2 = -x^{2/3} + 1$, VR: $[-10, 10]$ $[-6.7, 6.7]$. The intersection points
are $(\pm 8, -3)$ and $(\pm 1, 0)$. $Y_1 < Y_2$ on $[-10, -8) \cup (-1, 1) \cup (8, 10]$.

89. (a) Plot $(1990, 54{,}871{,}330)$, $(1991, 55{,}786{,}390)$, $(1992, 57{,}211{,}600)$,

    $(1993, 58{,}834{,}440)$, and $(1994, 59{,}332{,}200)$.

    (b) The number of cable subscribers is increasing each year.

$[1988, 1996]$ by $[54 \times 10^6, 61 \times 10^6]$ $\qquad$ $[1895, 2000]$ by $[0, 3000]$

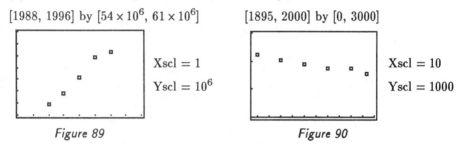

Xscl = 1 $\qquad\qquad\qquad\qquad$ Xscl = 10

Yscl = 10^6 $\qquad\qquad\qquad\qquad$ Yscl = 1000

Figure 89 $\qquad\qquad\qquad\qquad\qquad$ *Figure 90*

90. (a) Plot $(1900, 2226)$, $(1920, 2042)$, $(1940, 1878)$, $(1960, 1763)$, $(1980, 1745)$, and

    $(1993, 1556)$.

    (b) Find the midpoint of $(1920, 2042)$ and $(1940, 1878)$.

    $$\left(\frac{1920 + 1940}{2}, \frac{2042 + 1878}{2} \right) = (1930, 1960).$$

    The midpoint formula predicts 1960 daily newspapers published in the year 1930
    compared to the actual value of 1942 daily newspapers.

91. The viewing rectangles significantly affect the shape of the circle. Viewing rectangle
    (2) results in a graph that most looks like a circle. Viewing rectangles (3) and (4) are
    on the next page.

$[-2, 2]$ by $[-2, 2]$ $\qquad\qquad\qquad\qquad$ $[-3, 3]$ by $[-2, 2]$

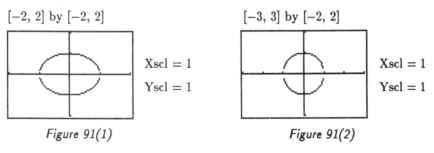

Xscl = 1 $\qquad\qquad\qquad\qquad$ Xscl = 1

Yscl = 1 $\qquad\qquad\qquad\qquad$ Yscl = 1

Figure 91(1) $\qquad\qquad\qquad\qquad\qquad$ *Figure 91(2)*

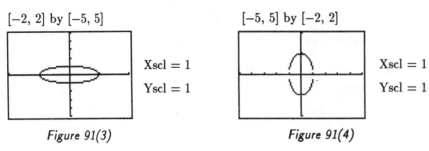

Figure 91(3)   Figure 91(4)

92 (a) From the graph there are two x–intercepts and two y–intercepts.

   (b) Using the free–moving cursor, one can conclude that $|x| + |y| < 5$ is true whenever the point (x, y) is located *inside* the diamond shape.

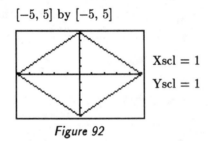

Figure 92

93 Assign $x^3 - \frac{9}{10}x^2 - \frac{43}{25}x + \frac{24}{25}$ to Y_1. After trying a standard viewing rectangle, we see that the x-intercepts are near the origin and we choose the viewing rectangle $[-6, 6]$ by $[-4, 4]$. This is simply one choice, not necessarily the best choice. For most [C] exercises, we have selected viewing rectangles that are in a $3:2$ proportion (horizontal : vertical) to maintain a true proportion. From the graph, there are three x-intercepts. Use a zoom or root feature to determine that they are approximately -1.2, 0.5, and 1.6.

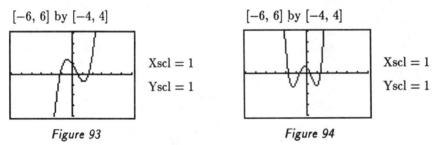

Figure 93   *Figure 94*

94 From the graph, there are four x-intercepts.

                        They are approximately -1.8, -0.7, 0.3 and 1.35.

95 Make the assignments $Y_1 = x^3 + x$, $Y_2 = \sqrt{1 - x^2}$, and $Y_3 = -Y_2$.

From the graph, there are two points of intersection.

They are approximately $(0.6, 0.8)$ and $(-0.6, -0.8)$.

$[-3, 3]$ by $[-2, 2]$ $[-3, 3]$ by $[-2, 2]$

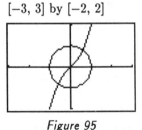
Xscl $= 1$

Yscl $= 1$

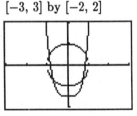
Xscl $= 1$

Yscl $= 1$

Figure 95   *Figure 96*

96 Make the assignments $Y_1 = 3x^4 - \frac{3}{2}$, $Y_2 = \sqrt{1 - x^2}$, and $Y_3 = -Y_2$.

From the graph, there are four points of intersection.

They are approximately $(\pm 0.9, 0.4)$ and $(\pm 0.7, -0.7)$.

97 Depending on the type of graphing utility used, you may need to solve for y first.

$x^2 + (y - 1)^2 = 1 \Rightarrow y = 1 \pm \sqrt{1 - x^2}$; $(x - \frac{5}{4})^2 + y^2 = 1 \Rightarrow y = \pm \sqrt{1 - (x - \frac{5}{4})^2}$.

Make the assignments $Y_1 = \sqrt{1 - x^2}$, $Y_2 = 1 + Y_1$, $Y_3 = 1 - Y_1$, $Y_4 = \sqrt{1 - (x - \frac{5}{4})^2}$,

and $Y_5 = -Y_4$. If a Y_5 is not available, you will need to use other function

assignments or alternate methods. For example, on the TI-81, you can graph Y_5 by

using DrawF $-Y_4$. Be sure to "turn off" Y_1 before graphing. From the graph, there

are two points of intersection.

They are approximately $(0.999, 0.968)$ and $(0.251, 0.032)$.

$[-3, 3]$ by $[-2, 2]$ $[-3, 3]$ by $[-2, 2]$

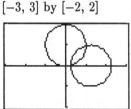
Xscl $= 1$

Yscl $= 1$

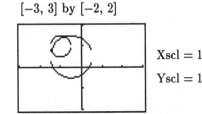
Xscl $= 1$

Yscl $= 1$

Figure 97   *Figure 98*

98 $(x + 1)^2 + (y - 1)^2 = \frac{1}{4} \Rightarrow y = 1 \pm \sqrt{\frac{1}{4} - (x + 1)^2}$; $(x + \frac{1}{2})^2 + (y - \frac{1}{2})^2 = 1 \Rightarrow$

$y = \frac{1}{2} \pm \sqrt{1 - (x + \frac{1}{2})^2}$. From the graph, there are two points of intersection.

They are approximately $(-0.79, 1.46)$ and $(-1.46, 0.79)$.

99 The cars are initially 4 miles apart. Their distance decreases to 0 when they meet on the highway after 2 minutes. Then, their distance starts to increase until it is 4 miles after a total of 4 minutes.

[0, 4] by [0, 4]   [0, 6] by [0, 20,000]

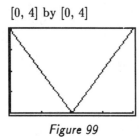   Xscl = 1
Yscl = 1

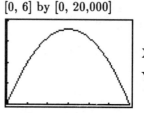   Xscl = 1
Yscl = 5000

Figure 99   *Figure 100*

100 At noon on Sunday the pool is empty since when $x = 0$, $A = 0$. It is then filled with water, until at noon on Wednesday ($x = 3$), it contains 18,000 gallons. It is then drained until at noon on Saturday ($x = 6$), it is empty again.

101 (a) $v = 1087\sqrt{(20 + 273)/273} \approx 1126$ ft/sec.

(b) Algebraically: $v = 1087\sqrt{\dfrac{T + 273}{273}} \Rightarrow 1000 = 1087\sqrt{\dfrac{T + 273}{273}} \Rightarrow$

$$T = \frac{1000^2 \times 273}{1087^2} - 273 \approx -42°\text{C}.$$

Graphically: Graph $Y_1 = 1087\sqrt{(T + 273)/273}$ and $Y_2 = 1000$.

At the point of their intersection, $T \approx -42°$C.

[−50, 50] by [900, 1200]   [14, 16] by [95, 105]

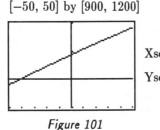   Xscl = 10
Yscl = 100

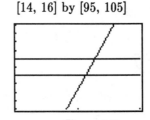   Xscl = 1
Yscl = 1

Figure 101   *Figure 102*

102 The horizontal lines intersect the graph of A at $s \approx 15.12$, 15.27. Thus, if $15.12 \le s \le 15.27$, then $99 \le A \le 101$.

1 $A(-3, 2),\ B(5, -4) \Rightarrow m_{AB} = \dfrac{(-4)-2}{5-(-3)} = \dfrac{-6}{8} = -\dfrac{3}{4}$

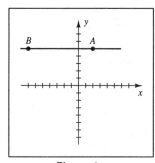

Figure 1

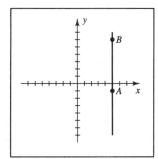

Figure 2

2 $A(4, -1),\ B(-6, -3) \Rightarrow m_{AB} = \dfrac{-3+1}{-6-4} = \dfrac{-2}{-10} = \dfrac{1}{5}$

3 $A(2, 5),\ B(-7, 5) \Rightarrow m_{AB} = \dfrac{5-5}{-7-2} = \dfrac{0}{-9} = 0$

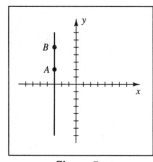

Figure 3

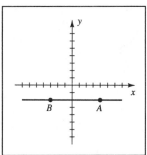

Figure 4

4 $A(5, -1),\ B(5, 6) \Rightarrow m_{AB} = \dfrac{6+1}{5-5} = \dfrac{7}{0} \Rightarrow m$ is undefined

5 $A(-3, 2),\ B(-3, 5) \Rightarrow m_{AB} = \dfrac{5-2}{-3-(-3)} = \dfrac{3}{0} \Rightarrow m$ is undefined

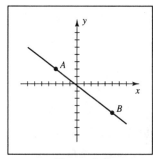

Figure 5

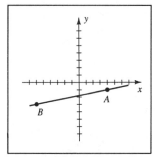

Figure 6

6 $A(4, -2),\ B(-3, -2) \Rightarrow m_{AB} = \dfrac{-2-(-2)}{-3-4} = \dfrac{0}{-7} = 0$

7 Show that the slopes of opposite sides are equal.

$A(-3, 1),\ B(5, 3),\ C(3, 0),\ D(-5, -2) \Rightarrow m_{AB} = \tfrac{1}{4} = m_{DC}$ and $m_{DA} = \tfrac{3}{2} = m_{CB}.$

$\boxed{8}$　Show that the slopes of one pair of opposite sides are equal.

$$A(2, 3),\ B(5, -1),\ C(0, -6),\ D(-6, 2) \Rightarrow m_{AB} = -\tfrac{4}{3} = m_{CD}.$$

$\boxed{9}$　Show that the slopes of opposite sides are equal (parallel lines) and the slopes of two

adjacent sides are negative reciprocals (perpendicular lines). $A(6, 15),$

$$B(11, 12),\ C(-1, -8),\ D(-6, -5) \Rightarrow m_{DA} = \tfrac{5}{3} = m_{CB} \text{ and } m_{AB} = -\tfrac{3}{5} = m_{DC}.$$

$\boxed{10}$　Show that adjacent sides are perpendicular.

$$A(1, 4),\ B(6, -4),\ C(-15, -6) \Rightarrow m_{AB} = -\tfrac{8}{5} \text{ and } m_{AC} = \tfrac{5}{8}.$$

$\boxed{11}$　$A(-1, -3)$ is 5 units to the left and 5 units down from $B(4, 2)$. D will have the

same relative position from $C(-7, 5)$, that is, $(-7-5, 5-5) = (-12, 0)$.

$\boxed{12}$　Let $E = M_{AB} = \left(\dfrac{x_1+x_2}{2}, \dfrac{y_1+y_2}{2}\right)$, $F = M_{BC} = \left(\dfrac{x_2+x_3}{2}, \dfrac{y_2+y_3}{2}\right)$,

$G = M_{CD} = \left(\dfrac{x_3+x_4}{2}, \dfrac{y_3+y_4}{2}\right)$, and $H = M_{AD} = \left(\dfrac{x_1+x_4}{2}, \dfrac{y_1+y_4}{2}\right)$.

The slopes of opposite sides are equal (or lines are vertical).

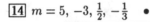

$$m_{EF} = m_{GH} = \frac{y_3-y_1}{x_3-x_1} \text{ and } m_{FG} = m_{EH} = \frac{y_4-y_2}{x_4-x_2}$$

$\boxed{13}$ $m = 3, -2, \tfrac{2}{3}, -\tfrac{1}{4}$　•

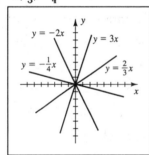

Figure 13

$\boxed{14}$ $m = 5, -3, \tfrac{1}{2}, -\tfrac{1}{3}$　•

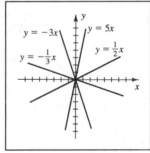

Figure 14

$\boxed{15}$ $P(3, 1);$　$m = \tfrac{1}{2}, -1, -\tfrac{1}{5}$　•

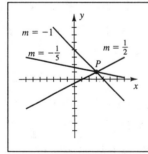

Figure 15

$\boxed{16}$ $P(-2, 4);$　$m = 1, -2, -\tfrac{1}{2}$　•

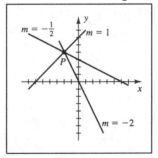

Figure 16

17 $y = x + 3,$ $y = x + 1,$ $y = -x + 1$ •

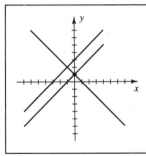

Figure 17   Figure 18

18 $y = -2x - 1,$ $y = -2x + 3,$ $y = \frac{1}{2}x + 3$ •

19 (a) Parallel to the y-axis implies the equation is of the form $x = k$.

The x-value of $A(5, -2)$ is 5, hence $x = 5$ is the equation.

(b) Perpendicular to the y-axis implies the equation is of the form $y = k$.

The y-value of $A(5, -2)$ is -2, hence $y = -2$ is the equation.

20 (a) The line through $A(-4, 2)$ and parallel to the x-axis is $y = 2$.

(b) The line through $A(-4, 2)$ and perpendicular to the x-axis is $x = -4$.

21 Using the point-slope form, the equation of the line through $A(5, -3)$ with slope -4

is $y + 3 = -4(x - 5) \Rightarrow y + 3 = -4x + 20 \Rightarrow 4x + y = 17$.

22 $A(-1, 4)$; slope $\frac{2}{3} \Rightarrow y - 4 = \frac{2}{3}(x + 1) \Rightarrow 3(y - 4) = 2(x + 1) \Rightarrow$

$$3y - 12 = 2x + 2 \Rightarrow 2x - 3y = -14.$$

23 $A(4, 0)$; slope $-3 \Rightarrow y - 0 = -3(x - 4) \Rightarrow y = -3x + 12 \Rightarrow 3x + y = 12$.

24 $A(0, -2)$; slope $5 \Rightarrow y + 2 = 5(x - 0) \Rightarrow y + 2 = 5x \Rightarrow 5x - y = 2$.

25 $A(4, -5)$, $B(-3, 6) \Rightarrow m_{AB} = -\frac{11}{7}$.

$$y + 5 = -\tfrac{11}{7}(x - 4) \Rightarrow 7y + 35 = -11x + 44 \Rightarrow 11x + 7y = 9.$$

26 $A(-1, 6)$, $B(5, 0) \Rightarrow m = -1$. $y - 0 = -1(x - 5) \Rightarrow y = -x + 5 \Rightarrow x + y = 5$.

27 $5x - 2y = 4 \Leftrightarrow y = \frac{5}{2}x - 2$. Using the same slope, $\frac{5}{2}$, with $A(2, -4)$,

gives us $y + 4 = \frac{5}{2}(x - 2) \Rightarrow 2y + 8 = 5x - 10 \Rightarrow 5x - 2y = 18$.

28 $x + 3y = 1 \Leftrightarrow y = -\frac{1}{3}x + \frac{1}{3}$. Using the same slope, $-\frac{1}{3}$, with $A(-3, 5)$,

gives us $y - 5 = -\frac{1}{3}(x + 3) \Rightarrow 3y - 15 = -x - 3 \Rightarrow x + 3y = 12$.

29 $2x - 5y = 8 \Leftrightarrow y = \frac{2}{5}x - \frac{8}{5}$. Using the negative reciprocal of $\frac{2}{5}$ for the slope,

$$y + 3 = -\tfrac{5}{2}(x - 7) \Rightarrow 2y + 6 = -5x + 35 \Rightarrow 5x + 2y = 29.$$

30 $3x + 2y = 7 \Leftrightarrow y = -\frac{3}{2}x + \frac{7}{2}$. Using the negative reciprocal of $-\frac{3}{2}$ for the slope,

$$y - 5 = \tfrac{2}{3}(x - 4) \Rightarrow 3y - 15 = 2x - 8 \Rightarrow 2x - 3y = -7.$$

31 $A(4, 0)$, $B(0, -3) \Rightarrow m = \frac{3}{4}$.

Using the slope-intercept form with $b = -3$ gives us $y = \frac{3}{4}x - 3$.

32 $A(-5, 0)$, $B(0, -1) \Rightarrow m = -\frac{1}{5}$. $b = -1 \Rightarrow y = -\frac{1}{5}x - 1$.

33 $A(5, 2)$, $B(-1, 4) \Rightarrow m = -\frac{1}{3}$.
$$y - 2 = -\frac{1}{3}(x - 5) \Rightarrow y = -\frac{1}{3}x + \frac{5}{3} + 2 \Rightarrow y = -\frac{1}{3}x + \frac{11}{3}.$$

34 $A(-2, 1)$, $B(3, 7) \Rightarrow m = \frac{6}{5}$. $y - 1 = \frac{6}{5}(x + 2) \Rightarrow y = \frac{6}{5}x + \frac{12}{5} + 1 \Rightarrow y = \frac{6}{5}x + \frac{17}{5}$.

35 $A(3, -1)$, $B(-2, 6) \Rightarrow M_{AB} = (\frac{1}{2}, \frac{5}{2})$ and $m_{AB} = -\frac{7}{5}$.
$$y - \frac{5}{2} = \frac{5}{7}(x - \frac{1}{2}) \Rightarrow 7y - \frac{35}{2} = 5x - \frac{5}{2} \Rightarrow 5x - 7y = -15.$$

36 $A(4, 2)$, $B(-2, 10) \Rightarrow M_{AB} = (1, 6)$ and $m_{AB} = -\frac{4}{3}$.
$$y - 6 = \frac{3}{4}(x - 1) \Rightarrow 4y - 24 = 3x - 3 \Rightarrow 3x - 4y = -21.$$

37 An equation of the line with slope -1 through the origin is
$$y - 0 = -1(x - 0), \text{ or } y = -x.$$

38 An equation of the line with slope 1 through the origin is $y - 0 = 1(x - 0)$, or $y = x$.

39 $2x = 15 - 3y \Rightarrow 3y = -2x + 15 \Rightarrow y = -\frac{2}{3}x + 5$; $m = -\frac{2}{3}$, $b = 5$

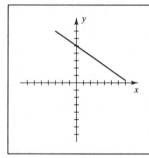

Figure 39

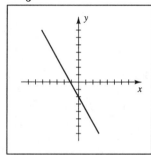

Figure 40

40 $7x = -4y - 8 \Rightarrow -4y = 7x + 8 \Rightarrow y = -\frac{7}{4}x - 2$; $m = -\frac{7}{4}$, $b = -2$

41 $4x - 3y = 9 \Rightarrow -3y = -4x + 9 \Rightarrow y = \frac{4}{3}x - 3$; $m = \frac{4}{3}$, $b = -3$

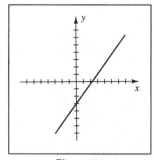

Figure 41

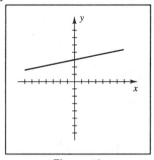

Figure 42

42 $x - 5y = -15 \Rightarrow -5y = -x - 15 \Rightarrow y = \frac{1}{5}x + 3$; $m = \frac{1}{5}$, $b = 3$

43 (a) An equation of the horizontal line with y-intercept 3 is $y = 3$.

   (b) An equation of the line through the origin with slope $-\frac{1}{2}$ is $y = -\frac{1}{2}x$.

   (c) An equation of the line with slope $-\frac{3}{2}$ and y-intercept 1 is $y = -\frac{3}{2}x + 1$.

   (d) An equation of the line through $(3, -2)$ with slope -1 is $y + 2 = -1(x - 3)$.

   Alternatively, we have a slope of -1 and a y-intercept of 1, i.e., $y = -x + 1$.

[44] (a) An equation of the vertical line with x-intercept -2 is $x = -2$.

(b) An equation of the line through the origin with slope $\frac{4}{3}$ is $y = \frac{4}{3}x$.

(c) An equation of the line with slope $\frac{1}{3}$ and y-intercept -2 is $y = \frac{1}{3}x - 2$.

(d) An equation of the line through $(-2, -5)$ with slope 3 is $y + 5 = 3(x + 2)$.

Alternatively, we have a slope of 3 and a y-intercept of 1, i.e., $y = 3x + 1$.

[45] $[4x - 2y = 6] \cdot \frac{1}{6} \Rightarrow \frac{2x}{3} - \frac{y}{3} = 1 \Rightarrow \frac{x}{\frac{3}{2}} + \frac{y}{-3} = 1$

[46] $[x - 3y = -2] \cdot \frac{1}{-2} \Rightarrow \frac{x}{-2} + \frac{3y}{2} = 1 \Rightarrow \frac{x}{-2} + \frac{y}{\frac{2}{3}} = 1$

[47] The radius of the circle is the vertical distance from the center of the circle to the line

$y = 5$, that is, $r = 5 - (-2) = 7$. An equation is $(x - 3)^2 + (y + 2)^2 = 49$.

[48] The line through the origin and P is perpendicular to the desired line.

This line has equation $y = \frac{4}{3}x$, so the desired line has slope $-\frac{3}{4}$.

$$y - 4 = -\frac{3}{4}(x - 3) \Rightarrow y = -\frac{3}{4}x + \frac{9}{4} + 4 \Rightarrow y = -\frac{3}{4}x + \frac{25}{4}.$$

[49] $L = 28 \Rightarrow 1.53t - 6.7 = 28 \Rightarrow t = \frac{28 + 6.7}{1.53} \approx 22.68$, or approximately 23 weeks.

[50] $S = 0.35 \Rightarrow 0.03 + 1.805C = 0.35 \Rightarrow C = \frac{0.35 - 0.03}{1.805} \approx 0.177$.

[51] (a) $L = 40 \Rightarrow W = 1.70(40) - 42.8 = 25.2$ tons

(b) Error in $L = \pm 2 \Rightarrow$ Error in $W = 1.70(\pm 2) = \pm 3.4$ tons

[52] (a) $L = at + b$ and $L = 24$ when $t = 0 \Rightarrow L = at + 24$.

$$L = 53 \text{ when } t = 7 \Rightarrow 53 = 7a + 24 \Rightarrow a = \frac{29}{7} \text{ and } L = \frac{29}{7}t + 24.$$

(b) From part (a), the slope is $\frac{29}{7}$ ft/month $= \frac{29}{210}$ ft/day ≈ 1.657 inches/day.

(c) $W = at + b$ and $W = 3$ when $t = 0 \Rightarrow W = at + 3$.

$$W = 23 \text{ when } t = 7 \Rightarrow 23 = 7a + 3 \Rightarrow a = \frac{20}{7} \text{ and } W = \frac{20}{7}t + 3.$$

(d) From part (c), the slope is $\frac{20}{7}$ tons/month $= \frac{2}{21}$ tons/day ≈ 190.476 pounds/day.

[53] (a) $y = mx = \dfrac{\text{change in } y \text{ from the beginning of the season}}{\text{change in } x \text{ from the beginning of the season}}(x) = \dfrac{5 - 0}{14 - 0}x = \dfrac{5}{14}x$.

(b) $x = 162 \Rightarrow y = \frac{5}{14}(162) \approx 58$.

[54] (a) $y = mx = \dfrac{\text{change in } y \text{ for the year}}{\text{change in } x \text{ for the year}}(x) = \dfrac{18,000 - 0}{(31 + 28 + 24) - 0}x = \dfrac{18,000}{83}x$.

(b) $x = 365 \Rightarrow y = \frac{18,000}{83}(365) \approx 79,157$.

[55] (a) Using the slope-intercept form, $W = mt + b = mt + 10$.

$$W = 30 \text{ when } t = 3 \Rightarrow 30 = 3m + 10 \Rightarrow m = \frac{20}{3} \text{ and } W = \frac{20}{3}t + 10.$$

(b) $t = 6 \Rightarrow W = \frac{20}{3}(6) + 10 \Rightarrow W = 50$ lb

(c) $W = 70 \Rightarrow 70 = \frac{20}{3}t + 10 \Rightarrow 60 = \frac{20}{3}t \Rightarrow t = 9$ years old

(d) The graph has endpoints at $(0, 10)$ and $(12, 90)$. See *Figure 55*.

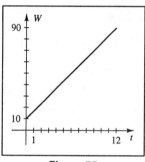

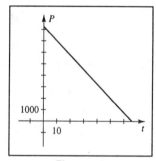

Figure 55   Figure 56

56 (a) Using the slope-intercept form, $P = mt + b = mt + 8250$. $P = 8125$ when $t = 1$

     {after one payment} $\Rightarrow 8125 = m + 8250 \Rightarrow m = -125$ and $P = -125t + 8250$.

   (b) $P = 5000 \Rightarrow -125t + 8250 = 5000 \Rightarrow -125t = -3250 \Rightarrow t = 26$ months

   (c) $\frac{8250}{125} = 66$ payments. The graph has endpoints at $(0, 8250)$ and $(66, 0)$.

57 Using $(10, 2480)$ and $(25, 2440)$,

$$\text{we have } H - 2440 = \frac{2440 - 2480}{25 - 10}(T - 25), \text{ or } H = -\frac{8}{3}T + \frac{7520}{3}.$$

58 (a) Using $(1800, 100)$ and $(5000, 40)$, we have

$$P - 40 = \frac{40 - 100}{5000 - 1800}(h - 5000), \text{ or } P = -\frac{3}{160}h + \frac{535}{4} \text{ for } 1800 \le h \le 5000.$$

   (b) $h = 2400 \Rightarrow P = -\frac{3}{160}(2400) + \frac{535}{4} = \frac{355}{4}$, or 88.75%.

59 (a) Using the slope-intercept form with $m = 0.032$ and $b = 13.5$,

$$\text{we have } T = 0.032t + 13.5.$$

   (b) $t = 2000 - 1915 = 85 \Rightarrow T = 0.032(85) + 13.5 = 16.22\,°C.$

60 (a) Using $(1870, 11.8)$ and $(1969, 13.5)$, we have $T - 13.5 = \frac{13.5 - 11.8}{1969 - 1870}(t - 1969)$.

   (b) $T = 12.5 \Rightarrow -1 = \frac{13.5 - 11.8}{1969 - 1870}(t - 1969) \Rightarrow -\frac{99}{1.7} = t - 1969 \Rightarrow t \approx 1910.76,$

$$\text{or during the year 1910.}$$

61 (a) Expenses $= (\$1000) + (5\% \text{ of } R) + (\$2600) + (50\% \text{ of } R) \Rightarrow E = 0.55R + 3600.$

   (b) Profit $=$ Revenue $-$ Expenses $\Rightarrow P = R - (0.55R + 3600) \Rightarrow P = 0.45R - 3600.$

   (c) *Break even* means P would be 0. $P = 0 \Rightarrow 0 = 0.45R - 3600 \Rightarrow 0.45R = 3600 \Rightarrow$

$$R = 3600(\tfrac{100}{45}) = \$8000/\text{month}$$

62 (a) $a = 100$ gives us $y = \frac{25}{6}(t + 1)$

       with endpoints $(0, \frac{25}{6})$ and $(12, \frac{325}{6})$,

       and $y = 8t$ with endpoints $(0, 0)$ and $(12, 96)$.

   (b) $\frac{1}{24}(t + 1)a = \frac{2}{25}ta \Rightarrow \frac{1}{24}(t + 1) = \frac{2}{25}t \Rightarrow$

       $25(t + 1) = 24(2t) \Rightarrow 25t + 25 = 48t \Rightarrow$

       $25 = 23t \Rightarrow t = \frac{25}{23} \approx 13$ months

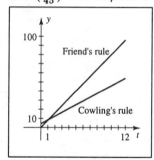

Figure 62

63 To determine if a target is hit, set $y = 0$ and solve for x.

(a) $y - 2 = -1(x - 1) \Rightarrow x + y = 3.$ $y = 0 \Rightarrow x = 3$ and a creature is hit.

(b) $y - \frac{5}{3} = -\frac{4}{9}(x - \frac{3}{2}) \Rightarrow 4x + 9y = 21.$ $y = 0 \Rightarrow x = 5.25$ and no creature is hit.

64 (a) $C = F$ and $C = \frac{5}{9}(F - 32) \Rightarrow F = \frac{5}{9}(F - 32) \Rightarrow 9F = 5F - 160 \Rightarrow$

$$4F = -160 \Rightarrow F = -40.$$

(b) $F = 2C$ and $C = \frac{5}{9}(F - 32) \Rightarrow C = \frac{5}{9}(2C - 32) \Rightarrow 9C = 10C - 160 \Rightarrow$

$$C = 160 \text{ and hence, } F = 320.$$

65 $s = \dfrac{v_2 - v_1}{h_2 - h_1} \Rightarrow 0.07 = \dfrac{v_2 - 22}{185 - 0} \Rightarrow v_2 = 22 + 0.07(185) = 34.95$ mi/hr.

66 From Exercise 65, the average wind shear is $s = \dfrac{v_2 - v_1}{h_2 - h_1}.$

We know $v_1 = 32$ at $h_1 = 20.$ We need to find v_2 at $h_2 = 200.$ $\dfrac{v_1}{v_2} = \left(\dfrac{h_1}{h_2}\right)^P \Rightarrow$

$$v_2 = v_1 \left(\frac{h_2}{h_1}\right)^P = 32\left(\frac{200}{20}\right)^{0.13}. \text{ Thus, } s = \frac{32(10^{0.13}) - 32}{200 - 20} \approx 0.062 \text{ (mi/hr)/ft.}$$

67 The slope of AB is $\dfrac{-1.11905 - (-1.3598)}{-0.55 - (-1.3)} = 0.321.$ Similarly, the slopes of BC and

CD are also $0.321.$ Therefore, the points all lie on the same line. Since the common

slope is $0.321,$ let $a = 0.321.$ $y = 0.321x + b \Rightarrow -1.3598 = 0.321(-1.3) + b \Rightarrow$

$b = -0.9425.$ Thus, the points are linearly related by the equation

$$y = 0.321x - 0.9425.$$

68 The slopes of AB and BC are both $-0.44,$ whereas the

slope of CD is approximately $-1.107.$ Thus, the points do not lie on the same line.

69 $x - 3y = -58 \Leftrightarrow y = (x + 58)/3$ and $3x - y = -70 \Leftrightarrow y = 3x + 70.$ Assign $(x + 58)/3$

to Y_1 and $y = 3x + 70$ to $Y_2.$ Using a standard viewing rectangle, we don't see the

lines. Zooming out gives us an indication where the lines intersect and by tracing

and zooming in, we find that the lines intersect at $(-19, 13).$

$[-30, 3]$ by $[-2, 20]$ $[-12, 12]$ by $[-2, 14]$

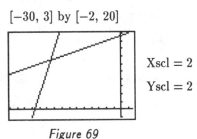

Xscl $= 2$

Yscl $= 2$

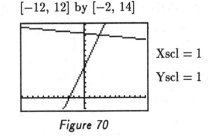

Xscl $= 1$

Yscl $= 1$

Figure 69   *Figure 70*

70 $x + 10y = 123 \Leftrightarrow y = (-x + 123)/10$ and $2x - y = -6 \Leftrightarrow y = 2x + 6.$ Assign

$(-x + 123)/10$ to Y_1 and $y = 2x + 6$ to $Y_2.$ Similar to Exercise 69, the lines intersect

at $(3, 12).$

71 From the graph, we can see that the points of intersection are $A(-0.8, -0.6)$, $B(4.8, -3.4)$, and $C(2, 5)$. The lines intersecting at A are perpendicular since they have slopes of 2 and $-\frac{1}{2}$. Since $d(A, B) = \sqrt{39.2}$ and $d(A, C) = \sqrt{39.2}$, the triangle is isosceles. Thus, the polygon is a right isosceles triangle.

$[-15, 15]$ by $[-10, 10]$　　　　　　　　$[-3, 3]$ by $[-2, 2]$

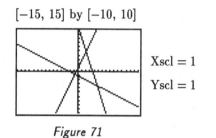
Xscl $= 1$
Yscl $= 1$

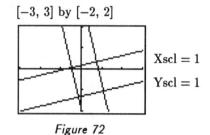
Xscl $= 1$
Yscl $= 1$

Figure 71　　　　　　　　　　　*Figure 72*

72 The equations of the lines can be rewritten as $y = \frac{1}{4.2}x + 0.17$, $y = -4.2x - 1.9$, $y = \frac{1}{4.2}x - 1.3$, and $y = -4.2x + 3.5$. From the graph, we can see that the points of intersection are approximately $A(0.75, 0.35)$, $B(1.08, -1.04)$, $C(-0.14, -1.33)$, and $D(-0.47, 0.059)$. The first and third lines are parallel as are the second and fourth lines. In addition, these pairs of lines are perpendicular to each other since their slopes are -4.2 and $\frac{1}{4.2}$. Since $d(A, B) \approx 1.43$ and $d(A, D) \approx 1.25$, it is not a square. Thus, the polygon is a rectangle.

73 The data appear to be linear. Using the two arbitrary points $(-7, -25)$ and $(4.6, 12.2)$, the slope of the line is $\dfrac{12.2 - (-25)}{4.6 - (-7)} \approx 3.2$. An equation of the line is $y + 25 = 3.2(x + 7) \Rightarrow y = 3.2x - 2.6$.

$[-8, 5]$ by $[-27, 15]$　　　　　　　　$[-1, 8]$ by $[-1, 5]$

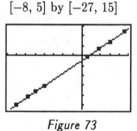
Xscl $= 1$
Yscl $= 5$

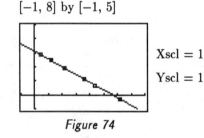
Xscl $= 1$
Yscl $= 1$

Figure 73　　　　　　　　　　　*Figure 74*

74 The data appear to be linear. Using the two arbitrary points $(0.4, 2.88)$ and $(6.2, -0.3)$, the slope of the line is $\dfrac{-0.3 - 2.88}{6.2 - 0.4} \approx -0.55$. An equation of the line is $y - 2.88 = -0.55(x - 0.4) \Rightarrow y = -0.55x + 3.1$.

75 (a)

[1980, 1988] by [300, 625]

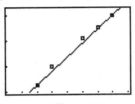

Xscl = 1

Yscl = 100

Figure 75

(b) To find a first approximation for the line use the arbitrary points (1982, 325) and (1987, 600). The resulting line is $y = 55x - 108{,}685$. Adjustments may be made to this equation.

(c) Let $y = 55x - 108{,}685$. When $x = 1984$, $y = 435$ and when $x = 1995$, $y = 1040$.

76 (a)

[1950, 1985] by [225, 240]

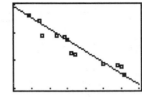

Xscl = 5

Yscl = 5

Figure 76

(b) For a first approximation for the line choose two points that appear to lie on the line using the TRACE mode. Two such points might be (1954, 238) and (1981, 227.3). These points determine the line

$$(T - 238) = \frac{227.3 - 238}{1981 - 1954}(Y - 1954) \Rightarrow T = -0.3963Y + 1012.36.$$

(c) $T = -0.3963(1985) + 1012.36 = 225.7$ seconds, which is 0.6 second fast.

(d) The slope of the line is approximately -0.4. This means that *on the average*, the record time for the mile has decreased by 0.4 sec/yr.

Chapter 1 Review Exercises

1 If $x \le -3$, then $x + 3 \le 0$, and $|x + 3| = -(x + 3) = -x - 3$.

2 If $2 < x < 3$, then $x - 2 > 0$ and $x - 3 < 0$. Thus, $(x - 2)(x - 3) < 0$ and

$$|(x - 2)(x - 3)| = -(x - 2)(x - 3), \text{ or, equivalently, } (2 - x)(x - 3).$$

3 $\left(\dfrac{a^{2/3}b^{3/2}}{a^2b}\right)^6 = \dfrac{a^4b^9}{a^{12}b^6} = \dfrac{b^3}{a^8}$

4 $(-2p^2q)^3\left(\dfrac{p}{4q^2}\right)^2 = (-8p^6q^3)\left(\dfrac{p^2}{16q^4}\right) = -\dfrac{p^8}{2q}$

5 $\left(\dfrac{xy^{-1}}{\sqrt{z}}\right)^4 \div \left(\dfrac{x^{1/3}y^2}{z}\right)^3 = \dfrac{x^4y^{-4}}{z^2} \cdot \dfrac{z^3}{xy^6} = \dfrac{x^3z}{y^{10}}$

6 $\left(\dfrac{-64x^3}{z^6y^9}\right)^{2/3} = \dfrac{(\sqrt[3]{-64})^2x^2}{z^4y^6} = \dfrac{16x^2}{z^4y^6}$

7 $\left[(a^{2/3}b^{-2})^3\right]^{-1} = (a^2b^{-6})^{-1} = a^{-2}b^6 = \dfrac{b^6}{a^2}$

8 $x^{-2} - y^{-1} = \dfrac{1}{x^2} - \dfrac{1}{y} = \dfrac{y - x^2}{x^2y}$

$\boxed{9}$ $\sqrt[3]{8x^5y^3z^4} = \sqrt[3]{8x^3y^3z^3}\sqrt[3]{x^2z} = 2xyz\sqrt[3]{x^2z}$

$\boxed{10}$ $\sqrt[4]{(-4a^3b^2c)^2} = \sqrt[4]{16a^6b^4c^2} = \sqrt[4]{2^4a^4b^4}\sqrt[4]{a^2c^2} = 2ab\sqrt[4]{(ac)^2} = 2ab\sqrt{ac}$

$\boxed{11}$ $\dfrac{1}{\sqrt{t}}\left(\dfrac{1}{\sqrt{t}} - 1\right) = \dfrac{1}{\sqrt{t}}\left(\dfrac{1}{\sqrt{t}} - \dfrac{\sqrt{t}}{\sqrt{t}}\right) = \dfrac{1}{\sqrt{t}}\left(\dfrac{1-\sqrt{t}}{\sqrt{t}}\right) = \dfrac{1-\sqrt{t}}{t}$

$\boxed{12}$ $\sqrt{\sqrt[3]{(c^3d^6)^4}} = \sqrt[6]{c^{12}d^{24}} = c^2d^4$
$\boxed{13}$ $\dfrac{\sqrt{12x^4y}}{\sqrt{3x^2y^5}} = \sqrt{\dfrac{12x^4y}{3x^2y^5}} = \sqrt{\dfrac{4x^2}{y^4}} = \dfrac{2x}{y^2}$

$\boxed{14}$ $\dfrac{3+\sqrt{x}}{3-\sqrt{x}} = \dfrac{3+\sqrt{x}}{3-\sqrt{x}} \cdot \dfrac{3+\sqrt{x}}{3+\sqrt{x}} = \dfrac{x+6\sqrt{x}+9}{9-x}$

$\boxed{15}$ $(3x^3 - 4x^2 + x - 7) + (x^4 - 2x^3 + 3x^2 + 5) = x^4 + x^3 - x^2 + x - 2$

$\boxed{16}$ $(x+4)(x+3) - (2x-1)(x-5) = (x^2 + 7x + 12) - (2x^2 - 11x + 5) = -x^2 + 18x + 7$

$\boxed{17}$ $(3a - 5b)(2a + 7b) = 6a^2 + 11ab - 35b^2$

$\boxed{18}$ $(4r^2 - 3s)^2 = (4r^2)^2 - 2(4r^2)(3s) + (3s)^2 = 16r^4 - 24r^2s + 9s^2$

$\boxed{19}$ $(13a^2 + 4b)(13a^2 - 4b) = (13a^2)^2 - (4b^2)^2 = 169a^4 - 16b^2$

$\boxed{20}$ $(2a + b)^3 = (2a)^3 + 3(2a)^2(b) + 3(2a)(b)^2 + (b)^3 = 8a^3 + 12a^2b + 6ab^2 + b^3$

$\boxed{21}$ $(3x + 2y)^2(3x - 2y)^2 = [(3x+2y)(3x-2y)]^2 = (9x^2 - 4y^2)^2 = 81x^4 - 72x^2y^2 + 16y^4$

$\boxed{22}$ $(a + b + c + d)^2 = a^2 + b^2 + c^2 + d^2 + 2(ab + ac + ad + bc + bd + cd)$

$\boxed{23}$ $28x^2 + 4x - 9 = (14x + 9)(2x - 1)$

$\boxed{24}$ $16a^4 + 24a^2b^2 + 9b^4 = (4a^2 + 3b^2)(4a^2 + 3b^2) = (4a^2 + 3b^2)^2$

$\boxed{25}$ $8x^3 + 64y^3 = 8(x^3 + 8y^3) = 8[(x)^3 + (2y)^3] = 8(x + 2y)(x^2 - 2xy + 4y^2)$

$\boxed{26}$ $u^3v^4 - u^6v = u^3v(v^3 - u^3) = u^3v(v - u)(v^2 + uv + u^2)$

$\boxed{27}$ $p^8 - q^8 = (p^4)^2 - (q^4)^2 = (p^4 + q^4)(p^4 - q^4) = (p^4 + q^4)(p^2 + q^2)(p^2 - q^2) =$
$$(p^4 + q^4)(p^2 + q^2)(p + q)(p - q)$$

$\boxed{28}$ $x^4 - 8x^3 + 16x^2 = x^2(x^2 - 8x + 16) = x^2(x - 4)(x - 4) = x^2(x - 4)^2$

$\boxed{29}$ $x^2 - 49y^2 - 14x + 49 = (x^2 - 14x + 49) - 49y^2 = (x - 7)^2 - (7y)^2 =$
$$(x - 7 + 7y)(x - 7 - 7y)$$

$\boxed{30}$ $x^5 - 4x^3 + 8x^2 - 32 = x^3(x^2 - 4) + 8(x^2 - 4) = (x^3 + 8)(x^2 - 4) =$
$$(x + 2)(x^2 - 2x + 4)(x + 2)(x - 2) = (x - 2)(x + 2)^2(x^2 - 2x + 4)$$

$\boxed{31}$ $\dfrac{2}{4x - 5} - \dfrac{5}{10x + 1} = \dfrac{2(10x + 1) - 5(4x - 5)}{(4x - 5)(10x + 1)} = \dfrac{27}{(4x - 5)(10x + 1)}$

$\boxed{32}$ $\dfrac{7}{x + 2} + \dfrac{3x}{(x + 2)^2} - \dfrac{5}{x} = \dfrac{7(x)(x + 2) + 3x(x) - 5(x + 2)^2}{x(x + 2)^2} =$

$$\dfrac{7x^2 + 14x + 3x^2 - 5x^2 - 20x - 20}{x(x + 2)^2} = \dfrac{5x^2 - 6x - 20}{x(x + 2)^2}$$

$\boxed{33}$ $\dfrac{x + x^{-2}}{1 + x^{-2}} = \dfrac{x + \frac{1}{x^2}}{1 + \frac{1}{x^2}} = \dfrac{\left(x + \frac{1}{x^2}\right) \cdot x^2}{\left(1 + \frac{1}{x^2}\right) \cdot x^2} = \dfrac{x^3 + 1}{x^2 + 1}$

$\boxed{34}$ $(a^{-1} + b^{-1})^{-1} = \left(\frac{1}{a} + \frac{1}{b}\right)^{-1} = \left(\frac{b + a}{ab}\right)^{-1} = \dfrac{ab}{a + b}$

$\boxed{35}$ $\dfrac{\frac{x}{x+2} - \frac{4}{x+2}}{x - 3 - \frac{6}{x+2}} = \dfrac{\frac{x-4}{x+2}}{\frac{(x-3)(x+2) - 6}{x+2}} = \dfrac{x-4}{x^2 - x - 12} = \dfrac{x-4}{(x+3)(x-4)} = \dfrac{1}{x+3}$

$\boxed{36}$ $\dfrac{(4 - x^2)(\frac{1}{3})(6x + 1)^{-2/3}(6) - (6x + 1)^{1/3}(-2x)}{(4 - x^2)^2} =$

$\dfrac{(6x + 1)^{-2/3}[2(4 - x^2) + 2x(6x + 1)]}{(4 - x^2)^2} = \dfrac{10x^2 + 2x + 8}{(6x + 1)^{2/3}(4 - x^2)^2} = \dfrac{2(5x^2 + x + 4)}{(6x + 1)^{2/3}(4 - x^2)^2}$

$\boxed{37}$ $\left[\dfrac{3x + 1}{5x + 7} = \dfrac{6x + 11}{10x - 3}\right] \cdot (5x + 7)(10x - 3) \Rightarrow (3x + 1)(10x - 3) = (6x + 11)(5x + 7) \Rightarrow$

$\qquad\qquad 30x^2 + x - 3 = 30x^2 + 97x + 77 \Rightarrow 96x = -80 \Rightarrow x = -\frac{5}{6}$

$\boxed{38}$ $2x^2 + 5x - 12 = 0 \Rightarrow (x + 4)(2x - 3) = 0 \Rightarrow x = -4, \frac{3}{2}$

$\boxed{39}$ $x(3x + 4) = 5 \Rightarrow 3x^2 + 4x - 5 = 0 \Rightarrow x = \dfrac{-4 \pm \sqrt{16 + 60}}{6} = \dfrac{-4 \pm 2\sqrt{19}}{6} = -\frac{2}{3} \pm \frac{1}{3}\sqrt{19}$

$\boxed{40}$ $4x^4 - 33x^2 + 50 = 0 \Rightarrow (4x^2 - 25)(x^2 - 2) \Rightarrow x^2 = \frac{25}{4}, 2 \Rightarrow x = \pm\frac{5}{2}, \pm\sqrt{2}$

$\boxed{41}$ $20x^3 + 8x^2 - 35x - 14 = 0 \Rightarrow 4x^2(5x + 2) - 7(5x + 2) = 0 \Rightarrow (4x^2 - 7)(5x + 2) = 0 \Rightarrow$

$\qquad\qquad\qquad\qquad\qquad\qquad\qquad x = \pm\frac{1}{2}\sqrt{7}, -\frac{2}{5}$

$\boxed{42}$ $|4x - 1| = 7 \Rightarrow 4x - 1 = 7$ or $4x - 1 = -7 \Rightarrow 4x = 8$ or $4x = -6 \Rightarrow x = 2$ or $x = -\frac{3}{2}$

$\boxed{43}$ $2|2x + 1| + 1 = 19 \Rightarrow 2|2x + 1| = 18 \Rightarrow |2x + 1| = 9 \Rightarrow$

$\qquad\qquad 2x + 1 = 9$ or $2x + 1 = -9 \Rightarrow 2x = 8$ or $2x = -10 \Rightarrow x = 4$ or $x = -5$

$\boxed{44}$ $\left[\dfrac{1}{x} + 6 = \dfrac{5}{\sqrt{x}}\right] \cdot x \Rightarrow 1 + 6x = 5\sqrt{x} \Rightarrow 6x - 5\sqrt{x} + 1 = 0 \Rightarrow$

$\qquad\qquad\qquad (2\sqrt{x} - 1)(3\sqrt{x} - 1) = 0 \Rightarrow \sqrt{x} = \frac{1}{2}, \frac{1}{3} \Rightarrow x = \frac{1}{4}, \frac{1}{9}$

$\boxed{45}$ $\sqrt{7x + 2} + x = 6 \Rightarrow (\sqrt{7x + 2})^2 = (6 - x)^2 \Rightarrow 7x + 2 = 36 - 12x + x^2 \Rightarrow$

$\qquad x^2 - 19x + 34 = 0 \Rightarrow (x - 2)(x - 17) = 0 \Rightarrow x = 2$ and 17 is an extraneous solution.

$\boxed{46}$ $\sqrt{3x + 1} - \sqrt{x + 4} = 1 \Rightarrow 3x + 1 = 1 + 2\sqrt{x + 4} + x + 4 \Rightarrow 2\sqrt{x + 4} = 2x - 4 \Rightarrow$

$\qquad (\sqrt{x + 4})^2 = (x - 2)^2 \Rightarrow x + 4 = x^2 - 4x + 4 \Rightarrow x^2 - 5x = 0 \Rightarrow x(x - 5) = 0 \Rightarrow$

$\qquad\qquad\qquad\qquad\qquad x = 5$ and 0 is an extraneous solution.

$\boxed{47}$ $10 - 7x < 4 + 2x \Rightarrow -9x < -6 \Rightarrow x > \frac{2}{3} \Leftrightarrow (\frac{2}{3}, \infty)$

$\boxed{48}$ $\left[-\frac{1}{2} < \dfrac{2x + 3}{5} < \frac{3}{2}\right] \cdot 10 \Rightarrow -5 < 4x + 6 < 15 \Rightarrow -11 < 4x < 9 \Rightarrow -\frac{11}{4} < x < \frac{9}{4} \Leftrightarrow$

$\qquad\qquad\qquad\qquad\qquad\qquad\qquad\qquad\qquad (-\frac{11}{4}, \frac{9}{4})$

$\boxed{49}$ $\dfrac{6}{10x + 3} < 0 \Rightarrow 10x + 3 < 0$ { since $6 > 0$ } $\Rightarrow x < -\frac{3}{10} \Leftrightarrow (-\infty, -\frac{3}{10})$

$\boxed{50}$ $|4x + 7| < 21 \Rightarrow -21 < 4x + 7 < 21 \Rightarrow -28 < 4x < 14 \Rightarrow -7 < x < \frac{7}{2} \Leftrightarrow (-7, \frac{7}{2})$

51 $2\,|\,3-x\,|\,+1>5 \Rightarrow 2\,|\,3-x\,|\,>4 \Rightarrow |\,3-x\,|\,>2 \Rightarrow$

$3-x>2$ or $3-x<-2 \Rightarrow 1>x$ or $5<x \Rightarrow x<1$ or $x>5 \Leftrightarrow (-\infty,\,1)\cup(5,\,\infty)$

52 $|\,16-3x\,|\,\geq 5 \Rightarrow 16-3x\geq 5$ or $16-3x\leq -5 \Rightarrow -3x\geq -11$ or $-3x\leq -21 \Rightarrow$

$x\leq \frac{11}{3}$ or $x\geq 7 \Leftrightarrow (-\infty,\,\frac{11}{3}]\cup[7,\,\infty)$

53 $10x^2+11x>6 \Rightarrow 10x^2+11x-6>0 \Rightarrow (2x+3)(5x-2)>0;\ (-\infty,\,-\frac{3}{2})\cup(\frac{2}{5},\,\infty)$

Resulting sign:	$\oplus$	$\ominus$	$\oplus$
Sign of $5x-2$:	$-$	$-$	$+$
Sign of $2x+3$:	$-$	$+$	$+$
x values:	$-3/2$		$2/5$

Resulting sign:	$\oplus$	$\ominus$	$\oplus$
Sign of $x-5$:	$-$	$-$	$+$
Sign of $x+2$:	$-$	$+$	$+$
x values:	-2		5

Diagram 53 / Diagram 54

54 $x(x-3)\leq 10 \Rightarrow x^2-3x-10\leq 0 \Rightarrow (x-5)(x+2)\leq 0;\ [-2,\,5]$

55 $\dfrac{x^2(3-x)}{x+2}\leq 0 \Rightarrow \dfrac{3-x}{x+2}\leq 0$ {include 0}; $(-\infty,\,-2)\cup\{0\}\cup[3,\,\infty)$

Resulting sign:	$\ominus$	$\oplus$	$\ominus$
Sign of $3-x$:	$+$	$+$	$-$
Sign of $x+2$:	$-$	$+$	$+$
x values:	-2		3

Resulting sign:	$\oplus$	$\ominus$	$\oplus$
Sign of $x-2$:	$-$	$-$	$+$
Sign of $x+3$:	$-$	$+$	$+$
x values:	-3		2

Diagram 55 / Diagram 56

56 $\dfrac{x^2-x-2}{x^2+4x+3}\leq 0 \Rightarrow \dfrac{(x-2)(x+1)}{(x+1)(x+3)}\leq 0 \Rightarrow \dfrac{x-2}{x+3}\leq 0$ {exclude -1} $(-3,\,-1)\cup(-1,\,2]$

57 $\dfrac{3}{2x+3}<\dfrac{1}{x-2} \Rightarrow \dfrac{3(x-2)-1(2x+3)}{(2x+3)(x-2)}<0 \Rightarrow \dfrac{x-9}{(2x+3)(x-2)}<0;\ (-\infty,\,-\frac{3}{2})\cup(2,\,9)$

Resulting sign:	$\ominus$	$\oplus$	$\ominus$	$\oplus$
Sign of $x-9$:	$-$	$-$	$-$	$+$
Sign of $x-2$:	$-$	$-$	$+$	$+$
Sign of $2x+3$:	$-$	$+$	$+$	$+$
x values:	$-3/2$	2		9

Resulting sign:	$\ominus$	$\oplus$	$\ominus$	$\oplus$
Sign of $x-5$:	$-$	$-$	$-$	$+$
Sign of $x+1$:	$-$	$-$	$+$	$+$
Sign of $x+5$:	$-$	$+$	$+$	$+$
x values:	-5	-1		5

Diagram 57 / Diagram 58

58 $\dfrac{x+1}{x^2-25}\leq 0 \Rightarrow \dfrac{x+1}{(x+5)(x-5)}\leq 0;\ (-\infty,\,-5)\cup[-1,\,5)$

59 $x^3>x^2 \Rightarrow x^2(x-1)>0 \Rightarrow x-1>0 \Rightarrow x>1 \Leftrightarrow (1,\,\infty)$

60 $(x^2-x)(x^2-5x+6)<0 \Rightarrow$

$x(x-1)(x-2)(x-3)<0;\ (0,\,1)\cup(2,\,3)$

Res. sign:	$\oplus$	$\ominus$	$\oplus$	$\ominus$	$\oplus$
$x-3$:	$-$	$-$	$-$	$-$	$+$
$x-2$:	$-$	$-$	$-$	$+$	$+$
$x-1$:	$-$	$-$	$+$	$+$	$+$
x:	$-$	$+$	$+$	$+$	$+$
x values:	0	1	2	3	

Diagram 60

61 $F=\dfrac{\pi P R^4}{8VL} \Rightarrow R^4=\dfrac{8FVL}{\pi P} \Rightarrow R=\pm\sqrt[4]{\dfrac{8FVL}{\pi P}} \Rightarrow R=\sqrt[4]{\dfrac{8FVL}{\pi P}}$ since $R>0$

$\boxed{62}$ $V = \frac{1}{3}\pi h(r^2 + R^2 + rR) \Rightarrow r^2 + Rr + R^2 - \frac{3V}{\pi h} = 0 \Rightarrow$

$(\pi h)r^2 + (\pi h R)r + (\pi h R^2 - 3V) = 0 \Rightarrow$

$$r = \frac{-\pi h R \pm \sqrt{\pi^2 h^2 R^2 - 4\pi h(\pi h R^2 - 3V)}}{2\pi h} = \frac{-\pi h R \pm \sqrt{12\pi h V - 3\pi^2 h^2 R^2}}{2\pi h}.$$

Since $r > 0$, we must use the plus sign, and $r = \dfrac{-\pi h R + \sqrt{12\pi h V - 3\pi^2 h^2 R^2}}{2\pi h}$.

$\boxed{63}$ $(3 + 8i)^2 = 3^2 + 2(3)(8i) + (8i)^2 = (9 - 64) + 48i = -55 + 48i$

$\boxed{64}$ $\dfrac{1}{9 - \sqrt{-4}} = \dfrac{1}{9 - 2i} = \dfrac{1}{9 - 2i} \cdot \dfrac{9 + 2i}{9 + 2i} = \dfrac{9 + 2i}{81 + 4} = \dfrac{9}{85} + \dfrac{2}{85}i$

$\boxed{65}$ $\dfrac{6 - 3i}{2 + 7i} = \dfrac{6 - 3i}{2 + 7i} \cdot \dfrac{2 - 7i}{2 - 7i} = \dfrac{(12 - 21) + (-42 - 6)i}{53} = -\dfrac{9}{53} - \dfrac{48}{53}i$

$\boxed{66}$ $\dfrac{20 - 8i}{4i} = \dfrac{4(5 - 2i)}{4i} = \dfrac{5 - 2i}{i} \cdot \dfrac{-i}{-i} = \dfrac{-5i + 2i^2}{-i^2} = \dfrac{-2 - 5i}{1} = -2 - 5i$

$\boxed{67}$ Show that $d(A, B)^2 + d(A, C)^2 = d(B, C)^2$, that is, $(\sqrt{80})^2 + (\sqrt{5})^2 = (\sqrt{85})^2$.

Area $= \frac{1}{2}bh = \frac{1}{2}(\sqrt{80})(\sqrt{5}) = \frac{1}{2}(4\sqrt{5})(\sqrt{5}) = 10.$

$\boxed{68}$ (a) $P(-5, 9), Q(-8, -7) \Rightarrow$

$$d(P, Q) = \sqrt{[-8 - (-5)]^2 + (-7 - 9)^2} = \sqrt{9 + 256} = \sqrt{265}.$$

(b) $P(-5, 9), Q(-8, -7) \Rightarrow M_{PQ} = \left(\dfrac{-5 + (-8)}{2}, \dfrac{9 + (-7)}{2}\right) = (-\frac{13}{2}, 1).$

(c) Let $R = (x, y)$. $Q = M_{PR} \Rightarrow (-8, -7) = \left(\dfrac{-5 + x}{2}, \dfrac{9 + y}{2}\right) \Rightarrow$

$-5 + x = -16$ and $9 + y = -14 \Rightarrow R = (-11, -23).$

$\boxed{69}$ Let $Q(0, y)$ be an arbitrary point on the y-axis. $13 = d(P, Q) \Rightarrow$

$13 = \sqrt{(0 - 12)^2 + (y - 6)^2} \Rightarrow 169 = 144 + y^2 - 12y + 36 \Rightarrow y^2 - 12y + 11 = 0 \Rightarrow$

$(y - 1)(y - 11) = 0 \Rightarrow y = 1, 11.$ The points are $(0, 1)$ and $(0, 11)$.

$\boxed{70}$ $d(P, Q) < 3 \Rightarrow \sqrt{(-2 - a)^2 + (a - 1)^2} < 3 \Rightarrow 4 + 4a + a^2 + a^2 - 2a + 1 < 9 \Rightarrow$

$2a^2 + 2a - 4 < 0 \Rightarrow a^2 + a - 2 < 0 \Rightarrow (a + 2)(a - 1) < 0 \Rightarrow -2 < a < 1.$

Use a sign diagram to establish the final answer.

$\boxed{71}$ The equation of a circle with center $C(7, -4)$ is $(x - 7)^2 + (y + 4)^2 = r^2.$

Letting $x = -3$ and $y = 3$ yields $(-10)^2 + 7^2 = r^2 \Rightarrow r^2 = 149.$

An equation is $(x - 7)^2 + (y + 4)^2 = 149.$

$\boxed{72}$ The center of the circle is the midpoint of $A(8, 10)$ and $B(-2, -14)$.

$M_{AB} = \left(\dfrac{8 + (-2)}{2}, \dfrac{10 + (-14)}{2}\right) = (3, -2).$ The radius of the circle is

$\frac{1}{2} \cdot d(A, B) = \frac{1}{2}\sqrt{(-2 - 8)^2 + (-14 - 10)^2} = \frac{1}{2}\sqrt{100 + 576} = \frac{1}{2} \cdot 26 = 13.$

An equation is $(x - 3)^2 + (y + 2)^2 = 13^2 = 169.$

$\boxed{73}$ We need to solve the equation for x.

$$(x+2)^2 + y^2 = 9 \Rightarrow (x+2)^2 = 9 - y^2 \Rightarrow x + 2 = \pm\sqrt{9-y^2} \Rightarrow x = -2 \pm \sqrt{9-y^2}.$$

Choose the term with the minus sign for the left half.

$\boxed{74}$ Show that the slopes of one pair of opposite sides are equal.

$$A(-3,\ 1),\ B(1,\ -1),\ C(4,\ 1),\ \text{and}\ D(3,\ 5) \Rightarrow m_{AD} = \tfrac{2}{3} = m_{BC}.$$

$\boxed{75}$ (a) $6x + 2y + 5 = 0 \Leftrightarrow y = -3x - \tfrac{5}{2}$. Using the same slope, -3, with $A(\tfrac{1}{2},\ -\tfrac{1}{3})$,

we have $y + \tfrac{1}{3} = -3(x - \tfrac{1}{2}) \Rightarrow 6y + 2 = -18x + 9 \Rightarrow 18x + 6y = 7$.

(b) Using the negative reciprocal of -3 for the slope,

$$y + \tfrac{1}{3} = \tfrac{1}{3}(x - \tfrac{1}{2}) \Rightarrow 6y + 2 = 2x - 1 \Rightarrow 2x - 6y = 3.$$

$\boxed{76}$ The radius of the circle is the distance from the line $x = 4$ to the x-value of the

center $C(-5,\ -1)$; $r = 4 - (-5) = 9$. An equation is $(x + 5)^2 + (y + 1)^2 = 81$.

$\boxed{77}$ $x^2 + y^2 - 4x + 10y + 26 = 0 \Rightarrow x^2 - 4x + \underline{\ 4\ } + y^2 + 10y + \underline{\ 25\ } = -26 + \underline{\ 4\ } + \underline{\ 25\ } \Rightarrow$

$(x - 2)^2 + (y + 5)^2 = 3 \Rightarrow C(2,\ -5)$. We want the equation of the line through

$(-3,\ 0)$ and $(2,\ -5)$. $y - 0 = \frac{-5-0}{2+3}(x + 3) \Rightarrow y = -1(x + 3) \Rightarrow x + y = -3$.

$\boxed{78}$ $P(4,\ -3)$ with $m = 5 \Rightarrow y + 3 = 5(x - 4) \Rightarrow y + 3 = 5x - 20 \Rightarrow 5x - y = 23$.

$\boxed{79}$ $A(-1,\ 2)$ and $B(3,\ -4) \Rightarrow M_{AB} = (1,\ -1)$ and $m_{AB} = -\tfrac{3}{2}$.

$$y + 1 = \tfrac{2}{3}(x - 1) \Rightarrow 3y + 3 = 2x - 2 \Rightarrow 2x - 3y = 5.$$

$\boxed{80}$ $x^2 + y^2 - 12y + 31 = 0 \Rightarrow x^2 + y^2 - 12y + \underline{\ 36\ } = -31 + \underline{\ 36\ } \Rightarrow x^2 + (y - 6)^2 = 5$.

$$C(0,\ 6);\ r = \sqrt{5}$$

$\boxed{81}$ $2y + 5x - 8 = 0 \Leftrightarrow y = -\tfrac{5}{2}x + 4$, a line with slope $-\tfrac{5}{2}$ and y-intercept 4;

x-intercept: $(1.6,\ 0)$

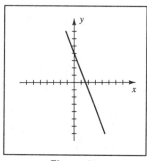

Figure 81

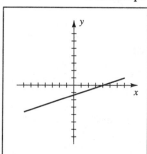

Figure 82

$\boxed{82}$ $x = 3y + 4 \Leftrightarrow y = \tfrac{1}{3}x - \tfrac{4}{3}$, a line with slope $\tfrac{1}{3}$ and y-intercept $-\tfrac{4}{3}$; x-intercept: $(4,\ 0)$

$\boxed{83}$ $9y + 2x^2 = 0 \Leftrightarrow y = -\frac{2}{9}x^2$, a parabola opening down; x- and y-intercept: $(0, 0)$

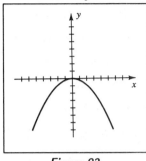

Figure 83

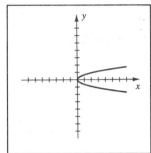

Figure 84

$\boxed{84}$ $3x - 7y^2 = 0 \Leftrightarrow x = \frac{7}{3}y^2$, a parabola opening to the right; x- and y-intercept: $(0, 0)$

$\boxed{85}$ $y = \sqrt{1 - x}$; x-intercept: $(1, 0)$, y-intercept: $(0, 1)$

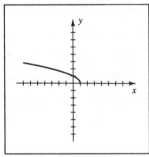

Figure 85

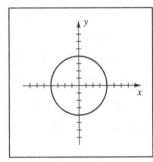

Figure 86

$\boxed{86}$ $y^2 = 16 - x^2 \Leftrightarrow x^2 + y^2 = 16$; x-intercepts: $(\pm 4, 0)$, y-intercepts: $(0, \pm 4)$

$\boxed{87}$ $x^2 + y^2 - 8x = 0 \Leftrightarrow x^2 - 8x + \underline{\ 16\ } + y^2 = \underline{\ 16\ } \Leftrightarrow (x - 4)^2 + y^2 = 16$;

$C(4, 0)$, $r = \sqrt{16} = 4$; x-intercepts: $(0, 0)$ and $(8, 0)$, y-intercept: $(0, 0)$

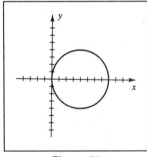

Figure 87

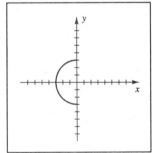

Figure 88

$\boxed{88}$ $x = -\sqrt{9 - y^2}$ is the left half of the circle $x^2 + y^2 = 9$;

x-intercept: $(-3, 0)$, y-intercepts: $(0, \pm 3)$

$\boxed{89}$ Using the intercept form, an equation is $\frac{x}{5} + \frac{y}{-2} = 1$, or, equivalently, $2x - 5y = 10$.

$\boxed{90}$ The midpoint of $(-7, 1)$ and $(3, 1)$ is $(-2, 1)$. This point is 5 units from either of the given points. An equation is $(x + 2)^2 + (y - 1)^2 = 5^2 = 25$.

91 Let P denote the principal that will be invested, and r the yield rate of the stock fund. Income$_\text{stocks}$ − 28% federal tax − 7% state tax = Income$_\text{bonds}$ ⇒

$(Pr) - 0.28(Pr) - 0.07(Pr) = 0.07186P \Rightarrow 1r - 0.28r - 0.07r = 0.07186 \Rightarrow$

$$0.65r = 0.07186 \Rightarrow r \approx 0.11055, \text{ or, } 11.055\%.$$

92 Let x denote the number of ounces of the vegetable portion, $10 - x$ the number of ounces of meat. Protein$_\text{vegetable}$ + Protein$_\text{meat}$ = Protein$_\text{total}$ $\Rightarrow \frac{1}{2}(x) + 1(10 - x) = 7$

$\Rightarrow -\frac{1}{2}x = -3 \Rightarrow x = 6$. Use 6 oz of vegetables and 4 oz of meat.

93 Let x denote the number of gallons of 20% solution, $120 - x$ the number of gallons of 50% solution. $20(x) + 50(120 - x) = 30(120)$ { all in % } $\Rightarrow 20 \cdot 120 = 30x \Rightarrow x = 80$.

Use 80 gal of the 20% solution and 40 gal of the 50% solution.

94 Let x denote the number of hours needed to fill an empty bin.

Using the hourly rates, $\left[\frac{1}{2} - \frac{1}{5} = \frac{1}{x}\right] \cdot 10x \Rightarrow 5x - 2x = 10 \Rightarrow 3x = 10 \Rightarrow x = \frac{10}{3}$ hr.

Since the bin was half-full at the start, $\frac{1}{2}x = \frac{1}{2} \cdot \frac{10}{3} = \frac{5}{3}$ hr, or, 1 hr 40 min.

95 (a) The eastbound car has distance $20t$ and the southbound car has distance

$$(-2 + 50t). \quad d^2 = (20t)^2 + (-2 + 50t)^2 \Rightarrow d = \sqrt{2900t^2 - 200t + 4}$$

(b) $104 = \sqrt{2900t^2 - 200t + 4} \Rightarrow 2900t^2 - 200t - 10{,}812 = 0 \Rightarrow$

$$725t^2 - 50t - 2703 = 0 \Rightarrow t = \frac{50 \pm \sqrt{7{,}841{,}200}}{1450} \{t > 0\} = \frac{5 + 2\sqrt{19{,}603}}{145} \approx 1.97,$$

or approximately 11:58 A.M.

96 Let l and w denote the length and width, respectively. $3l + 6w = 270 \Rightarrow w = 45 - \frac{1}{2}l$.

The total area is to be $10 \cdot 100 = 1000$ ft^2. Area $= lw \Rightarrow 1000 = l(45 - \frac{1}{2}l) \Rightarrow$

$2000 = 90l - l^2 \Rightarrow (l - 40)(l - 50) = 0 \Rightarrow l = 40, 50$ and $w = 25, 20$.

There are two arrangements: 40 ft × 25 ft and 50 ft × 20 ft.

97 Let x denote the length of one side of an end.

(a) $V = lwh \Rightarrow 48 = 6 \cdot x \cdot x \Rightarrow x^2 = 8 \Rightarrow x = 2\sqrt{2}$ ft

(b) $S = lw + 2wh + 2lh \Rightarrow 44 = 6x + 2(x^2) + 2(6x) \Rightarrow 44 = 2x^2 + 18x \Rightarrow$

$$x^2 + 9x - 22 = 0 \Rightarrow (x + 11)(x - 2) = 0 \Rightarrow x = 2 \text{ ft}$$

98 Let x denote the amount of yearly business.

Pay$_\text{B}$ > Pay$_\text{A}$ $\Rightarrow \$20{,}000 + 0.10x > \$25{,}000 + 0.05x \Rightarrow 0.05x > \$5000 \Rightarrow x > \$100{,}000$

99 $v > 1100 \Rightarrow 1087\sqrt{\dfrac{T}{273}} > 1100 \Rightarrow$

$$\sqrt{\frac{T}{273}} > \frac{1100}{1087} \Rightarrow \frac{T}{273} > \frac{(1100)^2}{(1087)^2} \Rightarrow T > \frac{273(1100)^2}{(1087)^2} \Rightarrow T > 279.57 \text{ K}$$

100 Let x denote the number of trees over 24. Then $24 + x$ represents the total number of trees planted per acre, and $600 - 12x$ represents the number of apples per tree. Total apples $= (\text{\# of trees})(\text{\# of apples per tree}) = (24 + x)(600 - 12x) = -12x^2 + 312x + 14{,}400$. Apples $\geq 16{,}416 \Rightarrow -12x^2 + 312x + 14{,}400 \geq 16{,}416 \Rightarrow -12x^2 + 312x - 2016 \geq 0 \Rightarrow x^2 - 26x + 168 \leq 0 \Rightarrow (x - 12)(x - 14) \leq 0 \Rightarrow$

$$12 \leq x \leq 14. \quad \text{Hence, 36 to 38 trees per acre should be planted.}$$

101 The slope of the ramp should be between $\frac{1}{12}$ and $\frac{1}{20}$. If the rise of the ramp is 3 feet, then the run should be between $3 \times 12 = 36$ ft and $3 \times 20 = 60$ ft. The range of the ramp lengths should be from $L = \sqrt{3^2 + 36^2} \approx 36.1$ ft to $L = \sqrt{3^2 + 60^2} \approx 60.1$ ft.

102 (a) 2000 corresponds to $t = 2000 - 1948 = 52$. $d = 175 + 1.75(52) = 266$ ft

(b) $d = 280 \Rightarrow 280 = 175 + 1.75t \Rightarrow t = \dfrac{280 - 175}{1.75} = \dfrac{420}{7} = 60$ yr, or 2008

103 The y-values are increasing slowly and can best be described by equation (3), $y = 3\sqrt{x - 0.5}$.

Chapter 1 Discussion Exercises

1 1 gallon ≈ 0.13368 ft^3 is a conversion factor that would help. The volume of the tank is 10,000 gallons ≈ 1336.8 ft^3. Use $V = \frac{4}{3}\pi r^3$ to determine the radius $r \approx 6.833$ ft and then use $S = 4\pi r^2$ to find the surface area—about 586.85 ft^2.

2 Squaring the right side gives us $(a + b)^2 = a^2 + 2ab + b^2$. Squaring the left side gives us $a^2 + b^2$. Now $a^2 + 2ab + b^2$ will equal $a^2 + b^2$ only if $2ab = 0$. The expression $2ab$ equals zero only if either $a = 0$ or $b = 0$.

3 We first need to determine the term that needs to be added and subtracted. If we add and subtract $10x$, we will obtain the square of a binomial—i.e., $(x^2 + 10x + 25) - 10x = (x + 5)^2 - 10x$. We can now factor this expression as the difference of two squares, $(x + 5)^2 - 10x = (x + 5 + \sqrt{10x})(x + 5 - \sqrt{10x})$.

4 The first expression can be evaluated at $x = 1$, whereas the second expression is undefined at $x = 1$.

5 They get close to the ratio of leading coefficients as x gets larger.

[6] $\dfrac{3x^2 - 5x - 2}{x^2 - 4} = \dfrac{(3x+1)(x-2)}{(x+2)(x-2)} = \dfrac{3x+1}{x+2}$.   Evaluating the original expression and the simplified expression with any $x \neq \pm 2$ gives us the same value. This evaluation does not prove that the expressions are equal for any value of x other than the one selected. The simplification proves that the expressions are equal for all values of x except $x = 2$.

[7]   Solve the equation $x^2 - xy + y^2 = 0$ for x.

$$x = \frac{y \pm \sqrt{y^2 - 4y^2}}{2} = \frac{y \pm \sqrt{-3y^2}}{2} = \frac{y \pm |y|\sqrt{3}\,i}{2}.$$

Since this equation has imaginary solutions, $x^2 - xy + y^2$ is not factorable over the reals. A similar argument holds for $x^2 + xy + y^2$.

[8]   The solutions are $x_1 = (-b + \sqrt{b^2 - 4ac})/(2a)$ and $x_2 = (-b - \sqrt{b^2 - 4ac})/(2a)$. The average is $(x_1 + x_2)/2 = \left(\frac{-2b}{2a}\right)/2 = -b/(2a)$. Suppose you solve the equation $-x^2 + 4x + 7 = 0$ and obtain the solutions $x_1 \approx -1.32$ and $x_2 \approx 5.32$. Averaging these numbers gives us the value 2, which we can easily see is equal to $-b/(2a)$

[9]   (a) $\dfrac{1}{\dfrac{a+bi}{c+di}} = \dfrac{c+di}{a+bi} \cdot \dfrac{a-bi}{a-bi} = \dfrac{ac + bd + (ad - bc)i}{a^2 + b^2} = \dfrac{ac + bd}{a^2 + b^2} + \dfrac{ad - bc}{a^2 + b^2}i$

(b)   Yes, try an example such as 3/4.

(c) a and b cannot both be 0 because then the denominator would be 0.

[10]   Since we don't know the value of x, we don't know the sign of $x - 2$, and hence we are unsure of whether or not to reverse the direction of the inequality sign.

[11]   (1) $a > 0$, $D \leq 0$: solution is $x \in \mathbb{R}$

(2) $a > 0$, $D > 0$: let $x_1 = (-b - \sqrt{D})/(2a)$ and $x_2 = (-b + \sqrt{D})/(2a) \Rightarrow$

solution is $(-\infty, x_1] \cup [x_2, \infty)$

(3) $a < 0$, $D < 0$: solution is $\{\ \}$

(4) $a < 0$, $D = 0$: solution is $x = -b/(2a)$

(5) $a < 0$, $D > 0$: solution is $[x_1, x_2]$

[12] (a) This problem is solved in three steps.

(i) First, we must determine the height of the cloud base using the formula in Exercise 66, $h = 227(T - D) = 227(80 - 68) = 2724$ ft.

(ii) Next, we must determine the temperature T at the cloud base.

From (i), the height of the cloud base is $h = 2724$ and

$$T = T_0 - \left(\frac{5.5}{1000}\right)h = 80 - \left(\frac{5.5}{1000}\right)2724 = 65.018°\,F.$$

(iii) Finally, we must solve the equation

$$T = B - \left(\frac{3}{1000}\right)h \text{ for } h, \text{ when } T = 32°\,F \text{ and } B = 65.018°\,F.$$

$$32 = 65.018 - \left(\frac{3}{1000}\right)h \Rightarrow h = (65.018 - 32)\left(\frac{1000}{3}\right) = 11{,}006 \text{ ft.}$$

(b) Following the procedure in part (a) and using $\frac{11}{2000}$ for $\frac{5.5}{1000}$, we obtain

$$h = \tfrac{1}{6}(2497D - 497G - 64{,}000).$$

[13] To determine the x-coordinate of R,

we want to start at x_1 and go $\frac{m}{n}$ of the way to x_2. We could write this as

$$x_3 = x_1 + \tfrac{m}{n}\Delta x = x_1 + \tfrac{m}{n}(x_2 - x_1) = x_1 + \tfrac{m}{n}x_2 - \tfrac{m}{n}x_1 = \left(1 - \tfrac{m}{n}\right)x_1 + \tfrac{m}{n}x_2.$$

Similarly, $y_3 = \left(1 - \tfrac{m}{n}\right)y_1 + \tfrac{m}{n}y_2.$

[14] Graphs of equations of the form $y = x^{p/q}$, where $x \geq 0$, and p and q are positive integers all pass through $(0, 0)$ and $(1, 1)$. If $p/q < 1$, the graph is above $y = x$ for $0 \leq x \leq 1$ and below $y = x$ for $x \geq 1$. The closer p/q is to 1, the closer $y = x^{p/q}$ is to $y = x$. If $p/q > 1$, the graph is below $y = x$ for $0 \leq x \leq 1$ and above $y = x$ for $x \geq 1$.

Chapter 2: Functions

2.1 Concept Check

1 What is the key idea to remember about a function? • To each element in the domain there corresponds exactly one element in the range.

2 Make quick sketches of each of the following functions: constant, identity, squaring, square root, cubing, cube root. What test do all of these graphs pass? • See Appendix II. The graphs pass the Vertical Line Test.

3 For an equation, what are the zeros of a function f? For a graph? • The zeros of a function f are solutions of the equation $f(x) = 0$. The zeros of a graph of the function f are the x-intercepts of the graph.

4 Why is the graph of $x = 3$ *not* the graph of a function? • Because the x-coordinate 3 corresponds to an infinite number of points on the graph of $x = 3$.

5 Let $y = f(x)$ be a polynomial. What is the domain of $\sqrt{f(x)}$? $\sqrt[3]{f(x)}$? $1/f(x)$? • The domain of $\sqrt{f(x)}$ consists of all x such that $f(x) \geq 0$ since the square root of a negative real number is not a real number. The domain of $\sqrt[3]{f(x)}$ consists of all x since the cube root of any real number is a real number. The domain of $1/f(x)$ consists of all x such that $f(x) \neq 0$ since division by zero is undefined.

6 State the type of variation that describes the relationship between y and x. (a) y is your taxable income and x is your tax bill. (b) y is the number of forest fires and x is the number of inches of rainfall. • (a) y is directly proportional to x. (b) y is inversely proportional to x.

2.1 Exercises

1 $f(x) = -x^2 - x - 4 \Rightarrow f(-2) = -4 + 2 - 4 = -6$, $f(0) = -4$, and $f(4) = -24$.

2 $f(x) = -x^3 - x^2 + 3 \Rightarrow f(-3) = 27 - 9 + 3 = 21$, $f(0) = 3$, and $f(2) = -9$.

3 $f(x) = \sqrt{x-4} - 3x \Rightarrow f(4) = -12$, $f(8) = -22$, and $f(13) = -36$.

4 $f(x) = \dfrac{x}{x-3} \Rightarrow f(-2) = \frac{2}{5}$, $f(0) = 0$, and $f(3)$ is undefined.

5 (a) $f(x) = 5x - 2 \Rightarrow f(a) = 5(a) - 2 = 5a - 2$ (b) $f(-a) = 5(-a) - 2 = -5a - 2$

   (c) $-f(a) = -1 \cdot (5a - 2) = -5a + 2$ (d) $f(a+h) = 5(a+h) - 2 = 5a + 5h - 2$

   (e) $f(a) + f(h) = (5a - 2) + (5h - 2) = 5a + 5h - 4$

   (f) $\dfrac{f(a+h) - f(a)}{h} = \dfrac{(5a + 5h - 2) - (5a - 2)}{h} = \dfrac{5h}{h} = 5$

6 (a) $f(x) = 3 - 4x \Rightarrow f(a) = 3 - 4(a) = 3 - 4a$ (b) $f(-a) = 3 - 4(-a) = 3 + 4a$

   (c) $-f(a) = -1 \cdot (3 - 4a) = 4a - 3$ (d) $f(a+h) = 3 - 4(a+h) = 3 - 4a - 4h$

(e) $f(a) + f(h) = (3 - 4a) + (3 - 4h) = 6 - 4a - 4h$

(f) $\dfrac{f(a+h) - f(a)}{h} = \dfrac{(3 - 4a - 4h) - (3 - 4a)}{h} = \dfrac{-4h}{h} = -4$

$\boxed{7}$ (a) $f(x) = x^2 - x + 3 \Rightarrow f(a) = (a)^2 - (a) + 3 = a^2 - a + 3$

(b) $f(-a) = (-a)^2 - (-a) + 3 = a^2 + a + 3$

(c) $-f(a) = -1 \cdot (a^2 - a + 3) = -a^2 + a - 3$

(d) $f(a+h) = (a+h)^2 - (a+h) + 3 = a^2 + 2ah + h^2 - a - h + 3$

(e) $f(a) + f(h) = (a^2 - a + 3) + (h^2 - h + 3) = a^2 + h^2 - a - h + 6$

(f) $\dfrac{f(a+h) - f(a)}{h} = \dfrac{(a^2 + 2ah + h^2 - a - h + 3) - (a^2 - a + 3)}{h} = \dfrac{2ah + h^2 - h}{h} =$

$$\dfrac{h(2a + h - 1)}{h} = 2a + h - 1$$

$\boxed{8}$ (a) $f(x) = 2x^2 + 3x - 7 \Rightarrow f(a) = 2(a)^2 + 3(a) - 7 = 2a^2 + 3a - 7$

(b) $f(-a) = 2(-a)^2 + 3(-a) - 7 = 2a^2 - 3a - 7$

(c) $-f(a) = -1 \cdot (2a^2 + 3a - 7) = -2a^2 - 3a + 7$

(d) $f(a+h) = 2(a+h)^2 + 3(a+h) - 7 = 2(a^2 + 2ah + h^2) + 3a + 3h - 7 =$

$$2a^2 + 4ah + 2h^2 + 3a + 3h - 7$$

(e) $f(a) + f(h) = (2a^2 + 3a - 7) + (2h^2 + 3h - 7) = 2a^2 + 2h^2 + 3a + 3h - 14$

(f) $\dfrac{f(a+h) - f(a)}{h} = \dfrac{(2a^2 + 4ah + 2h^2 + 3a + 3h - 7) - (2a^2 + 3a - 7)}{h} =$

$$\dfrac{4ah + 2h^2 + 3h}{h} = \dfrac{h(4a + 2h + 3)}{h} = 4a + 2h + 3$$

$\boxed{9}$ $\dfrac{f(x+h) - f(x)}{h} = \dfrac{[(x+h)^2 + 5] - [x^2 + 5]}{h} = \dfrac{(x^2 + 2xh + h^2 + 5) - (x^2 + 5)}{h} =$

$$\dfrac{2xh + h^2}{h} = \dfrac{h(2x + h)}{h} = 2x + h$$

$\boxed{10}$ $\dfrac{f(x+h) - f(x)}{h} = \dfrac{\dfrac{1}{(x+h)^2} - \dfrac{1}{x^2}}{h} = \dfrac{\dfrac{x^2 - (x+h)^2}{(x+h)^2 x^2}}{h} = \dfrac{x^2 - (x^2 + 2xh + h^2)}{hx^2(x+h)^2} =$

$$\dfrac{-2xh - h^2}{hx^2(x+h)^2} = -\dfrac{h(2x+h)}{hx^2(x+h)^2} = -\dfrac{2x+h}{x^2(x+h)^2}$$

$\boxed{11}$ $\dfrac{f(x) - f(a)}{x - a} = \dfrac{\sqrt{x-3} - \sqrt{a-3}}{x-a} = \dfrac{\sqrt{x-3} - \sqrt{a-3}}{x-a} \cdot \dfrac{\sqrt{x-3} + \sqrt{a-3}}{\sqrt{x-3} + \sqrt{a-3}} =$

$$\dfrac{(x-3) - (a-3)}{(x-a)(\sqrt{x-3} + \sqrt{a-3})} = \dfrac{x-a}{(x-a)(\sqrt{x-3} + \sqrt{a-3})} = \dfrac{1}{\sqrt{x-3} + \sqrt{a-3}}$$

$\boxed{12}$ $\dfrac{f(x) - f(a)}{x - a} = \dfrac{(x^3 - 2) - (a^3 - 2)}{x - a} = \dfrac{x^3 - a^3}{x - a} = \dfrac{(x-a)(x^2 + ax + a^2)}{x - a} = x^2 + ax + a^2$

13 (a) $g\left(\frac{1}{a}\right) = 4\left(\frac{1}{a}\right)^2 = \frac{4}{a^2}$ (b) $\frac{1}{g(a)} = \frac{1}{4(a)^2} = \frac{1}{4a^2}$

(c) $g(\sqrt{a}) = 4(\sqrt{a})^2 = 4a$ (d) $\sqrt{g(a)} = \sqrt{4a^2} = 2\,|\,a\,| = 2a$ since $a > 0$

14 (a) $g\left(\frac{1}{a}\right) = 2\left(\frac{1}{a}\right) - 5 = \frac{2}{a} - 5 = \frac{2 - 5a}{a}$ (b) $\frac{1}{g(a)} = \frac{1}{2(a) - 5} = \frac{1}{2a - 5}$

(c) $g(\sqrt{a}) = 2(\sqrt{a}) - 5 = 2\sqrt{a} - 5$ (d) $\sqrt{g(a)} = \sqrt{2a - 5}$

15 (a) $g\left(\frac{1}{a}\right) = \frac{2(1/a)}{(1/a)^2 + 1} = \frac{2/a}{1/a^2 + 1} \cdot \frac{a^2}{a^2} = \frac{2a}{1 + a^2} = \frac{2a}{a^2 + 1}$

(b) $\frac{1}{g(a)} = \frac{1}{\frac{2a}{a^2 + 1}} = \frac{a^2 + 1}{2a}$ (c) $g(\sqrt{a}) = \frac{2\sqrt{a}}{(\sqrt{a})^2 + 1} = \frac{2\sqrt{a}}{a + 1}$

(d) $\sqrt{g(a)} = \sqrt{\frac{2a}{a^2 + 1}} \cdot \frac{\sqrt{a^2 + 1}}{\sqrt{a^2 + 1}} = \frac{\sqrt{2a^3 + 2a}}{a^2 + 1}$

16 (a) $g\left(\frac{1}{a}\right) = \frac{(\frac{1}{a})^2}{\frac{1}{a} + 1} = \frac{\frac{1}{a^2}}{\frac{1 + a}{a}} \cdot \frac{a^2}{a^2} = \frac{1}{a(a + 1)}$ (b) $\frac{1}{g(a)} = \frac{1}{\frac{a^2}{a + 1}} = \frac{a + 1}{a^2}$

(c) $g(\sqrt{a}) = \frac{(\sqrt{a})^2}{\sqrt{a} + 1} \cdot \frac{\sqrt{a} - 1}{\sqrt{a} - 1} = \frac{a(\sqrt{a} - 1)}{a - 1}$

(d) $\sqrt{g(a)} = \sqrt{\frac{a^2}{a + 1}} \cdot \sqrt{\frac{a + 1}{a + 1}} = \frac{a\sqrt{a + 1}}{a + 1}$

17 (a) $[-3, 4]$ (b) $[-2, 2]$ (c) $f(1) = 0$

(d) $f(x) = 1 \Rightarrow x = -1, \frac{1}{2}, 2$ (e) $f(x) > 1 \Rightarrow x \in (-1, \frac{1}{2}) \cup (2, 4]$

18 (a) $[-5, 7]$ (b) $[-1, 2]$ (c) $f(1) = -1$

(d) $f(x) = 1 \Rightarrow x = -3, -1, 3, 5$ (e) $f(x) > 1 \Rightarrow x \in (-3, -1) \cup (3, 5)$

19 $f(x) = \sqrt{2x + 7}$ • $2x + 7 \geq 0 \Rightarrow x \geq -\frac{7}{2} \Leftrightarrow [-\frac{7}{2}, \infty)$

20 $f(x) = \sqrt{8 - 3x}$ • $8 - 3x \geq 0 \Rightarrow x \leq \frac{8}{3} \Leftrightarrow (-\infty, \frac{8}{3}]$

21 $f(x) = \sqrt{9 - x^2}$ • $9 - x^2 \geq 0 \Rightarrow 3 \geq \,|\,x\,| \Rightarrow -3 \leq x \leq 3 \Leftrightarrow [-3, 3]$

22 $f(x) = \sqrt{x^2 - 25}$ • $x^2 - 25 \geq 0 \Rightarrow \,|\,x\,| \geq 5 \Rightarrow x \geq 5$ or $x \leq -5 \Leftrightarrow$

$$(-\infty, -5] \cup [5, \infty)$$

23 $f(x) = \dfrac{x + 1}{x^3 - 4x}$ • $x^3 - 4x = 0 \Rightarrow x(x + 2)(x - 2) = 0 \Leftrightarrow \mathbb{R} - \{\,\pm 2, 0\,\}$

24 $f(x) = \dfrac{4x}{6x^2 + 13x - 5}$ • $6x^2 + 13x - 5 = 0 \Rightarrow (2x + 5)(3x - 1) = 0 \Leftrightarrow \mathbb{R} - \{-\frac{5}{2}, \frac{1}{3}\}$

25 $f(x) = \dfrac{\sqrt{2x - 3}}{x^2 - 5x + 4}$ • $x^2 - 5x + 4 = 0 \Rightarrow (x - 1)(x - 4) = 0 \Rightarrow x = 1, 4; \ 2x - 3 \geq 0$

$\Rightarrow x \geq \frac{3}{2}$. The domain is $[\frac{3}{2}, \infty)$, excluding 4, or, equivalently, $[\frac{3}{2}, 4) \cup (4, \infty)$

26 $f(x) = \dfrac{\sqrt{4x - 3}}{x^2 - 4}$ • $x^2 - 4 = 0 \Rightarrow (x + 2)(x - 2) = 0 \Rightarrow x = \pm 2;$

$$4x - 3 \geq 0 \Rightarrow x \geq \tfrac{3}{4} \Leftrightarrow [\tfrac{3}{4}, 2) \cup (2, \infty)$$

[27] $f(x) = \dfrac{x-4}{\sqrt{x-2}}$ • $x - 2 > 0 \Rightarrow x > 2 \Leftrightarrow (2, \infty)$

[28] $f(x) = \dfrac{1}{(x-3)\sqrt{x+3}}$ • $x + 3 > 0 \Rightarrow x > -3 \; \{x \neq 3\} \Leftrightarrow (-3, 3) \cup (3, \infty)$

[29] $f(x) = \sqrt{x+2} + \sqrt{2-x}$ • $x + 2 \geq 0 \Rightarrow x \geq -2; \; 2 - x \geq 0 \Rightarrow x \leq 2.$

The domain is the intersection of $x \geq -2$ and $x \leq 2$, that is, $[-2, 2]$.

[30] $f(x) = \sqrt{(x-2)(x-6)}$ •

$(x-2)(x-6) \geq 0 \Rightarrow x \leq 2$ or $x \geq 6$ { use a sign diagram } $\Rightarrow (-\infty, 2] \cup [6, \infty)$

[31] (b) $D = (-\infty, \infty)$, $R = (-\infty, \infty)$ (c) Increasing on $(-\infty, \infty)$

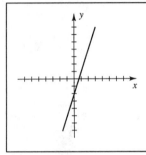

Figure 31

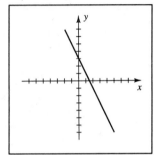

Figure 32

[32] (b) $D = (-\infty, \infty)$, $R = (-\infty, \infty)$ (c) Decreasing on $(-\infty, \infty)$

[33] (b) $D = (-\infty, \infty)$, $R = (-\infty, 4]$ (c) Increasing on $(-\infty, 0]$, decreasing on $[0, \infty)$

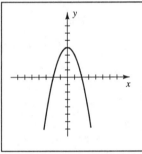

Figure 33

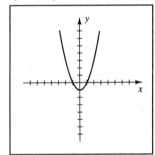

Figure 34

[34] (b) $D = (-\infty, \infty)$, $R = [-1, \infty)$ (c) Decreasing on $(-\infty, 0]$, increasing on $[0, \infty)$

[35] (b) $D = [-4, \infty)$, $R = [0, \infty)$ (c) Increasing on $[-4, \infty)$

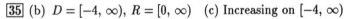

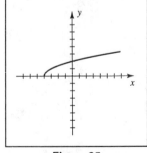

Figure 35

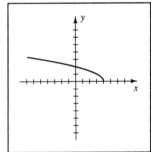

Figure 36

[36] (b) $D = (-\infty, 4]$, $R = [0, \infty)$ (c) Decreasing on $(-\infty, 4]$

37 (b) $D = (-\infty, \infty)$, $R = \{-2\}$ (c) Constant on $(-\infty, \infty)$

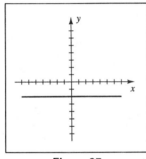

Figure 37

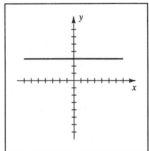

Figure 38

38 (b) $D = (-\infty, \infty)$, $R = \{3\}$ (c) Constant on $(-\infty, \infty)$

39 (b) $D = [-6, 6]$, $R = [-6, 0]$ (c) Decreasing on $[-6, 0]$, increasing on $[0, 6]$

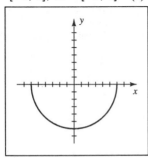

Figure 39

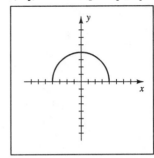

Figure 40

40 (b) $D = [-4, 4]$, $R = [0, 4]$ (c) Increasing on $[-4, 0]$, decreasing on $[0, 4]$

41 As in Example 7, $a = \dfrac{2-1}{3-(-3)} = \dfrac{1}{6}$ and f has the form $f(x) = \frac{1}{6}x + b$.

$\qquad f(3) = \frac{1}{6}(3) + b = \frac{1}{2} + b$. But $f(3) = 2$, so $\frac{1}{2} + b = 2 \Rightarrow b = \frac{3}{2}$, and $f(x) = \frac{1}{6}x + \frac{3}{2}$.

42 $a = \dfrac{-2-7}{4-(-2)} = -\dfrac{9}{6} = -\dfrac{3}{2} \Rightarrow f(x) = -\frac{3}{2}x + b$. $f(-2) = -\frac{3}{2}(-2) + b = 3 + b$ and

$\qquad\qquad\qquad\qquad\qquad f(-2) = 7 \Rightarrow 3 + b = 7 \Rightarrow b = 4$, and $f(x) = -\frac{3}{2}x + 4$.

Note: For Exercises 43–52, a good question to consider is "Given a particular value of x, can a unique value of y be found?" If the answer is yes, the value of y (general formula) is given. If no, two ordered pairs satisfying the relation having x in the first position are given.

43 $2y = x^2 + 5 \Rightarrow y = \dfrac{x^2 + 5}{2}$, a function

44 $x = 3y + 2 \Rightarrow x - 2 = 3y \Rightarrow y = \dfrac{x-2}{3}$, a function

45 $x^2 + y^2 = 4 \Rightarrow y^2 = 4 - x^2 \Rightarrow y = \pm\sqrt{4 - x^2}$, not a function, $(0, \pm 2)$

46 $y^2 - x^2 = 1 \Rightarrow y^2 = 1 + x^2 \Rightarrow y = \pm\sqrt{1 + x^2}$, not a function, $(0, \pm 1)$

47 $y = 3$ is a function since for any x,

$\qquad\qquad\qquad (x, 3)$ is the only ordered pair in W having x in the first position.

48 $x = 3$ is not a function, $(3, 0)$ and $(3, 1)$

49 Many ordered pairs with x-coordinate 0 satisfy $xy = 0$.

Two such ordered pairs are $(0, 0)$ and $(0, 1)$. Not a function

50 $x + y = 0 \Rightarrow y = -x$, a function

51 $|y| = |x| \Rightarrow \pm y = \pm x \Rightarrow y = \pm x$, not a function, $(1, \pm 1)$

52 Many ordered pairs with x-coordinate 3 (or any other number) satisfy $y < x$.

Two such ordered pairs are $(3, 1)$ and $(3, 2)$. Not a function

53 $V = lwh = (30 - 2x)(20 - 2x)(x) = 4x(15 - x)(10 - x)$

54 $S = 2\pi rh + 2(2\pi r^2) = 2\pi r(10) + 4\pi r^2 = 20\pi r + 4\pi r^2 = 4\pi r(5 + r)$

55 (a) $A = 500 \Rightarrow xy = 500 \Rightarrow y = \dfrac{500}{x}$

(b) $P = $ Linear feet of wall $= x + 2(y) + 2(x - 3) = 3x + 2\left(\dfrac{500}{x}\right) - 6.$

$$C = 100P = 300x + \dfrac{100{,}000}{x} - 600.$$

56 (a) $V = lwh \Rightarrow 6 = xy(1.5) \Rightarrow xy = 4 \Rightarrow y = \dfrac{4}{x}$

(b) Surface area $S = xy + 2(1.5)x + 2(1.5)y = x\left(\dfrac{4}{x}\right) + 3x + 3\left(\dfrac{4}{x}\right) = 4 + 3x + \dfrac{12}{x}$

57 $S(h) = 6(h - 25) + 100 = 6h - 150 + 100 = 6h - 50.$

58 $T(x) = \dfrac{125{,}000 \text{ BTUs}}{1 \text{ gallon of gas}} \cdot x \text{ gallons} \cdot \dfrac{\$0.342}{1{,}000{,}000 \text{ BTU}} = \$0.04275x.$

59 (a) Using $(6, 48)$ and $(7, 50.5)$, we have

$y - 48 = \dfrac{50.5 - 48}{7 - 6}(t - 6)$, or $y = 2.5t + 33.$

(b) The slope represents the

yearly increase in height, 2.5 in/yr.

(c) $t = 10 \Rightarrow y = 2.5(10) + 33 = 58$ in.

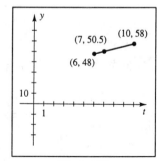

Figure 59

60 Let A denote the area of the contamination. A is linearly related to t, so $A = at + b$.

$A = 0$ when $t = 0 \Rightarrow b = 0$. $A = 40{,}000$ when $t = 40 \Rightarrow a = 1000$. Thus, $A = 1000t$.

Since the contamination is circular, $A = \pi r^2$. Hence, $\pi r^2 = 1000t \Rightarrow r = \sqrt{\dfrac{1000t}{\pi}}.$

61 The height of the balloon is $2t$. Using the Pythagorean theorem,

$$d^2 = 100^2 + (2t)^2 \Rightarrow d^2 = 2^2(50)^2 + 2^2 t^2 \Rightarrow d = 2\sqrt{t^2 + 2500}.$$

62 (a) By the Pythagorean theorem, $x^2 + y^2 = 15^2 \Rightarrow y = \sqrt{225 - x^2}.$

(b) $\mathcal{A} = \frac{1}{2}bh = \frac{1}{2}xy = \frac{1}{2}x\sqrt{225 - x^2}.$ The domain of this function is $-15 \le x \le 15$;

however, only $0 < x < 15$ will form triangles.

63 (a) $(CT)^2 + (PT)^2 = (PC)^2 \Rightarrow r^2 + y^2 = (h+r)^2 \Rightarrow r^2 + y^2 = h^2 + 2hr + r^2 \Rightarrow$

$$y^2 = h^2 + 2hr \; \{y > 0\} \Rightarrow y = \sqrt{h^2 + 2hr}$$

(b) $y = \sqrt{(200)^2 + 2(4000)(200)} = \sqrt{(200)^2(1+40)} = 200\sqrt{41} \approx 1280.6$ mi

64 (a) The dimensions L, 50, and $x - 2$ form a right triangle 2 feet off the ground.

$$\text{Thus, } L^2 = 50^2 + (x-2)^2 \Rightarrow L = \sqrt{2500 + (x-2)^2}.$$

(b) $L = 75 \Rightarrow 75^2 = 50^2 + (x-2)^2 \Rightarrow x - 2 = \pm\sqrt{3125} \Rightarrow x = 25\sqrt{5} + 2 \approx 57.9$ ft

65 Let y be the distance from the control booth to the beginning of the runway.

Then $y^2 = 300^2 + 20^2$ and, in a different plane, $d^2 = y^2 + x^2$.

$$\text{Solving for } d, \; d = \sqrt{y^2 + x^2} = \sqrt{90{,}400 + x^2}.$$

66 $\text{Time}_{\text{total}} = \text{Time}_{\text{rowing}} + \text{Time}_{\text{walking}}$ { use $t = d/r$ and $d(A, P) = 6 - x$ } $\Rightarrow$

$$T = \frac{\sqrt{2^2 + (6-x)^2}}{3} + \frac{x}{5} \Rightarrow T = \frac{\sqrt{x^2 - 12x + 40}}{3} + \frac{x}{5}$$

67 $F = kx.$ $F = 4$ and $x = 10.3 - 10 = 0.3 \Rightarrow 4 = k(0.3) \Rightarrow k = \frac{40}{3}.$ $F = \frac{40}{3}(1.5) = 20$ lb.

68 $T = kd^{3/2}.$ $365 = k(93)^{3/2} \Rightarrow k = \dfrac{365}{(93)^{3/2}}.$ $T = \dfrac{365}{(93)^{3/2}} \cdot (67)^{3/2} \approx 223.2$ days.

69 $R = k\dfrac{l}{d^2} = \dfrac{kl}{d^2}.$ $25 = \dfrac{k(100)}{(0.01)^2} \Rightarrow k = \dfrac{1}{40{,}000}.$ $R = \dfrac{50}{(40{,}000)(0.015)^2} = \dfrac{50}{9}$ ohms.

70 $F = k\dfrac{Q_1 Q_2}{d^2} = \dfrac{kQ_1 Q_2}{d^2}.$ $F_1 = \dfrac{kQ_1 Q_2}{d_1^2} = \dfrac{kQ_1 Q_2}{(\frac{1}{4}d)^2} = 16\left(\dfrac{kQ_1 Q_2}{d^2}\right) = 16F.$

The force F is multiplied by 16.

71 The square of the distance from the origin to the point (x, y) is $x^2 + y^2.$ $d = \dfrac{k}{x^2 + y^2}.$

If (x_1, y_1) is the new point that has density d_1, then

$$d_1 = \frac{k}{x_1^2 + y_1^2} = \frac{k}{(\frac{1}{3}x)^2 + (\frac{1}{3}y)^2} = \frac{k}{\frac{1}{9}x^2 + \frac{1}{9}y^2} = \frac{k}{\frac{1}{9}(x^2 + y^2)} = 9 \cdot \frac{k}{x^2 + y^2} = 9d.$$

The density d is multiplied by 9.

72 The distance from the origin to the point (x, y) is $\sqrt{x^2 + y^2}.$ $T = k/\sqrt{x^2 + y^2}.$

$T = 20$ and $P(3, 4) \Rightarrow 20 = k/5 \Rightarrow k = 100.$ $T = 100/\sqrt{24^2 + 7^2} = 100/25 = 4\,°C.$

73 (b) The maximum y-value of 0.75 occurs when $x \approx 0.55$ and

the minimum y-value of -0.75 occurs when $x \approx -0.55$.

Therefore, the range of f is approximately $[-0.75, 0.75]$.

(c) f is decreasing on $[-2, -0.55]$ and on $[0.55, 2]$. f is increasing on $[-0.55, 0.55]$.

$[-2, 2]$ by $[-2, 2]$ $[-1, 1]$ by $[-1, 1]$

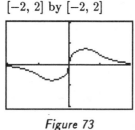 Xscl = 1
Yscl = 1

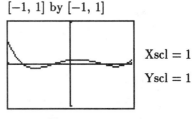 Xscl = 1
Yscl = 1

Figure 73   Figure 74

74 (b) The maximum y-value of 0.5 occurs when $x = -1$ and

the minimum y-value of -0.094 occurs when $x \approx -0.56$.

Therefore, the range of f is approximately $[-0.094, 0.5]$.

(c) f is decreasing on $[-1, -0.56]$ and on $[0.12, 0.75]$.

f is increasing on $[-0.56, 0.12]$ and on $[0.75, 1]$.

75 (b) The maximum y-value of 1 occurs when $x = 0$ and

the minimum y-value of -1.03 occurs when $x \approx 1.06$.

Therefore, the range of f is approximately $[-1.03, 1]$.

(c) f is decreasing on $[0, 1.06]$. f is increasing on $[-0.7, 0]$ and on $[1.06, 1.4]$.

$[-0.7, 1.4]$ by $[-1.1, 1]$ $[-4, 4]$ by $[-4, 4]$

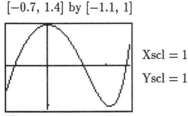 Xscl = 1
Yscl = 1

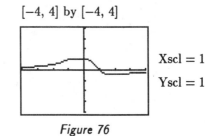 Xscl = 1
Yscl = 1

Figure 75   Figure 76

76 (b) The maximum y-value of 1.08 occurs when $x \approx -0.69$ and

the minimum y-value of -0.42 occurs when $x \approx 1.78$.

Therefore, the range of f is approximately $[-0.42, 1.08]$.

(c) f is decreasing on $[-0.69, 1.78]$. f is increasing on $[-4, -0.69]$ and on $[1.78, 4]$.

77 For each of (a)–(e), an assignment to Y_1, an appropriate viewing rectangle, and the solution(s) are listed.

(a) $Y_1 = (x\char94 5)\char94(1/3)$,   VR: $[-40, 40]$ by $[-40, 40]$, $x = 8$

(b) $Y_1 = (x\char94 4)\char94(1/3)$,   VR: $[-20, 20]$ by $[-20, 20]$, $x = \pm 8$

(c) $Y_1 = (x\char94 2)\char94(1/3)$,   VR: $[-40, 40]$ by $[-40, 40]$,   no real solutions

(d) $Y_1 = (x\char94 3)\char94(1/4)$,   VR: $[0, 650]$ by $[0, 650]$, $x = 625$

(e) $Y_1 = (x\char94 3)\char94(1/2)$,   VR: $[-30, 30]$ by $[-30, 30]$,   no real solutions

78 (a) $Y_1 = (x\char94 3)\char94(1/5)$,   VR: $[-250, 250]$ by $[-30, 30]$, $x = -243$

(b) $Y_1 = (x\char94 2)\char94(1/3)$,   VR: $[-130, 130]$ by $[0, 30]$, $x = \pm 125$

(c) $Y_1 = (x\char94 4)\char94(1/3)$,   VR: $[-50, 50]$ by $[-50, 50]$,   no real solutions

(d) $Y_1 = (x\char94 3)\char94(1/2)$,   VR: $[-5, 30]$ by $[-5, 30]$, $x = 9$

(e) $Y_1 = (x\char94 3)\char94(1/4)$,   VR: $[-10, 10]$ by $[-10, 10]$,   no real solutions

79 (a) First, we must determine the equation of the line that passes through the points (1985, 11,450) and (1994, 20,021).

$$y - 11,450 = \frac{20,021 - 11,450}{1994 - 1985}(x - 1985) = \frac{2857}{3}(x - 1985) \Rightarrow$$

$$y = \frac{2857}{3}x - \frac{5,636,795}{3}. \text{ Thus, let } f(x) = \frac{2857}{3}x - \frac{5,636,795}{3} \text{ and graph } f.$$

(b) The average annual increase in the price paid for a new car is equal to the slope:

$$\frac{2857}{3} \approx \$952.33.$$

(c) Graph $y = \dfrac{2857}{3}x - \dfrac{5,636,795}{3}$ and $y = 25,000$ on the same coordinate axes. Their point of intersection is approximately (1999.2, 25,000). Thus, according to this model, in the year 1999 the average price paid for a new car will be \$25,000.

[1984, 2005] by [10,000, 30,000]   [1984, 2005] by [10,000, 30,000]

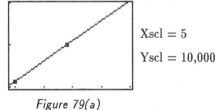   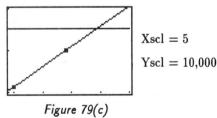

Xscl $= 5$ Xscl $= 5$

Yscl $= 10,000$ Yscl $= 10,000$

Figure 79(a)   *Figure 79(c)*

80 (a) $95 \times 63 = 5985$

(b) If a function is graphed in dot mode, only one pixel in each column of pixels on the screen can be darkened. Therefore, there are at most 95 pixels darkened.

Note: In connected mode this may not be true.

81 (a)

[0, 75] by [0, 600]

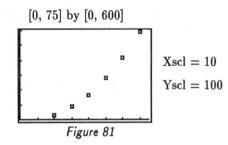

Xscl = 10

Yscl = 100

Figure 81

(b) The data and plot show that stopping distance is not a linear function of the speed. The distance required to stop a car traveling at 30 mi/hr is 86 ft whereas the distance required to stop a car traveling at 60 mi/hr is 414 ft. $\frac{414}{86} \approx 4.81$ rather than double.

(c) If you double the speed of a car, it requires almost *five* times the stopping distance. If stopping distance were a linear function of speed, doubling the speed would require approximately twice the stopping distance.

82 (a) $D = kS^{2.3} \Rightarrow k = \frac{D}{S^{2.3}}$. Using the 6 data points: $\frac{33}{20^{2.3}} \approx 0.0336$; $\frac{86}{30^{2.3}} \approx 0.0344$;

$\frac{167}{40^{2.3}} \approx 0.0345$; $\frac{278}{50^{2.3}} \approx 0.0343$; $\frac{414}{60^{2.3}} \approx 0.0337$; $\frac{593}{70^{2.3}} \approx 0.0338$. Let $k = 0.034$.

Thus, $D = 0.034S^{2.3}$.

(b) Graph the data together with

$Y_1 = 0.034x^{2.3}$.

[0, 75] by [0, 600]

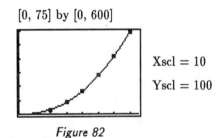

Xscl = 10

Yscl = 100

Figure 82

2.2 Exercises

2.2 Concept Check

1 Let f be an nth degree polynomial in x; that is,

$$f(x) = a_n x^n + a_{n-1} x^{n-1} + \cdots + a_1 x + a_0.$$

What condition on the a_i's ensures us that f is even? odd? • We must have the odd-numbered coefficients equal to zero; that is, $a_1 = 0$, $a_3 = 0$, ... The even-numbered coefficients must equal zero; that is, $a_0 = 0$, $a_2 = 0$, ...

2 Let c denote a positive real number. How does the graph of $y = f(x) + c$ compare to the graph of $y = f(x)$? How about the graph of $y = f(x + c)$ compared to that of $y = f(x)$? • The graph of $y = f(x) + c$ is shifted vertically upward a distance c from the graph of $y = f(x)$. The graph of $y = f(x + c)$ is shifted horizontally to the left a distance c from the graph of $y = f(x)$.

3 Let c denote a real number greater than 1. How does the graph of $y = cf(x)$ compare to the graph of $y = f(x)$? How about the graph of $y = f(cx)$ compared to that of $y = f(x)$? • The graph of $y = cf(x)$ is the graph of $y = f(x)$ stretched vertically by a factor c. The graph of $y = f(cx)$ is the graph of $y = f(x)$ compressed horizontally by a factor c.

4 What equation has the graph of the reflection of the graph of $y = f(x)$ through the x-axis? through the y-axis? • $y = -f(x)$; $y = f(-x)$

5 Write the absolute value function as a piecewise-defined function. •

$$f(x) = |x| = \begin{cases} x & \text{if } x \geq 0 \\ -x & \text{if } x < 0 \end{cases}$$

6 If the point $(3, -2)$ is on the graph of a function f, find the corresponding point on the graph of the given function.

(a) $y = f(x) - 3$ (b) $y = f(x - 4)$ (c) $y = \frac{1}{2}f(x)$

(d) $y = f(\frac{1}{3}x)$ (e) $y = f(-x)$ (f) $y = |f(x)|$ •

(a) $(3, -5)$ (b) $(7, -2)$ (c) $(3, -1)$ (d) $(9, -2)$ (e) $(-3, -2)$ (f) $(3, 2)$

2.2 Exercises

1 $f(x) = 5x^3 + 2x \Rightarrow f(-x) = 5(-x)^3 + 2(-x) = -5x^3 - 2x = -(5x^3 + 2x) = -f(x)$,

f is odd

2 $f(x) = |x| - 3 \Rightarrow f(-x) = |-x| - 3 = |x| - 3 = f(x)$, f is even

3 $f(x) = 3x^4 + 2x^2 - 5 \Rightarrow f(-x) = 3(-x)^4 + 2(-x)^2 - 5 = 3x^4 + 2x^2 - 5 = f(x)$,

f is even

4 $f(x) = 7x^5 - 4x^3 \Rightarrow f(-x) = 7(-x)^5 - 4(-x)^3 = -7x^5 + 4x^3 = -(7x^5 - 4x^3) = -f(x)$,

f is odd

5 $f(x) = 8x^3 - 3x^2 \Rightarrow f(-x) = 8(-x)^3 - 3(-x)^2 = -8x^3 - 3x^2 \neq \pm f(x)$,

f is neither even nor odd

6 $f(x) = 12 \Rightarrow f(-x) = 12 = f(x)$, f is even

7 $f(x) = \sqrt{x^2 + 4} \Rightarrow f(-x) = \sqrt{(-x)^2 + 4} = \sqrt{x^2 + 4} = f(x)$, f is even

8 $f(x) = 3x^2 - 5x + 1 \Rightarrow f(-x) = 3(-x)^2 - 5(-x) + 1 = 3x^2 + 5x + 1 \neq \pm f(x)$,

f is neither even nor odd

$\boxed{9}$ $f(x) = \sqrt[3]{x^3 - x} \Rightarrow f(-x) = \sqrt[3]{(-x)^3 - (-x)} = \sqrt[3]{-x^3 + x} = \sqrt[3]{-1(x^3 - x)} =$

$$\sqrt[3]{-1} \sqrt[3]{x^3 - x} = -\sqrt[3]{x^3 - x} = -f(x), \ f \text{ is odd}$$

$\boxed{10}$ $f(x) = x^3 - \frac{1}{x} \Rightarrow f(-x) = (-x)^3 - \frac{1}{-x} = -x^3 + \frac{1}{x} = -\left(x^3 - \frac{1}{x}\right) = -f(x), \ f \text{ is odd}$

$\boxed{11}$ $f(x) = |x| + c, \ c = -3, 1, 3$ •

Shift $g(x) = |x|$ down 3, up 1, and up 3 units, respectively.

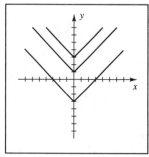

Figure 11

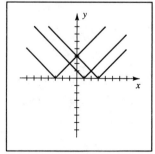

Figure 12

$\boxed{12}$ $f(x) = |x - c|, \ c = -3, 1, 3$ •

Shift $g(x) = |x|$ left 3, right 1, and right 3 units, respectively.

$\boxed{13}$ $f(x) = -x^2 + c, \ c = -4, 2, 4$ • Shift $g(x) = -x^2$ down 4, up 2, up 4, respectively.

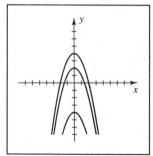

Figure 13

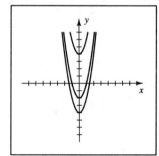

Figure 14

$\boxed{14}$ $f(x) = 2x^2 - c, \ c = -4, 2, 4$ •

Shift $g(x) = 2x^2$ up 4, down 2, down 4, respectively.

15 $f(x) = 2\sqrt{x} + c$, $c = -3, 0, 2$ • Shift $g(x) = 2\sqrt{x}$ down 3, up 2, respectively.

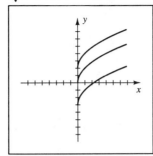

Figure 15

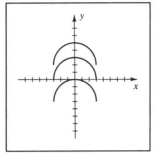

Figure 16

16 $f(x) = \sqrt{9 - x^2} + c$, $c = -3, 0, 2$ •

Shift $g(x) = \sqrt{9 - x^2}$ down 3, up 2, respectively.

17 $f(x) = \frac{1}{2}\sqrt{x - c}$, $c = -2, 0, 3$ • Shift $g(x) = \frac{1}{2}\sqrt{x}$ left 2, right 3, respectively.

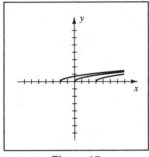

Figure 17

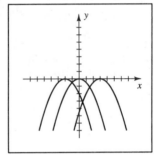

Figure 18

18 $f(x) = -\frac{1}{2}(x - c)^2$, $c = -2, 0, 3$ • Shift $g(x) = -\frac{1}{2}x^2$ left 2, right 3, respectively.

19 $f(x) = c\sqrt{4 - x^2}$, $c = -2, 1, 3$ •

For $c = -2$, reflect $g(x) = \sqrt{4 - x^2}$ through the x-axis and vertically stretch it by a

factor of 2. For $c = 3$, vertically stretch g by a factor of 3.

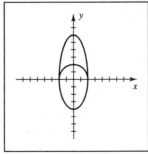

Figure 19

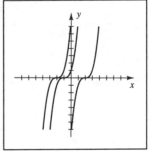

Figure 20

20 $f(x) = (x + c)^3$, $c = -2, 1, 2$ •

Shift $g(x) = x^3$ right 2, left 1, and left 2, respectively.

$\boxed{21}$ $f(x) = cx^3$, $c = -\frac{1}{3}$, 1, 2 • For $c = -\frac{1}{3}$, reflect $g(x) = x^3$ through the x-axis and
vertically compress it by a factor of $1/(1/3) = 3$.

For $c = 2$, vertically stretch g by a factor of 2.

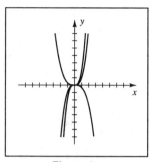

Figure 21

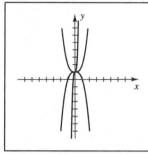

Figure 22

$\boxed{22}$ $f(x) = (cx)^3 + 1$, $c = -1$, 1, 4 • For $c = -1$, reflect $g(x) = x^3 + 1$ through the
y-axis. For $c = 4$, horizontally compress g by a factor of 4 { this could also be
considered as a vertical stretch by a factor of $4^3 = 64$ }.

$\boxed{23}$ $f(x) = \sqrt{cx} - 1$, $c = -1$, $\frac{1}{9}$, 4 •

For $c = -1$, reflect $g(x) = \sqrt{x} - 1$ through the y-axis. For $c = \frac{1}{9}$,
horizontally stretch g by a factor $1/(1/9) = 9$ { x-intercept changes from 1 to 9 }.

For $c = 4$, horizontally compress g by a factor 4 { x-intercept changes from 1 to $\frac{1}{4}$ }.

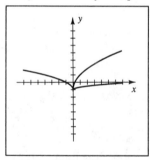

Figure 23

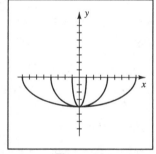

Figure 24

$\boxed{24}$ $f(x) = -\sqrt{16 - (cx)^2}$, $c = 1$, $\frac{1}{2}$, 4 • For $c = \frac{1}{2}$, horizontally stretch
$g(x) = -\sqrt{16 - x^2}$ by a factor of $1/(1/2) = 2$ { x-intercepts change from ± 4 to ± 8 }.
For $c = 4$, horizontally compress g by a factor of 4

{ x-intercepts change from ± 4 to ± 1 }.

$\boxed{25}$ $P(3, -2)$ { $x - 4$ [add 4 to the x-coordinate] } $\rightarrow (7, -2)$

{ $\times 2$ [multiply the y-coordinate by 2] } $\rightarrow (7, -4)$

{ $+1$ [add 1 to the y-coordinate] } $\rightarrow (7, -3)$

$\boxed{26}$ $P(-2, 1)$ { $2x$ [divide the x-coordinate by 2] } $\rightarrow (-1, 1)$

{ $\times -3$ [multiply the y-coordinate by -3] } $\rightarrow (-1, -3)$

{ -5 [subtract 5 from the y-coordinate] } $\rightarrow (-1, -8)$

27 (a) $y = f(x+3)$ • shift f left 3 units

(b) $y = f(x-3)$ • shift f right 3 units

(c) $y = f(x)+3$ • shift f up 3 units

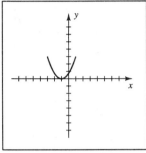

Figure 27(a)

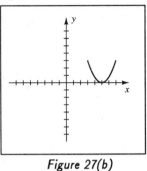

Figure 27(b)

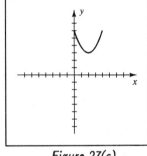

Figure 27(c)

(d) $y = f(x)-3$ • shift f down 3 units

(e) $y = -3f(x)$ •

   reflect f through the x-axis and vertically stretch it by a factor of 3

(f) $y = -\frac{1}{3}f(x)$ •

   reflect f through the x-axis and vertically compress it by a factor of $1/(1/3) = 3$

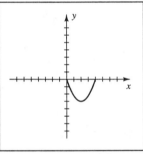

Figure 27(d)

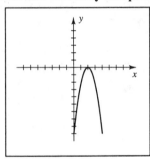

Figure 27(e)

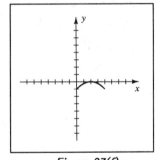

Figure 27(f)

(g) $y = f(-\frac{1}{2}x)$ •

   reflect f through the y-axis and horizontally stretch it by a factor of $1/(1/2) = 2$

(h) $y = f(2x)$ • horizontally compress f by a factor of 2

(i) $y = -f(x+2)-3$ • reflect f about the x-axis, shift it left 2 units and down 3

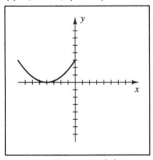

Figure 27(g)

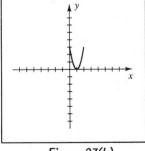

Figure 27(h)

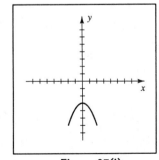

Figure 27(i)

(j) $y = f(x - 2) + 3$ •   shift f right 2 units and up 3

(k) $y = |f(x)|$ •   since no portion of the graph lies below the x-axis,
the graph is unchanged

(l) $y = f(|x|)$ •   include the reflection of the given graph through the y-axis
since all points have positive x-coordinates

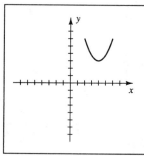

Figure 27(j)

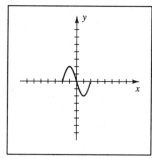

Figure 27(k)

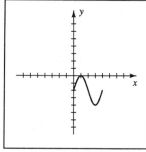

Figure 27(l)

28 (a) $y = f(x - 2)$ •   shift f right 2 units

     (b) $y = f(x + 2)$ •   shift f left 2 units

     (c) $y = f(x) - 2$ •   shift f down 2 units

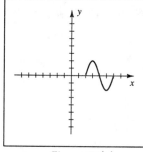

Figure 28(a)

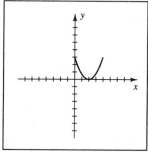

Figure 28(b)

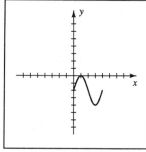

Figure 28(c)

     (d) $y = f(x) + 2$ •   shift f up 2 units

     (e) $y = -2f(x)$ •

reflect f through the x-axis and vertically stretch it by a factor of 2

     (f) $y = -\frac{1}{2}f(x)$ •

reflect f through the x-axis and vertically compress it by a factor of $1/(1/2) = 2$

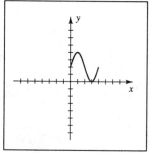

Figure 28(d)

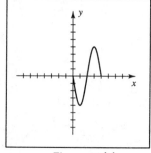

Figure 28(e)

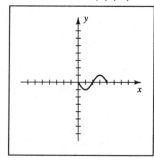

Figure 28(f)

(g) $y = f(-2x)$ •

　　　　　reflect f through the y-axis and horizontally compress it by a factor of 2

(h) $y = f(\frac{1}{2}x)$ •   horizontally stretch f by a factor of $1/(1/2) = 2$

(i) $y = -f(x+4) - 2$ •   reflect f about the x-axis, shift it left 4 units and down 2

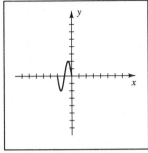
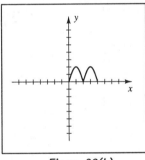
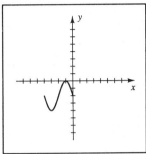

Figure 28(g) 　　　　　 *Figure 28(h)* 　　　　　 *Figure 28(i)*

(j) $y = f(x-4) + 2$ •   shift f right 4 units and up 2

(k) $y = |f(x)|$ •

　　　　　reflect the portion of the graph below the x-axis through the x-axis.

(l) $y = f(|x|)$ •   include the reflection of the given graph through the y-axis

　　　　　　　　　　　　since all points have positive x-coordinates

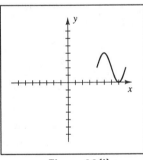
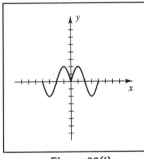

Figure 28(j) 　　　　　 *Figure 28(k)* 　　　　　 *Figure 28(l)*

29 (a) f is shifted left 9 units and up 1 $\Rightarrow y = f(x+9) + 1$

(b) f is reflected about the x-axis $\Rightarrow y = -f(x)$

(c) f is reflected about the x-axis and shifted left 7 units and down 1 $\Rightarrow$

$$y = -f(x+7) - 1$$

30 (a) f is shifted left 1 unit and up 1 $\Rightarrow y = f(x+1) + 1$

(b) f is reflected about the x-axis $\Rightarrow y = -f(x)$ { or $y = f(-x)$ }

(c) f is reflected about the x-axis and shifted right 2 units $\Rightarrow y = -f(x-2)$

31 (a) f is shifted left 4 units $\Rightarrow y = f(x+4)$

(b) f is shifted up 1 unit $\Rightarrow y = f(x) + 1$

(c) f is reflected about the y-axis $\Rightarrow y = f(-x)$

32 (a) f is shifted right 2 units and up 2 $\Rightarrow y = f(x-2)+2$

(b) f is reflected about the x-axis $\Rightarrow y = -f(x)$

(c) f is reflected about the x-axis and shifted left 4 units and up 2 $\Rightarrow$
$$y = -f(x+4)+2$$

33 $f(x) = \begin{cases} 3 & \text{if } x \le -1 \\ -2 & \text{if } x > -1 \end{cases}$

34 $f(x) = \begin{cases} -1 & \text{if } x \text{ is an integer} \\ -2 & \text{if } x \text{ is not an integer} \end{cases}$

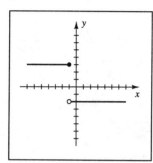

Figure 33

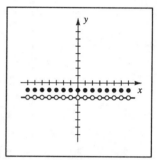

Figure 34

35 $f(x) = \begin{cases} 3 & \text{if } x < -2 \\ -x+1 & \text{if } |x| \le 2 \\ -3 & \text{if } x > 2 \end{cases}$

36 $f(x) = \begin{cases} -2x & \text{if } x < -1 \\ x^2 & \text{if } -1 \le x < 1 \\ -2 & \text{if } x \ge 1 \end{cases}$

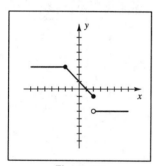

Figure 35

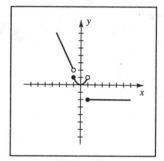

Figure 36

37 $f(x) = \begin{cases} x+2 & \text{if } x \le -1 \\ x^3 & \text{if } |x| < 1 \\ -x+3 & \text{if } x \ge 1 \end{cases}$

38 $f(x) = \begin{cases} x-3 & \text{if } x \le -2 \\ -x^2 & \text{if } -2 < x < 1 \\ -x+4 & \text{if } x \ge 1 \end{cases}$

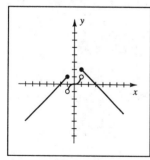

Figure 37

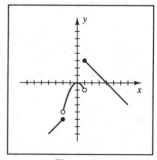

Figure 38

39 (a) $f(x) = [x - 3]$ • shift $g(x) = [x]$ right 3 units

(b) $f(x) = [x] - 3$ • shift g down 3 units, which is the same graph as in part (a).

(c) $f(x) = 2[x]$ • vertically stretch g by a factor of 2

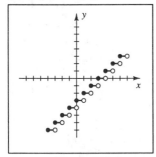

Figure 39(a)

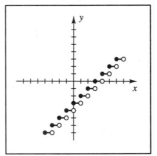

Figure 39(b)

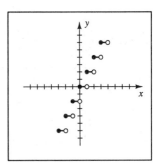

Figure 39(c)

(d) $f(x) = [2x]$ • horizontally compress g by a factor of 2

(e) $f(x) = [-x]$ • reflect g through the y-axis

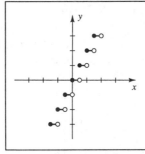

Figure 39(d)

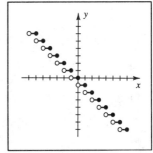

Figure 39(e)

40 (a) $f(x) = [x + 2]$ • shift $g(x) = [x]$ left 2 units

(b) $f(x) = [x] + 2$ • shift g up 2 units, which is the same graph as in part (a).

(c) $f(x) = \frac{1}{2}[x]$ • vertically compress g by a factor of $1/(1/2) = 2$

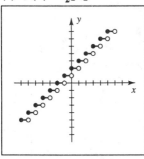

Figure 40(a)

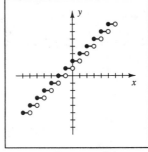

Figure 40(b)

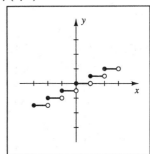

Figure 40(c)

(d) $f(x) = \left[\!\left[\frac{1}{2}x\right]\!\right]$ •   horizontally stretch g by a factor of $1/(1/2) = 2$

(e) $f(x) = -[\![-x]\!]$ •   reflect g through the y-axis and through the x-axis

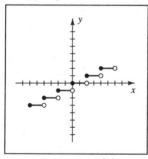

Figure 40(d)

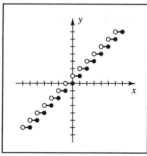

Figure 40(e)

41 The graph of $x = y^2$ is not the graph of a function because if $x > 0$,

two different points on the graph have x-coordinate x.

42 The graph of $x = -|y|$ is not the graph of a function because if $x < 0$,

two different points on the graph have x-coordinate x.

43 Reflect each portion of the graph that is below the x-axis through the x-axis.

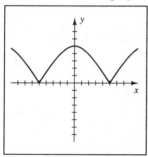

Figure 43

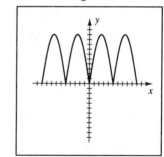

Figure 44

44 Same as Exercise 43.

45 $y = |9 - x^2|$ •   First sketch $y = 9 - x^2$,

then reflect the portions of the graph below the x-axis through the x-axis.

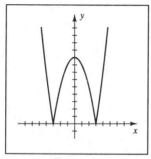

Figure 45

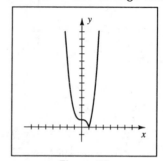

Figure 46

46 $y = |x^3 - 1|$ •

47 $y = |\sqrt{x} - 1|$ •

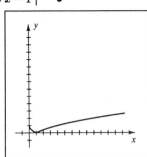

Figure 47

48 $y = ||x| - 1|$ •

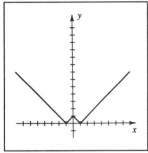

Figure 48

49 (a) For $y = -2f(x)$, multiply the y-coordinates by -2. $D = [-2, 6]$, $R = [-16, 8]$

(b) For $y = f(\frac{1}{2}x)$, multiply the x-coordinates by 2. $D = [-4, 12]$, $R = [-4, 8]$

(c) For $y = f(x - 3) + 1$, add 3 to the x-coordinates and add 1 to the y-coordinates.
$$D = [1, 9], R = [-3, 9]$$

(d) For $y = f(x + 2) - 3$, subtract 2 from the x-coordinates and subtract 3 from the y-coordinates. $D = [-4, 4]$, $R = [-7, 5]$

(e) For $y = f(-x)$, negate all x-coordinates. $D = [-6, 2]$, $R = [-4, 8]$

(f) For $y = -f(x)$, negate all y-coordinates. $D = [-2, 6]$, $R = [-8, 4]$

(g) $y = f(|x|)$ • Graphically, we can reflect all points with positive x-coordinates through the y-axis, so the domain $[-2, 6]$ becomes $[-6, 6]$. Algebraically, we are replacing x with $|x|$, so $-2 \le x \le 6$ becomes $-2 \le |x| \le 6$, which is equivalent $|x| \le 6$, or, equivalently, $-6 \le x \le 6$. The range stays the same because of the given assumptions: $f(2) = 8$ and $f(6) = -4$; that is, the full range is taken on for $x \ge 0$. Note that the range could not be determined if $f(-2)$ was equal to 8. $D = [-6, 6]$, $R = [-8, 4]$

(h) $y = |f(x)|$ • The points with y-coordinates having values from -4 to 0 will have values from 0 to 4, so the range will be $[0, 8]$. $D = [-2, 6]$, $R = [0, 8]$

50 (a) For $y = \frac{1}{2}f(x)$, multiply the y-coordinates by $\frac{1}{2}$. $D = [-6, -2]$, $R = [-5, -2]$

(b) For $y = f(2x)$, multiply the x-coordinates by $\frac{1}{2}$. $D = [-3, -1]$, $R = [-10, -4]$

(c) For $y = f(x - 2) + 5$, add 2 to the x-coordinates and add 5 to the y-coordinates.
$$D = [-4, 0], R = [-5, 1]$$

(d) For $y = f(x + 4) - 1$, subtract 4 from the x-coordinates and subtract 1 from the y-coordinates. $D = [-10, -6]$, $R = [-11, -5]$

(e) For $y = f(-x)$, negate all x-coordinates. $D = [2, 6]$, $R = [-10, -4]$

(f) For $y = -f(x)$, negate all y-coordinates. $D = [-6, -2]$, $R = [4, 10]$

(g) For $y = f(|x|)$, there is no graph since the domain of f consists of only negative values, -6 to -2, and $|x|$ is never negative.

(h) For $y = |f(x)|$, the negative y-coordinates having values from -10 to -4 will have values from 4 to 10. $D = [-6, -2]$, $R = [4, 10]$

51 If $x \leq 20,000$, then $T(x) = 0.15x$. If $x > 20,000$, then the tax is 15% of the first 20,000, which is 3000, plus 20% of the amount over 20,000. We may summarize and simplify as follows:

$$T(x) = \begin{cases} 0.15x & \text{if } x \leq 20,000 \\ 3000 + 0.20(x - 20,000) & \text{if } x > 20,000 \end{cases} = \begin{cases} 0.15x & \text{if } x \leq 20,000 \\ 0.20x - 1000 & \text{if } x > 20,000 \end{cases}$$

52 The cost is 0.25 for a 1-minute call. For an x-minute call, the cost is 0.25 plus 15¢ for each of the $x - 1$ additional minutes.

$$C(x) = \begin{cases} 0.25 & \text{if } x \leq 1 \\ 0.25 + 0.15(x - 1) & \text{if } x > 1 \end{cases} = \begin{cases} 0.25 & \text{if } x \leq 1 \\ 0.10 + 0.15x & \text{if } x > 1 \end{cases}$$

53 The author receives $1.20 on the first 10,000 copies,

$1.50 on the next 5000, and $1.80 on each additional copy.

$$R(x) = \begin{cases} 1.20x & \text{if } 0 \leq x \leq 10,000 \\ 12,000 + 1.50(x - 10,000) & \text{if } 10,000 < x \leq 15,000 \\ 19,500 + 1.80(x - 15,000) & \text{if } x > 15,000 \end{cases}$$

$$= \begin{cases} 1.20x & \text{if } 0 \leq x \leq 10,000 \\ 1.50x - 3000 & \text{if } 10,000 < x \leq 15,000 \\ 1.80x - 7500 & \text{if } x > 15,000 \end{cases}$$

54 The cost for 1000 kWh is $57.70 and

the cost for 5000 kWh is $57.70 + 4000(\$0.0532) = \$270.50$.

$$C(x) = \begin{cases} 0.0577x & \text{if } 0 \leq x \leq 1000 \\ 57.70 + 0.0532(x - 1000) & \text{if } 1000 < x \leq 5000 \\ 270.50 + 0.0511(x - 5000) & \text{if } x > 5000 \end{cases}$$

$$= \begin{cases} 0.0577x & \text{if } 0 \leq x \leq 1000 \\ 4.50 + 0.0532x & \text{if } 1000 < x \leq 5000 \\ 15.00 + 0.0511x & \text{if } x > 5000 \end{cases}$$

55 From a graph, we see that the solutions of $|1.3x + 2.8| = 1.2x + 5$ are approximately -3.12 and 22.00. It turns out that these are the exact solutions.

The solution is $(-3.12, 22.00)$.

56 The solutions of $|0.3x| - 2 = 2.2 - 0.63x^2$ are

approximately ± 2.35 { by symmetry }. The solution is $(-\infty, -2.35) \cup (2.35, \infty)$.

57 The solutions of $|1.2x^2 - 10.8| = 1.36x + 4.08$ are -3 and

approximately 1.87 and 4.13. The solution is $(-\infty, -3) \cup (-3, 1.87) \cup (4.13, \infty)$.

58 The solutions of $|\sqrt{16 - x^2} - 3| = 0.12x^2 - 0.3$ are approximately ± 3.60, ± 2.25

{ by symmetry }. The solution is $(-3.60, -2.25) \cup (2.25, 3.60)$.

59 Since $g(x) = f(x) + 4$, the graph of g can be obtained by shifting the graph of f upward a distance of 4.

$[-12, 12]$ by $[-8, 8]$

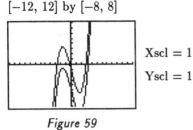

Xscl = 1

Yscl = 1

Figure 59

$[-12, 12]$ by $[-8, 8]$

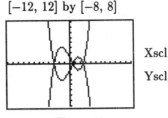

Xscl = 1

Yscl = 1

Figure 60

60 Since $g(x) = -f(x)$, the graph of g can be obtained reflecting the graph of f about the x–axis.

61 Since $g(x) = f(\frac{1}{2}x)$, the graph of g can be obtained by stretching the graph of f horizontally by a factor of 2.

$[-12, 12]$ by $[-8, 8]$

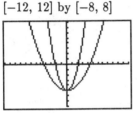

Xscl = 1

Yscl = 1

Figure 61

$[-12, 12]$ by $[-8, 8]$

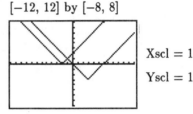

Xscl = 1

Yscl = 1

Figure 62

62 Since $g(x) = f(x - 5) - 3$, the graph of g can be obtained by shifting the graph of f horizontally to the right a distance of 5 and vertically downward a distance of 3.

63 Since $g(x) = |f(x)|$, the graph of g is the same as the graph of f if f is non-negative. If $f(x) < 0$, then the graph of f will be reflected about the x–axis.

$[-12, 12]$ by $[-8, 8]$

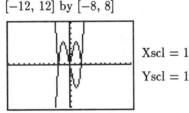

Xscl = 1

Yscl = 1

Figure 63

$[-12, 12]$ by $[-8, 8]$

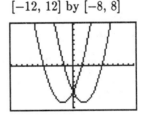

Xscl = 1

Yscl = 1

Figure 64

64 Since $g(x) = f(-x)$, the graph of g can be obtained from the graph of f by reflecting the graph of f about the y-axis.

65 (a) Option I gives $C_1 = 4(\$29.95) + \$0.25(500 - 200) = 119.80 + 75.00 = \$194.80$.

Option II gives $C_2 = 4(\$39.95) + \$0.15(500) = 159.80 + 75.00 = \$234.80$.

(b) Let x represent the mileage. The cost function for Option I is the piecewise linear function

$$C_1(x) = \begin{cases} 119.80 & \text{if } 0 \le x \le 200 \\ 119.80 + 0.25(x - 200) & \text{if } x > 200 \end{cases}$$

Option II is the linear function $C_2(x) = 159.8 + 0.15x$ for $x \ge 0$.

(c) Let $C_1 = Y_1$ and $C_2 = Y_2$.

Table $Y_1 = 119.80 + 0.25(x - 200)*(x > 200)$ and $Y_2 = 159.80 + 0.15x$

x	Y_1	Y_2	x	Y_1	Y_2
100	119.8	174.8	700	244.8	264.8
200	119.8	189.8	800	269.8	279.8
300	144.8	204.8	900	294.8	294.8
400	169.8	219.8	1000	319.8	309.8
500	194.8	234.8	1100	344.8	324.8
600	219.8	249.8	1200	369.8	339.8

(d) From the table, we see that the options are equal in cost for $x = 900$ miles. Option I is preferable if $x \in [0, 900)$ and Option II is preferable if $x > 900$.

2.3 Exercises

2.3 Concept Check

1 Does the graph of $y = 3 + 2x - x^2$ open upward or downward? • Since the coefficient of x^2, -1, is negative, the graph opens downward.

2 What is the vertex of the parabola with equation $y = -2(x + 3)^2 - 4$? Is it a minimum point or a maximum point on the parabola? • $V(-3, -4)$ is a maximum point since the graph of the parabola opens downward.

3 If the graph of a parabola has x-intercepts at $(-3, 0)$ and $(5, 0)$, what is the x-coordinate of the vertex of the parabola? • The x-coordinate of the vertex is halfway between the x-intercepts; that is, $(-3 + 5)/2 = 1$.

4 Let D denote the discriminant of the equation $f(x) = 0$, where $f(x) = ax^2 + bx + c$, and consider the graph of the parabola given by $y = f(x)$. How many x-intercepts does the graph have if $D > 0$? $D = 0$? $D < 0$? • The graph of $f(x) = ax^2 + bx + c$ has two x-intercepts if $D > 0$, one x-intercept if $D = 0$, and no x-intercepts if $D < 0$.

2.3 Exercises

1. $V(-3,\ 1) \Rightarrow y = a[x - (-3)]^2 + 1 \Rightarrow y = a(x+3)^2 + 1$

2. $V(4,\ -2) \Rightarrow y = a(x-4)^2 - 2$

3. $V(0,\ -3) \Rightarrow y = a(x-0)^2 - 3 \Rightarrow y = ax^2 - 3$

4. $V(-2,\ 0) \Rightarrow y = a[x - (-2)]^2 + 0 \Rightarrow y = a(x+2)^2$

5. $f(x) = -x^2 - 4x - 8 = -(x^2 + 4x + \underline{4}) - 8 + \underline{4} = -(x+2)^2 - 4$

6. $f(x) = x^2 - 6x + 11 = x^2 - 6x + \underline{9} + 11 - \underline{9} = (x-3)^2 + 2$

7. $f(x) = 2x^2 - 12x + 22 \Rightarrow \frac{1}{2}f(x) = x^2 - 6x + \underline{9} + 11 - \underline{9} = (x-3)^2 + 2 \Rightarrow$
$$f(x) = 2(x-3)^2 + 4$$

8. $f(x) = 5x^2 + 20x + 17 \Rightarrow \frac{1}{5}f(x) = x^2 + 4x + \underline{4} + \frac{17}{5} - \underline{4} = (x+2)^2 - \frac{3}{5} \Rightarrow$
$$f(x) = 5(x+2)^2 - 3$$

9. $f(x) = -3x^2 - 6x - 5 \Rightarrow -\frac{1}{3}f(x) = x^2 + 2x + \underline{1} + \frac{5}{3} - \underline{1} = (x+1)^2 + \frac{2}{3} \Rightarrow$
$$f(x) = -3(x+1)^2 - 2$$

10. $f(x) = -4x^2 + 16x - 13 \Rightarrow -\frac{1}{4}f(x) = x^2 - 4x + \underline{4} + \frac{13}{4} - \underline{4} = (x-2)^2 - \frac{3}{4} \Rightarrow$
$$f(x) = -4(x-2)^2 + 3$$

11. $f(x) = -\frac{3}{4}x^2 + 9x - 34 \Rightarrow -\frac{4}{3}f(x) = x^2 - 12x + \frac{136}{3} =$
$$x^2 - 12x + \underline{36} + \frac{136}{3} - \underline{36} = (x-6)^2 + \frac{28}{3} \Rightarrow f(x) = -\frac{3}{4}(x-6)^2 - 7$$

12. $f(x) = \frac{2}{5}x^2 - \frac{12}{5}x + \frac{23}{5} \Rightarrow$
$$\frac{5}{2}f(x) = x^2 - 6x + \frac{23}{2} = x^2 - 6x + \underline{9} + \frac{23}{2} - \underline{9} = (x-3)^2 + \frac{5}{2} \Rightarrow f(x) = \frac{2}{5}(x-3)^2 + 1$$

13. (a) $x^2 - 4x = 0 \Rightarrow x = \dfrac{4 \pm \sqrt{16-0}}{2} = 0,\ 4$

    (b) *Note:* Encourage students to recognize that the x-coordinate of the vertex,
$$-b/(2a),\ \text{is easily seen in part (a).}$$
$$f(x) = x^2 - 4x \Rightarrow -\frac{b}{2a} = -\frac{-4}{2(1)} = 2. \quad f(2) = -4 \text{ is a minimum since } a > 0.$$

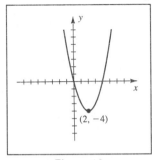

Figure 13

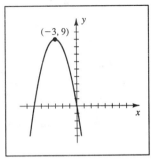

Figure 14

14. (a) $-x^2 - 6x = 0 \Rightarrow x = \dfrac{6 \pm \sqrt{36-0}}{-2} = -6,\ 0$

    (b) $f(x) = -x^2 - 6x \Rightarrow -\dfrac{b}{2a} = -\dfrac{-6}{2(-1)} = -3. \quad f(-3) = 9$ is a maximum since $a < 0$.

$\boxed{15}$ (a) $-12x^2 + 11x + 15 = 0 \Rightarrow x = \dfrac{-11 \pm \sqrt{121 + 720}}{-24} = \dfrac{-11 \pm 29}{-24} = -\dfrac{3}{4}, \dfrac{5}{3}$

(b) $f(x) = -12x^2 + 11x + 15 \Rightarrow -\dfrac{b}{2a} = -\dfrac{11}{2(-12)} = \dfrac{11}{24}.$

$f(\frac{11}{24}) = \dfrac{841}{48} \approx 17.52$ is a maximum since $a < 0$.

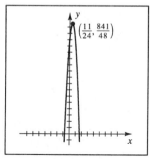

Figure 15

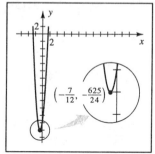

Figure 16

$\boxed{16}$ (a) $6x^2 + 7x - 24 = 0 \Rightarrow x = \dfrac{-7 \pm \sqrt{49 + 576}}{12} = \dfrac{-7 \pm 25}{12} = -\dfrac{8}{3}, \dfrac{3}{2}$

(b) $f(x) = 6x^2 + 7x - 24 \Rightarrow -\dfrac{b}{2a} = -\dfrac{7}{2(6)} = -\dfrac{7}{12}.$

$f(-\frac{7}{12}) = -\dfrac{625}{24} \approx -26.04$ is a minimum since $a > 0$.

$\boxed{17}$ (a) $9x^2 + 24x + 16 = 0 \Rightarrow x = \dfrac{-24 \pm \sqrt{576 - 576}}{18} = \dfrac{-24}{18} = -\dfrac{4}{3}$

(b) $f(x) = 9x^2 + 24x + 16 \Rightarrow -\dfrac{b}{2a} = -\dfrac{24}{2(9)} = -\dfrac{4}{3}.$

$f(-\frac{4}{3}) = 0$ is a minimum since $a > 0$.

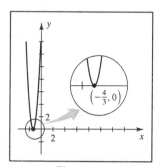

Figure 17

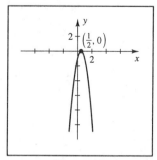

Figure 18

$\boxed{18}$ (a) $-4x^2 + 4x - 1 = 0 \Rightarrow x = \dfrac{-4 \pm \sqrt{16 - 16}}{-8} = \dfrac{-4}{-8} = \dfrac{1}{2}$

(b) $f(x) = -4x^2 + 4x - 1 \Rightarrow -\dfrac{b}{2a} = -\dfrac{4}{2(-4)} = \dfrac{1}{2}.$ $f(\frac{1}{2}) = 0$ is a maximum since $a < 0$.

19 (a) $x^2 + 4x + 9 = 0 \Rightarrow x = \dfrac{-4 \pm \sqrt{16 - 36}}{2}$. There are no x-intercepts.

(b) $f(x) = x^2 + 4x + 9 \Rightarrow -\dfrac{b}{2a} = -\dfrac{4}{2(1)} = -2$. $f(-2) = 5$ is a minimum since $a > 0$.

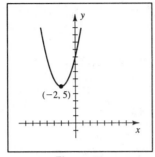

Figure 19

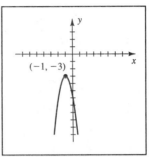

Figure 20

20 (a) $-3x^2 - 6x - 6 = 0 \Rightarrow x = \dfrac{6 \pm \sqrt{36 - 72}}{-6}$. There are no x-intercepts.

(b) $f(x) = -3x^2 - 6x - 6 \Rightarrow -\dfrac{b}{2a} = -\dfrac{-6}{2(-3)} = -1$.

$f(-1) = -3$ is a maximum since $a < 0$.

21 (a) $-2x^2 + 20x - 43 = 0 \Rightarrow x = \dfrac{-20 \pm \sqrt{400 - 344}}{-4} = 5 \pm \tfrac{1}{2}\sqrt{14} \approx 6.87, 3.13$

(b) $f(x) = -2x^2 + 20x - 43 \Rightarrow -\dfrac{b}{2a} = -\dfrac{20}{2(-2)} = 5$.

$f(5) = 7$ is a maximum since $a < 0$.

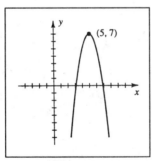

Figure 21

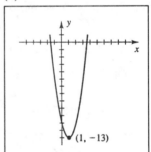

Figure 22

22 (a) $2x^2 - 4x - 11 = 0 \Rightarrow x = \dfrac{4 \pm \sqrt{16 + 88}}{4} = 1 \pm \tfrac{1}{2}\sqrt{26} \approx 3.55, -1.55$

(b) $f(x) = 2x^2 - 4x - 11 \Rightarrow -\dfrac{b}{2a} = -\dfrac{-4}{2(2)} = 1$.

$f(1) = -13$ is a minimum since $a > 0$.

23 $V(4, -1) \Rightarrow y = a(x - 4)^2 - 1$. $x = 0, y = 1 \Rightarrow 1 = a(0 - 4)^2 - 1 \Rightarrow 2 = 16a \Rightarrow a = \tfrac{1}{8}$.

Hence, $y = \tfrac{1}{8}(x - 4)^2 - 1$.

24 $V(2, 4) \Rightarrow y = a(x - 2)^2 + 4$. $x = 0, y = 0 \Rightarrow 0 = a(0 - 2)^2 + 4 \Rightarrow -4 = 4a \Rightarrow a = -1$.

Hence, $y = -(x - 2)^2 + 4$.

$\boxed{25}$ $V(-2, 4) \Rightarrow y = a(x + 2)^2 + 4$. $x = 1$, $y = 0 \Rightarrow 0 = a(1 + 2)^2 + 4 \Rightarrow -4 = 9a \Rightarrow$

$$a = -\tfrac{4}{9}. \text{ Hence, } y = -\tfrac{4}{9}(x + 2)^2 + 4.$$

$\boxed{26}$ $V(-1, -2) \Rightarrow y = a(x + 1)^2 - 2$. $x = 2$, $y = 3 \Rightarrow 3 = a(2 + 1)^2 - 2 \Rightarrow 5 = 9a \Rightarrow a = \tfrac{5}{9}$.

$$\text{Hence, } y = \tfrac{5}{9}(x + 1)^2 - 2.$$

$\boxed{27}$ $V(0, -2) \Rightarrow (h, k) = (0, -2)$. $x = 3$, $y = 25 \Rightarrow 25 = a(3 - 0)^2 - 2 \Rightarrow$

$$27 = 9a \Rightarrow a = 3. \text{ Hence, } y = 3(x - 0)^2 - 2, \text{ or } y = 3x^2 - 2.$$

$\boxed{28}$ $V(0, 5) \Rightarrow (h, k) = (0, 5)$. $x = 2$, $y = -3 \Rightarrow -3 = a(2 - 0)^2 + 5 \Rightarrow$

$$-8 = 4a \Rightarrow a = -2. \text{ Hence, } y = -2(x - 0)^2 + 5, \text{ or } y = -2x^2 + 5.$$

$\boxed{29}$ $V(3, 5) \Rightarrow y = a(x - 3)^2 + 5$. $x = 0$, $y = 0 \Rightarrow 0 = a(0 - 3)^2 + 5 \Rightarrow$

$$-5 = 9a \Rightarrow a = -\tfrac{5}{9}. \text{ Hence, } y = -\tfrac{5}{9}(x - 3)^2 + 5.$$

$\boxed{30}$ $V(4, -7) \Rightarrow y = a(x - 4)^2 - 7$. $x = -4$, $y = 0 \Rightarrow 0 = a(-4 - 4)^2 - 7 \Rightarrow$

$$7 = 64a \Rightarrow a = \tfrac{7}{64}. \text{ Hence, } y = \tfrac{7}{64}(x - 4)^2 - 7.$$

$\boxed{31}$ $V(1, 4) \Rightarrow y = a(x - 1)^2 + 4$. $x = -3$, $y = 0 \Rightarrow 0 = a(-3 - 1)^2 + 4 \Rightarrow$

$$-4 = 16a \Rightarrow a = -\tfrac{1}{4}. \text{ Hence, } y = -\tfrac{1}{4}(x - 1)^2 + 4.$$

$\boxed{32}$ $V(4, -48) \Rightarrow y = a(x - 4)^2 - 48$. $x = 0$, $y = 0 \Rightarrow 0 = a(0 - 4)^2 - 48 \Rightarrow$

$$48 = 16a \Rightarrow a = 3. \text{ Hence, } y = 3(x - 4)^2 - 48.$$

$\boxed{33}$ Let d denote the distance between the parabola and the line.

$$d = (\text{parabola}) - (\text{line}) = (-2x^2 + 4x + 3) - (x - 2) = -2x^2 + 3x + 5.$$

This relation is quadratic and the x-value of its maximum value is

$$-\frac{b}{2a} = -\frac{3}{2(-2)} = \frac{3}{4}. \text{ Thus, maximum } d = -2\left(\frac{3}{4}\right)^2 + 3\left(\frac{3}{4}\right) + 5 = \frac{49}{8} = 6.125.$$

$\boxed{34}$ As in #33, $d = (\text{line}) - (\text{parabola}) = (-x + 3) - (2x^2 + 8x + 4) = -2x^2 - 9x - 1$, and

$$-\frac{b}{2a} = -\frac{-9}{2(-2)} = -\frac{9}{4}. \text{ Thus, maximum } d = -2\left(-\frac{9}{4}\right)^2 - 9\left(-\frac{9}{4}\right) - 1 = \frac{73}{8} = 9.125.$$

Note: The applied problems can be solved using a variety of methods.

$\boxed{35}$ The vertex is located at $h = \dfrac{-b}{2a} = \dfrac{-2.867}{2(-0.058)} \approx 24.72$ km. Since $a < 0$,

$$\text{this will produce a maximum value.}$$

$\boxed{36}$ The vertex is located at $h = \dfrac{-b}{2a} = \dfrac{-3.811}{2(-0.078)} \approx 24.43$ km. Since $a < 0$,

$$\text{this will produce a maximum value.}$$

$\boxed{37}$ Since the x-intercepts are 0 and 21, the maximum will occur halfway between them,

$$\text{that is, when the infant weighs 10.5 lb.}$$

$\boxed{38}$ (a) M will be a maximum when $v = \dfrac{-b}{2a} = \dfrac{-5/2}{2(-1/30)} = \dfrac{75}{2}$, or 37.5 mi/hr.

(b) $v = \tfrac{75}{2} \Rightarrow M = -\tfrac{1}{30}\left(\tfrac{75}{2}\right)^2 + \tfrac{5}{2}\left(\tfrac{75}{2}\right) = -\tfrac{375}{8} + \tfrac{375}{4} = \tfrac{375}{8} = 46.875$ mi/gal.

39 (a) s will be a maximum when $t = \frac{-b}{2a} = \frac{-144}{2(-16)} = \frac{9}{2}$. $s\left(\frac{9}{2}\right) = 424$ ft.

(b) When $t = 0$, $s(t) = 100$ ft, which is the height of the building.

40 (a) $s = 0$ when $t = 12 \Rightarrow 0 = -16(12)^2 + v_0(12) \Rightarrow v_0 = 192$ ft/sec.

(b) Since the total flight is 12 seconds, the maximum height will occur when $t = 6$.
$$s(6) = -16(6)^2 + 192(6) = 576 \text{ ft.}$$

41 Let x and $40 - x$ denote the numbers, and their product P is $x(40 - x)$.

P has zeros at 0 and 40 and is a maximum (since $a < 0$) when $x = \frac{0 + 40}{2} = 20$.

The product will be a maximum when both numbers are 20.

42 Let x and $x - 40$ denote the numbers, and their product P is $x(x - 40)$.

P has zeros at 0 and 40 and is a minimum (since $a > 0$) when $x = \frac{0 + 40}{2} = 20$.

The product will be a minimum for $x = 20$ and $x - 40 = -20$.

43 (a) Perimeter $= 1000 \Rightarrow 3x + 4y = 1000 \Rightarrow y = 250 - \frac{3}{4}x$

(b) $A = xy = x\left(250 - \frac{3}{4}x\right) = -\frac{3}{4}x^2 + 250x$

(c) A will be a maximum when $x = \frac{-b}{2a} = \frac{-250}{2(-3/4)} = \frac{500}{3} = 166\frac{2}{3}$ ft.
$$y = 250 - \frac{3}{4}\left(\frac{500}{3}\right) = 125 \text{ ft.}$$

44 Represent the perimeter of the field by $2y + 4x = 1000$. $A = xy = x(500 - 2x)$.

A has zeros at 0 and 250 and will be a maximum when $x = \frac{0 + 250}{2} = 125$ yd.

$y = 500 - 2(125) = 250$ yd. The dimensions should be

125 yd by 250 yd with intermediate fences parallel to the short side.

45 The parabola has vertex $V\left(\frac{9}{2}, 3\right)$. Hence, the equation has the form $y = a\left(x - \frac{9}{2}\right)^2 + 3$.

Using the point $(9, 0)$ { or $(0, 0)$ }, we have $0 = a\left(9 - \frac{9}{2}\right)^2 + 3 \Rightarrow a = -\frac{4}{27}$.

Thus, the path may be described by $y = -\frac{4}{27}\left(x - \frac{9}{2}\right)^2 + 3$.

46 (a) Since $(0, 15)$ is on the graph, $c = 15$. Substituting $(175, 0)$ for (x, y) yields
$$0 = a(175)^2 + 175 + 15 \Rightarrow a = -\frac{190}{175^2} \text{ and } y = -\frac{190}{175^2}x^2 + x + 15.$$

(b) y will be a maximum when $x = \frac{-b}{2a} = \frac{-1}{2(-190/175^2)} = \frac{175^2}{380} \approx 80.59$.

The corresponding y-value is $\frac{8405}{152} \approx 55.3$ ft.

47 (a) Since the vertex is at $(0, 10)$, an equation for the parabola is $y = ax^2 + 10$.

Substituting $(200, 90)$ for (x, y) yields $a = \frac{1}{500}$ and $y = \frac{1}{500}x^2 + 10$.

(b) The cables are spaced 40 ft apart. Letting $x = 40, 80, 120$, and 160 gives us a

total length of $10 + 2\left(\frac{66}{5} + \frac{114}{5} + \frac{194}{5} + \frac{306}{5}\right) = 282$ ft.

48 (a) Substituting $x = 0$ and $m = 0$ into $m = 2ax + b$ yields $b = 0$.

Substituting $x = 800$ and $m = \frac{1}{5}$ into $m = 2ax$ yields $a = \frac{1}{8000}$, hence, $y = \frac{1}{8000}x^2$.

(b) Substitute $x = 800$ into $y = \frac{1}{8000}x^2$ to get $y = 80$. Thus, $B = (800, 80)$.

49 An equation describing the doorway is $y = ax^2 + 9$. Since the doorway is 6 feet wide at the base, $x = 3$ when $y = 0 \Rightarrow 0 = 9a + 9 \Rightarrow a = -1$. Thus, the equation is $y = -x^2 + 9$. To fit an 8 foot high box through the doorway, we must find x when $y = 8$. $y = 8 \Rightarrow 8 = -x^2 + 9 \Rightarrow x = \pm 1$. Hence, the box can only be 2 feet wide.

50 (a) $P = 24 \Rightarrow 2x + 2y = 24 \Rightarrow y = 12 - x$

   (b) $A = xy = x(12 - x)$

   (c) A is zero at 0 and 12 and will be a maximum when $x = \frac{0 + 12}{2} = 6$.

   Thus, the maximum value of A occurs if the rectangle is a square.

51 Let x denote the number of pairs of shoes that are ordered.

$$A(x) = \begin{cases} 40x & \text{if } x < 50 \\ (40 - 0.04x)x & \text{if } 50 \le x \le 600 \end{cases}$$

The maximum value of the first part of A is $(\$40)(49) = \$1960$. For the second part of A, $A = -0.04x^2 + 40x$ has a maximum when $x = \frac{-b}{2a} = \frac{-40}{2(-0.04)} = 500$ pairs.

$A(500) = 10{,}000 > 1960$, so $x = 500$ produces a maximum for both parts of A.

52 Let x denote the number of people in the group. The discount per person is $0.50(x - 30)$. The amount of money taken in by the agency may be expressed as:

$$A(x) = \begin{cases} 60x & \text{if } x \le 30 \\ [60 - 0.50(x - 30)]x & \text{if } 30 < x \le 90 \end{cases}$$

The maximum value of the first part of A is $(\$60)(30) = \$1800$. For the second part of A, $A = (75 - \frac{1}{2}x)x$ has a maximum when $x = 75$ { the x-intercepts are 0 and 150 }. This value corresponds to each person receiving a discount of $22.50 and hence, paying $37.50 for the tour. $A(75) = 2812.50 > 1800$, so $x = 75$ produces a maximum for both parts of A.

53 (a) Let y denote the number of $1 decreases in the monthly charge.

$R(y)$ = (# of customers)(monthly charge per customer)

   $= (5000 + 500y)(20 - y)$

   $= 500(10 + y)(20 - y)$

   Now let x denote the monthly charge, which is $20 - y$. R becomes $500[10 + (20 - x)](x) = 500x(30 - x)$.

   (b) R has x-intercepts at 0 and 30, and must have its vertex halfway between them at $x = 15$.

   Note that this gives us $y = 5$, and we have 7500 customers for a revenue of $112,500.

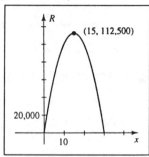

Figure 53

54 Let x denote the number of $10 increases in rent and $M(x)$ the monthly income. The number of occupied apartments is $180 - 5x$ and the rent per apartment is $300 + 10x$. $M(x) = (\text{\# of occupied apartments})(\text{rent per apartment}) = (180 - 5x)(300 + 10x) = 5 \cdot 10(36 - x)(30 + x)$. The x-intercepts of M are -30 and 36.

Hence, the maximum of M will occur when $x = \frac{-30 + 36}{2} = 3$.

The rent charged should be $300 + \$10(3) = \$330$.

55 From the graph, there are three points of intersection.

Their coordinates are approximately $(-0.57, 0.64)$, $(0.02, -0.27)$, and $(0.81, -0.41)$.

[−3, 3] by [−2, 2]

[−6, 6] by [−4, 4]

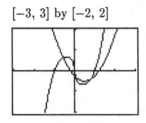

Xscl = 1
Yscl = 1

Figure 55

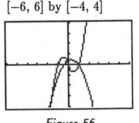

Xscl = 1
Yscl = 1

Figure 56

56 From the graph, there are three points of intersection.

Their coordinates are approximately $(-1.61, -2.99)$, $(-0.05, 0.37)$, and $(0.98, -0.06)$.

57 Since $a > 0$, all parabolas open upward. From the graph, we can see that smaller values of a result in the parabola opening wider while larger values of a result in the parabola becoming narrower.

[−8, 4] by [−1, 7]

[−6, 6] by [−2, 6]

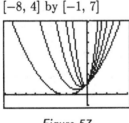

Xscl = 1
Yscl = 1

Figure 57

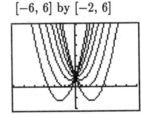

Xscl = 1
Yscl = 1

Figure 58

58 As $|b|$ increases, the graph of each parabola shifts downward. Negative values of b shift the parabola to the right while positive values of b shift the parabola to the left.

59 (a) Let January correspond to 1, February to 2, ..., and December to 12.

[0.5, 12] by [0, 8]

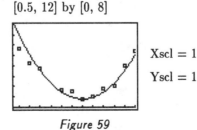

Xscl = 1
Yscl = 1

Figure 59

(b) Let $f(x) = a(x-h)^2 + k$. The vertex appears to occur near $(7, 0.8)$ Thus, $h = 7$ and $k = 0.8$. Using trial and error, a reasonable value for a is 0.17. Thus, let $f(x) = 0.17(x-7)^2 + 0.8$.

(c) $f(4) = 2.33$, compared to the actual value of 2.4 in.

60 (a) Overall, the data decreases slightly and then starts to increase, although there is an unexpected decrease in 1987.

[1980, 1995] by [5, 15]

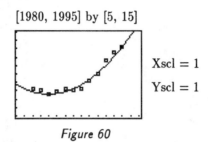

Xscl = 1

Yscl = 1

Figure 60

(b) Start by choosing a vertex. The lowest data point is $(1984, 7.6)$, so let $h = 1984$ and $k = 7.6$ in the equation $f(x) = a(x-h)^2 + k$. Choosing one more point will determine the parabola.

$$f(1993) = 13.3 \Rightarrow 13.3 = a(1993 - 1984)^2 + 7.6 \Rightarrow a \approx 0.07.$$

Let $f(x) = 0.07(x - 1984)^2 + 7.6$. f can be adjusted to give a slightly better fit.

61 (a) The equation of the line passing through $A(-800, -48)$ and $B(-500, 0)$ is $y = \frac{4}{25}x + 80$. The equation of the line passing through $D(500, 0)$ and $E(800, -48)$ is $y = -\frac{4}{25}x + 80$. Let $y = a(x - h)^2 + k$ be the equation of the parabola passing through the points $B(-500, 0)$, $C(0, 40)$, and $D(500, 0)$. The vertex is located at $(0, 40)$ so $y = a(x - 0)^2 + 40$. Since $D(500, 0)$ is on the graph, $0 = a(500 - 0)^2 + 40 \Rightarrow a = -\frac{1}{6250}$ and $y = -\frac{1}{6250}x^2 + 40$. Thus, let

$$f(x) = \begin{cases} \frac{4}{25}x + 80 & \text{if } -800 \le x < -500 \\ -\frac{1}{6250}x^2 + 40 & \text{if } -500 \le x \le 500 \\ -\frac{4}{25}x + 80 & \text{if } 500 < x \le 800 \end{cases}$$

(b) Graph the equations:

$$Y_1 = (4/25*x + 80)/(x < -500),$$
$$Y_2 = (-1/6250*x^2 + 40)/(x \ge -500 \text{ and } x \le 500),$$
$$Y_3 = (-4/25*x + 80)/(x > 500)$$

[−800, 800] by [−100, 200]

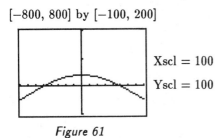

Xscl = 100

Yscl = 100

[−500, 2000] by [0, 800]

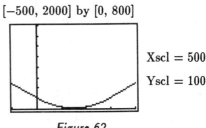

Xscl = 500

Yscl = 100

Figure 61

Figure 62

62 (a) The equation of the line passing through $A(-500, 243\frac{1}{3})$ and $B(0, 110)$ is $y = -\frac{4}{15}x + 110$. The equation of the line passing through $D(1500, 110)$ and $E(2000, 243\frac{1}{3})$ is $y = \frac{4}{15}x - 290$. Let $y = a(x-h)^2 + k$ be the equation of the parabola passing through the points $B(0, 110)$, $C(750, 10)$, and $D(1500, 110)$. The vertex is located at $(750, 10)$ so $y = a(x - 750)^2 + 10$. Since $D(1500, 110)$ is on the graph, $110 = a(1500 - 750)^2 + 10 \Rightarrow a = \frac{1}{5625}$; $y = \frac{1}{5625}(x - 750)^2 + 10$. Thus, let

$$f(x) = \begin{cases} -\frac{4}{15}x + 110 & \text{if } -500 \le x < 0 \\ \frac{1}{5625}(x - 750)^2 + 10 & \text{if } 0 \le x \le 1500 \\ \frac{4}{15}x - 290 & \text{if } 1500 < x \le 2000 \end{cases}$$

(b) Graph the equations:
$$Y_1 = (-4/15*x + 110)/(x < 0),$$
$$Y_2 = (1/5625*(x - 750)\hat{\ }2 + 10)/(x \ge 0 \text{ and } x \le 1500),$$
$$Y_3 = (4/15*x - 290)/(x > 1500)$$

63 (a) f must have zeros of 0 and 150. Thus, $f(x) = a(x - 0)(x - 150)$. Also, f will have a maximum of 100 occurring at $x = 75$. (The vertex will be midway between the zeros of f.) $a(75 - 0)(75 - 150) = 100 \Rightarrow a = \frac{100}{(75)(-75)} = -\frac{4}{225}$. $f(x) = -\frac{4}{225}(x)(x - 150) = -\frac{4}{225}x^2 + \frac{8}{3}x$.

(c) The value of k affects both the distance and the height traveled by the object. The distance and height decrease by a factor of $\frac{1}{k}$ when $k > 1$ and increase by a factor of $\frac{1}{k}$ when $0 < k < 1$.

[0, 180] by [0, 120]

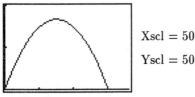

Xscl = 50

Yscl = 50

[0, 600] by [0, 400]

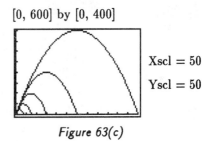

Xscl = 50

Yscl = 50

Figure 63(b)

Figure 63(c)

2.4 Exercises

| 2.4 Concept Check |

1 For the functions f and g, what is the domain of the sum $f + g$?   the difference $f - g$? the product fg? the quotient f/g?   • The domains of $f + g$, $f - g$, and fg are the intersection I of the domains of f and g. The domain of f/g is I excluding the zeros of g.

2 For the functions f and g, what is the domain of the composite function $(f \circ g)(x)$?   • The domain of $f \circ g$ is the set of all x in the domain of g such that $g(x)$ is in the domain of f.

3 Give a simple definition of a composite function.   • A composite function is a function of a function or it is a function of another function's values.

4 If $f(x) = -3x$ and $g(x) = \sqrt{x}$, what is $f(g(-2))$? What is $g(f(2))$?   • $f(g(-2))$ is not defined since -2 is not in the domain of g. $f(2) = -3(2) = -6$, but $g(f(2)) = g(-6)$ is not defined since -6 is not in the domain of g.

| 2.4 Exercises |

1 (a) $(f + g)(3) = f(3) + g(3) = 6 + 9 = 15$ (b) $(f - g)(3) = f(3) - g(3) = 6 - 9 = -3$
   (c) $(fg)(3) = f(3) \cdot g(3) = 6 \cdot 9 = 54$ (d) $(f/g)(3) = f(3)/g(3) = 6/9 = \frac{2}{3}$

2 (a) $(f + g)(3) = f(3) + g(3) = -9 + 5 = -4$
   (b) $(f - g)(3) = f(3) - g(3) = -9 - 5 = -14$
   (c) $(fg)(3) = f(3) \cdot g(3) = -9 \cdot 5 = -45$ (d) $(f/g)(3) = f(3)/g(3) = -9/5 = -\frac{9}{5}$

3 (a) $(f + g)(x) = f(x) + g(x) = (x^2 + 2) + (2x^2 - 1) = 3x^2 + 1$;
   $(f - g)(x) = f(x) - g(x) = (x^2 + 2) - (2x^2 - 1) = 3 - x^2$;
   $(fg)(x) = f(x) \cdot g(x) = (x^2 + 2) \cdot (2x^2 - 1) = 2x^4 + 3x^2 - 2$;
   $\left(\dfrac{f}{g}\right)(x) = \dfrac{f(x)}{g(x)} = \dfrac{x^2 + 2}{2x^2 - 1}$

   (b) The domain of $f + g$, $f - g$, and fg is the set of all real numbers, $\mathbb{R}$.

   (c) The domain of f/g is the same as in (b), except we must exclude the zeros of g.
   Hence, the domain of f/g is all real numbers except $\pm\frac{1}{2}\sqrt{2}$.

4 (a) $(f + g)(x) = f(x) + g(x) = (x^2 + x) + (x^2 - 3) = 2x^2 + x - 3$;
   $(f - g)(x) = f(x) - g(x) = (x^2 + x) - (x^2 - 3) = x + 3$;
   $(fg)(x) = f(x) \cdot g(x) = (x^2 + x) \cdot (x^2 - 3) = x^4 + x^3 - 3x^2 - 3x$;
   $\left(\dfrac{f}{g}\right)(x) = \dfrac{f(x)}{g(x)} = \dfrac{x^2 + x}{x^2 - 3}$

   (b) $\mathbb{R}$ (c) All real numbers except $\pm\sqrt{3}$

$\boxed{5}$ (a) $(f+g)(x) = f(x) + g(x) = \sqrt{x+5} + \sqrt{x+5} = 2\sqrt{x+5}$;

$(f-g)(x) = f(x) - g(x) = \sqrt{x+5} - \sqrt{x+5} = 0$;

$(fg)(x) = f(x) \cdot g(x) = \sqrt{x+5} \cdot \sqrt{x+5} = x+5$; $\left(\dfrac{f}{g}\right)(x) = \dfrac{f(x)}{g(x)} = \dfrac{\sqrt{x+5}}{\sqrt{x+5}} = 1$

(b) $[-5, \infty)$ (c) $(-5, \infty)$

$\boxed{6}$ (a) $(f+g)(x) = f(x) + g(x) = \sqrt{3-2x} + \sqrt{x+4}$;

$(f-g)(x) = f(x) - g(x) = \sqrt{3-2x} - \sqrt{x+4}$;

$(fg)(x) = f(x) \cdot g(x) = \sqrt{3-2x} \cdot \sqrt{x+4} = \sqrt{(3-2x)(x+4)}$;

$\left(\dfrac{f}{g}\right)(x) = \dfrac{f(x)}{g(x)} = \dfrac{\sqrt{3-2x}}{\sqrt{x+4}} = \sqrt{\dfrac{3-2x}{x+4}}$

(b) $[-4, \frac{3}{2}]$ (c) $(-4, \frac{3}{2}]$

$\boxed{7}$ (a) $(f+g)(x) = f(x) + g(x) = \dfrac{2x}{x-4} + \dfrac{x}{x+5} = \dfrac{2x(x+5) + x(x-4)}{(x-4)(x+5)} = \dfrac{3x^2 + 6x}{(x-4)(x+5)}$;

$(f-g)(x) = f(x) - g(x) = \dfrac{2x}{x-4} - \dfrac{x}{x+5} = \dfrac{2x(x+5) - x(x-4)}{(x-4)(x+5)} = \dfrac{x^2 + 14x}{(x-4)(x+5)}$;

$(fg)(x) = f(x) \cdot g(x) = \dfrac{2x}{x-4} \cdot \dfrac{x}{x+5} = \dfrac{2x^2}{(x-4)(x+5)}$;

$\left(\dfrac{f}{g}\right)(x) = \dfrac{f(x)}{g(x)} = \dfrac{2x/(x-4)}{x/(x+5)} = \dfrac{2(x+5)}{x-4}$

(b) All real numbers except -5 and 4 (c) All real numbers except -5, 0, and 4

$\boxed{8}$ (a) $(f+g)(x) = f(x) + g(x) = \dfrac{x}{x-2} + \dfrac{3x}{x+4} = \dfrac{x(x+4) + 3x(x-2)}{(x-2)(x+4)} = \dfrac{4x^2 - 2x}{(x-2)(x+4)}$;

$(f-g)(x) = f(x) - g(x) = \dfrac{x}{x-2} - \dfrac{3x}{x+4} = \dfrac{x(x+4) - 3x(x-2)}{(x-2)(x+4)} = \dfrac{-2x^2 + 10x}{(x-2)(x+4)}$;

$(fg)(x) = f(x) \cdot g(x) = \dfrac{x}{x-2} \cdot \dfrac{3x}{x+4} = \dfrac{3x^2}{(x-2)(x+4)}$;

$\left(\dfrac{f}{g}\right)(x) = \dfrac{f(x)}{g(x)} = \dfrac{x/(x-2)}{3x/(x+4)} = \dfrac{x+4}{3(x-2)}$

(b) All real numbers except -4 and 2 (c) All real numbers except -4, 0, and 2

$\boxed{9}$ (a) $(f \circ g)(x) = f(g(x)) = f(-x^2) = 2(-x^2) - 1 = -2x^2 - 1$

(b) $(g \circ f)(x) = g(f(x)) = g(2x-1) = -(2x-1)^2 = -(4x^2 - 4x + 1) = -4x^2 + 4x - 1$

(c) $(f \circ f)(x) = f(f(x)) = f(2x-1) = 2(2x-1) - 1 = (4x-2) - 1 = 4x - 3$

(d) $(g \circ g)(x) = g(g(x)) = g(-x^2) = -(-x^2)^2 = -(x^4) = -x^4$

$\boxed{10}$ (a) $(f \circ g)(x) = f(g(x)) = f(x-1) = 3(x-1)^2 = 3(x^2 - 2x + 1) = 3x^2 - 6x + 3$

(b) $(g \circ f)(x) = g(f(x)) = g(3x^2) = (3x^2) - 1 = 3x^2 - 1$

(c) $(f \circ f)(x) = f(f(x)) = f(3x^2) = 3(3x^2)^2 = 3(9x^4) = 27x^4$

(d) $(g \circ g)(x) = g(g(x)) = g(x-1) = (x-1) - 1 = x - 2$

Note: Let $h(x) = (f \circ g)(x) = f(g(x))$ and $k(x) = (g \circ f)(x) = g(f(x))$.

$h(-2)$ and $k(3)$ could be worked two ways, as in Example 3 in the text.

$\boxed{11}$ (a) $h(x) = f(3x + 7) = 2(3x + 7) - 5 = 6x + 9$

(b) $k(x) = g(2x - 5) = 3(2x - 5) + 7 = 6x - 8$

(c) Using the result from part (a), $h(-2) = 6(-2) + 9 = -12 + 9 = -3$.

(d) Using the result from part (b), $k(3) = 6(3) - 8 = 18 - 8 = 10$.

$\boxed{12}$ (a) $h(x) = f(6x - 1) = 5(6x - 1) + 2 = 30x - 3$

(b) $k(x) = g(5x + 2) = 6(5x + 2) - 1 = 30x + 11$

(c) Using the result from part (a), $h(-2) = 30(-2) - 3 = -60 - 3 = -63$.

(d) Using the result from part (b), $k(3) = 30(3) + 11 = 90 + 11 = 101$.

$\boxed{13}$ (a) $h(x) = f(5x) = 3(5x)^2 + 4 = 75x^2 + 4$

(b) $k(x) = g(3x^2 + 4) = 5(3x^2 + 4) = 15x^2 + 20$

(c) $h(-2) = 75(-2)^2 + 4 = 300 + 4 = 304$

(d) $k(3) = 15(3)^2 + 20 = 135 + 20 = 155$

$\boxed{14}$ (a) $h(x) = f(4x^2) = 3(4x^2) - 1 = 12x^2 - 1$

(b) $k(x) = g(3x - 1) = 4(3x - 1)^2 = 4(9x^2 - 6x + 1) = 36x^2 - 24x + 4$

(c) $h(-2) = 12(-2)^2 - 1 = 48 - 1 = 47$

(d) $k(3) = 36(3)^2 - 24(3) + 4 = 324 - 72 + 4 = 256$

$\boxed{15}$ (a) $h(x) = f(2x - 1) = 2(2x - 1)^2 + 3(2x - 1) - 4 = 8x^2 - 2x - 5$

(b) $k(x) = g(2x^2 + 3x - 4) = 2(2x^2 + 3x - 4) - 1 = 4x^2 + 6x - 9$

(c) $h(-2) = 8(-2)^2 - 2(-2) - 5 = 32 + 4 - 5 = 31$

(d) $k(3) = 4(3)^2 + 6(3) - 9 = 36 + 18 - 9 = 45$

$\boxed{16}$ (a) $h(x) = f(3x^2 - x + 2) = 5(3x^2 - x + 2) - 7 = 15x^2 - 5x + 3$

(b) $k(x) = g(5x - 7) = 3(5x - 7)^2 - (5x - 7) + 2 = 75x^2 - 215x + 156$

(c) $h(-2) = 15(-2)^2 - 5(-2) + 3 = 60 + 10 + 3 = 73$

(d) $k(3) = 75(3)^2 - 215(3) + 156 = 675 - 645 + 156 = 186$

$\boxed{17}$ (a) $h(x) = f(2x^3 - 5x) = 4(2x^3 - 5x) = 8x^3 - 20x$

(b) $k(x) = g(4x) = 2(4x)^3 - 5(4x) = 128x^3 - 20x$

(c) $h(-2) = 8(-2)^3 - 20(-2) = -64 + 40 = -24$

(d) $k(3) = 128(3)^3 - 20(3) = 3456 - 60 = 3396$

$\boxed{18}$ (a) $h(x) = f(3x) = (3x)^3 + 2(3x)^2 = 27x^3 + 18x^2$

(b) $k(x) = g(x^3 + 2x^2) = 3(x^3 + 2x^2) = 3x^3 + 6x^2$

(c) $h(-2) = 27(-2)^3 + 18(-2)^2 = -216 + 72 = -144$

(d) $k(3) = 3(3)^3 + 6(3)^2 = 81 + 54 = 135$

$\boxed{19}$ (a) $h(x) = f(-7) = |-7| = 7$ (b) $k(x) = g(|x|) = -7$

(c) $h(-2) = 7$ since $h(\text{any value}) = 7$ (d) $k(3) = -7$ since $k(\text{any value}) = -7$

$\boxed{20}$ (a) $h(x) = f(x^2) = 5$ (b) $k(x) = g(5) = (5)^2 = 25$

(c) $h(-2) = 5$ since $h(\text{any value}) = 5$ (d) $k(3) = 25$ since $k(\text{any value}) = 25$

$\boxed{21}$ (a) $h(x) = f(\sqrt{x+2}) = (\sqrt{x+2})^2 - 3(\sqrt{x+2}) = x + 2 - 3\sqrt{x+2}$. The domain of

$f \circ g$ is the set of all x in the domain of g, $x \geq -2$, such that $g(x)$ is in the

domain of f. Since the domain of f is $\mathbb{R}$, any value of $g(x)$ is in its domain.

Thus, the domain is all x such that $x \geq -2$.

(b) $k(x) = g(x^2 - 3x) = \sqrt{(x^2 - 3x) + 2} = \sqrt{x^2 - 3x + 2}$. The domain of $g \circ f$ is the

set of all x in the domain of f, $\mathbb{R}$, such that $f(x)$ is in the domain of g.

Since the domain of g is $x \geq -2$, we must solve $f(x) \geq -2$. $x^2 - 3x \geq -2 \Rightarrow$

$x^2 - 3x + 2 \geq 0 \Rightarrow (x-1)(x-2) \geq 0 \Rightarrow x \in (-\infty, 1] \cup [2, \infty)$ { use a sign

diagram }. Thus, the domain is all x such that $x \in (-\infty, 1] \cup [2, \infty)$.

$\boxed{22}$ (a) $h(x) = f(x^2 + 2x) = \sqrt{(x^2 + 2x) - 15} = \sqrt{x^2 + 2x - 15}$.

Domain of $g = \mathbb{R}$. Domain of $f = [15, \infty)$. $g(x) \geq 15 \Rightarrow x^2 + 2x \geq 15 \Rightarrow$

$x^2 + 2x - 15 \geq 0 \Rightarrow (x+5)(x-3) \geq 0 \Rightarrow x \in (-\infty, -5] \cup [3, \infty)$.

(b) $k(x) = g(\sqrt{x-15}) = (\sqrt{x-15})^2 + 2(\sqrt{x-15}) = x - 15 + 2\sqrt{x-15}$.

Domain of $f = [15, \infty)$. Domain of $g = \mathbb{R}$. Since $f(x)$ is always in the domain

of g, the domain of $g \circ f$ is the same as the domain of f, $[15, \infty)$.

$\boxed{23}$ (a) $h(x) = f(\sqrt{3x}) = (\sqrt{3x})^2 - 4 = 3x - 4$.

Domain of $g = [0, \infty)$. Domain of $f = \mathbb{R}$. Since $g(x)$ is always in the domain of

f, the domain of $f \circ g$ is the same as the domain of g, $[0, \infty)$.

(b) $k(x) = g(x^2 - 4) = \sqrt{3(x^2 - 4)} = \sqrt{3x^2 - 12}$.

Domain of $f = \mathbb{R}$. Domain of $g = [0, \infty)$.

$f(x) \geq 0 \Rightarrow x^2 - 4 \geq 0 \Rightarrow x^2 \geq 4 \Rightarrow |x| \geq 2 \Rightarrow x \in (-\infty, -2] \cup [2, \infty)$.

$\boxed{24}$ (a) $h(x) = f(\sqrt{x}) = -(\sqrt{x})^2 + 1 = -x + 1$.

Domain of $g = [0, \infty)$. Domain of $f = \mathbb{R}$. Since $g(x)$ is always in the domain of

f, the domain of $f \circ g$ is the same as the domain of g, $[0, \infty)$.

(b) $k(x) = g(-x^2 + 1) = \sqrt{-x^2 + 1}$. Domain of $f = \mathbb{R}$. Domain of $g = [0, \infty)$.

$f(x) \geq 0 \Rightarrow -x^2 + 1 \geq 0 \Rightarrow x^2 \leq 1 \Rightarrow |x| \leq 1 \Rightarrow x \in [-1, 1]$.

$\boxed{25}$ (a) $h(x) = f(\sqrt{x+5}) = \sqrt{\sqrt{x+5} - 2}$. Domain of $g = [-5, \infty)$. Domain of

$f = [2, \infty)$. $g(x) \geq 2 \Rightarrow \sqrt{x+5} \geq 2 \Rightarrow x + 5 \geq 4 \Rightarrow x \geq -1$ or $x \in [-1, \infty)$.

(b) $k(x) = g(\sqrt{x-2}) = \sqrt{\sqrt{x-2} + 5}$. Domain of $f = [2, \infty)$.

Domain of $g = [-5, \infty)$. $f(x) \geq -5 \Rightarrow \sqrt{x-2} \geq -5$. This is always true since

the result of a square root is nonnegative. The domain is $[2, \infty)$.

$\boxed{26}$ (a) $h(x) = f(\sqrt{x+2}) = \sqrt{3 - \sqrt{x+2}}$. Domain of $g = [-2, \infty)$.

Domain of $f = (-\infty, 3]$. $g(x) \le 3 \Rightarrow \sqrt{x+2} \le 3 \Rightarrow x + 2 \le 9 \Rightarrow x \le 7$.

We must remember that $x \ge -2$, hence, $-2 \le x \le 7$.

(b) $k(x) = g(\sqrt{3-x}) = \sqrt{\sqrt{3-x} + 2}$. Domain of $f = (-\infty, 3]$.

Domain of $g = [-2, \infty)$. $f(x) \ge -2 \Rightarrow \sqrt{3-x} \ge -2$. This is always true since

the result of a square root is nonnegative. The domain is $(-\infty, 3]$.

$\boxed{27}$ (a) $h(x) = f(\sqrt{x^2 - 16}) = \sqrt{3 - \sqrt{x^2 - 16}}$. Domain of $g = (-\infty, -4] \cup [4, \infty)$.

Domain of $f = (-\infty, 3]$. $g(x) \le 3 \Rightarrow \sqrt{x^2 - 16} \le 3 \Rightarrow x^2 - 16 \le 9 \Rightarrow x^2 \le 25 \Rightarrow$

$x \in [-5, 5]$. But $|x| \ge 4$ from the domain of g.

Hence, the domain of $f \circ g$ is $[-5, -4] \cup [4, 5]$.

(b) $k(x) = g(\sqrt{3-x}) = \sqrt{(\sqrt{3-x})^2 - 16} = \sqrt{3 - x - 16} = \sqrt{-x - 13}$.

Domain of $f = (-\infty, 3]$. Domain of $g = (-\infty, -4] \cup [4, \infty)$.

$f(x) \ge 4$ $\{f(x)$ cannot be less than $0\}$ $\Rightarrow \sqrt{3-x} \ge 4 \Rightarrow 3 - x \ge 16 \Rightarrow x \le -13$.

$\boxed{28}$ (a) $h(x) = f(\sqrt[3]{x-5}) = (\sqrt[3]{x-5})^3 + 5 = x - 5 + 5 = x$.

Domain of $g = \mathbb{R}$. Domain of $f = \mathbb{R}$. All values of $g(x)$ are in the domain of f.

Hence, the domain of $f \circ g$ is $\mathbb{R}$.

(b) $k(x) = g(x^3 + 5) = \sqrt[3]{(x^3 + 5) - 5} = \sqrt[3]{x^3} = x$.

Domain of $f = \mathbb{R}$. Domain of $g = \mathbb{R}$. All values of $f(x)$ are in the domain of g.

Hence, the domain of $g \circ f$ is $\mathbb{R}$.

$\boxed{29}$ (a) $h(x) = f\left(\dfrac{2x - 5}{3}\right) = \dfrac{3\left(\dfrac{2x-5}{3}\right) + 5}{2} = \dfrac{2x - 5 + 5}{2} = \dfrac{2x}{2} = x$.

Domain of $g = \mathbb{R}$. Domain of $f = \mathbb{R}$. All values of $g(x)$ are in the domain of f.

Hence, the domain of $f \circ g$ is $\mathbb{R}$.

(b) $k(x) = g\left(\dfrac{3x + 5}{2}\right) = \dfrac{2\left(\dfrac{3x+5}{2}\right) - 5}{3} = \dfrac{3x + 5 - 5}{3} = \dfrac{3x}{3} = x$.

Domain of $f = \mathbb{R}$. Domain of $g = \mathbb{R}$. All values of $f(x)$ are in the domain of g.

Hence, the domain of $g \circ f$ is $\mathbb{R}$.

$\boxed{30}$ (a) $h(x) = f(x - 1) = \dfrac{1}{(x-1) - 1} = \dfrac{1}{x - 2}$. Domain of $g = \mathbb{R}$. Domain of $f = \mathbb{R} - \{1\}$.

$g(x) \ne 1 \Rightarrow x - 1 \ne 1 \Rightarrow x \ne 2$. Hence, the domain of $f \circ g$ is $\mathbb{R} - \{2\}$.

(b) $k(x) = g\left(\dfrac{1}{x-1}\right) = \dfrac{1}{x-1} - 1 = \dfrac{1 - (x-1)}{x - 1} = \dfrac{2 - x}{x - 1}$.

Domain of $f = \mathbb{R} - \{1\}$. Domain of $g = \mathbb{R}$.

All values of $f(x)$ are in the domain of g. The domain of $g \circ f$ is $\mathbb{R} - \{1\}$.

31 (a) $h(x) = f\left(\frac{1}{x^3}\right) = \left(\frac{1}{x^3}\right)^2 = \frac{1}{x^6}$. Domain of $g = \mathbb{R} - \{0\}$. Domain of $f = \mathbb{R}$.

All values of $g(x)$ are in the domain of f. Hence, the domain of $f \circ g$ is $\mathbb{R} - \{0\}$.

(b) $k(x) = g(x^2) = \frac{1}{(x^2)^3} = \frac{1}{x^6}$. Domain of $f = \mathbb{R}$. Domain of $g = \mathbb{R} - \{0\}$.

All values of $f(x)$ are in the domain of g except for 0.

Since f is 0 when x is 0, the domain of $f \circ g$ is $\mathbb{R} - \{0\}$.

32 (a) $h(x) = f\left(\frac{3}{x}\right) = \frac{3/x}{(3/x) - 2} \cdot \frac{x}{x} = \frac{3}{3 - 2x}$.

Domain of $g = \mathbb{R} - \{0\}$. Domain of $f = \mathbb{R} - \{2\}$.

$g(x) \neq 2 \Rightarrow \frac{3}{x} \neq 2 \Rightarrow x \neq \frac{3}{2}$. Hence, the domain of $f \circ g$ is $\mathbb{R} - \{0, \frac{3}{2}\}$.

(b) $k(x) = g\left(\frac{x}{x - 2}\right) = \frac{3}{x/(x - 2)} = \frac{3x - 6}{x}$.

Domain of $f = \mathbb{R} - \{2\}$. Domain of $g = \mathbb{R} - \{0\}$.

$f(x) \neq 0 \Rightarrow \frac{x}{x - 2} \neq 0 \Rightarrow x \neq 0$. Hence, the domain of $g \circ f$ is $\mathbb{R} - \{0, 2\}$.

33 (a) $h(x) = f\left(\frac{x - 3}{x - 4}\right) = \dfrac{\frac{x - 3}{x - 4} - 1}{\frac{x - 3}{x - 4} - 2} \cdot \frac{x - 4}{x - 4} = \frac{x - 3 - 1(x - 4)}{x - 3 - 2(x - 4)} = \frac{1}{5 - x}$.

Domain of $g = \mathbb{R} - \{4\}$. Domain of $f = \mathbb{R} - \{2\}$.

$g(x) \neq 2 \Rightarrow \frac{x - 3}{x - 4} \neq 2 \Rightarrow x - 3 \neq 2x - 8 \Rightarrow x \neq 5$. The domain is $\mathbb{R} - \{4, 5\}$.

(b) $k(x) = g\left(\frac{x - 1}{x - 2}\right) = \dfrac{\frac{x - 1}{x - 2} - 3}{\frac{x - 1}{x - 2} - 4} \cdot \frac{x - 2}{x - 2} = \frac{x - 1 - 3(x - 2)}{x - 1 - 4(x - 2)} = \frac{-2x + 5}{-3x + 7}$.

Domain of $f = \mathbb{R} - \{2\}$. Domain of $g = \mathbb{R} - \{4\}$.

$f(x) \neq 4 \Rightarrow \frac{x - 1}{x - 2} \neq 4 \Rightarrow x - 1 \neq 4x - 8 \Rightarrow x \neq \frac{7}{3}$. The domain is $\mathbb{R} - \{2, \frac{7}{3}\}$.

34 (a) $h(x) = f\left(\frac{x - 5}{x + 4}\right) = \dfrac{\frac{x - 5}{x + 4} + 2}{\frac{x - 5}{x + 4} - 1} \cdot \frac{x + 4}{x + 4} = \frac{x - 5 + 2(x + 4)}{x - 5 - 1(x + 4)} = \frac{3x + 3}{-9} = \frac{-x - 1}{3}$.

Domain of $g = \mathbb{R} - \{-4\}$. Domain of $f = \mathbb{R} - \{1\}$.

$g(x) \neq 1 \Rightarrow \frac{x - 5}{x + 4} \neq 1 \Rightarrow x - 5 \neq x + 4$. This is always true —

so no additional values need to be excluded, and thus, the domain is $\mathbb{R} - \{-4\}$.

(b) $k(x) = g\left(\frac{x + 2}{x - 1}\right) = \dfrac{\frac{x + 2}{x - 1} - 5}{\frac{x + 2}{x - 1} + 4} \cdot \frac{x - 1}{x - 1} = \frac{x + 2 - 5(x - 1)}{x + 2 + 4(x - 1)} = \frac{-4x + 7}{5x - 2}$.

Domain of $f = \mathbb{R} - \{1\}$. Domain of $g = \mathbb{R} - \{-4\}$.

$f(x) \neq -4 \Rightarrow \frac{x + 2}{x - 1} \neq -4 \Rightarrow x + 2 \neq -4x + 4 \Rightarrow x \neq \frac{2}{5}$. The domain is $\mathbb{R} - \{\frac{2}{5}, 1\}$.

35 $(f \circ g)(x) = f(g(x)) = f(x + 3) = (x + 3)^2 - 2$.

$(f \circ g)(x) = 0 \Rightarrow (x + 3)^2 - 2 = 0 \Rightarrow (x + 3)^2 = 2 \Rightarrow x + 3 = \pm\sqrt{2} \Rightarrow x = -3 \pm \sqrt{2}$

36 $(f \circ g)(x) = f(g(x)) = f(2x - 1) = (2x - 1)^2 - (2x - 1) - 2 = 4x^2 - 6x.$

$\qquad (f \circ g)(x) = 0 \Rightarrow 4x^2 - 6x = 0 \Rightarrow 2x(2x - 3) = 0 \Rightarrow x = 0, \frac{3}{2}$

37 (a) $(f \circ g)(6) = f(g(6)) = f(8) = 5$ (b) $(g \circ f)(6) = g(f(6)) = g(7) = 6$

   (c) $(f \circ f)(6) = f(f(6)) = f(7) = 6$ (d) $(g \circ g)(6) = g(g(6)) = g(8) = 5$

38 (a) $(T \circ S)(1) = T(S(1)) = T(0) = 2$ (b) $(S \circ T)(1) = S(T(1)) = S(3) = 2$

   (c) $(T \circ T)(1) = T(T(1)) = T(3) = 0$ (d) $(S \circ S)(1) = S(S(1)) = S(0) = 1$

39 $(D \circ R)(x) = D(R(x)) = D(20x) =$

$$\sqrt{400 + (20x)^2} = \sqrt{400 + 400x^2} = \sqrt{400(1 + x^2)} = 20\sqrt{x^2 + 1}$$

40 $(S \circ D)(t) = S(D(t)) = S(2t + 5) = 4\pi(2t + 5)^2$

41 $(fg)(-x) = f(-x)g(-x) = -f(x)g(x) = -(fg)(x) \Rightarrow fg$ is an odd function.

42 If f is even and odd, then $f(-x) = f(x)$ and $f(-x) = -f(x)$.

   Thus, $f(x) = -f(x) \Rightarrow 2f(x) = 0 \Rightarrow f(x) = 0.$

$\qquad\qquad\qquad$ Hence, $f(x) = 0$ is a function that is both even and odd.

43 $(\text{ROUND2} \circ \text{SSTAX})(437.21) = \text{ROUND2}(\text{SSTAX}(437.21))$

$\qquad\qquad\qquad\qquad\qquad = \text{ROUND2}(0.0715 \cdot 437.21)$

$\qquad\qquad\qquad\qquad\qquad = \text{ROUND2}(31.260515) = 31.26$

44 (a) $(\text{CHR} \circ \text{ORD})(\text{``C''}) = \text{CHR}(\text{ORD}(\text{``C''})) = \text{CHR}(67) = \text{``C''}$

  (b) $\text{CHR}(\text{ORD}(\text{``A''}) + 3) = \text{CHR}(65 + 3) = \text{CHR}(68) = \text{``D''}$

45 $r = 6t$ and $A = \pi r^2 \Rightarrow A = \pi(6t)^2 = 36\pi t^2$ ft^2.

46 $V = \frac{4}{3}\pi r^3 \Rightarrow r^3 = \frac{3V}{4\pi} \Rightarrow r = \sqrt[3]{\frac{3V}{4\pi}}.$ $V = \frac{9}{2}\pi t \Rightarrow r = \sqrt[3]{\frac{27t}{8}} = \frac{3}{2}\sqrt[3]{t}$ ft.

47 $V = \frac{1}{3}\pi r^2 h = \frac{1}{3}\pi r^3 \Rightarrow r = \sqrt[3]{\frac{3V}{\pi}}.$ $V = 243\pi t \Rightarrow r = \sqrt[3]{729t} = 9\sqrt[3]{t}$ ft.

48 $x^2 + x^2 = y^2 \Rightarrow y^2 = 2x^2 \Rightarrow y = \sqrt{2}x.$ $y^2 + x^2 = d^2 \Rightarrow d^2 = 3x^2 \Rightarrow d = \sqrt{3}x.$

49 Let l denote the length of the rope. At $t = 0$, $l = 20$. At time t, $l = 20 + 5t$.

$\qquad h^2 + 20^2 = l^2 \Rightarrow h = \sqrt{(20 + 5t)^2 - 20^2} = \sqrt{25t^2 + 200t} = \sqrt{25(t^2 + 8t)} = 5\sqrt{t^2 + 8t}.$

50 The triangle has sides of length 28, 50, and $\sqrt{28^2 + 50^2} = \sqrt{3284} = 2\sqrt{821}.$

   Let $y = h - 2$. Using similar triangles and the fact that $d = 2t$,

$$\frac{y}{d} = \frac{28}{2\sqrt{821}} \Rightarrow y = \frac{14}{\sqrt{821}}d \Rightarrow h = \frac{28}{\sqrt{821}}t + 2.$$

51 From Exercise 65 of Section 2.1, $d = \sqrt{90{,}400 + x^2}$. Let $x = 500 + 150t$.

$$\text{Thus, } d = \sqrt{90{,}400 + (500 + 150t)^2} = 10\sqrt{225t^2 + 1500t + 3404}.$$

52 Consider the cable to be a right circular cylinder.

$A = 2\pi rh = \pi dh = 1200\pi d$ { $h = 1200$ inches } $\Rightarrow d = \frac{A}{1200\pi}$.

$A = -750t$, so $d =$ original value + change $= 4 - \frac{750t}{1200\pi} = 4 - \frac{5}{8\pi}t$ inches.

53 $y = (x^2 + 3x)^{1/3}$ • Suppose you were to find the value of y if x was equal to 3. Using a calculator, you might compute the value of $x^2 + 3x$ first, and then raise that result to the $\frac{1}{3}$ power. Thus, we would choose $y = u^{1/3}$ and $u = x^2 + 3x$.

54 For $y = \sqrt[4]{x^4 - 16}$, choose $u = x^4 - 16$ and $y = \sqrt[4]{u}$.

55 For $y = \frac{1}{(x-3)^4}$, choose $u = x - 3$ and $y = 1/u^4 = u^{-4}$.

56 For $y = 4 + \sqrt{x^2 + 1}$, choose $u = x^2 + 1$ and $y = 4 + \sqrt{u}$.

57 For $y = (x^4 - 2x^2 + 5)^5$, choose $u = x^4 - 2x^2 + 5$ and $y = u^5$.

58 For $y = \frac{1}{(x^2 + 3x - 5)^3}$, choose $u = x^2 + 3x - 5$ and $y = 1/u^3 = u^{-3}$.

59 For $y = \frac{\sqrt{x+4} - 2}{\sqrt{x+4} + 2}$, there is not a "simple" choice for y as in previous exercises.

One choice for u is $u = x + 4$. Then y would be $\frac{\sqrt{u} - 2}{\sqrt{u} + 2}$.

Another choice for u is $u = \sqrt{x+4}$. Then y would be $\frac{u-2}{u+2}$.

60 For $y = \frac{\sqrt[3]{x}}{1 + \sqrt[3]{x}}$, choose $u = \sqrt[3]{x}$ and $y = \frac{u}{1+u}$.

61 $(f \circ g)(x) = f(g(x)) =$

$$f(x^3 + 1) = \sqrt{x^3 + 1} - 1 = \left(\sqrt{x^3 + 1} - 1\right) \times \frac{\sqrt{x^3 + 1} + 1}{\sqrt{x^3 + 1} + 1} = \frac{x^3}{\sqrt{x^3 + 1} + 1}.$$

Thus, $(f \circ g)(0.0001) \approx \frac{(10^{-4})^3}{2} = 5 \times 10^{-13}$.

62 $f(1.12) \approx 0.321170$, $g(1.12) \approx 0.280105$, $f(5.2) \approx 4.106542$, and $f(f(5.2)) \approx 3.014835$

$$\Rightarrow \frac{(f+g)(1.12) - (f/g)(1.12)}{[(f \circ f)(5.2)]^2} = \frac{[f(1.12) + g(1.12)] - f(1.12)/g(1.12)}{\{f[f(5.2)]\}^2} \approx -0.059997$$

63 *Note:* Point out to students that Y_2 is actually f, Y_1 is the function we are replacing x with in f, and Y_3 is accepting Y_2's output values as its input values. Hence, Y_3 is a function of a function of a function.

(a) $y = -2f(x)$; $Y_1 = x$, graph $Y_3 = -2Y_2$ { turn off Y_1 and Y_2 };

see *Figure 63(a)* on the next page. $D = [-2, 6]$, $R = [-16, 8]$

Note: The graphs often do not show the correct endpoints—you need to change the viewing rectangle or zoom in to actually view them on the screen.

[−12, 12] by [−16, 8]   [−12, 12] by [−16, 8]

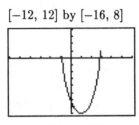
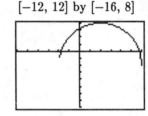

Xscl = 2   Xscl = 2

Yscl = 2   Yscl = 2

Figure 63(a)   *Figure 63(b)*

(b) $y = f(\frac{1}{2}x)$; $Y_1 = 0.5x$, graph Y_2; $D = [-4, 12]$, $R = [-4, 8]$

(c) $y = f(x - 3) + 1$; $Y_1 = x - 3$, graph $Y_3 = Y_2 + 1$; $D = [1, 9]$, $R = [-3, 9]$

[−12, 12] by [−6, 10]   [−12, 12] by [−8, 8]

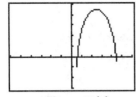
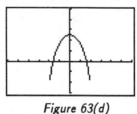

Xscl = 2   Xscl = 2

Yscl = 2   Yscl = 2

Figure 63(c)   *Figure 63(d)*

(d) $y = f(x + 2) - 3$; $Y_1 = x + 2$, graph $Y_3 = Y_2 - 3$; $D = [-4, 4]$, $R = [-7, 5]$

(e) $y = f(-x)$; $Y_1 = -x$, graph Y_2; $D = [-6, 2]$, $R = [-4, 8]$

[−12, 12] by [−8, 8]   [−12, 12] by [−8, 8]

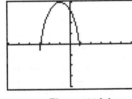
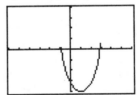

Xscl = 2   Xscl = 2

Yscl = 2   Yscl = 2

Figure 63(e)   *Figure 63(f)*

(f) $y = -f(x)$; $Y_1 = x$, graph $Y_3 = -Y_2$; $D = [-2, 6]$, $R = [-8, 4]$

(g) $y = f(|x|)$; $Y_1 = \text{abs } x$, graph Y_2; $D = [-6, 6]$, $R = [-4, 8]$

[−12, 12] by [−8, 8]   [−2, 6] by [0, 8]

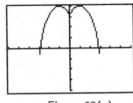
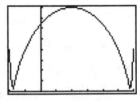

Xscl = 2   Xscl = 1

Yscl = 2   Yscl = 1

Figure 63(g)   *Figure 63(h)*

(h) $y = |f(x)|$; $Y_1 = x$, graph $Y_3 = \text{abs } Y_2$; $D = [-2, 6]$, $R = [0, 8]$

64 (a) $y = \frac{1}{2}f(x)$; $Y_1 = x$, graph $Y_3 = 0.5Y_2$; $D = [-6, -2]$, $R = [-5, -2]$

     (b) $y = f(2x)$; $Y_1 = 2x$, graph Y_2; $D = [-3, -1]$, $R = [-10, -4]$

     (c) $y = f(x - 2) + 5$; $Y_1 = x - 2$, graph $Y_3 = Y_2 + 5$; $D = [-4, 0]$, $R = [-5, 1]$

     (d) $y = f(x + 4) - 1$; $Y_1 = x + 4$, graph $Y_3 = Y_2 - 1$; $D = [-10, -6]$, $R = [-11, -5]$

(e) $y = f(-x)$; $Y_1 = -x$, graph Y_2; $D = [2, 6]$, $R = [-10, -4]$

(f) $y = -f(x)$; $Y_1 = x$, graph $Y_3 = -Y_2$; $D = [-6, -2]$, $R = [4, 10]$

(g) $y = f(|x|)$; No graph

(h) $y = |f(x)|$; $Y_1 = x$, graph $Y_3 = $ abs Y_2; $D = [-6, -2]$, $R = [4, 10]$

2.5 Exercises

2.5 Concept Check

1 Can an even function f have an inverse function? • Since an even function f has the property $f(-x) = f(x)$, it does not pass the Horizontal Line Test, so it is not one-to-one and hence, *cannot* have an inverse function.

2 Suppose a grading system assigns the grade of B to an average of 80%–89%. Is this grading function one-to-one? • No, because several domain elements (80%–89%) correspond to the *same* range element (B).

3 Suppose f is a one-to-one function whose graph is only in quadrant I. Where will the graph of f^{-1} be? • It is also in quadrant I since if (a, b) is a point on f (with $a > 0$, $b > 0$), then (b, a) is the point on the graph of f^{-1}.

4 If f is a one-to-one function with domain $[-\pi/2, \pi/2]$ and range $[-1, 1]$, what is the domain and range of f^{-1}? • f has domain $[-1, 1]$ and range $[-\pi/2, \pi/2]$.

2.5 Exercises

Note: We use the method illustrated in Example 1; however, the Horizontal Line Test or the theorem on increasing and decreasing functions could also be used.

1 Suppose $f(a) = f(b)$. $3a - 7 = 3b - 7 \Rightarrow 3a = 3b \Rightarrow a = b$.

Since $f(a) = f(b)$ implies that $a = b$, we conclude that f is one-to-one.

2 Suppose $f(a) = f(b)$. $\dfrac{1}{a-2} = \dfrac{1}{b-2} \Rightarrow a - 2 = b - 2 \Rightarrow a = b$. f is one-to-one.

3 Since $f(3) = f(-3) = 0$, but $3 \neq -3$, we conclude that f is *not* one-to-one.

4 For $f(x) = x^2 + 4$, $f(1) = 5 = f(-1)$. f is *not* one-to-one.

5 Suppose $f(a) = f(b)$ with $a, b \geq 0$. $\sqrt{a} = \sqrt{b} \Rightarrow (\sqrt{a})^2 = (\sqrt{b})^2 \Rightarrow a = b$.

f is one-to-one.

6 Suppose $f(a) = f(b)$. $\sqrt[3]{a} = \sqrt[3]{b} \Rightarrow (\sqrt[3]{a})^3 = (\sqrt[3]{b})^3 \Rightarrow a = b$. f is one-to-one.

7 For $f(x) = |x|$, $f(-1) = 1 = f(1)$. f is *not* one-to-one.

8 For $f(x) = 3$, $f(2) = 3 = f(4)$. f is *not* one-to-one.

9 For $f(x) = \sqrt{4 - x^2}$, $f(-1) = \sqrt{3} = f(1)$. f is *not* one-to-one.

10 Suppose $f(a) = f(b)$. $2a^3 - 4 = 2b^3 - 4 \Rightarrow 2a^3 = 2b^3 \Rightarrow a^3 = b^3 \Rightarrow a = b$.

f is one-to-one.

$\boxed{11}$ Suppose $f(a) = f(b)$. $\frac{1}{a} = \frac{1}{b} \Rightarrow a = b$. f is one-to-one.

$\boxed{12}$ For $f(x) = 1/x^2$, $f(-1) = 1 = f(1)$. f is *not* one-to-one.

$\boxed{13}$ $f(g(x)) = 3\left(\frac{x+2}{3}\right) - 2 = x + 2 - 2 = x$. $g(f(x)) = \frac{(3x-2)+2}{3} = \frac{3x}{3} = x$.

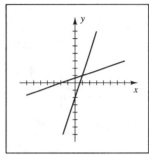

Figure 13

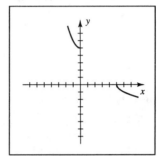

Figure 14

$\boxed{14}$ $f(g(x)) = (-\sqrt{x-5})^2 + 5 = x - 5 + 5 = x$.

     $g(f(x)) = -\sqrt{(x^2+5)-5} = -\sqrt{x^2} = -\,|\,x\,| = -(-x)$ { since $x \le 0$ } $= x$.

$\boxed{15}$ $f(g(x)) = -(\sqrt{3-x})^2 + 3 = -(3-x) + 3 = x$.

     $g(f(x)) = \sqrt{3-(-x^2+3)} = \sqrt{x^2} = |\,x\,| = x$ { since $x \ge 0$ }.

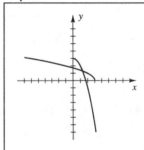

Figure 15

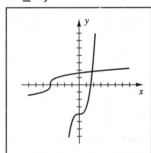

Figure 16

$\boxed{16}$ $f(g(x)) = (\sqrt[3]{x+4})^3 - 4 = x + 4 - 4 = x$. $g(f(x)) = \sqrt[3]{(x^3-4)+4} = \sqrt[3]{x^3} = x$.

$\boxed{17}$ $f(x) = 3x + 5 \Rightarrow y - 5 = 3x \Rightarrow x = \frac{y-5}{3} \Rightarrow f^{-1}(x) = \frac{x-5}{3}$

$\boxed{18}$ $f(x) = 7 - 2x \Rightarrow 2x = 7 - y \Rightarrow x = \frac{7-y}{2} \Rightarrow f^{-1}(x) = \frac{7-x}{2}$

$\boxed{19}$ $f(x) = \frac{1}{3x-2} \Rightarrow 3xy - 2y = 1 \Rightarrow 3xy = 2y + 1 \Rightarrow x = \frac{2y+1}{3y} \Rightarrow f^{-1}(x) = \frac{2x+1}{3x}$

$\boxed{20}$ $f(x) = \frac{1}{x+3} \Rightarrow xy + 3y = 1 \Rightarrow xy = 1 - 3y \Rightarrow x = \frac{1-3y}{y} \Rightarrow f^{-1}(x) = \frac{1-3x}{x}$

$\boxed{21}$ $f(x) = \frac{3x+2}{2x-5} \Rightarrow 2xy - 5y = 3x + 2 \Rightarrow 2xy - 3x = 5y + 2 \Rightarrow$

$$x(2y-3) = 5y + 2 \Rightarrow x = \frac{5y+2}{2y-3} \Rightarrow f^{-1}(x) = \frac{5x+2}{2x-3}$$

$\boxed{22}$ $f(x) = \frac{4x}{x-2} \Rightarrow xy - 2y = 4x \Rightarrow xy - 4x = 2y \Rightarrow x = \frac{2y}{y-4} \Rightarrow f^{-1}(x) = \frac{2x}{x-4}$

23 $f(x) = 2 - 3x^2$, $x \leq 0 \Rightarrow y + 3x^2 = 2 \Rightarrow$

$$x^2 = \frac{2-y}{3} \Rightarrow x = \pm\sqrt{\frac{2-y}{3}} \text{ \{choose minus since } x \leq 0 \} \Rightarrow f^{-1}(x) = -\sqrt{\frac{2-x}{3}}$$

24 $f(x) = 5x^2 + 2$, $x \geq 0 \Rightarrow y - 2 = 5x^2 \Rightarrow$

$$x^2 = \frac{y-2}{5} \Rightarrow x = \pm\sqrt{\frac{y-2}{5}} \text{ \{choose plus since } x \geq 0 \} \Rightarrow f^{-1}(x) = \sqrt{\frac{x-2}{5}}$$

25 $f(x) = 2x^3 - 5 \Rightarrow \frac{y+5}{2} = x^3 \Rightarrow x = \sqrt[3]{\frac{y+5}{2}} \Rightarrow f^{-1}(x) = \sqrt[3]{\frac{x+5}{2}}$

26 $f(x) = -x^3 + 2 \Rightarrow x^3 = 2 - y \Rightarrow x = \sqrt[3]{2-y} \Rightarrow f^{-1}(x) = \sqrt[3]{2-x}$

27 $f(x) = \sqrt{3-x} \Rightarrow y^2 = 3 - x \Rightarrow$

$$x = 3 - y^2 \text{ \{Since } y \geq 0 \text{ for } f, \ x \geq 0 \text{ for } f^{-1}. \} \Rightarrow f^{-1}(x) = 3 - x^2, \ x \geq 0$$

28 $f(x) = \sqrt{4 - x^2}$, $0 \leq x \leq 2 \Rightarrow y^2 = 4 - x^2 \Rightarrow x^2 = 4 - y^2 \Rightarrow$

$$x = \pm\sqrt{4 - y^2} \Rightarrow \text{\{choose plus since } 0 \leq x \leq 2 \} \Rightarrow f^{-1}(x) = \sqrt{4 - x^2}, \ 0 \leq x \leq 2$$

29 $f(x) = \sqrt[3]{x} + 1 \Rightarrow y - 1 = \sqrt[3]{x} \Rightarrow x = (y-1)^3 \Rightarrow f^{-1}(x) = (x-1)^3$

30 $f(x) = (x^3 + 1)^5 \Rightarrow \sqrt[5]{y} = x^3 + 1 \Rightarrow x^3 = \sqrt[5]{y} - 1 \Rightarrow$

$$x = \sqrt[3]{\sqrt[5]{y} - 1} \Rightarrow f^{-1}(x) = \sqrt[3]{\sqrt[5]{x} - 1}$$

31 $f(x) = x \Rightarrow y = x \Rightarrow x = y \Rightarrow f^{-1}(x) = x$

32 $f(x) = -x \Rightarrow y = -x \Rightarrow x = -y \Rightarrow f^{-1}(x) = -x$

33 $f(x) = x^2 - 4 \Rightarrow y = x^2 - 4 \Rightarrow y + 4 = x^2 \Rightarrow x = \pm\sqrt{y+4} \Rightarrow f^{-1}(x) = \sqrt{x+4}$ or

$$f^{-1}(x) = -\sqrt{x+4}. \text{ Since } f^{-1}(5) = -3, \text{ we choose } f^{-1}(x) = -\sqrt{x+4}.$$

34 $f(x) = x^2 - 4x + 3 \Rightarrow y = x^2 - 4x + 3 \Rightarrow x^2 - 4x + (3 - y) = 0 \Rightarrow$

$$x = \frac{4 \pm \sqrt{16 - 4(1)(3-y)}}{2} \Rightarrow x = 2 \pm \sqrt{y+1} \Rightarrow f^{-1}(x) = 2 + \sqrt{x+1} \text{ or}$$

$$f^{-1}(x) = 2 - \sqrt{x+1}. \text{ Since } f^{-1}(3) = 0, \text{ we choose } f^{-1}(x) = 2 - \sqrt{x+1}.$$

35 (b) $D = [-1, 2]$; $R = [\frac{1}{2}, 4]$ (c) $D_1 = R = [\frac{1}{2}, 4]$; $R_1 = D = [-1, 2]$

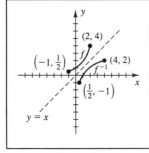

Figure 35

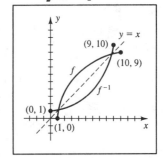

Figure 36

36 (b) $D = [1, 10]$; $R = [0, 9]$ (c) $D_1 = R = [0, 9]$; $R_1 = D = [1, 10]$

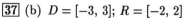

37 (b) $D = [-3, 3]$; $R = [-2, 2]$ (c) $D_1 = R = [-2, 2]$; $R_1 = D = [-3, 3]$

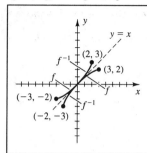

Figure 37

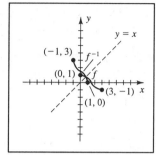

Figure 38

38 (b) $D = [0, 3]$; $R = [-1, 1]$ (c) $D_1 = R = [-1, 1]$; $R_1 = D = [0, 3]$

39 (a) Since f is one-to-one, an inverse exists.

$$\text{If } f(x) = ax + b, \text{ then } f^{-1}(x) = \frac{x - b}{a} \text{ for } a \neq 0.$$

(b) No, because a constant function is not one-to-one.

40 (1) If $P(a, b)$ is on the graph of f, then $f(a) = b$.

Also, $f^{-1}(f(a)) = f^{-1}(b)$ or $a = f^{-1}(b)$. So $Q(b, a)$ is on the graph of f^{-1}.

(2) $M_{PQ} = \left(\dfrac{a + b}{2}, \dfrac{b + a}{2} \right)$.

Since the x and y coordinates are equal, the point is on the line $y = x$.

(3) $m_{PQ} = \dfrac{a - b}{b - a} = -1$ and the slope of the line $y = x$ is 1. Since the slopes of the

lines are negative reciprocals of each other, the lines are perpendicular.

41 (a) $f(x) = -x + b \Rightarrow y = -x + b \Rightarrow x = -y + b$, or $f^{-1}(x) = -x + b$.

(b) $f(x) = \dfrac{ax + b}{cx - a}$ for $c \neq 0 \Rightarrow y = \dfrac{ax + b}{cx - a} \Rightarrow cyx - ya = ax + b \Rightarrow$

$cyx - ax = ay + b \Rightarrow x(cy - a) = ay + b \Rightarrow x = \dfrac{ay + b}{cy - a}$, or $f^{-1}(x) = \dfrac{ax + b}{cx - a}$.

(c) The graph of f is symmetric about the line $y = x$. Thus, $f(x) = f^{-1}(x)$.

42 (a) $f(x) = x^n$ for $x \geq 0$.   •   If n is odd, then $y = x^n \Rightarrow x = y^{1/n}$. If n is even,

then $y = x^n \Rightarrow x = \pm y^{1/n}$ { choose plus since $x \geq 0$ }, or $f^{-1}(x) = x^{1/n}$.

(b) $f(x) = x^{m/n}$ for $x \geq 0$ and m any positive integer.

$y = x^{m/n} \Rightarrow y^n = x^m \Rightarrow x = y^{n/m}$ { for the same reasons as in part (a) }.

43 From a graph of f, we see that f is always increasing. Thus, f is one-to-one.

$[-6, 6]$ by $[-4, 4]$ $[-2, 2]$ by $[-2.5, 0.5]$

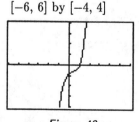

Xscl $= 1$

Yscl $= 1$

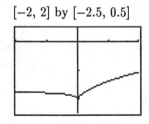

Xscl $= 1$

Yscl $= 1$

Figure 43   Figure 44

44 From a graph of f, we see that f is both decreasing and increasing near the point

$(0, -2)$. The horizontal line $y = -1.9$ will intersect the graph of f more than once.

Thus, f is not one-to-one. See *Figure 44* on the previous page.

45 (a) f decreases on $[-0.27, 1.22]$.

(b) Domain of g^{-1} is $[-0.20, 3.31]$; range of g^{-1} is $[-0.27, 1.22]$.

$[-1, 2]$ by $[-1, 4]$ $[-2, 2]$ by $[-1.33, 1.33]$

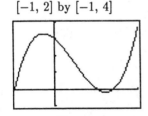   Xscl $= 1$ 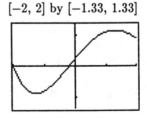   Xscl $= 1$
Yscl $= 1$ Yscl $= 1$

Figure 45   Figure 46

46 (a) $[-1.27, 1.31]$

(b) Domain of g^{-1} is $[-0.88, 1.14]$; range of g^{-1} is $[-1.27, 1.31]$.

47 The graph of f will be reflected about the line $y = x$.

$y = \sqrt[3]{x-1} \Rightarrow y^3 = x - 1 \Rightarrow x = y^3 + 1 \Rightarrow f^{-1}(x) = x^3 + 1$.

Graph $Y_1 = \sqrt[3]{x-1}$, $Y_2 = x^3 + 1$, and $Y_3 = x$.

$[-12, 12]$ by $[-8, 8]$ $[0, 12]$ by $[0, 8]$

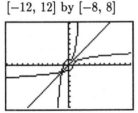   Xscl $= 1$ 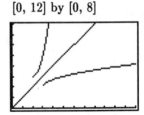   Xscl $= 1$
Yscl $= 1$ Yscl $= 1$

Figure 47   Figure 48

48 The graph of f will be reflected about the line $y = x$. $y = 2(x - 2)^2 + 3 \Rightarrow$

$\frac{y-3}{2} = (x-2)^2 \Rightarrow x - 2 = \pm\sqrt{\frac{y-3}{2}} \Rightarrow x = 2 \pm\sqrt{\frac{y-3}{2}}$. Let $f^{-1}(x) = 2 + \sqrt{\frac{x-3}{2}}$

since we must have $f^{-1}(x) \geq 2$.

Graph $Y_1 = (2(x-2)^2 + 3)/(x \geq 2)$, $Y_2 = 2 + \sqrt{\frac{x-3}{2}}$, and $Y_3 = x$.

49 (a) $V(23) = 35(23) = 805$ ft^3/min

(b) $V^{-1}(x) = \frac{1}{35}x$. Given an air circulation of x cubic feet per minute,

$V^{-1}(x)$ computes the maximum number of people that should be in the

restaurant at one time.

(c) $V^{-1}(2350) = \frac{1}{35}(2350) \approx 67.1 \Rightarrow$ the maximum number of people is 67.

50 (a)

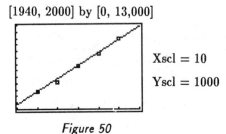

[1940, 2000] by [0, 13,000]

Xscl = 10

Yscl = 1000

Figure 50

(b) Use the two arbitrary points (1950, 2773) and (1990, 10819) to determine f.

$$m = \frac{10{,}819 - 2773}{1990 - 1950} = 201.15 \Rightarrow$$

$$y - 2773 = 201.15(x - 1950) = 201.15x - 392{,}242.5 \Rightarrow f(x) = 201.15x - 389{,}469.5$$

(c) $y = 201.15x - 389{,}469.5 \Rightarrow \dfrac{y + 389{,}469.5}{201.15} = x \Rightarrow f^{-1}(x) = \dfrac{x + 389{,}469.5}{201.15}.$

$f^{-1}(x)$ computes the year when x radio stations were on the air.

(d) $f^{-1}(7744) = \dfrac{7744 + 389{,}469.5}{201.15} \approx 1974.7 \approx 1975$

Chapter 2 Review Exercises

1 (a) $f(x) = \dfrac{x}{\sqrt{x+3}} \Rightarrow f(1) = \dfrac{1}{\sqrt{4}} = \dfrac{1}{2}$ (b) $f(-1) = -\dfrac{1}{\sqrt{2}}$ (c) $f(0) = \dfrac{0}{\sqrt{3}} = 0$

(d) $f(-x) = \dfrac{-x}{\sqrt{-x+3}} = -\dfrac{x}{\sqrt{3-x}}$ (e) $-f(x) = -1 \cdot f(x) = -\dfrac{x}{\sqrt{x+3}}$

(f) $f(x^2) = \dfrac{x^2}{\sqrt{x^2+3}}$ (g) $[f(x)]^2 = \left(\dfrac{x}{\sqrt{x+3}}\right)^2 = \dfrac{x^2}{x+3}$

2 $f(x) = \dfrac{-32(x^2 - 4)}{(9 - x^2)^{5/3}} \Rightarrow f(4) = \dfrac{(-)(+)}{(-)} = +.$ $f(4)$ is positive.

3 $f(x) = \dfrac{-2(x^2 - 20)(5 - x)}{(6 - x^2)^{4/3}} \Rightarrow f(4) = \dfrac{(-)(-)(+)}{(+)} = +.$ $f(4)$ is positive.

4 (a) $3x - 4 \ge 0 \Rightarrow x \ge \tfrac{4}{3};\ D = [\tfrac{4}{3}, \infty).$

     Since y is the result of a square root, $y \ge 0;\ R = [0, \infty).$

(b) $D =$ All real numbers except -3.

     Since y is the square of the nonzero term $\dfrac{1}{x+3},\ y > 0;\ R = (0, \infty).$

5 $\dfrac{f(a+h) - f(a)}{h} = \dfrac{[-(a+h)^2 + (a+h) + 5] - [-a^2 + a + 5]}{h} =$

$$\dfrac{-a^2 - 2ah - h^2 + a + h + 5 + a^2 - a - 5}{h} = \dfrac{-2ah - h^2 + h}{h} = \dfrac{h(-2a - h + 1)}{h} =$$

$$-2a - h + 1$$

6 $\dfrac{f(a+h)-f(a)}{h} = \dfrac{\frac{1}{a+h+2}-\frac{1}{a+2}}{h} = \dfrac{\frac{(a+2)-(a+h+2)}{(a+h+2)(a+2)}}{h} = \dfrac{-h}{(a+h+2)(a+2)h} =$

$$-\dfrac{1}{(a+h+2)(a+2)}$$

7 $f(x) = ax + b$ is the desired form. $a = \dfrac{7-2}{3-1} = \dfrac{5}{2}$. $f(x) = \dfrac{5}{2}x + b \Rightarrow$

$f(1) = \dfrac{5}{2} + b$, but $f(1) = 2$, so $\dfrac{5}{2} + b = 2$, and $b = -\dfrac{1}{2}$. Thus, $f(x) = \dfrac{5}{2}x - \dfrac{1}{2}$.

8 (a) $f(x) = \sqrt[3]{x^3 + 4x} \Rightarrow f(-x) = \sqrt[3]{(-x)^3 + 4(-x)} = \sqrt[3]{-1(x^3 + 4x)} = -\sqrt[3]{x^3 + 4x} =$

$$-f(x),\ f\ \text{is odd}$$

(b) $f(x) = \sqrt[3]{3x^2 - x^3} \Rightarrow f(-x) = \sqrt[3]{3(-x)^2 - (-x)^3} = \sqrt[3]{3x^2 + x^3} \neq \pm f(x),$

$$f\ \text{is neither even nor odd}$$

(c) $f(x) = \sqrt[3]{x^4 + 3x^2 + 5} \Rightarrow f(-x) = \sqrt[3]{(-x)^4 + 3(-x)^2 + 5} = \sqrt[3]{x^4 + 3x^2 + 5} = f(x),$

$$f\ \text{is even}$$

9 $y = (x-3)^2 - 2$ has vertex $(3, -2)$; x-intercepts: $(3 \pm \sqrt{2},\ 0)$, y-intercept: $(0, 7)$

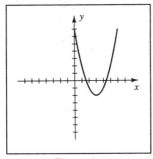

Figure 9

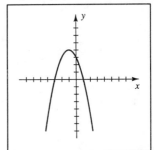

Figure 10

10 $y = -x^2 - 2x + 3 = -(x^2 + 2x + \underline{1}) + 3 + \underline{1} = -(x+1)^2 + 4;\ V(-1, 4);$

$$x\text{-intercepts: } (-3, 0)\text{ and }(1, 0),\ y\text{-intercept: } (0, 3)$$

11 (b) $D = \mathbb{R};\ R = \mathbb{R}$ (c) Decreasing on $(-\infty, \infty)$

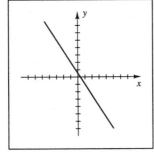

Figure 11

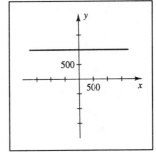

Figure 12

12 (b) $D = \mathbb{R};\ R = \{1000\}$ (c) Constant on $(-\infty, \infty)$

13 (b) $D = \mathbb{R}$; $R = [0, \infty)$ (c) Decreasing on $(-\infty, -3]$, increasing on $[-3, \infty)$

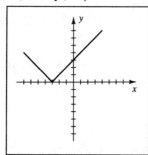

Figure 13

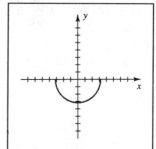

Figure 14

14 (b) $D = [-\sqrt{10}, \sqrt{10}]$; $R = [-\sqrt{10}, 0]$

 (c) Decreasing on $[-\sqrt{10}, 0]$, increasing on $[0, \sqrt{10}]$

15 (b) $D = [-1, \infty)$; $R = (-\infty, 1]$ (c) Decreasing on $[-1, \infty)$

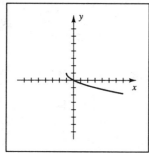

Figure 15

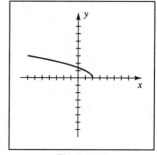

Figure 16

16 (b) $D = (-\infty, 2]$; $R = [0, \infty)$ (c) Decreasing on $(-\infty, 2]$

17 (b) $D = \mathbb{R}$; $R = (-\infty, 9]$ (c) Increasing on $(-\infty, 0]$, decreasing on $[0, \infty)$

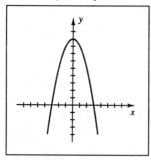

Figure 17

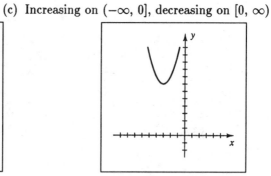

Figure 18

18 $f(x) = x^2 + 6x + 16 = x^2 + 6x + 9 + 7 = (x+3)^2 + 7$.   (b) $D = \mathbb{R}$; $R = [7, \infty)$

 (c) Decreasing on $(-\infty, -3]$, increasing on $[-3, \infty)$

19 (b) $D = \mathbb{R}$; $R = [0, \infty)$

(c) Decreasing on $(-\infty, 0]$, increasing on $[0, 2]$, constant on $[2, \infty)$

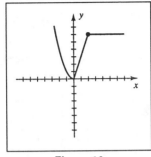

Figure 19

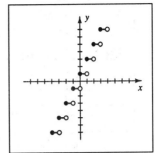

Figure 20

20 (b) $D = \mathbb{R}$; $R = \{\ldots, -3, -1, 1, 3, \ldots\}$

(c) Constant on $[n, n+1)$, where n is any integer

21 (a) $y = \sqrt{x}$

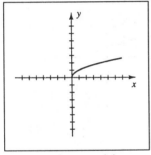

Figure 21(a)

(b) $y = \sqrt{x + 4}$

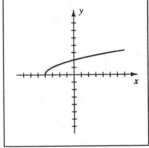

Figure 21(b)

(c) $y = \sqrt{x} + 4$

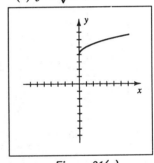

Figure 21(c)

(d) $y = 4\sqrt{x}$

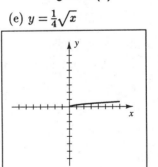

Figure 21(d)

(e) $y = \frac{1}{4}\sqrt{x}$

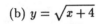

Figure 21(e)

(f) $y = -\sqrt{x}$

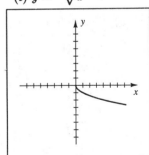

Figure 21(f)

$\boxed{22}$ (a) $y = f(x - 2)$ • shift f right 2 units

(b) $y = f(x) - 2$ • shift f down 2 units

(c) $y = f(-x)$ • reflect f through the y-axis

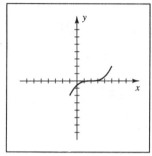 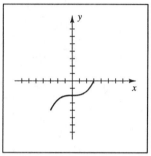 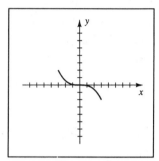

| *Figure 22(a)* | *Figure 22(b)* | *Figure 22(c)* |

(d) $y = f(2x)$ • horizontally compress f by a factor of 2

(e) $y = f(\frac{1}{2}x)$ • horizontally stretch f by a factor of $1/(1/2) = 2$

(f) $y = f^{-1}(x)$ • reflect f through the line $y = x$

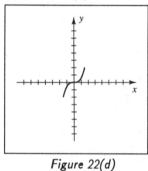 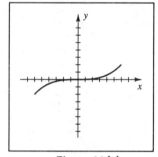 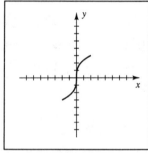

| *Figure 22(d)* | *Figure 22(e)* | *Figure 22(f)* |

(g) $y = |f(x)|$ •

reflect the portion of the graph below the x-axis through the x-axis.

(h) $y = f(|x|)$ • include the reflection of all points with positive x-coordinates

through the y-axis—results in the same graph as in part (g).

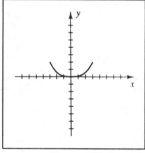 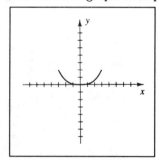

| *Figure 22(g)* | *Figure 22(h)* |

$\boxed{23}$ $V(2, -4)$ and $P(-2, 4)$ with $y = a(x - h)^2 + k \Rightarrow 4 = a(-2 - 2)^2 - 4 \Rightarrow$

$8 = 16a \Rightarrow a = \frac{1}{2}$. An equation is $y = \frac{1}{2}(x - 2)^2 - 4$.

$\boxed{24}$ The graph could be made by taking $y = |x|$ and reflecting it through the x-axis,

and then shifting that graph to the right 2 units and down 1 unit. $y = -|x - 2| - 1$

$\boxed{25}$ $f(x) = 5x^2 + 30x + 49 \Rightarrow -\dfrac{b}{2a} = -\dfrac{30}{2(5)} = -3.$ $f(-3) = 4$ is a minimum since $a > 0$.

$\boxed{26}$ $f(x) = -3x^2 + 30x - 82 \Rightarrow -\dfrac{b}{2a} = -\dfrac{30}{2(-3)} = 5.$ $f(5) = -7$ is a maximum since $a < 0$.

$\boxed{27}$ $f(x) = -12(x + 1)^2 - 37$ is in the standard form. $f(-1) = -37$ is a maximum.

$\boxed{28}$ $f(x) = 3(x + 2)(x - 10)$ has x-intercepts at -2 and 10. The vertex is halfway

between them at $x = 4$. $f(4) = 3 \cdot 6 \cdot (-6) = -108$ is a minimum.

$\boxed{29}$ $f(x) = -2x^2 + 12x - 14 = -2(x^2 - 6x + \underline{9}) - 14 + 18 = -2(x - 3)^2 + 4.$

$\boxed{30}$ $V(3, -2) \Rightarrow (h, k) = (3, -2)$ in $y = a(x - h)^2 + k$.

$x = 5$, $y = 4 \Rightarrow 4 = a(5 - 3)^2 - 2 \Rightarrow 6 = 4a \Rightarrow a = \frac{3}{2}$. Hence, $y = \frac{3}{2}(x - 3)^2 - 2$.

$\boxed{31}$ The domain of $f(x) = \sqrt{4 - x^2}$ is $[-2, 2]$. The domain of $g(x) = \sqrt{x}$ is $[0, \infty)$.

(a) The domain of fg is the intersection of those two domains, $[0, 2]$.

(b) The domain of f/g is the same as that of fg,

excluding any values that make g equal to 0. Thus, the domain of f/g is $(0, 2]$.

$\boxed{32}$ (a) $f(x) = 8x - 1$ and $g(x) = \sqrt{x - 2} \Rightarrow (f \circ g)(2) = f(g(2)) = f(0) = -1$

(b) $(g \circ f)(2) = g(f(2)) = g(15) = \sqrt{13}$

$\boxed{33}$ (a) $(f \circ g)(x) = f(g(x)) = 2(3x + 2)^2 - 5(3x + 2) + 1 = 18x^2 + 9x - 1$

(b) $(g \circ f)(x) = g(f(x)) = 3(2x^2 - 5x + 1) + 2 = 6x^2 - 15x + 5$

$\boxed{34}$ (a) $(f \circ g)(x) = f(g(x)) = \sqrt{3\left(\dfrac{1}{x^2}\right) + 2} = \sqrt{\dfrac{3 + 2x^2}{x^2}}$

(b) $(g \circ f)(x) = g(f(x)) = \dfrac{1}{(\sqrt{3x + 2})^2} = \dfrac{1}{3x + 2}.$

$\boxed{35}$ (a) $h(x) = f(\sqrt{x - 3}) = \sqrt{25 - (\sqrt{x - 3})^2} = \sqrt{25 - (x - 3)} = \sqrt{28 - x}.$

Domain of $g = [3, \infty)$. Domain of $f = [-5, 5]$.

$g(x) \le 5$ { $g(x)$ cannot be less than 0 } $\Rightarrow \sqrt{x - 3} \le 5 \Rightarrow$

$x - 3 \le 25 \Rightarrow x \le 28.$ $[3, \infty) \cap (-\infty, 28] = [3, 28]$

(b) $k(x) = g(\sqrt{25 - x^2}) = \sqrt{\sqrt{25 - x^2} - 3}.$

Domain of $f = [-5, 5]$. Domain of $g = [3, \infty)$.

$f(x) \ge 3 \Rightarrow \sqrt{25 - x^2} \ge 3 \Rightarrow 25 - x^2 \ge 9 \Rightarrow x^2 \le 16 \Rightarrow x \in [-4, 4].$

$\boxed{36}$ (a) $h(x) = f\left(\dfrac{2}{x}\right) = \dfrac{2/x}{3(2/x) + 2} \cdot \dfrac{x}{x} = \dfrac{2}{6 + 2x} = \dfrac{1}{x + 3}.$ Domain of $g = \mathbb{R} - \{0\}$.

Domain of $f = \mathbb{R} - \{-\frac{2}{3}\}$. $g(x) \ne -\frac{2}{3} \Rightarrow \frac{2}{x} \ne -\frac{2}{3} \Rightarrow x \ne -3$.

Hence, the domain of $f \circ g$ is $\mathbb{R} - \{-3, 0\}$.

(b) $k(x) = g\left(\dfrac{x}{3x+2}\right) = \dfrac{2}{x/(3x+2)} = \dfrac{6x+4}{x}$.

Domain of $f = \mathbb{R} - \{-\frac{2}{3}\}$. Domain of $g = \mathbb{R} - \{0\}$.

$f(x) \neq 0 \Rightarrow \dfrac{x}{3x+2} \neq 0 \Rightarrow x \neq 0$. Hence, the domain of $g \circ f$ is $\mathbb{R} - \{-\frac{2}{3}, 0\}$.

$\boxed{37}$ For $y = \sqrt[3]{x^2 - 5x}$, choose $u = x^2 - 5x$ and $y = \sqrt[3]{u}$.

$\boxed{38}$ Suppose $f(a) = f(b)$. $2a^3 - 5 = 2b^3 - 5 \Rightarrow 2a^3 = 2b^3 \Rightarrow a^3 = b^3 \Rightarrow a = b$.

Thus, f is a one-to-one function.

$\boxed{39}$ $f(x) = 10 - 15x \Rightarrow 15x = 10 - y \Rightarrow x = \dfrac{10-y}{15} \Rightarrow f^{-1}(x) = \dfrac{10-x}{15}$

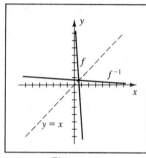

Figure 39

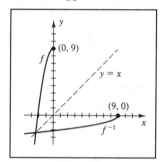

Figure 40

$\boxed{40}$ $f(x) = 9 - 2x^2, \; x \leq 0 \Rightarrow y + 2x^2 = 9 \Rightarrow$

$x^2 = \dfrac{9-y}{2} \Rightarrow x = \pm\sqrt{\dfrac{9-y}{2}}$ { choose minus since $x \leq 0$ } $\Rightarrow f^{-1}(x) = -\sqrt{\dfrac{9-x}{2}}$

$\boxed{41}$ (a) $f(1) = 2$ (b) $(f \circ f)(1) = f(f(1)) = f(2) = 4$

(c) $f(2) = 4$ and f is one-to-one $\Rightarrow f^{-1}(4) = 2$

(d) $f(x) = 4 \Rightarrow x = 2$ (e) $f(x) > 4 \Rightarrow x > 2$

$\boxed{42}$ Since f and g are one-to-one functions, we know that $f(2) = 7$, $f(4) = 2$, and

$g(2) = 5$ imply that $f^{-1}(7) = 2$, $f^{-1}(2) = 4$, and $g^{-1}(5) = 2$, respectively.

(a) $(g \circ f^{-1})(7) = g(f^{-1}(7)) = g(2) = 5$ (b) $(f \circ g^{-1})(5) = f(g^{-1}(5)) = f(2) = 7$

(c) $(f^{-1} \circ g^{-1})(5) = f^{-1}(g^{-1}(5)) = f^{-1}(2) = 4$

(d) $(g^{-1} \circ f^{-1})(2) = g^{-1}(f^{-1}(2)) = g^{-1}(4)$, which is not known.

$\boxed{43}$ (a) $V = at + b$ is the desired form. $V = 89,000$ when $t = 0 \Rightarrow V = at + 89,000$.

$V = 125,000$ when $t = 6 \Rightarrow 125,000 = 6a + 89,000 \Rightarrow a = \dfrac{36,000}{6} = 6000$ and hence,

$V = 6000t + 89,000.$

(b) $V = 103,000 \Rightarrow 103,000 = 6000t + 89,000 \Rightarrow t = \frac{7}{3}$, or $2\frac{1}{3}$.

$\boxed{44}$ (a) $F = aC + b$ is the desired form. $F = 32$ when $C = 0 \Rightarrow F = aC + 32$. $F = 212$

when $C = 100 \Rightarrow 212 = 100a + 32 \Rightarrow a = \frac{180}{100} = \frac{9}{5}$ and hence, $F = \frac{9}{5}C + 32$.

(b) If C increases $1°$, F increases $\left(\frac{9}{5}\right)°$, or $1.8°$.

45 Surface area $S = 2(4)(x) + (4)(y) = 8x + 4y$. Cost $C = 2(8x) + 5(4y) = 16x + 20y$.

(a) $C = 400 \Rightarrow 16x + 20y = 400 \Rightarrow 20y = -16x + 400 \Rightarrow y = -\frac{4}{5}x + 20$

(b) $V = lwh = (y)(4)(x) = 4xy = 4x(-\frac{4}{5}x + 20)$

46 $V = \pi r^2 h$ and $V = 24\pi \Rightarrow h = \frac{24}{r^2}$. $S = \pi r^2 + 2\pi r h = \pi r^2 + 2\pi r \cdot \frac{24}{r^2} = \pi r^2 + \frac{48\pi}{r}$.

$$C = (0.30)(\pi r^2) + (0.10)(\frac{48\pi}{r}) = \frac{3\pi r^2}{10} + \frac{48\pi}{10r} = \frac{3\pi(r^3 + 16)}{10r}.$$

47 (a) $V = (10 \text{ ft}^3 \text{ per minute})(t \text{ minutes}) = 10t$

(b) The height and length of the bottom triangular region are in the proportion 6–60, or 1–10, and the length is 10 times the height. When $0 \le h \le 6$, the volume is

$V = (\text{cross sectional area})(\text{pool width}) = \frac{1}{2}bh(40) = \frac{1}{2}(10h)(h)(40) = 200h^2 \text{ ft}^3$.

When $6 < h \le 9$, the triangular region is full and
$$V = 200(6)^2 + (h - 6)(80)(40) = 7200 + 3200(h - 6).$$

(c) $10t = 200h^2 \Rightarrow h = \sqrt{t/20}$;

$$0 \le h \le 6 \Rightarrow 0 \le \sqrt{t/20} \le 6 \Rightarrow 0 \le t/20 \le 36 \Rightarrow 0 \le t \le 720.$$

$$10t = 7200 + 3200(h - 6) \Rightarrow h - 6 = \frac{t - 720}{320} \Rightarrow h = 6 + \frac{t - 720}{320}; 6 < h \le 9 \Rightarrow$$

$$6 < 6 + \frac{t - 720}{320} \le 9 \Rightarrow 0 < \frac{t - 720}{320} \le 3 \Rightarrow 0 < t - 720 \le 960 \Rightarrow 720 < t \le 1680.$$

48 (a) Using similar triangles, $\frac{r}{x} = \frac{2}{4} \Rightarrow r = \frac{1}{2}x$.

(b) $\text{Volume}_{\text{cone}} + \text{Volume}_{\text{cup}} = \text{Volume}_{\text{total}} \Rightarrow \frac{1}{3}\pi r^2 h + \pi r^2 h = 5 \Rightarrow$

$$\frac{1}{3}\pi(\frac{1}{2}x)^2(x) + \pi(2)^2(y) = 5 \Rightarrow 5 - \frac{\pi}{12}x^3 = 4\pi y \Rightarrow y = \frac{5}{4\pi} - \frac{1}{48}x^3$$

49 (a) $\frac{y}{b} = \frac{y + h}{a} \Rightarrow ay = by + bh \Rightarrow y(a - b) = bh \Rightarrow y = \frac{bh}{a - b}$

(b) $V = \frac{1}{3}\pi a^2(y + h) - \frac{1}{3}\pi b^2 y = \frac{\pi}{3}[(a^2 - b^2)y + a^2 h] =$

$$\frac{\pi}{3}\left[(a^2 - b^2)\frac{bh}{a - b} + a^2 h\right] = \frac{\pi}{3}h[(a + b)b + a^2] = \frac{\pi}{3}h(a^2 + ab + b^2)$$

(c) $a = 6$, $b = 3$, $V = 600 \Rightarrow \frac{\pi}{3}h(6^2 + 6 \cdot 3 + 3^2) = 600 \Rightarrow h = \frac{1800}{63\pi} = \frac{200}{7\pi} \approx 9.1$ ft

50 Let k be the constant of variation. Then, $C = \frac{kDE}{Vt} \Rightarrow D = \left(\frac{Ct}{k}\right)\frac{V}{E}$, where $\frac{Ct}{k}$ is

constant. If V is twice its original value and E is $\frac{4}{5}$ of its original value, then

D becomes $\frac{2}{4/5} = \frac{5}{2} = 250\%$ of its original value. Thus, D increases by 250%.

51 $C = \frac{kP_1 P_2}{d^2}$; $2000 = \frac{k(10,000)(5000)}{(25)^2} \Rightarrow k = \frac{1}{40}$; $C = \frac{(10,000)(15,000)}{40(100)^2} = 375$

52 $P = kA^2 v^3$; $3000 = k[\pi(5)^2]^2(20)^3 \Rightarrow k = \frac{3}{5000\pi^2}$;

$$P = \frac{3}{5000\pi^2}[\pi(5)^2]^2(30)^3 = 10,125 \text{ watts}$$

$\boxed{53}$ Let t denote the time (in hr) after 1:00 P.M. If the starting point for ship B is the origin, then the locations of A and B are $-30 + 15t$ and $-10t$, respectively. Using the Pythagorean theorem, $d^2 = (-30 + 15t)^2 + (-10t)^2 = 325t^2 - 900t + 900$. The time at which the distance between the ships is minimal is the same as the time at which the square of the distance between the ships is minimal.

$$\text{Thus, } t = -\frac{b}{2a} = -\frac{-900}{2(325)} = \frac{18}{13}, \text{ or about 2:23 P.M.}$$

$\boxed{54}$ Let r denote the radius of the semicircles and x the length of the rectangle.

Perimeter = half-mile $\Rightarrow 2x + 2\pi r = \frac{1}{2} \Rightarrow x = -\pi r + \frac{1}{4}$.

$A = 2rx = 2r(-\pi r + \frac{1}{4}) = -2\pi r^2 + \frac{1}{2}r$. The maximum value of A occurs when

$$r = -\frac{b}{2a} = -\frac{1/2}{2(-2\pi)} = \frac{1}{8\pi} \text{ mi.} \quad x = -\pi\left(\frac{1}{8\pi}\right) + \frac{1}{4} = \frac{1}{8} \text{ mi.}$$

$\boxed{55}$ (a) $g = 32 \Rightarrow f(t) = -16t^2 + 16t$. Solving $f(t) = 0$ gives us $-16t(t-1) \Rightarrow t = 0, 1$.

The player is in the air for 1 second.

(b) $t = -\frac{b}{2a} = -\frac{16}{2(-16)} = \frac{1}{2}$. $f(\frac{1}{2}) = 4 \Rightarrow$ the player jumps 4 feet high.

(c) $g = \frac{32}{6} \Rightarrow f(t) = -\frac{8}{3}t^2 + 16t$. Solving $f(t) = 0$ yields $t = 0$ or 6.

The player would be in the air for 6 seconds on the moon.

$$t = -\frac{b}{2a} = -\frac{16}{2(-8/3)} = 3. \quad f(3) = 24 \Rightarrow \text{the player jumps 24 feet high.}$$

$\boxed{56}$ (a) Solving $-0.016x^2 + 1.6x = \frac{1}{5}x$ for x represents the intersection between the parabola and the line. $-0.08x^2 + 8x = x \Rightarrow 7x - \frac{8}{100}x^2 = 0 \Rightarrow x(7 - \frac{8}{100}x) = 0 \Rightarrow$

$x = 0, \frac{175}{2}$. The rocket lands at $(\frac{175}{2}, \frac{35}{2}) = (87.5, 17.5)$.

(b) The *difference d* between the parabola and the line is to be maximized here.

$d = (-0.016x^2 + 1.6x) - (\frac{1}{5}x) = -0.016x^2 + 1.4x$. d obtains a maximum when

$x = -\frac{b}{2a} = -\frac{1.4}{2(-0.016)} = 43.75$. The maximum height of the rocket

above the ground is $d = -0.016(43.75)^2 + 1.4(43.75) = 30.625$ units.

$\boxed{1}$ $f(x) = ax^2 + bx + c \Rightarrow$

$$\frac{f(x+h) - f(x)}{h} = \frac{\left[a(x+h)^2 + b(x+h) + c\right] - \left[ax^2 + bx + c\right]}{h}$$

$$= \frac{ax^2 + 2ahx + ah^2 + bx + bh + c - ax^2 - bx - c}{h}$$

$$= \frac{2ahx + ah^2 + bh}{h} = \frac{h(2ax + ah + b)}{h} = 2ax + ah + b$$

$\boxed{2}$ (a) About the x-axis • replace y with $-y$: $-y = \frac{1}{2}x - 3 \Rightarrow g(x) = -\frac{1}{2}x + 3$

(b) About the y-axis • replace x with $-x$: $y = \frac{1}{2}(-x) - 3 \Rightarrow g(x) = -\frac{1}{2}x - 3$

(c) About the line $y = 2$ • by examining the graphs of $f(x) = \frac{1}{2}x - 3$ and $y = 2$, we observe that the slope of the reflected line should be $-\frac{1}{2}$ and the y-intercept should be 5 units above $y = 2$ (since the y-intercept of f is 5 units below 2). Hence, $g(x) = -\frac{1}{2}x + 7$.

(d) About the line $x = 3$ • similar to part (c), the slope of g is $-\frac{1}{2}$. The x-intercept of f, 6, is 3 units to the right of $x = 3$, so the x-intercept of g should be 3 units to the left of $x = 3$. Hence, $g(x) = -\frac{1}{2}x$.

Note: An interesting generalization can be made for problems of the form of those in parts (a)–(d) which would be a worthwhile exploratory exercise in itself. It goes as follows: If the graph of $y = f(x)$ is reflected about the line $y = k$ (or $x = k$), how can you obtain the equation of the new graph? Answer: For $y = k$, replace y with $2k - y$; for $x = k$, replace x with $2k - x$.

(e) About the line $y = x$ • interchange x with y:

$$x = \frac{1}{2}y - 3 \Rightarrow \frac{1}{2}y = x + 3 \Rightarrow g(x) = 2x + 6$$

$\boxed{3}$ For the graph of $g(x) = \sqrt{f(x)}$, where $f(x) = ax^2 + bx + c$, consider 2 cases:

(1) $(a > 0)$ If f has 0 or 1 x-intercept(s), the domain of g is $\mathbb{R}$ and its range is $[\sqrt{k}, \infty)$, where k is the y-value of the vertex of f. If f has 2 x-intercepts (say x_1 and x_2 with $x_1 < x_2$), then the domain of g is $(-\infty, x_1] \cup [x_2, \infty)$ and its range is $[0, \infty)$. The general shape is similar to the v-shape of the graph of $y = \sqrt{a}\,|x|$.

(2) $(a < 0)$ If f has no x-intercepts, there is no graph of g. If f has 1 x-intercept, the graph of g consists of that point. If f has 2 x-intercepts, the domain of g is $[x_1, x_2]$ and the range is $[0, \sqrt{k}]$. The shape of g is that of the top half of an oval.

         The main advantage of graphing g as a composition (say $Y_1 = f$ and $Y_2 = \sqrt{Y_1}$ on a graphing calculator) is to observe the relationship between the range of f and the domain of g.

$\boxed{4}$ The values of the x-intercepts (if they exist) are found by using the quadratic formula $\left(x = -\dfrac{b}{2a} \pm \dfrac{\sqrt{b^2 - 4ac}}{2a} \right)$. Hence, the distance d from the axis of symmetry $(x = -b/(2a))$ to either x-intercept is $d = \dfrac{\sqrt{b^2 - 4ac}}{2\,|a|}$ and $d^2 = \dfrac{b^2 - 4ac}{4a^2}$. From page 148, the y-coordinate of the vertex is $h = c - \dfrac{b^2}{4a} = \dfrac{4ac - b^2}{4a}$.

$\dfrac{h}{d^2} = \dfrac{\frac{4ac - b^2}{4a}}{\frac{b^2 - 4ac}{4a^2}} = -\dfrac{4a^2(4ac - b^2)}{4a(b^2 - 4ac)} = -a$, so $h = -ad^2$. Note that this relationship also

reveals a connection between the discriminant D and the y-coordinate of the vertex, namely $h = -D^2/(4a)$.

$\boxed{5}$ The graph from Exercise 40(e) of Section 2.2 $(y = -[\![-x]\!])$ illustrates the concept of one of the most common billing methods with the open and closed endpoints reversed from those of the greatest integer function. Starting with $y = -[\![-x]\!]$ and adjusting for jumps every 15 minutes gives us $y = -[\![-x/15]\!]$. Since each quarter-hour charge is \$20, we multiply by 20 to obtain $y = -20[\![-x/15]\!]$. Because of the initial \$40 charge, we must add 40 to obtain the function $f(x) = 40 - 20[\![-x/15]\!]$.

6   $D = 0.0833x^2 - 0.4996x + 3.5491 \Rightarrow 0.0833x^2 - 0.4996x + (3.5491 - D) = 0.$

Solving for x with the quadratic formula yields

$$x = \frac{0.4996 \pm \sqrt{(-0.4996)^2 - 4(0.0833)(3.5491 - D)}}{2(0.0833)}, \text{ or, equivalently,}$$

$$x = \frac{4996 \pm \sqrt{33{,}320{,}000D - 93{,}295{,}996}}{1666}.$$

From *Figure 6* (a graph of D), we see that
$3 \le x \le 15$ corresponds to the right half of
the parabola. Hence, we choose the plus sign
in the equation for x.

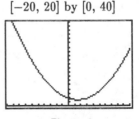

[−20, 20] by [0, 40]

Xscl = 2

Yscl = 2

Figure 6

7   (a) Let January correspond to 1, February to 2, ... , and December to 12.

[0.5, 12.5] by [0, 5]

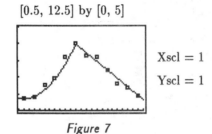

Xscl = 1

Yscl = 1

Figure 7

(b) The data points are (approximately) parabolic on the interval $[1, 6]$ and linear on
$[6, 12]$. Let $f_1(x) = a(x - h)^2 + k$ on $[1, 6]$ and $f_2(x) = mx + b$ on $[6, 12]$. On
$[1, 6]$, let the vertex $(h, k) = (1, 0.7)$. Since $(6, 4)$ is on the graph of f_1,
$f_1(6) = a(6 - 1)^2 + 0.7 = 4 \Rightarrow a = 0.132$. Thus, $f_1(x) = 0.132(x - 1)^2 + 0.7$ on
$[1, 6]$. Now, let $f_2(x) = mx + b$ pass through the points $(6, 4)$ and $(12, 0.9)$. An
equation of this line is approximately $(y - 4) = -0.517(x - 6)$. Thus,
let $f_2(x) = -0.517x + 7.102$ on $[6, 12]$.

$$f(x) = \begin{cases} 0.132(x - 1)^2 + 0.7 & \text{if } 1 \le x \le 6 \\ -0.517x + 7.102 & \text{if } 6 < x \le 12 \end{cases}$$

(c) To plot the piecewise function, let $Y_1 = (0.132(x - 1)\hat{\,}2 + 0.7)/(x \le 6)$ and
$Y_2 = (-0.517x + 7.102)/(x > 6)$. These assignments use the concept of Boolean
division. For example, when $(x \le 6)$ is false, the expression Y_1 will be undefined
(division by 0) and the calculator will not plot any values.

8 (a)

$[-15, 15]$ by $[-10, 10]$

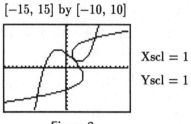

Xscl $= 1$

Yscl $= 1$

Figure 8

(b) If f is increasing, then f^{-1} moves from left to right. If f is decreasing, then f^{-1} moves from right to left.

(c) They can only occur on the line $y = x$.

Chapter 3: Polynomial and Rational Functions

3.1 Concept Check

1 List the figure number that corresponds to the equation.

(a) $y = 2x^4$ (b) $y = -3x^5$ (c) $y = -x^6$ (d) $y = 1.4x^3$

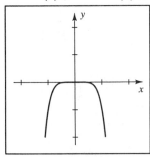

Figure I

Figure II

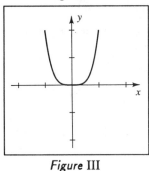

Figure III

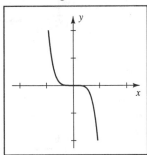

Figure IV

• (a) III (b) IV (c) I (d) II

2 Why doesn't $f(x) = [\![x]\!]$ satisfy the Intermediate Value Theorem on the interval $[2, 3]$? • The greatest integer function is not a polynomial function, which the Intermediate Value Theorem pertains to.

3 If x^2 is a factor of the polynomial f, then what happens to the graph of f at $x = 0$?
• The graph of f doesn't change sign at $x = 0$; that is, if it is positive (negative) to the left of $x = 0$, it is positive (negative) to the right of $x = 0$.

4 How many turning points can a polynomial of degree 5 have? • A polynomial of degree 5 could have at most 4 turning points.

5 If f is a polynomial with zeros at $x = -2$, 1, 3 and the solution to $f(x) > 0$ is $(-\infty, -2) \cup (1, 3)$, what is the solution to $f(x) < 0$? • $(-2, 1) \cup (3, \infty)$

6 If $x = 3$ and $x = 7$ are successive real zeros of a polynomial f, what can be said about $f(4)$ and $f(5)$? • They must have the same sign—either both positive or both negative.

3.1 Exercises

1 $f(x) = 2x^3 + c$ (a) $c = 3$ (b) $c = -3$ ●

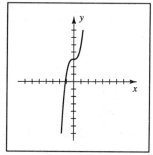

Figure 1(a)

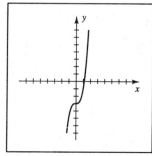

Figure 1(b)

2 $f(x) = -2x^3 + c$ (a) $c = -2$ (b) $c = 2$ ●

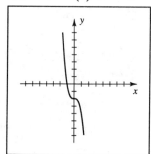

Figure 2(a)

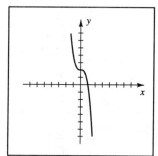

Figure 2(b)

3 $f(x) = ax^3 + 2$ (a) $a = 2$ (b) $a = -\frac{1}{3}$ ●

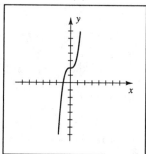

Figure 3(a)

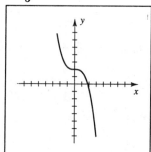

Figure 3(b)

4 $f(x) = ax^3 - 3$ (a) $a = -2$ (b) $a = \frac{1}{4}$ ●

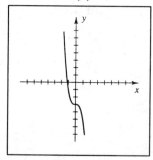

Figure 4(a)

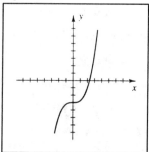

Figure 4(b)

⑤ $f(x) = x^3 - 4x^2 + 3x - 2$; $a = 3$, $b = 4$; $f(3) = -2 < 0$, $f(4) = 10 > 0$

By the intermediate value theorem for polynomial functions,

f takes on every value between -2 and 10 in the interval $[3, 4]$, namely, 0.

⑥ $f(x) = 2x^3 + 5x^2 - 3$; $a = -3$, $b = -2$; $f(-3) = -12 < 0$, $f(-2) = 1 > 0$

⑦ $f(x) = -x^4 + 3x^3 - 2x + 1$; $a = 2$, $b = 3$; $f(2) = 5 > 0$, $f(3) = -5 < 0$

⑧ $f(x) = 2x^4 + 3x - 2$; $a = \frac{1}{2}$, $b = \frac{3}{4}$; $f(\frac{1}{2}) = -\frac{3}{8} < 0$, $f(\frac{3}{4}) = \frac{113}{128} > 0$

⑨ $f(x) = x^5 + x^3 + x^2 + x + 1$; $a = -\frac{1}{2}$, $b = -1$; $f(-\frac{1}{2}) = \frac{19}{32} > 0$, $f(-1) = -1 < 0$

⑩ $f(x) = x^5 - 3x^4 - 2x^3 + 3x^2 - 9x - 6$; $a = 3$, $b = 4$; $f(3) = -60 < 0$, $f(4) = 134 > 0$

⑪ $f(x) = \frac{1}{4}x^3 - 2 = \frac{1}{4}(x^3 - 8) = \frac{1}{4}(x - 2)(x^2 + 2x + 4)$; $f(x) > 0$ if $x > 2$, $f(x) < 0$ if $x < 2$

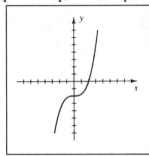

Figure 11

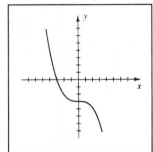

Figure 12

⑫ $f(x) = -\frac{1}{9}x^3 - 3 = -\frac{1}{9}(x^3 + 27) = -\frac{1}{9}(x + 3)(x^2 - 3x + 9)$;

$f(x) > 0$ if $x < -3$, $f(x) < 0$ if $x > -3$

⑬ $f(x) = -\frac{1}{16}x^4 + 1 = -\frac{1}{16}(x^4 - 16) = -\frac{1}{16}(x^2 + 4)(x + 2)(x - 2)$;

$f(x) > 0$ if $|x| < 2$, $f(x) < 0$ if $|x| > 2$

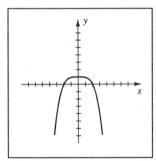

Figure 13

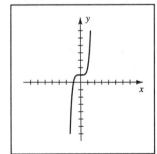

Figure 14

⑭ $f(x) = x^5 + 1 = (x + 1)(x^4 - x^3 + x^2 - x + 1)$; $f(x) > 0$ if $x > -1$, $f(x) < 0$ if $x < -1$

15 $f(x) = x^4 - 4x^2 = x^2(x+2)(x-2)$; $f(x) > 0$ if $|x| > 2$, $f(x) < 0$ if $0 < |x| < 2$

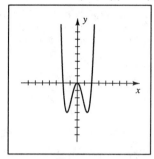

Figure 15

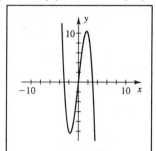

Figure 16

16 $f(x) = 9x - x^3 = x(3+x)(3-x)$;

$f(x) > 0$ if $x < -3$ or $0 < x < 3$, $f(x) < 0$ if $-3 < x < 0$ or $x > 3$

17 $f(x) = -x^3 + 3x^2 + 10x = -x(x^2 - 3x - 10) = -x(x+2)(x-5)$;

$f(x) > 0$ if $x < -2$ or $0 < x < 5$, $f(x) < 0$ if $-2 < x < 0$ or $x > 5$

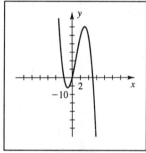

Figure 17

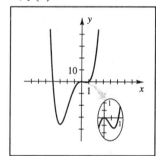

Figure 18

18 $f(x) = x^4 + 3x^3 - 4x^2 = x^2(x^2 + 3x - 4) = x^2(x+4)(x-1)$;

$f(x) > 0$ if $x < -4$ or $x > 1$, $f(x) < 0$ if $-4 < x < 0$ or $0 < x < 1$

19 $f(x) = \frac{1}{6}(x+2)(x-3)(x-4)$;

$f(x) > 0$ if $-2 < x < 3$ or $x > 4$, $f(x) < 0$ if $x < -2$ or $3 < x < 4$

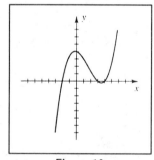

Figure 19

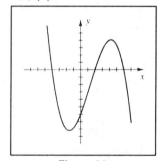

Figure 20

20 $f(x) = -\frac{1}{8}(x+4)(x-2)(x-6)$;

$f(x) > 0$ if $x < -4$ or $2 < x < 6$, $f(x) < 0$ if $-4 < x < 2$ or $x > 6$

$\boxed{21}$ $f(x) = x^3 + 2x^2 - 4x - 8 = x^2(x+2) - 4(x+2) = (x+2)^2(x-2);$

$f(x) > 0$ if $x > 2$, $f(x) < 0$ if $x < -2$ or $|x| < 2$

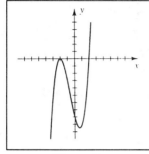

Figure 21

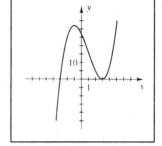

Figure 22

$\boxed{22}$ $f(x) = x^3 - 3x^2 - 9x + 27 = x^2(x-3) - 9(x-3) = (x-3)^2(x+3);$

$f(x) > 0$ if $|x| < 3$ or $x > 3$, $f(x) < 0$ if $x < -3$

$\boxed{23}$ $f(x) = x^4 - 6x^2 + 8 = (x^2 - 2)(x+2)(x-2);$

$f(x) > 0$ if $|x| > 2$ or $|x| < \sqrt{2}$, $f(x) < 0$ if $\sqrt{2} < |x| < 2$

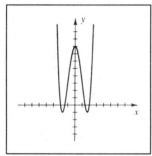

Figure 23

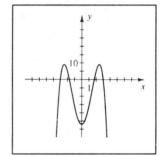

Figure 24

$\boxed{24}$ $f(x) = -x^4 + 12x^2 - 27 = (-x^2 + 3)(x^2 - 9) = -(x^2 - 3)(x+3)(x-3);$

$f(x) > 0$ if $\sqrt{3} < |x| < 3$, $f(x) < 0$ if $|x| > 3$ or $|x| < \sqrt{3}$

$\boxed{25}$ $f(x) = x^2(x+2)(x-1)^2(x-2);$

$f(x) > 0$ if $|x| > 2$, $f(x) < 0$ if $|x| < 2$, $x \neq 0$, $x \neq 1$

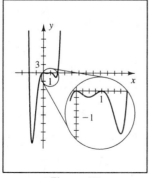

Figure 25

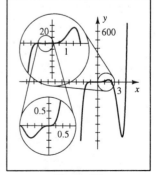

Figure 26

$\boxed{26}$ $f(x) = x^3(x+1)^2(x-2)(x-4);$

$f(x) > 0$ if $0 < x < 2$ or $x > 4$, $f(x) < 0$ if $x < 0$, $x \neq -1$ or $2 < x < 4$

$\boxed{27}$ If n is even, then $(-x)^n = x^n$ and hence $f(-x) = f(x)$. Thus, f is an even function.

$\boxed{28}$ If n is odd, then $(-x)^n = -x^n$ and hence $f(-x) = -f(x)$. Thus, f is an odd function.

$\boxed{29}$ $f(-1) = -4 - 6k$ and $f(-1) = 4 \Rightarrow -4 - 6k = 4 \Rightarrow k = -\frac{4}{3}$.

$\boxed{30}$ $f(2) = 16k - 32$ and $f(2) = 0 \Rightarrow 16k - 32 = 0 \Rightarrow k = 2$.

$f(x) = x^3 - 2x^2 - 16x + 32 = x^2(x - 2) - 16(x - 2) = (x + 4)(x - 4)(x - 2).$

The other two zeros are ± 4.

$\boxed{31}$ $P(x) = \frac{1}{2}(5x^3 - 3x) = \frac{1}{2}x(5x^2 - 3).$

$\quad P(x) > 0$ on $(-\frac{1}{5}\sqrt{15}, 0)$ and $(\frac{1}{5}\sqrt{15}, \infty)$.

$\quad P(x) < 0$ on $(-\infty, -\frac{1}{5}\sqrt{15})$ and $(0, \frac{1}{5}\sqrt{15})$.

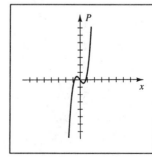

Figure 31

$\boxed{32}$ $x^2 = \dfrac{8 \pm 4\sqrt{2}}{16} = \dfrac{2 \pm \sqrt{2}}{4} \Rightarrow x = \pm\frac{1}{2}\sqrt{2 \pm \sqrt{2}} \approx \pm 0.92,\ \pm 0.38;$

$f(x) > 0$ if $|x| < \frac{1}{2}\sqrt{2 - \sqrt{2}}$ or $|x| > \frac{1}{2}\sqrt{2 + \sqrt{2}}$

$\boxed{33}$ (a) $V(x) = lwh = (30 - x - x)(20 - x - x)x = x(20 - 2x)(30 - 2x) =$

$4x(10 - x)(15 - x) = 4x(x - 10)(x - 15).$

(b) $V(x) > 0$ on $(0, 10)$ and $(15, \infty)$. Allowable values for x are in $(0, 10)$.

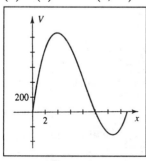

Figure 33

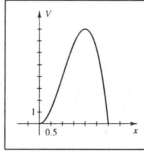

Figure 34

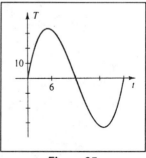

Figure 35

$\boxed{34}$ (a) Since we are disregarding the thickness of the lumber, 4 boards are y feet long
and 8 boards are x feet long. Total length $= 24 \Rightarrow 4y + 8x = 24 \Rightarrow y = 6 - 2x$.

$$V = x^2 y = x^2(6 - 2x) = 6x^2 - 2x^3.$$

(b) From part (a), $V = 6x^2 - 2x^3$, or, equivalently, $V = -2x^2(x - 3)$.

$\boxed{35}$ (a) $T = \frac{1}{20}t(t - 12)(t - 24) = 0 \Rightarrow t = 0, 12, 24.$ $T > 0$ for

$0 < t < 12$ {6 A.M. to 6 P.M.}; $T < 0$ for $12 < t < 24$ {6 P.M. to 6 A.M.}.

(c) 12 noon corresponds to $t = 6$, $T(6) = 32.4 > 32°F$ and $T(7) = 29.75 < 32°F$

36 (a) At the end of the board, $s = 10$.

Letting $d = 1$ and $L = 10$ yields $1 = 100c(20) \Rightarrow c = \frac{1}{2000}$.

(b) $s = 6.5 \Rightarrow d = (\frac{1}{2000})(6.5)^2[3(10) - 6.5] = 0.4964 < \frac{1}{2}$.

$s = 6.6 \Rightarrow d = (\frac{1}{2000})(6.6)^2[3(10) - 6.6] = 0.5097 > \frac{1}{2}$.

37 (a) $N(t) = -t^4 + 21t^2 + 100$

$= -(t^4 - 21t^2 - 100)$

$= -(t^2 - 25)(t^2 + 4)$

$= -(t + 5)(t - 5)(t^2 + 4)$

If $t > 0$, then $N(t) > 0$ for $0 < t < 5$.

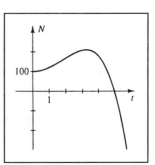

(b) The population becomes extinct when $N = 0$.

This occurs after 5 years.

Figure 37

38 (a) $R = 0 \Rightarrow -2t(2t^2 - 21) = 0 \Rightarrow t = \frac{1}{2}\sqrt{42}$ {for $t > 0$}.

The population ceases to grow after $\frac{1}{2}\sqrt{42} \approx 3.24$ years.

(b) $R > 0$ on $(0, \frac{1}{2}\sqrt{42})$

39 (a) $f(x) = 2x^4$, $g(x) = 2x^4 - 5x^2 + 1$, $h(x) = 2x^4 + 5x^2 - 1$, $k(x) = 2x^4 - x^3 + 2x$

x	$f(x)$	$g(x)$	$h(x)$	$k(x)$
-60	25,920,000	25,902,001	25,937,999	26,135,880
-40	5,120,000	5,112,001	5,127,999	5,183,920
-20	320,000	318,001	321,999	327,960
20	320,000	318,001	321,999	312,040
40	5,120,000	5,112,001	5,127,999	5,056,080
60	25,920,000	25,902,001	25,937,999	25,704,120

(b) As $|x|$ becomes large, the function values become similar.

(c) The term with the highest power of x: $2x^4$.

40 (a) $f(x) = -3x^3$, $g(x) = -3x^3 - x^2 + 1$, $h(x) = -3x^3 + x^2 - 1$, $k(x) = -3x^3 - 2x^2 + 2x$

Figures (3) and (4) are on the next page.

$[-2, 2]$ by $[-2, 2]$

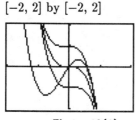

Xscl $= 1$

Yscl $= 1$

Figure 40(1)

$[-10, 10]$ by $[-10, 10]$

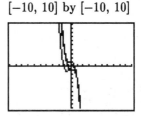

Xscl $= 1$

Yscl $= 1$

Figure 40(2)

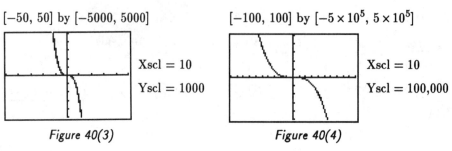

$[-50, 50]$ by $[-5000, 5000]$ Xscl = 10   Yscl = 1000

Figure 40(3)

$[-100, 100]$ by $[-5 \times 10^5, 5 \times 10^5]$ Xscl = 10   Yscl = 100,000

Figure 40(4)

(b) As the viewing rectangle increases the graphs look alike.

(c) Their end behavior is similar because their highest degree term is $-3x^3$. This term determines the shape of the graph when $|x|$ is large.

41 (a)

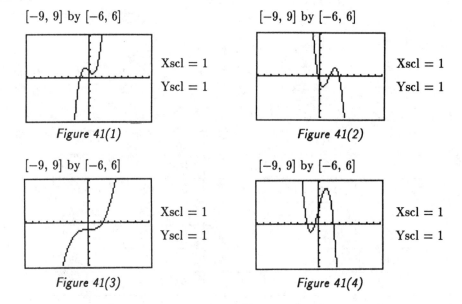

$[-9, 9]$ by $[-6, 6]$ Xscl = 1   Yscl = 1

Figure 41(1)

$[-9, 9]$ by $[-6, 6]$ Xscl = 1   Yscl = 1

Figure 41(2)

$[-9, 9]$ by $[-6, 6]$ Xscl = 1   Yscl = 1

Figure 41(3)

$[-9, 9]$ by $[-6, 6]$ Xscl = 1   Yscl = 1

Figure 41(4)

(b) (1) $f(x) = x^3 - x + 1$ • As x approaches ∞, $f(x)$ approaches ∞; as x approaches $-\infty$, $f(x)$ approaches $-\infty$

(2) $f(x) = -x^3 + 4x^2 - 3x - 1$ • As x approaches ∞, $f(x)$ approaches $-\infty$; as x approaches $-\infty$, $f(x)$ approaches ∞

(3) $f(x) = 0.1x^3 - 1$ • As x approaches ∞, $f(x)$ approaches ∞; as x approaches $-\infty$, $f(x)$ approaches $-\infty$

(4) $f(x) = -x^3 + 4x + 2$ • As x approaches ∞, $f(x)$ approaches $-\infty$; as x approaches $-\infty$, $f(x)$ approaches ∞

(c) For the cubic function $f(x) = ax^3 + bx^2 + cx + d$ with $a > 0$, $f(x)$ approaches ∞ as x approaches ∞ and $f(x)$ approaches $-\infty$ as x approaches $-\infty$. With $a < 0$, $f(x)$ approaches $-\infty$ as x approaches ∞ and $f(x)$ approaches ∞ as x approaches $-\infty$.

42 (a)

$[-9, 9]$ by $[-6, 6]$

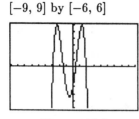

Xscl = 1

Yscl = 1

Figure 42(1)

$[-9, 9]$ by $[-6, 6]$

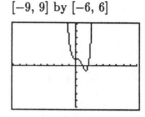

Xscl = 1

Yscl = 1

Figure 42(2)

$[-9, 9]$ by $[-6, 6]$

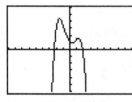

Xscl = 1

Yscl = 1

Figure 42(3)

$[-9, 9]$ by $[-6, 6]$

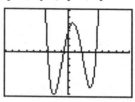

Xscl = 1

Yscl = 1

Figure 42(4)

(b) (1) $f(x) = -x^4 - 2x^3 + 5x^2 + 6x - 3$ • As x approaches ∞, $f(x)$ approaches $-\infty$; as x approaches $-\infty$, $f(x)$ approaches $-\infty$

(2) $f(x) = x^4 - 2x^3 + 1$ • As x approaches ∞, $f(x)$ approaches ∞; as x approaches $-\infty$, $f(x)$ approaches ∞

(3) $f(x) = -\frac{1}{2}x^4 + 2x^2 - x + 1$ • As x approaches ∞, $f(x)$ approaches $-\infty$; as x approaches $-\infty$, $f(x)$ approaches $-\infty$

(4) $f(x) = \frac{1}{5}x^4 - \frac{1}{2}x^3 - \frac{7}{3}x^2 + \frac{7}{2}x + 3$ • As x approaches ∞, $f(x)$ approaches ∞; as x approaches $-\infty$, $f(x)$ approaches ∞

(c) For the fourth–degree polynomial $f(x) = ax^4 + bx^3 + cx^2 + dx + e$ with $a > 0$, $f(x)$ approaches ∞ as $|x|$ approaches ∞ and with $a < 0$, $f(x)$ approaches $-\infty$ as $|x|$ approaches ∞.

43 From the graph, f has three zeros. They are approximately -1.89, 0.49, and 1.20.

$[-4.5, 4.5]$ by $[-3, 3]$

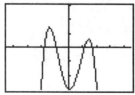

Xscl = 1

Yscl = 1

Figure 43

$[-4.5, 4.5]$ by $[-3, 3]$

Xscl = 1

Yscl = 1

Figure 44

44 From the graph, f has four zeros.

They are approximately -1.78, -0.91, 1.11, and 1.67.

45 From the graph, f has three zeros. They are approximately -1.88, 0.35, and 1.53.

[−4.5, 4.5] by [−3, 3]

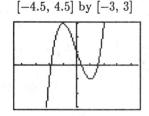

Xscl = 1

Yscl = 1

Figure 45

[−4.5, 4.5] by [−3, 3]

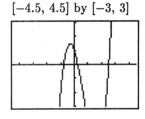

Xscl = 1

Yscl = 1

Figure 46

46 From the graph, f has three zeros. They are approximately -0.77, 0.26, and 2.52.

47 If $f(x) = x^3 + 5x - 2$ and $k = 1$, then $f(x) > k$ on $(0.56, \infty)$.

[−4.5, 4.5] by [−3, 3]

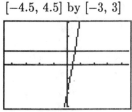

Xscl = 1

Yscl = 1

Figure 47

[−4.5, 4.5] by [−2, 4]

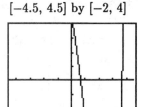

Xscl = 1

Yscl = 1

Figure 48

48 If $f(x) = x^4 - 4x^3 + 3x^2 - 8x + 5$ and $k = 3$, then $f(x) > k$ on $(-\infty, 0.27) \cup (3.73, \infty)$.

49 If $f(x) = x^5 - 2x^2 + 2$ and $k = -2$, then $f(x) > k$ on $(-1.10, \infty)$.

[−4.5, 4.5] by [−3, 3]

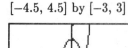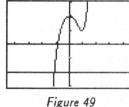

Xscl = 1

Yscl = 1

Figure 49

[−4.5, 4.5] by [−3, 3]

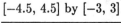

Xscl = 1

Yscl = 1

Figure 50

50 If $f(x) = x^4 - 2x^3 + 10x - 26$ and $k = -1$, then $f(x) > k$ on $(-\infty, -2.24) \cup (2.24, \infty)$.

51 From the graph, there are three points of intersection.

Their coordinates are approximately $(-1.29, -0.77)$, $(0.085, 2.66)$, and $(1.36, -0.42)$.

[−4.5, 4.5] by [−2, 4]

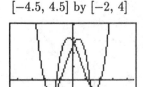

Xscl = 1

Yscl = 1

Figure 51

[−5.5, 5] by [−3, 4]

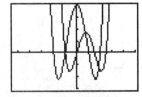

Xscl = 1

Yscl = 1

Figure 52

52 From the graph, there are three points of intersection.

Their coordinates are approximately $(-1, 0)$, $(0.71, 1.72)$, and $(1.87, -1.25)$.

53 (a)

[1975, 1995] by [20, 40]

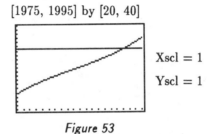

Xscl = 1

Yscl = 1

Figure 53

(b) Graph $Y_1 = 0.0014(x - 1975)^3 - 0.0388(x - 1975)^2 + 0.8783(x - 1975) + 23.82$ and $Y_2 = 34.4$. Their graphs intersect when $x \approx 1991.9792 \approx 1992$. There were 34.4 million recipients in 1992.

54 (a) The number of preschool children decreased during 1970 to 1976, but since then, it has increased.

[0, 25] by [3×10^5, 8×10^5]

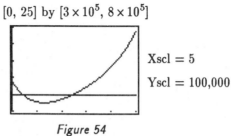

Xscl = 5

Yscl = 100,000

Figure 54

(b) $f(x) = 4.363x^4 - 236.3x^3 + 5527x^2 - 46,519x + 475,913 \Rightarrow f(6) \approx 350,385$

(c) Graph $Y_1 = f(x)$ and $Y_2 = 400,000$. There are two points of intersection at $x \approx 2.12, 12.30$. Thus, there were approximately 400,000 participants during the years 1972 and 1982.

3.2 Exercises

3.2 Concept Check

1 If a fifth-degree polynomial is divided by a second-degree polynomial, what is the degree of the quotient?   •   The quotient is a third-degree polynomial.

2 If a polynomial $f(x)$ is divided by $x + 3$ and the remainder is the same as $f(a)$, then what is the value of a?   •   Since $x + 3 = x - (-3)$, $a = -3$ by the Remainder Theorem.

3 If $f(4) = 0$, then the polynomial $f(x)$ has what factor?   •   If $f(4) = 0$, then $x - 4$ is a factor of $f(x)$.

4 Can you use synthetic division to divide $x^3 - 4x + 1$ by $x^2 + 3$?   •   No, synthetic division can only be used with divisors of the form $x - c$.

5 Given that $f(x) = x^3 - x^2 - 6x - 4 = (x^2 - 2x - 4)(x + 1)$, what point is on the graph of f?   •   Since $x + 1$ is a factor, $f(-1) = 0$ and so $(-1, 0)$ is on the graph of f.

3.2 Exercises

1–8 $f(x) =$ dividend; $p(x) =$ divisor •   ★ quotient; remainder

1 $f(x) = 2x^4 - x^3 - 3x^2 + 7x - 12$; $p(x) = x^2 - 3$ •   ★ $2x^2 - x + 3$; $4x - 3$

2 $f(x) = 3x^4 + 2x^3 - x^2 - x - 6$; $p(x) = x^2 + 1$ •   ★ $3x^2 + 2x - 4$; $-3x - 2$

3 $f(x) = 3x^3 + 2x - 4$; $p(x) = 2x^2 + 1$ •   ★ $\frac{3}{2}x$; $\frac{1}{2}x - 4$

4 $f(x) = 3x^3 - 5x^2 - 4x - 8$; $p(x) = 2x^2 + x$ •   ★ $\frac{3}{2}x - \frac{13}{4}$; $-\frac{3}{4}x - 8$

5 $f(x) = 7x + 2$; $p(x) = 2x^2 - x - 4$ •   ★ 0; $7x + 2$

6 $f(x) = -5x^2 + 3$; $p(x) = x^3 - 3x + 9$ •   ★ 0; $-5x^2 + 3$

7 $f(x) = 9x + 4$; $p(x) = 2x - 5$ •   ★ $\frac{9}{2}$; $\frac{53}{2}$

8 $f(x) = 7x^2 + 3x - 10$; $p(x) = x^2 - x + 10$ •   ★ 7; $10x - 80$

9   Dividing $f(x) = 3x^3 - x^2 + 5x - 4$ by $x - 2$ using either long division or synthetic division yields a remainder of 26.

10 Divide $f(x) = 2x^3 + 4x^2 - 3x - 1$ by $x - 3$ to obtain a remainder of 80.

11 Divide $f(x) = x^4 - 6x^2 + 4x - 8$ by $x + 3$ to obtain a remainder of 7.

12 Divide $f(x) = x^4 + 3x^2 - 12$ by $x + 2$ to obtain a remainder of 16.

13 Since $f(-3) = 0$, $x + 3$ is a factor of $f(x) = x^3 + x^2 - 2x + 12$.

14 Since $f(2) = 0$, $x - 2$ is a factor of $f(x) = x^3 + x^2 - 11x + 10$.

15 Since $f(-2) = 0$, $x + 2$ is a factor of $f(x) = x^{12} - 4096$.

16 Since $f(2) = 0$, $x - 2$ is a factor of $f(x) = x^4 - 3x^3 - 2x^2 + 5x + 6$.

Note: In Exercises 17–20, let $a = 1$.

17 f has degree 3 with zeros -2, 0, $5 \Rightarrow$

$$f(x) = a\big[x - (-2)\big](x - 0)(x - 5) = x(x + 2)(x - 5) = x(x^2 - 3x - 10) = x^3 - 3x^2 - 10x$$

18 f has degree 3 with zeros ± 2, $3 \Rightarrow$

$$f(x) = a(x + 2)(x - 2)(x - 3) = (x^2 - 4)(x - 3) = x^3 - 3x^2 - 4x + 12$$

19 f has degree 4 with zeros -2, ± 1, $4 \Rightarrow$

$$f(x) = a(x + 2)(x + 1)(x - 1)(x - 4) = (x^2 - 1)(x^2 - 2x - 8) = x^4 - 2x^3 - 9x^2 + 2x + 8$$

20 f has degree 4 with zeros -3, 0, 1, $5 \Rightarrow$

$$f(x) = a(x + 3)(x)(x - 1)(x - 5) = x(x^2 + 2x - 3)(x - 5) = x^4 - 3x^3 - 13x^2 + 15x$$

21 $2 \,\big|$
	2	−3	4	−5
		4	2	12
	2	1	6	7

The synthetic division indicates that the quotient is $2x^2 + x + 6$ and the remainder is 7.

22 $3x^3 - 4x^2 - x + 8$; $x + 4$ •   ★ $3x^2 - 16x + 63$; -244

23 $x^3 - 8x - 5$; $x + 3$ •   ★ $x^2 - 3x + 1$; -8

24 $5x^3 - 6x^2 + 15$; $x - 4$ •   ★ $5x^2 + 14x + 56$; 239

25 $3x^5 + 6x^2 + 7$; $x + 2$ •   ★ $3x^4 - 6x^3 + 12x^2 - 18x + 36$; -65

26 $-2x^4 + 10x - 3$; $x - 3$ •   ★ $-2x^3 - 6x^2 - 18x - 44$; -135

27 $4x^4 - 5x^2 + 1$; $x - \frac{1}{2}$ •   ★ $4x^3 + 2x^2 - 4x - 2$; 0

28 $9x^3 - 6x^2 + 3x - 4$; $x - \frac{1}{3}$ •   ★ $9x^2 - 3x + 2$; $-\frac{10}{3}$

29

$$\begin{array}{r|rrrr} 3 & 2 & 3 & -4 & 4 \\ & & 6 & 27 & 69 \\ \hline & 2 & 9 & 23 & 73 \end{array}$$

The synthetic division indicates that $f(3) = 73$.

30 $f(x) = -x^3 + 4x^2 + x$; $c = -2$ • $f(-2) = 22$

31 $f(x) = 0.3x^3 + 0.04x - 0.034$; $c = -0.2$ • $f(-0.2) = -0.0444$

32 $f(x) = 8x^5 - 3x^2 + 7$; $c = \frac{1}{2}$ • $f(\frac{1}{2}) = \frac{13}{2}$

33 $f(x) = x^2 + 3x - 5$; $c = 2 + \sqrt{3}$ • $f(2 + \sqrt{3}) = 8 + 7\sqrt{3}$

34 $f(x) = x^3 - 3x^2 - 8$; $c = 1 + \sqrt{2}$ • $f(1 + \sqrt{2}) = -10 - \sqrt{2}$

35 $f(x) = 3x^4 + 8x^3 - 2x^2 - 10x + 4$; $c = -2$ •   ★ $f(-2) = 0$

36 $f(x) = 4x^3 - 9x^2 - 8x - 3$; $c = 3$ •   ★ $f(3) = 0$

37 $f(x) = 4x^3 - 6x^2 + 8x - 3$; $c = \frac{1}{2}$ •   ★ $f(\frac{1}{2}) = 0$

38 $f(x) = 27x^4 - 9x^3 + 3x^2 + 6x + 1$; $c = -\frac{1}{3}$ •   ★ $f(-\frac{1}{3}) = 0$

39 $f(-2) = k^2 - 8k + 15$. This remainder must be zero if $f(x)$ is to be divisible by $x + 2$.

$$k^2 - 8k + 15 = 0 \Rightarrow k = 3, 5.$$

40 $f(1) = k^2 - 4k + 3$. As in the previous exercise, $k^2 - 4k + 3 = 0 \Rightarrow k = 1, 3$.

41 $f(c) = 3c^4 + c^2 + 5 \geq 5 \ \forall c \in \mathbb{R}$, that is, the remainder cannot be zero.

42 $f(c) = -c^4 - 3c^2 - 2 \leq -2 \ \forall c \in \mathbb{R}$, that is, the remainder cannot be zero.

43 $f(x) = 3x^{100} + 5x^{85} - 4x^{38} + 2x^{17} - 6 \Rightarrow f(-1) = 3 - 5 - 4 - 2 - 6 = -14$.

{ change sign on coefficients of odd powers of x }

44 If $f(x) = x^n - y^n$, then $f(y) = y^n - y^n = 0$. Hence, $x - y$ is a factor of f.

45 If $f(x) = x^n - y^n$ and n is even, then $f(-y) = (-y)^n - (y)^n = y^n - y^n = 0$.

Hence, $x + y$ is a factor of $x^n - y^n$.

46 If $f(x) = x^n + y^n$ and n is odd, then $f(-y) = (-y)^n + y^n = -y^n + y^n = 0$.

Hence, $x + y$ is a factor of $x^n + y^n$.

47 (a) $V = \pi r^2 h = \pi x^2 (6 - x)$

(b) The volume of the cylinder of radius 1 and altitude 5 is $\pi (1)^2 5 = 5\pi$.

$$5\pi = \pi x^2 (6 - x) \Rightarrow x^3 - 6x^2 + 5 = 0 \Rightarrow (x - 1)(x^2 - 5x - 5) = 0 \Rightarrow$$

$$x = 1, \frac{5 \pm \sqrt{45}}{2}. \quad \frac{5 + \sqrt{45}}{2} \approx 5.85 \text{ would be an allowable value of } x.$$

The point P is $P(x, y) = (\frac{1}{2}(5 + \sqrt{45}), \frac{1}{2}(7 - \sqrt{45}))$.

48 The width, depth, and diameter form a right triangle.

$w^2 + d^2 = 2^2 \Rightarrow d^2 = 4 - w^2 = \frac{7}{4}$ for $w = \frac{3}{2}$. $S = kwd^2 = k(\frac{3}{2})(\frac{7}{4}) = \frac{21}{8}k$. Now

$\frac{21}{8}k = kw(4 - w^2) \Rightarrow 8w^3 - 32w + 21 = 0 \Rightarrow (w - \frac{3}{2})(8w^2 + 12w - 14) = 0 \Rightarrow$

$$w = \frac{3}{2}, \frac{-3 \pm \sqrt{37}}{4}. \quad \frac{\sqrt{37} - 3}{4} \approx 0.77 \text{ would be an allowable value of } w.$$

49 (a) $A = lw = (2x)(y) = 2x(4 - x^2) = 8x - 2x^3$

(b) $A = 6 \Rightarrow 6 = 8x - 2x^3 \Rightarrow x^3 - 4x + 3 = 0 \Rightarrow (x - 1)(x^2 + x - 3) = 0 \Rightarrow$

$x = 1, \dfrac{-1 \pm \sqrt{13}}{2}. \quad \dfrac{\sqrt{13} - 1}{2}$ would be an allowable value of x.

The base would then be $\sqrt{13} - 1 \approx 2.61$.

50 (a) Let $\frac{3}{2} - 2r$ denote the length of the right circular cylinder portion of the capsule.

$V = \frac{4}{3}\pi r^3 + \pi r^2(\frac{3}{2} - 2r) = \pi r^2(\frac{4}{3}r + \frac{3}{2} - 2r) = \pi r^2(\frac{3}{2} - \frac{2}{3}r)$.

(b) The tablet has volume $\pi(\frac{1}{2})^2\frac{1}{3} = \frac{\pi}{12}$. $\frac{\pi}{12} = \pi r^2(\frac{3}{2} - \frac{2}{3}r) \Rightarrow$

$8r^3 - 18r^2 + 1 = 0 \Rightarrow (4r - 1)(2r^2 - 4r - 1) = 0 \Rightarrow r = \frac{1}{4}, 1 \pm \frac{1}{2}\sqrt{6}.$

$\frac{1}{4}$ cm is the only allowable solution.

51 If $f(x) = x^8 - 7.9x^5 - 0.8x^4 + x^3 + 1.2x - 9.81,$

then the remainder is $f(0.21) \approx -9.55$.

[-1, 1] by [-20, 0]

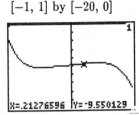

Xscl = 1

Yscl = 2

Figure 51

[-1, 1] by [-20, 0]

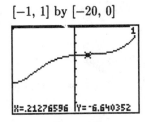

Xscl = 1

Yscl = 2

Figure 52

52 If $f(x) = 3.33x^6 - 2.5x^5 + 6.9x^3 - 4.1x^2 + 1.22x - 6.78,$

then the remainder is $f(0.21) \approx -6.64$.

53 $f(1.6) = -2k^4 + 2.56k^3 + 3.2k + 4.096$. Graph $y = -2k^4 + 2.56k^3 + 3.2k + 4.096$ (that

is, $y = -2x^4 + 2.56x^3 + 3.2x + 4.096$). From the graph, we see that $y = 0$ when

$k \approx -0.75, 1.96$. Thus, if k assumes either of these values, $f(1.6) = 0$ and f will be

divisible by $x - 1.6$ by the factor theorem.

[-9, 9] by [-3, 9]

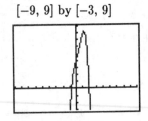

Xscl = 1

Yscl = 1

Figure 53

[-4.5, 4.5] by [-3, 3]

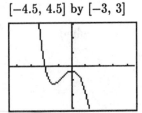

Xscl = 1

Yscl = 1

Figure 54

54 $f(-0.4) = -0.064k^5 - 0.4k^3 - 1.2k^2 - 0.336.$

Graph $y = -0.064k^5 - 0.4k^3 - 1.2k^2 - 0.336$. See *Figure 54*. From the graph, we see that $y = 0$ when $k \approx -1.98$. Thus, if k assumes this value, $f(-0.4) = 0$ and f will be divisible by $x + 0.4$ by the factor theorem.

3.3 Exercises

3.3 Concept Check

1 How many different complex zeros does a polynomial of degree $n > 0$ have? • At most n.

2 How many complex zeros does a polynomial of degree $n > 0$ have? • If a zero of multiplicity m is counted m times, then the polynomial has exactly n zeros.

3 Suppose you find three positive real zeros of $f(x)$, where f is given by $f(x) = x^5 - 9x^4 + 25x^3 - 15x^2 - 26x + 24$. What can you say about the other two zeros of $f(x)$? • There are four variations of sign in $f(x)$. Since we already have three positive real zeros, there must be four positive real zeros. Because there is only one variation of sign in $f(-x)$, the fifth zero of $f(x)$ must be a negative real number.

4 The polynomial $f(x) = 3x^4 - 12x^3 - 117x^2 + 258x + 840$ can be written as $f(x) = a(x + 5)(x + 2)(x - 4)(x - 7)$. What is the value of a? • The value of a is the leading coefficient of $f(x)$—in this case, 3.

5 Find the values of m and n (assume they are integers).

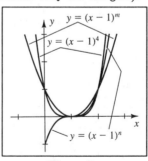

Figure 5

• Since the graph of $y = (x - 1)^m$ does not change sign as x increases through 1, m must be even; and since it increases slower than $y = (x - 1)^4$, m must equal 2. Since the graph of $y = (x - 1)^n$ changes sign from negative to positive as x increases through 1 and lies between $y = (x - 1)^2$ and $y = (x - 1)^4$, n must equal 3.

3.3 Exercises

1 $f(x) = a(x + 1)(x - 2)(x - 3);$

$f(-2) = a(-1)(-4)(-5) = 80 \Rightarrow -20a = 80 \Rightarrow a = -4$ ★ $-4x^3 + 16x^2 - 4x - 24$

$\boxed{2}$ $f(x) = a(x+5)(x-2)(x-4);$

$f(3) = a(8)(1)(-1) = -24 \Rightarrow -8a = -24 \Rightarrow a = 3$ $\bigstar \; 3x^3 - 3x^2 - 66x + 120$

$\boxed{3}$ $f(x) = a(x+4)(x-3)(x);$

$f(2) = a(6)(-1)(2) = -36 \Rightarrow -12a = -36 \Rightarrow a = 3$ $\bigstar \; 3x^3 + 3x^2 - 36x$

$\boxed{4}$ $f(x) = a(x+3)(x+2)(x);$

$f(-4) = a(-1)(-2)(-4) = 16 \Rightarrow -8a = 16 \Rightarrow a = -2$ $\bigstar \; -2x^3 - 10x^2 - 12x$

$\boxed{5}$ $f(x) = a(x+2i)(x-2i)(x-3);$

$f(1) = a(1+2i)(1-2i)(-2) = 20 \Rightarrow -10a = 20 \Rightarrow a = -2$ $\bigstar \; -2x^3 + 6x^2 - 8x + 24$

$\boxed{6}$ $f(x) = a(x+3i)(x-3i)(x-4);$

$f(-1) = a(-1+3i)(-1-3i)(-5) = 50 \Rightarrow -50a = 50 \Rightarrow a = -1$ $\bigstar \; -x^3 + 4x^2 - 9x + 36$

$\boxed{7}$ $f(x) = a(x+4)^2(x-3)^2 = (x^2+x-12)^2 \; \{\, a = 1 \,\} = x^4 + 2x^3 - 23x^2 - 24x + 144$

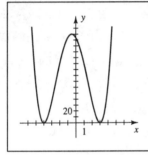

Figure 7

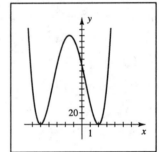

Figure 8

$\boxed{8}$ $f(x) = a(x+5)^2(x-2)^2 = (x^2+3x-10)^2 \; \{\, a = 1 \,\} = x^4 + 6x^3 - 11x^2 - 60x + 100.$

Note that the figure can be obtained by shifting *Figure 7* left 1 unit.

$\boxed{9}$ $f(x) = a(x)^3(x-3)^3$ so $f(2) = a(8)(-1) = -8a.$ But $f(2) = -24,$ so $-8a = -24,$ or,

$a = 3.$ $f(x) = 3(x)^3(x^3 - 9x^2 + 27x - 27) = 3x^6 - 27x^5 + 81x^4 - 81x^3.$

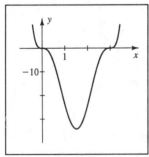

Figure 9

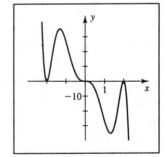

Figure 10

$\boxed{10}$ $f(x) = a(x)^3(x+2)^2(x-2)^2$ so $f(-1) = a(-1)(1)(9) = -9a.$

But $f(-1) = 27,$ so $-9a = 27,$ or, $a = -3.$

$$f(x) = -3x^3(x^2-4)^2 = -3x^3(x^4 - 8x^2 + 16) = -3x^7 + 24x^5 - 48x^3.$$

11 The graph has x-intercepts at -1, $\frac{3}{2}$, 3, and $f(0) = \frac{7}{2}$.

$f(x) = a(x+1)(x - \frac{3}{2})(x-3)$; $f(0) = a(1)(-\frac{3}{2})(-3) = \frac{7}{2} \Rightarrow \frac{9}{2}a = \frac{7}{2} \Rightarrow a = \frac{7}{9}$.

$$f(x) = \frac{7}{9}(x+1)(x - \frac{3}{2})(x-3)$$

12 The graph has x-intercepts at 0, 1, 3, 5, and $f(-1) = 4$.

$f(x) = a(x)(x-1)(x-3)(x-5)$; $f(-1) = a(-1)(-2)(-4)(-6) = 4 \Rightarrow$

$48a = 4 \Rightarrow a = \frac{1}{12}$. $f(x) = \frac{1}{12}x(x-1)(x-3)(x-5)$

13 3 is a zero of multiplicity one, 1 is a zero of multiplicity two, and $f(0) = 3$.

$f(x) = a(x-1)^2(x-3)$; $f(0) = a(1)(-3) = 3 \Rightarrow a = -1$. $f(x) = -1(x-1)^2(x-3)$.

14 4 is a zero of multiplicity one, 2 is a zero of multiplicity two, and $f(1) = -3$.

$f(x) = a(x-2)^2(x-4)$; $f(1) = a(1)(-3) = -3 \Rightarrow a = 1$. $f(x) = 1(x-2)^2(x-4)$.

15   ★ $-\frac{2}{3}$ (multiplicity 1); 0 (multiplicity 2); $\frac{5}{2}$ (multiplicity 3)

16   ★ -1 (multiplicity 4); 0 (multiplicity 1); $\frac{7}{3}$ (multiplicity 2)

17 $f(x) = 4x^5 + 12x^4 + 9x^3 = x^3(2x+3)^2$ ★ $-\frac{3}{2}$ (multiplicity 2); 0 (multiplicity 3)

18   ★ $\pm\frac{1}{2}\sqrt{5}$ (each of multiplicity 2)

19 $f(x) = (x^2 + x - 12)^3(x^2 - 9)^2 = (x+4)^3(x-3)^3(x+3)^2(x-3)^2$

★ -4 (multiplicity 3); -3 (multiplicity 2); 3 (multiplicity 5)

20 $f(x) = (6x^2 + 7x - 5)^4(4x^2 - 1)^2 = (3x+5)^4(2x-1)^4(2x+1)^2(2x-1)^2$

★ $-\frac{5}{3}$ (multiplicity 4); $-\frac{1}{2}$ (multiplicity 2); $\frac{1}{2}$ (multiplicity 6)

21 $f(x) = x^4 + 7x^2 - 144 = (x^2 + 16)(x+3)(x-3)$

★ $\pm 4i$, ± 3 (each of multiplicity 1)

22 $f(x) = x^4 + 21x^2 - 100 = (x^2 + 25)(x+2)(x-2)$

★ $\pm 5i$, ± 2 (each of multiplicity 1)

23 Using synthetic division, $f(x) = x^4 + 7x^3 + 13x^2 - 3x - 18 =$

$(x+3)(x^3 + 4x^2 + x - 6) = (x+3)^2(x^2 + x - 2) = (x+3)^2(x+2)(x-1)$.

24 $f(x) = x^4 - 9x^3 + 22x^2 - 32 = (x-4)^2(x-2)(x+1)$

25 $f(x) = x^6 - 4x^5 + 5x^4 - 5x^2 + 4x - 1 = (x-1)^5(x+1)$

26 $f(x) = x^5 + x^4 - 6x^3 - 14x^2 - 11x - 3 = (x+1)^4(x-3)$

Note: For the following exercises, let $f(x)$ denote the polynomial, P, the number of sign changes in $f(x)$, and N, the number of sign changes in $f(-x)$. The types of possible solutions are listed in the order positive, negative, nonreal complex.

27 There are 3 sign changes in $f(x) = 4x^3 - 6x^2 + x - 3$, so $P = 3$. There are no sign changes in $f(-x) = -4x^3 - 6x^2 - x - 3$, so $N = 0$, and there are no negative solutions of the given equation. The equation has either 3 positive solutions or 1 positive solution along with 2 nonreal complex solutions.   ★ 3, 0, 0 or 1, 0, 2

28 $5x^3 - 6x - 4 = 0$ •   P = 1, N = 2   ★ 1, 2, 0 or 1, 0, 2

29 $4x^3 + 2x^2 + 1 = 0$ •   P = 0, N = 1   ★ 0, 1, 2

30 $3x^3 - 4x^2 + 3x + 7 = 0$ •   P = 2, N = 1   ★ 2, 1, 0 or 0, 1, 2

31 $3x^4 + 2x^3 - 4x + 2 = 0$ •   P = 2, N = 2   ★ 2, 2, 0; 2, 0, 2; 0, 2, 2; 0, 0, 4

32 $2x^4 - x^3 + x^2 - 3x + 4 = 0$ •   P = 4, N = 0   ★ 4, 0, 0; 2, 0, 2; 0, 0, 4

33 $x^5 + 4x^4 + 3x^3 - 4x + 2 = 0$ • P = 2, N = 3   ★ 2, 3, 0; 2, 1, 2; 0, 3, 2; 0, 1, 4

34 $2x^6 + 5x^5 + 2x^2 - 3x + 4 = 0$ • P = 2, N = 2   ★ 2, 2, 2; 2, 0, 4; 0, 2, 4; 0, 0, 6

35 From the graph of $f(x) = x^3 - 4x^2 - 5x + 7$, we see that the bounds given by the theorem (5 and −2) are indeed the smallest and largest integers that are upper and lower bounds.

36 From the graph of $f(x) = 2x^3 - 5x^2 + 4x - 8$, we see that the least integer upper bound is 3 and the greatest integer lower bound is 2. According to the theorem, the greatest *negative* integer lower bound is −1 (the theorem gives no information about a greatest *positive* integer lower bound).

37 From the graph of $f(x) = x^4 - x^3 - 2x^2 + 3x + 6$, we see that there are no real zeros. The theorem gives us upper and lower bounds of 2 and −2, respectively.

38 Similar to Exercise 35 with $f(x) = 2x^4 - 9x^3 - 8x - 10$, upper bound 5, and lower bound −1.

39 Similar to Exercise 35 with $f(x) = 2x^5 - 13x^3 + 2x - 5$, upper bound 3, and lower bound −3.

40 Similar to Exercise 36 with $f(x) = 3x^5 + 2x^4 - x^3 - 8x^2 - 7$, upper bound 2, and lower bound 1.

41 $f(x) = a(x+1)^2(x-1)(x-2)^3$. $f(0) = a(1)(-1)(-8) = 8a$ and $f(0) = -2 \Rightarrow a = -\frac{1}{4}$.

42 $f(x) = a(x+2)(x+1)(x-2)^2$. $f(0) = a(2)(1)(4) = 8a$ and $f(0) = 1 \Rightarrow a = \frac{1}{8}$.

43 (a) $f(x) = a(x+3)^3(x+1)(x-2)^2$.

    (b) $a = 1$ and $x = 0 \Rightarrow f(0) = 1(3)^3(1)(-2)^2 = 108$.

44 (a) $f(x) = a(x+2)^3(x-3)^2$.

    (b) $a = -1$ and $x = 0 \Rightarrow f(0) = -1(2)^3(-3)^2 = -72$.

45 From the graph, we see that $f(x) = x^5 - 16.75x^3 + 12.75x^2 + 49.5x - 54$ has zeros of -4, -2, 1.5, and 3. There is a double root at 1.5. Since the leading coefficient of f is 1, we have $f(x) = 1(x+4)(x+2)(x-1.5)^2(x-3)$.

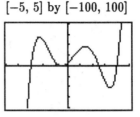

$[-5, 5]$ by $[-150, 150]$ $[-5, 5]$ by $[-100, 100]$

Xscl $= 1$

Yscl $= 25$

Xscl $= 1$

Yscl $= 25$

Figure 45   *Figure 46*

46 From the graph, we see that $f(x) = x^5 - 2.5x^4 - 12.75x^3 + 19.625x^2 + 27.625x + 7.5$ has zeros of -3, -0.5, 2.5, and 4. There is a double root at -0.5. Since the leading coefficient of f is 1, we have $f(x) = (x+3)(x+0.5)^2(x-2.5)(x-4)$.

47 Since the zeros are -2, 1, 2, and 3, the polynomial must have the form
$$f(x) = a(x+2)(x-1)(x-2)(x-3).$$
Now, $f(0) = a(2)(-1)(-2)(-3) = -12a$ and $f(0) = -24 \Rightarrow -12a = -24 \Rightarrow a = 2$.
Let $f(x) = 2(x+2)(x-1)(x-2)(x-3)$. Since f has been completely determined, we must check the remaining data point(s). $f(-1) = 2(1)(-2)(-3)(-4) = -48 \neq -52$.

Thus, a fourth-degree polynomial *does not* fit the data points.

48 $f(x) = a(x)(x+3)(x+1)(x-2)(x-3)$. $f(-2) = a(-2)(1)(-1)(-4)(-5) = 40a$ and $f(-2) = 5 \Rightarrow 40a = 5 \Rightarrow a = \frac{1}{8}$. Let $f(x) = \frac{1}{8}x(x+3)(x+1)(x-2)(x-3)$. $f(1) = \frac{1}{8}(1)(4)(2)(-1)(-2) = 2$. Thus, a fifth-degree polynomial *does* fit the data points.

49 $f(x) = a(x-2)(x-5.2)(x-10.1)$. $f(1.1) = a(-33.21) = -49.815 \Rightarrow a = 1.5$.
Let $f(x) = 1.5(x-2)(x-5.2)(x-10.1)$. $f(3.5) = 25.245$ and $f(6.4) = -29.304$.

Thus, a third-degree polynomial *does* fit the data points.

50 $f(x) = a(x-1.25)(x-2)(x-6.5)(x-10)$. $f(2.5) = a(18.75) = 56.25 \Rightarrow a = 3$.
Let $f(x) = 3(x-1.25)(x-2)(x-6.5)(x-10)$. $f(2.5) = 56.25$ and $f(3) = 128.625$.
However, $f(9) = -406.875 \neq -307.75$.

Thus, a fourth-degree polynomial *does not* fit the data points.

51 The zeros are 0, 5, 19, 24, and $f(12) = 10$. $f(t) = a(t)(t-5)(t-19)(t-24)$;
$f(12) = a(12)(7)(-7)(-12) = 10 \Rightarrow 7056a = 10 \Rightarrow a = \frac{5}{3528}$.
$$f(t) = \frac{5}{3528}t(t-5)(t-19)(t-24)$$

52 $f(x) = a(x-c_1)(x-c_2)(x-c_3)$;
$$f(c) = a(c-c_1)(c-c_2)(c-c_3) = 1 \Rightarrow a = \frac{1}{(c-c_1)(c-c_2)(c-c_3)}$$
$$f(x) = \frac{1}{(c-c_1)(c-c_2)(c-c_3)}(x-c_1)(x-c_2)(x-c_3)$$

53 The graph of f does not cross the x-axis at a zero of even multiplicity, but does cross the x-axis at a zero of odd multiplicity. The higher the multiplicity of a zero, the more horizontal the graph of f is near that zero.

[−3, 3] by [−2, 2]   [−3, 3] by [−2, 2]

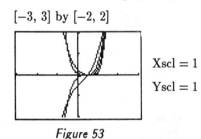

Xscl = 1   Xscl = 1
Yscl = 1   Yscl = 1

Figure 53   *Figure 54*

54 The conclusions from Exercise 53 do not change when there is more than one zero.

55 From the graph of f there are two zeros. They are −1.2 and 1.1. The zero at −1.2 has even multiplicity and the zero at 1.1 has odd multiplicity. Since f has degree 3, the zero at −1.2 must have multiplicity 2 and the zero at 1.1 has multiplicity 1.

[−3, 3] by [−3, 1]   [−3, 3] by [−2, 2]

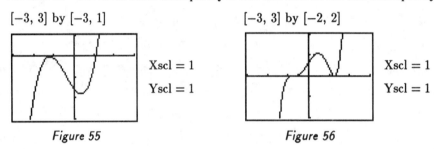

Xscl = 1   Xscl = 1
Yscl = 1   Yscl = 1

Figure 55   *Figure 56*

56 From the graph of f there are two zeros. They are −0.75 and 1.25. The zero at −0.75 has odd multiplicity and the zero at 1.25 has even multiplicity. Since f has degree 5, there are two possibilities for the multiplicity: −0.75 has multiplicity 1 and 1.25 has multiplicity 4, or −0.75 has multiplicity 3 and 1.25 has multiplicity 2. By careful inspection we can see that the graph of f levels off as it crosses the x-axis at −0.75. This means that the multiplicity of this zero is greater than 1. (See Exercises 53 and 54.) Thus, −0.75 has multiplicity 3 and 1.25 has multiplicity 2.

57 From the graph of $A(t) = -\frac{1}{2400}t^3 + \frac{1}{20}t^2 + \frac{7}{6}t + 340$, we see that $A = 400$ when $t \approx 27.1$. Thus, the carbon dioxide concentration will be 400 in $1980 + 27.1 = 2007.1$, or, during the year 2007.

[0, 60] by [0, 600]   [0, 60] by [−2, 2]

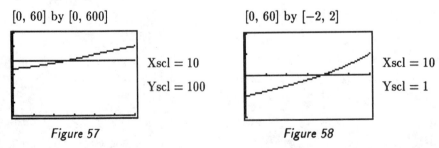

Xscl = 10   Xscl = 10
Yscl = 100   Yscl = 1

Figure 57   *Figure 58*

58 From the graph of $T(t) = \frac{21}{5,000,000}t^3 - \frac{127}{1,000,000}t^2 + \frac{1293}{50,000}t - 1$, we see that $T = 0$ when $t \approx 37.1$. Thus, the average temperature will have increased by $1\,°\text{C}$ in $1980 + 37.1 = 2017.1$, or, during the year 2017. See *Figure 58*.

59 (a) Graphing the data and the functions show that the best fit is $h(x)$.

(b) Since the temperature changes sign between April and May and between October and November, an average temperature of $0\,°\text{F}$ occurs when $4 \leq x \leq 5$ and $10 \leq x \leq 11$.

(c) Finding the zeros of h between 1 and 12 gives us $x \approx 4.02,\ 10.53$.

[0.5, 12.5] by [−30, 50]

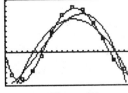

$\text{Xscl} = 1$

$\text{Yscl} = 10$

Figure 59

[0.5, 12.5] by [−20, 70]

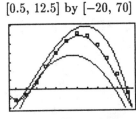

$\text{Xscl} = 1$

$\text{Yscl} = 10$

Figure 60

60 (a) Graphing the data and the functions show that the best fit is $h(x)$.

(b) Since the temperature changes sign between February and March and between November and December, an average temperature of $0\,°\text{F}$ occurs when $2 \leq x \leq 3$ and $11 \leq x \leq 12$.

(c) Finding the zeros of h between 1 and 12 gives us $x \approx 2.54,\ 11.42$.

61 Let $r = 6$ and $k = 0.7$. Graph $Y_1 = \frac{4k}{3}\pi r^3 - \pi x^2 r + \frac{1}{3}\pi x^3 = \frac{604.8\pi}{3} - 6\pi x^2 + \frac{1}{3}\pi x^3$ and determine the positive zeros. There are two zeros located at $x \approx 7.64,\ 15.47$. Since the sphere floats, it will not sink deeper than twice the radius, which is 12 centimeters. Thus, the pine sphere will sink approximately 7.64 centimeters into the water.

[−20, 20] by [−800, 800]

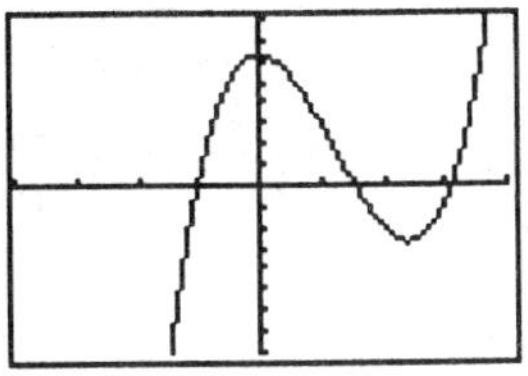

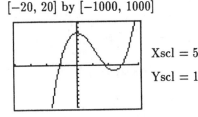

$\text{Xscl} = 5$

$\text{Yscl} = 100$

Figure 61

[−20, 20] by [−1000, 1000]

$\text{Xscl} = 5$

$\text{Yscl} = 100$

Figure 62

62 Let $r = 6$ and $k = 0.85$. Graph $Y_1 = \frac{4k}{3}\pi r^3 - \pi x^2 r + \frac{1}{3}\pi x^3 = \frac{734.4\pi}{3} - 6\pi x^2 + \frac{1}{3}\pi x^3$ and determine the positive zeros. There are two zeros located at $x \approx 9.07,\ 14.51$.

(continued)

Since the sphere floats, it will not sink deeper than twice the radius, which is 12. Thus, the oak sphere will sink approximately 9.07 centimeters into the water. This is slightly deeper than the pine sphere because the density of oak wood is greater than that of pine.

$\boxed{63}$ Let $r = 6$ and $k = 1$.   Graph $Y_1 = \frac{4k}{3}\pi r^3 - \pi x^2 r + \frac{1}{3}\pi x^3 = 288\pi - 6\pi x^2 + \frac{1}{3}\pi x^3$ and determine the positive zero. There is a zero at $x = 12$. This means that the entire sphere is just submerged. The sphere has the same density as water and neither sinks nor floats, much like a balloon filled with water.

$[-20, 20]$ by $[-1000, 1000]$

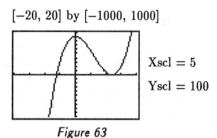

Xscl $= 5$

Yscl $= 100$

Figure 63

3.4 Exercises

3.4 Concept Check

$\boxed{1}$ What are the possible rational zeros of $f(x) = x^4 + 3x^3 - 4x^2 + 5x - 1$?   •   The possible rational zeros of f are ± 1.

$\boxed{2}$ The polynomial $f(x) = x^5 + 2x^4 - x - 2$ can be factored as $(x^3 + 2x^2 - x - 2)(x^2 + 1)$. Can it be factored further?   •   Yes, see the theorem on expressing a polynomial as a product of linear and quadratic factors. In this case,
$$x^3 + 2x^2 - x - 2 = (x + 1)(x - 1)(x + 2).$$

3.4 Exercises

$\boxed{1}$ Since $3 + 2i$ is a root, so is $3 - 2i$. Thus, the polynomial is of the form
$[x - (3 + 2i)][x - (3 - 2i)] = x^2 - 6x + 13$ { from the discussion on the top of p. 214 }.

$\boxed{2}$ $[x - (-4 + 3i)][x - (-4 - 3i)] = x^2 + 8x + 25$

$\boxed{3}$ $(x - 2)[x - (-2 - 5i)][x - (-2 + 5i)] = (x - 2)(x^2 + 4x + 29)$

$\boxed{4}$ $(x + 3)[x - (1 - 7i)][x - (1 + 7i)] = (x + 3)(x^2 - 2x + 50)$

$\boxed{5}$ $x(x + 1)[x - (3 + i)][x - (3 - i)] = x(x + 1)(x^2 - 6x + 10)$

$\boxed{6}$ $x(x - 2)[x - (-2 - i)][x - (-2 + i)] = x(x - 2)(x^2 + 4x + 5)$

$\boxed{7}$ $[x - (4 + 3i)][x - (4 - 3i)][x - (-2 + i)][x - (-2 - i)] = (x^2 - 8x + 25)(x^2 + 4x + 5)$

$\boxed{8}$ $[x - (3 + 5i)][x - (3 - 5i)][x - (-1 - i)][x - (-1 + i)] = (x^2 - 6x + 34)(x^2 + 2x + 2)$

$\boxed{9}$ $[x - (-2i)][x - (2i)][x - (1 - i)][x - (1 + i)] = x(x^2 + 4)(x^2 - 2x + 2)$

$\boxed{10}$ $[x-(3i)][x-(-3i)][x-(4+i)][x-(4-i)] = x(x^2+9)(x^2-8x+17)$

Note: Show that none of the possible rational roots listed satisfy the equation in 11–14.

$\boxed{11}$ $x^3 + 3x^2 - 4x + 6 = 0$ •   ★ $\pm 1, \pm 2, \pm 3, \pm 6$

$\boxed{12}$ $3x^3 - 4x^2 + 7x + 5 = 0$ •   ★ $\pm 1, \pm \frac{1}{3}, \pm 5, \pm \frac{5}{3}$

$\boxed{13}$ $x^5 - 3x^3 + 4x^2 + x - 2 = 0$ •   ★ $\pm 1, \pm 2$

$\boxed{14}$ $2x^5 + 3x^3 + 7 = 0$ •   ★ $\pm 1, \pm \frac{1}{2}, \pm 7, \pm \frac{7}{2}$

$\boxed{15}$ $x^3 - x^2 - 10x - 8 = 0$ •   ★ $-2, -1, 4$

$\boxed{16}$ $x^3 + x^2 - 14x - 24 = 0$ •   ★ $-3, -2, 4$

$\boxed{17}$ $2x^3 - 3x^2 - 17x + 30 = 0$ •   ★ $-3, 2, \frac{5}{2}$

$\boxed{18}$ $12x^3 + 8x^2 - 3x - 2 = 0$ •   ★ $-\frac{2}{3}, \pm \frac{1}{2}$

$\boxed{19}$ $x^4 + 3x^3 - 30x^2 - 6x + 56 = 0$ •   ★ $-7, \pm \sqrt{2}, 4$

$\boxed{20}$ $3x^5 - 10x^4 - 6x^3 + 24x^2 + 11x - 6 = 0$ •   ★ -1 (multiplicity 2), $\frac{1}{3}, 2, 3$

$\boxed{21}$ $6x^5 + 19x^4 + x^3 - 6x^2 = 0$ •   ★ $-3, -\frac{2}{3}, 0$ (multiplicity 2), $\frac{1}{2}$

$\boxed{22}$ $6x^4 + 5x^3 - 17x^2 - 6x = 0$ •   ★ $-2, -\frac{1}{3}, 0, \frac{3}{2}$

$\boxed{23}$ $8x^3 + 18x^2 + 45x + 27 = 0$ •   ★ $-\frac{3}{4}, -\frac{3}{4} \pm \frac{3}{4}\sqrt{7}\,i$

$\boxed{24}$ $3x^3 - x^2 + 11x - 20 = 0$ •   ★ $\frac{4}{3}, -\frac{1}{2} \pm \frac{1}{2}\sqrt{19}\,i$

$\boxed{25}$ $f(x) = 6x^5 - 23x^4 + 24x^3 + x^2 - 12x + 4$ has zeros at $-\frac{2}{3}, \frac{1}{2}, 1$ (mult. 2), and 2.

Thus, $f(x) = 6(x + \frac{2}{3})(x - \frac{1}{2})(x-1)^2(x-2) = (3x+2)(2x-1)(x-1)^2(x-2)$.

$\boxed{26}$ $f(x) = -6x^5 + 5x^4 + 14x^3 - 8x^2 - 8x + 3$ has zeros at -1 (mult. 2), $\frac{1}{3}, 1$, and $\frac{3}{2}$.

Thus, $f(x) = -6(x+1)^2(x - \frac{1}{3})(x-1)(x - \frac{3}{2}) = (x+1)^2(3x-1)(1-x)(2x-3)$.

$\boxed{27}$ From the graph, we see that $f(x) = 2x^3 - 25.4x^2 + 3.02x + 24.75$ has zeros of approximately $-0.9, 1.1$, and 12.5. Since the leading coefficient of f is 2, we have $f(x) = 2(x+0.9)(x-1.1)(x-12.5)$.

[−5, 15] by [−600, 100]   [−5, 5] by [−15, 15]

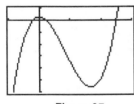   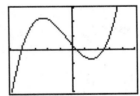

Xscl = 5   Xscl = 1

Yscl = 100   Yscl = 5

Figure 27   *Figure 28*

$\boxed{28}$ From the graph, we see that $f(x) = 0.5x^3 + 0.65x^2 - 5.365x + 1.5375$ has zeros of approximately $-4.1, 0.3$, and 2.5. Since the leading coefficient of f is 0.5, we have $f(x) = 0.5(x+4.1)(x-0.3)(x-2.5)$.

$\boxed{29}$ No. If i is a root, then $-i$ is also a root. Hence, the polynomial would have factors $x-1, x+1, x-i, x+i$ and therefore would be of degree greater than 3.

30 The theorem applies only to polynomials with real coefficients whereas the polynomial in question has nonreal complex coefficients.

31 Since n is odd and nonreal complex zeros occur in conjugate pairs for polynomials with real coefficients, there must be at least one real zero.

32 By the theorem on rational zeros, r is of the form c/d, where c is a factor of a_0 and d is a factor of a_n. Since a_n is 1, its divisors are ± 1.

Thus, r will be an integer and a factor of a_0.

33 (a) $V(x) = x(20 - 2x)(30 - 2x) = 1000 \Rightarrow 4x^3 - 100x^2 + 600x - 1000 = 0 \Rightarrow$
$4(x - 5)\left[x - (10 - 5\sqrt{2})\right]\left[x - (10 + 5\sqrt{2})\right] = 0$. The allowable range from Exercise 33 of Section 3.1 was $(0, 10)$, so discard $10 + 5\sqrt{2}$.

The two boxes having volume 1000 in^3 have dimensions
$$[\text{A}] \; 5 \times 10 \times 20 \text{ and } [\text{B}] \; (10 - 5\sqrt{2}) \times (10\sqrt{2}) \times (10 + 10\sqrt{2}).$$

(b) The surface area function is
$$S(x) = (20 - 2x)(30 - 2x) + 2(x)(20 - 2x) + 2(x)(30 - 2x) = -4x^2 + 600.$$
$S(5) = 500$ and $S(10 - 5\sqrt{2}) = 400\sqrt{2} \approx 565.7$ so box $[\text{A}]$ has less surface area.

34 From Exercise 34 in §3.1, $V(x) = x^2(6 - 2x)$. $V(x) = 4 \Rightarrow x^3 - 3x^2 + 2 = 0 \Rightarrow$
$$(x - 1)(x^2 - 2x - 2) = 0 \Rightarrow \{x > 0\} \; x = 1, \; 1 + \sqrt{3}.$$

35 (a) The sides of the triangle are x, $x + 1$, and $\sqrt{2x + 1}$.
$$A = \tfrac{1}{2}bh \Rightarrow 30 = \tfrac{1}{2}x\sqrt{2x + 1} \Rightarrow 2x^3 + x^2 - 3600 = 0.$$

(b) There is one sign change in $f(x) = 2x^3 + x^2 - 3600$.

By Descartes' rule of signs there is one positive real root.

Synthetically dividing 13 into f, we obtain a third row of 2, 27, 351, and 963.

These are all positive so 13 is an upper bound for the zeros of f.

(c) $f(x) = 0 \Rightarrow (x - 12)(2x^2 + 25x + 300) = 0$.

The legs of the triangle are 12 and 5, and the hypotenuse is 13.

36 $V(x) = 10\pi x^2 + \tfrac{4}{3}\pi x^3 = 27\pi \Rightarrow 4x^3 + 30x^2 - 81 = 0 \Rightarrow$
$$(2x - 3)(2x^2 + 18x + 27) = 0. \text{ The radius is 1.5 ft.}$$

37 (a) $\text{Volume}_{\text{total}} = \text{Volume}_{\text{cube}} + \text{Volume}_{\text{roof}}$
$$= x^3 + \tfrac{1}{2}bhx = x^3 + \tfrac{1}{2}(x)(6 - x)(x) = x^3 + \tfrac{1}{2}x^2(6 - x).$$

(b) $\text{Volume} = 80 \Rightarrow x^3 + 6x^2 - 160 = 0 \Rightarrow (x - 4)(x^2 + 10x + 40) = 0$.

The length of the side is 4 ft.

38 Form a triangle with the center pole and the midpoint of any side.

The hypotenuse (call it y) is the height of one of the triangular sides with base x.

$(\tfrac{1}{2}x)^2 + (8)^2 = y^2 \Rightarrow y = \sqrt{64 + \tfrac{1}{4}x^2}$. $\text{Area}_{\text{total}} = \text{Area}_{\text{base}} + \text{Area}_{4 \text{ sides}} =$

$(\text{side})(\text{side}) + 4(\frac{1}{2})(\text{base})(\text{height}) = x^2 + 4(\frac{1}{2})(x)\sqrt{64 + \frac{1}{4}x^2} = 384 \Rightarrow$

$$147{,}456 - 768x^2 + x^4 = 4x^2(64 + \frac{1}{4}x^2) \Rightarrow x^2 = 144 \Rightarrow x = 12.$$

39 $x^5 + 1.1x^4 - 3.21x^3 - 2.835x^2 + 2.7x + 0.62 = -1 \Leftrightarrow$

$x^5 + 1.1x^4 - 3.21x^3 - 2.835x^2 + 2.7x + 1.62 = 0.$

The graph of $y = x^5 + 1.1x^4 - 3.21x^3 - 2.835x^2 + 2.7x + 1.62$ intersects the x-axis three times. The zeros at -1.5 and 1.2 have even multiplicity (since the graph is tangent to the x-axis at these points) and the zero at -0.5 has odd multiplicity (since the graph crosses the x-axis at this point). Since the equation has degree 5, the only possibility is that the zeros at -1.5 and 1.2 have multiplicity 2 and the zero at -0.5 has multiplicity 1. Thus, the equation has no nonreal solutions.

$[-4.5, 4.5]$ by $[-3, 3]$ $[-4.5, 4.5]$ by $[-3, 3]$

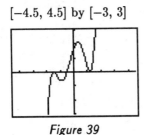

Xscl $= 1$

Yscl $= 1$

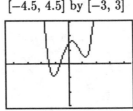

Xscl $= 1$

Yscl $= 1$

Figure 39   *Figure 40*

40 $x^4 - 0.4x^3 - 2.6x^2 + 1.1x + 3.5 = 2 \Leftrightarrow x^4 - 0.4x^3 - 2.6x^2 + 1.1x + 1.5 = 0.$ The graph of $y = x^4 - 0.4x^3 - 2.6x^2 + 1.1x + 1.5$ crosses the x-axis twice. There are two real zeros and they have odd multiplicity. By careful inspection we can see that the graph does not level off at either zero. Therefore, the zeros must have multiplicity 1. (See Exercises 53 and 54 in §3.3.) Since the equation has degree 4, there are two nonreal solutions.

41 Graph $y = x^4 + 1.4x^3 + 0.44x^2 - 0.56x - 0.96.$

From the graph, zeros are located at -1.2 and 0.8. Using synthetic division,

$\dfrac{x^4 + 1.4x^3 + 0.44x^2 - 0.56x - 0.96}{x + 1.2} = x^3 + 0.2x^2 + 0.2x - 0.8$ and

$\dfrac{x^3 + 0.2x^2 + 0.2x - 0.8}{x - 0.8} = x^2 + x + 1.$ The zeros of $x^2 + x + 1$ are $-\frac{1}{2} \pm \frac{\sqrt{3}}{2}i.$

Thus, the solutions to the equation are $-1.2,\ 0.8,\ -\frac{1}{2} \pm \frac{\sqrt{3}}{2}i.$

$[-4.5, 4.5]$ by $[-3, 3]$ $[-6.5, 7]$ by $[-3, 6]$

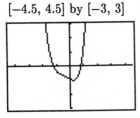

Xscl $= 1$

Yscl $= 1$

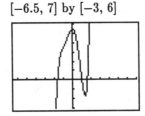

Xscl $= 1$

Yscl $= 1$

Figure 41   *Figure 42*

42 Graph $y = x^5 + 1.1x^4 - 2.62x^3 - 4.72x^2 - 0.2x + 5.44$. See *Figure 42*.

From the graph, zeros are located at -1.7, 1, and 1.6. Using synthetic division,

$$\frac{x^5 + 1.1x^4 - 2.62x^3 - 4.72x^2 - 0.2x + 5.44}{x + 1.7} = x^4 - 0.6x^3 - 1.6x^2 - 2x + 3.2,$$

$$\frac{x^4 - 0.6x^3 - 1.6x^2 - 2x + 3.2}{x - 1} = x^3 + 0.4x^2 - 1.2x - 3.2, \text{ and}$$

$$\frac{x^3 + 0.4x^2 - 1.2x - 3.2}{x - 1.6} = x^2 + 2x + 2. \text{ The zeros of } x^2 + 2x + 2 \text{ are } -1 \pm i.$$

Thus, the solutions to the equation are -1.7, 1, 1.6, $-1 \pm i$.

43 From the graph, we see that $D(h) = 0.4$ when $h \approx 10{,}200$.

Thus, the density of the atmosphere is 0.4 kg/m^3 at $10{,}200$ m.

[0, 30,000] by [0, 1.2]   [0, 1000] by [0, 5]

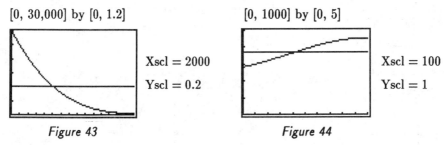

Xscl = 2000   Xscl = 100

Yscl = 0.2   Yscl = 1

     Figure 43   *Figure 44*

44 From the graph, we see that $D(h) = 3.7$ when $h \approx 418$. Thus, the density of the earth is 3.7 g/cm^3 at 418 m. (The graphs also intersect at $h \approx -674$ and $h \approx 1394$. However, these values are not in the domain of D.)

3.5 Exercises

3.5 Concept Check

1 If $f(x) = \dfrac{g(x)}{x - 2}$, where $g(x)$ is a polynomial, does f have a vertical asymptote at $x = 2$? • It depends. If $x - 2$ is not a factor of $g(x)$, then there is a vertical asymptote at $x = 2$. If $x - 2$ is a factor of $g(x)$, then there is a hole at $x = 2$.

2 What is the horizontal asymptote of f?   (a) $f(x) = \dfrac{3x^2 - 5x}{x^2 + 4x - 2}$ (b) $f(x) = \dfrac{3x - 5}{x^2 + 4x - 2}$ • (a) By (2) of the Theorem on Horizontal Asymptotes, $y = 3/1 = 3$ is the horizontal asymptote. (b) By (1) of the Theorem on Horizontal Asymptotes, $y = 0$ is the horizontal asymptote.

3.5 Exercises

1⃝ (b) D = all nonzero real numbers; $R = D$ (c) Decreasing on $(-\infty, 0)$ and on $(0, \infty)$

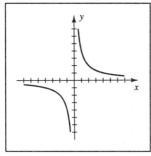

Figure 1

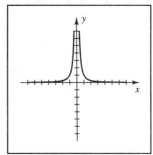

Figure 2

2⃝ (b) D = all nonzero real numbers; $R = (0, \infty)$

(c) Increasing on $(-\infty, 0)$, decreasing on $(0, \infty)$

3⃝ $f(x) = \dfrac{3}{x - 4}$ ●

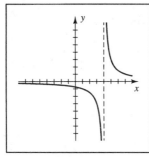

Figure 3

4⃝ $f(x) = \dfrac{-3}{x + 3}$ ●

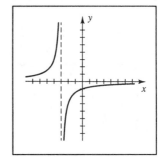

Figure 4

5⃝ $f(x) = \dfrac{-3x}{x + 2}$ ●

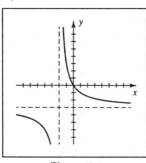

Figure 5

6⃝ $f(x) = \dfrac{4x}{2x - 5}$ ●

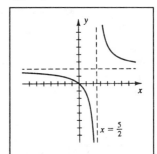

Figure 6

Note: Let I denote the point of intersection between the function and its horizontal or oblique asymptote. See Exercises 14 and 28 for more detailed work on finding I.

$\boxed{7}$ $f(x) = \dfrac{x-2}{x^2-x-6} = \dfrac{x-2}{(x+2)(x-3)}$; $I = (2,\,0)$

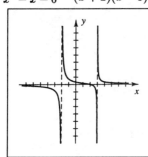

Figure 7

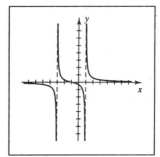

Figure 8

$\boxed{8}$ $f(x) = \dfrac{x+1}{x^2+2x-3} = \dfrac{x+1}{(x+3)(x-1)}$; $I = (-1,\,0)$

$\boxed{9}$ $f(x) = \dfrac{-4}{(x-2)^2}$ •

$\boxed{10}$ $f(x) = \dfrac{2}{(x+1)^2}$ •

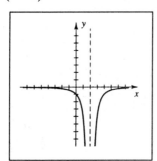

Figure 9

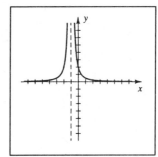

Figure 10

$\boxed{11}$ $f(x) = \dfrac{x-3}{x^2-1} = \dfrac{x-3}{(x+1)(x-1)}$; $I = (3,\,0)$

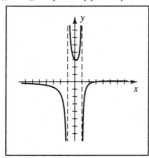

Figure 11

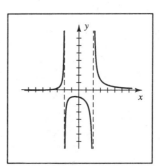

Figure 12

$\boxed{12}$ $f(x) = \dfrac{x+4}{x^2-4} = \dfrac{x+4}{(x+2)(x-2)}$; $I = (-4,\,0)$

13 $f(x) = \dfrac{2x^2 - 2x - 4}{x^2 + x - 12} = \dfrac{2(x+1)(x-2)}{(x+4)(x-3)}; \ I = (5, 2)$

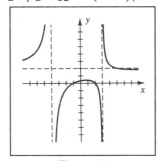

Figure 13

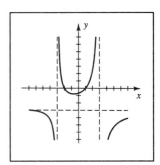

Figure 14

14 $f(x) = \dfrac{-3x^2 - 3x + 6}{x^2 - 9} = \dfrac{-3(x+2)(x-1)}{(x+3)(x-3)}$

$f(x) = -3 \Rightarrow \dfrac{-3x^2 - 3x + 6}{x^2 - 9} = -3 \Rightarrow -3x^2 - 3x + 6 = -3x^2 + 27 \Rightarrow$

$-3x = 21 \Rightarrow x = -7, \ I = (-7, -3).$

15 $f(x) = \dfrac{-x^2 - x + 6}{x^2 + 3x - 4} = \dfrac{-1(x+3)(x-2)}{(x+4)(x-1)}; \ I = (-1, -1)$

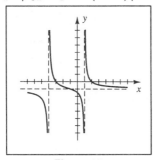

Figure 15

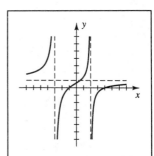

Figure 16

16 $f(x) = \dfrac{x^2 - 3x - 4}{x^2 + x - 6} = \dfrac{(x+1)(x-4)}{(x+3)(x-2)}; \ I = (\frac{1}{2}, 1)$

17 $f(x) = \dfrac{3x^2 - 3x - 36}{x^2 + x - 2} = \dfrac{3(x+3)(x-4)}{(x+2)(x-1)}; \ I = (-5, 3)$

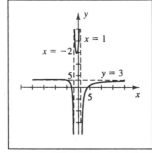

Figure 17

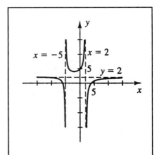

Figure 18

18 $f(x) = \dfrac{2x^2 + 4x - 48}{x^2 + 3x - 10} = \dfrac{2(x+6)(x-4)}{(x+5)(x-2)}; \ I = (-14, 2)$

[19] $f(x) = \dfrac{-2x^2 + 10x - 12}{x^2 + x} = \dfrac{-2(x-2)(x-3)}{(x+1)(x)}$; $I = (1, -2)$

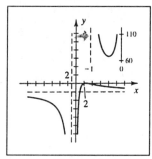

Figure 19

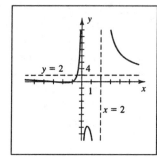

Figure 20

[20] $f(x) = \dfrac{2x^2 + 8x + 6}{x^2 - 2x} = \dfrac{2(x+3)(x+1)}{(x)(x-2)}$; $I = (-\frac{1}{2}, 2)$

[21] $f(x) = \dfrac{x-1}{x^3 - 4x} = \dfrac{x-1}{(x+2)(x)(x-2)}$; $I = (1, 0)$

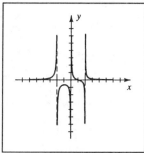

Figure 21

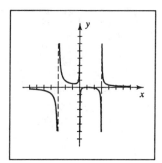

Figure 22

[22] $f(x) = \dfrac{x^2 - 2x + 1}{x^3 - 9x} = \dfrac{(x-1)^2}{(x+3)(x)(x-3)}$; $I = (1, 0)$

[23] $f(x) = \dfrac{-3x^2}{x^2 + 1}$; f is an even function

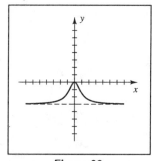

Figure 23

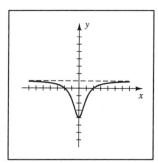

Figure 24

[24] $f(x) = \dfrac{x^2 - 4}{x^2 + 1} = \dfrac{(x+2)(x-2)}{x^2 + 1}$; f is an even function

$\boxed{25}$ $f(x) = \dfrac{x^2 - x - 6}{x + 1} = \dfrac{(x+2)(x-3)}{x+1} = x - 2 - \dfrac{4}{x+1}$.

The expression $\dfrac{4}{x+1} \to 0$ as $x \to \pm\infty$, so $y = x - 2$ is an oblique asymptote for f.

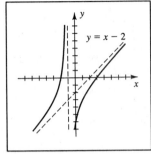

Figure 25

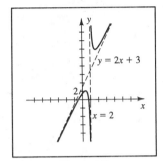

Figure 26

$\boxed{26}$ $f(x) = \dfrac{2x^2 - x - 3}{x - 2} = \dfrac{(x+1)(2x-3)}{x-2} = 2x + 3 + \dfrac{3}{x-2}$

$\boxed{27}$ $f(x) = \dfrac{8 - x^3}{2x^2} = \dfrac{(2-x)(4 + 2x + x^2)}{2x^2} = -\dfrac{1}{2}x + \dfrac{8}{2x^2}$

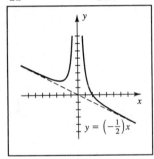

Figure 27

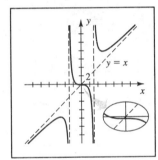

Figure 28

$\boxed{28}$ $f(x) = \dfrac{x^3 + 1}{x^2 - 9} = \dfrac{(x+1)(x^2 - x + 1)}{(x+3)(x-3)} = x + \dfrac{9x + 1}{x^2 - 9}$

$f(x) = x \Rightarrow \dfrac{x^3 + 1}{x^2 - 9} = x \Rightarrow x^3 + 1 = x^3 - 9x \Rightarrow x = -\dfrac{1}{9}, \ I = \left(-\dfrac{1}{9}, \ -\dfrac{1}{9}\right)$.

29 $f(x) = \dfrac{2x^2 + x - 6}{x^2 + 3x + 2} = \dfrac{(x+2)(2x-3)}{(x+2)(x+1)} = \dfrac{2x-3}{x+1}$ for $x \neq -2$;

To determine the value of y when $x = -2$, substitute -2 into $\dfrac{2x-3}{x+1}$ to get 7. There is a hole in the graph at $(-2, 7)$.

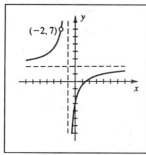

Figure 29

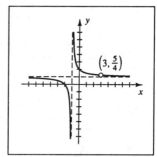

Figure 30

30 $f(x) = \dfrac{x^2 - x - 6}{x^2 - 2x - 3} = \dfrac{(x+2)(x-3)}{(x+1)(x-3)} = \dfrac{x+2}{x+1}$ for $x \neq 3$; hole at $(3, \frac{5}{4})$.

31 $f(x) = \dfrac{x-1}{1-x^2} = \dfrac{x-1}{(1+x)(1-x)} = \dfrac{-1}{x+1}$ for $x \neq 1$; hole at $(1, -\frac{1}{2})$

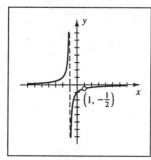

Figure 31

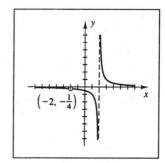

Figure 32

32 $f(x) = \dfrac{x+2}{x^2 - 4} = \dfrac{x+2}{(x+2)(x-2)} = \dfrac{1}{x-2}$ for $x \neq -2$; hole at $(-2, -\frac{1}{4})$

33 $f(x) = \dfrac{x^2 + x - 2}{x+2} = \dfrac{(x+2)(x-1)}{x+2} = x - 1$ for $x \neq -2$; hole at $(-2, -3)$

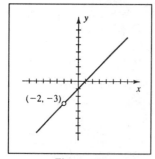

Figure 33

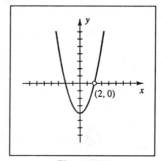

Figure 34

34 $f(x) = \dfrac{x^3 - 2x^2 - 4x + 8}{x-2} = \dfrac{(x^2-4)(x-2)}{x-2} = x^2 - 4$ for $x \neq 2$; hole at $(2, 0)$

35 $f(x) = \dfrac{x^2 + 4x + 4}{x^2 + 3x + 2} = \dfrac{(x+2)^2}{(x+1)(x+2)} = \dfrac{x+2}{x+1}$ for $x \neq -2$.

Note that the hole is on the x-axis at $(-2, 0)$.

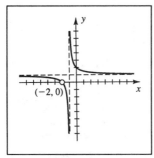

Figure 35

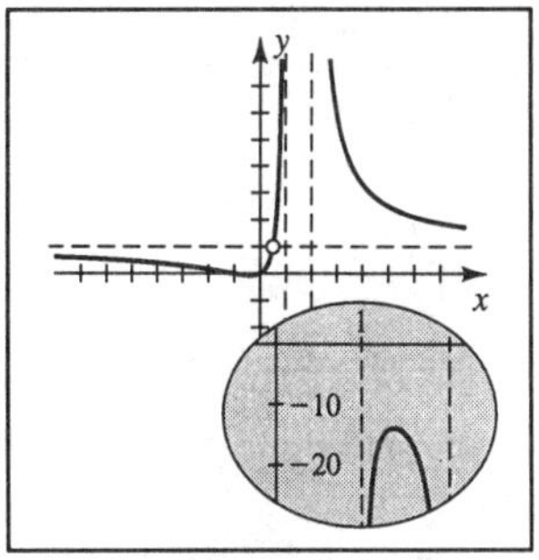

Figure 36

36 $f(x) = \dfrac{(x^2 + x)(2x - 1)}{(x^2 - 3x + 2)(2x - 1)} = \dfrac{x(x+1)(2x-1)}{(x-1)(x-2)(2x-1)} = \dfrac{x(x+1)}{(x-1)(x-2)}$ for $x \neq \frac{1}{2}$.

Note that the hole is on the horizontal asymptote at $(\frac{1}{2}, 1)$.

37 $f(x) = \dfrac{-1(x-3)}{x-4} = \dfrac{3-x}{x-4}$

38 $f(x) = \dfrac{a(x-2)}{x(x+2)}$; $f(3) = 1$ and $f(3) = \dfrac{a(1)}{3(5)} = \dfrac{a}{15} \Rightarrow a = 15$; $f(x) = \dfrac{15x - 30}{x^2 + 2x}$

39 $f(x) = \dfrac{a(x+1)(x-2)}{(x-1)(x+3)(x-2)}$; $f(0) = -2$ and $f(0) = \dfrac{a(1)}{(-1)(3)} = \dfrac{a}{-3} \Rightarrow a = 6$;

$$f(x) = \dfrac{6(x+1)(x-2)}{(x-1)(x+3)(x-2)} = \dfrac{6x^2 - 6x - 12}{x^3 - 7x + 6}$$

40 $f(x) = \dfrac{2(x+2)(x-1)x}{(x+1)(x-3)x} = \dfrac{2x^3 + 2x^2 - 4x}{x^3 - 2x^2 - 3x}$

41 (a) The radius of the outside cylinder is $(r + 0.5)$ ft and its height is $(h + 1)$ ft.

Since the volume is 16π ft^3, we have $16\pi = \pi(r + 0.5)^2(h + 1) \Rightarrow$

$$h = \dfrac{16}{(r + 0.5)^2} - 1.$$

(b) $V(r) = \pi r^2 h = \pi r^2 \left[\dfrac{16}{(r + 0.5)^2} - 1 \right]$

(c) r and h must both be positive. $h > 0 \Rightarrow \dfrac{16}{(r + 0.5)^2} - 1 > 0 \Rightarrow$

$16 > (r + 0.5)^2 \Rightarrow |r + 0.5| < 4 \Rightarrow -4.5 < r < 3.5$. The last inequality

combined with $r > 0$ means that the excluded values are $r \leq 0$ and $r \geq 3.5$.

42 $a = 100$ and $y = ta/(t + 12) \Rightarrow y = 100t/(t + 12)$.

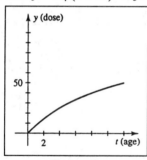

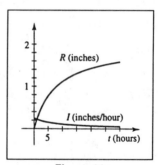

Figure 42   Figure 44

43 (a) Since 5 gallons of water flow into the tank each minute, $V(t) = 50 + 5t$. Since each additional gallon of water contains 0.1 lb of salt, $A(t) = 5(0.1)t = 0.5t$.

(b) $c(t) = \dfrac{A(t)}{V(t)} = \dfrac{0.5t}{50 + 5t} = \dfrac{t}{10t + 100}$ lb/gal

(c) As $t \to \infty$, $c(t) \to 0.1$ lb. of salt per gal.

44 (a) As t increases, the total number of inches of rain approaches the constant a.

(b) Note that at the start of the storm, $I = 0.25$ and $R = 0$, i.e.,

the intensity is greater than the accumulation. See *Figure 44*.

45 (a) $R > S \Rightarrow \dfrac{4500\,S}{S + 500} > S \Rightarrow \dfrac{S(S - 4000)}{S + 500} < 0 \; \{S > 0\} \Rightarrow 0 < S < 4000$

(b) The greatest possible number of offspring that survive to maturity is 4500, the horizontal asymptote value. 90% of 4500 is 4050. $R = 4050 \Rightarrow$

$$4050 = \frac{4500\,S}{S + 500} \Rightarrow 4050S + 2{,}025{,}000 = 4500S \Rightarrow 2{,}025{,}000 = 450S \Rightarrow S = 4500.$$

(c) 80% of 4500 is 3600. $R = 3600 \Rightarrow S = 2000$.

(d) A 125% increase $\left\{\dfrac{4500 - 2000}{2000} \times 100\right\}$ in the number S of spawners produces only

a 12.5% increase $\left\{\dfrac{4050 - 3600}{3600} \times 100\right\}$ in the number R of offspring surviving to maturity.

46 (a) $x = 20 \Rightarrow D \approx 229.4$ and $x = 25 \Rightarrow D = 189.1$; the density decreases

(b) As $x \to \infty$, $D \to 0$.

The density gets closer to 0 as the distance from the center increases.

(c) $D > 400 \Rightarrow \dfrac{5000x}{x^2 + 36} > 400 \Rightarrow$

$$25x > 2(x^2 + 36) \left\{ \text{multiply by } \tfrac{1}{200}(x^2 + 36), \text{ which is positive} \right\} \Rightarrow$$
$$2x^2 - 25x + 72 < 0 \Rightarrow (2x - 9)(x - 8) < 0 \Rightarrow 4.5 < x < 8$$

47 Assign $20x^2 + 80x + 72$ to Y_1, $10x^2 + 40x + 41$ to Y_2, and Y_1/Y_2 to Y_3. Zoom-in around $(-2, -8)$ to confirm that this a low point and that there is not a vertical asymptote at $x = -2$. To determine the vertical asymptotes, graph Y_2 only { turn off Y_3}, and look for its zeros. If these values are not zeros of the numerator, then they are the values of the vertical asymptotes. No vertical asymptotes in this case.

$[-9, 3]$ by $[-9, 3]$ $[-5, 9]$ by $[-1, 13]$

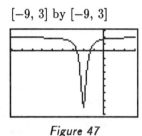
Xscl = 1
Yscl = 1

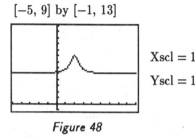
Xscl = 1
Yscl = 1

Figure 47   *Figure 48*

48 Similar to Exercise 47, there is a high point at $(2, 8)$. No vertical asymptotes.

49 $f(x) = \dfrac{(x-1)^2}{(x-0.999)^2}$ •   Note that the standard viewing rectangle gives the horizontal line $y = 1$. *Figure 49* was obtained by using Dot mode. An equation of the vertical asymptote is $x = 0.999$.

$[0.7, 1.3]$ by $[0.8, 1.2]$ $[-4, 8]$ by $[-1, 7]$

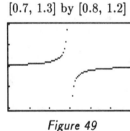
Xscl = 0.1
Yscl = 0.1

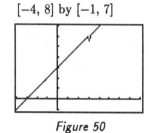
Xscl = 1
Yscl = 1

Figure 49   *Figure 50*

50 $f(x) = \dfrac{x^2 - 9.01}{x - 3}$ •   Note that the standard viewing rectangle gives a line,

but we recognize that there is a vertical asymptote at $x = 3$ since $x - 3$ is a factor of the denominator but not of the numerator.

51 (a) The graph of g is the horizontal line $y = 1$ with holes at $x = 0$, ± 1, ± 2, ± 3.

                              The TI-85/86 shows a small break in the line to indicate a hole.

   (b) The graph of h is the graph of p with holes at $x = 0$, ± 1, ± 2, ± 3.

52 (a) The graph of f is that of a seventh-degree polynomial with zeros at $x = 0$, ± 1, ± 2, ± 3. Its sign changes at each zero.

   (b) The graph of k has vertical asymptotes at $x = 0$, ± 1, ± 2, ± 3. Its sign changes at each asymptote. The values of k are reciprocals of the values of f—so as f gets larger, k gets smaller, and vice versa. Try graphing k with a viewing rectangle of $[-4, 4]$ by $[-0.5, 0.5]$.

1   Shift $y = x^3$ left 2 units. $f(x) > 0$ if $x > -2$, $f(x) < 0$ if $x < -2$.

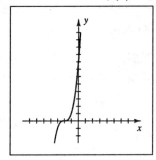

Figure 1

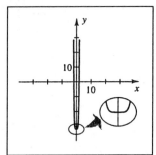

Figure 2

2   Shift $y = x^6$ down 32 units.
$$f(x) > 0 \text{ if } x < -\sqrt[6]{32} \text{ or } x > \sqrt[6]{32}, \; f(x) < 0 \text{ if } -\sqrt[6]{32} < x < \sqrt[6]{32}.$$

3 $f(x) = -\frac{1}{4}(x+2)(x-1)^2(x-3)$ has zeros at -2, 1 (multiplicity 2), and 3.
$$f(x) > 0 \text{ if } -2 < x < 1 \text{ or } 1 < x < 3, \; f(x) < 0 \text{ if } x < -2 \text{ or } x > 3.$$

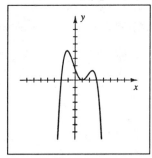

Figure 3

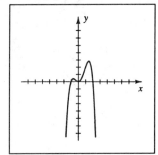

Figure 4

4 $f(x) = 2x^2 + x^3 - x^4 = x^2(2 + x - x^2) = -x^2(x-2)(x+1)$.
$$f(x) > 0 \text{ if } -1 < x < 0 \text{ or } 0 < x < 2, \; f(x) < 0 \text{ if } x < -1 \text{ or } x > 2.$$

5 $f(x) = x^3 + 2x^2 - 8x = x(x^2 + 2x - 8) = x(x+4)(x-2)$.
$$f(x) > 0 \text{ if } -4 < x < 0 \text{ or } x > 2, \; f(x) < 0 \text{ if } x < -4 \text{ or } 0 < x < 2.$$

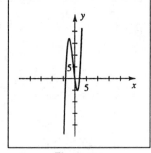

Figure 5

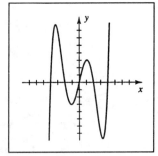

Figure 6

6 $f(x) = \frac{1}{15}(x^5 - 20x^3 + 64x) = \frac{1}{15}x(x^4 - 20x^2 + 64) = \frac{1}{15}x(x^2 - 4)(x^2 - 16) =$
$\frac{1}{15}x(x+2)(x-2)(x+4)(x-4)$. $f(x) > 0$ if $-4 < x < -2$, $0 < x < 2$, or $x > 4$,
$$f(x) < 0 \text{ if } x < -4, \; -2 < x < 0, \text{ or } 2 < x < 4.$$

[7] $f(0) = -9 < 100$ and $f(10) = 561 > 100$. By the intermediate value theorem for polynomial functions, f takes on every value between -9 and 561. Hence, there is at least one real number a in $[0, 10]$ such that $f(a) = 100$.

[8] Let $f(x) = x^5 - 3x^4 - 2x^3 - x + 1$. $f(0) = 1 > 0$ and $f(1) = -4 < 0$. By the intermediate value theorem for polynomial functions, f takes on every value between -4 and 1. Hence, there is at least one real number a in $[0, 1]$ such that $f(a) = 0$.

[9] $f(x) = 3x^5 - 4x^3 + x + 5$; $p(x) = x^3 - 2x + 7$ •   ★ $3x^2 + 2; -21x^2 + 5x - 9$

[10] $f(x) = 4x^3 - x^2 + 2x - 1$; $p(x) = x^2$ •   ★ $4x - 1; 2x - 1$

[11] Dividing $f(x) = -4x^4 + 3x^3 - 5x^2 + 7x - 10$ by $x + 2$ yields -132.

[12] If $f(x) = 2x^4 - 5x^3 - 4x^2 + 9$, then $f(3) = 0$ and $x - 3$ is a factor of f.

[13]   ★ $6x^4 - 12x^3 + 24x^2 - 52x + 104; -200$

[14]   ★ $2x^2 + (5 + 2\sqrt{2})x + (2 + 5\sqrt{2}); 11 + 2\sqrt{2}$

[15] $f(x) = a[x - (-3 + 5i)][x - (-3 - 5i)](x + 1) = a(x^2 + 6x + 34)(x + 1)$.
$f(1) = a(41)(2)$ and $f(1) = 4 \Rightarrow 82a = 4 \Rightarrow a = \frac{2}{41}$.
Hence, $f(x) = \frac{2}{41}(x^2 + 6x + 34)(x + 1)$.

[16] $f(x) = a[x - (1 - i)][x - (1 + i)](x - 3)(x) = ax(x^2 - 2x + 2)(x - 3)$.
$f(2) = a(2)(2)(-1)$ and $f(2) = -1 \Rightarrow -4a = -1 \Rightarrow a = \frac{1}{4}$.
Hence, $f(x) = \frac{1}{4}x(x^2 - 2x + 2)(x - 3)$.

[17] $f(x) = x^5(x + 3)^2$
$= x^5(x^2 + 6x + 9)$
$= x^7 + 6x^6 + 9x^5$

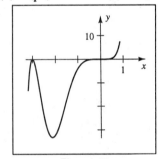

Figure 17

[18] Synthetically dividing $f(x) = x^5 - 4x^4 - 3x^3 + 34x^2 - 52x + 24$ by $x - 2$ three times gives us $(x - 2)^3(x^2 + 2x - 3)$. Hence, $f(x) = (x - 2)^3(x + 3)(x - 1)$.

[19] $f(x) = (x^2 - 2x + 1)^2(x^2 + 2x - 3) = [(x - 1)^2]^2(x + 3)(x - 1) = (x + 3)(x - 1)^5$
★ 1 (multiplicity 5); -3 (multiplicity 1)

[20] $f(x) = x^6 + 2x^4 + x^2 = x^2(x^4 + 2x^2 + 1) = x^2(x^2 + 1)^2$
★ 0, $\pm i$ (all have multiplicity 2)

$\boxed{21}$ (a) Let $f(x) = 2x^4 - 4x^3 + 2x^2 - 5x - 7$. Since there are 3 sign changes in $f(x)$ and 1

sign change in $f(-x)$, there are either 3 positive and 1 negative solution or

1 positive, 1 negative, and 2 nonreal complex solutions.

(b) Upper bound is 3, lower bound is -1

$\boxed{22}$ (a) Let $f(x) = x^5 - 4x^3 + 6x^2 + x + 4$. Since there are 2 sign changes in $f(x)$ and 3

sign changes in $f(-x)$, there are either 2 positive and 3 negative solutions;

2 positive, 1 negative, and 2 nonreal complex;

3 negative and 2 nonreal complex;

or   1 negative and 4 nonreal complex solutions.

(b) Upper bound is 2, lower bound is -3

$\boxed{23}$ Since there are only even powers, $7x^6 + 2x^4 + 3x^2 + 10 \geq 10$ for every real number x.

$\boxed{24}$ $x^4 + 9x^3 + 31x^2 + 49x + 30 = 0$ •   ★ $-3, -2, -2 \pm i$

$\boxed{25}$ $16x^3 - 20x^2 - 8x + 3 = 0$ •   ★ $-\frac{1}{2}, \frac{1}{4}, \frac{3}{2}$

$\boxed{26}$ $x^4 - 7x^2 + 6 = 0$ •   ★ $\pm\sqrt{6}, \pm 1$

$\boxed{27}$ $f(x) = \dfrac{-2}{(x+1)^2}$ • $\boxed{28}$ $f(x) = \dfrac{1}{(x-1)^3}$ •

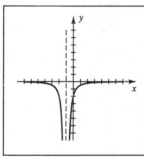

Figure 27

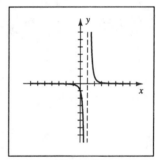

Figure 28

$\boxed{29}$ $f(x) = \dfrac{3x^2}{16 - x^2} = \dfrac{3x^2}{(4+x)(4-x)}$

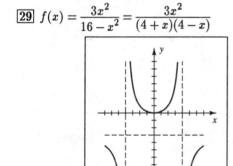

Figure 29

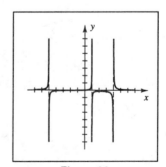

Figure 30

$\boxed{30}$ $f(x) = \dfrac{x}{(x+5)(x^2 - 5x + 4)} = \dfrac{x}{(x+5)(x-1)(x-4)}$

$\boxed{31}$ $f(x) = \dfrac{x^3 - 2x^2 - 8x}{-x^2 + 2x} = \dfrac{x(x^2 - 2x - 8)}{x(2 - x)} = \dfrac{(x - 4)(x + 2)}{2 - x}$ for $x \neq 0$; hole at $(0, -4)$

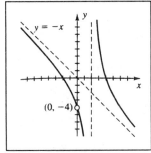

Figure 31

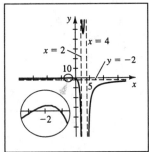

Figure 32

$\boxed{32}$ $f(x) = \dfrac{x^2 - 2x + 1}{x^3 - x^2 + x - 1} = \dfrac{(x - 1)(x - 1)}{x^2(x - 1) + 1(x - 1)} = \dfrac{(x - 1)^2}{(x^2 + 1)(x - 1)} = \dfrac{x - 1}{x^2 + 1}$ for $x \neq 1$;

hole at $(1, 0)$

$\boxed{33}$ $f(x) = \dfrac{3x^2 + x - 10}{x^2 + 2x} = \dfrac{(3x - 5)(x + 2)}{x(x + 2)} = \dfrac{3x - 5}{x}$ for $x \neq -2$

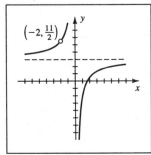

Figure 33

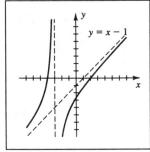

Figure 34

$\boxed{34}$ $f(x) = \dfrac{-2x^2 - 8x - 6}{x^2 - 6x + 8} = \dfrac{-2(x^2 + 4x + 3)}{(x - 2)(x - 4)} = \dfrac{-2(x + 1)(x + 3)}{(x - 2)(x - 4)}$

$\boxed{35}$ $f(x) = \dfrac{x^2 + 2x - 8}{x + 3} = \dfrac{(x + 4)(x - 2)}{x + 3} = x - 1 - \dfrac{5}{x + 3}$

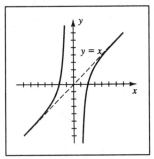

Figure 35

Figure 36

$\boxed{36}$ $f(x) = \dfrac{x^4 - 16}{x^3} = \dfrac{(x^2 + 4)(x + 2)(x - 2)}{x^3} = x - \dfrac{16}{x^3}$

$\boxed{37}$ (a) $l = 10$, $x = 10$, and $y = 2 \Rightarrow 2 = 30{,}000c \Rightarrow c = \frac{1}{15{,}000}$

(b) $y \approx 0.9754 < 1$ if $x = 6.1$, and $y \approx 1.0006 > 1$ if $x = 6.2$

38 (a) Edge AB has length $2\pi r$ where r is the radius of the cylinder.

$2\pi r = \sqrt{l^2 - x^2} \Rightarrow r^2 = \frac{1}{4\pi^2}(l^2 - x^2)$.

Now $V = \pi r^2 x = \pi \left[\frac{1}{4\pi^2}(l^2 - x^2) \right](x) = \frac{1}{4\pi} x(l^2 - x^2)$.

(b) If $x > 0$, $V > 0$ if $l^2 - x^2 > 0$ or $l > x$. Thus, when $0 < x < l$, $V > 0$.

39 $T = \frac{1}{20}t(t - 12)(t - 24) = 32 \Rightarrow t^3 - 36t^2 + 288t - 640 = 0$. Solving for t yields

$t = 4$ and $16 \pm 4\sqrt{6}$. Since $0 \le t \le 24$, $t = 4$ (10:00 A.M.) and

$t = 16 - 4\sqrt{6} \approx 6.2020$ (12:12 P.M.) are the times when the temperature was $32°$F.

40 $N(t) = -t^4 + 21t^2 + 100$ and $N(t) > 180 \Rightarrow t^4 - 21t^2 + 80 < 0 \Rightarrow (t^2 - 5)(t^2 - 16) < 0$.

The positive values of t satisfying this inequality are in the interval $(\sqrt{5}, 4)$.

41 (a) $R = \dfrac{kS^n}{S^n + a^n} = \dfrac{k}{1 + (a/S)^n}$. As S gets large, R approaches k.

(b) k is the maximum rate at which the liver can remove alcohol from the

bloodstream.

42 (a) $C(100) = \$2{,}000{,}000.00$ and

$C(90) \approx \$163{,}636.36$

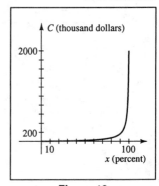

Figure 42

Chapter 3 Discussion Exercises

1 **For even-degreed polynomials:** the domain is **R** and the number of x-intercepts ranges from *zero* to the degree of the polynomial; if the leading coefficient is positive, the range is of the form $[c, \infty)$ and the general shape has $y \to \infty$ as $|x| \to \infty$; if the leading coefficient is negative, the range is of the form $(-\infty, c]$ and the general shape has $y \to -\infty$ as $|x| \to \infty$.

For odd-degreed polynomials: the domain is **R**, the range is **R**, and the number of x-intercepts ranges from *one* to the degree of the polynomial; if the leading coefficient is positive, then $y \to \infty$ as $x \to \infty$ and $y \to -\infty$ as $x \to \infty$, if the leading coefficient is negative, then $y \to -\infty$ as $x \to \infty$ and $y \to \infty$ as $x \to -\infty$.

2 After trying a few examples, students should come up with the conclusion that complex numbers can be used in the synthetic division process.

$\boxed{3}$ By long division, we obtain the quotient $2x^2 - 7x + 5$ with remainder -6. By synthetic division with $k = -3/2$, we obtain a bottom row of 4 -14 10 -6. The first three numbers are twice the coefficients of the quotient and the last number is the remainder. For the factor $ax + b$, we can use synthetic division with $k = -b/a$, and obtain a times the quotient and the remainder in the bottom row.

$\boxed{4}$ $f(x) = a(x-1)(x-2)(x-3)$. $f(0) = a(-6) = 6 \Rightarrow a = -1$. $f(-1) = 24 \neq 25 \Rightarrow$ the point cannot be on the polynomial.

$\boxed{5}$ After working Exercise 4, students should guess that 4 points specify a third-degree polynomial. They know that 2 points specify a first-degree polynomial, so a logical conclusion is that $n + 1$ points specify an n-degree polynomial.

$\boxed{6}$ Let us consider the polynomial

$$f(x) = a_n x^n + a_{n-1} x^{n-1} + \cdots + a_1 x + a_0,$$

where each coefficient a_k is a real number and $a_n \neq 0$. If $f(z) = 0$, then

$$a_n z^n + a_{n-1} z^{n-1} + \cdots + a_1 z + a_0 = 0.$$

If two complex numbers are equal, then so are their conjugates. Hence, the conjugate of the left-hand side of the last equation equals the conjugate of the right-hand side; that is,

$$\overline{a_n z^n + a_{n-1} z^{n-1} + \cdots + a_1 z + a_0} = \overline{0} = 0.$$

The fact that $\overline{0} = 0$ follows from $\overline{0} = \overline{0 + 0i} = 0 - 0i = 0$.

If z and w are complex numbers, then it can be shown that $\overline{z + w} = \overline{z} + \overline{w}$. More generally, the conjugate of *any* sum of complex numbers is the sum of the conjugates. Consequently,

$$\overline{a_n z^n} + \overline{a_{n-1} z^{n-1}} + \cdots + \overline{a_1 z} + \overline{a_0} = 0.$$

It can also be shown that $\overline{z \cdot w} = \overline{z} \cdot \overline{w}$, $\overline{z^n} = \overline{z}^n$ for every positive integer n, and $\overline{z} = z$ if and only if z is real. Thus, for every k,

$$\overline{a_k z^k} = \overline{a_k} \cdot \overline{z^k} = \overline{a_k} \cdot \overline{z}^k = a_k \overline{z}^k,$$

and therefore

$$a_n \overline{z}^n + a_{n-1} \overline{z}^{n-1} + \cdots + a_1 \overline{z} + a_0 = 0.$$

The last equation states that $f(\overline{z}) = 0$, which completes the proof.

$\boxed{7}$ If the common factor is never equal to zero for any real number, then it can be canceled and has no effect on its graph. Such a factor is $x^2 + 1$, and an example of a function is $f(x) = \dfrac{(x^2+1)(x-1)}{(x^2+1)(x-2)}$.

$\boxed{8}$ (a) The horizontal asymptote is $y = a/c$. Solving $f(x) = a/c$ gives us $\dfrac{ax+b}{cx+d} = \dfrac{a}{c} \Rightarrow$

$acx + bc = acx + ad \Rightarrow bc = ad \Rightarrow$ no solution, and f doesn't cross its horizontal asymptote.

(b) The horizontal asymptote is $y = a/d$. Solving $f(x) = a/d$ gives us

$$\frac{ax^2 + bx + c}{dx^2 + ex + f} = \frac{a}{d} \Rightarrow adx^2 + bdx + cd = adx^2 + aex + af \Rightarrow aex - bdx = cd - af \Rightarrow$$

$$x = \frac{cd - af}{ae - bd}, \text{ provided the denominator is not zero.}$$

$\boxed{9}$ Let x, $x+1$, and $x+2$ denote three consecutive integers. Their product is $x(x+1)(x+2) = x^3 + 3x^2 + 3x + 1$. Only $x+1$ or $x-1$ could be factors, and it turns out that $x+1$ is a factor three times. Thus, if you multiply three consecutive integers together and then add the second integer to that product, you obtain the cube of the second integer.

Chapter 4: Exponential and Logarithmic Functions

4.1 Concept Check

1. Do exponential functions have inverses? Why or why not? • Yes, because they are one-to-one.

2. Solve the equation $a^x = 0$, where $a > 0$. • There are no solutions since the function $y = a^x$ is never zero.

3. How do the graphs of $y = 3^{-x}$ and $y = 1/3^x$ differ? • Not at all—they are exactly the same decreasing exponential function.

4. Do you think the exponential model applies for a longer period of time when dealing with money or with bacterial growth? • The exponential model applies to money for any period of time, but must break down with bacterial growth due to limited resources and space.

4.1 Exercises

1. $7^{x+6} = 7^{3x-4} \Rightarrow x + 6 = 3x - 4 \Rightarrow 10 = 2x \Rightarrow x = 5$

2. $6^{7-x} = 6^{2x+1} \Rightarrow 7 - x = 2x + 1 \Rightarrow 6 = 3x \Rightarrow x = 2$

3. $3^{2x+3} = 3^{(x^2)} \Rightarrow 2x + 3 = x^2 \Rightarrow x^2 - 2x - 3 = 0 \Rightarrow (x-3)(x+1) = 0 \Rightarrow x = -1, 3$

4. $9^{(x^2)} = 3^{3x+2} \Rightarrow (3^2)^{(x^2)} = 3^{3x+2} \Rightarrow 3^{(2x^2)} = 3^{3x+2} \Rightarrow$
$$2x^2 = 3x + 2 \Rightarrow 2x^2 - 3x - 2 = 0 \Rightarrow (2x+1)(x-2) = 0 \Rightarrow x = -\tfrac{1}{2}, 2$$

5. $2^{-100x} = (0.5)^{x-4} \Rightarrow (2^{-1})^{100x} = \left(\tfrac{1}{2}\right)^{x-4} \Rightarrow \left(\tfrac{1}{2}\right)^{100x} = \left(\tfrac{1}{2}\right)^{x-4} \Rightarrow$
$$100x = x - 4 \Rightarrow 99x = -4 \Rightarrow x = -\tfrac{4}{99}$$

6. $\left(\tfrac{1}{2}\right)^{6-x} = 2 \Rightarrow \left(\tfrac{1}{2}\right)^{6-x} = \left(\tfrac{1}{2}\right)^{-1} \Rightarrow 6 - x = -1 \Rightarrow x = 7$

7. $4^{x-3} = 8^{4-x} \Rightarrow (2^2)^{x-3} = (2^3)^{4-x} \Rightarrow 2^{2x-6} = 2^{12-3x} \Rightarrow$
$$2x - 6 = 12 - 3x \Rightarrow 5x = 18 \Rightarrow x = \tfrac{18}{5}$$

8. $27^{x-1} = 9^{2x-3} \Rightarrow (3^3)^{x-1} = (3^2)^{2x-3} \Rightarrow 3^{3x-3} = 3^{4x-6} \Rightarrow$
$$3x - 3 = 4x - 6 \Rightarrow x = 3$$

9 (a) Let $F = f(x) = 2^x$. This graph goes through $(-1, \frac{1}{2})$, $(0, 1)$, and $(1, 2)$.

(b) $f(x) = -2^x$ •   reflect F through the x-axis

(c) $f(x) = 3 \cdot 2^x$ •   stretch F by a factor of 3

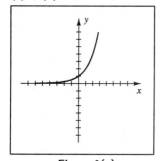

Figure 9(a)

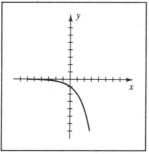

Figure 9(b)

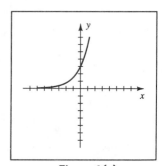

Figure 9(c)

(d) $f(x) = 2^{x+3}$ •   shift F left 3 units

(e) $f(x) = 2^x + 3$ •   shift F up 3 units

(f) $f(x) = 2^{x-3}$ •   shift F right 3 units

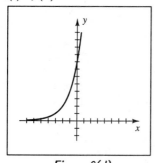

Figure 9(d)

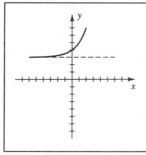

Figure 9(e)

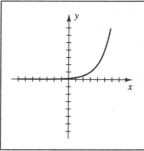

Figure 9(f)

(g) $f(x) = 2^x - 3$ •   shift F down 3 units

(h) $f(x) = 2^{-x}$ •   reflect F through the y-axis

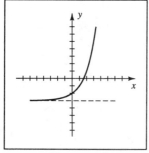

Figure 9(g)

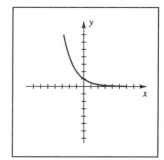

Figure 9(h)

(i) $f(x) = \left(\frac{1}{2}\right)^x$ • $\left(\frac{1}{2}\right)^x = (2^{-1})^x = 2^{-x}$, same graph as in part (h)

(j) $f(x) = 2^{3-x}$ • $2^{3-x} = 2^{-(x-3)}$, shift F right 3 units and reflect through the
line $x = 3$. Or, $2^{3-x} = 2^3 2^{-x} = 8\left(\frac{1}{2}\right)^x$, stretch $y = \left(\frac{1}{2}\right)^x$ by a factor of 8.

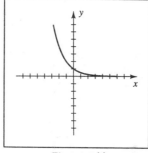

Figure 9(i)

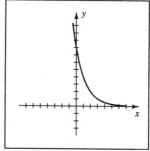

Figure 9(j)

10 (a) Let $F = f(x) = \left(\frac{1}{2}\right)^x$. This graph goes through $(-1, 2)$, $(0, 1)$, and $(1, \frac{1}{2})$.

(b) $f(x) = -\left(\frac{1}{2}\right)^x$ • reflect F through the x-axis

(c) $f(x) = 3 \cdot \left(\frac{1}{2}\right)^x$ • stretch F by a factor of 3

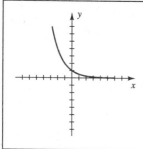

Figure 10(a)

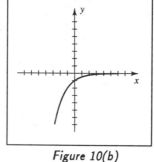

Figure 10(b)

Figure 10(c)

(d) $f(x) = \left(\frac{1}{2}\right)^{x+3}$ • shift F left 3 units

(e) $f(x) = \left(\frac{1}{2}\right)^x + 3$ • shift F up 3 units

(f) $f(x) = \left(\frac{1}{2}\right)^{x-3}$ • shift F right 3 units

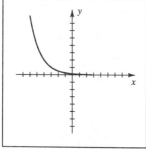

Figure 10(d)

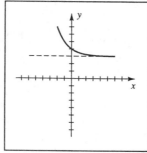

Figure 10(e)

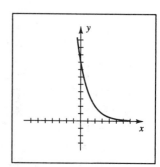

Figure 10(f)

(g) $f(x) = (\frac{1}{2})^x - 3$ •   shift F down 3 units

(h) $f(x) = (\frac{1}{2})^{-x}$ •   reflect F through the y-axis

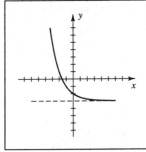

Figure 10(g)

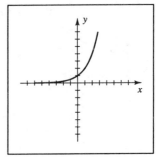

Figure 10(h)

(i) $f(x) = (\frac{1}{1/2})^x$ • $(\frac{1}{1/2})^x = (2)^x$, same graph as in part (h) or #9(a)

(j) $f(x) = (\frac{1}{2})^{3-x}$ • $(\frac{1}{2})^{3-x} = (\frac{1}{2})^{-(x-3)}$, shift F right 3 units and reflect through

the line $x = 3$. Or, $(\frac{1}{2})^{3-x} = (\frac{1}{2})^3(\frac{1}{2})^{-x} = \frac{1}{8} \cdot 2^x$, compress $y = 2^x$ by a factor of $\frac{1}{8}$.

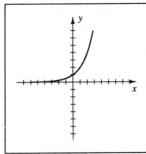

Figure 10(i)

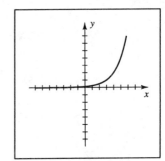

Figure 10(j)

$\boxed{11}$ $f(x) = (\frac{2}{5})^{-x} = \left[(\frac{2}{5})^{-1}\right]^x = (\frac{5}{2})^x$ •   goes through $(-1, \frac{2}{5})$, $(0, 1)$, and $(1, \frac{5}{2})$

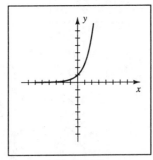

Figure 11

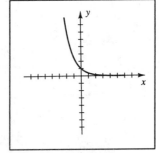

Figure 12

$\boxed{12}$ $f(x) = (\frac{2}{5})^x$ •   goes through $(-1, \frac{5}{2})$, $(0, 1)$, and $(1, \frac{2}{5})$

$\boxed{13}$ $f(x) = -(\frac{1}{2})^x + 4$ • reflect $y = (\frac{1}{2})^x$ through the x-axis and shift up 4 units

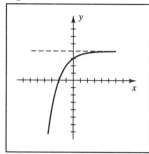

Figure 13

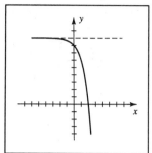

Figure 14

$\boxed{14}$ $f(x) = -3^x + 9$ • reflect $y = 3^x$ through the x-axis and shift up 9 units

$\boxed{15}$ $f(x) = 2^{|x|}$ • use the portion of $y = 2^x$ with $x \geq 0$ and

reflect it through the y-axis since f is even

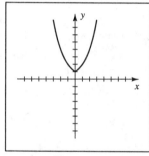

Figure 15

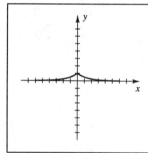

Figure 16

$\boxed{16}$ $f(x) = 2^{-|x|} = (\frac{1}{2})^{|x|}$ • use the portion of $y = (\frac{1}{2})^x$ with $x \geq 0$ and

reflect it through the y-axis since f is even

Note: For Exercises 17, 18, and 5 of the review exercises, refer to Example 5 in the text

for the basic graph of $y = a^{-x^2} = (\frac{1}{a})^{x^2}$, where $a > 1$.

$\boxed{17}$ $f(x) = 3^{1-x^2} = 3^1 3^{-x^2} = 3(\frac{1}{3})^{x^2}$ • stretch $y = (\frac{1}{3})^{x^2}$ by a factor of 3

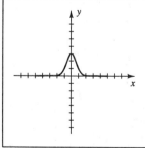

Figure 17

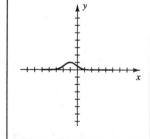

Figure 18

$\boxed{18}$ $f(x) = 2^{-(x+1)^2} = (\frac{1}{2})^{(x+1)^2}$ • shift $y = (\frac{1}{2})^{x^2}$ left 1 unit

$\boxed{19}$ $f(x) = 3^x + 3^{-x}$ •   if $x > 0$, f looks like $y = 3^x$ since 3^x dominates 3^{-x};

if $x < 0$, f looks like $y = 3^{-x}$ since 3^{-x} dominates 3^x

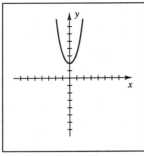

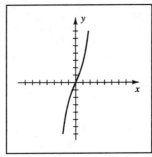

Figure 19   Figure 20

$\boxed{20}$ $f(x) = 3^x - 3^{-x}$ •   if $x > 0$, f looks like $y = 3^x$ since $0 < 3^{-x} < 1$;

if $x < 0$, f looks like $y = -3^{-x}$ since $0 < 3^x < 1$

$\boxed{21}$ (a) $N(t) = 100(0.9)^t \Rightarrow N(1) = 100(0.9)^1 = 90$

(b) $N(5) = 100(0.9)^5 \approx 59$ (c) $N(10) = 100(0.9)^{10} \approx 35$

$\boxed{22}$ (a) $A(t) = 10(0.8)^t \Rightarrow A(8) = 10(0.8)^8 \approx 1.68$ mg

(b) $\dfrac{A(t+1)}{A(t)} = \dfrac{10(0.8)^{t+1}}{10(0.8)^t} = 0.8$, that is, 80% remains, or 20% is eliminated

$\boxed{23}$ (a) 8:00 A.M. corresponds to $t = 1$ and $f(1) = 600\sqrt{3} \approx 1039$.

10:00 A.M. corresponds to $t = 3$ and $f(3) = 600(3\sqrt{3}) = 1800\sqrt{3} \approx 3118$.

11:00 A.M. corresponds to $t = 4$ and $f(4) = 600(9) = 5400$.

(b) The graph of f is an increasing exponential that passes through $(0, 600)$ and the

points in part (a).

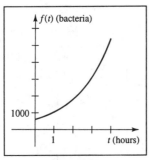

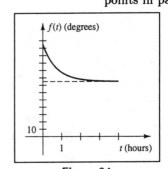

Figure 23   Figure 24

$\boxed{24}$ (a) 2:00 P.M. corresponds to $t = 1$ and $f(1) = 87.5°$.

3:30 P.M. corresponds to $t = \frac{5}{2}$ and $f(\frac{5}{2}) = 76.5625 \approx 76.6°$.

4:00 P.M. corresponds to $t = 3$ and $f(3) = 75.78125 \approx 75.8°$

(b) The endpoints are $(0, 125)$ and $(4, \approx 75.2)$.

$\boxed{25}$ (a) $f(5) = 100(2)^{-1} = 50$ mg; $f(10) = 100(2)^{-2} = 25$ mg;

$$f(12.5) = 100(2)^{-2.5} = \frac{100}{4\sqrt{2}} = \frac{25}{2}\sqrt{2} \approx 17.7 \text{ mg}$$

(b) The endpoints are $(0, 100)$ and $(30, 1.5625)$.

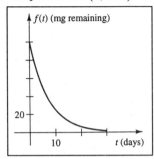

Figure 25

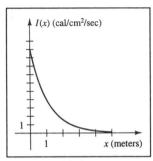

Figure 26

$\boxed{26}$ (a) $I(x) = 10(0.4)^x \Rightarrow I(2) = 10(0.4)^2 = 1.6$ calories/cm^2/sec

(b) The endpoints are $(0, 10)$ and $(5, 0.1024)$.

$\boxed{27}$ $q(t) = \frac{1}{2}q_0$ when $t = 1600 \Rightarrow \frac{1}{2}q_0 = q_0 2^{k(1600)} \Rightarrow 2^{-1} = 2^{1600k} \Rightarrow 1600k = -1 \Rightarrow$

$$k = -\frac{1}{1600}.$$

$\boxed{28}$ The endpoints of the graph of $q(t) = 10(\frac{4}{5})^t$ are $(0, 10)$ and $(10, \approx 1.07)$.

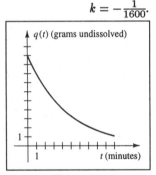

Figure 28

$\boxed{29}$ Using $A = P\left(1 + \frac{r}{n}\right)^{nt}$, we have $P = 1000$, $r = 0.12$, and $n = 12$.

Consider A to be a function of t, that is, $A(t) = 1000\left(1 + \frac{0.12}{12}\right)^{12t} = 1000(1.01)^{12t}$.

(a) $A(\frac{1}{12}) = \$1010.00$ (b) $A(\frac{6}{12}) \approx \$1061.52$

(c) $A(1) \approx \$1126.83$ (d) $A(20) \approx \$10,892.55$

$\boxed{30}$ $5000 = P\left(1 + \frac{0.10}{2}\right)^{2 \cdot 1} \Rightarrow P = \frac{5000}{(1.05)^2} \approx \$4535.15$

$\boxed{31}$ $C = 10,000 \Rightarrow V(t) = 7800(0.85)^{t-1}$

(a) $V(1) = \$7800$ (b) $V(4) \approx \$4790.18$, or \$4790 (c) $V(7) \approx \$2941.77$, or \$2942

$\boxed{32}$ The year 2010 corresponds to $t = 2010 - 1986 = 24$.

$$P = 80,000 \Rightarrow V = 80,000(1.05)^{24} = \$258,008.00.$$

$\boxed{33}$ $t = 2006 - 1626 = 380$; $A = \$24(1 + 0.06/4)^{4 \cdot 380} = \$161,657,351,965.80$.

$\boxed{34}$ $P = 500$, $r = 0.18$, and $n = 12 \Rightarrow A = 500\left(1 + \frac{0.18}{12}\right)^{12 \cdot 1} = 500(1.015)^{12} \approx \$597.81$

[35] (a) Examine the pattern formed by the value y in the year n.

year (n)	value (y)
0	y_0
1	$(1-a)y_0 = y_1$
2	$(1-a)y_1 = (1-a)\big[(1-a)y_0\big] = (1-a)^2 y_0 = y_2$
3	$(1-a)y_2 = (1-a)\big[(1-a)^2 y_0\big] = (1-a)^3 y_0 = y_3$

(b) $s = (1-a)^T y_0 \Rightarrow (1-a)^T = s/y_0 \Rightarrow 1 - a = \sqrt[T]{s/y_0} \Rightarrow a = 1 - \sqrt[T]{s/y_0}$

[36] (a) $t = \frac{100}{1000} = \frac{1}{10}$ millennium and

$N(\frac{1}{10}) = N_0(0.805)^{1/10} \approx 0.9785\, N_0.$

This is a 97.85% retention, or a 2.15% loss.

(b) The endpoints are $(0, 200)$ and $(5, \approx 67.61)$.

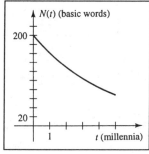

Figure 36

[37] (a) $r = 0.12$, $t = 30$, $L = 90{,}000 \Rightarrow k \approx 35.95$, $M \approx 925.75$

(b) $(360 \text{ payments}) \times \$925.75 - \$90{,}000 = \$243{,}270$

[38] $r = 0.10$, $t = 25$, $M = 800 \Rightarrow k \approx 12.06$, $L \approx \$88{,}037.78$

[39] $r = 0.15$, $t = 3$, $M = 220 \Rightarrow k \approx 1.56$, $L \approx \$6{,}346.40$

[40] (a) $r = 0.125$, $t = 2$, $L = 3000 \Rightarrow k \approx 1.28$, $M \approx \$141.92$

(b) $(24 \text{ payments}) \times \$141.92 - \$3000 = \$406.08$

[41] (a) $f(3) = 13^{\sqrt{3 + 1.1}} \approx 180.1206$ (b) $g(1.43) = \left(\frac{5}{42}\right)^{-1.43} \approx 20.9758$

(c) $h(1.06) = (2^{1.06} + 2^{-1.06})^{2(1.06)} \approx 7.3639$

[42] (a) $f(2.5) = 2^{\sqrt[3]{1 - 2.5}} \approx 0.4523$ (b) $g(2.1) = \left(\frac{2}{25} + 2.1\right)^{-3(2.1)} \approx 0.0074$

(c) $h(\sqrt{2}) = \dfrac{3^{-\sqrt{2}} + 5}{3^{\sqrt{2}} - 16} \approx -0.4624$

[43] Part (b) may be interpreted as doubling an investment at 8.5%.

(a) If $y = (1.085)^x$ and $x = 40$, then $y \approx 26.13$.   (b) If $y = 2$, then $x \approx 8.50$.

[0, 60] by [0, 40]   [0, 60] by [0, 40]

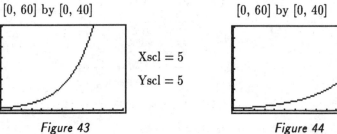

                                 Xscl = 5   Xscl = 5

                                 Yscl = 5   Yscl = 5

            Figure 43   *Figure 44*

44 Compare the doubling time in part (b) with the result in Exercise 43(b).

(a) If $y = (1.0525)^x$ and $x = 40$, then $y \approx 7.74$.   (b) If $y = 2$, then $x \approx 13.55$.

45 First graph $y = 1.4x^2 - 2.2^x - 1$. The x-intercepts will be the solutions of the

equation. From the graph, the solutions are $x \approx -1.02$, 2.14, and 3.62.

[−10.5, 10.5] by [−7, 7]

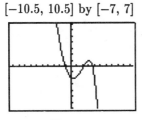 Xscl = 1
Yscl = 1

Figure 45

[−10.5, 10.5] by [−7, 7]

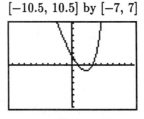 Xscl = 1
Yscl = 1

Figure 46

46 First graph $y = 1.21^{3x} + 1.4^{-1.1x} - 2x - 0.5$. The x-intercepts will be the solutions of

the equation. From the graph, the solutions are $x \approx 0.97$ and 3.41.

47 (a) See *Figure 47*. f is not one-to-one since

the horizontal line $y = -0.1$ intersects the graph of f more than once.

(b) The only zero of f is $x = 0$.

[−3, 3] by [−2, 2]

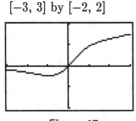 Xscl = 1
Yscl = 1

Figure 47

[−4, 4] by [−2.7, 2.7]

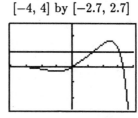 Xscl = 1
Yscl = 1

Figure 48

48 (a) Rewrite $f(x) = \pi^{0.6x} - 1.3^{(x^{1.8})}$ as $f(x) = \pi^{0.6x} - 1.3^{(x^{9/5})}$. f is not one-to-one

since the horizontal line $y = 1$ intersects the graph of f more than once.

(b) The zeros of f are $x \approx -3.33$, 0, and 3.33.

49 (a) f is increasing on $[-3.37, -1.19]$ and $[0.52, 1]$.
    f is decreasing on $[-4, -3.37]$ and $[-1.19, 0.52]$.

(b) The range of f on $[-4, 1]$ is approximately $[-1.79, 1.94]$.

[−4, 1] by [−2, 3]

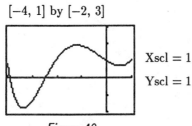 Xscl = 1
Yscl = 1

Figure 49

[−3, 3] by [−2, 2]

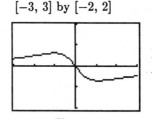 Xscl = 1
Yscl = 1

Figure 50

50 (a) f is increasing on $[-3, -1]$ and $[1.11, 3]$. f is decreasing on $[-1, 1.11]$.

(b) The range of f on $[-3, 3]$ is approximately $[-0.69, 0.62]$.

51 *Figure 51* is a graph of $N(t) = 1000(0.9)^t$.

By tracing and zooming, we can determine that $N = 500$ when $t \approx 6.58$ yr.

[0, 10] by [0, 1000]

[0, 20] by [0, 1]

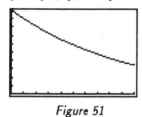

$Xscl = 1$

$Yscl = 100$

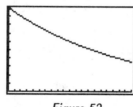

$Xscl = 1$

$Yscl = 0.1$

Figure 51

Figure 52

52 From a graph of $B(t) = (0.95)^t$, we determine that $B = 0.5$ when $t \approx 13.51$ yr.

53 Graph $y = 4(0.125)^{(0.25^x)}$. The line $y = k = 4$ is a horizontal asymptote for the

Gompertz function. The maximum number of sales of the product approaches k.

[0, 7.5] by [0, 5]

[0, 7.5] by [0, 5]

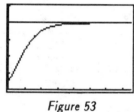

$Xscl = 1$

$Yscl = 1$

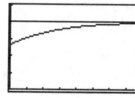

$Xscl = 1$

$Yscl = 1$

Figure 53

Figure 54

54 Graph $y = \dfrac{1}{0.25 + 0.125(0.625)^x}$. The line $y = 1/k = 4$ is a horizontal asymptote for

the logistic function. The maximum number of sales of the product approaches $1/k$.

55 From the graph, we determine that $A = 100{,}000$ when $n \approx 32.8$.

[0, 40] by [0, 200,000]

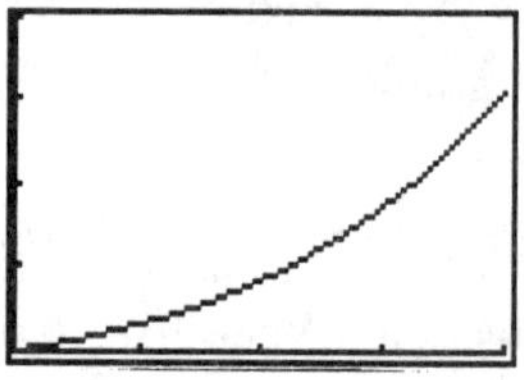

[0, 40] by [0, 200,000]

$Xscl = 10$

$Yscl = 50{,}000$

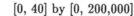

$Xscl = 10$

$Yscl = 50{,}000$

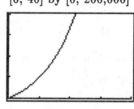

Figure 55

Figure 56

56 From the graph, we determine that $A = 100{,}000$ when $n \approx 15.4$.

57 (a) Let $x = 0$ correspond to 1910, $x = 20$ to 1930, ... , and $x = 85$ to 1995.

Graph the data together with the functions

$$f(x) = 0.809(1.094)^x \text{ and } g(x) = 0.375x^2 - 18.4x + 88.1.$$

[−10, 90] by [−200, 1500]   [−10, 90] by [−200, 1500]

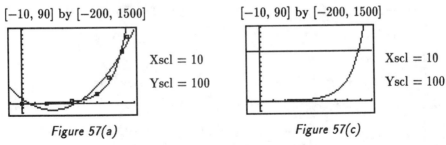

Xscl = 10   Xscl = 10

Yscl = 100   Yscl = 100

Figure 57(a)   *Figure 57(c)*

(b) The exponential function f best models the data.

(c) Graph $Y_1 = f(x)$ and $Y_2 = 1000$. The graphs intersect at $x \approx 79$, or in 1989.

58 (a) Change the date in the table to the number of days after August 12.

Graph the data together with the functions

$$f(t) = 653(1.028)^t \text{ and } g(t) = 54{,}700e^{-(t-200)^2/7500}.$$

t (days)	0	28	56	84	112	140	168
New Cases	506	1289	3487	9597	18,817	33,835	47,191

[0, 400] by [0, 60,000]   [0, 400] by [0, 60,000]

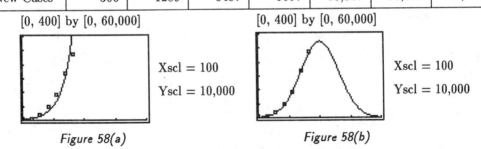

Xscl = 100   Xscl = 100

Yscl = 10,000   Yscl = 10,000

Figure 58(a)   *Figure 58(b)*

(b) The function g models Farr's prediction better than f since the graph of g attains
a maximum and then decreases.

(c) The maximum number of new cases occurred 200 days after August 12, which is
February 28, 1841. After this date, the number of new cases decreased.

4.2 Exercises

4.2 Concept Check

1 Refer to Example 1. Suppose Bank A offers quarterly compounding for your $1000
one-year investment and Bank B offers monthly compounding. Does it matter which
bank you choose to invest with? What if your principal is $10,000,000? ● Not
really—Bank B yields $0.73 more in interest in one year. With a $10,000,000
investment, the difference in interest is $7,235.79, which would seem to make Bank B
worth the drive for anyone.

☒ What type of compounding yields the largest gain in interest? • Continuously compounding yields the largest gain in interest of all the compounding types.

☒ If a population can be modeled by the formula $q = q_0 e^{0.1t}$, what happens to q as t increases? How about $q = q_0 e^{-0.1t}$? • By the Law of Growth (or Decay) Formula with $r = 0.1 > 0$, the population just keeps increasing. With $r = -0.1 < 0$, the population dies out (approaches 0).

☒ Which of the following could best be modeled by a Gompertz growth function: compound interest, bacterial growth, or radioactive decay? • Bacterial growth could be modeled by a Gompertz growth function, compound interest with an increasing exponential function, and radioactive decay with a decreasing exponential function.

| 4.2 Exercises |

☒ (a) $f(x) = e^{-x}$ • reflect $y = e^x$ through the y-axis

   (b) $f(x) = -e^x$ • reflect $y = e^x$ through the x-axis

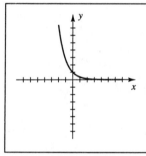

Figure 1(a)

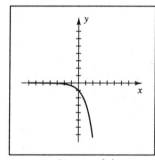

Figure 1(b)

☒ (a) $f(x) = e^{2x} = (e^x)^2$ • square the y values of $y = e^x$

   (b) $f(x) = 2e^x$ • vertically stretch $y = e^x$ by a factor of 2

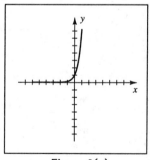

Figure 2(a)

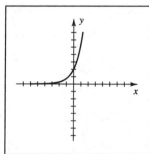

Figure 2(b)

$\boxed{3}$ (a) $f(x) = e^{x+4}$ •   shift $y = e^x$ left 4 units

     (b) $f(x) = e^x + 4$ •   shift $y = e^x$ up 4 units

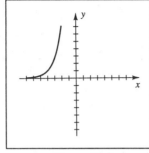

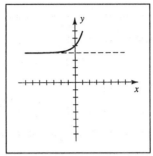

Figure 3(a)   Figure 3(b)

$\boxed{4}$ (a) $f(x) = e^{-2x}$ •   reflect $y = e^x$ through the y-axis and square the y values

     (b) $f(x) = -2e^x$ •   reflect $y = e^x$ through the x-axis and double the y values

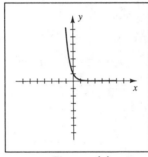

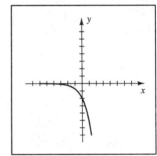

Figure 4(a)   Figure 4(b)

$\boxed{5}$ $A = Pe^{rt} = 1000e^{(0.0825)(5)} \approx \$1510.59$ $\boxed{6}$ $A = Pe^{rt} = 100e^{(0.125)(10)} \approx \$349.03$

$\boxed{7}$ $100{,}000 = Pe^{(0.11)(18)} \Rightarrow P = \dfrac{100{,}000}{e^{1.98}} \approx \$13{,}806.92$

$\boxed{8}$ $15{,}000 = Pe^{(0.095)(4)} \Rightarrow P = \dfrac{15{,}000}{e^{0.38}} \approx \$10{,}257.92$

$\boxed{9}$ $13{,}464 = 1000e^{(r)(20)} \Rightarrow e^{20r} = 13.464.$ Using a trial and error approach on a scientific calculator or tracing and zooming on a graphing calculator, we determine that $e^x \approx 13.464$ if $x \approx 2.6$. Thus, $20r = 2.6$ and $r = 0.13$ or 13%.

$\boxed{10}$ $890.20 = 400e^{(r)(16)} \Rightarrow e^{16r} = 2.2255.$ As in Exercise 9, $e^x \approx 2.2255$ if $x \approx 0.8$.

Thus, $16r = 0.8$ and $r = 0.05$ or 5%.

$\boxed{11}$ $e^{(x^2)} = e^{7x-12} \Rightarrow x^2 = 7x - 12 \Rightarrow x^2 - 7x + 12 = 0 \Rightarrow (x-3)(x-4) = 0 \Rightarrow x = 3, 4$

$\boxed{12}$ $e^{3x} = e^{2x-1} \Rightarrow 3x = 2x - 1 \Rightarrow x = -1$

$\boxed{13}$ $xe^x + e^x = 0 \Rightarrow e^x(x+1) = 0 \Rightarrow x = -1 \; \{e^x \neq 0\}$

$\boxed{14}$ $-x^2e^{-x} + 2xe^{-x} = 0 \Rightarrow xe^{-x}(-x+2) = 0 \Rightarrow x = 0, 2 \; \{e^{-x} \neq 0\}$

$\boxed{15}$ $x^3(4e^{4x}) + 3x^2e^{4x} = 0 \Rightarrow x^2e^{4x}(4x+3) = 0 \Rightarrow x = -\frac{3}{4}, 0 \; \{e^{4x} \neq 0\}$

$\boxed{16}$ $x^2(2e^{2x}) + 2xe^{2x} + e^{2x} + 2xe^{2x} = 0 \Rightarrow e^{2x}(2x^2 + 4x + 1) = 0 \Rightarrow x = -1 \pm \frac{1}{2}\sqrt{2}$

17 $\dfrac{(e^x + e^{-x})(e^x + e^{-x}) - (e^x - e^{-x})(e^x - e^{-x})}{(e^x + e^{-x})^2} =$

$$\dfrac{(e^{2x} + 2 + e^{-2x}) - (e^{2x} - 2 + e^{-2x})}{(e^x + e^{-x})^2} = \dfrac{4}{(e^x + e^{-x})^2}$$

18 $\dfrac{(e^x - e^{-x})^2 - (e^x + e^{-x})^2}{(e^x + e^{-x})^2} = \dfrac{(e^{2x} - 2 + e^{-2x}) - (e^{2x} + 2 + e^{-2x})}{(e^x + e^{-x})^2} = \dfrac{-4}{(e^x + e^{-x})^2}$

19 $W(t) = W_0 e^{kt}$; $t = 30 \Rightarrow W(30) = 68e^{(0.2)(30)} \approx 27{,}433$ mg, or 27.43 grams

20 $W(10) = W_0 e^{(0.21)(10)} = 575 \Rightarrow W_0 = \dfrac{575}{e^{2.1}} \approx 70.41$ mg

21 The year 2010 corresponds to $t = 2010 - 1980 = 30$. Using the law of growth formula
   with $q_0 = 227$ and $r = 0.007$, we have $N(t) = 227e^{0.007t}$.

$$\text{Thus, } N(30) = 227e^{(0.007)(30)} \approx 280.0 \text{ million.}$$

22 As in Exercise 21, 2010 corresponds to $t = 2010 - 1985 = 25$ and

$$N(25) = 762e^{(0.022)(25)} \approx 1{,}320.7 \text{ million.}$$

23 $N(10) = N_0 e^{-2}$. The percentage of the original number still alive after 10 years is

$$100 \times \left(\dfrac{N(10)}{N_0} \right) = 100e^{-2} \approx 13.5\%.$$

24 (a) $A_0 = 35$, $t = 2 \Rightarrow A(2) = 35e^{-0.0498} \approx 33.3$ units are available

   (b) $A(t) = 35$, $t = 2 \Rightarrow 35 = A_0 e^{-0.0498} \Rightarrow$

$$A_0 = 35e^{0.0498} \approx 36.8 \text{ units should be shipped}$$

25 2010 corresponds to $t = 2010 - 1978 = 32$; $N(32) = 5000e^{(0.0036)(32)} \approx 5610$

26 (a) $f(10) = 200(1 - 0.956e^{-0.18(10)}) \approx 168.4$ cm

   (b) $f(0) = 8.8$ cm. As $t \to \infty$, $0.956e^{-0.18t} \to 0$, and $f(t) \to 200$ cm.

27 $h = 40{,}000 \Rightarrow p = 29e^{-1.36} \approx 7.44$ in.

28 Consider A to be a function of t with $c = 50$.   (a) $A(30) = 50e^{-0.1485} \approx 43.10$ mg

   (b) $A(180) = 50e^{-0.891} \approx 20.51$ mg   (c) $A(365) = 50e^{-1.80675} \approx 8.21$ mg

29 $x = 1 \Rightarrow y = 79.041 + 6.39 - e^{2.268} \approx 75.77$ cm.

$$x = 1 \Rightarrow R = 6.39 + 0.993e^{2.268} \approx 15.98 \text{ cm/yr.}$$

30 (a) As t increases, $e^{-at} \to 0$ and $s \approx \dfrac{v_0}{a}$.   (b) $s \approx \dfrac{v_0}{a} = \dfrac{10}{8 \times 10^5} = 1.25 \times 10^{-5}$ m.

31 $2010 - 1971 = 39 \Rightarrow t = 39$ years. $A = 1.60e^{(0.05)(39)} \approx \$11.25$ per hour

32 Let P denote the cost of one acre in 1867.

$$P = \left(\dfrac{\$7{,}200{,}000}{586{,}400 \text{ mi}^2} \right) \left(\dfrac{1 \text{ mi}^2}{640 \text{ acres}} \right) (1 \text{ acre}) \approx \$0.02. \quad 2010 - 1867 = 143 \Rightarrow t = 143 \text{ years.}$$

$$A = Pe^{(0.03)(143)} = Pe^{4.29} \approx \$1.40.$$

$\boxed{33}$ (a) $\left(1 + \frac{0.07}{4}\right)^{4 \cdot 1} \approx 1.0719.$ $(1.0719 - 1) \times 100\% = 7.19\%$

(b) $e^{(0.07)(1)} \approx 1.0725.$ $(1.0725 - 1) \times 100\% = 7.25\%$

$\boxed{34}$ (a) $\left(1 + \frac{0.12}{4}\right)^{4 \cdot 1} \approx 1.1255.$ $(1.1255 - 1) \times 100\% = 12.55\%$

(b) $e^{(0.12)(1)} \approx 1.1275.$ $(1.1275 - 1) \times 100\% = 12.75\%$

$\boxed{35}$ It may be of interest to compare this graph with the graph of $y = (1.085)^x$ in
Exercise 43 of §4.1. Both are compounding functions with $r = 8.5\%$.
Note that $e^{0.085x} = (e^{0.085})^x \approx (1.0887)^x > (1.085)^x$ for $x > 0$.

(a) If $y = e^{0.085x}$ and $x = 40$, then $y \approx 29.96.$ (b) If $y = 2$, then $x \approx 8.15.$

    [0, 60] by [0, 40]   [0, 60] by [0, 40]

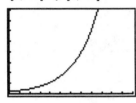
Xscl = 5
Yscl = 5

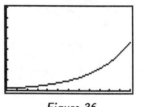
Xscl = 5
Yscl = 5

Figure 35   *Figure 36*

$\boxed{36}$ Compare with Exercise 44 of §4.1.

(a) If $y = e^{0.0525x}$ and $x = 40$, then $y \approx 8.17.$ (b) If $y = 2$, then $x \approx 13.20.$

$\boxed{37}$ (a) As $x \to \infty$, $e^{-x} \to 0$ and f will resemble $\frac{1}{2}e^x$.

As $x \to -\infty$, $e^x \to 0$ and f will resemble $-\frac{1}{2}e^x$.

(b) At $x = 0$, we will have a vertical asymptote. As $x \to \infty$, $f(x) \to \infty$, and $g(x) \to 0$.

As $x \to -\infty$, $f(x) \to -\infty$, and $g(x) \to 0$.

[−7.5, 7.5] by [−5, 5]

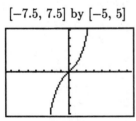
Xscl = 1
Yscl = 1

Figure 37(a)

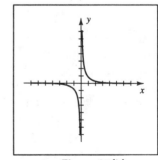

Figure 37(b)

38 (a) See Example 3.

(b) At $x = 0$, $f(x)$ and $g(x) = 1$. As $x \to \infty$ or $x \to -\infty$, $f(x) \to \infty$ and $g(x) \to 0$.

[−7.5, 7.5] by [−5, 5]

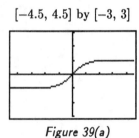

Xscl = 1

Yscl = 1

Figure 38(a)

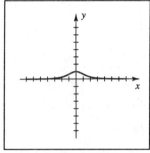

Figure 38(b)

39 (a) $f(x) = \dfrac{e^x - e^{-x}}{e^x + e^{-x}} = \dfrac{e^x - 1/e^x}{e^x + 1/e^x} \cdot \dfrac{e^x}{e^x} = \dfrac{e^{2x} - 1}{e^{2x} + 1}$.

At $x = 0$, $f(x) = 0$. As $x \to \infty$, $f(x) \to 1$. As $x \to -\infty$, $f(x) \to -1$.

(b) At $x = 0$, we will have a vertical asymptote. As $x \to \infty$, $g(x) \to 1$.

As $x \to -\infty$, $g(x) \to -1$.

[−4.5, 4.5] by [−3, 3]

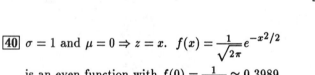

Xscl = 1

Yscl = 1

Figure 39(a)

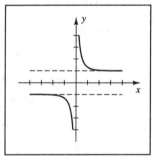

Figure 39(b)

40 $\sigma = 1$ and $\mu = 0 \Rightarrow z = x$. $f(x) = \dfrac{1}{\sqrt{2\pi}} e^{-x^2/2}$

is an even function with $f(0) = \dfrac{1}{\sqrt{2\pi}} \approx 0.3989$,

$f(\pm 1) = \dfrac{1}{\sqrt{2\pi e}} \approx 0.2420$, and $f(\pm 2) = \dfrac{1}{\sqrt{2\pi e^2}} \approx 0.0540$.

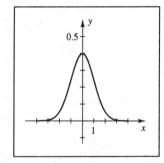

Figure 40

41 The approximate coordinates of the points where the graphs of f and g intersect are (−1.04, −0.92), (2.11, 2.44), and (8.51, 70.42). The region near the origin in *Figure 41(a)* is enhanced in *Figure 41(b)* (figures are on the next page). Thus, the solutions are $x \approx -1.04$, 2.11, and 8.51.

[−3, 11] by [−10, 80]   [−2.26, 3.34] by [−7.14, 8.57]

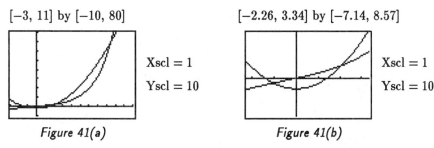

Xscl = 1   Xscl = 1
Yscl = 10   Yscl = 10

Figure 41(a)   *Figure 41(b)*

42 The approximate coordinates of the points where the graphs of f and g intersect are $(-0.93, 0.12)$, $(-0.25, 0.23)$, $(1.36, 1.17)$, and $(7.04, 341.46)$. The region near the origin in *Figure 42(a)* is enhanced in *Figure 42(b)*. Thus, the solutions are $x \approx -0.93$, -0.25, 1.36, and 7.04.

[−5, 8] by [−50, 400]   [−1.37, 1.79] by [−1.11, 2.06]

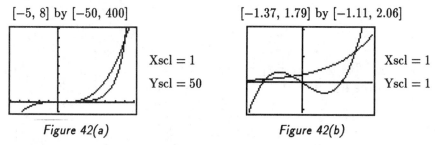

Xscl = 1   Xscl = 1
Yscl = 50   Yscl = 1

Figure 42(a)   *Figure 42(b)*

43 f is a more accurate approximation to e^x near $x = 0$,

whereas g is a more accurate approximation to e^x near $x = 1$.

[0, 4.5] by [0, 3]   [0, 4.5] by [0, 3]

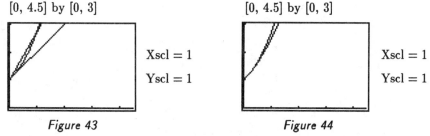

Xscl = 1   Xscl = 1
Yscl = 1   Yscl = 1

Figure 43   *Figure 44*

44 Both approximations are quite accurate for $0 \leq x \leq \frac{1}{2}$.

For $\frac{1}{2} \leq x \leq 1$, g is a more accurate approximation.
(Careful inspection will show that f is a more accurate near $x = 0$.)

45 From the graph, we determine that f has zeros at $x \approx 0.11$, 0.79, and 1.13.

[−2, 2.5] by [−1, 2]   [−6, 3] by [−3, 3]

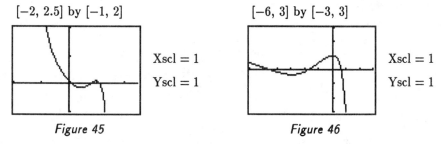

Xscl = 1   Xscl = 1
Yscl = 1   Yscl = 1

Figure 45   *Figure 46*

46 From the graph, we determine that f has zeros at $x \approx -4.54$, -1.71, and 0.65.

47 From the graph, there is a horizontal asymptote of $y \approx 2.71$.

f is approaching the value of e asymptotically.

[0, 200] by [0, 8]

[0, 200] by [0, 8]

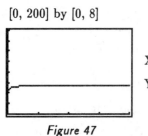

Xscl = 50

Yscl = 1

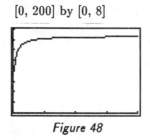

Xscl = 50

Yscl = 1

Figure 47

Figure 48

48 From the graph, there is a horizontal asymptote of $y \approx 7.32$.

f is approaching the value of e^2 (≈ 7.389) asymptotically.

49 $e^{-x} = x$ when $x \approx 0.567$.

[−4.5, 4.5] by [−3, 3]

[−4.5, 4.5] by [0, 6]

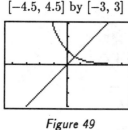

Xscl = 1

Yscl = 1

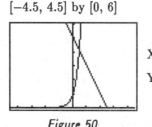

Xscl = 1

Yscl = 1

Figure 49

Figure 50

50 $e^{3x} = 5 - 2x$ when $x \approx 0.467$.

51 f is increasing on $[-1, \infty)$ and f is decreasing on $(-\infty, -1]$.

[−5.5, 5] by [−2, 5]

[−2, 2.5] by [−1, 2]

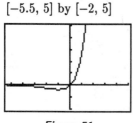

Xscl = 1

Yscl = 1

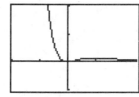

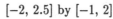

Xscl = 1

Yscl = 1

Figure 51

Figure 52

52 f is increasing on $[0, 1]$ and f is decreasing on $(-\infty, 0]$ and $[1, \infty)$.

53 (a) When $y = 0$ and $z = 0$, the equation becomes $C = \dfrac{2Q}{\pi v a b} e^{-h^2/(2b^2)}$.

As h increases, the concentration C decreases.

(b) When $z = 0$, the equation becomes $C = \dfrac{2Q}{\pi v a b} e^{-y^2/(2a^2)} e^{-h^2/(2b^2)}$.

As y increases, the concentration C decreases.

54 Graph $C = e^{-(z-100)^2/288} + e^{-(z+100)^2/288}$.   [0, 200] by [0, 1]

From the graph, we see that the concentration
of the pollution first increases as the height
increases and then decreases. The maximum
concentration occurs when $z = 100$ m.

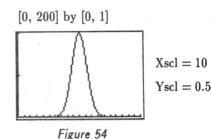

Xscl = 10

Yscl = 0.5

Figure 54

55 (a) Chose two arbitrary points that appear to lie on the curve such as (0, 1.225) and
(10,000, 0.414). $f(0) = Ce^0 = C = 1.225$ and $f(10{,}000) = 1.225e^{10{,}000k} = 0.414$.
To solve the last equation, graph $Y_1 = 1.225e^{10{,}000x}$ and $Y_2 = 0.414$. The
graphs intersect at $x \approx -0.0001085$. Thus, $f(x) = 1.225e^{-0.0001085x}$.

(b) $f(3000) \approx 0.885$ and $f(9000) \approx 0.461$.

[−1000, 10,100] by [0, 1.5]   [−10, 90] by [−100, 1600]

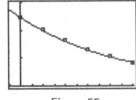

Xscl = 1000

Yscl = 0.5

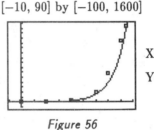

Xscl = 10

Yscl = 100

Figure 55   *Figure 56*

56 (a) Chose two arbitrary points that appear to lie on the curve such as (0, 0.7) and
(85, 1538.9). $A(0) = A_0e^0 = A_0 = 0.7$. $A(85) = 0.7e^{85k} = 1538.9$. To solve the
last equation, graph $Y_1 = 0.7e^{85x}$ and $Y_2 = 1538.9$. The graphs intersect at
$x \approx 0.09053527$. Thus, $A(x) = 0.7e^{0.09053527x}$.

(b) Graph $Y_1 = A(x)$ and $Y_2 = 1000$. The graphs intersect at $x \approx 80.2$. The federal
government first spent one trillion dollars in 1990.

4.3 Exercises

4.3 Concept Check

1 We know that $y = \ln x$ is an increasing function and we can compute that
$\ln 1{,}000{,}000 \approx 13.82$. What can we conclude about the graph of $y = \ln x$?   •   The
graph of $y = \ln x$ is an *extremely slowly* increasing function.

2 Why is $\log_3(-1)$ not a real number?   •   Because $3^x \neq -1$ for any real number x.

3 As $x \to \infty$, which function has larger values, $y = \log_2 x$ or $y = \log_3 x$?   • $y = \log_2 x$
is larger than $y = \log_3 x$ as $x \to \infty$.

4 About how long does it take money to double at 6%?   •   Using the rule of 72, we
have $72/6 = 12$ years.

4.3 Exercises

1. (a) $4^3 = 64 \Leftrightarrow \log_4 64 = 3$

    (b) $4^{-3} = \frac{1}{64} \Leftrightarrow \log_4 \frac{1}{64} = -3$

    (c) $t^r = s \Leftrightarrow \log_t s = r$

    (d) $3^x = 4 - t \Leftrightarrow \log_3 (4 - t) = x$

    (e) $5^{7t} = \frac{a+b}{a} \Leftrightarrow \log_5 \frac{a+b}{a} = 7t$

    (f) $(0.7)^t = 5.3 \Leftrightarrow \log_{0.7} (5.3) = t$

2. (a) $3^5 = 243 \Leftrightarrow \log_3 243 = 5$

    (b) $3^{-4} = \frac{1}{81} \Leftrightarrow \log_3 \frac{1}{81} = -4$

    (c) $c^p = d \Leftrightarrow \log_c d = p$

    (d) $7^x = 100p \Leftrightarrow \log_7 (100p) = x$

    (e) $3^{-2x} = \frac{P}{F} \Leftrightarrow \log_3 \frac{P}{F} = -2x$

    (f) $(0.9)^t = \frac{1}{2} \Leftrightarrow \log_{0.9} \left(\frac{1}{2}\right) = t$

3. (a) $\log_2 32 = 5 \Leftrightarrow 2^5 = 32$

    (b) $\log_3 \frac{1}{243} = -5 \Leftrightarrow 3^{-5} = \frac{1}{243}$

    (c) $\log_t r = p \Leftrightarrow t^p = r$

    (d) $\log_3 (x + 2) = 5 \Leftrightarrow 3^5 = (x + 2)$

    (e) $\log_2 m = 3x + 4 \Leftrightarrow 2^{3x+4} = m$

    (f) $\log_b 512 = \frac{3}{2} \Leftrightarrow b^{3/2} = 512$

4. (a) $\log_3 81 = 4 \Leftrightarrow 3^4 = 81$

    (b) $\log_4 \frac{1}{256} = -4 \Leftrightarrow 4^{-4} = \frac{1}{256}$

    (c) $\log_v w = q \Leftrightarrow v^q = w$

    (d) $\log_6 (2x - 1) = 3 \Leftrightarrow 6^3 = 2x - 1$

    (e) $\log_4 p = 5 - x \Leftrightarrow 4^{5-x} = p$

    (f) $\log_a 343 = \frac{3}{4} \Leftrightarrow a^{3/4} = 343$

5. $2a^{t/3} = 5 \Leftrightarrow a^{t/3} = \frac{5}{2} \Leftrightarrow t/3 = \log_a \frac{5}{2} \Leftrightarrow t = 3 \log_a \frac{5}{2}$

6. $3a^{4t} = 10 \Leftrightarrow a^{4t} = \frac{10}{3} \Leftrightarrow 4t = \log_a \frac{10}{3} \Leftrightarrow t = \frac{1}{4} \log_a \frac{10}{3}$

7. $A = Ba^{Ct} + D \Rightarrow A - D = Ba^{Ct} \Rightarrow$

$$\frac{A - D}{B} = a^{Ct} \Rightarrow Ct = \log_a \left(\frac{A - D}{B}\right) \Rightarrow t = \frac{1}{C} \log_a \left(\frac{A - D}{B}\right)$$

8. $L = Ma^{t/N} - P \Rightarrow L + P = Ma^{t/N} \Rightarrow$

$$\frac{L + P}{M} = a^{t/N} \Rightarrow \frac{t}{N} = \log_a \left(\frac{L + P}{M}\right) \Rightarrow t = N \log_a \left(\frac{L + P}{M}\right)$$

9. (a) $10^5 = 100{,}000 \Leftrightarrow \log 100{,}000 = 5$

    (b) $10^{-3} = 0.001 \Leftrightarrow \log 0.001 = -3$

    (c) $10^x = y + 1 \Leftrightarrow \log (y + 1) = x$

    (d) $e^7 = p \Leftrightarrow \ln p = 7$

    (e) $e^{2t} = 3 - x \Leftrightarrow \ln (3 - x) = 2t$

10. (a) $10^4 = 10{,}000 \Leftrightarrow \log 10{,}000 = 4$

    (b) $10^{-2} = 0.01 \Leftrightarrow \log 0.01 = -2$

    (c) $10^x = 38z \Leftrightarrow \log (38z) = x$

    (d) $e^4 = D \Leftrightarrow \ln D = 4$

    (e) $e^{0.1t} = x + 2 \Leftrightarrow \ln (x + 2) = 0.1t$

11. (a) $\log x = 50 \Leftrightarrow 10^{50} = x$

    (b) $\log x = 20t \Leftrightarrow 10^{20t} = x$

    (c) $\ln x = 0.1 \Leftrightarrow e^{0.1} = x$

    (d) $\ln w = 4 + 3x \Leftrightarrow e^{4+3x} = w$

    (e) $\ln (z - 2) = \frac{1}{6} \Leftrightarrow e^{1/6} = z - 2$

12. (a) $\log x = -8 \Leftrightarrow 10^{-8} = x$

    (b) $\log x = y - 2 \Leftrightarrow 10^{y-2} = x$

    (c) $\ln x = \frac{1}{2} \Leftrightarrow e^{1/2} = x$

    (d) $\ln z = 7 + x \Leftrightarrow e^{7+x} = z$

    (e) $\ln (t - 5) = 1.2 \Leftrightarrow e^{1.2} = t - 5$

$\boxed{13}$ (a) $\log_5 1 = 0$ (b) $\log_3 3 = 1$ (c) $\log_4(-2)$ is undefined, not possible

     (d) $\log_7 7^2 = 2$ (e) $3^{\log_3 8} = 8$ (f) $\log_5 125 = \log_5 5^3 = 3$

     (g) $\log_4 \frac{1}{16} = \log_4 4^{-2} = -2$

$\boxed{14}$ (a) $\log_8 1 = 0$ (b) $\log_9 9 = 1$ (c) $\log_5 0$ is undefined, not possible

     (d) $\log_6 6^7 = 7$ (e) $5^{\log_5 4} = 4$ (f) $\log_3 243 = \log_3 3^5 = 5$

     (g) $\log_2 128 = \log_2 2^7 = 7$

$\boxed{15}$ (a) $10^{\log 3} = 3$ (b) $\log 10^5 = 5$ (c) $\log 100 = \log 10^2 = 2$

     (d) $\log 0.0001 = \log 10^{-4} = -4$

     (e) $e^{\ln 2} = 2$ (f) $\ln e^{-3} = -3$ (g) $e^{2 + \ln 3} = e^2 e^{\ln 3} = e^2(3) = 3e^2$

$\boxed{16}$ (a) $10^{\log 7} = 7$ (b) $\log 10^{-6} = -6$ (c) $\log 100{,}000 = \log 10^5 = 5$

     (d) $\log 0.001 = \log 10^{-3} = -3$

     (e) $e^{\ln 8} = 8$ (f) $\ln e^{2/3} = \frac{2}{3}$ (g) $e^{1 + \ln 5} = e^1 e^{\ln 5} = e(5) = 5e$

$\boxed{17}$ $\log_4 x = \log_4(8 - x) \Rightarrow x = 8 - x \Rightarrow 2x = 8 \Rightarrow x = 4$

$\boxed{18}$ $\log_3(x + 4) = \log_3(1 - x) \Rightarrow x + 4 = 1 - x \Rightarrow 2x = -3 \Rightarrow x = -\frac{3}{2}$

$\boxed{19}$ $\log_5(x - 2) = \log_5(3x + 7) \Rightarrow x - 2 = 3x + 7 \Rightarrow 2x = -9 \Rightarrow x = -\frac{9}{2}$. $-\frac{9}{2}$ is extraneous

     since it makes either of the given logarithm expressions undefined; no solution.

$\boxed{20}$ $\log_7(x - 5) = \log_7(6x) \Rightarrow x - 5 = 6x \Rightarrow 5x = -5 \Rightarrow x = -1$. -1 is extraneous

     since it makes either of the given logarithm expressions undefined; no solution.

$\boxed{21}$ $\log x^2 = \log(-3x - 2) \Rightarrow x^2 = -3x - 2 \Rightarrow x^2 + 3x + 2 = 0 \Rightarrow (x + 1)(x + 2) = 0 \Rightarrow$

$$x = -1, -2$$

$\boxed{22}$ $\ln x^2 = \ln(12 - x) \Rightarrow x^2 = 12 - x \Rightarrow x^2 + x - 12 = 0 \Rightarrow (x + 4)(x - 3) = 0 \Rightarrow x = -4, 3$

$\boxed{23}$ $\log_3(x - 4) = 2 \Rightarrow x - 4 = 3^2 \Rightarrow x = 13$

$\boxed{24}$ $\log_2(x - 5) = 4 \Rightarrow x - 5 = 2^4 \Rightarrow x = 21$

$\boxed{25}$ $\log_9 x = \frac{3}{2} \Rightarrow x = 9^{3/2} = (9^{1/2})^3 = 3^3 = 27$

$\boxed{26}$ $\log_4 x = -\frac{3}{2} \Rightarrow x = 4^{-3/2} = (4^{-1/2})^3 = (\frac{1}{2})^3 = \frac{1}{8}$

$\boxed{27}$ $\ln x^2 = -2 \Rightarrow x^2 = e^{-2} = \frac{1}{e^2} \Rightarrow x = \pm\frac{1}{e}$

$\boxed{28}$ $\log x^2 = -4 \Rightarrow x^2 = 10^{-4} = \frac{1}{10{,}000} \Rightarrow x = \pm\frac{1}{100}$

$\boxed{29}$ $e^{2 \ln x} = 9 \Rightarrow (e^{\ln x})^2 = 9 \Rightarrow x^2 = 9 \Rightarrow x = \pm 3$; -3 is extraneous

$\boxed{30}$ $e^{-\ln x} = 0.2 \Rightarrow (e^{\ln x})^{-1} = 0.2 \Rightarrow x^{-1} = 0.2 \Rightarrow 1/x = 1/5 \Rightarrow x = 5$

31 (a) $f(x) = \log_4 x$ • This graph has a vertical asymptote of $x = 0$ and
goes through $(\frac{1}{4}, -1)$, $(1, 0)$, and $(4, 1)$. For reference purposes, call this $F(x)$.

(b) $f(x) = -\log_4 x$ • reflect F through the x-axis

(c) $f(x) = 2\log_4 x$ • vertically stretch F by a factor of 2

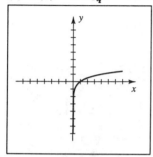

Figure 31(a)

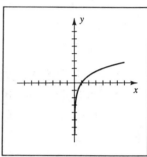

Figure 31(b)

Figure 31(c)

(d) $f(x) = \log_4(x + 2)$ • shift F left 2 units

(e) $f(x) = (\log_4 x) + 2$ • shift F up 2 units

(f) $f(x) = \log_4(x - 2)$ • shift F right 2 units

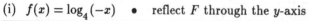

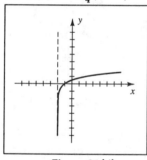

Figure 31(d)

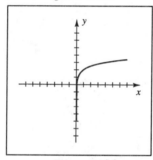

Figure 31(e)

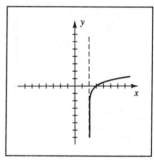

Figure 31(f)

(g) $f(x) = (\log_4 x) - 2$ • shift F down 2 units

(h) $f(x) = \log_4 |x|$ • include the reflection of F through the y-axis

(i) $f(x) = \log_4(-x)$ • reflect F through the y-axis

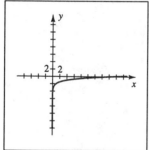

Figure 31(g)

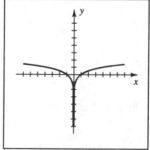

Figure 31(h)

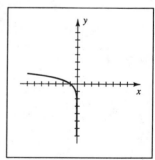

Figure 31(i)

(j) $f(x) = \log_4 (3 - x) = \log_4 [-(x - 3)]$ •

shift F 3 units right and reflect through the line $x = 3$

(k) $f(x) = |\log_4 x|$ •

reflect points with negative y-coordinates through the x-axis

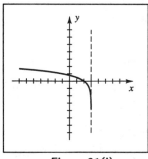

Figure 31(j)

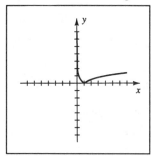

Figure 31(k)

32 The graphs are found in a manner similar to that of Exercise 31.

The graph of $y = \log_5 x$ goes through $(\frac{1}{5}, -1)$, $(1, 0)$, and $(5, 1)$.

33 $f(x) = \log x$ • goes through $(\frac{1}{10}, -1)$, $(1, 0)$, and $(10, 1)$

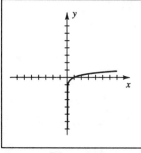

Figure 33

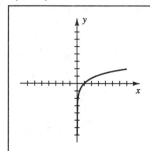

Figure 34

34 $f(x) = \ln x$ • goes through $(\frac{1}{e}, -1)$, $(1, 0)$, and $(e, 1)$

35 $f(x) = \log_2 |x - 5|$ • shift $y = \log_2 |x|$ right 5 units

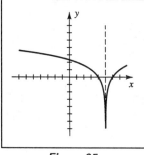

Figure 35

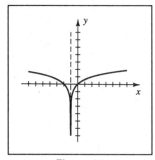

Figure 36

36 $f(x) = \log_3 |x + 1|$ • shift $y = \log_3 |x|$ left 1 unit

37 This is the basic "logarithm with base 2" graph, call it $F(x) = \log_2 x$. ★ $f(x) = \log_2 x$

38 the reflection of F through the x-axis ★ $f(x) = -\log_2 x$

39 shift F down 1 unit $\bigstar$ $f(x) = \log_2 x - 1$

40 shift F left 3 units $\bigstar$ $f(x) = \log_2 (x + 3)$

41 the reflection of F through the y-axis $\bigstar$ $f(x) = \log_2 (-x)$

42 shift F right 1 unit since the vertical asymptote is $x = 1$,

then reflect that graph through $x = 1$; $f(x) = \log_2 [-(x - 1)] = \log_2 (1 - x)$

43 the y-coordinates of F are doubled $\bigstar$ $f(x) = 2 \log_2 x$

44 the reflection of F through the y-axis is included with F $\bigstar$ $f(x) = \log_2 |x|$

45 (a) $\log x = 3.6274 \Rightarrow x = 10^{3.6274} \approx 4240.333$, or 4240 to three significant figures

(b) $\log x = 0.9469 \Rightarrow x = 10^{0.9469} \approx 8.849$, or 8.85

(c) $\log x = -1.6253 \Rightarrow x = 10^{-1.6253} \approx 0.023697$, or 0.0237

(d) $\ln x = 2.3 \Rightarrow x = e^{2.3} \approx 9.974$, or 9.97

(e) $\ln x = 0.05 \Rightarrow x = e^{0.05} \approx 1.051$, or 1.05

(f) $\ln x = -1.6 \Rightarrow x = e^{-1.6} \approx 0.2019$, or 0.202

46 (a) $\log x = 1.8965 \Rightarrow x = 10^{1.8965} \approx 78.795$, or 78.8

(b) $\log x = 4.9680 \Rightarrow x = 10^{4.968} \approx 92{,}896.639$, or 92,900

(c) $\log x = -2.2118 \Rightarrow x = 10^{-2.2118} \approx 0.00614$

(d) $\ln x = 3.7 \Rightarrow x = e^{3.7} \approx 40.447$, or 40.4

(e) $\ln x = 0.95 \Rightarrow x = e^{0.95} \approx 2.5857$, or 2.59

(f) $\ln x = -5 \Rightarrow x = e^{-5} \approx 0.00674$

47 $q = q_0 (2)^{-t/1600} \Rightarrow \frac{q}{q_0} = 2^{-t/1600} \Rightarrow -\frac{t}{1600} = \log_2 \left(\frac{q}{q_0} \right) \Rightarrow t = -1600 \log_2 \left(\frac{q}{q_0} \right)$

48 $Q = k(2)^{-t/5} \Rightarrow \frac{Q}{k} = 2^{-t/5} \Rightarrow -\frac{t}{5} = \log_2 \left(\frac{Q}{k} \right) \Rightarrow t = -5 \log_2 \left(\frac{Q}{k} \right)$

49 $I = 20e^{-Rt/L} \Rightarrow \frac{I}{20} = e^{-Rt/L} \Rightarrow \ln \left(\frac{I}{20} \right) = -\frac{Rt}{L} \Rightarrow t = -\frac{L}{R} \ln \left(\frac{I}{20} \right)$

50 $Q = Q_0 e^{kt} \Rightarrow \frac{Q}{Q_0} = e^{kt} \Rightarrow \ln \left(\frac{Q}{Q_0} \right) = kt \Rightarrow t = \frac{1}{k} \ln \left(\frac{Q}{Q_0} \right)$

51 $I = 10^a I_0 \Rightarrow R = \log \left(\frac{I}{I_0} \right) = \log \left(\frac{10^a I_0}{I_0} \right) = \log 10^a = a.$

Hence, for $10^2 I_0$, $10^4 I_0$, and $10^5 I_0$, the answers are: (a) 2   (b) 4   (c) 5

52 From the previous solution, these magnitudes are between $10^8 I_0$ and $10^9 I_0$.

53 $I = 10^a I_0 \Rightarrow \alpha = 10 \log \left(\frac{I}{I_0} \right) = 10 \log \left(\frac{10^a I_0}{I_0} \right) = 10 \log 10^a = 10a.$

Hence, for $10^1 I_0$, $10^3 I_0$, and $10^4 I_0$, the answers are: (a) 10   (b) 30   (c) 40

54 $\alpha = 140 \Rightarrow 140 = 10 \log \left(\frac{I}{I_0} \right) \Rightarrow \log \left(\frac{I}{I_0} \right) = 14 \Rightarrow \frac{I}{I_0} = 10^{14} \Rightarrow I = 10^{14} I_0.$

$\boxed{55}$ 1980 corresponds to $t = 0$ and $N(0) = 227$ million. $2 \cdot 227 = 227e^{0.007t} \Rightarrow$

$\qquad 2 = e^{0.007t} \Rightarrow \ln 2 = 0.007t \Rightarrow t \approx 99$, which corresponds to the year 2079.

Alternatively, using the doubling time formula, $t = (\ln 2)/r = (\ln 2)/0.007 \approx 99$.

$\boxed{56}$ 1985 corresponds to $t = 0$. $N(t) = 1500 \Rightarrow 1500 = 762e^{0.022t} \Rightarrow e^{0.022t} = \frac{1500}{762} \Rightarrow$

$\qquad 0.022t = \ln\left(\frac{1500}{762}\right) \Rightarrow t \approx 30.79$, which corresponds to the year 2015.

$\boxed{57}$ (a) $\ln W = \ln 2.4 + (1.84)h \Rightarrow W = e^{[\ln 2.4 + (1.84)h]} \Rightarrow W = e^{\ln 2.4} e^{1.84h} \Rightarrow$

$$W = 2.4e^{1.84h}$$

(b) $h = 1.5 \Rightarrow W = 2.4e^{(1.84)(1.5)} = 2.4e^{2.76} \approx 37.92$ kg

$\boxed{58}$ $25{,}000 = 6000e^{0.1t} \Rightarrow \frac{25}{6} = e^{0.1t} \Rightarrow 0.1t = \ln\left(\frac{25}{6}\right) \Rightarrow t = 10\ln\left(\frac{25}{6}\right) \approx 14.27$ yr

$\boxed{59}$ (a) $10 = 14.7e^{-0.0000385h} \Rightarrow h = -\frac{1}{0.0000385}\ln\left(\frac{10}{14.7}\right) \approx 10{,}007$ ft.

(b) At sea level, $h = 0$ and $p = 14.7$. Setting $p(h)$ equal to $\frac{1}{2}(14.7)$,

$\qquad$ and solving as in part (a), we have $h = -\frac{1}{0.0000385}\ln\left(\frac{1}{2}\right) \approx 18{,}004$ ft.

$\boxed{60}$ $\log P = a + \dfrac{b}{c+T} \Rightarrow P = 10^{a + b/(c+T)} \Rightarrow P = 10^a 10^{b/(c+T)}$

$\boxed{61}$ (a) $t = 0 \Rightarrow W = 2600(0.49)^3 \approx 305.9$ kg

(b) (1) From the graph, if $W = 1800$, t appears to be about 20.

$\quad$ (2) Solving the equation for t, we have $1800 = 2600\left(1 - 0.51e^{-0.075t}\right)^3 \Rightarrow$

$\qquad \frac{1800}{2600} = \left(1 - 0.51e^{-0.075t}\right)^3 \Rightarrow \sqrt[3]{\frac{9}{13}} = 1 - 0.51e^{-0.075t} \Rightarrow$

$\qquad e^{-0.075t} = \left(1 - \sqrt[3]{\frac{9}{13}}\right)\left(\frac{100}{51}\right) \{\text{call this } A\} \Rightarrow (-0.075)t = \ln A \Rightarrow t \approx 19.8$ yr.

$\boxed{62}$ $T = 50 \Rightarrow 50 = 325(e^{0.02t} - 1) \Rightarrow e^{0.02t} - 1 = \frac{2}{13} \Rightarrow e^{0.02t} = \frac{15}{13} \Rightarrow$

$\qquad 0.02t = \ln\frac{15}{13} \Rightarrow t = 50\ln\frac{15}{13} \approx 7.16$ yr

$\boxed{63}$ $D = 2 \Rightarrow 5.5e^{-0.1x} = 2 \Rightarrow e^{-0.1x} = \frac{4}{11} \Rightarrow -0.1x = \ln\frac{4}{11} \Rightarrow x = -10\ln\frac{4}{11}$ mi ≈ 10.1 mi

$\boxed{64}$ (a) $m = 6 - 2.5\log\left(\dfrac{10^{0.4} L_0}{L_0}\right) = 6 - 2.5\log 10^{0.4} = 6 - 2.5(0.4) = 6 - 1 = 5$

(b) $m = 6 - 2.5\log\left(\dfrac{L}{L_0}\right) \Rightarrow \log\left(\dfrac{L}{L_0}\right) = \dfrac{6 - m}{2.5} \Rightarrow \dfrac{L}{L_0} = 10^{(6 - m)/2.5} \Rightarrow$

$$L = L_0 10^{(6 - m)/2.5}$$

$\boxed{65}$ $A(t) = \frac{1}{2}A_0$ when $t = 8 \Rightarrow \frac{1}{2}A_0 = A_0 a^{-8} \Rightarrow a^{-8} = \frac{1}{2} \Rightarrow a^8 = 2 \Rightarrow a = 2^{1/8} \approx 1.09$.

$\boxed{66}$ Since the field is *currently* 2.5 times the safe level S, we let $A_0 = 2.5S$ and $A(t) = S$.

$\qquad S = 2.5Se^{-0.0239t} \Rightarrow 0.4 = e^{-0.0239t} \Rightarrow \ln 0.4 = -0.0239t \Rightarrow t = \dfrac{\ln 0.4}{-0.0239} \approx 38.3$ yr.

$\boxed{67}$ (a) Since $\log P$ is an increasing function, increasing the population increases the

$\qquad$ walking speed. Pedestrians have faster average walking speeds in large cities.

(b) $5 = 0.05 + 0.86\log P \Rightarrow 4.95 = 0.86\log P \Rightarrow P = 10^{4.95/0.86} \approx 570{,}000$

68 (a) Larger values of c cause F to decrease more rapidly.

This indicates that the chip will fail sooner and be less reliable.

(b) $c = 0.125$ and $F = 35\% \Rightarrow 0.35 = 1 - e^{-0.125t} \Rightarrow e^{-0.125t} = 0.65 \Rightarrow$

$$-0.125t = \ln 0.65 \Rightarrow t = \frac{\ln 0.65}{-0.125} \approx 3.45 \text{ yr.}$$

69 (a) $f(2) = \ln(2+1) + e^2 \approx 8.4877$

(b) $g(3.97) = \dfrac{(\log 3.97)^2 - \log 3.97}{4} \approx -0.0601$

70 (a) $f(1.95) = \log(2 \times 1.95^2 + 1) - 10^{-1.95} \approx 0.9235$

(b) $g(0.55) = \dfrac{0.55 - 3.4}{\ln 0.55 + 4} \approx -0.8377$

71 $x \ln x = 1$ when $x \approx 1.763$.

$[0, 4]$ by $[-1, 1.67]$ $[-3, 4.5]$ by $[-1, 4]$

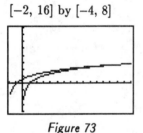

Xscl $= 1$

Yscl $= 1$

Figure 71

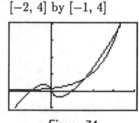

Xscl $= 1$

Yscl $= 1$

Figure 72

72 $\ln x + x = 0$ when $x \approx 0.567$.

73 The domain of g is $x > 0$. From the graph, we determine that f intersects g at about

14.90. Thus, $f(x) \geq g(x)$ on approximately $(0, 14.90)$.

$[-2, 16]$ by $[-4, 8]$ $[-2, 4]$ by $[-1, 4]$

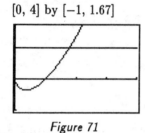

Xscl $= 1$

Yscl $= 1$

Figure 73

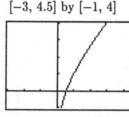

Xscl $= 1$

Yscl $= 1$

Figure 74

74 The graph of f intersects the graph of g four times—$x \approx -0.94$, -0.05, 1.59, and

3.28. Since f is not defined at $x = 0$, we must exclude $x = 0$. Thus, $f(x) \geq g(x)$ on

approximately $(-\infty, -0.94) \cup (-0.05, 0) \cup (0, 1.59) \cup (3.28, \infty)$.

75 (a) $R = 2.07 \ln \frac{242}{78} - 2.04 \approx 0.3037 \approx 30\%$.

(b) Graph $Y_1 = 2.07 \ln x - 2.04$ and $Y_2 = 0.75$.

From the graph, $R \approx 0.75$ when $x \approx 3.85$. See *Figure 75*.

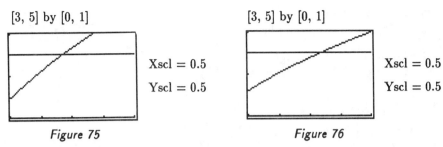

[3, 5] by [0, 1]   [3, 5] by [0, 1]

Xscl = 0.5   Xscl = 0.5

Yscl = 0.5   Yscl = 0.5

Figure 75   *Figure 76*

$\boxed{76}$ (a) $R = 1.36 \ln \frac{287}{65} - 1.19 \approx 0.8297 \approx 83\%$.

(b) Graph $Y_1 = 1.36 \ln x - 1.19$ and $Y_2 = 0.75$.

From the graph, $R \approx 0.75$ when $x \approx 4.16$.

4.4 Exercises

4.4 Concept Check

$\boxed{1}$ Does $\log x + \log y = \log (x + y)$? • $\log x + \log y = \log (xy)$, which is not, in general, equal to $\log (x + y)$.

$\boxed{2}$ For what values of x does $\log x^2 = 2 \log x$? • x must be a positive real number.

$\boxed{3}$ Is $x = 3$ a solution of the equation $\ln (x - 5) = \ln (x^2 - 11)$? • Substituting $x = 3$ into the equation gives us $\ln (-2) = \ln (-2)$. Since $\ln (-2)$ is not a real number, $x = 3$ is not a solution of the equation.

$\boxed{4}$ Can you find an example of a logarithmic function of the form $y = \log z$, where z is a function of x and the domain of the function is $x < 0$? • A couple examples are $z = -x$ and $z = 3 - x$.

4.4 Exercises

$\boxed{1}$ (a) $\log_4 (xz) = \log_4 x + \log_4 z$ (b) $\log_4 (y/x) = \log_4 y - \log_4 x$

(c) $\log_4 \sqrt[3]{z} = \log_4 z^{1/3} = \frac{1}{3} \log_4 z$

$\boxed{2}$ (a) $\log_3 (xyz) = \log_3 (xy) + \log_3 z = \log_3 x + \log_3 y + \log_3 z$

(b) $\log_3 (xz/y) = \log_3 (xz) - \log_3 y = \log_3 x + \log_3 z - \log_3 y$

(c) $\log_3 \sqrt[5]{y} = \log_3 y^{1/5} = \frac{1}{5} \log_3 y$

$\boxed{3}$ $\log_a \frac{x^3 w}{y^2 z^4} = \log_a x^3 w - \log_a y^2 z^4 = \log_a x^3 + \log_a w - (\log_a y^2 + \log_a z^4) =$

$$3 \log_a x + \log_a w - 2 \log_a y - 4 \log_a z$$

$\boxed{4}$ $\log_a \frac{y^5 w^2}{x^4 z^3} = \log_a y^5 w^2 - \log_a x^4 z^3 = \log_a y^5 + \log_a w^2 - (\log_a x^4 + \log_a z^3) =$

$$5 \log_a y + 2 \log_a w - 4 \log_a x - 3 \log_a z$$

$\boxed{5}$ $\log \frac{\sqrt[3]{z}}{x \sqrt{y}} = \log \sqrt[3]{z} - \log x \sqrt{y} = \log z^{1/3} - \log x - \log y^{1/2} = \frac{1}{3} \log z - \log x - \frac{1}{2} \log y$

$\boxed{6}$ $\log \frac{\sqrt{y}}{x^4 \sqrt[3]{z}} = \log \sqrt{y} - \log x^4 \sqrt[3]{z} = \log y^{1/2} - \log x^4 - \log y^{1/3} = \frac{1}{2} \log y - 4 \log x - \frac{1}{3} \log z$

7 $\ln\sqrt[4]{\dfrac{x^7}{y^5 z}} = \ln x^{7/4} - \ln y^{5/4} z^{1/4} = \ln x^{7/4} - \ln y^{5/4} - \ln z^{1/4} = \frac{7}{4}\ln x - \frac{5}{4}\ln y - \frac{1}{4}\ln z$

8 $\ln x\sqrt[3]{\dfrac{y^4}{z^5}} = \ln x + \ln y^{4/3} - \ln z^{5/3} = \ln x + \frac{4}{3}\ln y - \frac{5}{3}\ln z$

9 (a) $\log_3 x + \log_3(5y) = \log_3(x \cdot 5y) = \log_3(5xy)$

(b) $\log_3(2z) - \log_3 x = \log_3(2z/x)$　　　(c) $5\log_3 y = \log_3 y^5$

10 (a) $\log_4(3z) + \log_4 x = \log_4(3xz)$　　　(b) $\log_4 x - \log_4(7y) = \log_4[x/(7y)]$

(c) $\frac{1}{3}\log_4 w = \log_4 w^{1/3} = \log_4 \sqrt[3]{w}$

11 $2\log_a x + \frac{1}{3}\log_a(x-2) - 5\log_a(2x+3) = \log_a x^2 + \log_a(x-2)^{1/3} - \log_a(2x+3)^5 =$

$$\log_a x^2 \sqrt[3]{x-2} - \log_a(2x+3)^5 = \log_a \frac{x^2\sqrt[3]{x-2}}{(2x+3)^5}$$

12 $5\log_a x - \frac{1}{2}\log_a(3x-4) - 3\log_a(5x+1) = \log_a x^5 - \log_a(3x-4)^{1/2} - \log_a(5x+1)^3 =$

$$\log_a x^5 - \log_a \sqrt{3x-4}(5x+1)^3 = \log_a \frac{x^5}{\sqrt{3x-4}(5x+1)^3}$$

13 $\log(x^3 y^2) - 2\log x\sqrt[3]{y} - 3\log\left(\frac{x}{y}\right) = \log\dfrac{x^3 y^2}{x^2 y^{2/3}(x^3/y^3)} = \log\dfrac{y^{13/3}}{x^2}$

14 $2\log\dfrac{y^3}{x} - 3\log y + \frac{1}{2}\log x^4 y^2 = \log\dfrac{(y^6/x^2)(x^2 y)}{y^3} = \log y^4$

15 $\ln y^3 + \frac{1}{3}\ln(x^3 y^6) - 5\ln y = \ln y^3 + \ln(xy^2) - \ln y^5 = \ln[(xy^5)/y^5] = \ln x$

16 $2\ln x - 4\ln(1/y) - 3\ln(xy) = \ln x^2 - \ln(1/y^4) - \ln(x^3 y^3) =$

$$\ln x^2 - \left[\ln(1/y^4) + \ln(x^3 y^3)\right] = \ln x^2 - \ln(x^3/y) = \ln\frac{x^2}{x^3/y} = \ln(y/x)$$

17 $\log_6(2x-3) = \log_6 12 - \log_6 3 \Rightarrow \log_6(2x-3) = \log_6\frac{12}{3} \Rightarrow 2x - 3 = 4 \Rightarrow x = \frac{7}{2}$

18 $\log_4(3x+2) = \log_4 5 + \log_4 3 \Rightarrow \log_4(3x+2) = \log_4(5\cdot 3) \Rightarrow 3x + 2 = 15 \Rightarrow x = \frac{13}{3}$

19 $2\log_3 x = 3\log_3 5 \Rightarrow \log_3 x^2 = \log_3 5^3 \Rightarrow x^2 = 125 \Rightarrow x = \pm 5\sqrt{5};$

$-5\sqrt{5}$ is extraneous since it would make $\log_3 x$ undefined

20 $3\log_2 x = 2\log_2 3 \Rightarrow \log_2 x^3 = \log_2 3^2 \Rightarrow x^3 = 9 \Rightarrow x = \sqrt[3]{9}$

21 $\log x - \log(x+1) = 3\log 4 \Rightarrow \log\dfrac{x}{x+1} = \log 64 \Rightarrow$

$$\frac{x}{x+1} = 64 \Rightarrow x = 64x + 64 \Rightarrow x = -\tfrac{64}{63};\ -\tfrac{64}{63}\text{ is extraneous, no solution}$$

22 $\log(x+2) - \log x = 2\log 4 \Rightarrow \log\dfrac{x+2}{x} = \log 16 \Rightarrow x + 2 = 16x \Rightarrow x = \frac{2}{15}$

23 $\ln(-4-x) + \ln 3 = \ln(2-x) \Rightarrow \ln(-12-3x) = \ln(2-x) \Rightarrow$

$$-12 - 3x = 2 - x \Rightarrow 2x = -14 \Rightarrow x = -7$$

24 $\ln x + \ln(x+6) = \frac{1}{2}\ln 9 \Rightarrow \ln(x^2+6x) = \ln 3 \Rightarrow x^2 + 6x - 3 = 0 \Rightarrow$

$$x = \frac{-6\pm\sqrt{48}}{2} = -3 \pm 2\sqrt{3};\ -3 - 2\sqrt{3}\text{ is extraneous}$$

$\boxed{25}$ $\log_2(x+7) + \log_2 x = 3 \Rightarrow \log_2(x^2+7x) = 3 \Rightarrow x^2 + 7x = 8 \Rightarrow$

$$(x+8)(x-1) = 0 \Rightarrow x = -8, 1; \ -8 \text{ is extraneous}$$

$\boxed{26}$ $\log_6(x+5) + \log_6 x = 2 \Rightarrow \log_6(x^2+5x) = 2 \Rightarrow x^2 + 5x = 36 \Rightarrow$

$$(x+9)(x-4) = 0 \Rightarrow x = -9, 4; \ -9 \text{ is extraneous}$$

$\boxed{27}$ $\log_3(x+3) + \log_3(x+5) = 1 \Rightarrow \log_3(x^2+8x+15) = 1 \Rightarrow$

$$x^2 + 8x + 15 = 3 \Rightarrow (x+2)(x+6) = 0 \Rightarrow x = -6, -2; \ -6 \text{ is extraneous}$$

$\boxed{28}$ $\log_3(x-2) + \log_3(x-4) = 2 \Rightarrow \log_3(x^2-6x+8) = 2 \Rightarrow$

$$x^2 - 6x + 8 = 9 \Rightarrow x^2 - 6x - 1 = 0 \Rightarrow x = \frac{6 \pm \sqrt{40}}{2} = 3 \pm \sqrt{10}; \ 3 - \sqrt{10} \text{ is extraneous}$$

$\boxed{29}$ $\log(x+3) = 1 - \log(x-2) \Rightarrow \log(x+3) + \log(x-2) = 1 \Rightarrow$

$\log[(x+3)(x-2)] = 1 \Rightarrow x^2 + x - 6 = 10^1 \Rightarrow$

$$x^2 + x - 16 = 0 \Rightarrow x = \frac{-1+\sqrt{65}}{2} \approx 3.53; \ \frac{-1-\sqrt{65}}{2} \approx -4.53 \text{ is extraneous}$$

$\boxed{30}$ $\log(57x) = 2 + \log(x-2) \Rightarrow \log(57x) - \log(x-2) = 2 \Rightarrow$

$$\log \frac{57x}{x-2} = 2 \Rightarrow \frac{57x}{x-2} = 10^2 \Rightarrow 57x = 100x - 200 \Rightarrow 200 = 43x \Rightarrow x = \frac{200}{43}$$

$\boxed{31}$ $\ln x = 1 - \ln(x+2) \Rightarrow \ln x + \ln(x+2) = 1 \Rightarrow \ln[x(x+2)] = 1 \Rightarrow x^2 + 2x = e^1 \Rightarrow$

$$x^2 + 2x - e = 0 \Rightarrow x = \frac{-2+\sqrt{4+4e}}{2} = -1 + \sqrt{1+e} \approx 0.93;$$

$$-1 - \sqrt{1+e} \approx -2.93 \text{ is extraneous}$$

$\boxed{32}$ $\ln x = 1 + \ln(x+1) \Rightarrow \ln x - \ln(x+1) = 1 \Rightarrow \ln\left(\frac{x}{x+1}\right) = 1 \Rightarrow \frac{x}{x+1} = e^1 \Rightarrow$

$$x = ex + e \Rightarrow (1-e)x = e \Rightarrow x = \frac{e}{1-e} \approx -1.58 \text{ and is extraneous, no solution}$$

$\boxed{33}$ $f(x) = \log_3(3x) = \log_3 3 + \log_3 x = \log_3 x + 1$ • shift $y = \log_3 x$ up 1 unit

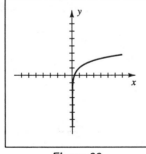

Figure 33

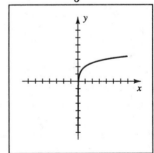

Figure 34

$\boxed{34}$ $f(x) = \log_4(16x) = \log_4 16 + \log_4 x = \log_4 x + 2$ • shift $y = \log_4 x$ up 2 units

35 $f(x) = 3\log_3 x$ •   vertically stretch $y = \log_3 x$ by a factor of 3

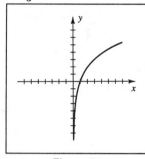

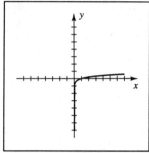

Figure 35   Figure 36

36 $f(x) = \frac{1}{3}\log_3 x$ •   vertically compress $y = \log_3 x$ by a factor of 3

37 $f(x) = \log_3(x^2) = 2\log_3 x$ •   Vertically stretch $y = \log_3 x$ by a factor of 2 and

include its reflection through the y-axis since the domain of the original function,

$$f(x) = \log_3(x^2), \text{ is } \mathbb{R} - \{0\}.$$

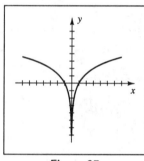

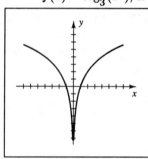

Figure 37   Figure 38

38 $f(x) = \log_2(x^2) = 2\log_2 x$ •   similar to Exercise 37

39 $f(x) = \log_2(x^3) = 3\log_2 x$ •   vertically stretch $y = \log_2 x$ by a factor of 3

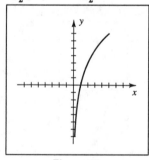

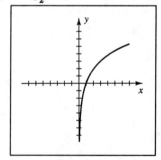

Figure 39   Figure 40

40 $f(x) = \log_3(x^3) = 3\log_3 x$ •   vertically stretch $y = \log_3 x$ by a factor of 3

41 $f(x) = \log_2 \sqrt{x} = \frac{1}{2}\log_2 x$ •   vertically compress $y = \log_2 x$ by a factor of 2

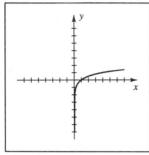

Figure 41

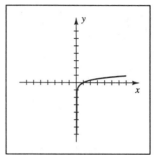

Figure 42

42 $f(x) = \log_2 \sqrt[3]{x} = \frac{1}{3}\log_2 x$ •   vertically compress $y = \log_2 x$ by a factor of 3

43 $f(x) = \log_3\left(\frac{1}{x}\right) = \log_3 x^{-1} = -\log_3 x$ •   reflect $y = \log_3 x$ through the x-axis

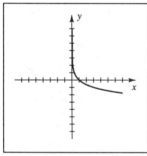

Figure 43

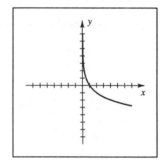

Figure 44

44 $f(x) = \log_2\left(\frac{1}{x}\right) = \log_2 x^{-1} = -\log_2 x$ •   reflect $y = \log_2 x$ through the x-axis

45 The values of $F(x) = \log_2 x$ are doubled and the reflection of F through the y-axis is included. The domain of f is $\mathbb{R} - \{0\}$ and $f(x) = \log_2 x^2$.

46 The domain of f is $\mathbb{R} - \{0\}$ and f has the same y-values as $F(x) = \log_2 x$.

Hence, $f(x) = \log_2 |x|$.

47 $F(x) = \log_2 x$ is shifted up 3 units.

Hence, $f(x) = 3 + \log_2 x = \log_2 2^3 + \log_2 x = \log_2 (8x)$.

48 $F(x) = \log_2 x$ is reflected through the x-axis and shifted up 1 unit.

Hence, $f(x) = -\log_2 x + 1 = \log_2 2 - \log_2 x = \log_2 \frac{2}{x}$.

49 $\log y = \log b - k \log x \Rightarrow \log y = \log b - \log x^k \Rightarrow \log y = \log \frac{b}{x^k} \Rightarrow y = \frac{b}{x^k}$

50 $p = p_0 e^{-ax} \Rightarrow \frac{p}{p_0} = e^{-ax} \Rightarrow \ln\left(\frac{p}{p_0}\right) = -ax \Rightarrow x = \frac{1}{a}\ln\left(\frac{p_0}{p}\right)$

$\boxed{51}$ $c = 0.5$ and $z_0 = 0.1 \Rightarrow$

$\quad v = c \ln (z/z_0)$

$\quad = (0.5) \ln (10z)$

$\quad = \frac{1}{2} (\ln 10 + \ln z) \approx \frac{1}{2} \ln z + 1.15.$

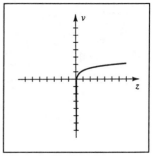

Figure 51

$\boxed{52}$ $y = 50\%$ of $y_0 \Rightarrow \frac{1}{2} y_0 = y_0 e^{-0.3821t} \Rightarrow \frac{1}{2} = e^{-0.3821t} \Rightarrow$

$$\ln \frac{1}{2} = -0.3821t \Rightarrow t = \frac{-\ln 2}{-0.3821} \approx 1.814 \text{ yr.}$$

$\boxed{53}$ (a) $R(x_0) = a \log \left(\frac{x_0}{x_0}\right) = a \log 1 = a \cdot 0 = 0$

$\quad$ (b) $R(2x) = a \log \left(\frac{2x}{x_0}\right) = a \left[\log 2 + \log \left(\frac{x}{x_0}\right)\right] = a \log 2 + a \log \left(\frac{x}{x_0}\right) = R(x) + a \log 2$

$\boxed{54}$ (a) $E(x_0) = E_0 e^{-x_0/x_0} = E_0 e^{-1} = \frac{1}{e} E_0$

$\quad$ (b) $E = E_0 - 99\% \, E_0 \Rightarrow (1 - 0.99) E_0 = E_0 e^{-x/x_0} \Rightarrow 0.01 = e^{-x/x_0} \Rightarrow$

$$-\frac{x}{x_0} = \ln (0.01) = -\ln 100 \Rightarrow x = (\ln 100) \, x_0 \approx 4.6 \, x_0$$

$\boxed{55}$ $\ln I_0 - \ln I = kx \Rightarrow \ln \frac{I_0}{I} = kx \Rightarrow x = \frac{1}{k} \ln \frac{I_0}{I} = \frac{1}{0.39} \ln 1.12 \approx 0.29 \text{ cm.}$

$\boxed{56}$ $\ln I_0 - \ln I = kx \Rightarrow \ln \frac{I_0}{I} = kx \Rightarrow \frac{I_0}{I} = e^{kx} = e^{(0.39)(0.24)} \approx 1.10 \Rightarrow \frac{I}{I_0} \approx 0.91.$

The intensity decreases by approximately 9%.

$\boxed{57}$ From the graph, the coordinates of the points of intersection are approximately

$\quad$ (1.01, 0.48) and (2.4, 0.86). $f(x) \geq g(x)$ on the intervals (0, 1.01] and [2.4, ∞).

[0, 6] by [−1, 3]   [0, 6] by [−1, 3]

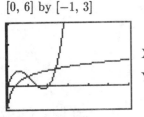   Xscl $= 1$ 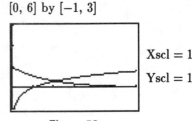   Xscl $= 1$

$\qquad\qquad\qquad$ Yscl $= 1$ $\qquad\qquad\qquad$ Yscl $= 1$

Figure 57   *Figure 58*

$\boxed{58}$ From the graph, the coordinates of the point of intersection are approximately

$\quad$ (2.08, 0.32). $f(x) \geq g(x)$ on the interval (0, 2.08].

59 Graph $y = e^{-x} - 2\log\left(1 + x^2\right) + 0.5x$ and estimate any x-intercepts. From the graph, we determine that the roots of the equation are approximately 1.41 and 6.59.

[0, 8] by [−1.67, 3.67]

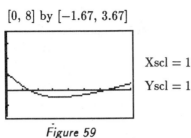

Xscl = 1
Yscl = 1

[−1, 5] by [−1, 3]

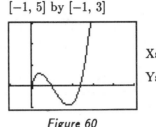

Xscl = 1
Yscl = 1

Figure 59   *Figure 60*

60 Graph $y = 0.3\ln x + x^3 - 3.1x^2 + 1.3x + 0.8$ and estimate any x-intercepts. From the graph, we determine that the roots of the equation are approximately 0.056 and 2.359 as well as $x = 1$.

61 (a) f is increasing on [0.2, 0.63] and [6.87, 16]. f is decreasing on [0.63, 6.87].

(b) The maximum value of f is 4.61 when $x = 16$.

The minimum value of f is approximately −3.31 when $x \approx 6.87$.

[0.2, 16] by [−4.77, 5.77]

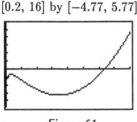

Xscl = 2
Yscl = 1

[0.2, 16] by [−6, 14]

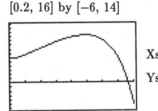

Xscl = 2
Yscl = 1

Figure 61   *Figure 62*

62 (a) f is increasing on [0.44, 9.76]. f is decreasing on [0.2, 0.44] and [9.76, 16].

(b) The maximum value of f is approximately 11.35 when $x \approx 9.76$.

The minimum value of f is approximately −4.9 when $x = 16$.

63 Graph $Y_1 = x\log x - \log x$ and $Y_2 = 5$. The graphs intersect at $x \approx 6.94$.

[−5, 10] by [−2, 8]

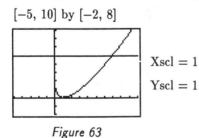

Xscl = 1
Yscl = 1

[−5, 10] by [−2, 8]

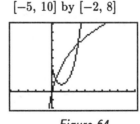

Xscl = 1
Yscl = 1

Figure 63   *Figure 64*

64 Graph $Y_1 = 0.3e^x - \ln x$ and $Y_2 = 4\ln\left(x + 1\right)$.

The graphs intersect at $x \approx 0.40, 3.12$.

65 Let $d = x$. Graph $Y_1 = I_0 - 20 \log x - kx = 70 - 20 \log x - 0.076x$ and $Y_2 = 20$.

At the point of intersection, $x \approx 115.3$. The distance is approximately 115 meters.

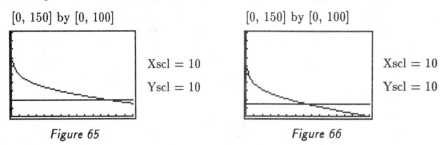

[0, 150] by [0, 100]   [0, 150] by [0, 100]

Xscl = 10   Xscl = 10

Yscl = 10   Yscl = 10

Figure 65   *Figure 66*

66 Let $d = x$. Graph $Y_1 = I_0 - 20 \log x - kx = 60 - 20 \log x - 0.11x$ and $Y_2 = 15$.

At the point of intersection, $x \approx 71.7$. The distance is approximately 72 meters.

4.5 Exercises

4.5 Concept Check

1 Do $\dfrac{\log 13}{\log 5}$ and $\dfrac{\ln 13}{\ln 5}$ represent the same real number?   •   Yes. By the Special

Change of Base Formulas, they both equal $\log_5 13$.

2 Are $\log_b a$ and $\log_a b$ reciprocals?   •   Yes, since $\log_b a = \dfrac{\log_a a}{\log_a b} = \dfrac{1}{\log_a b}$.

3 List two functions that can be entered into a graphing utility to graph $y = \log_4 x$.

Since most graphing utilities have log and ln functions available, either $y = \dfrac{\log x}{\log 4}$ or

$y = \dfrac{\ln x}{\ln 4}$ will produce the graph of $y = \log_4 x$.

4 Do you think an exponential model or a logistic model is more appropriate to describe the population of Earth?   •   An exponential model may be a good description for a period of time, but since there is a carrying capacity associated with the Earth's population, the logistic model seems more appropriate for a long period of time.

4.5 Exercises

1 (a) $5^x = 8 \Rightarrow \log 5^x = \log 8 \Rightarrow x \log 5 = \log 8 \Rightarrow x = \dfrac{\log 8}{\log 5} \approx 1.29$

  (b) $5^x = 8 \Rightarrow x = \log_5 8 = \dfrac{\log 8}{\log 5} \approx 1.29$

2 (a) $4^x = 3 \Rightarrow \log 4^x = \log 3 \Rightarrow x \log 4 = \log 3 \Rightarrow x = \dfrac{\log 3}{\log 4} \approx 0.79$

  (b) $4^x = 3 \Rightarrow x = \log_4 3 = \dfrac{\log 3}{\log 4} \approx 0.79$

$\boxed{3}$ (a) $3^{4-x} = 5 \Rightarrow \log(3^{4-x}) = \log 5 \Rightarrow (4-x)\log 3 = \log 5 \Rightarrow$

$\qquad 4 - x = \dfrac{\log 5}{\log 3} \Rightarrow x = 4 - \dfrac{\log 5}{\log 3} \approx 2.54.$ *Note:* The answer could also

$\qquad\qquad\qquad$ be written as $4 - \dfrac{\log 5}{\log 3} = \dfrac{4\log 3 - \log 5}{\log 3} = \dfrac{\log 81 - \log 5}{\log 3} = \dfrac{\log \frac{81}{5}}{\log 3}.$

$\qquad$ (b) $3^{4-x} = 5 \Rightarrow 4 - x = \log_3 5 \Rightarrow x = 4 - \dfrac{\log 5}{\log 3} \approx 2.54.$

$\boxed{4}$ (a) $\left(\frac{1}{3}\right)^x = 100 \Rightarrow \log\left(\frac{1}{3}\right)^x = \log 100 \Rightarrow x\log\frac{1}{3} = 2 \Rightarrow x = \dfrac{2}{-\log 3} \approx -4.19$

$\qquad$ (b) $\left(\frac{1}{3}\right)^x = 100 \Rightarrow x = \log_{(1/3)} 100 = \dfrac{\log 100}{\log \frac{1}{3}} = \dfrac{2}{-\log 3} \approx -4.19$

$\boxed{5}$ $\log_5 6 = \dfrac{\log 6}{\log 5}\left\{\text{or } \dfrac{\ln 6}{\ln 5}\right\} \approx 1.1133$ $\qquad\boxed{6}$ $\log_2 20 = \dfrac{\log 20}{\log 2} \approx 4.3219$

$\boxed{7}$ $\log_9 0.2 = \dfrac{\log 0.2}{\log 9} \approx -0.7325$ $\qquad\boxed{8}$ $\log_6 \frac{1}{2} = \dfrac{\log\frac{1}{2}}{\log 6} \approx -0.3869$

$\boxed{9}$ $\dfrac{\log_5 16}{\log_5 4} = \log_4 16 = \log_4 4^2 = 2$ $\qquad\boxed{10}$ $\dfrac{\log_7 243}{\log_7 3} = \log_3 243 = \log_3 3^5 = 5$

$\boxed{11}$ $3^{x+4} = 2^{1-3x} \Rightarrow (x+4)\log 3 = (1-3x)\log 2 \Rightarrow$

$\qquad x\log 3 + 4\log 3 = \log 2 - 3x\log 2 \Rightarrow x(\log 3 + 3\log 2) = \log 2 - 4\log 3 \Rightarrow$

$\qquad\qquad\qquad\qquad\qquad\qquad x = \dfrac{\log 2 - \log 81}{\log 3 + \log 8} \Rightarrow x = \dfrac{\log \frac{2}{81}}{\log 24} \approx -1.16$

$\boxed{12}$ $4^{2x+3} = 5^{x-2} \Rightarrow (2x+3)\log 4 = (x-2)\log 5 \Rightarrow$

$\qquad 2x\log 4 + 3\log 4 = x\log 5 - 2\log 5 \Rightarrow 2\log 5 + 3\log 4 = x(\log 5 - 2\log 4) \Rightarrow$

$\qquad\qquad\qquad\qquad\qquad\qquad x = \dfrac{\log 25 + \log 64}{\log 5 - \log 16} \Rightarrow x = \dfrac{\log 1600}{\log \frac{5}{16}} \approx -6.34$

$\boxed{13}$ $2^{2x-3} = 5^{x-2} \Rightarrow (2x-3)\log 2 = (x-2)\log 5 \Rightarrow$

$\qquad 2x\log 2 - 3\log 2 = x\log 5 - 2\log 5 \Rightarrow x(2\log 2 - \log 5) = 3\log 2 - 2\log 5 \Rightarrow$

$\qquad\qquad\qquad\qquad\qquad\qquad x = \dfrac{\log 8 - \log 25}{\log 4 - \log 5} \Rightarrow x = \dfrac{\log \frac{8}{25}}{\log \frac{4}{5}} \approx 5.11$

$\boxed{14}$ $3^{2-3x} = 4^{2x+1} \Rightarrow (2-3x)\log 3 = (2x+1)\log 4 \Rightarrow$

$\qquad 2\log 3 - 3x\log 3 = 2x\log 4 + \log 4 \Rightarrow 2\log 3 - \log 4 = x(2\log 4 + 3\log 3) \Rightarrow$

$\qquad\qquad\qquad\qquad\qquad\qquad x = \dfrac{\log 9 - \log 4}{\log 16 + \log 27} \Rightarrow x = \dfrac{\log \frac{9}{4}}{\log 432} \approx 0.13$

$\boxed{15}$ $2^{-x} = 8 \Rightarrow 2^{-x} = 2^3 \Rightarrow -x = 3 \Rightarrow x = -3$

$\boxed{16}$ $2^{-x^2} = 5 \Rightarrow -x^2 = \log_2 5 \Rightarrow x^2 = -\dfrac{\log 5}{\log 2}\left\{x^2 \ge 0\right\}$, no solution

$\boxed{17}$ $\log x = 1 - \log(x-3) \Rightarrow \log x + \log(x-3) = 1 \Rightarrow \log(x^2 - 3x) = 1 \Rightarrow$

$\qquad\qquad x^2 - 3x = 10^1 \Rightarrow (x-5)(x+2) = 0 \Rightarrow x = 5, -2; -2$ is extraneous

$\boxed{18}$ $\log{(5x+1)} = 2 + \log{(2x-3)} \Rightarrow \log{(5x+1)} - \log{(2x-3)} = 2 \Rightarrow$

$$\log\left(\frac{5x+1}{2x-3}\right) = 2 \Rightarrow \frac{5x+1}{2x-3} = 10^2 \Rightarrow 5x+1 = 200x - 300 \Rightarrow x = \frac{301}{195} \approx 1.54$$

$\boxed{19}$ $\log{(x^2+4)} - \log{(x+2)} = 2 + \log{(x-2)} \Rightarrow \log\left(\frac{x^2+4}{x+2}\right) - \log{(x-2)} = 2 \Rightarrow$

$$\log\left(\frac{x^2+4}{x^2-4}\right) = 2 \Rightarrow \frac{x^2+4}{x^2-4} = 10^2 \Rightarrow x^2 + 4 = 100x^2 - 400 \Rightarrow 404 = 99x^2 \Rightarrow$$

$$x = \pm\sqrt{\frac{404}{99}} = \pm\frac{2}{3}\sqrt{\frac{101}{11}} \approx \pm 2.02; \; -\frac{2}{3}\sqrt{\frac{101}{11}} \text{ is extraneous}$$

$\boxed{20}$ $\log{(x-4)} - \log{(3x-10)} = \log{(1/x)} \Rightarrow$

$$\log\left(\frac{x-4}{3x-10}\right) = \log\left(\frac{1}{x}\right) \Rightarrow \frac{x-4}{3x-10} = \frac{1}{x} \Rightarrow x^2 - 4x = 3x - 10 \Rightarrow$$

$$(x-2)(x-5) = 0 \Rightarrow x = 2, 5; \; 2 \text{ is extraneous}$$

$\boxed{21}$ $5^x + 125(5^{-x}) = 30 \Rightarrow \{\text{multiply by } 5^x\} \, (5^x)^2 - 30(5^x) + 125 = 0 \Rightarrow$

$$(5^x - 5)(5^x - 25) = 0 \Rightarrow 5^x = 5, 25 \Rightarrow 5^x = 5^1, 5^2 \Rightarrow x = 1, 2$$

$\boxed{22}$ $3(3^x) + 9(3^{-x}) = 28 \Rightarrow 3(3^x)^2 - 28(3^x) + 9 = 0 \Rightarrow$

$$[3(3^x) - 1](3^x - 9) = 0 \Rightarrow 3^x = \frac{1}{3}, 9 \Rightarrow 3^x = 3^{-1}, 3^2 \Rightarrow x = -1, 2$$

$\boxed{23}$ $4^x - 3(4^{-x}) = 8 \Rightarrow (4^x)^2 - 8(4^x) - 3 = 0 \Rightarrow$

$$4^x = \frac{8+\sqrt{76}}{2} \left\{ \text{since } 4^x > 0 \text{ and } \frac{8-\sqrt{76}}{2} < 0 \right\} = 4 + \sqrt{19} \Rightarrow$$

$$x = \log_4{(4+\sqrt{19})} = \frac{\log{(4+\sqrt{19})}}{\log 4} \approx 1.53$$

$\boxed{24}$ $2^x - 6(2^{-x}) = 6 \Rightarrow (2^x)^2 - 6(2^x) - 6 = 0 \Rightarrow$

$$2^x = \frac{6+\sqrt{60}}{2} \left\{ \text{since } 2^x > 0 \text{ and } \frac{6-\sqrt{60}}{2} < 0 \right\} = 3 + \sqrt{15} \Rightarrow$$

$$x = \log_2{(3+\sqrt{15})} = \frac{\log{(3+\sqrt{15})}}{\log 2} \approx 2.78$$

$\boxed{25}$ $\log{(x^2)} = (\log x)^2 \Rightarrow 2\log x = (\log x)^2 \Rightarrow (\log x)^2 - 2\log x = 0 \Rightarrow$

$$(\log x)(\log x - 2) = 0 \Rightarrow \log x = 0, 2 \Rightarrow x = 10^0, 10^2 \Rightarrow x = 1 \text{ or } 100$$

$\boxed{26}$ $\log{\sqrt{x}} = \sqrt{\log x} \Rightarrow \frac{1}{2}\log x = (\log x)^{1/2} \Rightarrow (\log x)^2 = 4\log x \Rightarrow$

$$(\log x)(\log x - 4) = 0 \Rightarrow \log x = 0, 4 \Rightarrow x = 10^0, 10^4 \Rightarrow x = 1 \text{ or } 10,000$$

$\boxed{27}$ $\log{(\log x)} = 2 \Rightarrow \log x = 10^2 = 100 \Rightarrow x = 10^{100}$

$\boxed{28}$ $\log{\sqrt{x^3-9}} = 2 \Rightarrow \sqrt{x^3 - 9} = 10^2 \Rightarrow x^3 - 9 = 10^4 \Rightarrow x = \sqrt[3]{10,009}$

$\boxed{29}$ $x^{\sqrt{\log x}} = 10^8 \Rightarrow \log\left(x^{\sqrt{\log x}}\right) = \log 10^8 \Rightarrow \sqrt{\log x}\,(\log x) = 8 \Rightarrow$

$$(\log x)^{3/2} = 8 \Rightarrow \log x = 8^{2/3} = 4 \Rightarrow x = 10,000$$

$\boxed{30}$ $\log{(x^3)} = (\log x)^3 \Rightarrow 3\log x = (\log x)^3 \Rightarrow (\log x)[(\log x)^2 - 3] = 0 \Rightarrow$

$$\log x = 0, \pm\sqrt{3} \Rightarrow x = 1, 10^{\sqrt{3}}, 10^{-\sqrt{3}}$$

Note: For Exercises 31–34 and 39–40 of the review exercises, let D denote the domain of the function determined by the original equation, and R its range. These are then the range and domain, respectively, of the equation listed in the answer.

$\boxed{31}$ $y = \dfrac{10^x + 10^{-x}}{2}$ $\{\, D = \mathbb{R},\ R = [1,\,\infty) \,\} \Rightarrow$

$2y = 10^x + 10^{-x}$ $\left\{\, \text{since } 10^{-x} = \dfrac{1}{10^x},\ \text{multiply by } 10^x \text{ to eliminate denominator} \,\right\} \Rightarrow$

$10^{2x} - 2y\,10^x + 1 = 0$ $\{\, \text{treat as a quadratic in } 10^x \,\} \Rightarrow$

$$10^x = \frac{2y \pm \sqrt{4y^2 - 4}}{2} = y \pm \sqrt{y^2 - 1} \Rightarrow x = \log\left(y \pm \sqrt{y^2 - 1}\right)$$

$\boxed{32}$ The solution is similar to that of Exercise 31.

$y = \dfrac{10^x - 10^{-x}}{2}$ $\{\, D = R = \mathbb{R} \,\} \Rightarrow 2y = 10^x - 10^{-x} \Rightarrow$

$10^{2x} - 2y\,10^x - 1 = 0 \Rightarrow 10^x = \dfrac{2y \pm \sqrt{4y^2 + 4}}{2} = y \pm \sqrt{y^2 + 1}$;

$\sqrt{y^2 + 1} > y$, so $y - \sqrt{y^2 + 1} < 0$, but $10^x > 0$ and thus, $x = \log\left(y + \sqrt{y^2 + 1}\right)$

$\boxed{33}$ $y = \dfrac{10^x - 10^{-x}}{10^x + 10^{-x}}$ $\{\, D = \mathbb{R},\ R = (-1,\,1) \,\} \Rightarrow y\,10^x + y\,10^{-x} = 10^x - 10^{-x} \Rightarrow$

$y\,10^{2x} + y = 10^{2x} - 1 \Rightarrow (y - 1)\,10^{2x} = -1 - y \Rightarrow$

$$10^{2x} = \frac{-1 - y}{y - 1} \Rightarrow 2x = \log\left(\frac{1 + y}{1 - y}\right) \Rightarrow x = \frac{1}{2}\log\left(\frac{1 + y}{1 - y}\right)$$

$\boxed{34}$ $y = \dfrac{10^x + 10^{-x}}{10^x - 10^{-x}}$ $\{\, D = \mathbb{R} - \{0\},\ R = (-\infty,\,-1) \cup (1,\,\infty) \,\} \Rightarrow$

$y\,10^x - y\,10^{-x} = 10^x + 10^{-x} \Rightarrow y\,10^{2x} - y = 10^{2x} + 1 \Rightarrow$

$$(y - 1)\,10^{2x} = y + 1 \Rightarrow 10^{2x} = \frac{y + 1}{y - 1} \Rightarrow 2x = \log\left(\frac{y + 1}{y - 1}\right) \Rightarrow x = \frac{1}{2}\log\left(\frac{y + 1}{y - 1}\right)$$

$\boxed{35}$ Use ln instead of log in Exercise 32. $x = \ln\left(y + \sqrt{y^2 + 1}\right)$

$\boxed{36}$ Use ln instead of log in Exercise 31. $x = \ln\left(y \pm \sqrt{y^2 - 1}\right)$

$\boxed{37}$ Use ln instead of log in Exercise 34. $x = \frac{1}{2}\ln\left(\dfrac{y + 1}{y - 1}\right)$

$\boxed{38}$ Use ln instead of log in Exercise 33. $x = \frac{1}{2}\ln\left(\dfrac{1 + y}{1 - y}\right)$

39 $f(x) = \log_2(x+3)$ • $x = 0 \Rightarrow$ y-intercept $= \log_2 3 = \dfrac{\log 3}{\log 2} \approx 1.5850$

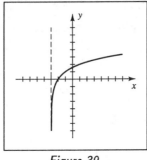

Figure 39

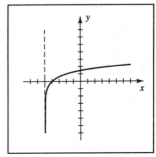

Figure 40

40 $f(x) = \log_3(x+5)$ • $x = 0 \Rightarrow$ y-intercept $= \log_3 5 = \dfrac{\log 5}{\log 3} \approx 1.4650$

41 $f(x) = 4^x - 3$ • $y = 0 \Rightarrow 4^x = 3 \Rightarrow$ x-intercept $= \log_4 3 = \dfrac{\log 3}{\log 4} \approx 0.7925$

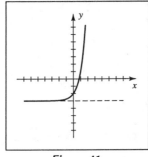

Figure 41

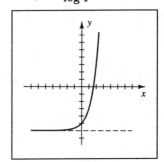

Figure 42

42 $f(x) = 3^x - 6$ • $y = 0 \Rightarrow 3^x = 6 \Rightarrow$ x-intercept $= \log_3 6 = \dfrac{\log 6}{\log 3} \approx 1.6309$

43 (a) vinegar: pH $\approx -\log(6.3 \times 10^{-3}) = -(\log 6.3 + \log 10^{-3}) = -(\log 6.3 - 3) =$

$$3 - \log 6.3 \approx 2.2$$

　(b) carrots: pH $\approx -\log(1.0 \times 10^{-5}) = 5 - \log 1.0 = 5$

　(c) sea water: pH $\approx -\log(5.0 \times 10^{-9}) = 9 - \log 5.0 \approx 8.3$

44 pH $= -\log[\text{H}^+] \Rightarrow [\text{H}^+] = 10^{-\text{pH}}$　　　　　(a) apples: $[\text{H}^+] = 10^{-3} = 0.001$

　(b) beer: $[\text{H}^+] = 10^{-4.2} \approx 0.0000631$　　　(c) milk: $[\text{H}^+] = 10^{-6.6} \approx 0.00000025$

45 $[\text{H}^+] < 10^{-7} \Rightarrow \log[\text{H}^+] < \log 10^{-7}$ { since log is an increasing function } $\Rightarrow$

　$\log[\text{H}^+] < -7 \Rightarrow -\log[\text{H}^+] > -(-7) \Rightarrow$ pH > 7 for basic solutions;

$$\text{similarly, pH} < 7 \text{ for acidic solutions.}$$

46 $1 < \text{pH} < 14 \Rightarrow 1 < -\log[\text{H}^+] < 14 \Rightarrow -1 > \log[\text{H}^+] > -14 \Rightarrow$

$$10^{-1} > 10^{\log[\text{H}^+]} > 10^{-14} \Rightarrow 10^{-14} < [\text{H}^+] < 10^{-1}$$

47 Solving $A = P(1+\frac{r}{n})^{nt}$ for t with $A = 2P$, $r = 0.06$, and $n = 12$ yields

　$2P = P(1+\frac{0.06}{12})^{12t} \Rightarrow 2 = (1.005)^{12t} \Rightarrow \ln 2 = 12t \ln(1.005) \Rightarrow$

$$t = \frac{\ln 2}{12 \ln(1.005)} \approx 11.58 \text{ yr, or about 11 years and 7 months.}$$

48 $A = P\left(1 + \frac{r}{n}\right)^{nt} \Rightarrow \frac{A}{P} = \left(1 + \frac{r}{n}\right)^{nt} \Rightarrow \ln\left(\frac{A}{P}\right) = nt \ln\left(1 + \frac{r}{n}\right) \Rightarrow t = \dfrac{\ln(A/P)}{n \ln\left(1 + \frac{r}{n}\right)}$

49 50% of the light reaching a depth of 13 meters corresponds to the equation

$\frac{1}{2}I_0 = I_0 c^{13}$. Solving for c, we have $c^{13} = \frac{1}{2} \Rightarrow c = \sqrt[13]{\frac{1}{2}} = 2^{-1/13}$.

Now letting $I = 0.01\,I_0$, $c = 2^{-1/13}$, and using the formula from Example 6,

$$x = \frac{\log(I/I_0)}{\log c} = \frac{\log[(0.01\,I_0)/I_0]}{\log 2^{-1/13}} = \frac{\log 10^{-2}}{-\frac{1}{13}\log 2} = \frac{26}{\log 2} \approx 86.4 \text{ m.}$$

50 Solving as in Exercise 49 with $x = 10$ cm $= 0.1$ m,

$$\frac{1}{2}I_0 = I_0 c^{0.1} \Rightarrow c^{1/10} = \frac{1}{2} \Rightarrow c = \frac{1}{1024}. \quad x = \frac{\log[(0.01\,I_0)/I_0]}{\log\left(\frac{1}{1024}\right)} = \frac{-2}{-\log 1024} \approx 0.664 \text{ m.}$$

51 (a) A is an increasing function that passes through

(0, 0), (5, ≈ 41), and (10, ≈ 65).

(b) $A = 50 \Rightarrow 50 = 100\left[1 - (0.9)^t\right] \Rightarrow$

$1 - (0.9)^t = 0.5 \Rightarrow (0.9)^t = 0.5 \Rightarrow$

$t = \log_{0.9}(0.5) = \dfrac{\log 0.5}{\log 0.9} \approx 6.58$ min.

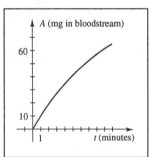

Figure 51

52 (a) $A(t) = 2 \Rightarrow 2 = 10(0.8)^t \Rightarrow 0.2 = (0.8)^t \Rightarrow t = \log_{0.8}(0.2) = \dfrac{\log 0.2}{\log 0.8} \approx 7.21$ hr

(b) $A(t) = \frac{1}{2}(10) \Rightarrow \frac{1}{2}(10) = 10(0.8)^t \Rightarrow t = \log_{0.8}(0.5) = \dfrac{\log 0.5}{\log 0.8} \approx 3.11$ hr

53 (a) $F = F_0(1 - m)^t \Rightarrow (1 - m)^t = \dfrac{F}{F_0} \Rightarrow t \log(1 - m) = \log\left(\dfrac{F}{F_0}\right) \Rightarrow t = \dfrac{\log(F/F_0)}{\log(1 - m)}$

(b) Using part (a) with $F = \frac{1}{2}F_0$ and $m = 0.00005$,

$$t = \frac{\log\frac{1}{2}}{\log 0.99995} \approx 13{,}863 \text{ generations.}$$

54 (a) $f(5) = 3 + 20\left[1 - e^{-0.1(5)}\right] \approx 10.87 \approx 11$; $\qquad$ [0, 36] by [0, 24]

$f(9) \approx 15$; $f(24) \approx 21$; $f(30) \approx 22$.

(b) The graph of $f(n) = 3 + 20(1 - e^{-0.1n})$

is shown in *Figure 54*.

(c) As $n \to \infty$, $e^{-0.1n} \to 0$, and $f(n) \to 23$.

Thus, there is a horizontal asymptote of 23.

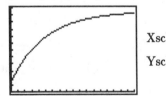

Xscl $= 2$

Yscl $= 2$

Figure 54

55 (a) $t = 10 \Rightarrow h = \dfrac{120}{1 + 200e^{-2}} \approx 4.28$ ft

(b) $50 = \dfrac{120}{1 + 200e^{-0.2t}} \Rightarrow 1 + 200e^{-0.2t} = \frac{120}{50} \Rightarrow e^{-0.2t} = \left(\frac{120}{50} - 1\right) \cdot \frac{1}{200} \Rightarrow$

$e^{-0.2t} = 0.007 \Rightarrow -0.2t = \ln 0.007 \Rightarrow t = \dfrac{\ln 0.007}{-0.2} \approx 24.8$ yr

56 (a) $T(2) = T_1 2^{-k} = (0.80)T_1 \Rightarrow 2^{-k} = 0.8 \Rightarrow -k = \log_2 0.8 \Rightarrow k = -\log_2 0.8 \approx 0.32$

(b) $T(4) = T_1(4)^{-k} = T_1(2^2)^{-k} = T_1(2^{-k})^2 = T_1(2^{\log_2 0.8})^2 = T_1(0.8)^2 = (0.64)T_1$

(c) $T(2n) = T_1(2n)^{-k} = 2^{-k}(T_1 n^{-k}) = 2^{\log_2 0.8} T(n) = (0.80)T(n)$

57 $\dfrac{v_0}{v_1} = \left(\dfrac{h_0}{h_1}\right)^P \Rightarrow \ln\dfrac{v_0}{v_1} = P\ln\dfrac{h_0}{h_1} \Rightarrow P = \dfrac{\ln(v_0/v_1)}{\ln(h_0/h_1)} = \dfrac{\ln(25/6)}{\ln(200/35)} \approx 0.82$

58 Without loss of generality, let $h_0 = 200$, $h_1 = 35$ and $v_0 > v_1$. Then $\dfrac{v_0}{v_1} > 1$ and $\ln\dfrac{v_0}{v_1}$

is positive. Since $P = \dfrac{\ln(v_0/v_1)}{\ln(h_0/h_1)} \approx 0.57\ln\dfrac{v_0}{v_1}$ and $y = \ln x$ is an increasing function,

P increases when the ratio $\dfrac{v_0}{v_1}$ increases. Since $v_0 > v_1 > 1$, if $\dfrac{v_0}{v_1}$ increases, then

$v_0 - v_1$ must also increase. Thus, $s = \dfrac{v_1 - v_0}{h_1 - h_0} = \dfrac{v_0 - v_1}{165}$ must increase.

Increasing values for P correspond with larger values for s.

59 When $x = 0$, $y = c2^0 = c = 4$. Thus, $y = 4(2)^{kx}$. Similarly, $x = 1 \Rightarrow$

$y = 4(2)^k = 3.249 \Rightarrow k = \log_2\left(\frac{3.249}{4}\right) \approx -0.300$. Thus, $y = 4(2)^{-0.3x}$. Checking the

remaining two points, we see that $x = 2 \Rightarrow y \approx 2.639$ and $x = 3 \Rightarrow y \approx 2.144$. The

points all lie on the graph of $y = 4(2)^{-0.3x}$ to within three-decimal-place accuracy.

60 When $x = 0$, $y = c2^0 = c = -0.3$. Thus, $y = -0.3(2)^{kx}$.

Similarly, $x = 0.5 \Rightarrow y = -0.3(2)^{0.5k} = -0.345 \Rightarrow k = 2\log_2\left(\frac{-0.345}{-0.3}\right) \approx 0.403$.

Thus, $y = -0.3(2)^{0.403x}$. Checking the remaining three points, we see that

$x = 1 \Rightarrow y \approx -0.397$, $x = 1.5 \Rightarrow y \approx -0.456$, and $x = 2 \Rightarrow y \approx -0.525$.

The points do not lie on the graph of $y = c2^{kx}$ to within three-decimal-place accuracy.

61 When $x = 0$, $y = c\log 10 = c = 1.5$. Thus, $y = 1.5\log(kx + 10)$.

Similarly, $x = 1 \Rightarrow y = 1.5\log(k + 10) = 1.619 \Rightarrow k + 10 = 10^{1.619/1.5} \Rightarrow$

$k = 10^{1.619/1.5} - 10 \approx 2.004$. Thus, $y = 1.5\log(2.004x + 10)$. Checking the

remaining two points, we see that $x = 2 \Rightarrow y \approx 1.720$, and $x = 3 \Rightarrow y \approx 1.807$. The

points do not all lie on the graph of $y = c2^{kx}$ to within three-decimal-place accuracy.

62 When $x = 0$, $y = c\log 10 = c = 0.7$. Thus, $y = 0.7\log(kx + 10)$.

Similarly, $x = 1 \Rightarrow y = 0.7\log(k + 10) = 0.782 \Rightarrow k + 10 = 10^{0.782/0.7} \Rightarrow$

$k = 10^{0.782/0.7} - 10 \approx 3.096$. Thus, $y = 0.7\log(3.096x + 10)$.

Checking the remaining three points, we see that $x = 2 \Rightarrow y \approx 0.847$,

$x = 3 \Rightarrow y \approx 0.900$, and $x = 4 \Rightarrow y \approx 0.945$. The points all lie on the graph of

$y = 0.7\log(3.096x + 10)$ to within three-decimal-place accuracy.

63 $h(5.3) = \log_4 5.3 - 2\log_8(1.2 \times 5.3) = \dfrac{\ln 5.3}{\ln 4} - \dfrac{2\ln 6.36}{\ln 8} \approx -0.5764$

64 $h(52.6) = 3\log_3(2 \times 52.6 - 1) + 7\log_2(52.6 + 0.2) = \dfrac{3\ln 104.2}{\ln 3} + \dfrac{7\ln 52.8}{\ln 2} \approx 52.7450$

65 From the graph of $y = x - \ln(0.3x) - 3\log_3 x$,

we see that there are *no* x-intercepts, and hence, no roots of the equation.

[−1, 17] by [−1, 11]

[0, 3] by [−1, 1]

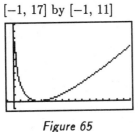

Xscl = 1

Yscl = 1

Figure 65

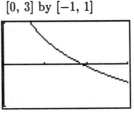

Xscl = 1

Yscl = 1

Figure 66

66 Graph $y = 2\log 2x - \log_3 x^2$ and estimate any x-intercepts.

From the graph, we see that the root of the equation is approximately 1.88.

67 The graphs of $f(x) = x$ and $g(x) = 3\log_2 x$ intersect at approximately $(1.37, 1.37)$

and $(9.94, 9.94)$. Hence, the solutions of the equation $f(x) = g(x)$ are 1.37 and 9.94.

[−1, 17] by [−1, 11]

[−1, 2] by [−1, 1]

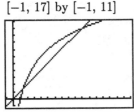

Xscl = 1

Yscl = 1

Figure 67

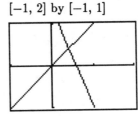

Xscl = 1

Yscl = 1

Figure 68

68 The graphs of $f(x) = x$ and $g(x) = -x^2 - \log_5 x$ intersect at approximately

$(0.40, 0.40)$. Hence, the solution of the equation $f(x) = g(x)$ is 0.40.

69 From the graph, we see that the graphs of f and g intersect at three points. Their

coordinates are approximately $(-0.32, 0.50)$, $(1.52, -1.33)$, and $(6.84, -6.65)$. The

region near the origin in *Figure 69(a)* is enhanced in *Figure 69(b)*. Thus, $f(x) > g(x)$

on $(-\infty, -0.32)$ and $(1.52, 6.84)$.

[−5, 10] by [−8, 2]

[−1.53, 2.26] by [−2.92, 1.05]

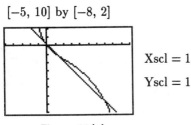

Xscl = 1

Yscl = 1

Figure 69(a)

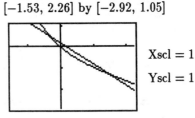

Xscl = 1

Yscl = 1

Figure 69(b)

70 From the graph, we see that the graphs of f and g intersect at two points. Their coordinates are approximately (2.68, 1.70) and (5.30, 2.88). Thus, $f(x) > g(x)$ on (2.68, 5.30).

$[-8, 19]$ by $[-13, 5]$

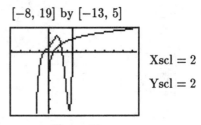

Xscl $= 2$
Yscl $= 2$

Figure 70

71 (1) The graph of $n(t) = 85e^{t/3}$ is increasing rapidly and soon becomes greater than 100. It is doubtful that the average score would improve dramatically without any review.

$[0, 5]$ by $[0, 200]$ $[0, 5]$ by $[0, 100]$

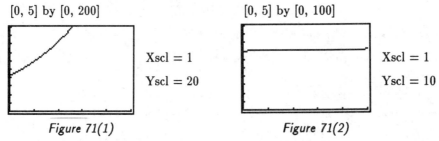

Xscl $= 1$ Xscl $= 1$
Yscl $= 20$ Yscl $= 10$

Figure 71(1)   *Figure 71(2)*

(2) The graph of $n(t) = 70 + \ln(t+1)$ is also increasing. It is incorrect because $n(0) = 70 \neq 85$. Also, one would not expect the average score to improve without any review.

(3) The graph of $n(t) = 86 - e^t$ decreases rapidly to zero. The *average* score probably would not be zero after 5 weeks.

$[0, 5]$ by $[0, 100]$ $[0, 5]$ by $[0, 100]$

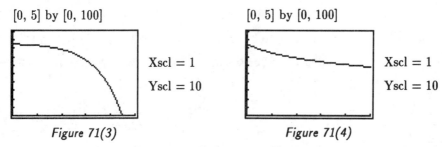

Xscl $= 1$ Xscl $= 1$
Yscl $= 10$ Yscl $= 10$

Figure 71(3)   *Figure 71(4)*

(4) The graph of $n(t) = 85 - 15\ln(t+1)$ is decreasing. During the first weeks it decreases most rapidly and then starts to level off. Of the four functions, this function seems to best model the situation.

72 (1) $T(t) = 212 - 50t$ decreases at a constant rate of 50°F each hour. Initially the temperature is 212°F but after 3 hours the temperature of the water is 62°F, which is cooler than the room.

[0, 5] by [0, 250]

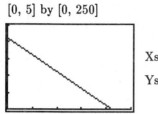

Xscl = 1

Yscl = 50

Figure 72(1)

[0, 5] by [0, 250]

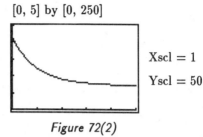

Xscl = 1

Yscl = 50

Figure 72(2)

(2) $T(t) = 140e^{-t} + 72$ is initially 212°F, cools rapidly at first and then gradually approaches a temperature of 72°F. This equation best models the situation.

(3) $T(t) = 212e^{-t}$ is initially 212°F, but decreases rapidly to 29°F in approximately 2 hours.

[0, 5] by [0, 250]

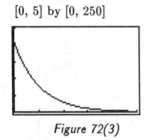

Xscl = 1

Yscl = 50

Figure 72(3)

[0, 5] by [0, 250]

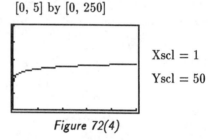

Xscl = 1

Yscl = 50

Figure 72(4)

(4) $T(t) = 72 + 10 \ln(140t + 1)$ is initially 72°F and is an increasing function.

73 (a) The ozone level is decreasing by 11% per year. The fraction of ozone remaining x years after April 1992 is given by the function $f(x) = (0.89)^x$. We must approximate x when $f(x) = 0.5$. Using a table, $f(x) = 0.5$ when $x \approx 6$. Thus, in 1998 the ozone level would be 50% of its normal amount.

x	1	2	3	4	5	6	7
$f(x)$	0.89	0.79	0.70	0.63	0.56	0.50	0.44

(b) $(0.89)^t = 0.5 \Rightarrow \ln(0.89)^t = \ln 0.5 \Rightarrow t \ln 0.89 = \ln 0.5 \Rightarrow$

$$t = \frac{\ln 0.5}{\ln 0.89} \approx 5.948, \text{ or in 1998.}$$

74 (a) Let $f(t)$ be the increased likelihood of skin cancer. f is increasing by a factor of 1.07 each year. Thus, we must solve $f(t) = (1.07)^t = 2$. Graph $Y_1 = (1.07)^t$ and $Y_2 = 2$. The point of intersection occurs at $x \approx 10.2448 \approx 10.2$ years.

[0, 15] by [0, 3]

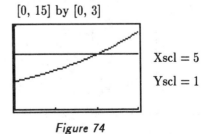

Xscl = 5

Yscl = 1

Figure 74

(b) $(1.07)^t = 2 \Rightarrow \ln(1.07)^t = \ln 2 \Rightarrow t \ln 1.07 = \ln 2 \Rightarrow$

$$t = \frac{\ln 2}{\ln 1.07} \approx 10.2448 \approx 10.2 \text{ yr.}$$

Chapter 4 Review Exercises

1 $f(x) = 3^{x+2}$ •   shift $y = 3^x$ left 2 units

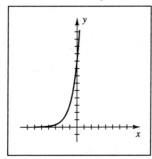

Figure 1   Figure 2

2 $f(x) = \left(\frac{3}{5}\right)^x$ •   goes through $\left(-1, \frac{5}{3}\right)$, $(0, 1)$, and $\left(1, \frac{3}{5}\right)$

3 $f(x) = \left(\frac{3}{2}\right)^{-x} = \left(\frac{2}{3}\right)^x$ •   goes through $\left(-1, \frac{3}{2}\right)$, $(0, 1)$, and $\left(1, \frac{2}{3}\right)$

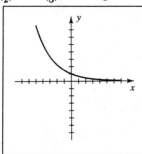
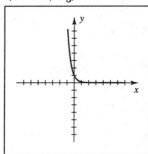

Figure 3   Figure 4

4 $f(x) = 3^{-2x} = (3^{-2})^x = \left(\frac{1}{9}\right)^x$ •   goes through $(-1, 9)$, $(0, 1)$, and $\left(1, \frac{1}{9}\right)$

5 $f(x) = 3^{-x^2} = \left(\frac{1}{3}\right)^{x^2}$ •   see the note in §4.1 before Exercise 17

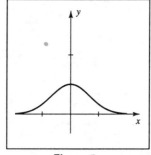
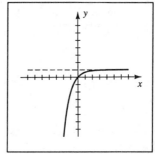

Figure 5   Figure 6

6 $f(x) = 1 - 3^{-x} = -\left(\frac{1}{3}\right)^x + 1$ •

reflect $y = \left(\frac{1}{3}\right)^x$ through the x-axis and shift it up 1 unit

$\boxed{7}$ $f(x) = e^{x/2} = (e^{1/2})^x \approx (1.65)^x$ • goes through $(-1, 1/\sqrt{e})$, $(0, 1)$, and $(1, \sqrt{e})$;

or approximately $(-1, 0.61)$, $(0, 1)$, and $(1, 1.65)$

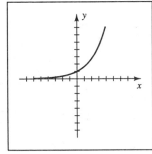

Figure 7

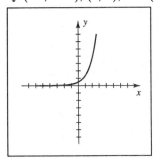

Figure 8

$\boxed{8}$ $f(x) = \frac{1}{2}e^x$ • vertically compress $y = e^x$ by a factor of 2

$\boxed{9}$ $f(x) = e^{x-2}$ • shift $y = e^x$ right 2 units

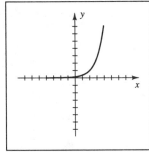

Figure 9

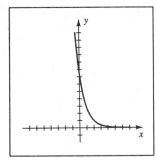

Figure 10

$\boxed{10}$ $f(x) = e^{2-x} = e^{-(x-2)} = (\frac{1}{e})^{x-2}$ • the graph of $y = (\frac{1}{e})^x$ is just the graph of

$y = e^x$ reflected through the y-axis; shift it right 2 units

$\boxed{11}$ $f(x) = \log_6 x$ • goes through $(\frac{1}{6}, -1)$, $(1, 0)$, and $(6, 1)$

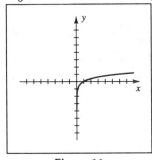

Figure 11

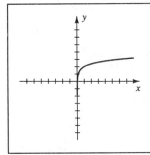

Figure 12

$\boxed{12}$ $f(x) = \log_6 (36x) = \log_6 36 + \log_6 x = \log_6 6^2 + \log_6 x = \log_6 x + 2$ •

shift $y = \log_6 x$ up 2 units

[13] $f(x) = \log_4(x^2) = 2\log_4 x$ • stretch $y = \log_4 x$ by a factor of 2 and include its

reflection through the y-axis since the domain of the original function is $\mathbb{R} - \{0\}$

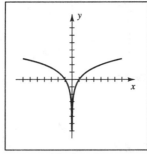

Figure 13

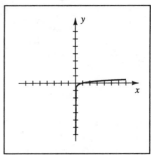

Figure 14

[14] $f(x) = \log_4 \sqrt[3]{x} = \log_4 x^{1/3} = \frac{1}{3}\log_4 x$ •

vertically compress $y = \log_4 x$ by a factor of 3

[15] $f(x) = \log_2(x + 4)$ • shift $y = \log_2 x$ left 4 units

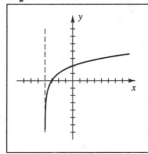

Figure 15

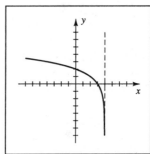

Figure 16

[16] $f(x) = \log_2(4 - x) = \log_2[-(x - 4)]$ •

shift $y = \log_2 x$ four units right and reflect through the line $x = 4$

[17] (a) $\log_2 \frac{1}{16} = \log_2 2^{-4} = -4$ (b) $\log_\pi 1 = 0$ (c) $\ln e = 1$

(d) $6^{\log_6 4} = 4$ (e) $\log 1{,}000{,}000 = \log 10^6 = 6$

(f) $10^{3\log 2} = 10^{\log 2^3} = 2^3 = 8$ (g) $\log_4 2 = \log_4 4^{1/2} = \frac{1}{2}$

[18] (a) $\log_5 \sqrt[3]{5} = \log_5 5^{1/3} = \frac{1}{3}$ (b) $\log_5 1 = 0$ (c) $\log 10 = 1$

(d) $e^{\ln 5} = 5$ (e) $\log\log 10^{10} = \log(\log 10^{10}) = \log(10) = 1$

(f) $e^{2\ln 5} = e^{\ln 5^2} = 5^2 = 25$ (g) $\log_{27} 3 = \log_{27} 27^{1/3} = \frac{1}{3}$

[19] $2^{3x-1} = \frac{1}{2} \Rightarrow 2^{3x-1} = 2^{-1} \Rightarrow 3x - 1 = -1 \Rightarrow 3x = 0 \Rightarrow x = 0$

[20] $\log \sqrt{x} = \log(x - 6) \Rightarrow \sqrt{x} = x - 6 \Rightarrow x = x^2 - 12x + 36 \Rightarrow$

$$x^2 - 13x + 36 = 0 \Rightarrow (x - 4)(x - 9) = 0 \Rightarrow x = 4, 9; \; 4 \text{ is extraneous}$$

[21] $\log_8(x - 5) = \frac{2}{3} \Rightarrow x - 5 = 8^{2/3} = 4 \Rightarrow x = 9$

[22] $\log_4(x + 1) = 2 + \log_4(3x - 2) \Rightarrow \log_4(x + 1) - \log_4(3x - 2) = 2 \Rightarrow$

$$\log_4\left(\frac{x + 1}{3x - 2}\right) = 2 \Rightarrow \frac{x + 1}{3x - 2} = 16 \Rightarrow x + 1 = 48x - 32 \Rightarrow x = \frac{33}{47}$$

$\boxed{23}$ $2\ln(x+3) - \ln(x+1) = 3\ln 2 \Rightarrow \ln\dfrac{(x+3)^2}{x+1} = \ln 2^3 \Rightarrow (x+3)^2 = 8(x+1) \Rightarrow$

$$x^2 + 6x + 9 = 8x + 8 \Rightarrow x^2 - 2x + 1 = 0 \Rightarrow (x-1)^2 = 0 \Rightarrow x = 1$$

$\boxed{24}$ $\log \sqrt[4]{x+1} = \frac{1}{2} \Rightarrow (x+1)^{1/4} = 10^{1/2} \Rightarrow x + 1 = 10^2 \Rightarrow x = 99$

$\boxed{25}$ $2^{5-x} = 6 \Rightarrow 5 - x = \log_2 6 \Rightarrow x = 5 - \dfrac{\log 6}{\log 2}$, or $\dfrac{\log \frac{16}{3}}{\log 2}$

$\boxed{26}$ $3^{(x^2)} = 7 \Rightarrow x^2 = \log_3 7 \Rightarrow x^2 = \dfrac{\log 7}{\log 3} \Rightarrow x = \pm\sqrt{\dfrac{\log 7}{\log 3}}$

$\boxed{27}$ $2^{5x+3} = 3^{2x+1} \Rightarrow (5x+3)\log 2 = (2x+1)\log 3 \Rightarrow$

$$5x\log 2 + 3\log 2 = 2x\log 3 + \log 3 \Rightarrow x(5\log 2 - 2\log 3) = \log 3 - 3\log 2 \Rightarrow$$

$$x = \frac{\log 3 - \log 8}{\log 32 - \log 9} = \frac{\log\frac{3}{8}}{\log\frac{32}{9}}$$

$\boxed{28}$ $\log_3(3x) = \log_3 x + \log_3(4-x) \Rightarrow \log_3(3x) = \log_3\big[x(4-x)\big] \Rightarrow 3x = 4x - x^2 \Rightarrow$

$$x^2 - x = 0 \Rightarrow x(x-1) = 0 \Rightarrow x = 0, 1; \ 0 \text{ is extraneous}$$

$\boxed{29}$ $\log_4 x = \sqrt[3]{\log_4 x} \Rightarrow \log_4 x = (\log_4 x)^{1/3} \Rightarrow (\log_4 x)^3 = \log_4 x \Rightarrow$

$$\log_4 x\Big[(\log_4 x)^2 - 1\Big] = 0 \Rightarrow \log_4 x = 0 \text{ or } \log_4 x = \pm 1 \Rightarrow x = 1 \text{ or } x = 4, \tfrac{1}{4}$$

$\boxed{30}$ $e^{x+\ln 4} = 3e^x \Rightarrow e^x e^{\ln 4} = 3e^x \Rightarrow 4e^x = 3e^x \Rightarrow e^x = 0$, which is never true.

There is no real solution.

$\boxed{31}$ $10^{2\log x} = 5 \Rightarrow 10^{\log x^2} = 5 \Rightarrow x^2 = 5 \Rightarrow x = \pm\sqrt{5}; -\sqrt{5}$ is extraneous

$\boxed{32}$ $e^{\ln(x+1)} = 3 \Rightarrow x + 1 = 3 \Rightarrow x = 2$

$\boxed{33}$ $x^2(-2xe^{-x^2}) + 2xe^{-x^2} = 0 \Rightarrow 2xe^{-x^2}(-x^2 + 1) = 0 \Rightarrow x = 0, \pm 1 \left\{e^{-x^2} \neq 0\right\}$

$\boxed{34}$ $e^x + 2 = 8e^{-x} \Rightarrow e^{2x} + 2e^x - 8 = 0 \Rightarrow (e^x + 4)(e^x - 2) = 0 \Rightarrow e^x = -4, 2 \Rightarrow$

$$x = \ln 2 \text{ since } e^x \neq -4$$

$\boxed{35}$ (a) $\log x^2 = \log(6-x) \Rightarrow x^2 = 6 - x \Rightarrow x^2 + x - 6 = 0 \Rightarrow (x+3)(x-2) = 0 \Rightarrow$

$$x = -3, 2$$

(b) $2\log x = \log(6-x) \Rightarrow \log x^2 = \log(6-x)$, which is the equation in part (a).

This equation has the same solutions provided they are in the domain.

But -3 is extraneous, so 2 is the only solution.

$\boxed{36}$ (a) $\ln(e^x)^2 = 16 \Rightarrow 2\ln e^x = 16 \Rightarrow 2x = 16 \Rightarrow x = 8$

(b) $\ln e^{(x^2)} = 16 \Rightarrow x^2 = 16 \Rightarrow x = \pm 4$

$\boxed{37}$ $\log x^4 \sqrt[3]{y^2/z} = \log(x^4 y^{2/3} z^{-1/3}) = \log x^4 + \log y^{2/3} + \log z^{-1/3} =$

$$4\log x + \tfrac{2}{3}\log y - \tfrac{1}{3}\log z$$

$\boxed{38}$ $\log(x^2/y^3) + 4\log y - 6\log\sqrt{xy} = \log\left(\dfrac{x^2}{y^3}\right) + \log y^4 - \log(x^3 y^3)$

$$= \log\left(\frac{x^2 y}{x^3 y^3}\right) = \log\left(\frac{1}{xy^2}\right) = -\log(xy^2)$$

39 $y = \dfrac{1}{10^x + 10^{-x}}$ $\left\{ D = \mathbb{R},\ R = (0, \tfrac{1}{2}] \right\} \Rightarrow y\,10^x + y\,10^{-x} = 1 \Rightarrow$

$y\,10^{2x} + y = 10^x \Rightarrow y\,10^{2x} - 10^x + y = 0 \Rightarrow 10^x = \dfrac{1 \pm \sqrt{1 - 4y^2}}{2y} \Rightarrow$

$$x = \log\left(\dfrac{1 \pm \sqrt{1 - 4y^2}}{2y}\right)$$

40 $y = \dfrac{1}{10^x - 10^{-x}}$ $\left\{ D = R = \mathbb{R} - \{0\} \right\} \Rightarrow y\,10^x - y\,10^{-x} = 1 \Rightarrow$

$y\,10^{2x} - y = 10^x \Rightarrow y\,10^{2x} - 10^x - y = 0 \Rightarrow 10^x = \dfrac{1 \pm \sqrt{1 + 4y^2}}{2y}.$

There are 2 cases to consider.

(1) If $y < 0$, then $\dfrac{1 - \sqrt{1 + 4y^2}}{2y} > 0$, so $x = \log\left(\dfrac{1 - \sqrt{1 + 4y^2}}{2y}\right)$.

(2) If $y > 0$, then $\dfrac{1 + \sqrt{1 + 4y^2}}{2y} > 0$, so $x = \log\left(\dfrac{1 + \sqrt{1 + 4y^2}}{2y}\right)$.

41 (a) $x = \ln 6.6 \approx 1.89$ (b) $\log x = 1.8938 \Rightarrow x = 10^{1.8938} \approx 78.3$

    (c) $\ln x = -0.75 \Rightarrow x = e^{-0.75} \approx 0.472$

42 (a) $x = \log 8.4 \approx 0.924$ (b) $\log x = -2.4260 \Rightarrow x = 10^{-2.4260} \approx 0.00375$

    (c) $\ln x = 1.8 \Rightarrow x = e^{1.8} \approx 6.05$

43 (a) For $y = \log_2(x + 1)$, $D = (-1, \infty)$ and $R = \mathbb{R}$.

    (b) $y = \log_2(x + 1) \Rightarrow x = \log_2(y + 1) \Rightarrow 2^x = y + 1 \Rightarrow y = 2^x - 1,$

$$D = \mathbb{R},\ R = (-1, \infty)$$

44 (a) For $y = 2^{3 - x} - 2$, $D = \mathbb{R}$ and $R = (-2, \infty)$.

    (b) $y = 2^{3 - x} - 2 \Rightarrow x = 2^{3 - y} - 2 \Rightarrow x + 2 = 2^{3 - y} \Rightarrow \log_2(x + 2) = 3 - y \Rightarrow$

$$y = 3 - \log_2(x + 2),\ D = (-2, \infty),\ R = \mathbb{R}$$

45 (a) $Q(0) = 2(3^0) = 2$ {in thousands}, or 2000

    (b) $Q(\tfrac{10}{60}) = 2000(3^{1/6}) \approx 2401$; $Q(\tfrac{30}{60}) = 2000(3^{1/2}) \approx 3464$; $Q(1) = 2(3) = 6000$

46 $A = P\left(1 + \dfrac{r}{n}\right)^{nt} = 1000\left(1 + \dfrac{0.12}{4}\right)^{4 \cdot 1} \approx \$1125.51$

47 (a) $N = 64(0.5)^{t/8} = 64\left[(0.5)^{1/8}\right]^t \approx 64(0.917)^t$

    (b) $N = \tfrac{1}{2}N_0 \Rightarrow \tfrac{1}{2}N_0 = N_0(0.5)^{t/8} \Rightarrow$

        $\left(\tfrac{1}{2}\right)^1 = \left(\tfrac{1}{2}\right)^{t/8} \Rightarrow 1 = t/8 \Rightarrow t = 8$ days

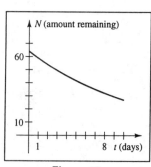

Figure 47

48 $t = 0$ and $N = 1000 \Rightarrow N_0 = 1000$. $t = 3$ and $N = 600 \Rightarrow 600 = 1000(a^c)^3 \Rightarrow$

$$(a^c)^3 = \frac{600}{1000} \Rightarrow a^c = \left(\frac{3}{5}\right)^{1/3} \Rightarrow N = 1000\left(\frac{3}{5}\right)^{t/3}, \text{ with } a = \frac{3}{5} \text{ and } c = \frac{1}{3}.$$

49 (a) $A = Pe^{rt} \Rightarrow 35{,}000 = 10{,}000e^{0.11t} \Rightarrow e^{0.11t} = 3.5 \Rightarrow 0.11t = \ln 3.5 \Rightarrow t \approx 11.39$ yr

(b) $2 \cdot 10{,}000 = 10{,}000e^{0.11t} \Rightarrow e^{0.11t} = 2 \Rightarrow 0.11t = \ln 2 \Rightarrow t \approx 6.30$ yr.

Alternatively, using the doubling time formula, $t = (\ln 2)/r = (\ln 2)/0.11 \approx 6.30$.

50 $I(t) = 1\%$ of $I_0 \Rightarrow \frac{1}{100}I_0 = I_0 e^{-Rt/L} \Rightarrow \frac{1}{100} = e^{-Rt/L} \Rightarrow \ln\frac{1}{100} = -\frac{Rt}{L} \Rightarrow$

$$t = (-\ln 100)\left(-\frac{L}{R}\right) = (\ln 100)\frac{L}{R} \approx 4.6\frac{L}{R}$$

51 (a) $\alpha = 10\log\left(\frac{I}{I_0}\right) \Rightarrow \frac{\alpha}{10} = \log\left(\frac{I}{I_0}\right) \Rightarrow 10^{\alpha/10} = \frac{I}{I_0} \Rightarrow I = I_0 10^{\alpha/10}$

(b) Let $I(\alpha)$ be the intensity corresponding to α decibels.

$$I(\alpha+1) = I_0 10^{(\alpha+1)/10} = I_0 10^{\alpha/10}10^{1/10} = I(\alpha)\,10^{1/10} \approx 1.26\,I(\alpha),$$

which represents a 26% increase in $I(\alpha)$.

52 $L = a(1 - be^{-kt}) \Rightarrow \frac{L}{a} = 1 - be^{-kt} \Rightarrow be^{-kt} = \frac{a - L}{a} \Rightarrow$

$$e^{-kt} = \frac{a-L}{ab} \Rightarrow -kt = \ln\left(\frac{a-L}{ab}\right) \Rightarrow t = -\frac{1}{k}\ln\left(\frac{a-L}{ab}\right)$$

53 $R = 2.3\log(A + 3000) - 5.1 \Rightarrow \dfrac{R + 5.1}{2.3} = \log(A + 3000) \Rightarrow$

$$A + 3000 = 10^{(R+5.1)/2.3} \Rightarrow A = 10^{(R+5.1)/2.3} - 3000$$

54 As in Exercise 53, $A = 10^{(R+7.5)/2.3} - 34{,}000$. Thus, $\dfrac{A_1}{A_2} = \dfrac{10^{(R+5.1)/2.3} - 3000}{10^{(R+7.5)/2.3} - 34{,}000}$.

55 $R = 4 \Rightarrow 2.3\log(A + 14{,}000) - 6.6 = 4 \Rightarrow \log(A + 14{,}000) = \frac{10.6}{2.3} \Rightarrow$

$$A = 10^{106/23} - 14{,}000 \approx 26{,}615.9 \text{ mi}^2.$$

56 $p = 29e^{-0.000034h} \Rightarrow \dfrac{p}{29} = e^{-0.000034h} \Rightarrow \ln\left(\frac{p}{29}\right) = -0.000034h \Rightarrow$

$$h = \frac{\ln(p/29)}{-0.000034} \Rightarrow h = \frac{\ln(29/p)}{0.000034}$$

57 Substituting $v = 0$ and $m = m_1 + m_2$ in $v = -a\ln m + b$ yields

$0 = -a\ln(m_1 + m_2) + b$. Thus, $b = a\ln(m_1 + m_2)$. At burnout, $m = m_1$,

and hence, $v = -a\ln m_1 + b = -a\ln m_1 + a\ln(m_1 + m_2)$

$$= a[\ln(m_1 + m_2) - \ln m_1] \Rightarrow v = a\ln\left(\frac{m_1 + m_2}{m_1}\right)$$

58 (a) $\log n = 7.7 - (0.9)R \Rightarrow n = 10^{7.7 - 0.9R}$

(b) $R = 4, 5,$ and $6 \Rightarrow n \approx 12{,}589;\ 1585;$ and 200

59 (a) $\log E = 11.4 + (1.5)R \Rightarrow E = 10^{11.4 + 1.5R}$

(b) $R = 8.4 \Rightarrow E = 10^{24}$ ergs

60 Let $q(t) = \frac{1}{2}q_0$. $\frac{1}{2}q_0 = q_0 e^{-0.0063t} \Rightarrow \frac{1}{2} = e^{-0.0063t} \Rightarrow \ln\frac{1}{2} = -0.0063t \Rightarrow$

$$-\ln 2 = -0.0063t \Rightarrow t = \frac{\ln 2}{0.0063} \approx 110 \text{ days}$$

[61] $t = 2 \Rightarrow h \approx 86.8$ cm and $R = 9.715$ cm/yr

[62] $I = \frac{V}{R}(1 - e^{-Rt/L}) \Rightarrow \frac{RI}{V} = 1 - e^{-Rt/L} \Rightarrow$

$$e^{-Rt/L} = \left(\frac{V - RI}{V}\right) \Rightarrow -\frac{Rt}{L} = \ln\left(\frac{V - RI}{V}\right) \Rightarrow t = -\frac{L}{R}\ln\left(\frac{V - RI}{V}\right)$$

[63] (a) $x = 4\% \Rightarrow T = -8310\ln(0.04) \approx 26{,}749$ yr.

(b) $T = 10{,}000 \Rightarrow 10{,}000 = -8310\ln x \Rightarrow x = e^{-10{,}000/8310} \approx 0.30$, or 30%.

[64] Using the doubling time formula, $t = (\ln 2)/r = (\ln 2)/0.041 \approx 16.91$ yr.

[65] $N(t) = \frac{1}{2}N_0 \Rightarrow \frac{1}{2}N_0 = N_0(0.805)^t \Rightarrow 2^{-1} = (0.805)^t \Rightarrow \ln(2^{-1}) = \ln(0.805)^t \Rightarrow$

$$-\ln 2 = t\ln(0.805) \Rightarrow t = -\frac{\ln 2}{\ln(0.805)} \approx 3.196 \text{ millennia, or } 3196 \text{ yr}$$

Chapter 4 Discussion Exercises

[1] (a) The y-intercept is a, so it increases as a does. The graph flattens out as a increases.

(b) Graph $Y_1 = \frac{a}{2}(e^{x/a} + e^{-x/a}) + (30 - a)$ on $[-20,\ 20]$ by $[30,\ 32]$ and check for $Y_1 < 32$ at $x = 20$. In this case it turns out that $a = 101$ is the smallest integer value that satisfies the conditions, so an equation is

$$y = \frac{101}{2}(e^{x/101} + e^{-x/101}) - 71.$$

[2] Sum the values of R for $t = 1$ to $t = x$ so that the sum is 50. Summing R for $t = 1$ to $t = 7$ years gives 49.329 tons. The answer using the formula is about 7.16 years.

[3] (a) $x^y = y^x \Rightarrow \ln(x^y) = \ln(y^x) \Rightarrow y\ln x = x\ln y \Rightarrow \frac{\ln x}{x} = \frac{\ln y}{y}$

(b) Once you find two values of $(\ln x)/x$ that are the same (such as 0.36652), you know that the corresponding x-values, x_1 and x_2, satisfy the relationship $(x_1)^{x_2} \approx (x_2)^{x_1}$. In particular, when $(\ln x)/x \approx 0.36652$, we find that $x_1 \approx 2.50$ and $x_2 \approx 2.97$. Note that $2.50^{2.97} \approx 2.97^{2.50} \approx 15.20$.

(c) Note that $f(e) = \frac{1}{e}$. Any horizontal line $y = k$, with $0 < k < \frac{1}{e}$, will intersect the graph at the two points $\left(x_1, \frac{\ln x_1}{x_1}\right)$ and $\left(x_2, \frac{\ln x_2}{x_2}\right)$, where $1 < x_1 < e$ and $x_2 > e$.

4 (a) $y_1 = (1.085)^x$ could be considered to be the value of an investment growing at
8.5% per year with no compounding. $y_2 = e^{0.085x}$ could be considered to be the
value of an investment growing at 8.5% per year compounded continuously. In
part (a) of the exercises, $x = 40 \Rightarrow y_1 \approx 26.13$ and $y_2 \approx 29.96$. In part (b) of the
exercises, $y = 2 \Rightarrow x_1 \approx 8.50$ and $x_2 \approx 8.15$. The answers in part (b) could be
considered to be the doubling time for the investments.

(b) $y_3 = (1 + 0.085/12)^{12x}$ would be greater than y_1, but less than y_2 (closer to y_2).

(c) An estimate of 29 and 8.2 would be reasonable. You would believe that these are
correct because they are much closer to the continuously compounded interest
values than the simple interest values. Actual values are 29.61 and 8.18.

5 Logarithm law 3 states that it is valid only for positive real numbers, so $y = \log_3 (x^2)$
is equivalent to $y = 2 \log_3 x$ only for $x > 0$. The domain of $y = \log_3 (x^2)$ is $\mathbb{R} - \{0\}$,
whereas the domain of $y = 2 \log_3 x$ is $x > 0$.

6 (a) $U =$ compound interest amount $-$ accumulated amt. $=$

$$P\left(1 + \frac{r}{12}\right)^{12t} - \frac{12M\left[(1 + r/12)^{12t} - 1\right]}{r}.$$

Note that P is the loan amount L and we use 12 for n because there are monthly
payments.

(b) $U = 90{,}000\left(1 + \frac{0.12}{12}\right)^{12x} -$

$$\frac{12(925.75)\left[(1 + 0.12/12)^{12x} - 1\right]}{0.12}.$$

[0, 35] by [0, 100,000]

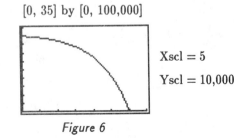

Xscl $= 5$

Yscl $= 10{,}000$

Figure 6

(c) $x = 10$ years $\Rightarrow U = \$84{,}076.50$. $U = \$45{,}000 \Rightarrow x \approx 24.425$ years.

(d) The points (0, 90,000) and (30, 0) must be on the graph. The graph must be
decreasing—more near $x = 30$ than in the beginning.

(e) It is an excellent approximation, but we must remember that payments are only
made every month—not for every value of x. *Note:* You may want to loosely
discuss discrete vs. continuous models at this time.

7 There are 4 points of intersection. Listed in order of difficulty to find we have:
$(-0.9999011, \ 0.00999001)$, $(-0.0001, \ 0.01)$, $(100, \ 0.01105111)$, and $(36{,}102.844,$
$4.6928 \times 10^{13})$. Exponential function values (with base > 1) are greater than
polynomial function values (with leading term positive) for very large values of x.

[8]   There are 3 points of intersection. Listed in order of difficulty to find we have (x, x) with $x \approx 0.44239443$, 4.1770774, and $5{,}503.6647$. The y-values for $y = x$ eventually will be larger than the y-values for $y = (\ln x)^n$.

[9] $60{,}000 = 40{,}000b^5 \Rightarrow b = \sqrt[5]{1.5} \approx 1.0844717712$, or 8.44717712%. Mentally—it would take $70/8.5 \approx 8^+$ years to double and there would be about $40/8 = 5$ doubling periods, $2^5 = 32$ and $32 \cdot \$40{,}000 = \$1{,}280{,}000$.

$$\text{Actual} = \$40{,}000(1 + 0.0844717712)^{40} = \$1{,}025{,}156.25.$$

[10] (a) The formula in Exercise 59, $\log E = 11.4 + 1.5\,R$, gives E in terms of ergs and 1 joule $= 10^7$ ergs. The earthquake released about 1.122×10^{15} joules of energy, so about 3.5 earthquakes are equivalent to one 1-megaton bomb. About 425 1-megaton bombs are equivalent to the Mount St. Helens eruption.

(b) $E = 1.7 \times 10^{18} \Rightarrow R = (\log E - 11.4)/1.5 = 9.22$.   No, the highest recorded reading is about 8.9 in the 1933 earthquake in Japan. The worst death toll by an earthquake was in 1201 in the Near East—it killed an estimated 1.1 million people.

[11] On the TI-82/83, enter the sum of the days, $\{0, 5168, 6728, 8136, 8407, 8735, 8857, 9010\}$, and the averages, $\{1003.16, 2002.25, 3004.46, 4003.33, 5023.55, 6010.00, 7022.44, 8038.88\}$, in L_1 and L_2, respectively. Use ExpReg under STAT CALC to obtain $y = ab^x$, where $a = 838.6243588$ and $b = 1.000218653$. Plot the data along with the exponential function and the line $y = 15{,}000$. The functions intersect at approximately 13,191. This value corresponds to December 26, 2008. *Note:* The TI-83 has a convenient "day between dates" function for problems of this nature.

Using the first and last milestone figures and the continuously compounded interest formula gives us $A = Pe^{rt} \Leftrightarrow 8038.88 = 1003.16e^{r(9010)} \Rightarrow$ $r \approx 0.0002309805496$ (daily) or about 8.43% annually. *Note:* The Dow was 100.25 on 1/12/1906. You may want to include this information and examine the differences it makes in any type of prediction.

A discussion of practical considerations should lead to mention of crashes, corrections, and the validity of any model over too long of a period of time.

Chapter 5: The Trigonometric Functions

5.1 Concept Check

1 One radian is equivalent to how many degrees (to the nearest integer)?   •   One radian is equivalent to about 57 degrees.

2 What is the length of the arc of a circle of radius r that subtends a central angle of 1 radian?   •   It is r—see the Definition of Radian Measure and Figure 7(a).

3 If $\theta = 3$ is in standard position, in which quadrant does its terminal side lie?   • Since $\frac{\pi}{2} < 3 < \pi$, the terminal side of $\theta = 3$ lies in quadrant II.

4 Comment on the following statement: The arc of length on a circle of radius $r = 2$ cm which subtends a central angle of measure $\theta = 45°$ is equal to $r\theta = 2(45) = 90$ cm.

   •   To apply the Formula for the Length of a Circular Arc, the angle θ must be in *radians.* So $r\theta = 2(\frac{\pi}{4}) = \frac{\pi}{2}$ cm is the correct arc length.

5.1 Exercises

Note: Exer. 1–4: The answers listed are the smallest (in magnitude) two positive coterminal angles and two negative coterminal angles.

1 (a) $120° + 1(360°) = 480°,$ $\qquad$ $120° + 2(360°) = 840°;$

$\qquad$ $120° - 1(360°) = -240°,$ $\qquad$ $120° - 2(360°) = -600°$

$\quad$ (b) $135° + 1(360°) = 495°,$ $\qquad$ $135° + 2(360°) = 855°;$

$\qquad$ $135° - 1(360°) = -225°,$ $\qquad$ $135° - 2(360°) = -585°$

$\quad$ (c) $-30° + 1(360°) = 330°,$ $\qquad$ $-30° + 2(360°) = 690°;$

$\qquad$ $-30° - 1(360°) = -390°,$ $\qquad$ $-30° - 2(360°) = -750°$

2 (a) $240° \rightarrow 600°, 960°, -120°, -480°$

$\quad$ (b) $315° \rightarrow 675°, 1035°, -45°, -405°$

$\quad$ (c) $-150° \rightarrow 210°, 570°, -510°, -870°$

3 (a) $620° - 1(360°) = 260°,$ $\qquad$ $620° + 1(360°) = 980°;$

$\qquad$ $620° - 2(360°) = -100°,$ $\qquad$ $620° - 3(360°) = -460°$

$\quad$ (b) $\frac{5\pi}{6} + 1(2\pi) = \frac{5\pi}{6} + \frac{12\pi}{6} = \frac{17\pi}{6},$ $\quad$ $\frac{5\pi}{6} + 2(2\pi) = \frac{5\pi}{6} + \frac{24\pi}{6} = \frac{29\pi}{6};$

$\qquad$ $\frac{5\pi}{6} - 1(2\pi) = \frac{5\pi}{6} - \frac{12\pi}{6} = -\frac{7\pi}{6},$ $\quad$ $\frac{5\pi}{6} - 2(2\pi) = \frac{5\pi}{6} - \frac{24\pi}{6} = -\frac{19\pi}{6}$

$\quad$ (c) $-\frac{\pi}{4} + 1(2\pi) = -\frac{\pi}{4} + \frac{8\pi}{4} = \frac{7\pi}{4},$ $\quad$ $-\frac{\pi}{4} + 2(2\pi) = -\frac{\pi}{4} + \frac{16\pi}{4} = \frac{15\pi}{4};$

$\qquad$ $-\frac{\pi}{4} - 1(2\pi) = -\frac{\pi}{4} - \frac{8\pi}{4} = -\frac{9\pi}{4},$ $\quad$ $-\frac{\pi}{4} - 2(2\pi) = -\frac{\pi}{4} - \frac{16\pi}{4} = -\frac{17\pi}{4}$

4 (a) $570° \rightarrow 210°, 930°, -150°, -510°$

$\quad$ (b) $\frac{2\pi}{3} \rightarrow \frac{8\pi}{3}, \frac{14\pi}{3}, -\frac{4\pi}{3}, -\frac{10\pi}{3}$

$\quad$ (c) $-\frac{5\pi}{4} \rightarrow \frac{3\pi}{4}, \frac{11\pi}{4}, -\frac{13\pi}{4}, -\frac{21\pi}{4}$

$\boxed{5}$ (a) $90° - 5°17'34'' = 84°42'26''$ (b) $90° - 32.5° = 57.5°$

$\boxed{6}$ (a) $90° - 63°4'15'' = 26°55'45''$ (b) $90° - 82.73° = 7.27°$

$\boxed{7}$ (a) $180° - 48°51'37'' = 131°8'23''$ (b) $180° - 136.42° = 43.58°$

$\boxed{8}$ (a) $180° - 152°12'4'' = 27°47'56''$ (b) $180° - 15.9° = 164.1°$

Note: Multiply each degree measure by $\frac{\pi}{180}$ to obtain the listed radian measure.

$\boxed{9}$ (a) $150° \cdot \frac{\pi}{180} = \frac{5 \cdot 30\pi}{6 \cdot 30} = \frac{5\pi}{6}$ (b) $\)° \cdot \frac{\pi}{180} = -\frac{60\pi}{3 \cdot 60} = -\frac{\pi}{3}$

     (c) $225° \cdot \frac{\pi}{180} = \frac{5 \cdot 45\pi}{4 \cdot 45} = \frac{5\pi}{4}$

$\boxed{10}$ (a) $120° \cdot \frac{\pi}{180} = \frac{2 \cdot 60\pi}{3 \cdot 60} = \frac{2\pi}{3}$ (b) $-135° \cdot \frac{\pi}{180} = -\frac{3 \cdot 45\pi}{4 \cdot 45} = -\frac{3\pi}{4}$

     (c) $210° \cdot \frac{\pi}{180} = \frac{7 \cdot 30\pi}{6 \cdot 30} = \frac{7\pi}{6}$

$\boxed{11}$ (a) $450° \cdot \frac{\pi}{180} = \frac{5 \cdot 90\pi}{2 \cdot 90} = \frac{5\pi}{2}$ (b) $72° \cdot \frac{\pi}{180} = \frac{2 \cdot 36\pi}{5 \cdot 36} = \frac{2\pi}{5}$

     (c) $100° \cdot \frac{\pi}{180} = \frac{5 \cdot 20\pi}{9 \cdot 20} = \frac{5\pi}{9}$

$\boxed{12}$ (a) $630° \cdot \frac{\pi}{180} = \frac{7 \cdot 90\pi}{2 \cdot 90} = \frac{7\pi}{2}$ (b) $54° \cdot \frac{\pi}{180} = \frac{3 \cdot 18\pi}{10 \cdot 18} = \frac{3\pi}{10}$

     (c) $95° \cdot \frac{\pi}{180} = \frac{19 \cdot 5\pi}{36 \cdot 5} = \frac{19\pi}{36}$

Note: Multiply each radian measure by $\frac{180}{\pi}$ to obtain the listed degree measure.

$\boxed{13}$ (a) $\frac{2\pi}{3} \cdot \left(\frac{180}{\pi}\right)° = \left(\frac{2 \cdot 3 \cdot 60\pi}{3\pi}\right)° = 120°$ (b) $\frac{11\pi}{6} \cdot \left(\frac{180}{\pi}\right)° = \left(\frac{11 \cdot 30 \cdot 6\pi}{6\pi}\right)° = 330°$

     (c) $\frac{3\pi}{4} \cdot \left(\frac{180}{\pi}\right)° = \left(\frac{3 \cdot 45 \cdot 4\pi}{4\pi}\right)° = 135°$

$\boxed{14}$ (a) $\frac{5\pi}{6} \cdot \left(\frac{180}{\pi}\right)° = \left(\frac{5 \cdot 30 \cdot 6\pi}{6\pi}\right)° = 150°$ (b) $\frac{4\pi}{3} \cdot \left(\frac{180}{\pi}\right)° = \left(\frac{4 \cdot 60 \cdot 3\pi}{3\pi}\right)° = 240°$

     (c) $\frac{11\pi}{4} \cdot \left(\frac{180}{\pi}\right)° = \left(\frac{11 \cdot 45 \cdot 4\pi}{4\pi}\right)° = 495°$

$\boxed{15}$ (a) $-\frac{7\pi}{2} \cdot \left(\frac{180}{\pi}\right)° = -\left(\frac{7 \cdot 90 \cdot 2\pi}{2\pi}\right)° = -630°$ (b) $7\pi \cdot \left(\frac{180}{\pi}\right)° = (7 \cdot 180)° = 1260°$

     (c) $\frac{\pi}{9} \cdot \left(\frac{180}{\pi}\right)° = \left(\frac{20 \cdot 9\pi}{9\pi}\right)° = 20°$

$\boxed{16}$ (a) $-\frac{5\pi}{2} \cdot \left(\frac{180}{\pi}\right)° = -\left(\frac{5 \cdot 90 \cdot 2\pi}{2\pi}\right)° = -450°$ (b) $9\pi \cdot \left(\frac{180}{\pi}\right)° = (9 \cdot 180)° = 1620°$

     (c) $\frac{\pi}{16} \cdot \left(\frac{180}{\pi}\right)° = \left(\frac{45 \cdot 4\pi}{4 \cdot 4\pi}\right)° = \left(\frac{45}{4}\right)° = 11.25°$

$\boxed{17}$ $2 \cdot \left(\frac{180}{\pi}\right)° \approx 114.59156° = 114° + 0.59156°$.

Since $60' = 1°$, we have $0.59156° = 0.59156\,(60') = 35.4936'$.

Since $60'' = 1'$, we have $0.4936' = 0.4936\,(60'') \approx 30''$. $\therefore$ 2 radians $\approx 114°35'30''$

$\boxed{18}$ $1.5 \cdot \left(\frac{180}{\pi}\right)° \approx 85.943669°$; $0.943669\,(60') = 56.62014'$; $0.62014\,(60'') \approx 37''$.

$\therefore$ 1.5 radians $\approx 85°56'37''$

$\boxed{19}$ $5 \cdot \left(\frac{180}{\pi}\right)° \approx 286.4789°$; $0.4789\,(60') = 28.734'$; $0.734\,(60'') \approx 44''$.

$\therefore$ 5 radians $\approx 286°28'44''$

$\boxed{20}$ $4 \cdot \left(\frac{180}{\pi}\right)° \approx 229.18312°$; $0.18312\,(60') = 10.9872'$; $0.9872\,(60'') \approx 59''$.

$\therefore$ 4 radians $\approx 229°10'59''$

$\boxed{21}$ $37°41' = \left(37 + \frac{41}{60}\right)° \approx 37.6833°$ $\boxed{22}$ $83°17' = \left(83 + \frac{17}{60}\right)° \approx 83.2833°$

$\boxed{23}$ $115°26'27'' = \left(115 + \frac{26}{60} + \frac{27}{3600}\right)° \approx 115.4408°$

$\boxed{24}$ $258°39'52'' = \left(258 + \frac{39}{60} + \frac{52}{3600}\right)° \approx 258.6644°$

25 $0.169\,(60') = 10.14'$; $0.14\,(60'') = 8.4''$; $\therefore 63.169° \approx 63°10'8''$

26 $0.864\,(60') = 51.84'$; $0.84\,(60'') = 50.4''$; $\therefore 12.864° \approx 12°51'50''$

27 $0.6215\,(60') = 37.29'$; $0.29\,(60'') = 17.4''$; $\therefore 310.6215° \approx 310°37'17''$

28 $0.7238\,(60') = 43.428'$; $0.428\,(60'') = 25.68''$; $\therefore 81.7238° \approx 81°43'26''$

29 $s = r\theta \Rightarrow r = \frac{s}{\theta} = \frac{10}{4} = 2.5$ cm

30 $s = r\theta \Rightarrow r = \frac{s}{\theta} = \frac{3}{20 \cdot \frac{\pi}{180}} = \frac{27}{\pi} \approx 8.59$ km

31 (a) $s = r\theta = 8 \cdot (45 \cdot \frac{\pi}{180}) = 8 \cdot \frac{\pi}{4} = 2\pi \approx 6.28$ cm

　　(b) $A = \frac{1}{2}r^2\theta = \frac{1}{2}(8)^2(\frac{\pi}{4}) = 8\pi \approx 25.13$ cm^2

32 (a) $s = r\theta = 9 \cdot (120 \cdot \frac{\pi}{180}) = 9 \cdot \frac{2\pi}{3} = 6\pi \approx 18.85$ cm

　　(b) $A = \frac{1}{2}r^2\theta = \frac{1}{2}(9)^2(\frac{2\pi}{3}) = 27\pi \approx 84.82$ cm^2

33 (a) $s = r\theta \Rightarrow \theta = \frac{s}{r} = \frac{7}{4} = 1.75$ radians; $\frac{7}{4} \cdot (\frac{180}{\pi})° = (\frac{315}{\pi})° \approx 100.27°$

　　(b) $A = \frac{1}{2}r^2\theta = \frac{1}{2}(4)^2(\frac{7}{4}) = 14$ cm^2

34 (a) $\theta = \frac{s}{r} = \frac{3(12)}{20} = \frac{9}{5} = 1.8$ radians; $\frac{9}{5} \cdot (\frac{180}{\pi})° = (\frac{324}{\pi})° \approx 103.13°$

　　(b) $A = \frac{1}{2}r^2\theta = \frac{1}{2}(20)^2(\frac{9}{5}) = 360$ in^2

35 (a) $s = r\theta = (\frac{1}{2} \cdot 16)(50 \cdot \frac{\pi}{180}) = 8 \cdot \frac{5\pi}{18} = \frac{20\pi}{9} \approx 6.98$ m

　　(b) $A = \frac{1}{2}r^2\theta = \frac{1}{2}(8)^2(\frac{5\pi}{18}) = \frac{80\pi}{9} \approx 27.93$ m^2

36 (a) $s = r\theta = (\frac{1}{2} \cdot 120)(2.2) = 60(2.2) = 132$ cm

　　(b) $A = \frac{1}{2}r^2\theta = \frac{1}{2}(60)^2(2.2) = 3960$ cm^2

37 radius $= \frac{1}{2} \cdot 8000$ miles $= 4000$ miles

　　(a) $s = r\theta = 4000\,(60 \cdot \frac{\pi}{180}) = \frac{4000\pi}{3} \approx 4189$ miles

　　(b) $s = r\theta = 4000\,(45 \cdot \frac{\pi}{180}) = 1000\pi \approx 3142$ miles

　　(c) $s = r\theta = 4000\,(30 \cdot \frac{\pi}{180}) = \frac{2000\pi}{3} \approx 2094$ miles

　　(d) $s = r\theta = 4000\,(10 \cdot \frac{\pi}{180}) = \frac{2000\pi}{9} \approx 698$ miles

　　(e) $s = r\theta = 4000\,(1 \cdot \frac{\pi}{180}) = \frac{200\pi}{9} \approx 70$ miles

38 $1' = (\frac{1}{60})°$; $s = r\theta = 4000\,(\frac{1}{60} \cdot \frac{\pi}{180}) = \frac{10\pi}{27} \approx 1.16$ mi

39 $\theta = \frac{s}{r} = \frac{500}{4000} = \frac{1}{8}$ radian; $(\frac{1}{8})(\frac{180}{\pi})° = (\frac{45}{2\pi})° \approx 7°10'$

40 A point on the perimeter of the core is moving 264 ft in 1 sec.

　　The radius of the core is 100 ft. $s = r\theta \Rightarrow$

$$\theta = \frac{s}{r} = \frac{264}{100} = 2.64 \text{ rad/sec} = 158.4 \text{ rad/min} = \frac{158.4}{2\pi} \text{ rev/min} \approx 25.2 \text{ rev/min.}$$

41 23 hours, 56 minutes, and 4 seconds $= 23(60)^2 + 56(60) + 4 = 86{,}164$ sec.

　　Since the earth turns through 2π radians in 86,164 seconds,

$$\text{it rotates through } \frac{2\pi}{86{,}164} \approx 7.29 \times 10^{-5} \text{ radians in one second.}$$

42 Using the result from Exercise 41, the distance s traveled in 1 second will be

$$s = r\theta \approx (3963.3)\left(\tfrac{2\pi}{86,164}\right) \approx 0.29 \text{ mi/sec, or, } 1040 \text{ mi/hr.}$$

43 (a) $\left(40 \, \tfrac{\text{rev}}{\text{min}}\right)\left(2\pi \, \tfrac{\text{rad}}{\text{rev}}\right) = 80\pi \, \tfrac{\text{rad}}{\text{min}}$

(b) $s = r\theta = (5 \text{ in}) \cdot 80\pi = 400\pi$ in.

$$\text{Linear speed} = 400\pi \text{ in/min} = \tfrac{100\pi}{3} \text{ ft/min} \approx 104.72 \text{ ft/min.}$$

44 (a) $\left(2400 \, \tfrac{\text{rev}}{\text{min}}\right)\left(2\pi \, \tfrac{\text{rad}}{\text{rev}}\right) = 4800\pi \, \tfrac{\text{rad}}{\text{min}}$

(b) $s = r\theta = (9 \text{ in}) \cdot 4800\pi = 43,200\pi$ in.

$$\text{Linear speed} = 43,200\pi \text{ in/min} = 3600\pi \text{ ft/min.}$$

45 (a) As in Exercise 43, $(33\tfrac{1}{3})(2\pi) = \tfrac{200\pi}{3}$ and $45(2\pi) = 90\pi$.

(b) $s = r\theta = (\tfrac{1}{2} \cdot 12)(\tfrac{200\pi}{3}) = 400\pi$ in. Linear speed $= 400\pi$ in/min $= \tfrac{100\pi}{3}$ ft/min.

$s = r\theta = (\tfrac{1}{2} \cdot 7)(90\pi) = 315\pi$ in. Linear speed $= 315\pi$ in/min $= \tfrac{105\pi}{4}$ ft/min.

46 $\dfrac{60 \text{ miles}}{\text{hour}} = \dfrac{60 \text{ miles}}{\text{hour}} \cdot \dfrac{1 \text{ hour}}{60 \text{ minutes}} \cdot \dfrac{5280 \text{ feet}}{\text{mile}} \cdot \dfrac{12 \text{ inches}}{\text{foot}} = \dfrac{63,360 \text{ inches}}{\text{minute}}.$

A point of the circumference of the tire moves $2\pi r = 2\pi(\tfrac{1}{2} \cdot 22) = 22\pi$ inches each revolution. Thus, the number of revolutions per minute is

$$\dfrac{63,360 \text{ inches}}{\text{minute}} \cdot \dfrac{1 \text{ revolution}}{22\pi \text{ inches}} = \dfrac{31,680 \text{ revolutions}}{11\pi \text{ minute}} \approx 916.73 \text{ rpm.}$$

47 (a) $s = r\theta = (\tfrac{1}{2} \cdot 3)(\tfrac{7\pi}{4}) = \tfrac{21\pi}{8} \approx 8.25$ ft

(b) $s = r\theta \Rightarrow d = (\tfrac{1}{2} \cdot 3)\theta \Rightarrow \theta = (\tfrac{2}{3}d)$ radians

48 $\theta = \tfrac{s}{r} = \dfrac{6 \text{ in}}{4 \text{ ft}} = \dfrac{6 \text{ in}}{48 \text{ in}} = \tfrac{1}{8}$ radian $\approx 7.162°$ or $7°10'$

49 Area$_{\text{small}} = \tfrac{1}{2}r^2\theta = \tfrac{1}{2}\left(\tfrac{1}{2} \cdot 18\right)^2 \cdot \left(\tfrac{2\pi}{6}\right) = \tfrac{27\pi}{2}$. Area$_{\text{large}} = \tfrac{1}{2}\left(\tfrac{1}{2} \cdot 26\right)^2 \cdot \left(\tfrac{2\pi}{8}\right) = \tfrac{169\pi}{8}$.

Cost$_{\text{small}} = \tfrac{27\pi}{2} \div 2 \approx 21.21$ in^2/dollar. Cost$_{\text{large}} = \tfrac{169\pi}{8} \div 3 \approx 22.12$ in^2/dollar.

The large slice provides slightly more pizza per dollar.

50 Let s_1 and s_2 denote the lengths of the chain around the sprockets with radii r_1 and r_2, respectively. Thus, $s_1 = r_1\theta_1$ and $s_2 = r_2\theta_2$.

The lengths of chain s_1 and s_2 are equal. $s_2 = s_1 \Rightarrow r_2\theta_2 = r_1\theta_1 \Rightarrow \theta_2 = \dfrac{r_1\theta_1}{r_2}$.

51 $\dfrac{40 \text{ miles}}{\text{hour}} = \dfrac{40 \text{ miles}}{\text{hour}} \cdot \dfrac{1 \text{ hour}}{3600 \text{ seconds}} \cdot \dfrac{5280 \text{ feet}}{\text{mile}} \cdot \dfrac{12 \text{ inches}}{\text{foot}} = \dfrac{704 \text{ inches}}{\text{second}}.$

The circumference of the wheel is $2\pi(14)$ inches. The back sprocket then rotates $\tfrac{704}{28\pi}$ revolutions per second or $\tfrac{704}{28\pi} \cdot 2\pi = \tfrac{352}{7}$ radians per second. The front sprocket's angular speed is given by $\theta_1 = \dfrac{r_2\theta_2}{r_1} = \dfrac{2 \cdot \tfrac{352}{7}}{5} = \tfrac{704}{35} \approx 20.114$ radians per second

or 3.2 revolutions per second or 192.08 revolutions per minute.

52 $0.0017 \text{ rad/yr} = 0.0017\left(\tfrac{180}{\pi}\right)°/\text{yr}.$

If x is the number of years required, then $5 = \dfrac{0.0017(180)}{\pi}x \Rightarrow x = \tfrac{5\pi}{0.306} \approx 51.3.$

| 5.2 Exercises |

| 5.2 Concept Check |

1. List the pairs of trigonometric functions that are reciprocals. • The pairs of trigonometric functions that are reciprocals are: sine and cosecant, cosine and secant, tangent and cotangent.

2. List the pairs of trigonometric functions that have the same domain. • The pairs of trigonometric functions that have the same domain are: sine and cosine, tangent and secant, cotangent and cosecant.

3. Comment on the following scenario: Suppose you enter $\sin x$ on your calculator, where x is any real number, and your calculator returns the value 1.4. • Since $-1 \leq \sin x \leq 1$, the value 1.4 cannot be returned by a calculator—it must be broken.

4. Are identities valid for all values? • No—identities that contain fractions are valid for all values of the variables such that no denominator is zero.

5. For what values of θ for $0 < \theta < 2\pi$ is $\sqrt{\sin^2 \theta} = \sin \theta$? • $\sqrt{\sin^2 \theta} = |\sin \theta| = \sin \theta$ if $\sin \theta > 0$, that is, $0 < \theta < \pi$.

| 5.2 Exercises |

Note: Answers are in the order *sin, cos, tan, cot, sec, csc* for any exercises that require the values of the six trigonometric functions.

1. $\sin \theta = \dfrac{\text{opp}}{\text{hyp}} = \dfrac{4}{5}$; $\cos \theta = \dfrac{\text{adj}}{\text{hyp}} = \dfrac{3}{5}$; $\tan \theta = \dfrac{\text{opp}}{\text{adj}} = \dfrac{4}{3}$;

$$\cot \theta = \frac{1}{\tan \theta} = \frac{3}{4}; \ \sec \theta = \frac{1}{\cos \theta} = \frac{5}{3}; \ \csc \theta = \frac{1}{\sin \theta} = \frac{5}{4}$$

2. $\sin \theta = \dfrac{\text{opp}}{\text{hyp}} = \dfrac{8}{17}$; $\cos \theta = \dfrac{\text{adj}}{\text{hyp}} = \dfrac{15}{17}$; $\tan \theta = \dfrac{\text{opp}}{\text{adj}} = \dfrac{8}{15}$ ★ $\dfrac{8}{17}, \dfrac{15}{17}, \dfrac{8}{15}, \dfrac{15}{8}, \dfrac{17}{15}, \dfrac{17}{8}$

3. Using the Pythagorean theorem, $\text{adj} = \sqrt{(\text{hyp})^2 - (\text{opp})^2} = \sqrt{5^2 - 2^2} = \sqrt{21}$.

★ $\dfrac{2}{5}, \dfrac{\sqrt{21}}{5}, \dfrac{2}{\sqrt{21}}, \dfrac{\sqrt{21}}{2}, \dfrac{5}{\sqrt{21}}, \dfrac{5}{2}$

4. Using the Pythagorean theorem, $\text{opp} = \sqrt{(\text{hyp})^2 - (\text{adj})^2} = \sqrt{3^2 - 1^2} = \sqrt{8}$.

★ $\dfrac{\sqrt{8}}{3}, \dfrac{1}{3}, \sqrt{8}, \dfrac{1}{\sqrt{8}}, 3, \dfrac{3}{\sqrt{8}}$

5. Using the Pythagorean theorem, $\text{hyp} = \sqrt{(\text{adj})^2 + (\text{opp})^2} = \sqrt{a^2 + b^2}$.

★ $\dfrac{a}{\sqrt{a^2 + b^2}}, \dfrac{b}{\sqrt{a^2 + b^2}}, \dfrac{a}{b}, \dfrac{b}{a}, \dfrac{\sqrt{a^2 + b^2}}{b}, \dfrac{\sqrt{a^2 + b^2}}{a}$

6. $\text{opp} = \sqrt{c^2 - a^2}$

★ $\dfrac{\sqrt{c^2 - a^2}}{c}, \dfrac{a}{c}, \dfrac{\sqrt{c^2 - a^2}}{a}, \dfrac{a}{\sqrt{c^2 - a^2}}, \dfrac{c}{a}, \dfrac{c}{\sqrt{c^2 - a^2}}$

$\boxed{7}$ adj $= \sqrt{c^2 - b^2}$ ★ $\dfrac{b}{c}$, $\dfrac{\sqrt{c^2-b^2}}{c}$, $\dfrac{b}{\sqrt{c^2-b^2}}$, $\dfrac{\sqrt{c^2-b^2}}{b}$, $\dfrac{c}{\sqrt{c^2-b^2}}$, $\dfrac{c}{b}$

$\boxed{8}$ hyp $= \sqrt{a^2 + a^2} = \sqrt{2a^2} = \sqrt{2}\,a \Rightarrow \sin\theta = \dfrac{a}{\sqrt{2}\,a} = \dfrac{1}{\sqrt{2}}$, or, $\dfrac{\sqrt{2}}{2}$.

   $\cos\theta = \dfrac{a}{\sqrt{2}\,a} = \dfrac{1}{\sqrt{2}}$ and $\tan\theta = \dfrac{a}{a} = 1$.   ★ $\dfrac{\sqrt{2}}{2}$, $\dfrac{\sqrt{2}}{2}$, 1, 1, $\sqrt{2}$, $\sqrt{2}$

$\boxed{9}$ $\sin 30° = \dfrac{4}{x} \Rightarrow \dfrac{1}{2} = \dfrac{4}{x} \Rightarrow x = 8$; $\tan 30° = \dfrac{4}{y} \Rightarrow \dfrac{\sqrt{3}}{3} = \dfrac{4}{y} \Rightarrow y = 4\sqrt{3}$

$\boxed{10}$ $\sin 60° = \dfrac{3}{x} \Rightarrow \dfrac{\sqrt{3}}{2} = \dfrac{3}{x} \Rightarrow x = 2\sqrt{3}$; $\tan 60° = \dfrac{3}{y} \Rightarrow \sqrt{3} = \dfrac{3}{y} \Rightarrow y = \sqrt{3}$

$\boxed{11}$ $\sin 45° = \dfrac{7}{x} \Rightarrow \dfrac{\sqrt{2}}{2} = \dfrac{7}{x} \Rightarrow x = 7\sqrt{2}$; $\tan 45° = \dfrac{7}{y} \Rightarrow 1 = \dfrac{7}{y} \Rightarrow y = 7$

$\boxed{12}$ $\sin 30° = \dfrac{x}{10} \Rightarrow \dfrac{1}{2} = \dfrac{x}{10} \Rightarrow x = 5$; $\cos 30° = \dfrac{y}{10} \Rightarrow \dfrac{\sqrt{3}}{2} = \dfrac{y}{10} \Rightarrow y = 5\sqrt{3}$

$\boxed{13}$ $\sin 60° = \dfrac{x}{8} \Rightarrow \dfrac{\sqrt{3}}{2} = \dfrac{x}{8} \Rightarrow x = 4\sqrt{3}$; $\cos 60° = \dfrac{y}{8} \Rightarrow \dfrac{1}{2} = \dfrac{y}{8} \Rightarrow y = 4$

$\boxed{14}$ $\sin 45° = \dfrac{x}{4} \Rightarrow \dfrac{\sqrt{2}}{2} = \dfrac{x}{4} \Rightarrow x = 2\sqrt{2}$; $\cos 45° = \dfrac{y}{4} \Rightarrow \dfrac{\sqrt{2}}{2} = \dfrac{y}{4} \Rightarrow y = 2\sqrt{2}$

Note: It may help to sketch a triangle as shown for Exercises 15 and 19.

   Use the Pythagorean theorem to find the remaining side.

$\boxed{15}$ $(\text{adj})^2 + (\text{opp})^2 = (\text{hyp})^2 \Rightarrow (\text{adj})^2 + 3^2 = 5^2 \Rightarrow \text{adj} = \sqrt{25-9} = 4$.   ★ $\dfrac{3}{5}$, $\dfrac{4}{5}$, $\dfrac{3}{4}$, $\dfrac{4}{3}$, $\dfrac{5}{4}$, $\dfrac{5}{3}$

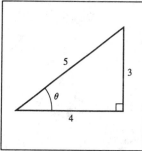

Figure 15

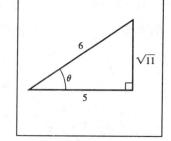

Figure 19

$\boxed{16}$ $8^2 + (\text{opp})^2 = 17^2 \Rightarrow \text{opp} = \sqrt{289-64} = 15$.   ★ $\dfrac{15}{17}$, $\dfrac{8}{17}$, $\dfrac{15}{8}$, $\dfrac{8}{15}$, $\dfrac{17}{8}$, $\dfrac{17}{15}$

$\boxed{17}$ $12^2 + 5^2 = (\text{hyp})^2 \Rightarrow \text{hyp} = \sqrt{144+25} = 13$.   ★ $\dfrac{5}{13}$, $\dfrac{12}{13}$, $\dfrac{5}{12}$, $\dfrac{12}{5}$, $\dfrac{13}{12}$, $\dfrac{13}{5}$

$\boxed{18}$ $7^2 + 24^2 = (\text{hyp})^2 \Rightarrow \text{hyp} = \sqrt{49+576} = 25$.   ★ $\dfrac{24}{25}$, $\dfrac{7}{25}$, $\dfrac{24}{7}$, $\dfrac{7}{24}$, $\dfrac{25}{7}$, $\dfrac{25}{24}$

$\boxed{19}$ $5^2 + (\text{opp})^2 = 6^2 \Rightarrow \text{opp} = \sqrt{36-25} = \sqrt{11}$.   ★ $\dfrac{\sqrt{11}}{6}$, $\dfrac{5}{6}$, $\dfrac{\sqrt{11}}{5}$, $\dfrac{5}{\sqrt{11}}$, $\dfrac{6}{5}$, $\dfrac{6}{\sqrt{11}}$

$\boxed{20}$ $(\text{adj})^2 + 1^2 = 4^2 \Rightarrow \text{adj} = \sqrt{16-1} = \sqrt{15}$.   ★ $\dfrac{1}{4}$, $\dfrac{\sqrt{15}}{4}$, $\dfrac{1}{\sqrt{15}}$, $\sqrt{15}$, $\dfrac{4}{\sqrt{15}}$, 4

$\boxed{21}$ Let h denote the height of the tree.

$$\tan\theta = \frac{\text{opp}}{\text{adj}} \Rightarrow \tan 60° = \frac{h}{200} \Rightarrow h = 200\sqrt{3} \approx 346.4 \text{ ft}$$

$\boxed{22}$ Let d denote the distance to the base of the mountain.

$$\cot\theta = \frac{\text{adj}}{\text{opp}} \Rightarrow \cot 30° = \frac{d}{12{,}400} \Rightarrow d = 12{,}400\sqrt{3} \approx 21{,}477.4 \text{ ft}$$

[23] Let d be the distance that it was moved. $\sin 9° = \frac{30}{d} \Rightarrow d = \frac{30}{\sin 9°} \approx 192$ ft

[24] Let h be the height of the top of the sign.

$$\tan 78.87° = \frac{h}{200} \Rightarrow h = 200\tan 78.87° \approx 1017 \text{ ft}$$

[25] $\sin\theta = \frac{1.22\lambda}{D} \Rightarrow D = \frac{1.22\lambda}{\sin\theta} = \frac{1.22 \times 550 \times 10^{-9}}{\sin 0.00003769°} \approx 1.02$ meters

[26] (a) $A = \frac{1}{2}\pi R^2(1 + \cos 0°) = \frac{1}{2}\pi R^2(2) = \pi R^2 = \pi(1080)^2 = 1{,}166{,}400\pi \approx 3{,}664{,}354 \text{ mi}^2$

(b) $A = \frac{1}{2}\pi R^2(1 + \cos 180°) = \frac{1}{2}\pi R^2(0) = 0 \text{ mi}^2$

(c) $A = \frac{1}{2}\pi R^2(1 + \cos 90°) = \frac{1}{2}\pi R^2(1) = \frac{1}{2}\pi R^2 = \frac{\pi}{2}(1080)^2 = 583{,}200\pi \approx 1{,}832{,}177 \text{ mi}^2$

(d) $A = \frac{1}{2}\pi R^2(1 + \cos 103°) \approx \frac{1}{2}\pi R^2(0.77505) \approx 0.38752\pi(1080)^2 \approx 1{,}420{,}027 \text{ mi}^2$

[27] *Note:* Be sure that your calculator is in degree mode.

(a) $\sin 42° \approx 0.6691$ (b) $\cos 77° \approx 0.2250$

(c) $\csc 123° = \frac{1}{\sin 123°} \approx 1.1924$ (d) $\sec(-190°) = \frac{1}{\cos(-190°)} \approx -1.0154$

[28] (a) $\tan 282° \approx -4.7046$ (b) $\cot(-81°) = \frac{1}{\tan(-81°)} \approx -0.1584$

(c) $\sec 202° = \frac{1}{\cos 202°} \approx -1.0785$ (d) $\sin 97° \approx 0.9925$

[29] *Note:* Be sure that your calculator is in radian mode.

(a) $\cot\frac{\pi}{13} = \frac{1}{\tan(\pi/13)} \approx 4.0572$ (b) $\csc 1.32 = \frac{1}{\sin 1.32} \approx 1.0323$

(c) $\cos(-8.54) \approx -0.6335$ (d) $\tan\frac{3\pi}{7} \approx 4.3813$

[30] (a) $\sin(-0.11) \approx -0.1098$ (b) $\sec\frac{31}{27} = \frac{1}{\cos(31/27)} \approx 2.4380$

(c) $\tan\left(-\frac{3}{13}\right) \approx -0.2350$ (d) $\cos 2.4\pi \approx 0.3090$

[31] (a) Since $1 + \tan^2 4\beta = \sec^2 4\beta$, $\tan^2 4\beta - \sec^2 4\beta = -1$.

(b) $4\tan^2\beta - 4\sec^2\beta = 4(\tan^2\beta - \sec^2\beta) = 4(-1) = -4$

[32] (a) Since $1 + \cot^2 3\alpha = \csc^2 3\alpha$, $\csc^2 3\alpha - \cot^2 3\alpha = 1$.

(b) $3\csc^2\alpha - 3\cot^2\alpha = 3(\csc^2\alpha - \cot^2\alpha) = 3(1) = 3$

[33] (a) $5\sin^2\theta + 5\cos^2\theta = 5(\sin^2\theta + \cos^2\theta) = 5(1) = 5$

(b) $5\sin^2(\theta/4) + 5\cos^2(\theta/4) = 5\left[\sin^2(\theta/4) + \cos^2(\theta/4)\right] = 5(1) = 5$

[34] (a) $7\sec^2\gamma - 7\tan^2\gamma = 7(\sec^2\gamma - \tan^2\gamma) = 7(1) = 7$

(b) $7\sec^2(\gamma/3) - 7\tan^2(\gamma/3) = 7\left[\sec^2(\gamma/3) - \tan^2(\gamma/3)\right] = 7(1) = 7$

[35] $\dfrac{\sin^3\theta + \cos^3\theta}{\sin\theta + \cos\theta} = \dfrac{(\sin\theta + \cos\theta)(\sin^2\theta - \sin\theta\cos\theta + \cos^2\theta)}{\sin\theta + \cos\theta} =$

$$\sin^2\theta - \sin\theta\cos\theta + \cos^2\theta = (\sin^2\theta + \cos^2\theta) - \sin\theta\cos\theta = 1 - \sin\theta\cos\theta$$

[36] $\dfrac{\cot^2\alpha - 4}{\cot^2\alpha - \cot\alpha - 6} = \dfrac{(\cot\alpha + 2)(\cot\alpha - 2)}{(\cot\alpha - 3)(\cot\alpha + 2)} = \dfrac{\cot\alpha - 2}{\cot\alpha - 3}$

$$\boxed{37}\ \frac{2-\tan\theta}{2\csc\theta-\sec\theta}=\frac{2-\dfrac{\sin\theta}{\cos\theta}}{2\cdot\dfrac{1}{\sin\theta}-\dfrac{1}{\cos\theta}}=\frac{\dfrac{2\cos\theta-\sin\theta}{\cos\theta}}{\dfrac{2\cos\theta-\sin\theta}{\sin\theta\cos\theta}}=\frac{\dfrac{1}{1}}{\dfrac{1}{\sin\theta}}=\sin\theta$$

$$\boxed{38}\ \frac{\csc\theta+1}{(1/\sin^2\theta)+\csc\theta}=\frac{\csc\theta+1}{\csc^2\theta+\csc\theta}=\frac{\csc\theta+1}{\csc\theta(\csc\theta+1)}=\frac{1}{\csc\theta}=\sin\theta$$

$$\boxed{39}\ \cot\theta=\frac{\cos\theta}{\sin\theta}\ \{\text{cotangent identity}\,\}=\frac{\sqrt{1-\sin^2\theta}}{\sin\theta}\ \{\sin^2\theta+\cos^2\theta=1\,\}$$

$$\boxed{40}\ \tan\theta=\frac{\sin\theta}{\cos\theta}\ \{\text{tangent identity}\,\}=\frac{\sqrt{1-\cos^2\theta}}{\cos\theta}\ \{\sin^2\theta+\cos^2\theta=1\,\}$$

$$\boxed{41}\ \sec\theta=\frac{1}{\cos\theta}\ \{\text{reciprocal identity}\,\}=\frac{1}{\sqrt{1-\sin^2\theta}}$$

$$\boxed{42}\ \csc\theta=\frac{1}{\sin\theta}\ \{\text{reciprocal identity}\,\}=\frac{1}{\sqrt{1-\cos^2\theta}}$$

$$\boxed{43}\ \text{One solution is}\ \sin\theta=\sqrt{1-\cos^2\theta}=\sqrt{1-\frac{1}{\sec^2\theta}}=\frac{\sqrt{\sec^2\theta-1}}{\sec\theta}.$$

$$\text{Alternatively,}\ \sin\theta=\frac{\sin\theta/\cos\theta}{1/\cos\theta}=\frac{\tan\theta}{\sec\theta}=\frac{\sqrt{\sec^2\theta-1}}{\sec\theta}\ \{1+\tan^2\theta=\sec^2\theta\,\}.$$

$$\boxed{44}\ \cos\theta=\frac{\cos\theta/\sin\theta}{1/\sin\theta}=\frac{\cot\theta}{\csc\theta}=\frac{\cot\theta}{\sqrt{1+\cot^2\theta}}\ \{1+\cot^2\theta=\csc^2\theta\,\}$$

$$\boxed{45}\ \cos\theta\sec\theta=\cos\theta\,(1/\cos\theta)=1 \qquad\qquad \boxed{46}\ \tan\theta\cot\theta=\tan\theta\,(1/\tan\theta)=1$$

$$\boxed{47}\ \sin\theta\sec\theta=\sin\theta\,(1/\cos\theta)=\sin\theta/\cos\theta=\tan\theta$$

$$\boxed{48}\ \sin\theta\cot\theta=\sin\theta\,(\cos\theta/\sin\theta)=\cos\theta$$

$$\boxed{49}\ \frac{\csc\theta}{\sec\theta}=\frac{1/\sin\theta}{1/\cos\theta}=\frac{\cos\theta}{\sin\theta}=\cot\theta \qquad\qquad \boxed{50}\ \cot\theta\sec\theta=\frac{\cos\theta}{\sin\theta}\cdot\frac{1}{\cos\theta}=\frac{1}{\sin\theta}=\csc\theta$$

$$\boxed{51}\ (1+\cos 2\theta)(1-\cos 2\theta)=1-\cos^2 2\theta=\sin^2 2\theta$$

$$\boxed{52}\ \cos^2 2\theta-\sin^2 2\theta=\cos^2 2\theta-(1-\cos^2 2\theta)=2\cos^2 2\theta-1$$

$$\boxed{53}\ \cos^2\theta\,(\sec^2\theta-1)=\cos^2\theta\,(\tan^2\theta)=\cos^2\theta\cdot\frac{\sin^2\theta}{\cos^2\theta}=\sin^2\theta$$

$$\boxed{54}\ (\tan\theta+\cot\theta)\tan\theta=\tan^2\theta+\cot\theta\tan\theta=\tan^2\theta+1=\sec^2\theta$$

$$\boxed{55}\ \frac{\sin(\theta/2)}{\csc(\theta/2)}+\frac{\cos(\theta/2)}{\sec(\theta/2)}=\frac{\sin(\theta/2)}{1/\sin(\theta/2)}+\frac{\cos(\theta/2)}{1/\cos(\theta/2)}=\sin^2(\theta/2)+\cos^2(\theta/2)=1$$

$$\boxed{56}\ 1-2\sin^2(\theta/2)=1-2(1-\cos^2(\theta/2))=1-2+2\cos^2(\theta/2)=2\cos^2(\theta/2)-1$$

$$\boxed{57}\ (1+\sin\theta)(1-\sin\theta)=1-\sin^2\theta=\cos^2\theta=\frac{1}{\sec^2\theta}$$

$$\boxed{58}\ (1-\sin^2\theta)(1+\tan^2\theta)=(\cos^2\theta)(\sec^2\theta)=\cos^2\theta\,(1/\cos^2\theta)=1$$

$$\boxed{59}\ \sec\theta-\cos\theta=\frac{1}{\cos\theta}-\cos\theta=\frac{1-\cos^2\theta}{\cos\theta}=\frac{\sin^2\theta}{\cos\theta}=\frac{\sin\theta}{\cos\theta}\cdot\sin\theta=\tan\theta\sin\theta$$

$$\boxed{60}\ \frac{\sin\theta+\cos\theta}{\cos\theta}=\frac{\sin\theta}{\cos\theta}+\frac{\cos\theta}{\cos\theta}=\tan\theta+1=1+\tan\theta$$

61 $(\cot\theta + \csc\theta)(\tan\theta - \sin\theta) = \cot\theta\,\tan\theta - \cot\theta\,\sin\theta + \csc\theta\,\tan\theta - \csc\theta\,\sin\theta$

$$= \frac{1}{\tan\theta}\tan\theta - \frac{\cos\theta}{\sin\theta}\sin\theta + \frac{1}{\sin\theta}\frac{\sin\theta}{\cos\theta} - \frac{1}{\sin\theta}\sin\theta$$

$$= 1 - \cos\theta + \frac{1}{\cos\theta} - 1 = -\cos\theta + \sec\theta = \sec\theta - \cos\theta$$

62 $\cot\theta + \tan\theta = \dfrac{\cos\theta}{\sin\theta} + \dfrac{\sin\theta}{\cos\theta} = \dfrac{\cos^2\theta + \sin^2\theta}{\sin\theta\,\cos\theta} = \dfrac{1}{\sin\theta\,\cos\theta} = \dfrac{1}{\sin\theta}\cdot\dfrac{1}{\cos\theta} = \csc\theta\,\sec\theta$

63 $\sec^2 3\theta\,\csc^2 3\theta = (1 + \tan^2 3\theta)(1 + \cot^2 3\theta) = 1 + \tan^2 3\theta + \cot^2 3\theta + 1 =$
$$\sec^2 3\theta + \csc^2 3\theta$$

64 $\dfrac{1 + \cos^2 3\theta}{\sin^2 3\theta} = \dfrac{1}{\sin^2 3\theta} + \dfrac{\cos^2 3\theta}{\sin^2 3\theta} = \csc^2 3\theta + \cot^2 3\theta = \csc^2 3\theta + (\csc^2 3\theta - 1) =$
$$2\csc^2 3\theta - 1$$

65 $\log\csc\theta = \log\left(\dfrac{1}{\sin\theta}\right) = \log 1 - \log\sin\theta = 0 - \log\sin\theta = -\log\sin\theta$

66 $\log\tan\theta = \log\left(\dfrac{\sin\theta}{\cos\theta}\right) = \log\sin\theta - \log\cos\theta$

67 $x = 4$ and $y = -3 \Rightarrow r = \sqrt{4^2 + (-3)^2} = 5.$

$\sin\theta = y/r = -\frac{3}{5}$, $\cos\theta = x/r = \frac{4}{5}$, and $\tan\theta = y/x = -\frac{3}{4}$. $\star$ $-\frac{3}{5}, \frac{4}{5}, -\frac{3}{4}, -\frac{4}{3}, \frac{5}{4}, -\frac{5}{3}$

68 $x = -8$ and $y = -15 \Rightarrow r = \sqrt{(-8)^2 + (-15)^2} = 17.$ $\star$ $-\frac{15}{17}, -\frac{8}{17}, \frac{15}{8}, \frac{8}{15}, -\frac{17}{8}, -\frac{17}{15}$

69 $x = -2$ and $y = -5 \Rightarrow r = \sqrt{(-2)^2 + (-5)^2} = \sqrt{29}.$

$\star$ $-\dfrac{5}{\sqrt{29}}, -\dfrac{2}{\sqrt{29}}, \dfrac{5}{2}, \dfrac{2}{5}, -\dfrac{\sqrt{29}}{2}, -\dfrac{\sqrt{29}}{5}$

70 $x = -1$ and $y = 2 \Rightarrow r = \sqrt{(-1)^2 + 2^2} = \sqrt{5}.$ $\star$ $\dfrac{2}{\sqrt{5}}, -\dfrac{1}{\sqrt{5}}, -2, -\dfrac{1}{2}, -\sqrt{5}, \dfrac{\sqrt{5}}{2}$

71 Since the terminal side of θ is in QII, choose x to be negative.

If $x = -1$, then $y = 4$ and $(-1, 4)$ is a point on the terminal side of θ.

$x = -1$ and $y = 4 \Rightarrow r = \sqrt{(-1)^2 + 4^2} = \sqrt{17}.$ $\star$ $\dfrac{4}{\sqrt{17}}, -\dfrac{1}{\sqrt{17}}, -4, -\dfrac{1}{4}, -\sqrt{17}, \dfrac{\sqrt{17}}{4}$

72 Since the terminal side of θ is in QIV, choose x to be positive.

If $x = 3$, then $y = -5$ and $(3, -5)$ is a point on the terminal side of θ.

$x = 3$ and $y = -5 \Rightarrow r = \sqrt{3^2 + (-5)^2} = \sqrt{34}.$ $\star$ $-\dfrac{5}{\sqrt{34}}, \dfrac{3}{\sqrt{34}}, -\dfrac{5}{3}, -\dfrac{3}{5}, \dfrac{\sqrt{34}}{3}, -\dfrac{\sqrt{34}}{5}$

73 An equation of the line is $y = \frac{4}{3}x$. If $x = 3$, then $y = 4$ and $(3, 4)$ is a point on the

terminal side of θ. $x = 3$ and $y = 4 \Rightarrow r = \sqrt{3^2 + 4^2} = 5.$ $\star$ $\frac{4}{5}, \frac{3}{5}, \frac{4}{3}, \frac{3}{4}, \frac{5}{3}, \frac{5}{4}$

74 An equation of the line bisecting the third quadrant is $y = x$.

If $x = -1$, then $y = -1$ and $(-1, -1)$ is a point on the terminal side of θ.

$x = -1$ and $y = -1 \Rightarrow r = \sqrt{(-1)^2 + (-1)^2} = \sqrt{2}.$ $\star$ $-\dfrac{\sqrt{2}}{2}, -\dfrac{\sqrt{2}}{2}, 1, 1, -\sqrt{2}, -\sqrt{2}$

$\boxed{75}$ $2y - 7x + 2 = 0 \Leftrightarrow y = \frac{7}{2}x - 1$. Thus, the slope of the given line is $\frac{7}{2}$.

An equation of the line through the origin with that slope is $y = \frac{7}{2}x$.

If $x = -2$, then $y = -7$ and $(-2, -7)$ is a point on the terminal side of θ.

$x = -2$ and $y = -7 \Rightarrow r = \sqrt{(-2)^2 + (-7)^2} = \sqrt{53}$.

$$\star \quad -\frac{7}{\sqrt{53}}, \; -\frac{2}{\sqrt{53}}, \; \frac{7}{2}, \frac{2}{7}, \; -\frac{\sqrt{53}}{2}, \; -\frac{\sqrt{53}}{7}$$

$\boxed{76}$ $m_{AB} = \frac{-2-4}{3-1} = -3$. An equation of the line through the origin with a slope of -3 is

$y = -3x$. If $x = -1$, then $y = 3$ and $(-1, 3)$ is a point on the terminal side of θ.

$x = -1$ and $y = 3 \Rightarrow r = \sqrt{(-1)^2 + 3^2} = \sqrt{10}$. $\quad \star \; \frac{3}{\sqrt{10}}, \; -\frac{1}{\sqrt{10}}, \; -3, \; -\frac{1}{3}, \; -\sqrt{10}, \; \frac{\sqrt{10}}{3}$

Note: U denotes *undefined.*

$\boxed{77}$ (a) For $\theta = 90°$, choose $x = 0$ and $y = 1$. $r = 1$. $\qquad\qquad \star$ 1, 0, U, 0, U, 1

(b) For $\theta = 0°$, choose $x = 1$ and $y = 0$. $r = 1$. $\qquad\qquad \star$ 0, 1, 0, U, 1, U

(c) For $\theta = \frac{7\pi}{2}$, choose $x = 0$ and $y = -1$. $r = 1$. $\qquad\quad \star$ -1, 0, U, 0, U, -1

(d) For $\theta = 3\pi$, choose $x = -1$ and $y = 0$. $r = 1$. $\qquad\quad \star$ 0, -1, 0, U, -1, U

$\boxed{78}$ (a) For $\theta = 180°$, choose $x = -1$ and $y = 0$. $r = 1$. $\qquad \star$ 0, -1, 0, U, -1, U

(b) For $\theta = -90°$, choose $x = 0$ and $y = -1$. $r = 1$. $\qquad \star$ -1, 0, U, 0, U, -1

(c) For $\theta = 2\pi$, choose $x = 1$ and $y = 0$. $r = 1$. $\qquad\quad \star$ 0, 1, 0, U, 1, U

(d) For $\theta = \frac{5\pi}{2}$, choose $x = 0$ and $y = 1$. $r = 1$. $\qquad\quad \star$ 1, 0, U, 0, U, 1

$\boxed{79}$ (a) $\cos\theta > 0 \Rightarrow \theta$ is in QI or QIV. $\sin\theta < 0 \Rightarrow \theta$ is in QIII or QIV. $\therefore \theta$ is in QIV.

(b) $\sin\theta < 0 \Rightarrow \theta$ is in QIII or QIV. $\cot\theta > 0 \Rightarrow \theta$ is in QI or QIII. $\therefore \theta$ is in QIII.

(c) $\csc\theta > 0 \Rightarrow \theta$ is in QI or QII. $\sec\theta < 0 \Rightarrow \theta$ is in QII or QIII. $\therefore \theta$ is in QII.

(d) $\sec\theta < 0 \Rightarrow \theta$ is in QII or QIII. $\tan\theta > 0 \Rightarrow \theta$ is in QI or QIII. $\therefore \theta$ is in QIII.

$\boxed{80}$ (a) $\tan\theta < 0 \Rightarrow \theta$ is in QII or QIV. $\cos\theta > 0 \Rightarrow \theta$ is in QI or QIV. $\therefore \theta$ is in QIV.

(b) $\sec\theta > 0 \Rightarrow \theta$ is QI or QIV. $\tan\theta < 0 \Rightarrow \theta$ is in QII or QIV. $\therefore \theta$ is in QIV.

(c) $\csc\theta > 0 \Rightarrow \theta$ is in QI or QII. $\cot\theta < 0 \Rightarrow \theta$ is in QII or QIV. $\therefore \theta$ is in QII.

(d) $\cos\theta < 0 \Rightarrow \theta$ is in QII or QIII. $\csc\theta < 0 \Rightarrow \theta$ is in QIII or QIV. $\therefore \theta$ is in QIII.

Note: Exer. 81–88: Steps to determine 2 function values using only the fundamental identities are shown. The other 3 function values are just the reciprocals of those given and are listed in the answer.

$\boxed{81}$ $\tan\theta = -\frac{3}{4}$ and $\sin\theta > 0 \Rightarrow \theta$ is in QII. $\sec\theta = -\sqrt{1 + \tan^2\theta} = -\sqrt{1 + \frac{9}{16}} = -\frac{5}{4}$.

$\tan\theta = \frac{\sin\theta}{\cos\theta} \Rightarrow -\frac{3}{4} = \frac{\sin\theta}{-4/5} \Rightarrow \sin\theta = \frac{3}{5}$ $\qquad\qquad \star \; \frac{3}{5}, \; -\frac{4}{5}, \; -\frac{3}{4}, \; -\frac{4}{3}, \; -\frac{5}{4}, \frac{5}{3}$

$\boxed{82}$ $\cot\theta = \frac{3}{4}$ and $\cos\theta < 0 \Rightarrow \theta$ is in QIII. $\csc\theta = -\sqrt{1 + \cot^2\theta} = -\sqrt{1 + \frac{9}{16}} = -\frac{5}{4}$;

$\cot\theta = \frac{\cos\theta}{\sin\theta} \Rightarrow \frac{3}{4} = \frac{\cos\theta}{-4/5} \Rightarrow \cos\theta = -\frac{3}{5}$ $\qquad\qquad \star \; -\frac{4}{5}, \; -\frac{3}{5}, \frac{4}{3}, \frac{3}{4}, \; -\frac{5}{3}, \; -\frac{5}{4}$

83 $\sin\theta = -\frac{5}{13}$ and $\sec\theta > 0 \Rightarrow \theta$ is in QIV. $\cos\theta = \sqrt{1-\sin^2\theta} = \sqrt{1-\frac{25}{169}} = \frac{12}{13}$.

$\tan\theta = \frac{\sin\theta}{\cos\theta} = \frac{-5/13}{12/13} = -\frac{5}{12}$

$\bigstar \ -\frac{5}{13}, \frac{12}{13}, -\frac{5}{12}, -\frac{12}{5}, \frac{13}{12}, -\frac{13}{5}$

84 $\cos\theta = \frac{1}{2}$ and $\sin\theta < 0 \Rightarrow \theta$ is in QIV. $\sin\theta = -\sqrt{1-\cos^2\theta} = -\sqrt{1-\frac{1}{4}} = -\frac{\sqrt{3}}{2}$.

$\tan\theta = \frac{\sin\theta}{\cos\theta} = \frac{-\sqrt{3}/2}{1/2} = -\sqrt{3}$

$\bigstar \ -\frac{\sqrt{3}}{2}, \frac{1}{2}, -\sqrt{3}, -\frac{1}{\sqrt{3}}, 2, -\frac{2}{\sqrt{3}}$

85 $\cos\theta = -\frac{1}{3}$ and $\sin\theta < 0 \Rightarrow \theta$ is in QIII. $\sin\theta = -\sqrt{1-\cos^2\theta} = -\sqrt{1-\frac{1}{9}} = -\frac{\sqrt{8}}{3}$.

$\tan\theta = \frac{\sin\theta}{\cos\theta} = \frac{-\sqrt{8}/3}{-1/3} = \sqrt{8} = 2\sqrt{2}$

$\bigstar \ -\frac{\sqrt{8}}{3}, -\frac{1}{3}, \sqrt{8}, \frac{1}{\sqrt{8}}, -3, -\frac{3}{\sqrt{8}}$

86 $\csc\theta = 5$ and $\cot\theta < 0 \Rightarrow \theta$ is in QII. $\cot\theta = -\sqrt{\csc^2\theta - 1} = -\sqrt{25-1} = -\sqrt{24}$.

$\cot\theta = \frac{\cos\theta}{\sin\theta} \Rightarrow -\sqrt{24} = \frac{\cos\theta}{1/5} \Rightarrow \cos\theta = -\frac{\sqrt{24}}{5}$

$\bigstar \ \frac{1}{5}, -\frac{\sqrt{24}}{5}, -\frac{1}{\sqrt{24}}, -\sqrt{24}, -\frac{5}{\sqrt{24}}, 5$

87 $\sec\theta = -4$ and $\csc\theta > 0 \Rightarrow \theta$ is in QII. $\tan\theta = -\sqrt{\sec^2\theta - 1} = -\sqrt{16-1} = -\sqrt{15}$.

$\tan\theta = \frac{\sin\theta}{\cos\theta} \Rightarrow -\sqrt{15} = \frac{\sin\theta}{-1/4} \Rightarrow \sin\theta = \frac{\sqrt{15}}{4}$

$\bigstar \ \frac{\sqrt{15}}{4}, -\frac{1}{4}, -\sqrt{15}, -\frac{1}{\sqrt{15}}, -4, \frac{4}{\sqrt{15}}$

88 $\sin\theta = \frac{2}{5}$ and $\cos\theta < 0 \Rightarrow \theta$ is in QII. $\cos\theta = -\sqrt{1-\sin^2\theta} = -\sqrt{1-\frac{4}{25}} = -\frac{\sqrt{21}}{5}$.

$\tan\theta = \frac{\sin\theta}{\cos\theta} = \frac{2/5}{-\sqrt{21}/5} = -\frac{2}{\sqrt{21}}$

$\bigstar \ \frac{2}{5}, -\frac{\sqrt{21}}{5}, -\frac{2}{\sqrt{21}}, -\frac{\sqrt{21}}{2}, -\frac{5}{\sqrt{21}}, \frac{5}{2}$

89 $\sqrt{\sec^2\theta - 1} = \sqrt{\tan^2\theta} = |\tan\theta| = -\tan\theta$ since $\tan\theta < 0$ if $\pi/2 < \theta < \pi$

90 $\sqrt{1+\cot^2\theta} = \sqrt{\csc^2\theta} = |\csc\theta| = \csc\theta$ since $\csc\theta > 0$ if $0 < \theta < \pi$

91 $\sqrt{1+\tan^2\theta} = \sqrt{\sec^2\theta} = |\sec\theta| = \sec\theta$ since $\sec\theta > 0$ if $3\pi/2 < \theta < 2\pi$

92 $\sqrt{\csc^2\theta - 1} = \sqrt{\cot^2\theta} = |\cot\theta| = -\cot\theta$ since $\cot\theta < 0$ if $3\pi/2 < \theta < 2\pi$

93 $\sqrt{\sin^2(\theta/2)} = |\sin(\theta/2)| = -\sin(\theta/2)$ since

$\sin(\theta/2) < 0$ if $2\pi < \theta < 4\pi \ \{2\pi < \theta < 4\pi \Rightarrow \pi < \theta/2 < 2\pi\}$

94 $\sqrt{\cos^2(\theta/2)} = |\cos(\theta/2)| = \cos(\theta/2)$ since

$\cos(\theta/2) > 0$ if $0 < \theta < \pi \ \{0 < \theta/2 < \pi/2\}$

5.3 Exercises

5.3 Concept Check

1 On the unit circle U, the radian measure of an angle θ is equivalent to what? ●
On the unit circle U, the radian measure of an angle θ is equivalent to the length of
the arc that subtends θ.

2 If $P(t) = (a, b)$ is a point on the unit circle U as described in Example 2, what are
the coordinates of $P(t + k\pi)$, where k is any odd integer? ● $P(t + k\pi) = (-a, -b)$
for any odd integer k; that is, the coordinates have opposite signs of those of $P(t)$.

3 Suppose f is a function that assigns the positive integers to a day of the week as follows: $f(1) = $ Sunday, $f(2) = $ Monday, ..., $f(7) = $ Saturday. What is $f(7003)$? • Since the period of f is 7, $f(7003) = f(3 + 7 \cdot 1000) = f(3) = $ Tuesday.

4 Which two trigonometric functions have graphs that are symmetric with respect to the y-axis? • The cosine and secant functions are even, so their graphs are symmetric with respect to the y-axis.

5 How many solutions does the equation $\sec x = 0$ have? • None, since $\sec x \geq 1$ or $\sec x \leq -1$.

6 If T denotes any one of the six trigonometric functions, is it true that $T(t + 2\pi) = T(t)$? • Yes—adding 2π to any real number just gets us back to the original point on the unit circle.

5.3 Exercises

1 $P(-\frac{15}{17}, \frac{8}{17}) \Rightarrow \sin t = y = \frac{8}{17}$, $\cos t = x = -\frac{15}{17}$, $\tan t = y/x = -\frac{8}{15}$, $\cot t = x/y = -\frac{15}{8}$,
$$\sec t = 1/x = -\frac{17}{15}, \ \csc t = 1/y = \frac{17}{8}$$

2 $P(\frac{4}{5}, \frac{3}{5})$ gives us $\frac{3}{5}, \frac{4}{5}, \frac{3}{4}, \frac{4}{3}, \frac{5}{4}, \frac{5}{3}$.

3 $P(\frac{24}{25}, -\frac{7}{25})$ gives us $-\frac{7}{25}, \frac{24}{25}, -\frac{7}{24}, -\frac{24}{7}, \frac{25}{24}, -\frac{25}{7}$.

4 $P(-\frac{5}{13}, -\frac{12}{13})$ gives us $-\frac{12}{13}, -\frac{5}{13}, \frac{12}{5}, \frac{5}{12}, -\frac{13}{5}, -\frac{13}{12}$.

5 $P(t) = (\frac{3}{5}, \frac{4}{5}) \Rightarrow P(t + \pi) = P(t - \pi) = (-\frac{3}{5}, -\frac{4}{5})$,
$$P(-t) = (\tfrac{3}{5}, -\tfrac{4}{5}), \ P(-t - \pi) = (-\tfrac{3}{5}, \tfrac{4}{5})$$

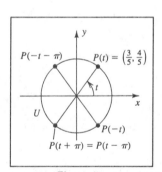

Figure 5

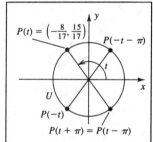

Figure 6

6 $P(t) = (-\frac{8}{17}, \frac{15}{17}) \Rightarrow P(t + \pi) = P(t - \pi) = (\frac{8}{17}, -\frac{15}{17})$,
$$P(-t) = (-\tfrac{8}{17}, -\tfrac{15}{17}), \ P(-t - \pi) = (\tfrac{8}{17}, \tfrac{15}{17})$$

7 $P(t) = (-\frac{12}{13}, -\frac{5}{13}) \Rightarrow P(t + \pi) = P(t - \pi) = (\frac{12}{13}, \frac{5}{13})$,
$$P(-t) = (-\tfrac{12}{13}, \tfrac{5}{13}), \ P(-t - \pi) = (\tfrac{12}{13}, -\tfrac{5}{13})$$

8 $P(t) = (\frac{7}{25}, -\frac{24}{25}) \Rightarrow P(t + \pi) = P(t - \pi) = (-\frac{7}{25}, \frac{24}{25})$,
$$P(-t) = (\tfrac{7}{25}, \tfrac{24}{25}), \ P(-t - \pi) = (-\tfrac{7}{25}, -\tfrac{24}{25})$$

Note: U denotes *undefined.*

⑨ (a) $t = 2\pi \Rightarrow P(x, y) = (1, 0)$.

The exact values of the trigonometric functions at t are 0, 1, 0, U, 1, U.

(b) $t = -3\pi \Rightarrow P(x, y) = (-1, 0)$. 0, -1, 0, U, -1, U

⑩ (a) $t = -\pi \Rightarrow P(x, y) = (-1, 0)$. 0, -1, 0, U, -1, U

(b) $t = 6\pi \Rightarrow P(x, y) = (1, 0)$. 0, 1, 0, U, 1, U

⑪ (a) $t = \frac{3\pi}{2} \Rightarrow P(x, y) = (0, -1)$. -1, 0, U, 0, U, -1

(b) $t = -\frac{7\pi}{2} \Rightarrow P(x, y) = (0, 1)$. 1, 0, U, 0, U, 1

⑫ (a) $t = \frac{5\pi}{2} \Rightarrow P(x, y) = (0, 1)$. 1, 0, U, 0, U, 1

(b) $t = -\frac{\pi}{2} \Rightarrow P(x, y) = (0, -1)$. -1, 0, U, 0, U, -1

⑬ (a) $t = \frac{9\pi}{4} \Rightarrow P(x, y) = \left(\frac{\sqrt{2}}{2}, \frac{\sqrt{2}}{2}\right)$. $\frac{\sqrt{2}}{2}, \frac{\sqrt{2}}{2}, 1, 1, \sqrt{2}, \sqrt{2}$

(b) $t = -\frac{5\pi}{4} \Rightarrow P(x, y) = \left(-\frac{\sqrt{2}}{2}, \frac{\sqrt{2}}{2}\right)$. $\frac{\sqrt{2}}{2}, -\frac{\sqrt{2}}{2}, -1, -1, -\sqrt{2}, \sqrt{2}$

⑭ (a) $t = \frac{3\pi}{4} \Rightarrow P(x, y) = \left(-\frac{\sqrt{2}}{2}, \frac{\sqrt{2}}{2}\right)$. $\frac{\sqrt{2}}{2}, -\frac{\sqrt{2}}{2}, -1, -1, -\sqrt{2}, \sqrt{2}$

(b) $t = -\frac{7\pi}{4} \Rightarrow P(x, y) = \left(\frac{\sqrt{2}}{2}, \frac{\sqrt{2}}{2}\right)$. $\frac{\sqrt{2}}{2}, \frac{\sqrt{2}}{2}, 1, 1, \sqrt{2}, \sqrt{2}$

⑮ (a) $t = \frac{5\pi}{4} \Rightarrow P(x, y) = \left(-\frac{\sqrt{2}}{2}, -\frac{\sqrt{2}}{2}\right)$. $-\frac{\sqrt{2}}{2}, -\frac{\sqrt{2}}{2}, 1, 1, -\sqrt{2}, -\sqrt{2}$

(b) $t = -\frac{\pi}{4} \Rightarrow P(x, y) = \left(\frac{\sqrt{2}}{2}, -\frac{\sqrt{2}}{2}\right)$. $-\frac{\sqrt{2}}{2}, \frac{\sqrt{2}}{2}, -1, -1, \sqrt{2}, -\sqrt{2}$

⑯ (a) $t = \frac{7\pi}{4} \Rightarrow P(x, y) = \left(\frac{\sqrt{2}}{2}, -\frac{\sqrt{2}}{2}\right)$. $-\frac{\sqrt{2}}{2}, \frac{\sqrt{2}}{2}, -1, -1, \sqrt{2}, -\sqrt{2}$

(b) $t = -\frac{3\pi}{4} \Rightarrow P(x, y) = \left(-\frac{\sqrt{2}}{2}, -\frac{\sqrt{2}}{2}\right)$. $-\frac{\sqrt{2}}{2}, -\frac{\sqrt{2}}{2}, 1, 1, -\sqrt{2}, -\sqrt{2}$

⑰ (a) $\sin(-90°) = -\sin 90° = -1$ (b) $\cos\left(-\frac{3\pi}{4}\right) = \cos\frac{3\pi}{4} = -\frac{\sqrt{2}}{2}$

(c) $\tan(-45°) = -\tan 45° = -1$

⑱ (a) $\sin\left(-\frac{3\pi}{2}\right) = -\sin\frac{3\pi}{2} = -(-1) = 1$ (b) $\cos(-225°) = \cos 225° = -\frac{\sqrt{2}}{2}$

(c) $\tan(-\pi) = -\tan \pi = 0$

⑲ (a) $\cot\left(-\frac{3\pi}{4}\right) = -\cot\frac{3\pi}{4} = -(-1) = 1$ (b) $\sec(-180°) = \sec 180° = -1$

(c) $\csc\left(-\frac{3\pi}{2}\right) = -\csc\frac{3\pi}{2} = -(-1) = 1$

⑳ (a) $\cot(-225°) = -\cot 225° = -1$ (b) $\sec\left(-\frac{\pi}{4}\right) = \sec\frac{\pi}{4} = \sqrt{2}$

(c) $\csc(-45°) = -\csc 45° = -\sqrt{2}$

㉑ $\sin(-x)\sec(-x) = (-\sin x)\sec x = (-\sin x)(1/\cos x) = -\tan x$

㉒ $\csc(-x)\cos(-x) = (-\csc x)\cos x = (-1/\sin x)(\cos x) = -\cot x$

23 $\dfrac{\cot(-x)}{\csc(-x)} = \dfrac{-\cot x}{-\csc x} = \dfrac{\cos x/\sin x}{1/\sin x} = \cos x$

24 $\dfrac{\sec(-x)}{\tan(-x)} = \dfrac{\sec x}{-\tan x} = -\dfrac{1/\cos x}{\sin x/\cos x} = -\dfrac{1}{\sin x} = -\csc x$

25 $\dfrac{1}{\cos(-x)} - \tan(-x)\sin(-x) = \dfrac{1}{\cos x} - (-\tan x)(-\sin x) =$

$$\dfrac{1}{\cos x} - \dfrac{\sin x}{\cos x}\sin x = \dfrac{1-\sin^2 x}{\cos x} = \dfrac{\cos^2 x}{\cos x} = \cos x$$

26 $\cot(-x)\cos(-x) + \sin(-x) = -\cot x \cos x - \sin x =$

$$-\dfrac{\cos x}{\sin x}\cos x - \sin x = -\dfrac{\cos^2 x + \sin^2 x}{\sin x} = -\dfrac{1}{\sin x} = -\csc x$$

27 (a) As $x \to 0^+$, $\sin x \to \underline{\;0\;}$ (b) As $x \to -\frac{\pi}{2}^-$, $\sin x \to \underline{\;-1\;}$

28 (a) As $x \to \pi^+$, $\sin x \to \underline{\;0\;}$ (b) As $x \to \frac{\pi}{6}^-$, $\sin x \to \frac{1}{2}$

29 (a) As $x \to \frac{\pi}{4}^+$, $\cos x \to \underline{\;\sqrt{2}/2\;}$ (b) As $x \to \pi^-$, $\cos x \to \underline{\;-1\;}$

30 (a) As $x \to 0^+$, $\cos x \to \underline{\;1\;}$ (b) As $x \to -\frac{\pi}{3}^-$, $\cos x \to \frac{1}{2}$

31 (a) As $x \to \frac{\pi}{4}^+$, $\tan x \to \underline{\;1\;}$ (b) As $x \to \frac{\pi}{2}^+$, $\tan x \to \underline{\;-\infty\;}$

32 (a) As $x \to 0^+$, $\tan x \to \underline{\;0\;}$ (b) As $x \to -\frac{\pi}{2}^-$, $\tan x \to \underline{\;\infty\;}$

33 (a) As $x \to -\frac{\pi}{4}^-$, $\cot x \to \underline{\;-1\;}$ (b) As $x \to 0^+$, $\cot x \to \underline{\;\infty\;}$

34 (a) As $x \to \frac{\pi}{6}^+$, $\cot x \to \underline{\;\sqrt{3}\;}$ (b) As $x \to \pi^-$, $\cot x \to \underline{\;-\infty\;}$

35 (a) As $x \to \frac{\pi}{2}^-$, $\sec x \to \underline{\;\infty\;}$ (b) As $x \to \frac{\pi}{4}^+$, $\sec x \to \underline{\;\sqrt{2}\;}$

36 (a) As $x \to \frac{\pi}{2}^+$, $\sec x \to \underline{\;-\infty\;}$ (b) As $x \to 0^-$, $\sec x \to \underline{\;1\;}$

37 (a) As $x \to 0^-$, $\csc x \to \underline{\;-\infty\;}$ (b) As $x \to \frac{\pi}{2}^+$, $\csc x \to \underline{\;1\;}$

38 (a) As $x \to \pi^+$, $\csc x \to \underline{\;-\infty\;}$ (b) As $x \to \frac{\pi}{4}^-$, $\csc x \to \underline{\;\sqrt{2}\;}$

39 Refer to Figure 32 and the accompanying table. We see that $\sin\frac{3\pi}{2} = -1$.

     Since the period of the sine is 2π, the second value in $[0, 4\pi]$ is $\frac{3\pi}{2} + 2\pi = \frac{7\pi}{2}$.

40 $\sin x = 1$ •   ★ $\frac{\pi}{2}, \frac{5\pi}{2}$

41 $\sin x = \frac{1}{2}$ •   ★ $\frac{\pi}{6}, \frac{5\pi}{6}, \frac{13\pi}{6}, \frac{17\pi}{6}$

42 $\sin x = -\sqrt{2}/2$ •   ★ $\frac{5\pi}{4}, \frac{7\pi}{4}, \frac{13\pi}{4}, \frac{15\pi}{4}$

43 $\cos x = 1$ •   ★ $0, 2\pi, 4\pi$

44 $\cos x = -1$ •   ★ $\pi, 3\pi$

45 Refer to Figure 34 and the accompanying table. We see that $\cos\frac{\pi}{4} = \cos\frac{7\pi}{4} = \frac{\sqrt{2}}{2}$.

     Since the period of the cosine is 2π,

            other values in $[0, 4\pi]$ are $\frac{\pi}{4} + 2\pi = \frac{9\pi}{4}$ and $\frac{7\pi}{4} + 2\pi = \frac{15\pi}{4}$.

46 $\cos x = -\frac{1}{2}$ •   ★ $\frac{2\pi}{3}, \frac{4\pi}{3}, \frac{8\pi}{3}, \frac{10\pi}{3}$

47 Refer to Figure 37. In the interval $(-\frac{\pi}{2}, \frac{\pi}{2})$, $\tan x = 1$ only if $x = \frac{\pi}{4}$. Since the

     period of the tangent is π, the desired value in the interval $(\frac{\pi}{2}, \frac{3\pi}{2})$ is $\frac{\pi}{4} + \pi = \frac{5\pi}{4}$.

$\boxed{48}$ $\tan x = \sqrt{3}$ •   ★ $\frac{\pi}{3}, \frac{4\pi}{3}$

$\boxed{49}$ $\tan x = 0$ •   ★ $0, \pi$

$\boxed{50}$ $\tan x = -1/\sqrt{3}$ •   ★ $-\frac{\pi}{6}, \frac{5\pi}{6}$

$\boxed{51}$ $y = \sin x$; $[-2\pi, 2\pi]$; $a = \frac{1}{2}$ • Refer to Figure 32. $\sin x = \frac{1}{2} \Rightarrow x = \frac{\pi}{6}$ and $\frac{5\pi}{6}$.

Also, $\frac{\pi}{6} - 2\pi = -\frac{11\pi}{6}$ and $\frac{5\pi}{6} - 2\pi = -\frac{7\pi}{6}$. $\sin x > \frac{1}{2}$ when the graph is above the horizontal line $y = \frac{1}{2}$. $\sin x < \frac{1}{2}$ when the graph is below the horizontal line $y = \frac{1}{2}$.

★ (a) $-\frac{11\pi}{6}, -\frac{7\pi}{6}, \frac{\pi}{6}, \frac{5\pi}{6}$ (b) $-\frac{11\pi}{6} < x < -\frac{7\pi}{6}$ and $\frac{\pi}{6} < x < \frac{5\pi}{6}$

(c) $-2\pi \le x < -\frac{11\pi}{6}, -\frac{7\pi}{6} < x < \frac{\pi}{6}$, and $\frac{5\pi}{6} < x \le 2\pi$

$\boxed{52}$ $y = \cos x$; $[0, 4\pi]$; $a = \frac{\sqrt{3}}{2}$ •   ★ (a) $\frac{\pi}{6}, \frac{11\pi}{6}, \frac{13\pi}{6}, \frac{23\pi}{6}$

(b) $0 \le x < \frac{\pi}{6}, \frac{11\pi}{6} < x < \frac{13\pi}{6}$, and $\frac{23\pi}{6} < x \le 4\pi$ (c) $\frac{\pi}{6} < x < \frac{11\pi}{6}$ and $\frac{13\pi}{6} < x < \frac{23\pi}{6}$

$\boxed{53}$ $y = \cos x$; $[-2\pi, 2\pi]$; $a = -\frac{1}{2}$ •   ★ (a) $-\frac{4\pi}{3}, -\frac{2\pi}{3}, \frac{2\pi}{3}, \frac{4\pi}{3}$

(b) $-2\pi \le x < -\frac{4\pi}{3}, -\frac{2\pi}{3} < x < \frac{2\pi}{3}$, and $\frac{4\pi}{3} < x \le 2\pi$

(c) $-\frac{4\pi}{3} < x < -\frac{2\pi}{3}$ and $\frac{2\pi}{3} < x < \frac{4\pi}{3}$

$\boxed{54}$ $y = \sin x$; $[0, 4\pi]$; $a = -\frac{\sqrt{2}}{2}$ •   ★ (a) $\frac{5\pi}{4}, \frac{7\pi}{4}, \frac{13\pi}{4}, \frac{15\pi}{4}$

(b) $0 \le x < \frac{5\pi}{4}, \frac{7\pi}{4} < x < \frac{13\pi}{4}$, and $\frac{15\pi}{4} < x \le 4\pi$ (c) $\frac{5\pi}{4} < x < \frac{7\pi}{4}$ and $\frac{13\pi}{4} < x < \frac{15\pi}{4}$

$\boxed{55}$ $y = 2 + \sin x$ • shift $y = \sin x$ up 2 units

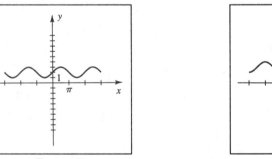

Figure 55   Figure 56

$\boxed{56}$ $y = 3 + \cos x$ • shift $y = \cos x$ up 3 units

$\boxed{57}$ $y = \cos x - 2$ • shift $y = \cos x$ down 2 units

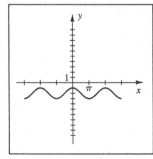   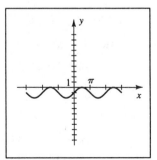

Figure 57   Figure 58

$\boxed{58}$ $y = \sin x - 1$ • shift $y = \sin x$ down 1 unit, x-intercepts are at $x = \frac{\pi}{2} + 2\pi n$

$\boxed{59}$ $y = 1 + \tan x$ • shift $y = \tan x$ up 1 unit, x-intercepts are at $x = -\frac{\pi}{4} + \pi n$

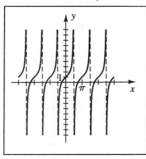

Figure 59

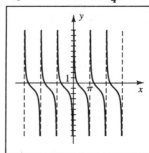

Figure 60

$\boxed{60}$ $y = \cot x - 1$ • shift $y = \cot x$ down 1 unit, x-intercepts are at $x = \frac{\pi}{4} + \pi n$

$\boxed{61}$ $y = \sec x - 2$ •

shift $y = \sec x$ down 2 units, x-intercepts are at $x = \frac{\pi}{3} + 2\pi n, \frac{5\pi}{3} + 2\pi n$

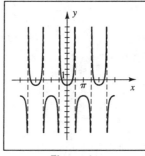

Figure 61

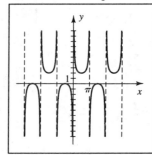

Figure 62

$\boxed{62}$ $y = 1 + \csc x$ • shift $y = \csc x$ up 1 unit, x-intercepts are at $x = \frac{3\pi}{2} + 2\pi n$

$\boxed{63}$ (a) As we move from left to right, the function rises on the intervals

$$[-2\pi, -\tfrac{3\pi}{2}), (-\tfrac{3\pi}{2}, -\pi], [0, \tfrac{\pi}{2}), \text{ and } (\tfrac{\pi}{2}, \pi].$$

(b) $[-\pi, -\frac{\pi}{2}), (-\frac{\pi}{2}, 0], [\pi, \frac{3\pi}{2}), (\frac{3\pi}{2}, 2\pi]$

$\boxed{64}$ (a) $[-\frac{3\pi}{2}, -\pi), (-\pi, -\frac{\pi}{2}], [\frac{\pi}{2}, \pi), (\pi, \frac{3\pi}{2}]$ (b) $(-2\pi, -\frac{3\pi}{2}], [-\frac{\pi}{2}, 0), (0, \frac{\pi}{2}], [\frac{3\pi}{2}, 2\pi)$

$\boxed{65}$ (a) The tangent function increases on *all* intervals on which it is defined.

Between -2π and 2π,

these intervals are $[-2\pi, -\frac{3\pi}{2}), (-\frac{3\pi}{2}, -\frac{\pi}{2}), (-\frac{\pi}{2}, \frac{\pi}{2}), (\frac{\pi}{2}, \frac{3\pi}{2}),$ and $(\frac{3\pi}{2}, 2\pi]$.

(b) The tangent function is *never* decreasing on any interval for which it is defined.

$\boxed{66}$ (a) The cotangent function is *never* increasing on any interval for which it is defined.

(b) The cotangent function decreases on *all* intervals on which it is defined.

Between -2π and 2π, these intervals are $(-2\pi, -\pi), (-\pi, 0), (0, \pi),$ and $(\pi, 2\pi)$.

$\boxed{69}$ (a) From $(1, 0)$, move counterclockwise on the unit circle to the point at the tick

marked 4. The projection of this point on the y-axis,

approximately -0.7 or -0.8, is the value of $\sin 4$.

(b) From $(1, 0)$, move clockwise 1.2 units to about 5.1.

As in part (a), $\sin(-1.2)$ is about -0.9.

(c) Draw the horizontal line $y = 0.5$.

This line intersects the circle at about 0.5 and 2.6.

70 (a) As in part (a) of Exercise 69, $\sin 2$ is about 0.9.

(b) As in part (b) of Exercise 69, $\sin(-2.3)$ is about -0.8.

(c) As in part (c) of Exercise 69,

the horizontal line $y = -0.2$ intersects the circle at about 3.3 and 6.1.

71 (a) From $(1, 0)$, move counterclockwise on the unit circle to the point at the tick marked 4. The projection of this point on the x-axis,

approximately -0.6 or -0.7, is the value of $\cos 4$.

(b) Proceeding as in part (a), $\cos(-1.2)$ is about 0.4.

(c) Draw the vertical line $x = -0.6$.

This line intersects the circle at about 2.2 and 4.1.

72 (a) As in part (a) of Exercise 71, $\cos 2$ is about -0.5.

(b) As in part (b) of Exercise 71, $\cos(-2.3)$ is about -0.7.

(c) As in part (c) of Exercise 71,

the vertical line $x = 0.2$ intersects the circle at about 1.4 and 4.9.

73 (a) Note that midnight occurs when $t = -6$.

Time	Temp.	Humidity	Time	Temp.	Humidity
12 A.M.	60	60	12 P.M.	60	60
3 A.M.	52	74	3 P.M.	68	46
6 A.M.	48	80	6 P.M.	72	40
9 A.M.	52	74	9 P.M.	68	46

(b) Since $T(t) = -12\cos\left(\frac{\pi}{12}t\right) + 60$, its maximum is $60 + 12 = 72\,°\text{F}$ at $t = 12$ or 6:00 P.M., and its minimum is $60 - 12 = 48\,°\text{F}$ at $t = 0$ or 6:00 A.M. Since $H(t) = 20\cos\left(\frac{\pi}{12}t\right) + 60$, its maximum is $60 + 20 = 80\%$ at $t = 0$ or 6:00 A.M., and its minimum is $60 - 20 = 40\%$ at $t = 12$ or 6:00 P.M.

(c) When the temperature increases, the relative humidity decreases and vice versa. As the temperature cools, the air can hold less moisture and the relative humidity increases. Because of this phenomenon, fog often occurs during the evening hours rather than in the middle of the day.

74 (a) Since the elbow joint does not bend and the arm has a constant length, the robotic hand moves in a circular arc. Therefore, its height h is equal to $h = 153 \sin \theta + 50 = 153 \sin\left(\frac{\pi}{12}t\right) + 50$. If $0 \le \theta \le \pi/2$, then $0 \le t \le 6$.

t (sec)	0	1	2	3	4	5	6
θ (rad)	0	$\pi/12$	$\pi/6$	$\pi/4$	$\pi/3$	$5\pi/12$	$\pi/2$
h (cm)	50.00	89.60	126.50	158.19	182.50	197.79	203.00

(b) From the table, it is obvious that the height of the arm does not increase at a constant rate. Instead, it increases at a slower rate as θ increases at a constant rate. During the first second of time, the hand's height increases by $89.6 - 50 = 39.6$ cm, whereas during the sixth second its height increased by only $203 - 197.79 = 5.21$ cm.

(c) The total distance traveled by the hand is determined by the circular arc with a radius of 153 cm, subtending an angle of $\pi/2$.

Thus, $s = r\theta = 153(\pi/2) = 76.5\pi \approx 240.33$ cm.

75 Graph $y = \sin(x^2)$ and $y = 0.5$ on the same coordinate plane. From the graph, we see that $\sin(x^2)$ assumes the value of 0.5 at $x \approx \pm 0.72$, ± 1.62, ± 2.61, ± 2.98.

[$-\pi$, π] by [-2.09, 2.09]   [0, 25] by [-8.33, 8.33]

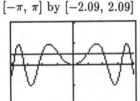 Xscl $= \pi/4$
Yscl $= 1$

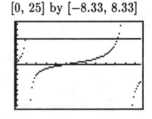 Xscl $= 2$
Yscl $= 1$

Figure 75   Figure 76

76 Graph $y = \tan(\sqrt{x})$ and $y = 5$ on the same coordinate plane. From the graph, we see that $\tan(\sqrt{x})$ assumes the value of 5 at $x \approx 1.89$, 20.39. *Figure 76* was obtained by using Dot Mode. Note that the vertical asymptotes are at $\sqrt{x} = \frac{\pi}{2}$, $\frac{3\pi}{2}$ or $x = \frac{\pi^2}{4} \approx 2.47$, $\frac{9\pi^2}{4} \approx 22.21$.

77 We see that the graph of $y = x \sin x$ assumes a maximum value of approximately 1.82 at $x \approx \pm 2.03$, and a minimum value of -4.81 at $x \approx \pm 4.91$.

[-2π, 2π] by [-5.19, 3.19]   [-2π, 2π] by [-4.19, 4.19]

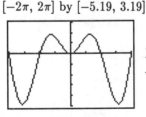 Xscl $= \pi/2$
Yscl $= 1$

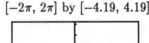 Xscl $= \pi/2$
Yscl $= 1$

Figure 77   Figure 78

[78] We see that the graph of $y = \sin^2 x \cos x$ assumes a maximum value of approximately 0.38 at $x \approx \pm 0.96$, ± 5.33, and a minimum value of -0.38 at $x \approx \pm 2.19$, ± 4.10. See *Figure 78*.

[79] As $x \to 0^+$, $f(x) = \dfrac{1 - \cos x}{x} \to 0$.

[−1, 1] by [−0.67, 0.67]

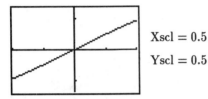

Xscl = 0.5
Yscl = 0.5

Figure 79

[80] As $x \to 0^+$, $f(x) = \dfrac{6x - 6\sin x}{x^3} \to 1$.

[−2, 2] by [−1.33, 1.33]

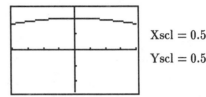

Xscl = 0.5
Yscl = 0.5

Figure 80

[81] As $x \to 0^+$, $f(x) = x \cot x \to 1$.

[−2, 2] by [−1.33, 1.33]

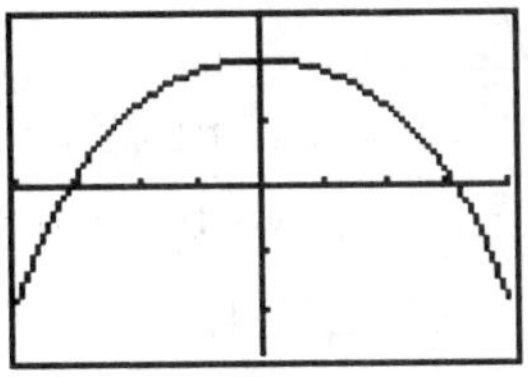

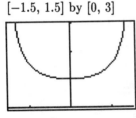

Xscl = 0.5
Yscl = 0.5

Figure 81

[82] As $x \to 0^+$, $f(x) = \dfrac{x + \tan x}{\sin x} \to 2$.

[−1.5, 1.5] by [0, 3]

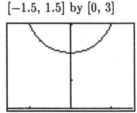

Xscl = 1
Yscl = 1

Figure 82

[83] As $x \to 0^+$, $f(x) = \dfrac{\tan x}{x} \to 1$.

[−1.5, 1.5] by [0, 3]

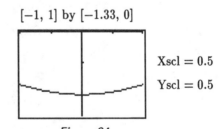

Xscl = 1
Yscl = 1

Figure 83

[84] As $x \to 0^+$, $f(x) = \dfrac{\cos\left(x + \frac{1}{2}\pi\right)}{x} \to -1$.

[−1, 1] by [−1.33, 0]

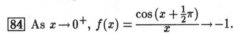

Xscl = 0.5
Yscl = 0.5

Figure 84

5.4 Exercises

5.4 Concept Check

[1] What are the allowable values for a reference angle?   •   Since a reference angle is acute, it can only take on values between 0 and 90 degrees.

[2] What can you expect when you enter $\sin^{-1} 2$ on your calculator?   •   You should expect an error message of some type since the sine function values are between -1 and 1, inclusive.

$\boxed{3}$ What can you expect when you enter $\tan^{-1} x$ on your calculator, where x is any real number? • The calculator will return a number between $-\pi/2$ and $\pi/2$, or between $-90°$ and $90°$.

$\boxed{4}$ If $\cos \theta = k$, where $0 \le \theta < 2\pi$ and $-1 < k < 0$, how many solutions for θ are there? In which quadrants are they? • There are two solutions, one in the second quadrant and one in the third quadrant.

5.4 Exercises

Note: Let θ_C denote the coterminal angle of θ such that $0° \le \theta_C < 360°$ { or $0 \le \theta_C < 2\pi$ }.

       The following formulas are then used in the solutions { on text page 344 }.

       (1) If θ_C is in QI, then $\theta_R = \theta_C$.

       (2) If θ_C is in QII, then $\theta_R = 180° - \theta_C$ { or $\pi - \theta_C$ }.

       (3) If θ_C is in QIII, then $\theta_R = \theta_C - 180°$ { or $\theta_C - \pi$ }.

       (4) If θ_C is in QIV, then $\theta_R = 360° - \theta_C$ { or $2\pi - \theta_C$ }.

Note: It may be easier to simply draw the angles when explaining the solutions.

$\boxed{1}$ (a) Since $240°$ is in QIII, $\theta_R = 240° - 180° = 60°$.

     (b) Since $340°$ is in QIV, $\theta_R = 360° - 340° = 20°$.

     (c) $\theta_C = -202° + 1(360°) = 158° \in$ QII. $\theta_R = 180° - 158° = 22°$.

     (d) $\theta_C = -660° + 2(360°) = 60° \in$ QI. $\theta_R = 60°$.

$\boxed{2}$ (a) Since $165°$ is in QII, $\theta_R = 180° - 165° = 15°$.

     (b) Since $275°$ is in QIV, $\theta_R = 360° - 275° = 85°$.

     (c) $\theta_C = -110° + 1(360°) = 250° \in$ QIII. $\theta_R = 250° - 180° = 70°$.

     (d) $\theta_C = 400° - 1(360°) = 40° \in$ QI. $\theta_R = 40°$.

$\boxed{3}$ (a) Since $\frac{3\pi}{4}$ is in QII, $\theta_R = \pi - \frac{3\pi}{4} = \frac{\pi}{4}$.

     (b) Since $\frac{4\pi}{3}$ is in QIII, $\theta_R = \frac{4\pi}{3} - \pi = \frac{\pi}{3}$.

     (c) $\theta_C = -\frac{\pi}{6} + 1(2\pi) = \frac{11\pi}{6} \in$ QIV. $\theta_R = 2\pi - \frac{11\pi}{6} = \frac{\pi}{6}$.

     (d) $\theta_C = \frac{9\pi}{4} - 1(2\pi) = \frac{\pi}{4} \in$ QI. $\theta_R = \frac{\pi}{4}$.

$\boxed{4}$ (a) Since $\frac{7\pi}{4}$ is in QIV, $\theta_R = 2\pi - \frac{7\pi}{4} = \frac{\pi}{4}$.

     (b) Since $\frac{2\pi}{3}$ is in QII, $\theta_R = \pi - \frac{2\pi}{3} = \frac{\pi}{3}$.

     (c) $\theta_C = -\frac{3\pi}{4} + 1(2\pi) = \frac{5\pi}{4} \in$ QIII. $\theta_R = \frac{5\pi}{4} - \pi = \frac{\pi}{4}$.

     (d) $\theta_C = -\frac{23\pi}{6} + 2(2\pi) = \frac{\pi}{6} \in$ QI. $\theta_R = \frac{\pi}{6}$.

$\boxed{5}$ (a) Since $\frac{\pi}{2} < 3 < \pi$, θ is in QII and $\theta_R = \pi - 3 \approx 0.14$, or $8.1°$.

     (b) $\theta_C = -2 + 1(2\pi) = 2\pi - 2 \approx 4.28$.

         Since $\pi < 4.28 < \frac{3\pi}{2}$, θ_C is in QIII and $\theta_R = (2\pi - 2) - \pi = \pi - 2 \approx 1.14$, or $65.4°$.

     (c) Since $\frac{3\pi}{2} < 5.5 < 2\pi$, θ is in QIV and $\theta_R = 2\pi - 5.5 \approx 0.78$, or $44.9°$.

    (d) The number of revolutions formed by θ is $\frac{100}{2\pi} \approx 15.92$, so

        $\theta_C = 100 - 15(2\pi) = 100 - 30\pi \approx 5.75$. Since $\frac{3\pi}{2} < 5.75 < 2\pi$,

        θ_C is in QIV and $\theta_R = 2\pi - (100 - 30\pi) = 32\pi - 100 \approx 0.53$, or $30.4°$.

        Alternatively, if your calculator is capable of computing trigonometric functions

            of large values, then computing $\sin^{-1}(\sin 100) \approx -0.53 \Rightarrow \theta_R = 0.53$, or $30.4°$.

6 (a) Since $\frac{3\pi}{2} < 6 < 2\pi$, θ is in QIV and $\theta_R = 2\pi - 6 \approx 0.28$, or $16.2°$.

    (b) $\theta_C = -4 + 1(2\pi) = 2\pi - 4 \approx 2.28$.

        Since $\frac{\pi}{2} < 2.28 < \pi$, θ_C is in QII and $\theta_R = \pi - (2\pi - 4) = 4 - \pi \approx 0.86$, or $49.2°$.

    (c) Since $\pi < 4.5 < \frac{3\pi}{2}$, θ is in QIII and $\theta_R = 4.5 - \pi \approx 1.36$, or $77.8°$.

    (d) As in Exercise 5(d), $\frac{80}{2\pi} \approx 12.73$, so $\theta_C = 80 - 12(2\pi) = 80 - 24\pi \approx 4.60$. Since

        $\pi < 4.60 < \frac{3\pi}{2}$, θ_C is in QIII and $\theta_R = (80 - 24\pi) - \pi = 80 - 25\pi \approx 1.46$, or $83.7°$.

            Alternatively, $\sin^{-1}(\sin 80) \approx -1.46 \Rightarrow \theta_R = 1.46$, or $83.7°$.

Note: For the following problems, we use the theorem on reference angles before

        evaluating.

7 (a) $\sin \frac{2\pi}{3} = \sin \frac{\pi}{3} = \frac{\sqrt{3}}{2}$ (b) $\sin\left(-\frac{5\pi}{4}\right) = \sin \frac{3\pi}{4} = \sin \frac{\pi}{4} = \frac{\sqrt{2}}{2}$

8 (a) $\sin 210° = -\sin 30° = -\frac{1}{2}$ (b) $\sin(-315°) = \sin 45° = \frac{\sqrt{2}}{2}$

9 (a) $\cos 150° = -\cos 30° = -\frac{\sqrt{3}}{2}$ (b) $\cos(-60°) = \cos 300° = \cos 60° = \frac{1}{2}$

10 (a) $\cos \frac{5\pi}{4} = -\cos \frac{\pi}{4} = -\frac{\sqrt{2}}{2}$ (b) $\cos\left(-\frac{11\pi}{6}\right) = \cos \frac{\pi}{6} = \frac{\sqrt{3}}{2}$

11 (a) $\tan \frac{5\pi}{6} = -\tan \frac{\pi}{6} = -\frac{\sqrt{3}}{3}$ (b) $\tan\left(-\frac{\pi}{3}\right) = \tan \frac{5\pi}{3} = -\tan \frac{\pi}{3} = -\sqrt{3}$

12 (a) $\tan 330° = -\tan 30° = -\frac{\sqrt{3}}{3}$ (b) $\tan(-225°) = \tan 135° = -\tan 45° = -1$

13 (a) $\cot 120° = -\cot 60° = -\frac{\sqrt{3}}{3}$ (b) $\cot(-150°) = \cot 210° = \cot 30° = \sqrt{3}$

14 (a) $\cot \frac{3\pi}{4} = -\cot \frac{\pi}{4} = -1$ (b) $\cot\left(-\frac{2\pi}{3}\right) = \cot \frac{4\pi}{3} = \cot \frac{\pi}{3} = \frac{\sqrt{3}}{3}$

15 (a) $\sec \frac{2\pi}{3} = -\sec \frac{\pi}{3} = -2$ (b) $\sec\left(-\frac{\pi}{6}\right) = \sec \frac{11\pi}{6} = \sec \frac{\pi}{6} = \frac{2}{\sqrt{3}}$

16 (a) $\sec 135° = -\sec 45° = -\sqrt{2}$ (b) $\sec(-210°) = \sec 150° = -\sec 30° = -\frac{2}{\sqrt{3}}$

17 (a) $\csc 240° = -\csc 60° = -\frac{2}{\sqrt{3}}$ (b) $\csc(-330°) = \csc 30° = 2$

18 (a) $\csc \frac{3\pi}{4} = \csc \frac{\pi}{4} = \sqrt{2}$ (b) $\csc\left(-\frac{2\pi}{3}\right) = \csc \frac{4\pi}{3} = -\csc \frac{\pi}{3} = -\frac{2}{\sqrt{3}}$

19 (a) Using the degree mode on a calculator, $\sin 73°20' \approx 0.958$.

    (b) Using the radian mode on a calculator, $\cos 0.68 \approx 0.778$.

20 (a) $\cos 38°30' \approx 0.783$ (b) $\sin 1.48 \approx 0.996$

21 (a) $\tan 21°10' \approx 0.387$ (b) $\cot 1.13 \approx 0.472$

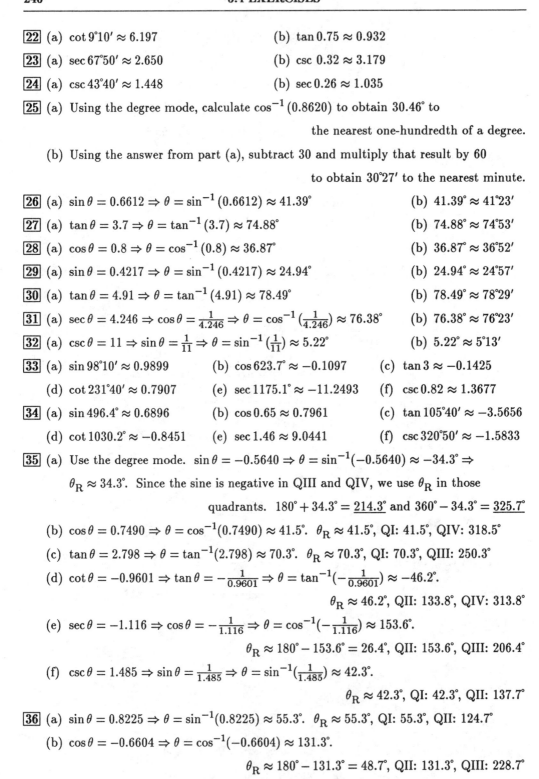

22 (a) $\cot 9°10' \approx 6.197$ (b) $\tan 0.75 \approx 0.932$

23 (a) $\sec 67°50' \approx 2.650$ (b) $\csc 0.32 \approx 3.179$

24 (a) $\csc 43°40' \approx 1.448$ (b) $\sec 0.26 \approx 1.035$

25 (a) Using the degree mode, calculate $\cos^{-1}(0.8620)$ to obtain 30.46° to

the nearest one-hundredth of a degree.

  (b) Using the answer from part (a), subtract 30 and multiply that result by 60

to obtain 30°27' to the nearest minute.

26 (a) $\sin\theta = 0.6612 \Rightarrow \theta = \sin^{-1}(0.6612) \approx 41.39°$ (b) $41.39° \approx 41°23'$

27 (a) $\tan\theta = 3.7 \Rightarrow \theta = \tan^{-1}(3.7) \approx 74.88°$ (b) $74.88° \approx 74°53'$

28 (a) $\cos\theta = 0.8 \Rightarrow \theta = \cos^{-1}(0.8) \approx 36.87°$ (b) $36.87° \approx 36°52'$

29 (a) $\sin\theta = 0.4217 \Rightarrow \theta = \sin^{-1}(0.4217) \approx 24.94°$ (b) $24.94° \approx 24°57'$

30 (a) $\tan\theta = 4.91 \Rightarrow \theta = \tan^{-1}(4.91) \approx 78.49°$ (b) $78.49° \approx 78°29'$

31 (a) $\sec\theta = 4.246 \Rightarrow \cos\theta = \frac{1}{4.246} \Rightarrow \theta = \cos^{-1}\left(\frac{1}{4.246}\right) \approx 76.38°$ (b) $76.38° \approx 76°23'$

32 (a) $\csc\theta = 11 \Rightarrow \sin\theta = \frac{1}{11} \Rightarrow \theta = \sin^{-1}\left(\frac{1}{11}\right) \approx 5.22°$ (b) $5.22° \approx 5°13'$

33 (a) $\sin 98°10' \approx 0.9899$ (b) $\cos 623.7° \approx -0.1097$ (c) $\tan 3 \approx -0.1425$

    (d) $\cot 231°40' \approx 0.7907$ (e) $\sec 1175.1° \approx -11.2493$ (f) $\csc 0.82 \approx 1.3677$

34 (a) $\sin 496.4° \approx 0.6896$ (b) $\cos 0.65 \approx 0.7961$ (c) $\tan 105°40' \approx -3.5656$

    (d) $\cot 1030.2° \approx -0.8451$ (e) $\sec 1.46 \approx 9.0441$ (f) $\csc 320°50' \approx -1.5833$

35 (a) Use the degree mode. $\sin\theta = -0.5640 \Rightarrow \theta = \sin^{-1}(-0.5640) \approx -34.3° \Rightarrow$

$\theta_R \approx 34.3°$. Since the sine is negative in QIII and QIV, we use θ_R in those

quadrants. $180° + 34.3° = \underline{214.3°}$ and $360° - 34.3° = \underline{325.7°}$

  (b) $\cos\theta = 0.7490 \Rightarrow \theta = \cos^{-1}(0.7490) \approx 41.5°$. $\theta_R \approx 41.5°$, QI: 41.5°, QIV: 318.5°

  (c) $\tan\theta = 2.798 \Rightarrow \theta = \tan^{-1}(2.798) \approx 70.3°$. $\theta_R \approx 70.3°$, QI: 70.3°, QIII: 250.3°

  (d) $\cot\theta = -0.9601 \Rightarrow \tan\theta = -\frac{1}{0.9601} \Rightarrow \theta = \tan^{-1}\left(-\frac{1}{0.9601}\right) \approx -46.2°$.

$\theta_R \approx 46.2°$, QII: 133.8°, QIV: 313.8°

  (e) $\sec\theta = -1.116 \Rightarrow \cos\theta = -\frac{1}{1.116} \Rightarrow \theta = \cos^{-1}\left(-\frac{1}{1.116}\right) \approx 153.6°$.

$\theta_R \approx 180° - 153.6° = 26.4°$, QII: 153.6°, QIII: 206.4°

  (f) $\csc\theta = 1.485 \Rightarrow \sin\theta = \frac{1}{1.485} \Rightarrow \theta = \sin^{-1}\left(\frac{1}{1.485}\right) \approx 42.3°$.

$\theta_R \approx 42.3°$, QI: 42.3°, QII: 137.7°

36 (a) $\sin\theta = 0.8225 \Rightarrow \theta = \sin^{-1}(0.8225) \approx 55.3°$. $\theta_R \approx 55.3°$, QI: 55.3°, QII: 124.7°

  (b) $\cos\theta = -0.6604 \Rightarrow \theta = \cos^{-1}(-0.6604) \approx 131.3°$.

$\theta_R \approx 180° - 131.3° = 48.7°$, QII: 131.3°, QIII: 228.7°

  (c) $\tan\theta = -1.5214 \Rightarrow \theta = \tan^{-1}(-1.5214) \approx -56.7°$.

$\theta_R \approx 56.7°$, QII: 123.3°, QIV: 303.3°

(d) $\cot\theta = 1.3752 \Rightarrow \tan\theta = \frac{1}{1.3752} \Rightarrow \theta = \tan^{-1}(\frac{1}{1.3752}) \approx 36.0°.$

$\theta_R \approx 36.0°$, QI: $36.0°$, QIII: $216.0°$

(e) $\sec\theta = 1.4291 \Rightarrow \cos\theta = \frac{1}{1.4291} \Rightarrow \theta = \cos^{-1}(\frac{1}{1.4291}) \approx 45.6°.$

$\theta_R \approx 45.6°$, QI: $45.6°$, QIV: $314.4°$

(f) $\csc\theta = -2.3179 \Rightarrow \sin\theta = -\frac{1}{2.3179} \Rightarrow \theta = \sin^{-1}(-\frac{1}{2.3179}) \approx -25.6°.$

$\theta_R \approx 25.6°$, QIII: $205.6°$, QIV: $334.4°$

$\boxed{37}$ (a) Use the radian mode. $\sin\theta = 0.4195 \Rightarrow \theta = \sin^{-1}(0.4195) \approx 0.43.$

$\theta_R \approx 0.43$ is one answer. Since the sine is positive in QI and QII,

we also use the reference angle for θ in quadrant II. QII: $\pi - 0.43 \approx 2.71$

(b) $\cos\theta = -0.1207 \Rightarrow \theta = \cos^{-1}(-0.1207) \approx 1.69$ is one answer. Since 1.69 is in QII,

$\theta_R \approx \pi - 1.69 \approx 1.45.$ The cosine is also negative in QIII. QIII: $\pi + 1.45 \approx 4.59$

(c) $\tan\theta = -3.2504 \Rightarrow \theta = \tan^{-1}(-3.2504) \approx -1.27 \Rightarrow \theta_R \approx 1.27.$

QII: $\pi - 1.27 \approx 1.87$, QIV: $2\pi - 1.27 \approx 5.01$

(d) $\cot\theta = 2.6815 \Rightarrow \tan\theta = \frac{1}{2.6815} \Rightarrow \theta = \tan^{-1}(\frac{1}{2.6815}) \approx 0.36 \Rightarrow$

$\theta_R \approx 0.36$ is one answer. QIII: $\pi + 0.36 \approx 3.50$

(e) $\sec\theta = 1.7452 \Rightarrow \cos\theta = \frac{1}{1.7452} \Rightarrow \theta = \cos^{-1}(\frac{1}{1.7452}) \approx 0.96 \Rightarrow$

$\theta_R \approx 0.96$ is one answer. QIV: $2\pi - 0.96 \approx 5.32$

(f) $\csc\theta = -4.8521 \Rightarrow \sin\theta = -\frac{1}{4.8521} \Rightarrow \theta = \sin^{-1}(-\frac{1}{4.8521}) \approx -0.21 \Rightarrow \theta_R \approx 0.21.$

QIII: $\pi + 0.21 \approx 3.35$, QIV: $2\pi - 0.21 \approx 6.07$

$\boxed{38}$ (a) $\sin\theta = -0.0135 \Rightarrow \theta = \sin^{-1}(-0.0135) \approx -0.01 \Rightarrow \theta_R \approx 0.01.$

QIII: $\pi + 0.01 \approx 3.15$; QIV: $2\pi - 0.01 \approx 6.27$

(b) $\cos\theta = 0.9235 \Rightarrow \theta = \cos^{-1}(0.9235) \approx 0.39 \Rightarrow \theta_R \approx 0.39$ is one answer.

QIV: $2\pi - 0.39 \approx 5.89$

(c) $\tan\theta = 0.42 \Rightarrow \theta = \tan^{-1}(0.42) \approx 0.40 \Rightarrow \theta_R \approx 0.40$ is one answer.

QIII: $\pi + 0.40 \approx 3.54$

(d) $\cot\theta = -2.731 \Rightarrow \tan\theta = -\frac{1}{2.731} \Rightarrow \theta = \tan^{-1}(-\frac{1}{2.731}) \approx -0.35 \Rightarrow \theta_R \approx 0.35.$

QII: $\pi - 0.35 \approx 2.79$, QIV: $2\pi - 0.35 \approx 5.93$

(e) $\sec\theta = -3.51 \Rightarrow \cos\theta = -\frac{1}{3.51} \Rightarrow \theta = \cos^{-1}(-\frac{1}{3.51}) \approx 1.86$ is one answer.

Since 1.86 is in QII, $\theta_R \approx \pi - 1.86 \approx 1.28.$ QIII: $\pi + 1.28 \approx 4.42$

(f) $\csc\theta = 1.258 \Rightarrow \sin\theta = \frac{1}{1.258} \Rightarrow \theta = \sin^{-1}(\frac{1}{1.258}) \approx 0.92 \Rightarrow \theta_R \approx 0.92$ is one answer.

QII: $\pi - 0.92 \approx 2.22$

$\boxed{39}$ $\ln I_0 - \ln I = kx \sec\theta \Rightarrow$

$$\ln\frac{I_0}{I} = kx \sec\theta \Rightarrow x = \frac{1}{k \sec\theta} \ln\frac{I_0}{I} = \frac{1}{1.88 \sec 12°} \ln 1.72 \approx 0.28 \text{ cm}.$$

40 $\ln\frac{I_0}{I} = kx\sec\theta \Rightarrow \sec\theta = \frac{1}{kx}\ln\frac{I_0}{I} \Rightarrow \cos\theta = \frac{kx}{\ln(I_0/I)} = \frac{1.88(0.31)}{\ln 2.05} \approx 0.8119 \Rightarrow$

$$\theta \approx 35.7°.$$

41 (a) The solar radiation R will equal R_0 when $\cos\theta = \sin\phi = 1$. This occurs when

$\theta = 0°$ and $\phi = 90°$, and corresponds to when the sun is just rising in the east.

(b) The sun located in the southeast corresponds to $\phi = 45°$.

$$R/R_0 = \cos\theta\,\sin\phi = \cos 60°\,\sin 45° = \frac{1}{2}\cdot\frac{\sqrt{2}}{2} = \frac{\sqrt{2}}{4} \approx 35\%.$$

42 (a) $d = 2\pi\left(\frac{vR}{0.52\cos\phi}\right)^{1/3} = 2\pi\left(\frac{45\cdot 6369}{0.52\cos 48°}\right)^{1/3} \approx 589$ km.

(b) Since $\cos\phi$ decreases as ϕ increases from $0°$ to $90°$,

and $\cos\phi$ is in the denominator of the expression, d increases as ϕ increases.

43 $\sin\theta = \frac{b}{c} \Rightarrow \sin 60° = \frac{b}{18} \Rightarrow b = 18\sin 60° = 18\cdot\frac{\sqrt{3}}{2} = 9\sqrt{3} \approx 15.6$. $\cos\theta = \frac{a}{c} \Rightarrow$

$\cos 60° = \frac{a}{18} \Rightarrow a = 18\cos 60° = 18\cdot\frac{1}{2} = 9$. The hand is located at $(9, 9\sqrt{3})$.

44 The arm's initial length is $\sqrt{12^2 + 12^2} = \sqrt{288}$. $\tan\theta_1 = \frac{b}{a} = \frac{12}{12} = 1 \Rightarrow \theta_1 = 45°$ is the

arm's initial angle. The new arm length is $\sqrt{(-16)^2 + 10^2} = \sqrt{356}$. The new angle

has $\tan\theta_2 = \frac{b}{a} = \frac{10}{-16} = -\frac{5}{8}$. Since θ_2 is in quadrant II, $\theta_2 \approx 148°$. Thus, the arm

must increase its length by $\sqrt{356} - \sqrt{288} \approx 1.9$ inches and rotate $\theta_2 - \theta_1 \approx 103°$

counterclockwise.

5.5 Exercises

5.5 Concept Check

1 If $y = a\sin(bx + c)$ or $y = a\cos(bx + c)$ $(a \neq 0,\ b \neq 0)$, what are the amplitude,
period, and phase shift of the graph of y? • The amplitude is $|a|$, the period is $\frac{2\pi}{|b|}$,
and the phase shift is $-c/b$.

2 For $y = a\sin(bx + c)$ $(a \neq 0,\ b \neq 0)$, what purpose is served by solving the inequality
$0 \leq bx + c \leq 2\pi$ for x? • Solving the inequality $0 \leq bx + c \leq 2\pi$ for x gives an
interval that contains exactly one cycle of the graph.

3 What is the phase shift of $y = \sin(x + \pi/2)$? What familiar function has the same
graph as $y = \sin(x + \pi/2)$? • The phase shift of $y = \sin(x + \pi/2)$ is $-\pi/2$ and its
graph is the same as that of $y = \cos x$.

4 Find the equation of the graph in *Figure 4* knowing that it is of the form $y = a \sin x$.

- The graph is that of $y = \sin x$ stretched vertically by a factor of 3 and reflected about the x-axis, so $a = -3$ and the equation is $y = -3 \sin x$.

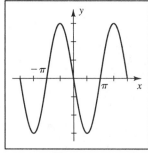

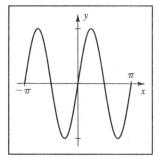

Figure 4   Figure 5

5 Find the equation of the graph in *Figure 5* knowing that it is of the form $y = \sin bx$.

- The normal cycle of the sine, 2π, is reduced to π; that is, the graph of $y = \sin x$ has been horizontally compressed by a factor of 2. So $b = 2$ and the equation is $y = \sin 2x$.

5.5 Exercises

Note: Exer. 1–4: We will refer to $y = \sin x$ as just $\sin x$ ($y = \cos x$ as $\cos x$, etc.).

For the form $y = a \sin bx$, the amplitude is $|a|$ and the period is $\dfrac{2\pi}{|b|}$.

These are merely listed in the answer along with the values of the x-intercepts.

1 (a) $y = 4 \sin x$ • stretch $\sin x$ by a factor of 4   ★ 4, 2π, x-int. @ πn

(b) $y = \sin 4x$ • horizontally compress $\sin x$ by a factor of 4   ★ 1, $\frac{\pi}{2}$, x-int. @ $\frac{\pi}{4}n$

(c) $y = \frac{1}{4} \sin x$ • compress $\sin x$ by a factor of 4   ★ $\frac{1}{4}$, 2π, x-int. @ πn

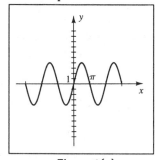

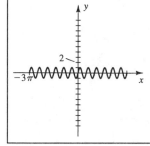

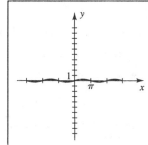

Figure 1(a)   Figure 1(b)   Figure 1(c)

(d) $y = \sin\frac{1}{4}x$ •   horizontally stretch $\sin x$ by a factor of 4   ★ 1, 8π, x-int. @ $4\pi n$

(e) $y = 2\sin\frac{1}{4}x$ •   stretch the graph in part (d) by a factor of 2

★ 2, 8π, x-int. @ $4\pi n$

(f) $y = \frac{1}{2}\sin 4x$ •   compress the graph in part (b) by a factor of 2

★ $\frac{1}{2}$, $\frac{\pi}{2}$, x-int. @ $\frac{\pi}{4}n$

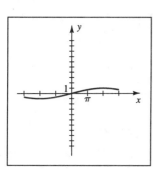

Figure 1(d)

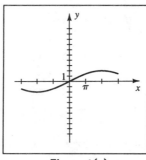

Figure 1(e)

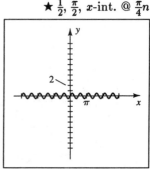

Figure 1(f)

(g) $y = -4\sin x$ •   reflect the graph in part (a) through the x-axis

★ 4, 2π, x-int. @ πn

(h) $y = \sin(-4x) = -\sin 4x$ •   reflect the graph in part (b) through the x-axis

★ 1, $\frac{\pi}{2}$, x-int. @ $\frac{\pi}{4}n$

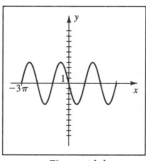

Figure 1(g)

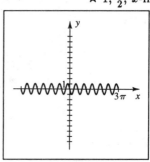

Figure 1(h)

[2] (a) $y = 4\cos x$ •   stretch $\cos x$ by a factor of 4   ★ 4, 2π, x-int. @ $\frac{\pi}{2} + \pi n$

(b) $y = \cos 4x$ •   horizontally compress $\cos x$ by a factor of 4

★ 1, $\frac{\pi}{2}$, x-int. @ $\frac{\pi}{8} + \frac{\pi}{4}n$

(c) $y = \frac{1}{4}\cos x$ •   compress $\cos x$ by a factor of 4   ★ $\frac{1}{4}$, 2π, x-int. @ $\frac{\pi}{2} + \pi n$

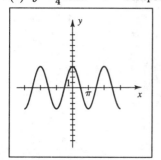

Figure 2(a)

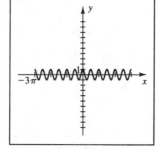

Figure 2(b)

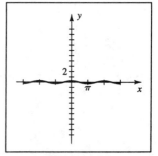

Figure 2(c)

(d) $y = \cos\frac{1}{4}x$ • horizontally stretch $\cos x$ by a factor of 4

★ $1, 8\pi$, x-int. @ $2\pi + 4\pi n$

(e) $y = 2\cos\frac{1}{4}x$ • stretch the graph in part (d) by a factor of 2

★ $2, 8\pi$, x-int. @ $2\pi + 4\pi n$

(f) $y = \frac{1}{2}\cos 4x$ • compress the graph in part (b) by a factor of 2

★ $\frac{1}{2}, \frac{\pi}{2}$, x-int. @ $\frac{\pi}{8} + \frac{\pi}{4}n$

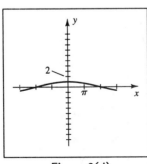

Figure 2(d)

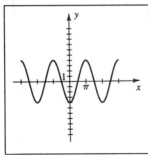

Figure 2(e)

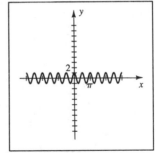

Figure 2(f)

(g) $y = -4\cos x$ • reflect the graph in part (a) through the x-axis

★ $4, 2\pi$, x-int. @ $\frac{\pi}{2} + \pi n$

(h) $y = \cos(-4x) = \cos 4x$ • same as the graph in part (b)

★ $1, \frac{\pi}{2}$, x-int. @ $\frac{\pi}{8} + \frac{\pi}{4}n$

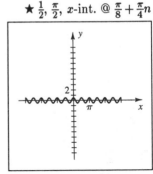

Figure 2(g)

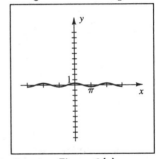

Figure 2(h)

3 (a) $y = 3\cos x$ • stretch $\cos x$ by a factor of 3 ★ $3, 2\pi$, x-int. @ $\frac{\pi}{2} + \pi n$

(b) $y = \cos 3x$ • horizontally compress $\cos x$ by a factor of 3

★ $1, \frac{2\pi}{3}$, x-int. @ $\frac{\pi}{6} + \frac{\pi}{3}n$

(c) $y = \frac{1}{3}\cos x$ • compress $\cos x$ by a factor of 3 ★ $\frac{1}{3}, 2\pi$, x-int. @ $\frac{\pi}{2} + \pi n$

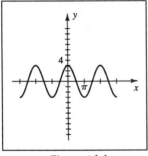

Figure 3(a)

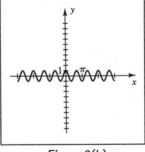

Figure 3(b)

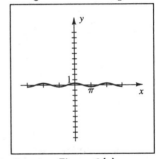

Figure 3(c)

(d) $y = \cos\frac{1}{3}x$ • horizontally stretch $\cos x$ by a factor of 3

★ 1, 6π, x-int. @ $\frac{3\pi}{2} + 3\pi n$

(e) $y = 2\cos\frac{1}{3}x$ • stretch the graph in part (d) by a factor of 2

★ 2, 6π, x-int. @ $\frac{3\pi}{2} + 3\pi n$

(f) $y = \frac{1}{2}\cos 3x$ • compress the graph in part (b) by a factor of 2

★ $\frac{1}{2}$, $\frac{2\pi}{3}$, x-int. @ $\frac{\pi}{6} + \frac{\pi}{3}n$

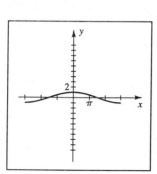
Figure 3(d)

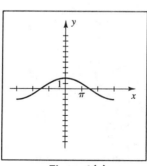
Figure 3(e)

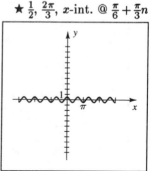
Figure 3(f)

(g) $y = -3\cos x$ • reflect the graph in part (a) through the x-axis

★ 3, 2π, x-int. @ $\frac{\pi}{2} + \pi n$

(h) $y = \cos(-3x) = \cos 3x$ • same as the graph in part (b)

★ 1, $\frac{2\pi}{3}$, x-int. @ $\frac{\pi}{6} + \frac{\pi}{3}n$

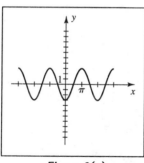
Figure 3(g)

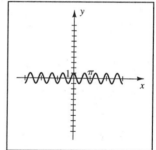
Figure 3(h)

4 (a) $y = 3\sin x$ • stretch $\sin x$ by a factor of 3   ★ 3, 2π, x-int. @ πn

(b) $y = \sin 3x$ • horizontally compress $\sin x$ by a factor of 3   ★ 1, $\frac{2\pi}{3}$, x-int. @ $\frac{\pi}{3}n$

(c) $y = \frac{1}{3}\sin x$ • compress $\sin x$ by a factor of 3   ★ $\frac{1}{3}$, 2π, x-int. @ πn

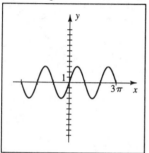
Figure 4(a)

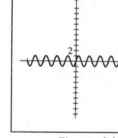
Figure 4(b)

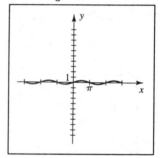
Figure 4(c)

(d) $y = \sin\frac{1}{3}x$ • horizontally stretch $\sin x$ by a factor of 3 ★ 1, 6π, x-int. @ $3\pi n$

(e) $y = 2\sin\frac{1}{3}x$ • stretch the graph in part (d) by a factor of 2

★ 2, 6π, x-int. @ $3\pi n$

(f) $y = \frac{1}{2}\sin 3x$ • compress the graph in part (b) by a factor of 2

★ $\frac{1}{2}$, $\frac{2\pi}{3}$, x-int. @ $\frac{\pi}{3}n$

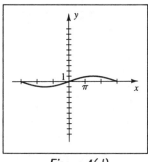

Figure 4(d)

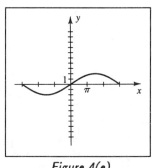

Figure 4(e)

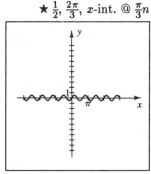

Figure 4(f)

(g) $y = -3\sin x$ • reflect the graph in part (a) through the x-axis

★ 3, 2π, x-int. @ πn

(h) $y = \sin(-3x) = -\sin 3x$ • reflect the graph in part (b) through the x-axis

★ 1, $\frac{2\pi}{3}$, x-int. @ $\frac{\pi}{3}n$

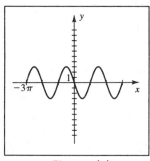

Figure 4(g)

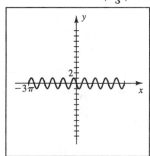

Figure 4(h)

Note: We will write $y = a\sin(bx + c)$ in the form $y = a\sin\left[b\left(x + \frac{c}{b}\right)\right]$. From this form we have the amplitude, $|a|$, the period, $\frac{2\pi}{|b|}$, and the phase shift, $-\frac{c}{b}$. We will also list the interval that corresponds to $[0, 2\pi]$ for the sine functions and $[-\frac{\pi}{2}, \frac{3\pi}{2}]$ for the cosine functions—other intervals could certainly be used. See Exercises 17 and 29 for representative examples.

5 See the *Note* on the previous page.

$y = \sin\left(x - \frac{\pi}{2}\right)$ • $0 \le x - \frac{\pi}{2} \le 2\pi \Rightarrow \frac{\pi}{2} \le x \le \frac{5\pi}{2}$  ★ $1, 2\pi, \frac{\pi}{2}, \left[\frac{\pi}{2}, \frac{5\pi}{2}\right]$

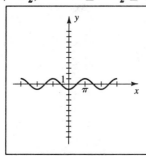

Figure 5

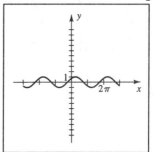

Figure 6

6 $y = \sin\left(x + \frac{\pi}{4}\right)$ • $0 \le x + \frac{\pi}{4} \le 2\pi \Rightarrow -\frac{\pi}{4} \le x \le \frac{7\pi}{4}$ ★ $1, 2\pi, -\frac{\pi}{4}, \left[-\frac{\pi}{4}, \frac{7\pi}{4}\right]$

7 $y = 3\sin\left(x + \frac{\pi}{6}\right)$ • $0 \le x + \frac{\pi}{6} \le 2\pi \Rightarrow -\frac{\pi}{6} \le x \le \frac{11\pi}{6}$ ★ $3, 2\pi, -\frac{\pi}{6}, \left[-\frac{\pi}{6}, \frac{11\pi}{6}\right]$

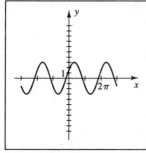

Figure 7

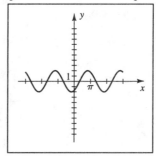

Figure 8

8 $y = 2\sin\left(x - \frac{\pi}{3}\right)$ • $0 \le x - \frac{\pi}{3} \le 2\pi \Rightarrow \frac{\pi}{3} \le x \le \frac{7\pi}{3}$ ★ $2, 2\pi, \frac{\pi}{3}, \left[\frac{\pi}{3}, \frac{7\pi}{3}\right]$

9 $y = \cos\left(x + \frac{\pi}{2}\right)$ • $-\frac{\pi}{2} \le x + \frac{\pi}{2} \le \frac{3\pi}{2} \Rightarrow -\pi \le x \le \pi$ ★ $1, 2\pi, -\frac{\pi}{2}, \left[-\pi, \pi\right]$

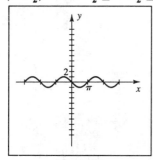

Figure 9

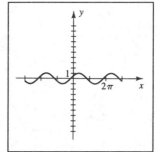

Figure 10

10 $y = \cos\left(x - \frac{\pi}{3}\right)$ • $-\frac{\pi}{2} \le x - \frac{\pi}{3} \le \frac{3\pi}{2} \Rightarrow -\frac{\pi}{6} \le x \le \frac{11\pi}{6}$ ★ $1, 2\pi, \frac{\pi}{3}, \left[-\frac{\pi}{6}, \frac{11\pi}{6}\right]$

11 $y = 4\cos\left(x - \frac{\pi}{4}\right)$ • $-\frac{\pi}{2} \leq x - \frac{\pi}{4} \leq \frac{3\pi}{2} \Rightarrow -\frac{\pi}{4} \leq x \leq \frac{7\pi}{4}$ ★ $4, 2\pi, \frac{\pi}{4}, \left[-\frac{\pi}{4}, \frac{7\pi}{4}\right]$

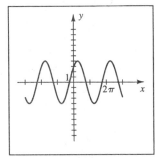

Figure 11

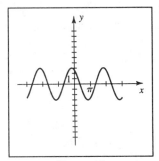

Figure 12

12 $y = 3\cos\left(x + \frac{\pi}{6}\right)$ • $-\frac{\pi}{2} \leq x + \frac{\pi}{6} \leq \frac{3\pi}{2} \Rightarrow -\frac{2\pi}{3} \leq x \leq \frac{4\pi}{3}$ ★ $3, 2\pi, -\frac{\pi}{6}, \left[-\frac{2\pi}{3}, \frac{4\pi}{3}\right]$

13 $y = \sin(2x - \pi) + 1 = \sin\left[2\left(x - \frac{\pi}{2}\right)\right] + 1.$

$0 \leq 2x - \pi \leq 2\pi \Rightarrow \pi \leq 2x \leq 3\pi \Rightarrow \frac{\pi}{2} \leq x \leq \frac{3\pi}{2}$ ★ $1, \pi, \frac{\pi}{2}, \left[\frac{\pi}{2}, \frac{3\pi}{2}\right]$

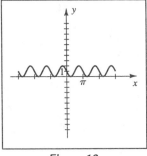

Figure 13

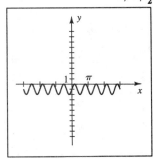

Figure 14

14 $y = -\sin(3x + \pi) - 1 = -\sin\left[3\left(x + \frac{\pi}{3}\right)\right] - 1.$

$0 \leq 3x + \pi \leq 2\pi \Rightarrow -\pi \leq 3x \leq \pi \Rightarrow -\frac{\pi}{3} \leq x \leq \frac{\pi}{3}$ ★ $1, \frac{2\pi}{3}, -\frac{\pi}{3}, \left[-\frac{\pi}{3}, \frac{\pi}{3}\right]$

15 $y = -\cos(3x + \pi) - 2 = -\cos\left[3\left(x + \frac{\pi}{3}\right)\right] - 2.$

$-\frac{\pi}{2} \leq 3x + \pi \leq \frac{3\pi}{2} \Rightarrow -\frac{3\pi}{2} \leq 3x \leq \frac{\pi}{2} \Rightarrow -\frac{\pi}{2} \leq x \leq \frac{\pi}{6}$ ★ $1, \frac{2\pi}{3}, -\frac{\pi}{3}, \left[-\frac{\pi}{2}, \frac{\pi}{6}\right]$

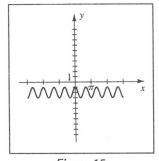

Figure 15

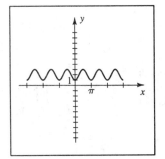

Figure 16

16 $y = \cos(2x - \pi) + 2 = \cos\left[2\left(x - \frac{\pi}{2}\right)\right] + 2.$

$-\frac{\pi}{2} \leq 2x - \pi \leq \frac{3\pi}{2} \Rightarrow \frac{\pi}{2} \leq 2x \leq \frac{5\pi}{2} \Rightarrow \frac{\pi}{4} \leq x \leq \frac{5\pi}{4}$ ★ $1, \pi, \frac{\pi}{2}, \left[\frac{\pi}{4}, \frac{5\pi}{4}\right]$

$\boxed{17}$ $y = -2\sin(3x - \pi) = -2\sin\left[3\left(x - \frac{\pi}{3}\right)\right].$ Amplitude $= |-2| = 2.$ The first negative

sign has the effect of reflecting the graph of $y = 2\sin(3x - \pi)$ through the x-axis.

Period $= \frac{2\pi}{|3|} = \frac{2\pi}{3},$ phase shift $= -\left(-\frac{\pi}{3}\right) = \frac{\pi}{3},$ $\quad 0 \le 3x - \pi \le 2\pi \Rightarrow \pi \le 3x \le 3\pi \Rightarrow$

$\frac{\pi}{3} \le x \le \pi.$ ★ $2, \frac{2\pi}{3}, \frac{\pi}{3}, [\frac{\pi}{3}, \pi]$

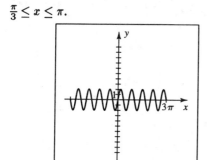

Figure 17

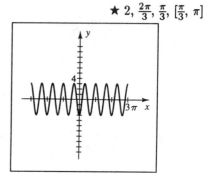

Figure 18

$\boxed{18}$ $y = 3\cos(3x - \pi) = 3\cos\left[3\left(x - \frac{\pi}{3}\right)\right].$

$\quad -\frac{\pi}{2} \le 3x - \pi \le \frac{3\pi}{2} \Rightarrow \frac{\pi}{2} \le 3x \le \frac{5\pi}{2} \Rightarrow \frac{\pi}{6} \le x \le \frac{5\pi}{6}$ ★ $3, \frac{2\pi}{3}, \frac{\pi}{3}, [\frac{\pi}{6}, \frac{5\pi}{6}]$

$\boxed{19}$ $y = \sin\left(\frac{1}{2}x - \frac{\pi}{3}\right) = \sin\left[\frac{1}{2}\left(x - \frac{2\pi}{3}\right)\right].$ $\quad 0 \le \frac{1}{2}x - \frac{\pi}{3} \le 2\pi \Rightarrow \frac{\pi}{3} \le \frac{1}{2}x \le \frac{7\pi}{3} \Rightarrow \frac{2\pi}{3} \le x \le \frac{14\pi}{3}$

                                                    ★ $1, 4\pi, \frac{2\pi}{3}, [\frac{2\pi}{3}, \frac{14\pi}{3}]$

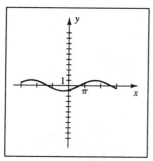

Figure 19

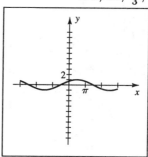

Figure 20

$\boxed{20}$ $y = \sin\left(\frac{1}{2}x + \frac{\pi}{4}\right) = \sin\left[\frac{1}{2}\left(x + \frac{\pi}{2}\right)\right].$ $\quad 0 \le \frac{1}{2}x + \frac{\pi}{4} \le 2\pi \Rightarrow -\frac{\pi}{4} \le \frac{1}{2}x \le \frac{7\pi}{4} \Rightarrow -\frac{\pi}{2} \le x \le \frac{7\pi}{2}$

                                                    ★ $1, 4\pi, -\frac{\pi}{2}, [-\frac{\pi}{2}, \frac{7\pi}{2}]$

$\boxed{21}$ $y = 6\sin \pi x$ $\quad \bullet \quad 0 \le \pi x \le 2\pi \Rightarrow 0 \le x \le 2$ ★ $6, 2, 0, [0, 2]$

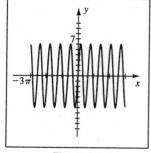

Figure 21

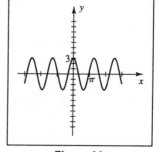

Figure 22

$\boxed{22}$ $y = 3\cos\frac{\pi}{2}x$ $\quad \bullet \quad -\frac{\pi}{2} \le \frac{\pi}{2}x \le \frac{3\pi}{2} \Rightarrow -1 \le x \le 3$ ★ $3, 4, 0, [-1, 3]$

$\boxed{23}$ $y = 2\cos\frac{\pi}{2}x$ • $-\frac{\pi}{2} \le \frac{\pi}{2}x \le \frac{3\pi}{2} \Rightarrow -1 \le x \le 3$ ★ $2, 4, 0, [-1, 3]$

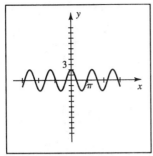

Figure 23

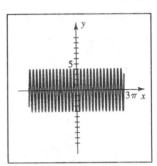

Figure 24

$\boxed{24}$ $y = 4\sin 3\pi x$ • $0 \le 3\pi x \le 2\pi \Rightarrow 0 \le x \le \frac{2}{3}$ ★ $4, \frac{2}{3}, 0, [0, \frac{2}{3}]$

$\boxed{25}$ $y = \frac{1}{2}\sin 2\pi x$ • $0 \le 2\pi x \le 2\pi \Rightarrow 0 \le x \le 1$ ★ $\frac{1}{2}, 1, 0, [0, 1]$

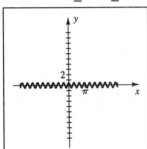

Figure 25

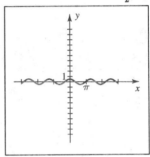

Figure 26

$\boxed{26}$ $y = \frac{1}{2}\cos\frac{\pi}{2}x$ • $-\frac{\pi}{2} \le \frac{\pi}{2}x \le \frac{3\pi}{2} \Rightarrow -1 \le x \le 3$ ★ $\frac{1}{2}, 4, 0, [-1, 3]$

$\boxed{27}$ $y = 5\sin\left(3x - \frac{\pi}{2}\right) = 5\sin\left[3\left(x - \frac{\pi}{6}\right)\right]$. $0 \le 3x - \frac{\pi}{2} \le 2\pi \Rightarrow \frac{\pi}{2} \le 3x \le \frac{5\pi}{2} \Rightarrow \frac{\pi}{6} \le x \le \frac{5\pi}{6}$

★ $5, \frac{2\pi}{3}, \frac{\pi}{6}, [\frac{\pi}{6}, \frac{5\pi}{6}]$

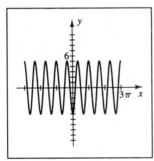

Figure 27

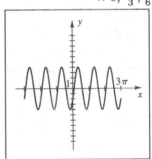

Figure 28

$\boxed{28}$ $y = -4\cos\left(2x + \frac{\pi}{3}\right) = -4\cos\left[2\left(x + \frac{\pi}{6}\right)\right]$.

$-\frac{\pi}{2} \le 2x + \frac{\pi}{3} \le \frac{3\pi}{2} \Rightarrow -\frac{5\pi}{6} \le 2x \le \frac{7\pi}{6} \Rightarrow -\frac{5\pi}{12} \le x \le \frac{7\pi}{12}$ ★ $4, \pi, -\frac{\pi}{6}, [-\frac{5\pi}{12}, \frac{7\pi}{12}]$

$\boxed{29}$ $y = 3\cos\left(\frac{1}{2}x - \frac{\pi}{4}\right) = 3\cos\left[\frac{1}{2}\left(x - \frac{\pi}{2}\right)\right]$. Amplitude $= |3| = 3$, period $= \dfrac{2\pi}{|1/2|} = 4\pi$,

phase shift $= -\left(-\frac{\pi}{2}\right) = \frac{\pi}{2}$, $-\frac{\pi}{2} \le \frac{1}{2}x - \frac{\pi}{4} \le \frac{3\pi}{2} \Rightarrow -\frac{\pi}{4} \le \frac{1}{2}x \le \frac{7\pi}{4} \Rightarrow -\frac{\pi}{2} \le x \le \frac{7\pi}{2}$.

★ $3,\ 4\pi,\ \frac{\pi}{2},\ \left[-\frac{\pi}{2}, \frac{7\pi}{2}\right]$

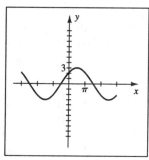

Figure 29

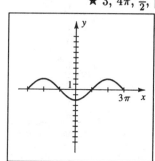

Figure 30

$\boxed{30}$ $y = -2\sin\left(\frac{1}{2}x + \frac{\pi}{2}\right) = -2\sin\left[\frac{1}{2}(x + \pi)\right]$.

$0 \le \frac{1}{2}x + \frac{\pi}{2} \le 2\pi \Rightarrow -\frac{\pi}{2} \le \frac{1}{2}x \le \frac{3\pi}{2} \Rightarrow -\pi \le x \le 3\pi$ ★ $2,\ 4\pi,\ -\pi,\ [-\pi, 3\pi]$

$\boxed{31}$ $y = -5\cos\left(\frac{1}{3}x + \frac{\pi}{6}\right) = -5\cos\left[\frac{1}{3}\left(x + \frac{\pi}{2}\right)\right]$.

$-\frac{\pi}{2} \le \frac{1}{3}x + \frac{\pi}{6} \le \frac{3\pi}{2} \Rightarrow -\frac{2\pi}{3} \le \frac{1}{3}x \le \frac{4\pi}{3} \Rightarrow -2\pi \le x \le 4\pi$ ★ $5,\ 6\pi,\ -\frac{\pi}{2},\ [-2\pi, 4\pi]$

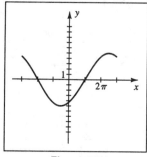

Figure 31

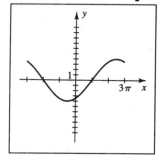

Figure 32

$\boxed{32}$ $y = 4\sin\left(\frac{1}{3}x - \frac{\pi}{3}\right) = 4\sin\left[\frac{1}{3}(x - \pi)\right]$. $0 \le \frac{1}{3}x - \frac{\pi}{3} \le 2\pi \Rightarrow \frac{\pi}{3} \le \frac{1}{3}x \le \frac{7\pi}{3} \Rightarrow \pi \le x \le 7\pi$

★ $4,\ 6\pi,\ \pi,\ [\pi, 7\pi]$

$\boxed{33}$ $y = 3\cos(\pi x + 4\pi) = 3\cos[\pi(x + 4)]$.

$-\frac{\pi}{2} \le \pi x + 4\pi \le \frac{3\pi}{2} \Rightarrow -\frac{9\pi}{2} \le \pi x \le -\frac{5\pi}{2} \Rightarrow -\frac{9}{2} \le x \le -\frac{5}{2}$ ★ $3,\ 2,\ -4,\ \left[-\frac{9}{2}, -\frac{5}{2}\right]$

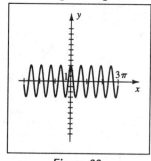

Figure 33

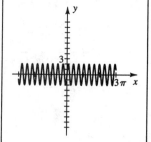

Figure 34

$\boxed{34}$ $y = -2\sin(2\pi x + \pi) = -2\sin\left[2\pi\left(x + \frac{1}{2}\right)\right]$.

$0 \le 2\pi x + \pi \le 2\pi \Rightarrow -\pi \le 2\pi x \le \pi \Rightarrow -\frac{1}{2} \le x \le \frac{1}{2}$ ★ $2,\ 1,\ -\frac{1}{2},\ \left[-\frac{1}{2}, \frac{1}{2}\right]$

$\boxed{35}$ $y = -\sqrt{2}\sin\left(\frac{\pi}{2}x - \frac{\pi}{4}\right) = -\sqrt{2}\sin\left[\frac{\pi}{2}\left(x - \frac{1}{2}\right)\right]$.

$0 \le \frac{\pi}{2}x - \frac{\pi}{4} \le 2\pi \Rightarrow \frac{\pi}{4} \le \frac{\pi}{2}x \le \frac{9\pi}{4} \Rightarrow \frac{1}{2} \le x \le \frac{9}{2}$ ★ $\sqrt{2}$, 4, $\frac{1}{2}$, $[\frac{1}{2}, \frac{9}{2}]$

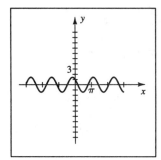

Figure 35

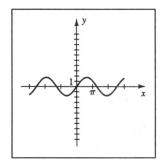

Figure 36

$\boxed{36}$ $y = \sqrt{3}\cos\left(\frac{\pi}{4}x - \frac{\pi}{2}\right) = \sqrt{3}\cos\left[\frac{\pi}{4}(x - 2)\right]$.

$-\frac{\pi}{2} \le \frac{\pi}{4}x - \frac{\pi}{2} \le \frac{3\pi}{2} \Rightarrow 0 \le \frac{\pi}{4}x \le 2\pi \Rightarrow 0 \le x \le 8$ ★ $\sqrt{3}$, 8, 2, [0, 8]

$\boxed{37}$ $y = -2\sin(2x - \pi) + 3 = -2\sin\left[2\left(x - \frac{\pi}{2}\right)\right] + 3$.

$0 \le 2x - \pi \le 2\pi \Rightarrow \pi \le 2x \le 3\pi \Rightarrow \frac{\pi}{2} \le x \le \frac{3\pi}{2}$ ★ 2, π, $\frac{\pi}{2}$, $[\frac{\pi}{2}, \frac{3\pi}{2}]$

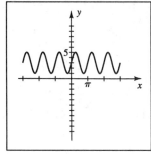

Figure 37

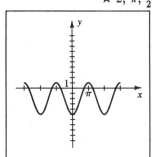

Figure 38

$\boxed{38}$ $y = 3\cos(x + 3\pi) - 2$ • $-\frac{\pi}{2} \le x + 3\pi \le \frac{3\pi}{2} \Rightarrow -\frac{7\pi}{2} \le x \le -\frac{3\pi}{2}$

★ 3, 2π, -3π, $[-\frac{7\pi}{2}, -\frac{3\pi}{2}]$

$\boxed{39}$ $y = 5\cos(2x + 2\pi) + 2 = 5\cos\left[2(x + \pi)\right] + 2$.

$-\frac{\pi}{2} \le 2x + 2\pi \le \frac{3\pi}{2} \Rightarrow -\frac{5\pi}{2} \le 2x \le -\frac{\pi}{2} \Rightarrow -\frac{5\pi}{4} \le x \le -\frac{\pi}{4}$ ★ 5, π, $-\pi$, $[-\frac{5\pi}{4}, -\frac{\pi}{4}]$

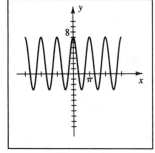

Figure 39

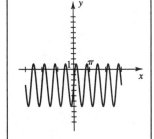

Figure 40

$\boxed{40}$ $y = -4\sin(3x - \pi) - 3 = -4\sin\left[3\left(x - \frac{\pi}{3}\right)\right] - 3$.

$0 \le 3x - \pi \le 2\pi \Rightarrow \pi \le 3x \le 3\pi \Rightarrow \frac{\pi}{3} \le x \le \pi$ ★ 4, $\frac{2\pi}{3}$, $\frac{\pi}{3}$, $[\frac{\pi}{3}, \pi]$

$\boxed{41}$ (a) The amplitude a is 4 and the period {from $-\pi$ to π} is 2π.

The phase shift is the first negative zero that occurs before a maximum, $-\pi$.

(b) Period $= \frac{2\pi}{b} \Rightarrow 2\pi = \frac{2\pi}{b} \Rightarrow b = 1$. Phase shift $= -\frac{c}{b} \Rightarrow -\pi = -\frac{c}{1} \Rightarrow c = \pi$.

Hence, $y = a\sin(bx + c) = 4\sin(x + \pi)$.

$\boxed{42}$ (a) The amplitude a is 3 and the period {from $-\frac{\pi}{4}$ to $\frac{3\pi}{4}$} is π.

The phase shift is the first negative zero that occurs before a maximum, $-\frac{\pi}{4}$.

(b) Period $= \frac{2\pi}{b} \Rightarrow \pi = \frac{2\pi}{b} \Rightarrow b = 2$. Phase shift $= -\frac{c}{b} \Rightarrow -\frac{\pi}{4} = -\frac{c}{2} \Rightarrow c = \frac{\pi}{2}$.

Hence, $y = a\sin(bx + c) = 3\sin(2x + \frac{\pi}{2})$.

$\boxed{43}$ (a) The amplitude a is 2 and the period {from -3 to 1} is 4.

The phase shift is the first negative zero that occurs before a maximum, -3.

(b) Period $= \frac{2\pi}{b} \Rightarrow 4 = \frac{2\pi}{b} \Rightarrow b = \frac{\pi}{2}$. Phase shift $= -\frac{c}{b} \Rightarrow -3 = -\frac{c}{\pi/2} \Rightarrow c = \frac{3\pi}{2}$.

Hence, $y = a\sin(bx + c) = 2\sin(\frac{\pi}{2}x + \frac{3\pi}{2})$.

$\boxed{44}$ (a) The amplitude a is 3 and the period {from $-\frac{1}{4}$ to $\frac{3}{4}$ (or 0 to 1)} is 1.

The phase shift is the first negative zero that occurs before a maximum, $-\frac{1}{4}$.

(b) Period $= \frac{2\pi}{b} \Rightarrow 1 = \frac{2\pi}{b} \Rightarrow b = 2\pi$. Phase shift $= -\frac{c}{b} \Rightarrow -\frac{1}{4} = -\frac{c}{2\pi} \Rightarrow c = \frac{\pi}{2}$.

Hence, $y = a\sin(bx + c) = 3\sin(2\pi x + \frac{\pi}{2})$.

$\boxed{45}$ In the first second, there are 2 complete cycles. Thus, the period is $\frac{1}{2}$.

$$\frac{2\pi}{b} = \frac{1}{2} \Rightarrow b = 4\pi.$$

$\boxed{46}$ $\frac{2\pi}{b} = 24$ hours $\Rightarrow b = \frac{\pi}{12}$. The light intensity would be 0 at $t = 0$ and $t = 12$.

The light intensity is 510 at $t = 6$. $I = 510\sin(\frac{\pi}{12}t)$

$\boxed{47}$ $\frac{1}{4}$ sec $= \frac{1}{2}$ period $\Rightarrow$ period $= \frac{1}{2}$ sec.

$$\frac{2\pi}{b} = \frac{1}{2} \Rightarrow b = 4\pi \text{ and the amplitude is } 8. \quad a = 8 \text{ and } b = 4\pi \Rightarrow y = 8\sin 4\pi t.$$

$\boxed{48}$ (a) Period $= 23 \Rightarrow \frac{2\pi}{b} = 23 \Rightarrow b = \frac{2\pi}{23}$. Similarly, $b = \frac{2\pi}{28}$ and $b = \frac{2\pi}{33}$.

(b) physical: $y = \sin(\frac{2\pi}{23}x) = \sin(\frac{2\pi}{23} \cdot 7670) \approx 0.136$, or 13.6%

emotional: $y = \sin(\frac{2\pi}{28}x) = \sin(\frac{2\pi}{28} \cdot 7670) \approx -0.434$, or -43.4%

intellectual: $y = \sin(\frac{2\pi}{33}x) = \sin(\frac{2\pi}{33} \cdot 7670) \approx 0.458$, or 45.8%

49 $f(t) = \frac{1}{2}\cos\left[\frac{\pi}{6}\left(t - \frac{11}{2}\right)\right]$, amplitude $= \frac{1}{2}$, period $= \frac{2\pi}{\pi/6} = 12$, phase shift $= \frac{11}{2}$

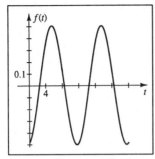

Figure 49

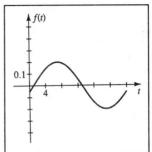

Figure 50

50 $f(t) = \frac{1}{5}\cos\left[\frac{\pi}{12}(t - 7)\right]$, amplitude $= \frac{1}{5}$, period $= \frac{2\pi}{\pi/12} = 24$, phase shift $= 7$

51 $D(t) = 6\sin\left[\frac{2\pi}{365}(t - 79)\right] + 12$, amplitude $= 6$, period $= \frac{2\pi}{2\pi/365} = 365$,

phase shift $= 79$, range $= \underline{12 - 6}$ to $\underline{12 + 6}$ or 6 to 18

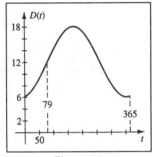

Figure 51

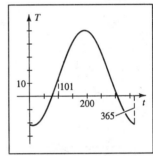

Figure 52

52 (a) $T(t) = 36\sin\left[\frac{2\pi}{365}(t - 101)\right] + 14$, amplitude $= 36$, period $= \frac{2\pi}{2\pi/365} = 365$,

phase shift $= 101$, range $= \underline{14 - 36}$ to $\underline{14 + 36}$ or -22 to 50

(b) The coldest day will occur when the argument of the sine is $-\frac{\pi}{2}$.

$\{\frac{3\pi}{2}, \frac{7\pi}{2},$ etc. could also be used – they would result in another year's minimum $\}$

$\frac{2\pi}{365}(t - 101) = -\frac{\pi}{2} \Rightarrow t - 101 = -\frac{365}{4} \Rightarrow t = 9.75.$

Since $t = 0$ corresponds to January 1, $t = 10$ would correspond to $\underline{\text{January 11}}$.

53 The temperature is $20\,°\text{F}$ at 9:00 A.M. ($t = 0$). It increases to a high of $35\,°\text{F}$ at 3:00
P.M. ($t = 6$) and then decreases to $20\,°\text{F}$ at 9:00 P.M. ($t = 12$). It continues to decrease
to a low of $5\,°\text{F}$ at 3:00 A.M. ($t = 18$). It then rises to $20\,°\text{F}$ at 9:00 A.M. ($t = 24$).

[0, 24] by [0, 40]   [0, 24] by [40, 120]

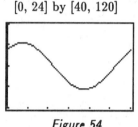

Xscl = 4   Xscl = 4

Yscl = 4   Yscl = 20

Figure 53   *Figure 54*

54 The temperature is approximately $95.6\,°\text{F}$ at 9:00 A.M. ($t = 0$). It increases to a high
of $102\,°\text{F}$ at noon ($t = 3$) and then decreases to $58\,°\text{F}$ at midnight ($t = 15$). The
temperature then rises to $95.6\,°\text{F}$ at 9:00 A.M. ($t = 24$).

Note: Exer. 55–58: The period is 24 hours. Thus, $24 = \frac{2\pi}{b} \Rightarrow b = \frac{\pi}{12}$.

55 A high of $10\,°\text{C}$ and a low of $-10\,°\text{C}$ imply that $d = 0$ and $a = 10$. The average
temperature of $0\,°\text{C}$ will occur 6 hours after the low at 4 A.M., which corresponds to
$t = 10$. Letting this correspond to the first zero of the sine function, we have

$$f(t) = 10\sin\left[\tfrac{\pi}{12}(t - 10)\right] + 0 = 10\sin\left(\tfrac{\pi}{12}t - \tfrac{5\pi}{6}\right) \text{ with } a = 10,\ b = \tfrac{\pi}{12},\ c = -\tfrac{5\pi}{6},\ d = 0.$$

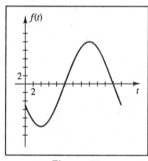

Figure 55

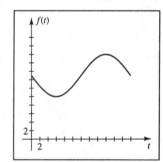

Figure 56

56 A high of $20\,°\text{C}$ and a low of $10\,°\text{C}$ imply that $d = 15$ and $a = 5$. Since $f(t)$ is
decreasing at midnight, the average temperature of $15\,°\text{C}$ (before the high of $20\,°\text{C}$)
would occur at noon, which corresponds to $t = 12$. Letting this correspond to the
first zero of the sine function, we have $f(t) = 5\sin\left[\tfrac{\pi}{12}(t - 12)\right] + 15 =$

$$5\sin\left(\tfrac{\pi}{12}t - \pi\right) + 15 \text{ with } a = 5,\ b = \tfrac{\pi}{12},\ c = -\pi,\ d = 15.$$

[57] A high of 30°C and a low of 10°C imply that $d = 20$ and $a = 10$. The average temperature of 20°C at 9 A.M. corresponds to $t = 9$. Letting this correspond to the first zero of the sine function, we have $f(t) = 10\sin\left[\frac{\pi}{12}(t-9)\right] + 20 \Rightarrow$

$$f(t) = 10\sin\left(\frac{\pi}{12}t - \frac{3\pi}{4}\right) + 20 \text{ with } a = 10, \ b = \frac{\pi}{12}, \ c = -\frac{3\pi}{4}, \ d = 20.$$

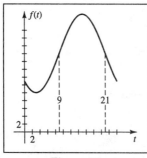

Figure 57

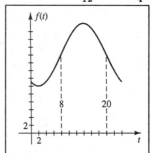

Figure 58

[58] A high of 28°C with an average of 20°C imply that the low is 12°C, $d = 20$ and $a = 8$. It was 20°C at 8 A.M., which corresponds to $t = 8$. Letting this correspond to the first zero of the sine function, we have $f(t) = 8\sin\left[\frac{\pi}{12}(t-8)\right] + 20 \Rightarrow$

$$f(t) = 8\sin\left(\frac{\pi}{12}t - \frac{2\pi}{3}\right) + 20 \text{ with } a = 8, \ b = \frac{\pi}{12}, \ c = -\frac{2\pi}{3}, \ d = 20.$$

[59] (b) Since the period is 12 months, $12 = \frac{2\pi}{b} \Rightarrow b = \frac{\pi}{6}$. The maximum precipitation is

6.1 and the minimum is 0.2, so the sine wave is centered vertically at $d = \frac{6.1 + 0.2}{2} = 3.15$ and its amplitude is $a = \frac{6.1 - 0.2}{2} = 2.95$. Since the maximum precipitation occurs at $t = 1$ (January), we must have $bt + c = \frac{\pi}{2} \Rightarrow$ $\frac{\pi}{6}(1) + c = \frac{\pi}{2} \Rightarrow c = \frac{\pi}{3}$. Thus, $P(t) = a\sin(bt + c) + d = 2.95\sin\left(\frac{\pi}{6}t + \frac{\pi}{3}\right) + 3.15$.

$$[0.5, 24.5] \text{ by } [-1, 8]$$

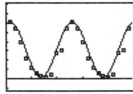

Xscl = 4

Yscl = 1

Figure 59

[60] (a) See *Figure 60(a & b)*.

(b) The maximum depth is 34.3 feet and the minimum depth is 18 feet. Thus, the amplitude of D is $a = \frac{34.3 - 18}{2} = 8.15$ and it is centered vertically at $d = \frac{34.3 + 18}{2} = 26.15$. The time between maximum depths is approximately 13 hours. Thus, $b = \frac{2\pi}{13}$. The maximum of D occurs at $t = 3$. It follows that $bt + c = \frac{\pi}{2} \Rightarrow \frac{2\pi}{13}(3) + c = \frac{\pi}{2} \Rightarrow c = \frac{\pi}{26}$. Thus, $D(t) = 8.15\sin\left(\frac{2\pi}{13}t + \frac{\pi}{26}\right) + 26.15$.

(c) Graph $Y_1 = 8.15 \sin\left(\frac{2\pi}{13}x + \frac{\pi}{26}\right) + 26.15$ and $Y_2 = 24$ on $[0, 30]$. $Y_1 < Y_2$ { the depth is less than 24 } $\Rightarrow x \in (6.8, 12.2) \cup (19.8, 25.2)$. This corresponds to the time intervals from 6:48 A.M. to 12:12 P.M. and from 7:48 P.M. to 1:12 A.M.

[0, 23] by [0, 50]   [0, 30] by [0, 50]

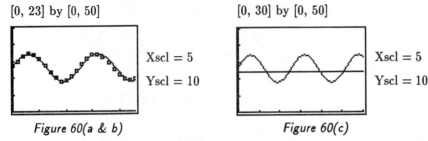

Xscl = 5   Xscl = 5
Yscl = 10   Yscl = 10

Figure 60(a & b)   *Figure 60(c)*

61 (b) Since the period is 12 months, $b = \frac{2\pi}{12} = \frac{\pi}{6}$. From the table, the maximum number of daylight hours is 18.72 and the minimum is 5.88. Thus, the sine wave is centered vertically at $d = \dfrac{18.72 + 5.88}{2} = 12.3$ and its amplitude is $a = \dfrac{18.72 - 5.88}{2} = 6.42$. Since the maximum daylight occurs at $t = 7$ (July), we must have $bt + c = \frac{\pi}{2} \Rightarrow \frac{\pi}{6}(7) + c = \frac{\pi}{2} \Rightarrow c = -\frac{2\pi}{3}$.

$$\text{Thus, } D(t) = a\sin(bt + c) + d = 6.42\sin\left(\tfrac{\pi}{6}t - \tfrac{2\pi}{3}\right) + 12.3.$$

[0.5, 24.5] by [0, 20]   [0.5, 24.5] by [0, 20]

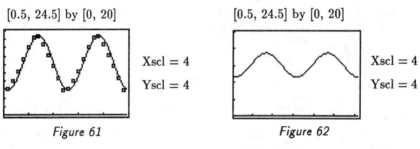

Xscl = 4   Xscl = 4
Yscl = 4   Yscl = 4

Figure 61   *Figure 62*

62 (a) We have $a = \dfrac{15.02 - 9.32}{2} = 2.85$ and $d = \dfrac{15.02 + 9.32}{2} = 12.17$. Since the period is 12 months, $b = \frac{2\pi}{12} = \frac{\pi}{6}$. The maximum should occur on June 21 { when $t = 6.7$ }. $\frac{\pi}{6}(6.7) + c = \frac{\pi}{2} \Rightarrow c = -\frac{3.7\pi}{6}$. Thus, $D(t) = 2.85\sin\left(\frac{\pi}{6}t - \frac{3.7\pi}{6}\right) + 12.17$.

(c) $D(2) \approx 9.96$ hr { true = 10.17 } and $D(9) \approx 13.19$ hr { true = 13.08 }.

63 As $x \to 0^-$ or as $x \to 0^+$,

y oscillates between -1 and 1 and does not approach a unique value.

[−2, 2] by [−1.33, 1.33]

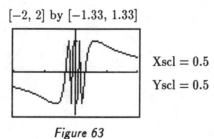

Xscl = 0.5
Yscl = 0.5

Figure 63

$\boxed{64}$ As $x \to 0^-$ or as $x \to 0^+$, y appears to approach 0. You should try at least one zoom-in to obtain a better view of the region near the origin, as shown in *Figure 64(b)*.

[−2, 2] by [−1.33, 1.33]

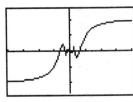

Xscl = 0.5
Yscl = 0.5

Figure 64(a)

[−0.2, 0.2] by [−0.13, 0.13]

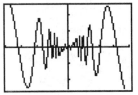

Xscl = 0.05
Yscl = 0.05

Figure 64(b)

$\boxed{65}$ As $x \to 0^-$ or as $x \to 0^+$, y appears to approach 2.

[−2, 2] by [−0.33, 2.33]

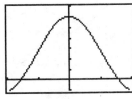

Xscl = 0.5
Yscl = 0.5

Figure 65

[−2, 2] by [−2.2, 2.2]

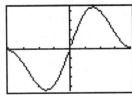

Xscl = 0.5
Yscl = 0.5

Figure 66

$\boxed{66}$ As $x \to 0^-$ or as $x \to 0^+$, y appears to approach 0.

$\boxed{67}$ From the graph, we see that there is a horizontal asymptote of $y = 4$.

[−20, 20] by [−1, 5]

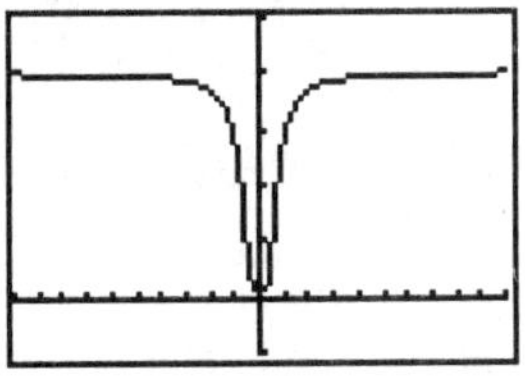

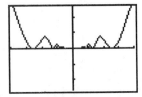

Xscl = 2
Yscl = 1

Figure 67(a)

[−1, 1] by [−0.67, 0.67]

Xscl = 0.25
Yscl = 0.25

Figure 67(b)

$\boxed{68}$ From the graph, we see that there is a horizontal asymptote of $y = 0$.

[−20, 20] by [−2, 2]

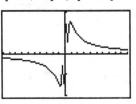

Xscl = 2
Yscl = 1

Figure 68

69 Graph $Y_1 = \cos 3x$ and $Y_2 = \frac{1}{2}x - \sin x$.

From the graph, Y_1 intersects Y_2 at $x \approx -1.63, -0.45, 0.61, 1.49, 2.42$.

Thus, $\cos 3x \geq \frac{1}{2}x - \sin x$ on $[-\pi, -1.63] \cup [-0.45, 0.61] \cup [1.49, 2.42]$.

$[-\pi, \pi]$ by $[-2.09, 2.09]$ $[-\pi, \pi]$ by $[-2.09, 2.09]$

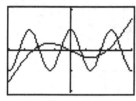
Xscl $= \pi/4$

Yscl $= 1$

Figure 69

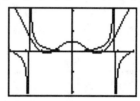
Xscl $= \pi/4$

Yscl $= 1$

Figure 70

70 Graph $Y_1 = \frac{1}{4}\tan\left(\frac{1}{3}x^2\right)$ and $Y_2 = \frac{1}{2}\cos 2x + \frac{1}{5}x^2$. From the graph, Y_1 intersects Y_2 at $x \approx \pm 0.87$. $y = \frac{1}{4}\tan\left(\frac{1}{3}x^2\right)$ is undefined when $\frac{1}{3}x^2 = \frac{\pi}{2}$, or $x = \pm\sqrt{\frac{3\pi}{2}} \approx \pm 2.17$. Thus, $\frac{1}{4}\tan\left(\frac{1}{3}x^2\right) < \frac{1}{2}\cos 2x + \frac{1}{5}x^2$ on $[-\pi, \sqrt{3\pi/2}) \cup (-0.87, 0.87) \cup (\sqrt{3\pi/2}, \pi]$. *Figure 70* was run in Connected Mode—run it in Dot Mode to remove the vertical asymptote.

5.6 Exercises

5.6 Concept Check

1 Is it true that the tangent function is increasing everywhere?   •   Not quite—it is increasing on every interval on which it is defined.

2 For $y = a\tan(bx + c)$ $(a \neq 0, b \neq 0)$, what is the period of its graph?   •   The period of $y = a\tan(bx + c)$ is $\pi/|b|$.

3 How many solutions does the equation $\csc x = 0.5$ have?   •   None, because $|\csc x| \geq 1$.

4 In terms of the graph of the cosecant, what feature corresponds to the zeros of the sine curve?   •   The asymptotes of the cosecant graph are at the same values of x as the zeros of the sine curve.

5 In terms of the graph of the secant, what feature corresponds to the turning points of the cosine curve?   •   The high (low) points on the cosine curve are the low (high) points on the graph of the secant.

5.6 Exercises

| 1 | $y = 4 \tan x$ | • | stretch $\tan x$ by a factor of 4 | ★ π |

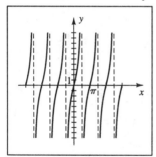

Figure 1

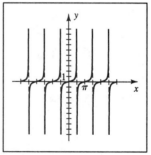

Figure 2

| 2 | $y = \frac{1}{4} \tan x$ | • | compress $\tan x$ by a factor of 4 | ★ π |

| 3 | $y = 3 \cot x$ | • | stretch $\cot x$ by a factor of 3 | ★ π |

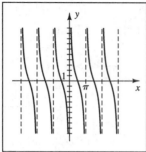

Figure 3

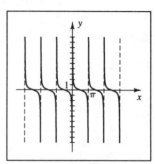

Figure 4

| 4 | $y = \frac{1}{3} \cot x$ | • | compress $\cot x$ by a factor of 3 | ★ π |

| 5 | $y = 2 \csc x$ | • | stretch $\csc x$ by a factor of 2, $f(\frac{\pi}{2}) = 2$ | ★ 2π |

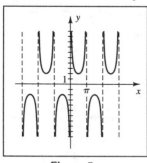

Figure 5

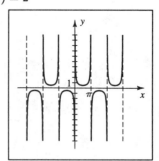

Figure 6

| 6 | $y = \frac{1}{2} \csc x$ | • | compress $\csc x$ by a factor of 2, $f(\frac{\pi}{2}) = \frac{1}{2}$ | ★ 2π |

$\boxed{7}$ $y = 3\sec x$ • stretch $\sec x$ by a factor of 3, $f(0) = 3$ ★ 2π

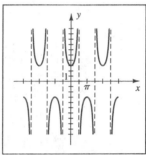

Figure 7

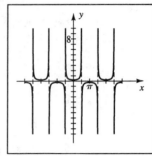

Figure 8

$\boxed{8}$ $y = \frac{1}{4}\sec x$ • compress $\sec x$ by a factor of 4, $f(0) = \frac{1}{4}$ ★ 2π

Note: The vertical asymptotes of each function are denoted by *VA* @ $x = $.

The periods for the tangent and cotangent graphs are $\pi/|b|$.

The periods for the secant and cosecant graphs are $2\pi/|b|$.

$\boxed{9}$ $y = \tan\left(x - \frac{\pi}{4}\right)$ • shift $\tan x$ right $\frac{\pi}{4}$ units, *VA* @ $x = -\frac{\pi}{4} + \pi n$

$-\frac{\pi}{2} \le x - \frac{\pi}{4} \le \frac{\pi}{2} \Rightarrow -\frac{\pi}{4} \le x \le \frac{3\pi}{4}$ ★ π

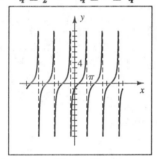

Figure 9

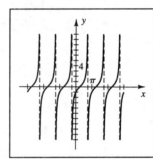

Figure 10

$\boxed{10}$ $y = \tan\left(x + \frac{3\pi}{4}\right)$ • shift $\tan x$ left $\frac{3\pi}{4}$ units, *VA* @ $x = -\frac{5\pi}{4} + \pi n$

$-\frac{\pi}{2} \le x + \frac{3\pi}{4} \le \frac{\pi}{2} \Rightarrow -\frac{5\pi}{4} \le x \le -\frac{\pi}{4}$ ★ π

$\boxed{11}$ $y = \tan 2x$ • horizontally compress $\tan x$ by a factor of 2, *VA* @ $x = -\frac{\pi}{4} + \frac{\pi}{2}n$

$-\frac{\pi}{2} \le 2x \le \frac{\pi}{2} \Rightarrow -\frac{\pi}{4} \le x \le \frac{\pi}{4}$ ★ $\frac{\pi}{2}$

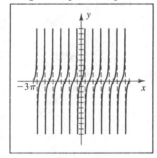

Figure 11

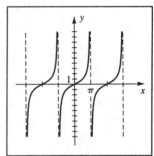

Figure 12

$\boxed{12}$ $y = \tan\frac{1}{2}x$ • horizontally stretch $\tan x$ by a factor of 2, *VA* @ $x = -\pi + 2\pi n$

$-\frac{\pi}{2} \le \frac{1}{2}x \le \frac{\pi}{2} \Rightarrow -\pi \le x \le \pi$ ★ 2π

$\boxed{13}$ $y = \tan\frac{1}{4}x$ •   horizontally stretch $\tan x$ by a factor of 4, VA @ $x = -2\pi + 4\pi n$

$-\frac{\pi}{2} \le \frac{1}{4}x \le \frac{\pi}{2} \Rightarrow -2\pi \le x \le 2\pi$ ★ 4π

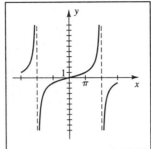

Figure 13

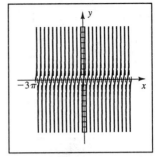

Figure 14

$\boxed{14}$ $y = \tan 4x$ •   horizontally compress $\tan x$ by a factor of 4, VA @ $x = -\frac{\pi}{8} + \frac{\pi}{4}n$

$-\frac{\pi}{2} \le 4x \le \frac{\pi}{2} \Rightarrow -\frac{\pi}{8} \le x \le \frac{\pi}{8}$ ★ $\frac{\pi}{4}$

$\boxed{15}$ $y = 2\tan\left(2x + \frac{\pi}{2}\right) = 2\tan\left[2\left(x + \frac{\pi}{4}\right)\right].$

$-\frac{\pi}{2} \le 2x + \frac{\pi}{2} \le \frac{\pi}{2} \Rightarrow -\pi \le 2x \le 0 \Rightarrow -\frac{\pi}{2} \le x \le 0$, VA @ $x = \frac{\pi}{2}n$ ★ $\frac{\pi}{2}$

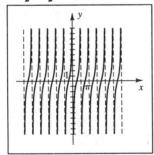

Figure 15

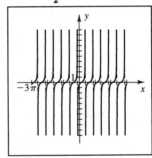

Figure 16

$\boxed{16}$ $y = \frac{1}{3}\tan\left(2x - \frac{\pi}{4}\right) = \frac{1}{3}\tan\left[2\left(x - \frac{\pi}{8}\right)\right].$

$-\frac{\pi}{2} \le 2x - \frac{\pi}{4} \le \frac{\pi}{2} \Rightarrow -\frac{\pi}{4} \le 2x \le \frac{3\pi}{4} \Rightarrow -\frac{\pi}{8} \le x \le \frac{3\pi}{8}$, VA @ $x = -\frac{\pi}{8} + \frac{\pi}{2}n$ ★ $\frac{\pi}{2}$

$\boxed{17}$ $y = -\frac{1}{4}\tan\left(\frac{1}{2}x + \frac{\pi}{3}\right) = -\frac{1}{4}\tan\left[\frac{1}{2}\left(x + \frac{2\pi}{3}\right)\right].$

$-\frac{\pi}{2} \le \frac{1}{2}x + \frac{\pi}{3} \le \frac{\pi}{2} \Rightarrow -\frac{5\pi}{6} \le \frac{1}{2}x \le \frac{\pi}{6} \Rightarrow -\frac{5\pi}{3} \le x \le \frac{\pi}{3}$, VA @ $x = -\frac{5\pi}{3} + 2\pi n$ ★ 2π

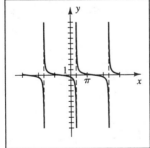

Figure 17

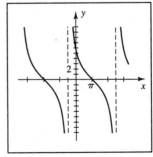

Figure 18

$\boxed{18}$ $y = -3\tan\left(\frac{1}{3}x - \frac{\pi}{3}\right) = -3\tan\left[\frac{1}{3}(x - \pi)\right].$

$-\frac{\pi}{2} \le \frac{1}{3}x - \frac{\pi}{3} \le \frac{\pi}{2} \Rightarrow -\frac{\pi}{6} \le \frac{1}{3}x \le \frac{5\pi}{6} \Rightarrow -\frac{\pi}{2} \le x \le \frac{5\pi}{2}$, VA @ $x = -\frac{\pi}{2} + 3\pi n$ ★ 3π

19 $y = \cot\left(x - \frac{\pi}{2}\right)$ • $0 \le x - \frac{\pi}{2} \le \pi \Rightarrow \frac{\pi}{2} \le x \le \frac{3\pi}{2}$, VA @ $x = \frac{\pi}{2} + \pi n$ ★ π

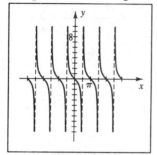

Figure 19

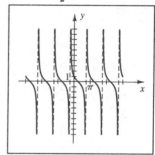

Figure 20

20 $y = \cot\left(x + \frac{\pi}{4}\right)$ • $0 \le x + \frac{\pi}{4} \le \pi \Rightarrow -\frac{\pi}{4} \le x \le \frac{3\pi}{4}$, VA @ $x = -\frac{\pi}{4} + \pi n$ ★ π

21 $y = \cot 2x$ • $0 \le 2x \le \pi \Rightarrow 0 \le x \le \frac{\pi}{2}$, VA @ $x = \frac{\pi}{2}n$ ★ $\frac{\pi}{2}$

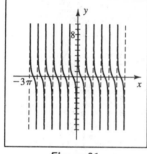

Figure 21

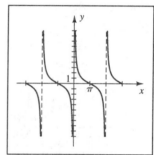

Figure 22

22 $y = \cot\frac{1}{2}x$ • $0 \le \frac{1}{2}x \le \pi \Rightarrow 0 \le x \le 2\pi$, VA @ $x = 2\pi n$ ★ 2π

23 $y = \cot\frac{1}{3}x$ • $0 \le \frac{1}{3}x \le \pi \Rightarrow 0 \le x \le 3\pi$, VA @ $x = 3\pi n$ ★ 3π

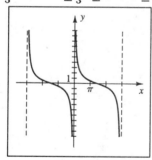

Figure 23

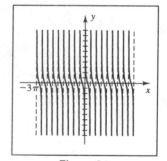

Figure 24

24 $y = \cot 3x$ • $0 \le 3x \le \pi \Rightarrow 0 \le x \le \frac{\pi}{3}$, VA @ $x = \frac{\pi}{3}n$ ★ $\frac{\pi}{3}$

$\boxed{25}$ $y = 2\cot\left(2x + \frac{\pi}{2}\right) = 2\cot\left[2\left(x + \frac{\pi}{4}\right)\right].$

$0 \le 2x + \frac{\pi}{2} \le \pi \Rightarrow -\frac{\pi}{2} \le 2x \le \frac{\pi}{2} \Rightarrow -\frac{\pi}{4} \le x \le \frac{\pi}{4},\ VA\ @\ x = -\frac{\pi}{4} + \frac{\pi}{2}n$ $\bigstar\ \frac{\pi}{2}$

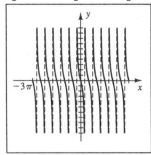

Figure 25

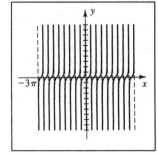

Figure 26

$\boxed{26}$ $y = -\frac{1}{3}\cot(3x - \pi) = -\frac{1}{3}\cot\left[3\left(x - \frac{\pi}{3}\right)\right].$

$0 \le 3x - \pi \le \pi \Rightarrow \pi \le 3x \le 2\pi \Rightarrow \frac{\pi}{3} \le x \le \frac{2\pi}{3},\ VA\ @\ x = \frac{\pi}{3} + \frac{\pi}{3}n$ $\bigstar\ \frac{\pi}{3}$

$\boxed{27}$ $y = -\frac{1}{2}\cot\left(\frac{1}{2}x + \frac{\pi}{4}\right) = -\frac{1}{2}\cot\left[\frac{1}{2}\left(x + \frac{\pi}{2}\right)\right].$

$0 \le \frac{1}{2}x + \frac{\pi}{4} \le \pi \Rightarrow -\frac{\pi}{4} \le \frac{1}{2}x \le \frac{3\pi}{4} \Rightarrow -\frac{\pi}{2} \le x \le \frac{3\pi}{2},\ VA\ @\ x = -\frac{\pi}{2} + 2\pi n$ $\bigstar\ 2\pi$

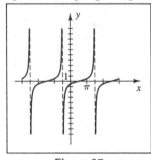

Figure 27

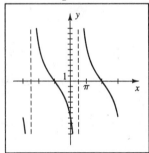

Figure 28

$\boxed{28}$ $y = 4\cot\left(\frac{1}{3}x - \frac{\pi}{6}\right) = 4\cot\left[\frac{1}{3}\left(x - \frac{\pi}{2}\right)\right].$

$0 \le \frac{1}{3}x - \frac{\pi}{6} \le \pi \Rightarrow \frac{\pi}{6} \le \frac{1}{3}x \le \frac{7\pi}{6} \Rightarrow \frac{\pi}{2} \le x \le \frac{7\pi}{2},\ VA\ @\ x = \frac{\pi}{2} + 3\pi n$ $\bigstar\ 3\pi$

$\boxed{29}$ $y = \sec\left(x - \frac{\pi}{2}\right)$ $\bullet$ $-\frac{\pi}{2} \le x - \frac{\pi}{2} \le \frac{\pi}{2} \Rightarrow 0 \le x \le \pi,\ VA\ @\ x = \pi n$ $\bigstar\ 2\pi$

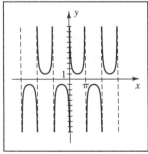

Figure 29

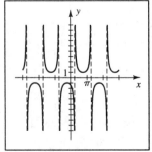

Figure 30

$\boxed{30}$ $y = \sec\left(x - \frac{3\pi}{4}\right)$ $\bullet$ $-\frac{\pi}{2} \le x - \frac{3\pi}{4} \le \frac{\pi}{2} \Rightarrow \frac{\pi}{4} \le x \le \frac{5\pi}{4},\ VA\ @\ x = \frac{\pi}{4} + \pi n$ $\bigstar\ 2\pi$

31 $y = \sec 2x$ • $-\frac{\pi}{2} \le 2x \le \frac{\pi}{2} \Rightarrow -\frac{\pi}{4} \le x \le \frac{\pi}{4}$, $VA @ x = -\frac{\pi}{4} + \frac{\pi}{2}n$ ★ π

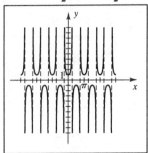

Figure 31

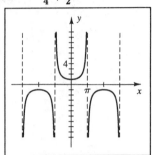

Figure 32

32 $y = \sec\frac{1}{2}x$ • $-\frac{\pi}{2} \le \frac{1}{2}x \le \frac{\pi}{2} \Rightarrow -\pi \le x \le \pi$, $VA @ x = -\pi + 2\pi n$ ★ 4π

33 $y = \sec\frac{1}{3}x$ • $-\frac{\pi}{2} \le \frac{1}{3}x \le \frac{\pi}{2} \Rightarrow -\frac{3\pi}{2} \le x \le \frac{3\pi}{2}$, $VA @ x = -\frac{3\pi}{2} + 3\pi n$ ★ 6π

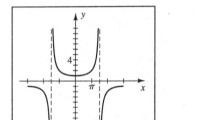

Figure 33

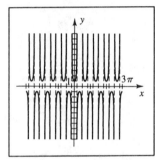

Figure 34

34 $y = \sec 3x$ • $-\frac{\pi}{2} \le 3x \le \frac{\pi}{2} \Rightarrow -\frac{\pi}{6} \le x \le \frac{\pi}{6}$, $VA @ x = -\frac{\pi}{6} + \frac{\pi}{3}n$ ★ $\frac{2\pi}{3}$

35 $y = 2\sec\left(2x - \frac{\pi}{2}\right) = 2\sec\left[2\left(x - \frac{\pi}{4}\right)\right]$.

$-\frac{\pi}{2} \le 2x - \frac{\pi}{2} \le \frac{\pi}{2} \Rightarrow 0 \le 2x \le \pi \Rightarrow 0 \le x \le \frac{\pi}{2}$, $VA @ x = \frac{\pi}{2}n$ ★ π

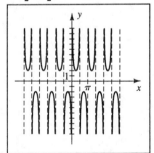

Figure 35

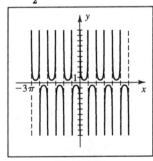

Figure 36

36 $y = \frac{1}{2}\sec\left(2x - \frac{\pi}{2}\right) = \frac{1}{2}\sec\left[2\left(x - \frac{\pi}{4}\right)\right]$.

$-\frac{\pi}{2} \le 2x - \frac{\pi}{2} \le \frac{\pi}{2} \Rightarrow 0 \le 2x \le \pi \Rightarrow 0 \le x \le \frac{\pi}{2}$, $VA @ x = \frac{\pi}{2}n$ ★ π

37 $y = -\frac{1}{3}\sec\left(\frac{1}{2}x + \frac{\pi}{4}\right) = -\frac{1}{3}\sec\left[\frac{1}{2}\left(x + \frac{\pi}{2}\right)\right].$

$-\frac{\pi}{2} \le \frac{1}{2}x + \frac{\pi}{4} \le \frac{\pi}{2} \Rightarrow -\frac{3\pi}{4} \le \frac{1}{2}x \le \frac{\pi}{4} \Rightarrow -\frac{3\pi}{2} \le x \le \frac{\pi}{2},$ $VA @ x = -\frac{3\pi}{2} + 2\pi n$ ★ 4π

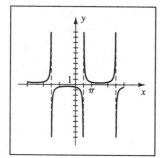

Figure 37

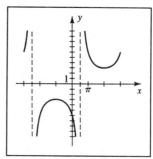

Figure 38

38 $y = -3\sec\left(\frac{1}{3}x + \frac{\pi}{3}\right) = -3\sec\left[\frac{1}{3}(x + \pi)\right].$

$-\frac{\pi}{2} \le \frac{1}{3}x + \frac{\pi}{3} \le \frac{\pi}{2} \Rightarrow -\frac{5\pi}{6} \le \frac{1}{3}x \le \frac{\pi}{6} \Rightarrow -\frac{5\pi}{2} \le x \le \frac{\pi}{2},$ $VA @ x = -\frac{5\pi}{2} + 3\pi n$ ★ 6π

39 $y = \csc\left(x - \frac{\pi}{2}\right)$ • $0 \le x - \frac{\pi}{2} \le \pi \Rightarrow \frac{\pi}{2} \le x \le \frac{3\pi}{2},$ $VA @ x = \frac{\pi}{2} + \pi n$ ★ 2π

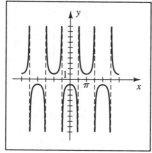

Figure 39

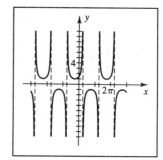

Figure 40

40 $y = \csc\left(x + \frac{3\pi}{4}\right)$ • $0 \le x + \frac{3\pi}{4} \le \pi \Rightarrow -\frac{3\pi}{4} \le x \le \frac{\pi}{4},$ $VA @ x = -\frac{3\pi}{4} + \pi n$ ★ 2π

41 $y = \csc 2x$ • $0 \le 2x \le \pi \Rightarrow 0 \le x \le \frac{\pi}{2},$ $VA @ x = \frac{\pi}{2}n$ ★ π

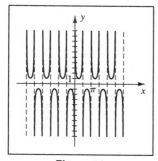

Figure 41

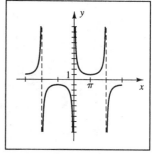

Figure 42

42 $y = \csc\frac{1}{2}x$ • $0 \le \frac{1}{2}x \le \pi \Rightarrow 0 \le x \le 2\pi,$ $VA @ x = 2\pi n$ ★ 4π

$\boxed{43}$ $y = \csc\frac{1}{3}x$ $\quad\bullet\quad$ $0 \le \frac{1}{3}x \le \pi \Rightarrow 0 \le x \le 3\pi$, VA @ $x = 3\pi n$ $\qquad\qquad$ $\star\ 6\pi$

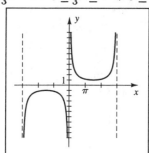

Figure 43

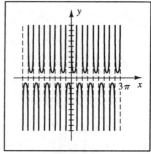

Figure 44

$\boxed{44}$ $y = \csc 3x$ $\quad\bullet\quad$ $0 \le 3x \le \pi \Rightarrow 0 \le x \le \frac{\pi}{3}$, VA @ $x = \frac{\pi}{3}n$ $\qquad\qquad$ $\star\ \frac{2\pi}{3}$

$\boxed{45}$ $y = 2\csc\left(2x + \frac{\pi}{2}\right) = 2\csc\left[2(x + \frac{\pi}{4})\right]$.

$0 \le 2x + \frac{\pi}{2} \le \pi \Rightarrow -\frac{\pi}{2} \le 2x \le \frac{\pi}{2} \Rightarrow -\frac{\pi}{4} \le x \le \frac{\pi}{4}$, VA @ $x = -\frac{\pi}{4} + \frac{\pi}{2}n$ $\qquad$ $\star\ \pi$

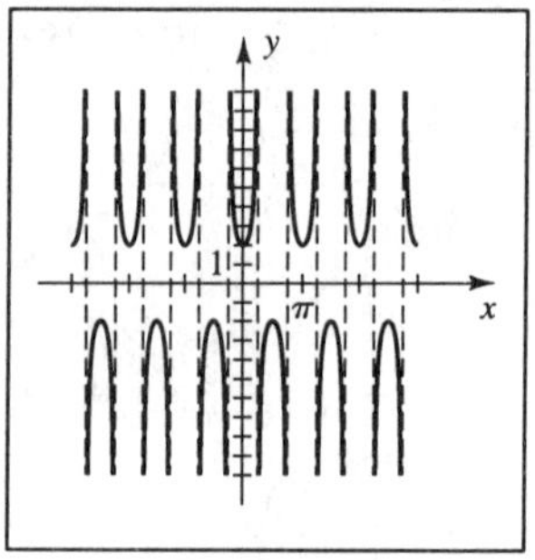

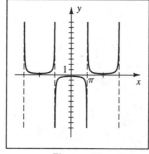

Figure 45

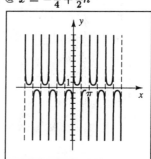

Figure 46

$\boxed{46}$ $y = -\frac{1}{2}\csc(2x - \pi) = -\frac{1}{2}\csc\left[2(x - \frac{\pi}{2})\right]$.

$0 \le 2x - \pi \le \pi \Rightarrow \pi \le 2x \le 2\pi \Rightarrow \frac{\pi}{2} \le x \le \pi$, VA @ $x = \frac{\pi}{2}n$ $\qquad\qquad$ $\star\ \pi$

$\boxed{47}$ $y = -\frac{1}{4}\csc\left(\frac{1}{2}x + \frac{\pi}{2}\right) = -\frac{1}{4}\csc\left[\frac{1}{2}(x + \pi)\right]$.

$0 \le \frac{1}{2}x + \frac{\pi}{2} \le \pi \Rightarrow -\frac{\pi}{2} \le \frac{1}{2}x \le \frac{\pi}{2} \Rightarrow -\pi \le x \le \pi$, VA @ $x = -\pi + 2\pi n$ $\qquad\qquad$ $\star\ 4\pi$

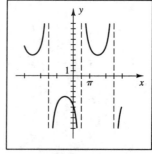

Figure 47

Figure 48

$\boxed{48}$ $y = 4\csc\left(\frac{1}{2}x - \frac{\pi}{4}\right) = 4\csc\left[\frac{1}{2}(x - \frac{\pi}{2})\right]$.

$0 \le \frac{1}{2}x - \frac{\pi}{4} \le \pi \Rightarrow \frac{\pi}{4} \le \frac{1}{2}x \le \frac{5\pi}{4} \Rightarrow \frac{\pi}{2} \le x \le \frac{5\pi}{2}$, VA @ $x = \frac{\pi}{2} + 2\pi n$ $\qquad\qquad$ $\star\ 4\pi$

49 $y = \tan \frac{\pi}{2} x$ • horizontally stretch $\tan x$ by a factor of $2/\pi$, *VA* @ $x = -1 + 2n$

$-\frac{\pi}{2} \le \frac{\pi}{2} x \le \frac{\pi}{2} \Rightarrow -1 \le x \le 1$ ★ 2

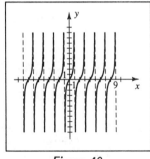

Figure 49

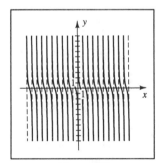

Figure 50

50 $y = \cot \pi x$ • $0 \le \pi x \le \pi \Rightarrow 0 \le x \le 1$, *VA* @ $x = n$ ★ 1

51 $y = \csc 2\pi x$ • $0 \le 2\pi x \le \pi \Rightarrow 0 \le x \le \frac{1}{2}$, *VA* @ $x = \frac{1}{2} n$ ★ 1

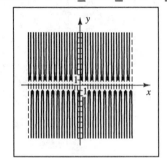

Figure 51

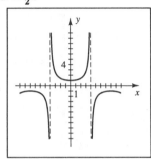

Figure 52

52 $y = \sec \frac{\pi}{8} x$ • $-\frac{\pi}{2} \le \frac{\pi}{8} x \le \frac{\pi}{2} \Rightarrow -4 \le x \le 4$, *VA* @ $x = -4 + 8n$ ★ 16

53 Reflecting the graph of $y = \cot x$ about the x-axis, which is $y = -\cot x$, gives us the graph of $y = \tan\left(x + \frac{\pi}{2}\right)$. If we shift this graph to the left (or right), we will obtain the graph of $y = \tan x$. Thus, one equation is $y = -\cot\left(x + \frac{\pi}{2}\right)$.

54 Shifting the graph of $y = \csc x$ to the left $\frac{\pi}{2}$ units gives us the graph of $y = \sec x$.

Thus, one equation is $y = \csc\left(x + \frac{\pi}{2}\right)$.

55 $y = |\sin x|$ •

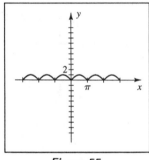

Figure 55

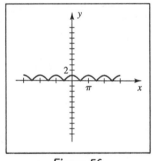

Figure 56

56 $y = |\cos x|$ •

57 $y = |\sin x| + 2$ •

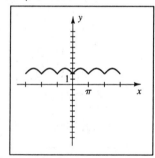

Figure 57

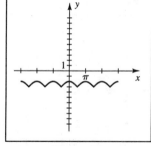

Figure 58

58 $y = |\cos x| - 3$ •

59 $y = -|\cos x| + 1$ •

60 $y = -|\sin x| - 2$ •

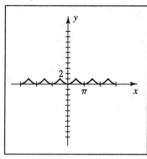

Figure 59

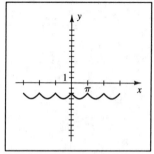

Figure 60

61 $y = x + \cos x$ •

62 $y = x - \sin x$ •

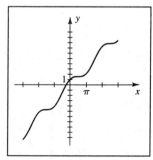

Figure 61

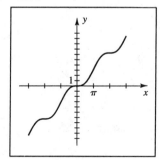

Figure 62

63 $y = 2^{-x} \cos x$ •

64 $y = e^x \sin x$ •

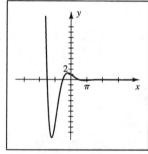

Figure 63

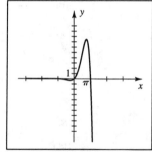

Figure 64

65 $y = |x| \sin x$ •

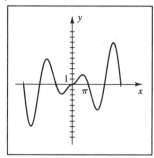

Figure 65

66 $y = |x| \cos x$ •

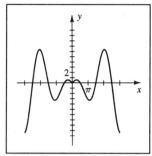

Figure 66

67 $f(x) = \tan(0.5x)$; $\qquad g(x) = \tan[0.5(x + \pi/2)]$ • Since $g(x) = f(x + \pi/2)$,

the graph of g can be obtained by shifting the graph of f left a distance of $\frac{\pi}{2}$.

$[-2\pi, 2\pi]$ by $[-4, 4]$

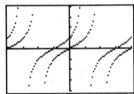

Xscl $= \pi/2$
Yscl $= 1$

Figure 67

$[-2\pi, 2\pi]$ by $[-4, 4]$

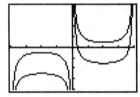

Xscl $= \pi/2$
Yscl $= 1$

Figure 68

68 $f(x) = 0.5 \csc(0.5x)$; $\qquad g(x) = 0.5 \csc(0.5x) - 2$ • Since $g(x) = f(x) - 2$,

the graph of g can be obtained by shifting the graph of f downward a distance of 2.

69 $f(x) = 0.5 \sec 0.5x$; $\qquad g(x) = 0.5 \sec[0.5(x - \pi/2)] - 1$ •

Since $g(x) = f(x - \pi/2) - 1$, the graph of g can be obtained by shifting the graph of f

horizontally to the right a distance of $\frac{\pi}{2}$ and vertically downward a distance of 1.

$[-2\pi, 2\pi]$ by $[-4, 4]$

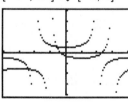

Xscl $= \pi/2$
Yscl $= 1$

Figure 69

$[-2\pi, 2\pi]$ by $[-4, 4]$

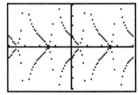

Xscl $= \pi/2$
Yscl $= 1$

Figure 70

70 $f(x) = \tan x - 1$; $\qquad g(x) = -\tan x + 1$ • Since $g(x) = -f(x)$,

the graph of g can be obtained by reflecting the graph of f about the x–axis.

71 $f(x) = 3\cos 2x$; $g(x) = |3\cos 2x| - 1$ •   Since $g(x) = |f(x)| - 1$,

the graph of g can be obtained from the graph of f by reflecting it about the x–axis

when $f(x) < 0$ and then shifting that graph downward a distance of 1.

$[-2\pi,\ 2\pi]$ by $[-4,\ 4]$ $[-2\pi,\ 2\pi]$ by $[-4,\ 4]$

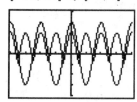
Xscl $= \pi/2$

Yscl $= 1$

Figure 71

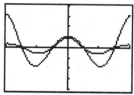
Xscl $= \pi/2$

Yscl $= 1$

Figure 72

72 $f(x) = 1.2^{-x}\cos x$; $g(x) = 1.2^x\cos x$ •

Since $g(x) = 1.2^x\cos x = 1.2^{-(-x)}\cos(-x) = f(-x)$, the graph of g can be obtained

from the graph of f by reflecting the graph of f about the y–axis.

73 The damping factor of $y = e^{-x/4}\sin 4x$ is $e^{-x/4}$.

$[-2\pi,\ 2\pi]$ by $[-4.19,\ 4.19]$ $[-2\pi,\ 2\pi]$ by $[-4.19,\ 4.19]$

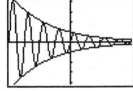
Xscl $= \pi/2$

Yscl $= 1$

Figure 73

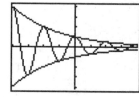
Xscl $= \pi/2$

Yscl $= 1$

Figure 74

74 The damping factor of $y = 3^{-x/5}\cos 2x$ is $3^{-x/5}$.

75 From the graph, we see that the maximum occurs at the approximate coordinates

$(-2.76, 3.09)$, and the minimum occurs at the approximate coordinates $(1.23, -3.68)$.

$[-\pi,\ \pi]$ by $[-4,\ 4]$ $[-\pi,\ \pi]$ by $[-4,\ 4]$

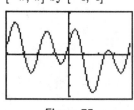
Xscl $= \pi/4$

Yscl $= 1$

Figure 75

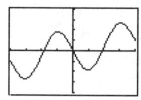
Xscl $= \pi/4$

Yscl $= 1$

Figure 76

76 From the graph, we see that the maximum occurs at the approximate coordinates

$(2.40, 2.68)$, and the minimum occurs at the approximate coordinates $(-2.40, -2.68)$.

$\boxed{77}$ From the graph, we see that f is increasing and one-to-one between

$a \approx -0.70$ and $b \approx 0.12$. Thus, the interval is approximately $[-0.70, 0.12]$.

$[-2, 2]$ by $[-1.33, 1.33]$ $[-3, 3]$ by $[-1, 3]$

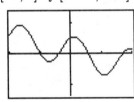
$\text{Xscl} = 1$
$\text{Yscl} = 1$

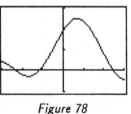
$\text{Xscl} = 1$
$\text{Yscl} = 1$

Figure 77   *Figure 78*

$\boxed{78}$ From the graph, we see that f is increasing and one-to-one between

$a \approx -1.70$ and $b \approx 0.70$. Thus, the interval is approximately $[-1.70, 0.70]$.

$\boxed{79}$ Graph $Y_1 = \cos(2x - 1) + \sin 3x$ and $Y_2 = \sin \frac{1}{3}x + \cos x$.

From the graph, Y_1 intersects Y_2 at $x \approx -1.31, 0.11, 0.95, 2.39$.

Thus, $\cos(2x - 1) + \sin 3x \geq \sin \frac{1}{3}x + \cos x$ on $[-\pi, -1.31] \cup [0.11, 0.95] \cup [2.39, \pi]$.

$[-\pi, \pi]$ by $[-2.09, 2.09]$ $[-\pi, \pi]$ by $[-2.09, 2.09]$

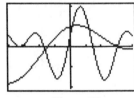
$\text{Xscl} = \pi/4$
$\text{Yscl} = 1$

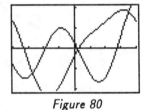
$\text{Xscl} = \pi/4$
$\text{Yscl} = 1$

Figure 79   *Figure 80*

$\boxed{80}$ Graph $Y_1 = \frac{1}{2}\cos 2x + 2\cos(x - 2)$ and $Y_2 = 2\cos(1.5x + 1) + \sin(x - 1)$.

From the graph, Y_1 intersects Y_2 at $x \approx -2.16, 0.15, 2.76$. Thus,

$\frac{1}{2}\cos 2x + 2\cos(x - 2) < 2\cos(1.5x + 1) + \sin(x - 1)$ on $(-2.16, 0.15) \cup (2.76, \pi]$.

$\boxed{81}$ (a) $\theta = 0 \Rightarrow I = \frac{1}{2}I_0[1 + \cos(\pi \sin 0)] = \frac{1}{2}I_0[1 + \cos(0)] = \frac{1}{2}I_0(2) = I_0$.

(b) $\theta = \pi/3 \Rightarrow I = \frac{1}{2}I_0[1 + \cos(\pi \sin(\pi/3))] \approx 0.044 I_0$.

(c) $\theta = \pi/7 \Rightarrow I = \frac{1}{2}I_0[1 + \cos(\pi \sin(\pi/7))] \approx 0.603 I_0$.

$\boxed{82}$ (a) The intensity $I = \frac{1}{2}I_0[1 + \cos(\pi \sin \theta)]$ will be maximum when $\cos(\pi \sin \theta) = 1 \Rightarrow$

$\pi \sin \theta = 0 \Rightarrow \sin \theta = 0 \Rightarrow \theta = 0, \pi$. Thus, the intensity is maximum in the east

and west directions. The intensity I will be minimum when $\cos(\pi \sin \theta) = -1 \Rightarrow$

$\pi \sin \theta = \pm \pi \Rightarrow \sin \theta = \pm 1 \Rightarrow \theta = \frac{\pi}{2}, \frac{3\pi}{2}$. There is no signal in the north and

south directions so that it wouldn't interfere with a radio station at the same

wavelength to the north or south.

(b) Graph $Y_1 = \frac{1}{2}[1 + \cos(\pi \sin \theta)]$ and $Y_2 = \frac{1}{3}$. There are four points of intersection on $[0, 2\pi)$. They occur at $\theta \approx 0.654$, 2.488, 3.795, 5.629.

$$[0, 2\pi] \text{ by } [0, 1.5]$$

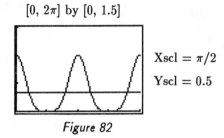

$\text{Xscl} = \pi/2$

$\text{Yscl} = 0.5$

Figure 82

83 (a) The damping factor is $A_0 e^{-\alpha z}$.

(b) The phase shift at depth z_0 is given by $kt - \alpha z_0 = 0 \Rightarrow t = \frac{\alpha}{k} z_0$.

(c) At the surface, $z = 0$. Hence, $S = A_0 \sin kt$ and the amplitude at the surface is A_0. $\text{Amplitude}_{\text{wave}} = \frac{1}{2} \text{Amplitude}_{\text{surface}} \Rightarrow$

$$A_0 e^{-\alpha z} = \frac{1}{2} A_0 \Rightarrow e^{-\alpha z} = \frac{1}{2} \Rightarrow -\alpha z = \ln \frac{1}{2} \Rightarrow z = \frac{-\ln 2}{-\alpha} = \frac{\ln 2}{\alpha}.$$

5.7 Exercises

5.7 Concept Check

1 What do all the triangles in this section have in common? • All the triangles in this section have a right angle.

2 Can you solve $\triangle ABC$ given angles α and β? • No—knowing the three angles ($\gamma = 90°$) of a triangle does not enable us to solve $\triangle ABC$ since we cannot find any of the sides.

3 The direction N25°E is how many degrees north of due east? • Since N25°E is 25° east of due north, it is $90° - 25° = 65°$ north of due east.

4 Angles of elevation and depression are measured with respect to what? • The angles of elevation and depression are measured with respect to the angle that the line of sight makes with a horizontal line from the observer.

5 If an object in simple harmonic motion makes one complete oscillation in 10 seconds, what is its frequency? • The frequency is $\frac{1}{10}$, which means that one-tenth of an oscillation takes place each second.

5.7 Exercises

Note: The missing values are found in terms of the given values.

We could also use proportions to find the remaining parts.

1 $\beta = 90° - \alpha = 60°$. $\tan \alpha = \frac{a}{b} \Rightarrow a = b \tan \alpha = 20(\frac{1}{3}\sqrt{3}) = \frac{20}{3}\sqrt{3}$.

$\sec \alpha = \frac{c}{b} \Rightarrow c = b \sec \alpha = 20(\frac{2}{3}\sqrt{3}) = \frac{40}{3}\sqrt{3}$.

$\boxed{2}$ $\alpha = 90° - \beta = 45°$. $\cot \beta = \frac{a}{b} \Rightarrow a = b \cot \beta = 35(1) = 35$.

$$\csc \beta = \frac{c}{b} \Rightarrow c = b \csc \beta = 35(\sqrt{2}) = 35\sqrt{2}.$$

$\boxed{3}$ $\alpha = 90° - \beta = 45°$. $\cos \beta = \frac{a}{c} \Rightarrow a = c \cos \beta = 30(\frac{1}{2}\sqrt{2}) = 15\sqrt{2}$.

$$b = a \text{ in a } 45°-45°-90° \,\triangle\,.$$

$\boxed{4}$ $\beta = 90° - \alpha = 30°$. $\sin \alpha = \frac{a}{c} \Rightarrow a = c \sin \alpha = 6(\frac{1}{2}\sqrt{3}) = 3\sqrt{3}$.

$$\cos \alpha = \frac{b}{c} \Rightarrow b = c \cos \alpha = 6(\frac{1}{2}) = 3.$$

$\boxed{5}$ $\tan \alpha = \frac{a}{b} = \frac{5}{5} = 1 \Rightarrow \alpha = 45°$. $\beta = 90° - \alpha = 45°$.

$$c = \sqrt{a^2 + b^2} = \sqrt{25 + 25} = \sqrt{50} = 5\sqrt{2}.$$

$\boxed{6}$ $\sin \alpha = \frac{a}{c} = \frac{4\sqrt{3}}{8} = \frac{\sqrt{3}}{2} \Rightarrow \alpha = 60°$. $\beta = 90° - \alpha = 30°$.

$$b = \sqrt{c^2 - a^2} = \sqrt{64 - 48} = \sqrt{16} = 4.$$

$\boxed{7}$ $\cos \alpha = \frac{b}{c} = \frac{5\sqrt{3}}{10\sqrt{3}} = \frac{1}{2} \Rightarrow \alpha = 60°$. $\beta = 90° - \alpha = 30°$.

$$a = \sqrt{c^2 - b^2} = \sqrt{300 - 75} = \sqrt{225} = 15.$$

$\boxed{8}$ $\cos \alpha = \frac{b}{c} = \frac{7\sqrt{2}}{14} = \frac{\sqrt{2}}{2} \Rightarrow \alpha = 45°$. $\beta = 90° - \alpha = 45°$.

$$a = \sqrt{c^2 - b^2} = \sqrt{196 - 98} = \sqrt{98} = 7\sqrt{2}.$$

$\boxed{9}$ $\beta = 90° - \alpha = 53°$. $\tan \alpha = \frac{a}{b} \Rightarrow a = b \tan \alpha = 24 \tan 37° \approx 18$.

$$\sec \alpha = \frac{c}{b} \Rightarrow c = b \sec \alpha = 24 \sec 37° \approx 30.$$

$\boxed{10}$ $\alpha = 90° - \beta = 25°40'$. $\tan \beta = \frac{b}{a} \Rightarrow b = a \tan \beta = 20.1 \tan 64°20' \approx 41.8$.

$$\sec \beta = \frac{c}{a} \Rightarrow c = a \sec \beta = 20.1 \sec 64°20' \approx 46.4.$$

$\boxed{11}$ $\alpha = 90° - \beta = 18°9'$. $\cot \beta = \frac{a}{b} \Rightarrow a = b \cot \beta = 240.0 \cot 71°51' \approx 78.7$.

$$\csc \beta = \frac{c}{b} \Rightarrow c = b \csc \beta = 240.0 \csc 71°51' \approx 252.6.$$

$\boxed{12}$ $\beta = 90° - \alpha = 58°50'$. $\cot \alpha = \frac{b}{a} \Rightarrow b = a \cot \alpha = 510 \cot 31°10' \approx 843$.

$$\csc \alpha = \frac{c}{a} \Rightarrow c = a \csc \alpha = 510 \csc 31°10' \approx 985.$$

$\boxed{13}$ $\tan \alpha = \frac{a}{b} = \frac{25}{45} \Rightarrow \alpha \approx 29°$. $\beta = 90° - \alpha \approx 61°$.

$$c = \sqrt{a^2 + b^2} = \sqrt{625 + 2025} = \sqrt{2650} \approx 51.$$

$\boxed{14}$ $\tan \alpha = \frac{a}{b} = \frac{31}{9.0} \Rightarrow \alpha \approx 74°$. $\beta = 90° - \alpha \approx 16°$.

$$c = \sqrt{a^2 + b^2} = \sqrt{961 + 81} = \sqrt{1042} \approx 32.$$

$\boxed{15}$ $\cos \alpha = \frac{b}{c} = \frac{2.1}{5.8} \Rightarrow \alpha \approx 69°$. $\beta = 90° - \alpha \approx 21°$.

$$a = \sqrt{c^2 - b^2} = \sqrt{33.64 - 4.41} = \sqrt{29.23} \approx 5.4.$$

$\boxed{16}$ $\sin \alpha = \frac{a}{c} = \frac{0.42}{0.68} \Rightarrow \alpha \approx 38°$. $\beta = 90° - \alpha \approx 52°$.

$$b = \sqrt{c^2 - a^2} = \sqrt{0.4624 - 0.1764} = \sqrt{0.286} \approx 0.53.$$

$\boxed{17}$ $\cos \alpha = \frac{b}{c} \Rightarrow b = c \cos \alpha$ $\boxed{18}$ $\sin \beta = \frac{b}{c} \Rightarrow b = c \sin \beta$

$\boxed{19}$ $\cot \beta = \frac{a}{b} \Rightarrow a = b \cot \beta$ $\boxed{20}$ $\tan \alpha = \frac{a}{b} \Rightarrow a = b \tan \alpha$

$\boxed{21}$ $\csc \alpha = \frac{c}{a} \Rightarrow c = a \csc \alpha$ $\boxed{22}$ $\sec \beta = \frac{c}{a} \Rightarrow c = a \sec \beta$

23   $a^2 + b^2 = c^2 \Rightarrow b^2 = c^2 - a^2 \Rightarrow b = \sqrt{c^2 - a^2}$

24   $a^2 + b^2 = c^2 \Rightarrow c = \sqrt{a^2 + b^2}$

25   Let h denote the height of the kite and $x = h - 4$.

$$\sin 60° = \frac{x}{500} \Rightarrow x = 500(\tfrac{1}{2}\sqrt{3}) = 250\sqrt{3}, \quad h = 250\sqrt{3} + 4 \approx 437 \text{ ft}$$

26   $\cot 68° = \frac{x}{15} \Rightarrow x = 15 \cot 68° \approx 6.1$ m.

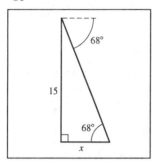

Figure 26

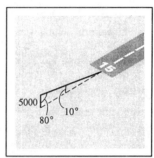

Figure 27

27   $\sin 10° = \frac{5000}{x} \Rightarrow x = 5000 \csc 10° \approx 28{,}793.85$, or 28,800 ft.

28   Let l denote the length of the wire. $\cos 58°20' = \frac{40}{l} \Rightarrow l = 40 \sec 58°20' \approx 76.2$ m

29   $\tan 72°40' = \frac{d}{50} \Rightarrow d \approx 160$ m.

30   (a) $\tan \theta = \frac{h}{d} \Rightarrow h = d \tan \theta$ (b) $h = 1000 \tan 59° \approx 1664$ m

31   Let h denote the altitude. $\sin 75° = \frac{h}{10{,}000} \Rightarrow h \approx 9659$ ft.

32   Let d denote the distance the plane travels. $\sin 10° = 15{,}000/d \Rightarrow d = 15{,}000 \csc 10°.$

At 250 ft/sec, it will take $\dfrac{d}{250} = \dfrac{15{,}000 \csc 10°}{250} \approx 345.5$ seconds or 5.76 minutes.

33   (a)   The bridge section is 75 ft. long. $\sin 35° = \frac{d - 15}{75} \Rightarrow d = 75 \sin 35° + 15 \approx 58$ ft.

(b)   Let x be the horizontal distance from the end of a bridge section to a point

directly underneath the end of the section. $\cos 35° = \frac{x}{75} \Rightarrow x = 75 \cos 35°.$

The distance is $150 - 2x \approx 27$ ft.

34   The lower section has a horizontal length of $x_1 = 15 \cot 25°$ and a slide length of

$s_1 = 15 \csc 25° \approx 35.5$.   The upper section has a horizontal length of $x_2 = 15 \cot 35°$

and a slide length of $s_2 = 15 \csc 35° \approx 26.2$.

The middle section has a slide length of $s_3 = 100 - x_1 - x_2 \approx 46.4$.

The total slide length is $s_1 + s_2 + s_3 \approx 35.5 + 26.2 + 46.4 = 108.1$ ft.

35   Let α denote the angle of elevation. $\tan \alpha = \frac{5}{4} \Rightarrow \alpha \approx 51°20'$.

36   $\sin \alpha = \frac{5}{24} \Rightarrow \alpha \approx 12°$

37   Let D denote the position of the duck and t the number of seconds required for a

direct hit. $\sin \varphi = \dfrac{\overline{AD}}{\overline{OD}} = \dfrac{7t}{25t} \Rightarrow \sin \varphi = \dfrac{7}{25} \Rightarrow \varphi \approx 16.3°$

38 (a) $\sin\alpha = \frac{4}{9} \Rightarrow \alpha \approx 26.4°$ (b) $\sin 40° = \frac{h}{9} \Rightarrow h \approx 5.8$ m

39 Let h denote the height of the tower.

$$\tan 21°20'24'' = \tan 21.34° = \frac{h}{5280} \Rightarrow h = 5280\tan 21.34° \approx 2063 \text{ ft.}$$

40 Maximum elongation $\theta_{\max}$ will occur when the line of sight from the earth to Venus is tangent to the orbit of Venus. Since a tangent line to a circle is perpendicular to a radius, maximum elongation will occur when the angle determined by the sun,

Venus, and the earth is 90°. $\sin(\theta_{\max}) = \dfrac{D_v}{D_e} = \dfrac{68,000,000}{91,500,000} = \dfrac{68}{91.5} \Rightarrow \theta_{\max} \approx 48°.$

41 The central angle of a section of the Pentagon has measure $360°/5 = 72°$.

Bisecting that angle, we have an angle of $36°$ whose opposite side is $\frac{921}{2}$.

The height h is given by $\tan 36° = \dfrac{\frac{921}{2}}{h} \Rightarrow h = \dfrac{921}{2\tan 36°}$.

Area $= 5(\frac{1}{2}bh) = 5(\frac{1}{2})(921)\left(\dfrac{921}{2\tan 36°}\right) \approx 1,459,379 \text{ ft}^2.$

42 The central angle of a section of the octagon has an angle

measure of $\dfrac{360°}{8} = 45°$. Bisecting that angle forms a right

triangle with a hypotenuse of 12 cm.

$\sin 22.5° = \frac{x}{12} \Rightarrow x = 12\sin 22.5°.$

There are 8 sides of length $2x$.

Hence, the perimeter is $16x = 192\sin 22.5° \approx 73.5$ cm.

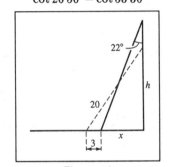

Figure 42

43 The diagonal of the base is $\sqrt{8^2 + 6^2} = 10$. $\tan\theta = \frac{4}{10} \Rightarrow \theta \approx 21.8°$

44 $V = \frac{1}{3}\pi r^2 h \Leftrightarrow 20 = \frac{1}{3}\pi(2)^2 h \Rightarrow h = \frac{15}{\pi}.$

$$\tan\frac{\beta}{2} = \frac{r}{h} = \frac{2}{15/\pi} \Rightarrow \frac{\beta}{2} \approx 22.728°, \text{ and } \beta \approx 45.5°.$$

45 $\cot 53°30' = \frac{x}{h} \Rightarrow x = h\cot 53°30'.$ $\cot 26°50' = \dfrac{x+25}{h} \Rightarrow x + 25 = h\cot 26°50' \Rightarrow$

$x = h\cot 26°50' - 25.$ Thus, $h\cot 53°30' = h\cot 26°50' - 25 \Rightarrow$

$$25 = h\cot 26°50' - h\cot 53°30' \Rightarrow h = \dfrac{25}{\cot 26°50' - \cot 53°30'} \approx 20.2 \text{ m.}$$

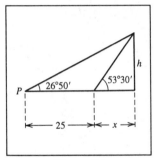

Figure 45

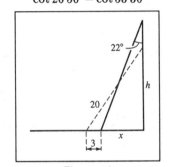

Figure 46

46 (a) *Figure 46* is on the previous page. $\sin 22° = \frac{x}{20} \Rightarrow x = 20 \sin 22° \approx 7.49$ ft.

(b) $\cos 22° = \frac{h}{20} \Rightarrow h \approx 18.54$ ft, the original height of the ladder.

Let $x = 20 \sin 22° + 3$ and then $h = \sqrt{20^2 - x^2} \approx 17.03$ ft.

Hence, the top of the ladder moved from 18.54 to 17.03 or approximately 1.51 ft.

47 When the angle of elevation is 19°20′, $\tan 19°20′ = \frac{h_1}{110} \Rightarrow h_1 = 110 \tan 19°20′$.

When the angle of elevation is 31°50′, $\tan 31°50′ = \frac{h_2}{110} \Rightarrow h_2 = 110 \tan 31°50′$.

$$h_2 - h_1 \approx 68.29 - 38.59 = 29.7 \text{ km.}$$

48 $\tan 12°50′ = \frac{8.2}{y} \Rightarrow y \approx 36.0.$ $\tan 31°20′ = \frac{x}{y} \Rightarrow x \approx 21.9.$

The height is $x + 8.2$, or 30.1 m.

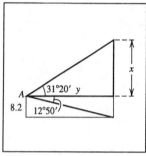

Figure 48

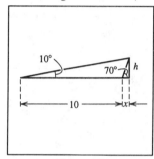

Figure 52

49 $\sin 65.8° = \dfrac{r}{r + 380} \Rightarrow r \sin 65.8° + 380 \sin 65.8° = r \Rightarrow$

$$r - r \sin 65.8° = 380 \sin 65.8° \Rightarrow r = \frac{380 \sin 65.8°}{1 - \sin 65.8°} \approx 3944 \text{ mi.}$$

50 Let h denote the length of the antenna and θ the angle opposite the garage.

$$\tan \theta = \frac{16}{100} \Rightarrow \theta \approx 9.09°. \quad \alpha = 12° + 9.09° = 21.09°. \quad \tan 21.09° = \frac{h + 16}{100} \Rightarrow$$

$$h + 16 = 100 \tan 21.09° \Rightarrow h = 100 \tan 21.09° - 16 \approx 22.6 \text{ ft.}$$

51 Let d be the distance traveled. $\tan 42° = \dfrac{10,000}{d} \Rightarrow d = 10,000 \cot 42°.$

Converting to mi/hr, we have $\dfrac{10,000 \cot 42° \text{ ft}}{1 \text{ minute}} \cdot \dfrac{60 \text{ minutes}}{1 \text{ hour}} \cdot \dfrac{1 \text{ mile}}{5280 \text{ ft}} \approx 126$ mi/hr.

52 See *Figure 52*. The motorist travels a distance of 10 km. Now $\tan 10° = \dfrac{h}{x + 10} \Rightarrow$

$x = h \cot 10° - 10$ and $\tan 70° = \frac{h}{x} \Rightarrow x = h \cot 70°.$ $h \cot 10° - 10 = h \cot 70° \Rightarrow$

$$h = \frac{10}{\cot 10° - \cot 70°} \approx 1.88 \text{ km.}$$

$\boxed{53}$ (a) As in Exercise 49, there is a right angle formed on the earth's surface.

Bisecting angle θ and forming a right triangle, we have

$$\cos\frac{\theta}{2} = \frac{R}{R+a} = \frac{4000}{26,300}. \quad \text{Thus, } \frac{\theta}{2} \approx 81.25° \Rightarrow \theta \approx 162.5°.$$

The percentage of the equator that is within signal range is $\frac{162.5°}{360°} \times 100 \approx 45\%$.

(b) Each satellite has a signal range of more than $120°$,

and thus all 3 will cover all points on the equator.

$\boxed{54}$ (a) Bisect θ and form a right triangle with

angle $\frac{\theta}{2}$, adjacent side $R - d$, and hypotenuse R.

$$\cos\frac{\theta}{2} = \frac{R-d}{R} \Rightarrow R\cos\frac{\theta}{2} = R - d \Rightarrow d = R - R\cos\frac{\theta}{2} \Rightarrow d = R(1 - \cos\frac{\theta}{2}).$$

(b) From Exercise 53, $\cos\frac{\theta}{2} = \frac{40}{263}$. The portion of the planet's surface that is within

signal range is $\dfrac{\text{surface area of spherical cap}}{\text{surface area of earth}} = \dfrac{2\pi Rd}{4\pi R^2} = \dfrac{d}{2R} = \dfrac{R(1-\cos\frac{\theta}{2})}{2R} =$

$$\frac{1-\cos\frac{\theta}{2}}{2} = \frac{1 - \frac{40}{263}}{2} = \frac{223}{526} \approx 0.424 \text{ or } 42.4\%.$$

$\boxed{55}$ Let $x = h - c$. $\sin\alpha = \frac{x}{d} \Rightarrow x = d\sin\alpha$. $h = x + c = d\sin\alpha + c$.

$\boxed{56}$ $\cot\alpha = \frac{x}{d} \Rightarrow x = d\cot\alpha$

$\boxed{57}$ Let x denote the distance from the base of the tower to the closer point.

$$\cot\beta = \frac{x}{h} \Rightarrow x = h\cot\beta. \quad \cot\alpha = \frac{x+d}{h} \Rightarrow x + d = h\cot\alpha \Rightarrow x = h\cot\alpha - d.$$

Thus, $h\cot\beta = h\cot\alpha - d \Rightarrow d = h\cot\alpha - h\cot\beta \Rightarrow d = h(\cot\alpha - \cot\beta) \Rightarrow$

$$h = \frac{d}{\cot\alpha - \cot\beta}.$$

$\boxed{58}$ The central angle of a section of an n-sided polygon has an angle measure of $\frac{360°}{n}$.

Bisecting that angle forms a right triangle with a hypotenuse r and opposite side x.

$$\sin\left(\frac{1}{2} \cdot \frac{360°}{n}\right) = \sin\left(\frac{180}{n}\right)° = \frac{x}{r} \Rightarrow x = r\sin\left(\frac{180}{n}\right)°. \quad \text{There are } n \text{ sides of length } 2x.$$

Hence, the perimeter P is $2nx = 2nr\sin\left(\frac{180}{n}\right)°$.

$\boxed{59}$ When the angle of elevation is α, $\tan\alpha = \frac{h_1}{d} \Rightarrow h_1 = d\tan\alpha$.

When the angle of elevation is β, $\tan\beta = \frac{h_2}{d} \Rightarrow h_2 = d\tan\beta$.

$$h = h_2 - h_1 = d\tan\beta - d\tan\alpha = d(\tan\beta - \tan\alpha).$$

$\boxed{60}$ Let x and y denote the sides as labeled in *Figure 48*. We see that $\cot\beta = \frac{y}{d} \Rightarrow$

$y = d\cot\beta$. Also, $\tan\alpha = \frac{x}{y} \Rightarrow x = y\tan\alpha = d\cot\beta\tan\alpha$.

Hence, $h = d + x = d + d\cot\beta\tan\alpha = d(1 + \cot\beta\tan\alpha)$.

$\boxed{61}$ The bearing from P to A is $90° - 20° = 70°$ east of north and is denoted by N70°E.

The bearings for B, C, and D are N40°W, S15°W, and S25°E, respectively.

62 The bearings for A, B, C, and D are N15°E, N30°W, S80°W, and S55°E, respectively.

63 (a) The ships form a right triangle with legs of 48 miles
and 27 miles. The distance between the two ships is

$$\sqrt{27^2 + 48^2} \approx 55 \text{ miles.}$$

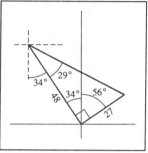

(b) The angle between the side of length 48 and the
hypotenuse is found by solving $\tan \alpha = \frac{27}{48}$ for α.
Now $\alpha \approx 29°$, so the second ship is approximately
$29° + 34° = \text{S63°E}$ of the first ship.

Figure 63

64 Let F denote the point of the fire.

$\angle BAF = 90° - 35°50' = 54°10'$ and $\angle ABF = 90° - 54°10' = 35°50'$.

Thus, $\angle BFA = 90°$. If d denotes the distance AF, then $\cos 54°10' = \frac{d}{5} \Rightarrow d \approx 2.9$ mi.

65 The plane's flight forms a right triangle with legs 180 miles and 270 miles.

The distance from A to the airplane is then $\sqrt{180^2 + 270^2} \approx 324.5$ mi.

66 (a) The plane's flight forms two legs (400 mi each) of a right triangle. The
hypotenuse of this 45°–45°–90° triangle is $400\sqrt{2}$. The plane is in the direction
$153° - 45° = 108°$ from point A (18° below the horizontal). It must take the
direction $270° + 18° = 288°$ to get back to A.

(b) At 400 mi/hr, it will take the plane $\sqrt{2}$ hr to travel $400\sqrt{2}$ mi.

67 Amplitude, 10 cm; period $= \frac{2\pi}{6\pi} = \frac{1}{3}$ sec; frequency $= \frac{6\pi}{2\pi} = 3$ oscillations/sec. The point
is at the origin at $t = 0$. It moves upward with decreasing speed, reaching the point
with coordinate 10 when $6\pi t = \frac{\pi}{2}$ or $t = \frac{1}{12}$. It then reverses direction and moves
downward, gaining speed until it reaches the origin when $6\pi t = \pi$ or $t = \frac{1}{6}$. It
continues downward with decreasing speed, reaching the point with coordinate -10
when $6\pi t = \frac{3\pi}{2}$ or $t = \frac{1}{4}$. It then reverses direction and moves upward with increasing
speed, returning to the origin when $6\pi t = 2\pi$ or $t = \frac{1}{3}$ to complete one oscillation.
Another approach is to simply model this movement in terms of proportions of the
sine curve. For one period, the sine increases for $\frac{1}{4}$ period, decreases for $\frac{1}{2}$ period, and
increases for its last $\frac{1}{4}$ period.

68 Amplitude, $\frac{1}{3}$ cm; period $= \frac{2\pi}{\pi/4} = 8$ sec; frequency $= \frac{\pi/4}{2\pi} = \frac{1}{8}$ oscillation/sec. The point
is at $d = \frac{1}{3}$ cm when $t = 0$. It then decreases in height until $\frac{\pi}{4}t = \pi$ or $t = 4$ where it
obtains a minimum of $d = -\frac{1}{3}$. It then reverses direction and increases to a height of
$d = \frac{1}{3}$ when $\frac{\pi}{4}t = 2\pi$ or $t = 8$ to complete one oscillation.

69 Amplitude, $4\,\text{cm}$; period $= \frac{2\pi}{3\pi/2} = \frac{4}{3}$ sec; frequency $= \frac{3\pi/2}{2\pi} = \frac{3}{4}$ oscillation/sec. The point is at $d = 4$ when $t = 0$. It then decreases in height until $\frac{3\pi}{2}t = \pi$ or $t = \frac{2}{3}$ where it obtains a minimum of $d = -4$. It then reverses direction and increases to a height of $d = 4$ when $\frac{3\pi}{2}t = 2\pi$ or $t = \frac{4}{3}$ to complete one oscillation.

70 Amplitude, $6\,\text{cm}$; period $= \frac{2\pi}{2\pi/3} = 3$ sec; frequency $= \frac{2\pi/3}{2\pi} = \frac{1}{3}$ oscillation/sec. The point is at the origin at $t = 0$. It will obtain a maximum height of 6 when $\frac{2\pi}{3}t = \frac{\pi}{2}$ or $t = \frac{3}{4}$. It then decreases in height until it obtains a minimum of -6 when $\frac{2\pi}{3}t = \frac{3\pi}{2}$ or $t = \frac{9}{4}$. It then reverses direction and returns to the origin when $\frac{2\pi}{3}t = 2\pi$ or $t = 3$ to complete one oscillation.

71 Period $= 3 \Rightarrow \frac{2\pi}{\omega} = 3 \Rightarrow \omega = \frac{2\pi}{3}$. Amplitude $= 5 \Rightarrow a = 5$. $d = 5\cos\frac{2\pi}{3}t$

72 $\frac{1}{2}$ oscillation per minute $\Rightarrow \frac{\omega}{2\pi} = \frac{1}{2} \Rightarrow \omega = \pi$. Amplitude $= 4 \Rightarrow a = 4$. $d = 4\sin\pi t$

73 (a) period $= 30 \Rightarrow \frac{2\pi}{\omega} = 30 \Rightarrow \omega = \frac{\pi}{15}$. When $t = 0$, the wave is at its highest point, thus, we use the cosine function. $y = 25\cos\frac{\pi}{15}t$, where t is in minutes.

(b) 180 ft/sec $= 10,800$ ft/min.

$10,800$ ft/min for 30 minutes is a distance of $324,000$ ft, or $61\frac{4}{11}$ miles.

74 (a) $y = a\sin bt = 8\sin\frac{\pi}{6}t \Rightarrow a = 8$ and $b = \frac{\pi}{6}$.

Thus, the wave has an amplitude of 8 ft and its period is $\frac{2\pi}{b} = \frac{2\pi}{\pi/6} = 12$ min.

(b) The wave moves 21 km every 12 min.

The wave's velocity is $\frac{21}{12} = 1.75$ km/min, or, 105 km/hr.

Chapter 5 Review Exercises

1 $330° \cdot \frac{\pi}{180} = \frac{11 \cdot 30\pi}{6 \cdot 30} = \frac{11\pi}{6}$; $405° \cdot \frac{\pi}{180} = \frac{9 \cdot 45\pi}{4 \cdot 45} = \frac{9\pi}{4}$;

$-150° \cdot \frac{\pi}{180} = -\frac{5 \cdot 30\pi}{6 \cdot 30} = -\frac{5\pi}{6}$; $240° \cdot \frac{\pi}{180} = \frac{4 \cdot 60\pi}{3 \cdot 60} = \frac{4\pi}{3}$;

$36° \cdot \frac{\pi}{180} = \frac{36\pi}{5 \cdot 36} = \frac{\pi}{5}$

2 $\frac{9\pi}{2} \cdot \left(\frac{180}{\pi}\right)° = \left(\frac{9 \cdot 90 \cdot 2\pi}{2\pi}\right)° = 810°$; $-\frac{2\pi}{3} \cdot \left(\frac{180}{\pi}\right)° = -\left(\frac{2 \cdot 60 \cdot 3\pi}{3\pi}\right)° = -120°$;

$\frac{7\pi}{4} \cdot \left(\frac{180}{\pi}\right)° = \left(\frac{7 \cdot 45 \cdot 4\pi}{4\pi}\right)° = 315°$; $5\pi \cdot \left(\frac{180}{\pi}\right)° = \left(\frac{5 \cdot 180 \cdot \pi}{\pi}\right)° = 900°$;

$\frac{\pi}{5} \cdot \left(\frac{180}{\pi}\right)° = \left(\frac{36 \cdot 5\pi}{5\pi}\right)° = 36°$

3 (a) $\theta = \frac{s}{r} = \frac{20\,\text{cm}}{2\,\text{m}} = \frac{20\,\text{cm}}{2(100)\,\text{cm}} = 0.1\,\text{radian}$

(b) $A = \frac{1}{2}r^2\theta = \frac{1}{2}(2)^2(0.1) = 0.2\,\text{m}^2$

4 (a) $s = r\theta = (15 \cdot \frac{1}{2})(70 \cdot \frac{\pi}{180}) = \frac{35\pi}{12} \approx 9.16$ cm

(b) $A = \frac{1}{2}r^2\theta = \frac{1}{2}(15 \cdot \frac{1}{2})^2(70 \cdot \frac{\pi}{180}) = \frac{175\pi}{16} \approx 34.4$ cm^2

5 $\sin 60° = \frac{9}{x} \Rightarrow \frac{\sqrt{3}}{2} = \frac{9}{x} \Rightarrow x = 6\sqrt{3}$; $\tan 60° = \frac{9}{y} \Rightarrow \sqrt{3} = \frac{9}{y} \Rightarrow y = 3\sqrt{3}$

6 $\sin 45° = \frac{x}{7} \Rightarrow \frac{\sqrt{2}}{2} = \frac{x}{7} \Rightarrow x = \frac{7}{2}\sqrt{2}$; $\cos 45° = \frac{y}{7} \Rightarrow \frac{\sqrt{2}}{2} = \frac{y}{7} \Rightarrow y = \frac{7}{2}\sqrt{2}$

7 $1 + \tan^2\theta = \sec^2\theta \Rightarrow \tan^2\theta = \sec^2\theta - 1 \Rightarrow \tan\theta = \sqrt{\sec^2\theta - 1}$

8 $1 + \cot^2\theta = \csc^2\theta \Rightarrow \cot^2\theta = \csc^2\theta - 1 \Rightarrow \cot\theta = \sqrt{\csc^2\theta - 1}$

9 $\sin\theta\,(\csc\theta - \sin\theta) = \sin\theta\,\csc\theta - \sin^2\theta = 1 - \sin^2\theta = \cos^2\theta$

10 $\cos\theta\,(\tan\theta + \cot\theta) =$

$$\cos\theta \cdot \frac{\sin\theta}{\cos\theta} + \cos\theta \cdot \frac{\cos\theta}{\sin\theta} = \sin\theta + \frac{\cos^2\theta}{\sin\theta} = \frac{\sin^2\theta + \cos^2\theta}{\sin\theta} = \frac{1}{\sin\theta} = \csc\theta$$

11 $(\cos^2\theta - 1)(\tan^2\theta + 1) = (\cos^2\theta - 1)(\sec^2\theta) = \cos^2\theta\,\sec^2\theta - \sec^2\theta = 1 - \sec^2\theta$

12 $\dfrac{\sec\theta - \cos\theta}{\tan\theta} = \dfrac{\dfrac{1}{\cos\theta} - \cos\theta}{\dfrac{\sin\theta}{\cos\theta}} = \dfrac{\dfrac{1 - \cos^2\theta}{\cos\theta}}{\dfrac{\sin\theta}{\cos\theta}} = \dfrac{\dfrac{\sin^2\theta}{\cos\theta}}{\dfrac{\sin\theta}{\cos\theta}} = \dfrac{\dfrac{\sin\theta}{\cos\theta}}{\dfrac{1}{\cos\theta}} = \dfrac{\tan\theta}{\sec\theta}$

13 $\dfrac{1 + \tan^2\theta}{\tan^2\theta} = \dfrac{1}{\tan^2\theta} + \dfrac{\tan^2\theta}{\tan^2\theta} = \cot^2\theta + 1 = \csc^2\theta$

14 $\dfrac{\sec\theta + \csc\theta}{\sec\theta - \csc\theta} = \dfrac{\dfrac{1}{\cos\theta} + \dfrac{1}{\sin\theta}}{\dfrac{1}{\cos\theta} - \dfrac{1}{\sin\theta}} = \dfrac{\dfrac{\sin\theta + \cos\theta}{\cos\theta\,\sin\theta}}{\dfrac{\sin\theta - \cos\theta}{\cos\theta\,\sin\theta}} = \dfrac{\sin\theta + \cos\theta}{\sin\theta - \cos\theta}$

15 $\dfrac{\cot\theta - 1}{1 - \tan\theta} = \dfrac{\dfrac{\cos\theta}{\sin\theta} - 1}{1 - \dfrac{\sin\theta}{\cos\theta}} = \dfrac{\dfrac{\cos\theta - \sin\theta}{\sin\theta}}{\dfrac{\cos\theta - \sin\theta}{\cos\theta}} = \dfrac{(\cos\theta - \sin\theta)\cos\theta}{(\cos\theta - \sin\theta)\sin\theta} = \dfrac{\cos\theta}{\sin\theta} = \cot\theta$

16 $\dfrac{1 + \sec\theta}{\tan\theta + \sin\theta} = \dfrac{1 + \dfrac{1}{\cos\theta}}{\dfrac{\sin\theta}{\cos\theta} + \dfrac{\sin\theta\,\cos\theta}{\cos\theta}} = \dfrac{\dfrac{\cos\theta + 1}{\cos\theta}}{\dfrac{\sin\theta\,(1 + \cos\theta)}{\cos\theta}} = \dfrac{1}{\sin\theta} = \csc\theta$

17 $\dfrac{\tan(-\theta) + \cot(-\theta)}{\tan\theta} = \dfrac{-\tan\theta - \cot\theta}{\tan\theta} = -\dfrac{\tan\theta}{\tan\theta} - \dfrac{\cot\theta}{\tan\theta} = -1 - \cot^2\theta = -(1 + \cot^2\theta) =$

$$-\csc^2\theta$$

18 $-\dfrac{1}{\csc(-\theta)} - \dfrac{\cot(-\theta)}{\sec(-\theta)} = -\dfrac{1}{-\csc\theta} - \dfrac{-\cot\theta}{\sec\theta} = \sin\theta + \dfrac{\cos\theta/\sin\theta}{1/\cos\theta} = \sin\theta + \dfrac{\cos^2\theta}{\sin\theta} =$

$$\dfrac{\sin^2\theta + \cos^2\theta}{\sin\theta} = \dfrac{1}{\sin\theta} = \csc\theta$$

19 $\text{opp} = \sqrt{\text{hyp}^2 - \text{adj}^2} = \sqrt{7^2 - 4^2} = \sqrt{33}.$ $\bigstar$ $\dfrac{\sqrt{33}}{7}, \dfrac{4}{7}, \dfrac{\sqrt{33}}{4}, \dfrac{4}{\sqrt{33}}, \dfrac{7}{4}, \dfrac{7}{\sqrt{33}}$

[20] (a) $x = 30$ and $y = -40 \Rightarrow r = \sqrt{30^2 + (-40)^2} = 50.$ ★ (a) $-\frac{4}{5}, \frac{3}{5}, -\frac{4}{3}, -\frac{3}{4}, \frac{5}{3}, -\frac{5}{4}$

(b) $2x + 3y + 6 = 0 \Leftrightarrow y = -\frac{2}{3}x - 2$, so the slope of the given line is $-\frac{2}{3}$.

The line through the origin with that slope is $y = -\frac{2}{3}x$.

If $x = -3$, then $y = 2$ and $(-3, 2)$ is a point on the terminal side of θ.

$$x = -3 \text{ and } y = 2 \Rightarrow r = \sqrt{(-3)^2 + 2^2} = \sqrt{13}.$$

$$\text{★ (b)} \; \frac{2}{\sqrt{13}}, -\frac{3}{\sqrt{13}}, -\frac{2}{3}, -\frac{3}{2}, -\frac{\sqrt{13}}{3}, \frac{\sqrt{13}}{2}$$

(c) For $\theta = -90°$, choose $x = 0$ and $y = -1$. r is 1.   ★ (c) $-1, 0, U, 0, U, -1$

[21] (a) $\sec\theta < 0 \Rightarrow P$ is in QII or QIII. $\sin\theta > 0 \Rightarrow P$ is in QI or QII. $\therefore P$ is in QII.

(b) $\cot\theta > 0 \Rightarrow P$ is in QI or QIII. $\csc\theta < 0 \Rightarrow P$ is in QIII or QIV. $\therefore P$ is in QIII.

(c) $\cos\theta > 0 \Rightarrow P$ is in QI or QIV. $\tan\theta < 0 \Rightarrow P$ is in QII or QIV. $\therefore P$ is in QIV.

[22] (a) $\tan\theta = \frac{\sin\theta}{\cos\theta} = -\frac{4}{3}$; the other values are just the reciprocals

(b) $\cot\theta = \frac{\cos\theta}{\sin\theta} = \frac{\csc\theta}{\sec\theta} \Rightarrow -\frac{3}{2} = \frac{\sqrt{13}/2}{\sec\theta} \Rightarrow \sec\theta = -\frac{\sqrt{13}}{3}$

[23] $P(7\pi) = P(\pi) = (-1, 0).$ $P(-\frac{5\pi}{2}) = P(-\frac{\pi}{2}) = (0, -1).$ $P(\frac{9\pi}{2}) = P(\frac{\pi}{2}) = (0, 1).$

$$P(-\tfrac{3\pi}{4}) = (-\tfrac{\sqrt{2}}{2}, -\tfrac{\sqrt{2}}{2}). \quad P(18\pi) = P(0) = (1, 0). \quad P(\tfrac{\pi}{6}) = (\tfrac{\sqrt{3}}{2}, \tfrac{1}{2}).$$

[24] $P(t + 3\pi) = P(t + \pi) = P(t - \pi) = (\frac{3}{5}, \frac{4}{5}).$

$$P(-t) = (-\tfrac{3}{5}, \tfrac{4}{5}). \quad P(2\pi - t) = P(-t + 2\pi) = (-\tfrac{3}{5}, \tfrac{4}{5}).$$

[25] (a) $\theta = \frac{5\pi}{4} \Rightarrow \theta_R = \frac{5\pi}{4} - \pi = \frac{\pi}{4}.$ $\theta = -\frac{5\pi}{6} \Rightarrow \theta_C = \frac{7\pi}{6}$ and $\theta_R = \frac{7\pi}{6} - \frac{\pi}{6} = \frac{\pi}{6}.$

$$\theta = -\tfrac{9\pi}{8} \Rightarrow \theta_C = \tfrac{7\pi}{8} \text{ and } \theta_R = \pi - \tfrac{7\pi}{8} = \tfrac{\pi}{8}.$$

(b) $\theta = 245° \Rightarrow \theta_R = 245° - 180° = 65°.$ $\theta = 137° \Rightarrow \theta_R = 180° - 137° = 43°.$

$$\theta = 892° \Rightarrow \theta_C = 172° \text{ and } \theta_R = 180° - 172° = 8°.$$

[26] (a) For $\theta = \frac{9\pi}{2}$, choose $x = 0$ and $y = 1$. $r = 1.$ ★ (a) $1, 0, U, 0, U, 1$

(b) For $\theta = -\frac{5\pi}{4}$, choose $x = -1$ and $y = 1$. $r = \sqrt{2}.$

$$\text{★ (b)} \; \frac{\sqrt{2}}{2}, -\frac{\sqrt{2}}{2}, -1, -1, -\sqrt{2}, \sqrt{2}$$

(c) For $\theta = 0$, choose $x = 1$ and $y = 0$. $r = 1.$ ★ (c) $0, 1, 0, U, 1, U$

(d) For $\theta = \frac{11\pi}{6}$, choose $x = \sqrt{3}$ and $y = -1$. $r = 2.$

$$\text{★ (d)} \; -\frac{1}{2}, \frac{\sqrt{3}}{2}, -\frac{\sqrt{3}}{3}, -\sqrt{3}, \frac{2}{\sqrt{3}}, -2$$

[27] (a) $\cos 225° = -\cos 45° = -\frac{\sqrt{2}}{2}$ (b) $\tan 150° = -\tan 30° = -\frac{\sqrt{3}}{3}$

(c) $\sin\left(-\frac{\pi}{6}\right) = -\sin\frac{\pi}{6} = -\frac{1}{2}$ (d) $\sec\frac{4\pi}{3} = -\sec\frac{\pi}{3} = -2$

(e) $\cot\frac{7\pi}{4} = -\cot\frac{\pi}{4} = -1$ (f) $\csc 300° = -\csc 60° = -\frac{2}{\sqrt{3}}$

[28] $\sin\theta = -0.7604 \Rightarrow \theta = \sin^{-1}(-0.7604) \approx -49.5° \Rightarrow \theta_R \approx 49.5°.$

Since the sine is negative in QIII and QIV, and the secant is positive in QIV,

we want the fourth-quadrant angle having $\theta_R = 49.5°$. $360° - 49.5° = 310.5°$

29 $y = 5\cos x$ •   stretch $\cos x$ by a factor of 5   ★ 5, 2π, x-int. @ $\frac{\pi}{2} + \pi n$

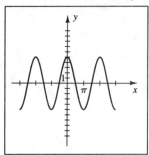

Figure 29

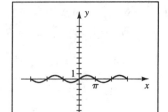

Figure 30

30 $y = \frac{2}{3}\sin x$ •   compress $\sin x$ by a factor of $\frac{3}{2}$ { or multiply by $\frac{2}{3}$ }

★ $\frac{2}{3}$, 2π, x-int. @ πn

31 $y = \frac{1}{3}\sin 3x$ •   horizontally compress $\sin x$ by a factor of 3 and

compress that graph by a factor of 3   ★ $\frac{1}{3}$, $\frac{2\pi}{3}$, x-int. @ $\frac{\pi}{3} n$

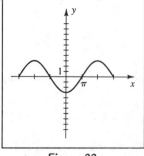

Figure 31

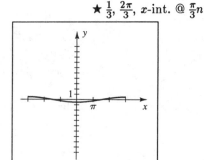

Figure 32

32 $y = -\frac{1}{2}\cos\frac{1}{3}x$ •   horizontally stretch $\cos x$ by a factor of 3, compress by a factor of

2, and reflect that graph through the x-axis   ★ $\frac{1}{2}$, 6π, x-int. @ $\frac{3\pi}{2} + 3\pi n$

33 $y = -3\cos\frac{1}{2}x$ •   horizontally stretch $\cos x$ by a factor of 2, stretch that graph by a

factor of 3, and reflect that graph through the x-axis   ★ 3, 4π, x-int. @ $\pi + 2\pi n$

Figure 33

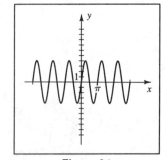

Figure 34

34 $y = 4\sin 2x$ •   horizontally compress $\sin x$ by a factor of 2 and stretch that graph

by a factor of 4   ★ 4, π, x-int. @ $\frac{\pi}{2} n$

$\boxed{35}$ $y = 2\sin\pi x$ • horizontally compress $\sin x$ by a factor of π, and stretch that graph

by a factor of 2 $\star$ 2, 2, x-int. @ n

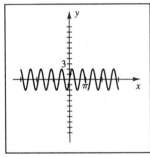

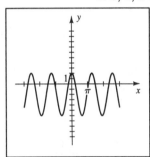

Figure 35   Figure 36

$\boxed{36}$ $y = 4\cos\frac{\pi}{2}x - 2$ • horizontally compress $\cos x$ by a factor of $\pi/2$,

stretch that graph by a factor of 4, and shift the last graph 2 units down

$\star$ 4, 4, x-int. @ $\frac{2}{3} + 4n$, $\frac{10}{3} + 4n$

Note: Let a denote the amplitude and p the period.

$\boxed{37}$ (a) $a = |-1.43| = 1.43$, $\frac{3}{4}p = 1.5 \Rightarrow p = 2$

(b) $b = \frac{2\pi}{p} = \frac{2\pi}{2} = \pi$, $y = 1.43\sin\pi x$

$\boxed{38}$ (a) $a = |-3.27| = 3.27$, $\frac{1}{4}p = \frac{3\pi}{4} \Rightarrow p = 3\pi$

(b) $b = \frac{2\pi}{p} = \frac{2\pi}{3\pi} = \frac{2}{3}$, $y = -3.27\sin\frac{2}{3}x$

$\boxed{39}$ (a) Since the y-intercept is -3, $a = |-3| = 3$.

The second positive x-intercept is π, so $\frac{3}{4}p = \pi \Rightarrow p = \frac{4\pi}{3}$.

(b) $b = \frac{2\pi}{p} = \frac{2\pi}{4\pi/3} = \frac{3}{2}$, $y = -3\cos\frac{3}{2}x$

$\boxed{40}$ (a) Since the y-intercept is 2, $a = |2| = 2$.

The first positive x-intercept is 1, so $\frac{1}{4}p = 1 \Rightarrow p = 4$.

(b) $b = \frac{2\pi}{p} = \frac{2\pi}{4} = \frac{\pi}{2}$, $y = 2\cos\frac{\pi}{2}x$.

$\boxed{41}$ $y = 2\sin(x - \frac{2\pi}{3})$ • $0 \le x - \frac{2\pi}{3} \le 2\pi \Rightarrow \frac{2\pi}{3} \le x \le \frac{8\pi}{3}$

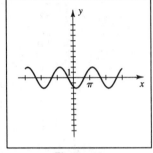

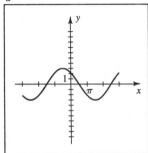

Figure 41   Figure 42

$\boxed{42}$ $y = -3\sin(\frac{1}{2}x - \frac{\pi}{4}) = -3\sin[\frac{1}{2}(x - \frac{\pi}{2})]$.

$0 \le \frac{1}{2}x - \frac{\pi}{4} \le 2\pi \Rightarrow \frac{\pi}{4} \le \frac{1}{2}x \le \frac{9\pi}{4} \Rightarrow \frac{\pi}{2} \le x \le \frac{9\pi}{2}$

43 $y = -4\cos\left(x + \frac{\pi}{6}\right)$ • $-\frac{\pi}{2} \le x + \frac{\pi}{6} \le \frac{3\pi}{2} \Rightarrow -\frac{2\pi}{3} \le x \le \frac{4\pi}{3}$

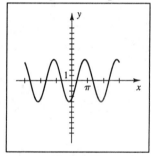

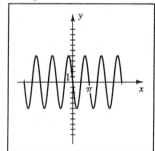

Figure 43   Figure 44

44 $y = 5\cos\left(2x + \frac{\pi}{2}\right) = 5\cos\left[2\left(x + \frac{\pi}{4}\right)\right]$.

   $-\frac{\pi}{2} \le 2x + \frac{\pi}{2} \le \frac{3\pi}{2} \Rightarrow -\pi \le 2x \le \pi \Rightarrow -\frac{\pi}{2} \le x \le \frac{\pi}{2}$

45 $y = 2\tan\left(\frac{1}{2}x - \pi\right) = 2\tan\left[\frac{1}{2}(x - 2\pi)\right]$.

   $-\frac{\pi}{2} \le \frac{1}{2}x - \pi \le \frac{\pi}{2} \Rightarrow \frac{\pi}{2} \le \frac{1}{2}x \le \frac{3\pi}{2} \Rightarrow \pi \le x \le 3\pi$, VA @ $x = \pi + 2\pi n$

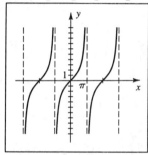

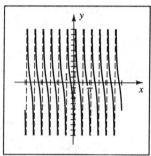

Figure 45   Figure 46

46 $y = -3\tan\left(2x + \frac{\pi}{3}\right) = -3\tan\left[2\left(x + \frac{\pi}{6}\right)\right]$.

   $-\frac{\pi}{2} \le 2x + \frac{\pi}{3} \le \frac{\pi}{2} \Rightarrow -\frac{5\pi}{6} \le 2x \le \frac{\pi}{6} \Rightarrow -\frac{5\pi}{12} \le x \le \frac{\pi}{12}$, VA @ $x = -\frac{5\pi}{12} + \frac{\pi}{2}n$

47 $y = -4\cot\left(2x - \frac{\pi}{2}\right) = -4\cot\left[2\left(x - \frac{\pi}{4}\right)\right]$.

   $0 \le 2x - \frac{\pi}{2} \le \pi \Rightarrow \frac{\pi}{2} \le 2x \le \frac{3\pi}{2} \Rightarrow \frac{\pi}{4} \le x \le \frac{3\pi}{4}$, VA @ $x = \frac{\pi}{4} + \frac{\pi}{2}n$

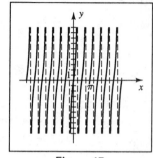

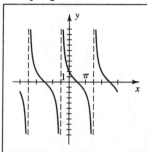

Figure 47   Figure 48

48 $y = 2\cot\left(\frac{1}{2}x + \frac{\pi}{4}\right) = 2\cot\left[\frac{1}{2}\left(x + \frac{\pi}{2}\right)\right]$.

   $0 \le \frac{1}{2}x + \frac{\pi}{4} \le \pi \Rightarrow -\frac{\pi}{4} \le \frac{1}{2}x \le \frac{3\pi}{4} \Rightarrow -\frac{\pi}{2} \le x \le \frac{3\pi}{2}$, VA @ $x = -\frac{\pi}{2} + 2\pi n$

49 $y = \sec\left(\frac{1}{2}x + \pi\right) = \sec\left[\frac{1}{2}(x + 2\pi)\right]$.

$-\frac{\pi}{2} \le \frac{1}{2}x + \pi \le \frac{\pi}{2} \Rightarrow -\frac{3\pi}{2} \le \frac{1}{2}x \le -\frac{\pi}{2} \Rightarrow -3\pi \le x \le -\pi$, VA @ $x = -3\pi + 2\pi n$

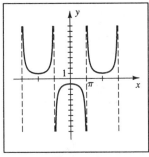

Figure 49

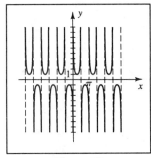

Figure 50

50 $y = \sec\left(2x - \frac{\pi}{2}\right) = \sec\left[2(x - \frac{\pi}{4})\right]$.

$-\frac{\pi}{2} \le 2x - \frac{\pi}{2} \le \frac{\pi}{2} \Rightarrow 0 \le 2x \le \pi \Rightarrow 0 \le x \le \frac{\pi}{2}$, VA @ $x = \frac{\pi}{2}n$

51 $y = \csc\left(2x - \frac{\pi}{4}\right) = \csc\left[2(x - \frac{\pi}{8})\right]$.

$0 \le 2x - \frac{\pi}{4} \le \pi \Rightarrow \frac{\pi}{4} \le 2x \le \frac{5\pi}{4} \Rightarrow \frac{\pi}{8} \le x \le \frac{5\pi}{8}$, VA @ $x = \frac{\pi}{8} + \frac{\pi}{2}n$

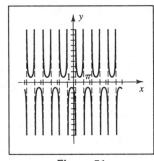

Figure 51

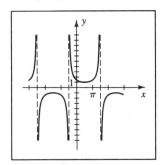

Figure 52

52 $y = \csc\left(\frac{1}{2}x + \frac{\pi}{4}\right) = \csc\left[\frac{1}{2}(x + \frac{\pi}{2})\right]$.

$0 \le \frac{1}{2}x + \frac{\pi}{4} \le \pi \Rightarrow -\frac{\pi}{4} \le \frac{1}{2}x \le \frac{3\pi}{4} \Rightarrow -\frac{\pi}{2} \le x \le \frac{3\pi}{2}$, VA @ $x = -\frac{\pi}{2} + 2\pi n$

53 $\alpha = 90° - \beta = 30°$. $\cot \beta = \frac{a}{b} \Rightarrow a = b \cot \beta = 40(\frac{1}{3}\sqrt{3}) \approx 23$.

$$\csc \beta = \frac{c}{b} \Rightarrow c = b \csc \beta = 40(\frac{2}{3}\sqrt{3}) \approx 46.$$

54 $\beta = 90° - \alpha = 35°20'$. $\tan \alpha = \frac{a}{b} \Rightarrow a = b \tan \alpha = 220 \tan 54°40' \approx 310$.

$$\sec \alpha = \frac{c}{b} \Rightarrow c = b \sec \alpha = 220 \sec 54°40' \approx 380.$$

55 $\tan \alpha = \frac{a}{b} = \frac{62}{25} \Rightarrow \alpha \approx 68°$. $\beta = 90° - \alpha \approx 22°$.

$$c = \sqrt{a^2 + b^2} = \sqrt{3844 + 625} = \sqrt{4469} \approx 67.$$

56 $\sin \alpha = \frac{a}{c} = \frac{9.0}{41} \Rightarrow \alpha \approx 13°$. $\beta = 90° - \alpha \approx 77°$.

$$b = \sqrt{c^2 - a^2} = \sqrt{1681 - 81} = \sqrt{1600} = 40.$$

57 (a) $\left(\dfrac{545 \text{ rev}}{1 \text{ min}}\right)\left(\dfrac{2\pi \text{ rad}}{1 \text{ rev}}\right)\left(\dfrac{1 \text{ min}}{60 \text{ sec}}\right) = \dfrac{109\pi}{6}$ rad/sec ≈ 57 rad/sec

   (b) $d = 22.625$ ft $\Rightarrow C = \pi d = 22.625\pi$ ft.

$$\left(\dfrac{22.625\pi \text{ ft}}{1 \text{ rev}}\right)\left(\dfrac{545 \text{ rev}}{1 \text{ min}}\right)\left(\dfrac{1 \text{ mile}}{5280 \text{ ft}}\right)\left(\dfrac{60 \text{ min}}{1 \text{ hour}}\right) \approx 440.2 \text{ mi/hr}$$

58 Let h denote the height of the tower. $\tan 79.2° = \dfrac{h}{200} \Rightarrow h \approx 1048$ ft.

59 $\Delta f = \dfrac{2fv}{c} \Rightarrow v = \dfrac{c(\Delta f)}{2f} = \dfrac{186{,}000 \times 10^8}{2 \times 10^{14}} = 0.093$ mi/sec

60 The angle φ has an adjacent side of $\frac{1}{2}(230 \text{ m})$, or 115 m. $\tan \varphi = \frac{147}{115} \Rightarrow \varphi \approx 52°$.

61 Let d denote the distance from Venus to the sun.

$$\sin 47° = \dfrac{d}{92{,}900{,}000} \Rightarrow d \approx 67{,}942{,}759 \text{ mi., or approximately } 67{,}900{,}000 \text{ mi.}$$

62 The depth of the cone is 4 inches and its slant height is 5 inches.

Thus, $4^2 + r^2 = 5^2 \Rightarrow r = 3$ inches. The circumference of the rim of the cone is

$$2\pi r = 6\pi. \text{ On the circle, } \theta = \tfrac{s}{r} = \tfrac{6\pi}{5} \text{ radians} = 216°.$$

63 Let A denote the point at the 36° angle. Let Q denote the highest point of the mountain and P denote Q's projection such that $\angle APQ = 90°$. Let x denote the distance from the left end of the mountain to P and let y denote the distance from the right end of the mountain to P. $\cot 36° = \dfrac{x + 200}{260} \Rightarrow x = 260 \cot 36° - 200.$

$$\cot 47° = \dfrac{y + 150}{260} \Rightarrow y = 260 \cot 47° - 150. \quad x + y \approx 250 \text{ ft.}$$

64 (a) Let h denote the height of the building and x the distance between the two buildings. $\tan 59° = \dfrac{h - 50}{x}$ and $\tan 62° = \dfrac{h}{x} \Rightarrow h = x \tan 59° + 50$ and

$$h = x \tan 62° \Rightarrow x \tan 62° - x \tan 59° = 50 \Rightarrow x = \dfrac{50}{\tan 62° - \tan 59°} \approx 231.0 \text{ ft.}$$

   (b) From part (a), $h = x \tan 62° \approx 434.5$ ft.

65 (a) Let $x = \overline{QR}$. $\cot \beta = \dfrac{x}{h} \Rightarrow x = h \cot \beta$. $\cot \alpha = \dfrac{d + x}{h} \Rightarrow x = h \cot \alpha - d$.

   Thus, $h \cot \beta = h \cot \alpha - d \Rightarrow d = h(\cot \alpha - \cot \beta) \Rightarrow h = \dfrac{d}{\cot \alpha - \cot \beta}.$

   (b) $d = 2$ miles, $\alpha = 15°$, and $\beta = 20° \Rightarrow h = \dfrac{2}{\cot 15° - \cot 20°} \approx 2.03$, or 2 miles.

66 (a) Extend the two boundary lines for h { call these l_{top} and l_{bottom} } to the right until they intersect a line l extended down from the front edge of the building. Let x denote the distance from the intersection of the incline and l_{bottom} to l and y the distance on l from l_{top} to the lower left corner of the building.

$$\cos \alpha = \tfrac{x}{d} \Rightarrow x = d \cos \alpha. \quad \sin \alpha = \dfrac{h + y}{d} \Rightarrow y = d \sin \alpha - h. \quad \tan \theta = \dfrac{y + T}{x} \Rightarrow$$
$$T = x \tan \theta - y = d \cos \alpha \tan \theta - d \sin \alpha + h = h + d(\cos \alpha \tan \theta - \sin \alpha).$$

   (b) $T = 6 + 50(\cos 15° \tan 31.4° - \sin 15°) \approx 6 + 50(0.3308) \approx 22.54$ ft.

67 (a) $\cos\theta = \frac{15}{s} \Rightarrow s = \frac{15}{\cos\theta}$. $E = \frac{5000\cos\theta}{s^2} = \frac{5000\cos\theta}{225/\cos^2\theta} = \frac{200}{9}\cos^3\theta$.

$$\theta = 30° \Rightarrow E = \frac{200}{9}(\tfrac{1}{2}\sqrt{3})^3 = \frac{200}{9}(\tfrac{3}{8}\sqrt{3}) = \frac{25}{3}\sqrt{3} \approx 14.43 \text{ ft-candles}$$

(b) $E = \frac{1}{2}E_{\max} \Rightarrow \frac{200}{9}\cos^3\theta = \frac{1}{2}(\frac{200}{9}\cos^3 0°) \Rightarrow \cos^3\theta = \frac{1}{2} \Rightarrow \cos\theta = \sqrt[3]{\frac{1}{2}} \Rightarrow \theta \approx 37.47°$

68 (a) Let $x = \overline{PT}$ and $y = \overline{QT}$. Now $x^2 + d^2 = y^2$, $h = x\sin\alpha$, and $h = y\sin\beta$.

$$d^2 = y^2 - x^2 = \frac{h^2}{\sin^2\beta} - \frac{h^2}{\sin^2\alpha} = \frac{h^2(\sin^2\alpha - \sin^2\beta)}{\sin^2\alpha\sin^2\beta} \Rightarrow h^2 = \frac{d^2\sin^2\alpha\sin^2\beta}{\sin^2\alpha - \sin^2\beta} \Rightarrow$$

$$h = \frac{d\sin\alpha\sin\beta}{\sqrt{\sin^2\alpha - \sin^2\beta}}.$$

(b) $\alpha = 30°$, $\beta = 20°$, and $d = 10 \Rightarrow h = \frac{10\sin 30°\sin 20°}{\sqrt{\sin^2 30° - \sin^2 20°}} \approx 4.69$ miles.

69 (a) Let d denote the distance from the end of the bracket to the wall.

$$\cos 30° = \frac{d}{85.5} \Rightarrow d = (85.5)(\tfrac{1}{2}\sqrt{3}) \approx 74.05 \text{ in.}$$

(b) Let y denote the side opposite 30°. $\sin 30° = \frac{y}{85.5} \Rightarrow y = 42.75$ in.

Thus, the distance from the ceiling to the top of the screen is the

(length of the bracket $+ y -$ one-half the height of the screen) $=$

$$(18'' + 42.75'' - 36'') = 24.75''.$$

70 (a) $\sin\theta = \frac{\frac{1}{2}x}{a} \Rightarrow x = 2a\sin\theta$. The area of one face is $\frac{1}{2}$(base)(height) $= \frac{1}{2}xa$.

$$S = 4(\tfrac{1}{2}ax) = 2ax = 2a(2a\sin\theta) = 4a^2\sin\theta.$$

(b) $\cos\theta = \frac{y}{a} \Rightarrow y = a\cos\theta$.

$$V = \frac{1}{3}(\text{base area})(\text{height}) = \frac{1}{3}x^2 y = \frac{1}{3}(2a\sin\theta)^2(a\cos\theta) = \frac{4}{3}a^3\sin^2\theta\cos\theta.$$

71 (a) Let $\theta = \angle PCQ$. Since $\angle BPC = 90°$, $\cos\theta = \frac{R}{R+h} \Rightarrow$

$$R + h = R\sec\theta \Rightarrow h = R\sec\theta - R. \text{ Since } \theta = \frac{s}{R}, h = R\sec\frac{s}{R} - R.$$

(b) $h = R\left(\sec\frac{s}{R} - 1\right) = 4000\left(\sec\frac{50}{4000} - 1\right) \approx 0.31252\,\text{mi} \approx 1650\,\text{ft}$.

72 $y = 1 - 1\cos\left(\frac{1}{2}\pi x/10\right) = -\cos\left(\frac{\pi}{20}x\right) + 1$.

For $0 \le x \le 10$,

$$0 \le \tfrac{\pi}{20}x \le \tfrac{\pi}{2}$$

$$\Rightarrow 1 \ge \cos\left(\tfrac{\pi}{20}x\right) \ge 0$$

$$\Rightarrow -1 \le -\cos\left(\tfrac{\pi}{20}x\right) \le 0$$

$$\Rightarrow 0 \le -\cos\left(\tfrac{\pi}{20}x\right) + 1 \le 1$$

$$\Rightarrow 0 \le y \le 1.$$

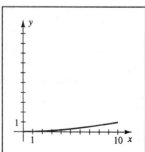

Figure 72

$\boxed{73}$ The range of temperatures is $0.6\,°F$, so $a = 0.3$. $\frac{2\pi}{b} = 24 \Rightarrow b = \frac{\pi}{12}$. The average

temperature occurs at 11 A.M., 6 hours before the high at 5 P.M., which corresponds

to $t = 11$. The argument of the sine is then $\frac{\pi}{12}(t - 11)$, or $\frac{\pi}{12}t - \frac{11\pi}{12}$. Thus,

$$y = 98.6 + (0.3)\sin\left(\frac{\pi}{12}t - \frac{11\pi}{12}\right) \{ \text{ or equivalently, } y = 98.6 + (0.3)\sin\left(\frac{\pi}{12}t + \frac{13\pi}{12}\right) \}.$$

$\boxed{74}$ (a) $p = \frac{2\pi}{\pi/6} = 12$ months

(b) The highest temperature will occur when the argument of the sine is $\frac{\pi}{2}$.

$\frac{\pi}{6}(t - 3) = \frac{\pi}{2} \Rightarrow t - 3 = 3 \Rightarrow t = 6$ months.

This is July 1st and the temperature is $20.8\,°C$, or $69.44\,°F$.

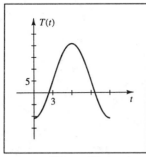

Figure 74

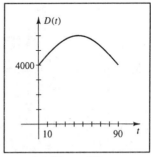

Figure 75

$\boxed{75}$ (a) $p = \frac{2\pi}{\pi/90} = 180\,\text{days}$

(b) As in Exercise 74, $\frac{\pi}{90}t = \frac{\pi}{2} \Rightarrow t = 45$ days into summer.

$\boxed{76}$ (a) The cork is in simple harmonic motion. At $t = 0$, its height is 13 ft.

It decreases until $t = 1$, reaching a minimum of 11 ft.

It then increases, reaching a maximum of 13 ft at $t = 2$.

(b) From part (a), the cork is rising for $1 \le t \le 2$.

Chapter 5 Discussion Exercises

$\boxed{1}$ On the TI-82/83 with $a = 15$, there is an indication that there are 15 sine waves on

each side of the y-axis, but the minimums and maximums do not get to -1 and 1,

respectively. With $a = 30$, the number of sine waves is undetectable—there simply

aren't enough pixels for any degree of clarity. With $a = 45$, there are 2 sine waves on

each side of the y-axis—there should be 45!

2 Divide 10^{k+1} by 2π, subtract the greatest integer of that result from itself, leaving only a fractional part of 2π radians. Multiply that result by 2π to give you a number between 0 and 2π, and then take the sine of that value. On the TI-82/83, $k = 11$. To find $\sin(10^{12})$, enter 10^{12}, divide by 2π, take fPart Ans to obtain .89 {fPart is under the NUM submenu from the MATH key}, multiply by 2π, and take the sine of that result. Thus, $\sin(10^{12}) \approx \sin(5.59203) \approx -0.6374$.

3 The sum on the left-side of the equation can never be greater than 3—no solutions.

4 A discussion should bring out the following comments:

(1) the trigonometric functions are all periodic functions,

(2) periodic functions can't be one-to-one functions,

(3) for a function to have an inverse it must be one-to-one;

and come up with the conclusion that any one of the trigonometric functions cannot have an inverse unless its domain is restricted.

5 The graph of $y_1 = x$, $y_2 = \sin x$, and $y_3 = \tan x$ in the suggested viewing rectangle, $[-0.1, 0.1]$ by $[-0.1, 0.1]$, indicates that their values are very close to each other near $x = 0$—in fact, the graphs of the functions are indistinguishable. Creating a table of values on the order of 10^{-10} also shows that all three functions are nearly equal.

6 (a) Consider the track as a unit circle. The 2 km can then be thought of as an angle measurement of 2 radians. Thus, $x = \cos 2 \approx -0.4161$ and $y = \sin 2 \approx 0.9093$.

(b) Since the diameter is 2 km, the radius is 1 km and the circumference is 2π km. $\frac{500}{2\pi} \approx 79.577472$ revolutions. Subtracting the 79 whole laps and multiplying the remainder by 2π we obtain $(2\pi)(0.577472) \approx 3.6283607$ radians. Thus, $x \approx \cos(3.6283607) \approx -0.8838$ and $y \approx \sin(3.6283607) \approx -0.4678$. Alternatively, $x = \cos 500 \approx -0.8838$ and $y = \sin 500 \approx -0.4678$.

$\boxed{7}$ (a) S is at $(0, -1)$ on the rectangular coordinate system. Starting at S, subtract 1 from the 2 km to get to the circular portion of the track. Now consider $t = (1 + \frac{3\pi}{2})$ as the radian measurement of the track in Discussion Exercise 6. $\{\frac{3\pi}{2}$ to get to the bottom of the circle and 1 to make the second km.$\}$ $x = \cos t + 1 \approx 1.8415$ and $y = \sin t \approx -0.5403$.

   (b) The perimeter of the track is $(4 + 2\pi)$ km. $\frac{500}{4 + 2\pi} \approx 48.623066$ laps. $(4 + 2\pi)(0.623066) \approx 6.4071052$. To determine where this places us on the track, start at S and subtract 1 $\{$ to get to $(1, -1)\}$, subtract π $\{$ to get to $(1, 1)\}$, and subtract 2 $\{$ to get to $(-1, 1)\}$. This is about 0.26551259. Now consider $t = (0.26551259 + \frac{\pi}{2})$ as the radian measurement of the track in Discussion Exercise 6. $x \approx \cos t - 1 \approx -1.2624$ and $y \approx \sin t \approx 0.9650$.

$\boxed{8}$ (a) $\omega = \dfrac{5000 \text{ rev}}{1 \text{ minute}} \times \dfrac{1 \text{ minute}}{60 \text{ seconds}} \times \dfrac{2\pi \text{ radians}}{1 \text{ revolution}} = \dfrac{500\pi}{3} \approx 523.6$ radian/sec.

   (b) Since the depth is 18, we have $d = 18$. The radius is 5 inches, so $a = 5$. Thus, $D(t) = a \cos(\omega t + c) + d = 5 \cos\left(\frac{500\pi}{3}t + c\right) + 18$. Since the point is initially at a depth of 23 inches, $D = 23$ when $t = 0$. Substituting, we have $23 = 5 \cos(c) + 18 \Rightarrow \cos c = 1 \Rightarrow c = 0$. Hence, $D(t) = 5 \cos\left(\frac{500\pi}{3}t\right) + 18$.

   (c) Graph $Y_1 = 5 \cos\left(\frac{500\pi}{3}x\right) + 18$ on the interval $[0, 0.12]$. From the graph, we see that the propeller completes approximately 10 revolutions in 0.12 seconds.

$[0, 0.12]$ by $[0, 25]$

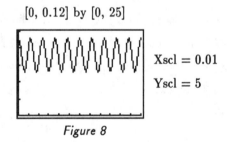

Xscl = 0.01

Yscl = 5

Figure 8

Chapter 6: Analytic Trigonometry

1 $\csc\theta - \sin\theta = \dfrac{1}{\sin\theta} - \sin\theta = \dfrac{1-\sin^2\theta}{\sin\theta} = \dfrac{\cos^2\theta}{\sin\theta} = \dfrac{\cos\theta}{\sin\theta}\cdot\cos\theta = \cot\theta\,\cos\theta$

2 $\sin x + \cos x \cot x = \sin x + \cos x\cdot\dfrac{\cos x}{\sin x} = \dfrac{\sin^2 x + \cos^2 x}{\sin x} = \dfrac{1}{\sin x} = \csc x$

3 $\dfrac{\sec^2 2u - 1}{\sec^2 2u} = 1 - \dfrac{1}{\sec^2 2u} = 1 - \cos^2 2u = \sin^2 2u$

4 $\tan t + 2\cos t \csc t = \dfrac{\sin t}{\cos t} + \dfrac{2\cos t}{\sin t} = \dfrac{\sin^2 t + 2\cos^2 t}{\cos t \sin t} =$

$$\dfrac{1-\cos^2 t + 2\cos^2 t}{\cos t \sin t} = \dfrac{1+\cos^2 t}{\cos t \sin t} = \dfrac{1}{\cos t \sin t} + \dfrac{\cos t}{\sin t} = \sec t \csc t + \cot t$$

5 $\dfrac{\csc^2\theta}{1+\tan^2\theta} = \dfrac{\csc^2\theta}{\sec^2\theta} = \dfrac{1/\sin^2\theta}{1/\cos^2\theta} = \dfrac{\cos^2\theta}{\sin^2\theta} = \left(\dfrac{\cos\theta}{\sin\theta}\right)^2 = \cot^2\theta$

6 $(\tan u + \cot u)(\cos u + \sin u) =$

$$\left(\dfrac{\sin u}{\cos u} + \dfrac{\cos u}{\sin u}\right)(\cos u + \sin u) = \left(\dfrac{\sin^2 u + \cos^2 u}{\cos u \sin u}\right)(\cos u + \sin u) =$$

$$\left(\dfrac{1}{\cos u \sin u}\right)(\cos u + \sin u) = \dfrac{\cos u}{\cos u \sin u} + \dfrac{\sin u}{\cos u \sin u} = \dfrac{1}{\sin u} + \dfrac{1}{\cos u} = \csc u + \sec u$$

7 $\dfrac{1+\cos 3t}{\sin 3t} + \dfrac{\sin 3t}{1+\cos 3t} = \dfrac{(1+\cos 3t)^2 + \sin^2 3t}{\sin 3t\,(1+\cos 3t)} =$

$$\dfrac{1 + 2\cos 3t + \cos^2 3t + \sin^2 3t}{\sin 3t\,(1+\cos 3t)} = \dfrac{2+2\cos 3t}{\sin 3t\,(1+\cos 3t)} = \dfrac{2(1+\cos 3t)}{\sin 3t\,(1+\cos 3t)} = 2\csc 3t$$

8 $\tan^2\alpha - \sin^2\alpha = \dfrac{\sin^2\alpha}{\cos^2\alpha} - \sin^2\alpha = \sin^2\alpha\left(\dfrac{1}{\cos^2\alpha} - 1\right) = (\sec^2\alpha - 1)\sin^2\alpha = \tan^2\alpha\,\sin^2\alpha$

9 $\dfrac{1}{1-\cos\gamma} + \dfrac{1}{1+\cos\gamma} = \dfrac{1+\cos\gamma + 1 - \cos\gamma}{1-\cos^2\gamma} = \dfrac{2}{\sin^2\gamma} = 2\csc^2\gamma$

10 $\dfrac{1+\csc 3\beta}{\sec 3\beta} - \cot 3\beta = \dfrac{1}{\sec 3\beta} + \dfrac{\csc 3\beta}{\sec 3\beta} - \cot 3\beta = \cos 3\beta + \dfrac{\cos 3\beta}{\sin 3\beta} - \cot 3\beta = \cos 3\beta$

11 $(\sec u - \tan u)(\csc u + 1) = \left(\dfrac{1}{\cos u} - \dfrac{\sin u}{\cos u}\right)\left(\dfrac{1}{\sin u} + 1\right) =$

$$\left(\dfrac{1-\sin u}{\cos u}\right)\left(\dfrac{1+\sin u}{\sin u}\right) = \dfrac{1-\sin^2 u}{\cos u \sin u} = \dfrac{\cos^2 u}{\cos u \sin u} = \dfrac{\cos u}{\sin u} = \cot u$$

12 $\dfrac{\cot\theta - \tan\theta}{\sin\theta + \cos\theta} = \dfrac{\dfrac{\cos\theta}{\sin\theta} - \dfrac{\sin\theta}{\cos\theta}}{\sin\theta + \cos\theta} = \dfrac{\dfrac{\cos^2\theta - \sin^2\theta}{\sin\theta\,\cos\theta}}{\sin\theta + \cos\theta} = \dfrac{(\cos\theta + \sin\theta)(\cos\theta - \sin\theta)}{\sin\theta\,\cos\theta\,(\sin\theta + \cos\theta)} =$

$$\dfrac{\cos\theta - \sin\theta}{\sin\theta\,\cos\theta} = \dfrac{\cos\theta}{\sin\theta\,\cos\theta} - \dfrac{\sin\theta}{\sin\theta\,\cos\theta} = \dfrac{1}{\sin\theta} - \dfrac{1}{\cos\theta} = \csc\theta - \sec\theta$$

13 $\csc^4 t - \cot^4 t = (\csc^2 t + \cot^2 t)(\csc^2 t - \cot^2 t) = (\csc^2 t + \cot^2 t)(1) = \csc^2 t + \cot^2 t$

14 $\cos^4 2\theta + \sin^2 2\theta = (\cos^2 2\theta)^2 + \sin^2 2\theta = (1 - \sin^2 2\theta)^2 + \sin^2 2\theta =$

$$1 - 2\sin^2 2\theta + \sin^4 2\theta + \sin^2 2\theta = 1 - \sin^2 2\theta + \sin^4 2\theta = \cos^2 2\theta + \sin^4 2\theta$$

15 $\dfrac{\cos\beta}{1-\sin\beta} = \dfrac{\cos\beta}{1-\sin\beta}\cdot\dfrac{1+\sin\beta}{1+\sin\beta} = \dfrac{\cos\beta\,(1+\sin\beta)}{1-\sin^2\beta} = \dfrac{\cos\beta\,(1+\sin\beta)}{\cos^2\beta} = \dfrac{1+\sin\beta}{\cos\beta} =$

$$\dfrac{1}{\cos\beta} + \dfrac{\sin\beta}{\cos\beta} = \sec\beta + \tan\beta$$

16 $\dfrac{1}{\csc y - \cot y} = \dfrac{1}{\csc y - \cot y}\cdot\dfrac{\csc y + \cot y}{\csc y + \cot y} = \dfrac{\csc y + \cot y}{\csc^2 y - \cot^2 y} = \dfrac{\csc y + \cot y}{1} = \csc y + \cot y$

17 $\dfrac{\tan^2 x}{\sec x + 1} = \dfrac{\sec^2 x - 1}{\sec x + 1} = \dfrac{(\sec x + 1)(\sec x - 1)}{\sec x + 1} = \sec x - 1 = \dfrac{1}{\cos x} - 1 = \dfrac{1 - \cos x}{\cos x}$

18 $\dfrac{\cot x}{\csc x + 1} = \dfrac{\cot x}{\csc x + 1}\cdot\dfrac{\csc x - 1}{\csc x - 1} = \dfrac{\cot x\,(\csc x - 1)}{\csc^2 x - 1} = \dfrac{\cot x\,(\csc x - 1)}{\cot^2 x} = \dfrac{\csc x - 1}{\cot x}$

19 $\dfrac{\cot 4u - 1}{\cot 4u + 1} = \dfrac{\dfrac{1}{\tan 4u} - 1}{\dfrac{1}{\tan 4u} + 1} = \dfrac{\dfrac{1 - \tan 4u}{\tan 4u}}{\dfrac{1 + \tan 4u}{\tan 4u}} = \dfrac{1 - \tan 4u}{1 + \tan 4u}$

20 $\dfrac{1 + \sec 4x}{\sin 4x + \tan 4x} = \dfrac{1 + \dfrac{1}{\cos 4x}}{\sin 4x + \dfrac{\sin 4x}{\cos 4x}} = \dfrac{\dfrac{\cos 4x + 1}{\cos 4x}}{\dfrac{\sin 4x \cos 4x + \sin 4x}{\cos 4x}} = \dfrac{\cos 4x + 1}{\sin 4x\,(\cos 4x + 1)} =$

$$\dfrac{1}{\sin 4x} = \csc 4x$$

21 $\sin^4 r - \cos^4 r = (\sin^2 r - \cos^2 r)(\sin^2 r + \cos^2 r) = (\sin^2 r - \cos^2 r)(1) = \sin^2 r - \cos^2 r$

22 $\sin^4\theta + 2\sin^2\theta\,\cos^2\theta + \cos^4\theta = (\sin^2\theta + \cos^2\theta)^2 = (1)^2 = 1$

23 $\tan^4 k - \sec^4 k = (\tan^2 k - \sec^2 k)(\tan^2 k + \sec^2 k) = (-1)(\sec^2 k - 1 + \sec^2 k) =$

$$(-1)(2\sec^2 k - 1) = 1 - 2\sec^2 k$$

24 $\sec^4 u - \sec^2 u = \sec^2 u\,(\sec^2 u - 1) = (1 + \tan^2 u)(\tan^2 u) = \tan^2 u + \tan^4 u$

25 $(\sec t + \tan t)^2 = \left(\dfrac{1}{\cos t} + \dfrac{\sin t}{\cos t}\right)^2 = \left(\dfrac{1 + \sin t}{\cos t}\right)^2 = \dfrac{(1 + \sin t)^2}{\cos^2 t} =$

$$\dfrac{(1 + \sin t)^2}{1 - \sin^2 t} = \dfrac{(1 + \sin t)^2}{(1 + \sin t)(1 - \sin t)} = \dfrac{1 + \sin t}{1 - \sin t}$$

26 $RS = (1 - \sin^4\gamma)\sec^4\gamma = \sec^4\gamma - \dfrac{\sin^4\gamma}{\cos^4\gamma} = \sec^4\gamma - \tan^4\gamma =$

$$(\sec^2\gamma - \tan^2\gamma)(\sec^2\gamma + \tan^2\gamma) = (1)(\sec^2\gamma + \tan^2\gamma) = \sec^2\gamma + \tan^2\gamma = LS$$

27 $(\sin^2\theta + \cos^2\theta)^3 = (1)^3 = 1$

28 $\dfrac{\sin t}{1 - \cos t} = \dfrac{\sin t}{1 - \cos t}\cdot\dfrac{1 + \cos t}{1 + \cos t} = \dfrac{\sin t\,(1 + \cos t)}{1 - \cos^2 t} = \dfrac{\sin t\,(1 + \cos t)}{\sin^2 t} = \dfrac{1 + \cos t}{\sin t} =$

$$\dfrac{1}{\sin t} + \dfrac{\cos t}{\sin t} = \csc t + \cot t$$

29 $\dfrac{1 + \csc\beta}{\cot\beta + \cos\beta} = \dfrac{1 + \dfrac{1}{\sin\beta}}{\dfrac{\cos\beta}{\sin\beta} + \cos\beta} = \dfrac{\dfrac{\sin\beta + 1}{\sin\beta}}{\dfrac{\cos\beta + \cos\beta\,\sin\beta}{\sin\beta}} = \dfrac{\sin\beta + 1}{\cos\beta\,(1 + \sin\beta)} = \dfrac{1}{\cos\beta} = \sec\beta$

30 $\dfrac{\cos^3 x - \sin^3 x}{\cos x - \sin x} = \dfrac{(\cos x - \sin x)(\cos^2 x + \cos x\,\sin x + \sin^2 x)}{\cos x - \sin x} = 1 + \sin x\,\cos x$

31 $(\csc t - \cot t)^4(\csc t + \cot t)^4 =$

$$[(\csc t - \cot t)(\csc t + \cot t)]^4 = (\csc^2 t - \cot^2 t)^4 = (1)^4 = 1$$

32 $(a \cos t - b \sin t)^2 + (a \sin t + b \cos t)^2 =$

$(a^2 \cos^2 t - 2ab \cos t \sin t + b^2 \sin^2 t) + (a^2 \sin^2 t + 2ab \sin t \cos t + b^2 \cos^2 t) =$

$$a^2(\cos^2 t + \sin^2 t) + b^2(\sin^2 t + \cos^2 t) = a^2 + b^2$$

33 RS $= \dfrac{\tan \alpha + \tan \beta}{1 - \tan \alpha \tan \beta} = \dfrac{\dfrac{\sin \alpha}{\cos \alpha} + \dfrac{\sin \beta}{\cos \beta}}{1 - \dfrac{\sin \alpha}{\cos \alpha} \cdot \dfrac{\sin \beta}{\cos \beta}} = \dfrac{\dfrac{\sin \alpha \cos \beta + \cos \alpha \sin \beta}{\cos \alpha \cos \beta}}{\dfrac{\cos \alpha \cos \beta - \sin \alpha \sin \beta}{\cos \alpha \cos \beta}} =$

$$\dfrac{\sin \alpha \cos \beta + \cos \alpha \sin \beta}{\cos \alpha \cos \beta - \sin \alpha \sin \beta} = \text{LS}$$

Note: We could obtain the RS by dividing

the numerator and denominator of the LS by $(\cos \alpha \cos \beta)$.

34 $\dfrac{\tan u - \tan v}{1 + \tan u \tan v} = \dfrac{\dfrac{1}{\cot u} - \dfrac{1}{\cot v}}{1 + \dfrac{1}{\cot u} \cdot \dfrac{1}{\cot v}} = \dfrac{\dfrac{\cot v - \cot u}{\cot u \cot v}}{\dfrac{\cot u \cot v + 1}{\cot u \cot v}} = \dfrac{\cot v - \cot u}{\cot u \cot v + 1}$

35 $\dfrac{\tan \alpha}{1 + \sec \alpha} + \dfrac{1 + \sec \alpha}{\tan \alpha} = \dfrac{\tan^2 \alpha + (1 + \sec \alpha)^2}{(1 + \sec \alpha) \tan \alpha} = \dfrac{\sec^2 \alpha - 1 + 1 + 2 \sec \alpha + \sec^2 \alpha}{(1 + \sec \alpha) \tan \alpha} =$

$$\dfrac{2 \sec^2 \alpha + 2 \sec \alpha}{(1 + \sec \alpha) \tan \alpha} = \dfrac{2 \sec \alpha (\sec \alpha + 1) \cot \alpha}{1 + \sec \alpha} = \dfrac{2}{\cos \alpha} \cdot \dfrac{\cos \alpha}{\sin \alpha} = \dfrac{2}{\sin \alpha} = 2 \csc \alpha$$

36 $\dfrac{\csc x}{1 + \csc x} - \dfrac{\csc x}{1 - \csc x} = \dfrac{\csc x(1 - \csc x) - \csc x(1 + \csc x)}{1 - \csc^2 x} =$

$$\dfrac{\csc x - \csc^2 x - \csc x - \csc^2 x}{1 - \csc^2 x} = \dfrac{-2 \csc^2 x}{-\cot^2 x} = \dfrac{2/\sin^2 x}{\cos^2 x/\sin^2 x} = \dfrac{2}{\cos^2 x} = 2 \sec^2 x$$

37 $\dfrac{1}{\tan \beta + \cot \beta} = \dfrac{1}{\dfrac{\sin \beta}{\cos \beta} + \dfrac{\cos \beta}{\sin \beta}} = \dfrac{1}{\dfrac{\sin^2 \beta + \cos^2 \beta}{\cos \beta \sin \beta}} = \sin \beta \cos \beta$

38 $\dfrac{\cot y - \tan y}{\sin y \cos y} = \dfrac{\dfrac{\cos y}{\sin y} - \dfrac{\sin y}{\cos y}}{\sin y \cos y} = \dfrac{\dfrac{\cos^2 y - \sin^2 y}{\sin^2 y \cos^2 y}}{} =$

$$\dfrac{\cos^2 y}{\sin^2 y \cos^2 y} - \dfrac{\sin^2 y}{\sin^2 y \cos^2 y} = \dfrac{1}{\sin^2 y} - \dfrac{1}{\cos^2 y} = \csc^2 y - \sec^2 y$$

39 $\sec \theta + \csc \theta - \cos \theta - \sin \theta = \dfrac{1}{\cos \theta} - \cos \theta + \dfrac{1}{\sin \theta} - \sin \theta = \dfrac{1 - \cos^2 \theta}{\cos \theta} + \dfrac{1 - \sin^2 \theta}{\sin \theta} =$

$$\dfrac{\sin^2 \theta}{\cos \theta} + \dfrac{\cos^2 \theta}{\sin \theta} = \sin \theta \cdot \dfrac{\sin \theta}{\cos \theta} + \cos \theta \cdot \dfrac{\cos \theta}{\sin \theta} = \sin \theta \tan \theta + \cos \theta \cot \theta$$

40 $\sin^3 t + \cos^3 t = (\sin t + \cos t)(\sin^2 t - \sin t \cos t + \cos^2 t) = (1 - \sin t \cos t)(\sin t + \cos t)$

41 RS $= \sec^4 \phi - 4 \tan^2 \phi = (\sec^2 \phi)^2 - 4 \tan^2 \phi = (1 + \tan^2 \phi)^2 - 4 \tan^2 \phi =$

$$1 + 2 \tan^2 \phi + \tan^4 \phi - 4 \tan^2 \phi = 1 - 2 \tan^2 \phi + \tan^4 \phi = (1 - \tan^2 \phi)^2 = \text{LS}$$

42 $\cos^4 w + 1 - \sin^4 w = \cos^4 w + 1 - (1 - \cos^2 w)^2 =$

$$\cos^4 w + 1 - (1 - 2 \cos^2 w + \cos^4 w) = 2 \cos^2 w$$

43 $\dfrac{\cot(-t)+\tan(-t)}{\cot t}=\dfrac{-\cot t-\tan t}{\cot t}=-\dfrac{\cot t}{\cot t}-\dfrac{\tan t}{\cot t}=-(1+\tan^2 t)=-\sec^2 t$

44 $\dfrac{\csc(-t)-\sin(-t)}{\sin(-t)}=\dfrac{-\csc t+\sin t}{-\sin t}=\dfrac{\csc t}{\sin t}-\dfrac{\sin t}{\sin t}=\csc^2 t-1=\cot^2 t$

45 $\log 10^{\tan t}=\log_{10}10^{\tan t}=\tan t$, since $\log_a a^x=x$

46 $10^{\log|\sin t|}=10^{\log_{10}|\sin t|}=|\sin t|$, since $a^{\log_a x}=x$

47 $\ln\cot x=\ln(\cot x)=\ln(\tan x)^{-1}=-\ln(\tan x)=-\ln\tan x$

48 $\ln\sec\theta=\ln(\sec\theta)=\ln(\cos\theta)^{-1}=-\ln(\cos\theta)=-\ln\cos\theta$

49 $\ln|\sec\theta+\tan\theta|=\ln\left|\dfrac{(\sec\theta+\tan\theta)(\sec\theta-\tan\theta)}{\sec\theta-\tan\theta}\right|=\ln\left|\dfrac{\sec^2\theta-\tan^2\theta}{\sec\theta-\tan\theta}\right|=$

$\ln\left|\dfrac{1}{\sec\theta-\tan\theta}\right|=\ln|1|-\ln|\sec\theta-\tan\theta|=-\ln|\sec\theta-\tan\theta|\ \{\ln 1=0\}$

50 $\ln|\csc x-\cot x|=\ln\left|\dfrac{(\csc x-\cot x)(\csc x+\cot x)}{\csc x+\cot x}\right|=\ln\left|\dfrac{\csc^2 x-\cot^2 x}{\csc x+\cot x}\right|=$

$\ln\left|\dfrac{1}{\csc x+\cot x}\right|=\ln|1|-\ln|\csc x+\cot x|=-\ln|\csc x+\cot x|$

51 $\cos^2 t=1-\sin^2 t\Rightarrow\cos t=\pm\sqrt{1-\sin^2 t}$. Hence, choose any t such that $\cos t<0$.

$\quad\quad$ Using $t=\pi$, LS $=\cos\pi=-1$. RS $=\sqrt{1-\sin^2\pi}=1$. Since $-1\neq 1$, LS $\neq$ RS.

52 $(\sin t+\cos t)^2=\sin^2 t+2\cos t\sin t+\cos^2 t$. Hence, choose any t except 0 or $\frac{\pi}{2}$ and

$\quad$ their coterminal angles. Using $t=\pi$, LS $=\sqrt{\sin^2\pi+\cos^2\pi}=1$.

$\quad\quad\quad\quad$ RS $=\sin\pi+\cos\pi=0+(-1)=-1$. Since $1\neq-1$, LS $\neq$ RS.

53 $\sqrt{\sin^2 t}=|\sin t|=\pm\sin t$. Hence, choose any t such that $\sin t<0$.

$\quad\quad$ Using $t=\frac{3\pi}{2}$, LS $=\sqrt{(-1)^2}=1$. RS $=\sin\frac{3\pi}{2}=-1$. Since $1\neq-1$, LS $\neq$ RS.

54 $\sec^2 t=\tan^2 t+1\Rightarrow\sec t=\pm\sqrt{\tan^2 t+1}$. Hence, choose any t such that $\sec t<0$.

$\quad$ Using $t=\frac{3\pi}{4}$, LS $=\sec\frac{3\pi}{4}=-\sqrt{2}$. RS $=\sqrt{(-1)^2+1}=\sqrt{2}$.

$\quad\quad\quad\quad\quad\quad\quad\quad\quad\quad\quad\quad$ Since $-\sqrt{2}\neq\sqrt{2}$, LS $\neq$ RS.

55 $(\sin\theta+\cos\theta)^2=\sin^2\theta+2\sin\theta\cos\theta+\cos^2\theta$. Hence, choose any θ such that

$\quad$ $\sin\theta\cos\theta\neq 0$. Using $\theta=\frac{\pi}{4}$, LS $=(\frac{1}{2}\sqrt{2}+\frac{1}{2}\sqrt{2})^2=(\sqrt{2})^2=2$.

$\quad\quad\quad\quad$ RS $=(\frac{1}{2}\sqrt{2})^2+(\frac{1}{2}\sqrt{2})^2=\frac{1}{2}+\frac{1}{2}=1$. Since $2\neq 1$, LS $\neq$ RS.

56 $\log(1/\sin t)=-\log\sin t\neq(\log\sin t)^{-1}$. $\log\sin t$ is defined if $\sin t>0$. If $\sin t>0$,

$\quad$ $\log\sin t\leq 0$ since $\sin t\leq 1$ and $-\log\sin t\geq 0$. $(\log\sin t)^{-1}<0$ when defined so

$\quad$ LS is never equal to RS. Using $t=\frac{\pi}{6}$, LS $=\log 2$. RS $=1/\log\frac{1}{2}=-1/\log 2$.

$\quad\quad\quad\quad\quad\quad\quad\quad$ Since $\log 2\neq-1/\log 2$, LS $\neq$ RS.

57 $\cos(-t)=-\cos t$. Choose any t such that $\cos t\neq-\cos t$, i.e., any t such that

$\quad$ $\cos t\neq 0$. Using $t=\pi$, LS $=\cos(-\pi)=-1$. RS $=-\cos\pi=-(-1)=1$.

$\quad\quad\quad\quad\quad\quad\quad\quad\quad\quad\quad\quad$ Since $-1\neq 1$, LS $\neq$ RS.

58 From the unit circle, $\sin(t + \pi) = -\sin t$. Choose any t such that $-\sin t \neq \sin t$, i.e., any t such that $\sin t \neq 0$. Using $t = \frac{\pi}{2}$, LS $= \sin\frac{3\pi}{2} = -1$.

$$\text{RS} = \sin\frac{\pi}{2} = 1. \text{ Since } -1 \neq 1, \text{ LS} \neq \text{RS}.$$

59 Don't confuse $\cos(\sec t) = 1$ with $\cos t \cdot \sec t = 1$. Choose any t such that $\sec t \neq 2\pi n$.

$$\text{Using } t = \frac{\pi}{4}, \text{ LS} = \cos(\sec\tfrac{\pi}{4}) = \cos\sqrt{2} \neq 1 = \text{RS}.$$

60 Don't confuse $\cot(\tan\theta) = 1$ with $\cot\theta \cdot \tan\theta = 1$. Choose any θ such that

$$\tan\theta \neq \tfrac{\pi}{4} + \pi n. \text{ Using } \theta = \tfrac{\pi}{4}, \text{ LS} = \cot(\tan\tfrac{\pi}{4}) = \cot 1 \neq 1 = \text{RS}.$$

61 $\sin^2 t - 4\sin t - 5 = 0 \Rightarrow (\sin t - 5)(\sin t + 1) = 0$.

$$\text{Choose any } t \text{ such that } \sin t \neq -1. \text{ Using } t = \pi, \text{ LS} = -5 \neq 0 = \text{RS}.$$

62 $3\cos^2\theta + \cos\theta - 2 = 0 \Rightarrow (3\cos\theta - 2)(\cos\theta + 1) = 0$. Choose any θ such

$$\text{that } \cos\theta \neq \tfrac{2}{3}, -1. \text{ Using } \theta = \tfrac{\pi}{2}, \text{ LS} = -2 \neq 0 = \text{RS}.$$

Note: Exer. 63–66: Use $\sqrt{a^2 - x^2} = a\cos\theta$ because

$$\sqrt{a^2 - x^2} = \sqrt{a^2 - a^2\sin^2\theta} = \sqrt{a^2(1 - \sin^2\theta)} = \sqrt{a^2\cos^2\theta} = |a|\,|\cos\theta| = a\cos\theta$$

$$\text{since } \cos\theta > 0 \text{ if } -\tfrac{\pi}{2} < \theta < \tfrac{\pi}{2} \text{ and } a > 0.$$

63 $(a^2 - x^2)^{3/2} = (\sqrt{a^2 - x^2})^3 = (a\cos\theta)^3 = a^3\cos^3\theta$

64 $\dfrac{\sqrt{a^2 - x^2}}{x} = \dfrac{a\cos\theta}{a\sin\theta} = \cot\theta$

65 $\dfrac{x^2}{\sqrt{a^2 - x^2}} = \dfrac{a^2\sin^2\theta}{a\cos\theta} = a \cdot \dfrac{\sin\theta}{\cos\theta} \cdot \sin\theta = a\tan\theta\sin\theta$

66 $\dfrac{1}{x\sqrt{a^2 - x^2}} = \dfrac{1}{(a\sin\theta)(a\cos\theta)} = \dfrac{1}{a^2}\csc\theta\sec\theta$

Note: Exer. 67–70: Use $\sqrt{a^2 + x^2} = a\sec\theta$ because

$$\sqrt{a^2 + x^2} = \sqrt{a^2 + a^2\tan^2\theta} = \sqrt{a^2(1 + \tan^2\theta)} = \sqrt{a^2\sec^2\theta} = |a|\,|\sec\theta| =$$

$$a\sec\theta \text{ since } \sec\theta > 0 \text{ if } -\tfrac{\pi}{2} < \theta < \tfrac{\pi}{2} \text{ and } a > 0.$$

67 $\sqrt{a^2 + x^2} = a\sec\theta$

68 $\dfrac{1}{\sqrt{a^2 + x^2}} = \dfrac{1}{a\sec\theta} = \dfrac{1}{a}\cos\theta$

69 $\dfrac{1}{x^2 + a^2} = \dfrac{1}{(\sqrt{a^2 + x^2})^2} = \dfrac{1}{(a\sec\theta)^2} = \dfrac{1}{a^2\sec^2\theta} = \dfrac{1}{a^2}\cos^2\theta$

70 $\dfrac{(x^2 + a^2)^{3/2}}{x} = \dfrac{(\sqrt{a^2 + x^2})^3}{x} = \dfrac{(a\sec\theta)^3}{a\tan\theta} = a^2\sec^2\theta \cdot \dfrac{1/\cos\theta}{\sin\theta/\cos\theta} = a^2\sec^2\theta\csc\theta$

Note: Exer. 71–74: Use $\sqrt{x^2 - a^2} = a\tan\theta$ because

$$\sqrt{x^2 - a^2} = \sqrt{a^2\sec^2\theta - a^2} = \sqrt{a^2(\sec^2\theta - 1)} = \sqrt{a^2\tan^2\theta} = |a|\,|\tan\theta| =$$

$$a\tan\theta \text{ since } \tan\theta > 0 \text{ if } 0 < \theta < \tfrac{\pi}{2} \text{ and } a > 0.$$

71 $\sqrt{x^2 - a^2} = a\tan\theta$

$\boxed{72}$ $\dfrac{1}{x^2\sqrt{x^2-a^2}} = \dfrac{1}{(a^2\sec^2\theta)(a\tan\theta)} = \dfrac{1}{a^3}\cos^2\theta\cot\theta$

$\boxed{73}$ $x^3\sqrt{x^2-a^2} = (a^3\sec^3\theta)(a\tan\theta) = a^4\sec^3\theta\tan\theta$

$\boxed{74}$ $\dfrac{\sqrt{x^2-a^2}}{x^2} = \dfrac{a\tan\theta}{a^2\sec^2\theta} = \dfrac{1}{a}\cdot\dfrac{\sin\theta/\cos\theta}{1/\cos\theta}\cdot\dfrac{1}{\sec\theta} = \dfrac{1}{a}\sin\theta\cos\theta$

$\boxed{75}$ The graph of f appears to be that of $y = g(x) = -1$.

$$\dfrac{\sin^2 x - \sin^4 x}{(1-\sec^2 x)\cos^4 x} = \dfrac{\sin^2 x(1-\sin^2 x)}{-\tan^2 x\,\cos^4 x} = \dfrac{\sin^2 x\,\cos^2 x}{-(\sin^2 x/\cos^2 x)\cos^4 x} = \dfrac{\sin^2 x\,\cos^2 x}{-\sin^2 x\,\cos^2 x} = -1$$

$\boxed{76}$ The graph of f appears to be that of $y = g(x) = \sin x$.

$$\dfrac{\sin x - \sin^3 x}{\cos^4 x + \cos^2 x\,\sin^2 x} = \dfrac{\sin x(1-\sin^2 x)}{\cos^2 x(\cos^2 x + \sin^2 x)} = \dfrac{\sin x\,\cos^2 x}{\cos^2 x(1)} = \sin x$$

$\boxed{77}$ The graph of f appears to be that of $y = g(x) = \cos x$.

$$\sec x\,(\sin x\,\cos x + \cos^2 x) - \sin x = \sec x\,\cos x\,(\sin x + \cos x) - \sin x =$$
$$(\sin x + \cos x) - \sin x = \cos x$$

$\boxed{78}$ The graph of f appears to be that of $y = g(x) = 1$.

$$\dfrac{\sin^3 x + \sin x\,\cos^2 x}{\csc x} + \dfrac{\cos^3 x + \cos x\,\sin^2 x}{\sec x} =$$
$$\dfrac{\sin x(\sin^2 x + \cos^2 x)}{\csc x} + \dfrac{\cos x(\cos^2 x + \sin^2 x)}{\sec x} = \dfrac{\sin x}{\csc x} + \dfrac{\cos x}{\sec x} = \sin^2 x + \cos^2 x = 1$$

6.2 Exercises

$\boxed{1}$ In $[0, 2\pi)$, $\sin x = -\dfrac{\sqrt{2}}{2}$ only if $x = \dfrac{5\pi}{4}, \dfrac{7\pi}{4}$. __All solutions__ would include these angles plus all angles coterminal with them. Hence, $x = \dfrac{5\pi}{4} + 2\pi n, \dfrac{7\pi}{4} + 2\pi n$.

$\boxed{2}$ $\cos t = -1 \Rightarrow t = \pi + 2\pi n$, or, equivalently, $(2n+1)\pi$.

$\boxed{3}$ $\tan\theta = \sqrt{3} \Rightarrow \theta = \dfrac{\pi}{3} + \pi n$.

$\boxed{4}$ $\cot\alpha = -\dfrac{1}{\sqrt{3}} \Rightarrow \tan\alpha = -\sqrt{3} \Rightarrow \alpha = \dfrac{2\pi}{3} + \pi n$.

$\boxed{5}$ $\sec\beta = 2 \Rightarrow \cos\beta = \dfrac{1}{2} \Rightarrow \beta = \dfrac{\pi}{3} + 2\pi n, \dfrac{5\pi}{3} + 2\pi n$.

$\boxed{6}$ $\csc\gamma = \sqrt{2} \Rightarrow \sin\gamma = \dfrac{1}{\sqrt{2}} \Rightarrow \gamma = \dfrac{\pi}{4} + 2\pi n, \dfrac{3\pi}{4} + 2\pi n$.

$\boxed{7}$ $\sin x = \dfrac{\pi}{2}$ has no solution since $\dfrac{\pi}{2} > 1$, which is not in the range $[-1, 1]$.

$\boxed{8}$ $\cos x = -\dfrac{\pi}{3}$ has no solution since $-\dfrac{\pi}{3} < -1$, which is not in the range $[-1, 1]$.

$\boxed{9}$ $\cos\theta = \dfrac{1}{\sec\theta}$ is true for all values for which the equation is defined.

★ All θ except $\theta = \dfrac{\pi}{2} + \pi n$

$\boxed{10}$ $\csc\theta\sin\theta = 1$ is true for all values for which the equation is defined.

★ All θ except $\theta = \pi n$

11 $2\cos 2\theta - \sqrt{3} = 0 \Rightarrow \cos 2\theta = \frac{\sqrt{3}}{2} \Rightarrow 2\theta = \frac{\pi}{6} + 2\pi n, \frac{11\pi}{6} + 2\pi n \Rightarrow \theta = \frac{\pi}{12} + \pi n, \frac{11\pi}{12} + \pi n$

12 $2\sin 3\theta + \sqrt{2} = 0 \Rightarrow \sin 3\theta = -\frac{\sqrt{2}}{2} \Rightarrow 3\theta = \frac{5\pi}{4} + 2\pi n, \frac{7\pi}{4} + 2\pi n \Rightarrow$

$$\theta = \frac{5\pi}{12} + \frac{2\pi}{3}n, \frac{7\pi}{12} + \frac{2\pi}{3}n$$

13 $\sqrt{3}\tan \frac{1}{3}t = 1 \Rightarrow \tan \frac{1}{3}t = \frac{1}{\sqrt{3}} \Rightarrow \frac{1}{3}t = \frac{\pi}{6} + \pi n \Rightarrow t = \frac{\pi}{2} + 3\pi n$

14 $\cos \frac{1}{4}x = -\frac{\sqrt{2}}{2} \Rightarrow \frac{1}{4}x = \frac{3\pi}{4} + 2\pi n, \frac{5\pi}{4} + 2\pi n \Rightarrow x = 3\pi + 8\pi n, 5\pi + 8\pi n$

15 $\sin\left(\theta + \frac{\pi}{4}\right) = \frac{1}{2} \Rightarrow \theta + \frac{\pi}{4} = \frac{\pi}{6} + 2\pi n, \frac{5\pi}{6} + 2\pi n \Rightarrow \theta = -\frac{\pi}{12} + 2\pi n, \frac{7\pi}{12} + 2\pi n$

16 $\cos\left(x - \frac{\pi}{3}\right) = -1 \Rightarrow x - \frac{\pi}{3} = \pi + 2\pi n \Rightarrow x = \frac{4\pi}{3} + 2\pi n$

17 $\sin\left(2x - \frac{\pi}{3}\right) = \frac{1}{2} \Rightarrow 2x - \frac{\pi}{3} = \frac{\pi}{6} + 2\pi n, \frac{5\pi}{6} + 2\pi n \Rightarrow 2x = \frac{\pi}{2} + 2\pi n, \frac{7\pi}{6} + 2\pi n \Rightarrow$

$$x = \frac{\pi}{4} + \pi n, \frac{7\pi}{12} + \pi n$$

18 $\cos\left(4x - \frac{\pi}{4}\right) = \frac{\sqrt{2}}{2} \Rightarrow 4x - \frac{\pi}{4} = \frac{\pi}{4} + 2\pi n, \frac{7\pi}{4} + 2\pi n \Rightarrow$

$$4x = \frac{\pi}{2} + 2\pi n, 2\pi + 2\pi n \text{ \{ or just } 2\pi n \text{ \}} \Rightarrow x = \frac{\pi}{8} + \frac{\pi}{2}n, \frac{\pi}{2}n$$

19 $2\cos t + 1 = 0 \Rightarrow \cos t = -\frac{1}{2} \Rightarrow t = \frac{2\pi}{3} + 2\pi n, \frac{4\pi}{3} + 2\pi n$

20 $\cot \theta + 1 = 0 \Rightarrow \cot \theta = -1 \Rightarrow \theta = \frac{3\pi}{4} + \pi n$

21 $\tan^2 x = 1 \Rightarrow \tan x = \pm 1 \Rightarrow x = \frac{\pi}{4} + \pi n, \frac{3\pi}{4} + \pi n$, or simply $\frac{\pi}{4} + \frac{\pi}{2}n$

22 $4\cos \theta - 2 = 0 \Rightarrow \cos \theta = \frac{1}{2} \Rightarrow \theta = \frac{\pi}{3} + 2\pi n, \frac{5\pi}{3} + 2\pi n$

23 $(\cos \theta - 1)(\sin \theta + 1) = 0 \Rightarrow \cos \theta = 1$ or $\sin \theta = -1 \Rightarrow \theta = 2\pi n$ or $\theta = \frac{3\pi}{2} + 2\pi n$

24 $2\cos x = \sqrt{3} \Rightarrow \cos x = \frac{\sqrt{3}}{2} \Rightarrow x = \frac{\pi}{6} + 2\pi n, \frac{11\pi}{6} + 2\pi n$

25 $\sec^2 \alpha - 4 = 0 \Rightarrow \sec^2 \alpha = 4 \Rightarrow \sec \alpha = \pm 2 \Rightarrow$

$$\alpha = \frac{\pi}{3} + 2\pi n, \frac{5\pi}{3} + 2\pi n, \frac{2\pi}{3} + 2\pi n, \frac{4\pi}{3} + 2\pi n, \text{ or simply } \frac{\pi}{3} + \pi n, \frac{2\pi}{3} + \pi n$$

26 $3 - \tan^2 \beta = 0 \Rightarrow \tan^2 \beta = 3 \Rightarrow \tan \beta = \pm \sqrt{3} \Rightarrow \beta = \frac{\pi}{3} + \pi n, \frac{2\pi}{3} + \pi n$

27 $\sqrt{3} + 2\sin \beta = 0 \Rightarrow \sin \beta = -\frac{\sqrt{3}}{2} \Rightarrow \beta = \frac{4\pi}{3} + 2\pi n, \frac{5\pi}{3} + 2\pi n$

28 $4\sin^2 x - 3 = 0 \Rightarrow \sin^2 x = \frac{3}{4} \Rightarrow \sin x = \pm \frac{\sqrt{3}}{2} \Rightarrow x = \frac{\pi}{3} + \pi n, \frac{2\pi}{3} + \pi n$

29 $\cot^2 x - 3 = 0 \Rightarrow \cot^2 x = 3 \Rightarrow \cot x = \pm \sqrt{3} \Rightarrow x = \frac{\pi}{6} + \pi n, \frac{5\pi}{6} + \pi n$

30 $(\sin t - 1)\cos t = 0 \Rightarrow \sin t = 1$ or $\cos t = 0 \Rightarrow$

$$t = \frac{\pi}{2} + 2\pi n \text{ or } t = \frac{\pi}{2} + \pi n, \text{ or simply } \frac{\pi}{2} + \pi n$$

31 $(2\sin \theta + 1)(2\cos \theta + 3) = 0 \Rightarrow \sin \theta = -\frac{1}{2}$ or $\sin \theta = -\frac{3}{2} \Rightarrow$

$$\theta = \frac{7\pi}{6} + 2\pi n, \frac{11\pi}{6} + 2\pi n \text{ \{ } \sin \theta = -\frac{3}{2} \text{ has no solutions \}}$$

32 $(2\sin u - 1)(\cos u - \sqrt{2}) = 0 \Rightarrow \sin u = \frac{1}{2}$ or $\cos u = \sqrt{2} \Rightarrow$

$$u = \frac{\pi}{6} + 2\pi n, \frac{5\pi}{6} + 2\pi n \text{ \{ } \cos u = \sqrt{2} \text{ has no solutions \}}$$

33 $\sin 2x \left(\csc 2x - 2\right) = 0 \Rightarrow 1 - 2\sin 2x = 0 \Rightarrow \sin 2x = \frac{1}{2} \Rightarrow$

$$2x = \frac{\pi}{6} + 2\pi n, \frac{5\pi}{6} + 2\pi n \Rightarrow x = \frac{\pi}{12} + \pi n, \frac{5\pi}{12} + \pi n$$

34 $\tan \alpha + \tan^2 \alpha = 0 \Rightarrow \tan \alpha (1 + \tan \alpha) = 0 \Rightarrow \tan \alpha = 0, -1 \Rightarrow \alpha = \pi n, \frac{3\pi}{4} + \pi n$

35 $\cos (\ln x) = 0 \Rightarrow \ln x = \frac{\pi}{2} + \pi n \Rightarrow x = e^{(\pi/2) + \pi n}$

36 $\ln(\sin x) = 0 \Rightarrow \sin x - 1 \rightarrow x = \frac{\pi}{2} + 2\pi n$

37 $\cos\left(2x - \frac{\pi}{4}\right) = 0 \Rightarrow 2x - \frac{\pi}{4} = \frac{\pi}{2} + \pi n \Rightarrow 2x = \frac{3\pi}{4} + \pi n \Rightarrow x = \frac{3\pi}{8} + \frac{\pi}{2}n.$

x will be in the interval $[0, 2\pi)$ if $n = 0, 1, 2,$ or 3. Thus, $x = \frac{3\pi}{8}, \frac{7\pi}{8}, \frac{11\pi}{8}, \frac{15\pi}{8}$.

38 $\sin\left(3x - \frac{\pi}{4}\right) = 1 \Rightarrow 3x - \frac{\pi}{4} = \frac{\pi}{2} + 2\pi n \Rightarrow 3x = \frac{3\pi}{4} + 2\pi n \Rightarrow x = \frac{\pi}{4} + \frac{2\pi}{3}n.$

x will be in the interval $[0, 2\pi)$ if $n = 0, 1,$ or 2. Thus, $x = \frac{\pi}{4}, \frac{11\pi}{12}, \frac{19\pi}{12}$.

39 $2 - 8\cos^2 t = 0 \Rightarrow \cos^2 t = \frac{1}{4} \Rightarrow \cos t = \pm\frac{1}{2} \Rightarrow t = \frac{\pi}{3}, \frac{2\pi}{3}, \frac{4\pi}{3}, \frac{5\pi}{3}$

40 $\cot^2\theta - \cot\theta = 0 \Rightarrow \cot\theta(\cot\theta - 1) = 0 \Rightarrow \cot\theta = 0, 1 \Rightarrow \theta = \frac{\pi}{2}, \frac{3\pi}{2}, \frac{\pi}{4}, \frac{5\pi}{4}$

41 $2\sin^2 u = 1 - \sin u \Rightarrow 2\sin^2 u + \sin u - 1 = 0 \Rightarrow (2\sin u - 1)(\sin u + 1) = 0 \Rightarrow$

$$\sin u = \frac{1}{2}, -1 \Rightarrow u = \frac{\pi}{6}, \frac{5\pi}{6}, \frac{3\pi}{2}$$

42 $2\cos^2 t + 3\cos t + 1 = 0 \Rightarrow (2\cos t + 1)(\cos t + 1) = 0 \Rightarrow \cos t = -\frac{1}{2}, -1 \Rightarrow t = \frac{2\pi}{3}, \frac{4\pi}{3}, \pi$

43 $\tan^2 x \sin x = \sin x \Rightarrow \tan^2 x \sin x - \sin x = 0 \Rightarrow \sin x(\tan^2 x - 1) = 0 \Rightarrow$

$$\sin x = 0 \text{ or } \tan x = \pm 1 \Rightarrow x = 0, \pi, \frac{\pi}{4}, \frac{3\pi}{4}, \frac{5\pi}{4}, \frac{7\pi}{4}$$

44 $\sec\beta\csc\beta = 2\csc\beta \Rightarrow \sec\beta\csc\beta - 2\csc\beta = 0 \Rightarrow \csc\beta(\sec\beta - 2) = 0 \Rightarrow$

$$\csc\beta = 0 \text{ or } \sec\beta = 2 \Rightarrow \beta = \frac{\pi}{3}, \frac{5\pi}{3} \; \{\csc\beta = 0 \text{ has no solutions}\}$$

45 $2\cos^2\gamma + \cos\gamma = 0 \Rightarrow \cos\gamma(2\cos\gamma + 1) = 0 \Rightarrow \cos\gamma = 0, -\frac{1}{2} \Rightarrow \gamma = \frac{\pi}{2}, \frac{3\pi}{2}, \frac{2\pi}{3}, \frac{4\pi}{3}$

46 $\sin x - \cos x = 0 \Rightarrow \sin x = \cos x \Rightarrow \tan x = 1 \Rightarrow x = \frac{\pi}{4}, \frac{5\pi}{4}$

47 $\sin^2\theta + \sin\theta - 6 = 0 \Rightarrow (\sin\theta + 3)(\sin\theta - 2) = 0 \Rightarrow \sin\theta = -3, 2.$

There are *no solutions* for either equation.

48 $2\sin^2 u + \sin u - 6 = 0 \Rightarrow (2\sin u - 3)(\sin u + 2) = 0 \Rightarrow \sin u = \frac{3}{2}, -2.$

There are *no solutions* for either equation.

49 $1 - \sin t = \sqrt{3}\cos t$ ●   Square both sides to obtain an equation in either sin or cos.

$(1 - \sin t)^2 = (\sqrt{3}\cos t)^2 \Rightarrow 1 - 2\sin t + \sin^2 t = 3\cos^2 t \Rightarrow$

$\sin^2 t - 2\sin t + 1 = 3(1 - \sin^2 t) \Rightarrow 4\sin^2 t - 2\sin t - 2 = 0 \Rightarrow$

$2\sin^2 t - \sin t - 1 = 0 \Rightarrow (2\sin t + 1)(\sin t - 1) = 0 \Rightarrow \sin t = -\frac{1}{2}, 1 \Rightarrow$

$t = \frac{7\pi}{6}, \frac{11\pi}{6}, \frac{\pi}{2}$. Since each side of the equation was squared,

the solutions must be checked in the original equation. $\frac{7\pi}{6}$ is an extraneous solution.

50 $\cos\theta - \sin\theta = 1 \Rightarrow \cos\theta = 1 + \sin\theta \Rightarrow \cos^2\theta = 1 + 2\sin\theta + \sin^2\theta \Rightarrow$

$1 - \sin^2\theta = 1 + 2\sin\theta + \sin^2\theta \Rightarrow 2\sin^2\theta + 2\sin\theta = 0 \Rightarrow$

$2\sin\theta(\sin\theta + 1) = 0 \Rightarrow \sin\theta = 0, -1 \Rightarrow \theta = 0, \pi, \frac{3\pi}{2}$. π is an extraneous solution.

51 $\cos\alpha + \sin\alpha = 1 \Rightarrow \cos\alpha = 1 - \sin\alpha \Rightarrow \cos^2\alpha = 1 - 2\sin\alpha + \sin^2\alpha \Rightarrow$

$1 - \sin^2\alpha = 1 - 2\sin\alpha + \sin^2\alpha \Rightarrow 2\sin^2\alpha - 2\sin\alpha = 0 \Rightarrow$

$2\sin\alpha(\sin\alpha - 1) = 0 \Rightarrow \sin\alpha = 0, 1 \Rightarrow \alpha = 0, \pi, \frac{\pi}{2}$. π is an extraneous solution.

52 $\sqrt{3}\sin t + \cos t = 1 \Rightarrow \sqrt{3}\sin t = 1 - \cos t \Rightarrow 3\sin^2 t = 1 - 2\cos t + \cos^2 t \Rightarrow$

$3(1 - \cos^2 t) = 1 - 2\cos t + \cos^2 t \Rightarrow 4\cos^2 t - 2\cos t - 2 = 0 \Rightarrow$

$2\cos^2 t - \cos t - 1 = 0 \Rightarrow (2\cos t + 1)(\cos t - 1) = 0 \Rightarrow \cos t = -\frac{1}{2}, 1 \Rightarrow$

$t = \frac{2\pi}{3}, \frac{4\pi}{3}, 0.$ $\frac{4\pi}{3}$ is an extraneous solution.

53 $2\tan t - \sec^2 t = 0 \Rightarrow 2\tan t - (1 + \tan^2 t) = 0 \Rightarrow \tan^2 t - 2\tan t + 1 = 0 \Rightarrow$

$(\tan t - 1)^2 = 0 \Rightarrow \tan t = 1 \Rightarrow t = \frac{\pi}{4}, \frac{5\pi}{4}$

54 $\tan\theta + \sec\theta = 1 \Rightarrow \sec^2\theta = (1 - \tan\theta)^2 \Rightarrow 1 + \tan^2\theta = 1 - 2\tan\theta + \tan^2\theta \Rightarrow$

$2\tan\theta = 0 \Rightarrow \theta = 0, \pi.$ π is an extraneous solution.

55 $\cot\alpha + \tan\alpha = \csc\alpha\sec\alpha \Rightarrow \dfrac{\cos\alpha}{\sin\alpha} + \dfrac{\sin\alpha}{\cos\alpha} = \dfrac{1}{\sin\alpha\cos\alpha} \Rightarrow$

$\dfrac{\cos^2\alpha + \sin^2\alpha}{\sin\alpha\cos\alpha} = \dfrac{1}{\sin\alpha\cos\alpha}.$ This is an identity and is true for *all numbers in* $[0, 2\pi)$

except $0, \frac{\pi}{2}, \pi,$ and $\frac{3\pi}{2}$ since these values make the original equation undefined.

56 $\sin x + \cos x \cot x = \csc x \Rightarrow \sin x + \cos x \cdot \dfrac{\cos x}{\sin x} = \dfrac{1}{\sin x} \Rightarrow \dfrac{\sin^2 x + \cos^2 x}{\sin x} = \dfrac{1}{\sin x}.$

This is an identity and is true for *all numbers in* $[0, 2\pi)$ *except* 0 and π

since these values make the original equation undefined.

57 $2\sin^3 x + \sin^2 x - 2\sin x - 1 = 0 \Rightarrow \sin^2 x(2\sin x + 1) - 1(2\sin x + 1) = 0 \Rightarrow$

$(\sin^2 x - 1)(2\sin x + 1) = 0 \Rightarrow \sin x = \pm 1, -\frac{1}{2} \Rightarrow x = \frac{\pi}{2}, \frac{3\pi}{2}, \frac{7\pi}{6}, \frac{11\pi}{6}$

58 $\sec^5\theta = 4\sec\theta \Rightarrow \sec\theta(\sec^4\theta - 4) = 0 \Rightarrow \sec\theta = 0$ or $\sec^2\theta = \pm 2 \Rightarrow$

$\sec\theta = \pm\sqrt{2}$ {since $\sec\theta \ne 0$ and $\sec^2\theta \ne -2$} $\Rightarrow \theta = \frac{\pi}{4}, \frac{3\pi}{4}, \frac{5\pi}{4}, \frac{7\pi}{4}$

59 $2\tan t\csc t + 2\csc t + \tan t + 1 = 0 \Rightarrow 2\csc t(\tan t + 1) + 1(\tan t + 1) \Rightarrow$

$(2\csc t + 1)(\tan t + 1) = 0 \Rightarrow \csc t = -\frac{1}{2}$ or $\tan t = -1 \Rightarrow t = \frac{3\pi}{4}, \frac{7\pi}{4}$ {since $\csc t \ne -\frac{1}{2}$}

60 $2\sin v\csc v - \csc v = 4\sin v - 2 \Rightarrow 2\sin v\csc v - \csc v - 4\sin v + 2 = 0 \Rightarrow$

$\csc v(2\sin v - 1) - 2(2\sin v - 1) = 0 \Rightarrow (\csc v - 2)(2\sin v - 1) = 0 \Rightarrow$

$\csc v = 2$ or $\sin v = \frac{1}{2} \Rightarrow v = \frac{\pi}{6}, \frac{5\pi}{6}.$ The equations are equivalent.

61 $\sin^2 t - 4\sin t + 1 = 0 \Rightarrow \sin t = \dfrac{4 \pm \sqrt{12}}{2} = 2 \pm \sqrt{3}.$

$(2 + \sqrt{3}) > 1$ is not in the range of the sine, so $\sin t = 2 - \sqrt{3} \Rightarrow$

$t = 15°30'$ or $164°30'$ {to the nearest ten minutes}

62 $\cos^2 t - 4\cos t + 2 = 0 \Rightarrow \cos t = \dfrac{4 \pm \sqrt{8}}{2} = 2 \pm \sqrt{2}.$

$(2 + \sqrt{2}) > 1$ is not in the range of the cosine, so $\cos t = 2 - \sqrt{2} \Rightarrow$

$t = 54°10'$ or $305°50'$ {to the nearest ten minutes}

63 $\tan^2\theta + 3\tan\theta + 2 = 0 \Rightarrow (\tan\theta + 1)(\tan\theta + 2) = 0 \Rightarrow$

$\tan\theta = -1, -2 \Rightarrow \theta = 135°, 315°, 116°30', 296°30'$

64 $2\tan^2 x - 3\tan x - 1 = 0 \Rightarrow \tan x = \dfrac{3 \pm \sqrt{17}}{4} \Rightarrow x = 60°40', 240°40', 164°20', 344°20'$

65 $12\sin^2 u - 5\sin u - 2 = 0 \Rightarrow (3\sin u - 2)(4\sin u + 1) = 0 \Rightarrow \sin u = \frac{2}{3}, -\frac{1}{4} \Rightarrow$

$$u = 41°50', 138°10', 194°30', 345°30'$$

66 $5\cos^2\alpha + 3\cos\alpha - 2 = 0 \Rightarrow (5\cos\alpha - 2)(\cos\alpha + 1) = 0 \Rightarrow \cos\alpha = \frac{2}{5}, -1 \Rightarrow$

$$\alpha = 66°30', 293°30', 180°$$

67 $y > 12.5 \Rightarrow 25\cos\frac{\pi}{15}t > 12.5 \Rightarrow \cos\frac{\pi}{15}t > \frac{1}{2} \Rightarrow -\frac{\pi}{3} < \frac{\pi}{15}t < \frac{\pi}{3} \Rightarrow -5 < t < 5 \Rightarrow$

$$y > 12.5 \text{ for about } 5 - (-5) = 10 \text{ minutes of each 30-minute period.}$$

68 The low temperature will be below $-4°F$ when $T < -4$.

$$T < -4 \Rightarrow 36\sin\left[\frac{2\pi}{365}(t - 101)\right] + 14 < -4 \Rightarrow \sin\left[\frac{2\pi}{365}(t - 101)\right] < -\frac{1}{2} \Rightarrow$$

$$\frac{7\pi}{6} < \frac{2\pi}{365}(t - 101) < \frac{11\pi}{6} \Rightarrow \frac{2555}{12} < t - 101 < \frac{4015}{12} \Rightarrow \frac{3767}{12} < t < \frac{5227}{12} \Rightarrow$$

$$313\frac{11}{12} < t < 435\frac{7}{12} \Rightarrow T < -4 \text{ for } 435\frac{7}{12} - 313\frac{11}{12} = 121\frac{2}{3} \text{ days.}$$

69 (b) July: $T(7) = 83°F$; October: $T(10) = 56.5°F$.

    (c) Graph $Y_1 = 26.5\sin\left(\frac{\pi}{6}x - \frac{2\pi}{3}\right) + 56.5$ and $Y_2 = 69$. Their graphs intersect at $t \approx 4.94, 9.06$ on $[1, 13]$. The average high temperature is above $69°F$ approximately May through September.

    (d) A sine function is periodic and varies between a maximum and minimum value. Average monthly high temperatures are also seasonal with a 12-month period. Therefore, a sine function is a reasonable function to model these temperatures.

[1, 25] by [0, 100]   [1, 25] by [0, 100]

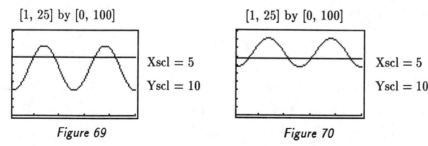

Xscl = 5   Xscl = 5

Yscl = 10   Yscl = 10

         Figure 69   *Figure 70*

70 (b) April: $T(4) = 75°F$; December: $T(12) \approx 60.3°F$.

    (c) Graph $Y_1 = 17\cos\left(\frac{\pi}{6}x - \frac{7\pi}{6}\right) + 75$ and $Y_2 = 67$. Their graphs intersect at $t \approx 3.06, 10.94$ on the interval $[1, 13]$. The average high temperature is below $67°F$ approximately November through March.

71 $I = \frac{1}{2}I_M$ and $D = 12 \Rightarrow \frac{1}{2}I_M = I_M\sin^3\frac{\pi}{12}t \Rightarrow \sin^3\frac{\pi}{12}t = \frac{1}{2} \Rightarrow \sin\frac{\pi}{12}t = \sqrt[3]{\frac{1}{2}} \Rightarrow$

$\frac{\pi}{12}t \approx 0.9169$ and 2.2247 $\{\pi - 0.9169 \approx 2.2247$ is the reference angle for 0.9169 in

$$\text{QII.}\} \Rightarrow t \approx 3.50 \text{ and } t \approx 8.50$$

72 $I = \frac{1}{2}I_M$ and $D = 12 \Rightarrow \frac{1}{2}I_M = I_M\sin^2\frac{\pi}{12}t \Rightarrow \sin^2\frac{\pi}{12}t = \frac{1}{2} \Rightarrow \sin\frac{\pi}{12}t = \pm\sqrt{\frac{1}{2}}$.

The sine is positive since if $0 \leq t \leq D$, then $0 \leq \frac{\pi t}{D} \leq \pi$.

$$\text{Thus, } \frac{\pi}{12}t = \frac{\pi}{4} \text{ and } \frac{\pi}{12}t = \frac{3\pi}{4} \Rightarrow t = 3 \text{ and } t = 9.$$

$\boxed{73}$ (a) $I > 0.75\,I_M \Rightarrow I_M \sin^3 \frac{\pi}{12}t > 0.75\,I_M \Rightarrow \sin^3 \frac{\pi}{12}t > \frac{3}{4} \Rightarrow \sin \frac{\pi}{12}t > \sqrt[3]{\frac{3}{4}} \Rightarrow$

$1.1398 < \frac{\pi}{12}t < 2.0018 \Rightarrow 4.3538 < t < 7.6462$, or approximately 3.29 hours.

(b) $I > 0.75\,I_M \Rightarrow I_M \sin^2 \frac{\pi}{12}t > 0.75\,I_M \Rightarrow \sin^2 \frac{\pi}{12}t > \frac{3}{4} \Rightarrow \sin \frac{\pi}{12}t > \frac{1}{2}\sqrt{3} \Rightarrow$

$\frac{\pi}{3} < \frac{\pi}{12}t < \frac{2\pi}{3} \Rightarrow 4 < t < 8$, or 4 hours.

$\boxed{74}$ (a) On the surface, $x = 0$. Thus, $T = T_0 e^{-\lambda(0)} \sin(\omega t - \lambda(0)) = T_0 \sin \omega t$.

Since the period is 24 hours, $24 = \frac{2\pi}{\omega}$, or $\omega = \frac{\pi}{12}$.

The formula for the temperature at the surface is then $T = T_0 \sin \frac{\pi}{12}t$.

(b) T will be a minimum when $\sin \frac{\pi}{12}t$ equals -1.

$\sin \frac{\pi}{12}t = -1 \Rightarrow \frac{\pi}{12}t = \frac{3\pi}{2} + 2\pi n \Rightarrow t = 18 + 24n$ for $n = 0, 1, 2, \ldots$.

(c) If $\lambda = 2.5$ and $x = 1$, then $T = T_0 e^{-2.5} \sin\left(\frac{\pi}{12}t - 2.5\right)$. As in part (b),

$\sin\left(\frac{\pi}{12}t - 2.5\right) = -1 \Rightarrow \frac{\pi}{12}t - \frac{5}{2} = -\frac{\pi}{2} + 2\pi n \Rightarrow \frac{\pi}{12}t = \frac{5 - \pi}{2} + 2\pi n \Rightarrow$

$t = \frac{6(5 - \pi)}{\pi} + 24n$ for $n = 0, 1, 2, \ldots \approx 3.55 + 24n$ for $n = 0, 1, 2, \ldots$.

$\left\{\text{If } \frac{3\pi}{2} \text{ is used instead of } -\frac{\pi}{2}, \text{ then } n = -1, 0, 1, 2, \ldots.\right\}$

$\boxed{75}$ (a) $N(t) = 1000 \cos \frac{\pi}{5}t + 4000$, amplitude $= 1000$,

period $= \frac{2\pi}{\pi/5} = 10$ years

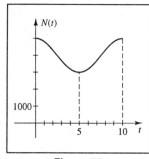

(b) $N > 4500 \Rightarrow 1000 \cos \frac{\pi}{5}t + 4000 > 4500 \Rightarrow$

$\cos \frac{\pi}{5}t > \frac{1}{2} \Rightarrow 0 \le \frac{\pi}{5}t < \frac{\pi}{3}$ and $\frac{5\pi}{3} < \frac{\pi}{5}t \le 2\pi \Rightarrow$

$0 \le t < \frac{5}{3}$ and $\frac{25}{3} < t \le 10$

Figure 75

$\boxed{76}$ $F > 55{,}000 \Rightarrow 26{,}000 \sin\left[\frac{\pi}{6}(t - 5.5)\right] + 34{,}000 > 55{,}000 \Rightarrow \sin\left[\frac{\pi}{6}(t - 5.5)\right] > \frac{21}{26} \Rightarrow$

$\{\text{approximate values}\}\ 0.94 < \frac{\pi}{6}(t - 5.5) < 2.20 \Rightarrow 1.8 < t - 5.5 < 4.2 \Rightarrow$

$7.3 < t < 9.7 \Rightarrow F > 55{,}000$ for about 2.4 months.

$\boxed{77}$ $\frac{1}{2} + \cos x = 0 \Rightarrow \cos x = -\frac{1}{2} \Rightarrow x = -\frac{4\pi}{3}, -\frac{2\pi}{3}, \frac{2\pi}{3}$, and $\frac{4\pi}{3}$ $\{\text{for } x \text{ in } [-2\pi, 2\pi]\}$

for A, B, C, and D, respectively. The corresponding y values are found by using

$y = \frac{1}{2}x + \sin x$ with each of the above values. The points are:

$A(-\frac{4\pi}{3}, -\frac{2\pi}{3} + \frac{1}{2}\sqrt{3})$, $B(-\frac{2\pi}{3}, -\frac{\pi}{3} - \frac{1}{2}\sqrt{3})$, $C(\frac{2\pi}{3}, \frac{\pi}{3} + \frac{1}{2}\sqrt{3})$, and $D(\frac{4\pi}{3}, \frac{2\pi}{3} - \frac{1}{2}\sqrt{3})$

$\boxed{78}$ $4 \cos 2x - \sin 2x = 0 \Rightarrow 4 \cos 2x = \sin 2x \Rightarrow 4 = \tan 2x \Rightarrow 2x \approx 1.3258 + \pi n \Rightarrow$

$x \approx 0.6629 + \frac{\pi}{2}n$ for $n = 0, 1, 2, \ldots$, or $0.66, 2.23, 3.80, 5.38, \ldots$.

$\boxed{79}$ $-10 = 20 \sin(60\pi t - 6\pi) \Rightarrow \sin(60\pi t - 6\pi) = -\frac{1}{2} \Rightarrow 60\pi t_1 - 6\pi = \frac{7\pi}{6} + 2\pi n$ or

$60\pi t_2 - 6\pi = \frac{11\pi}{6} + 2\pi n \Rightarrow 60t_1 = \frac{43}{6} + 2n$ or $60t_2 = \frac{47}{6} + 2n \Rightarrow t_1 = \frac{43}{360} + \frac{1}{30}n$ or

$t_2 = \frac{47}{360} + \frac{1}{30}n$. $t_1 > 0 \Rightarrow \frac{1}{30}n > -\frac{43}{360} \Rightarrow n > -\frac{43}{12}$. If $n = -3$, then $t_1 = \frac{7}{360}$.

$t_2 > 0 \Rightarrow \frac{1}{30}n > -\frac{47}{360} \Rightarrow n > -\frac{47}{12}$. If $n = -3$, then $t_1 = \frac{11}{360}$. Thus, $t = \frac{7}{360}$ sec.

80 $20 = 40\sin(100\pi t - 4\pi) \Rightarrow \sin(100\pi t - 4\pi) = \frac{1}{2} \Rightarrow 100\pi t_1 - 4\pi = \frac{\pi}{6} + 2\pi n$ or

$100\pi t_2 - 4\pi = \frac{5\pi}{6} + 2\pi n \Rightarrow 100 t_1 = \frac{25}{6} + 2n$ or $100 t_2 = \frac{29}{6} + 2n \Rightarrow t_1 = \frac{25}{600} + \frac{1}{50}n$ or

$t_2 = \frac{29}{600} + \frac{1}{50}n.$ $t_1 > 0 \Rightarrow \frac{1}{50}n > -\frac{25}{600} \Rightarrow n > -\frac{25}{12}.$ If $n = -2$, then $t_1 = \frac{1}{600}.$

$\qquad t_2 > 0 \Rightarrow \frac{1}{50}n > -\frac{29}{600} \Rightarrow n > -\frac{29}{12}.$ If $n = -2$, then $t_2 = \frac{5}{600}.$ Thus, $t = \frac{1}{600}$ sec.

81 Graph $y = \cos x$ and $y = 0.3$ on the same coordinate plane.

$\qquad$ The points of intersection are located at $x \approx 1.27$, 5.02, and $\cos x$ is less than 0.3

$\qquad\qquad$ between these values. Therefore, $\cos x \geq 0.3$ on $[0, 1.27] \cup [5.02, 2\pi]$.

$[0, 2\pi]$ by $[-2.09, 2.09]$ $\qquad\qquad\qquad\qquad$ $[0, 2\pi]$ by $[-2.09, 2.09]$

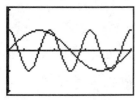
$\qquad$ Xscl $= \pi/4$
$\qquad$ Yscl $= 1$

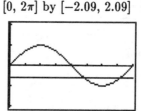
$\qquad$ Xscl $= \pi/4$
$\qquad$ Yscl $= 1$

$\qquad\qquad$ *Figure 81* $\qquad\qquad\qquad\qquad\qquad\qquad$ *Figure 82*

82 Graph $y = \sin x$ and $y = -0.6$ on the same coordinate plane.

$\qquad$ The points of intersection are located at $x \approx 3.79$, 5.64.

$\qquad\qquad$ From the graph, we see that $\sin x < -0.6$ on $(3.79, 5.64)$.

83 Graph $y = \cos 3x$ and $y = \sin x$ on the same coordinate plane.

$\qquad$ The points of intersection are located at $x \approx 0.39$, 1.96, 2.36, 3.53, 5.11, 5.50.

$\qquad$ From the graph, we see that $\cos 3x$ is less than $\sin x$ on

$\qquad\qquad\qquad (0.39, 1.96) \cup (2.36, 3.53) \cup (5.11, 5.50)$.

$[0, 2\pi]$ by $[-2.09, 2.09]$ $\qquad\qquad\qquad\qquad$ $[0, 2\pi]$ by $[-2.09, 2.09]$

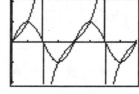
$\qquad$ Xscl $= \pi/4$
$\qquad$ Yscl $= 1$

$\qquad$ Xscl $= \pi/4$
$\qquad$ Yscl $= 1$

$\qquad\qquad$ *Figure 83* $\qquad\qquad\qquad\qquad\qquad\qquad$ *Figure 84*

84 Graph $y = \tan x$ and $y = \sin 2x$ on the same coordinate plane.

$\qquad$ The points of intersection are located at $x \approx 0$, 0.79, 2.36, π, 3.93, 5.50, 2π.

$\qquad$ $\tan x$ is undefined at $\frac{\pi}{2}$ and $\frac{3\pi}{2}$. From the graph, we see that $\tan x \leq \sin 2x$ on

$\qquad\qquad\qquad [0, 0.79] \cup (\frac{\pi}{2}, 2.36] \cup [\pi, 3.93] \cup (\frac{3\pi}{2}, 5.50]$.

85 (a) The largest zero occurs when $x \approx 0.6366$.

   (b) As x becomes large, the graph of $f(x) = \cos(1/x)$ approaches the horizontal asymptote $y = 1$.

   (c) There appears to be an infinite number of zeros on $[0,\, c]$ for any $c > 0$.

$[0,\, 3]$ by $[-1.5,\, 1.5]$ $[0,\, 3]$ by $[-1.5,\, 1.5]$

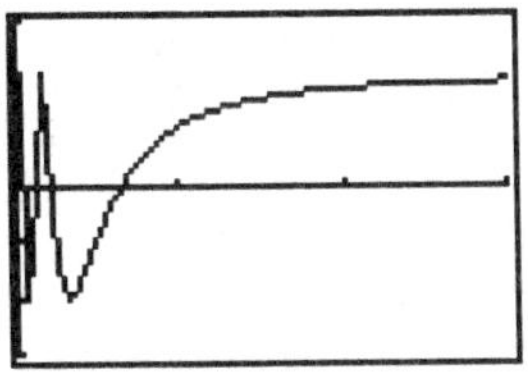

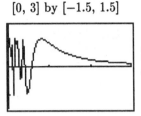

Xscl = 1   Xscl = 1

Yscl = 1   Yscl = 1

Figure 85   *Figure 86*

86 (a) The largest zero occurs when $x \approx 0.5642$.

   (b) As x becomes large, the graph of $f(x) = \sin(1/x^2)$ approaches the horizontal asymptote $y = 0$.

   (c) There appears to be an infinite number of zeros on $[0,\, c]$ for any $c > 0$.

Note: Exer. 87–90: Graph $Y_1 = M$ and $Y_2 = \theta + e \sin \theta$ and approximate the value of θ such that $Y_1 = Y_2$.

87 Mercury: $Y_1 = 5.241$ and $Y_2 = \theta + 0.206 \sin \theta$ intersect when $\theta \approx 5.400$ (radians).

$[0,\, 12]$ by $[0,\, 8]$ $[0,\, 12]$ by $[0,\, 8]$

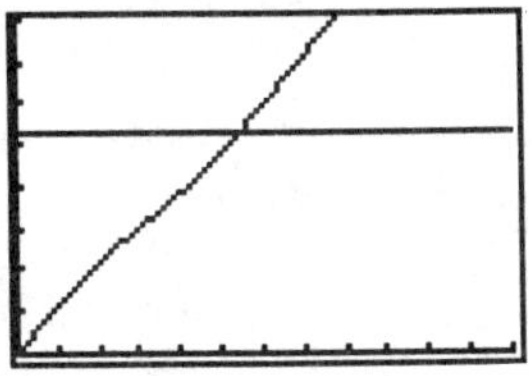

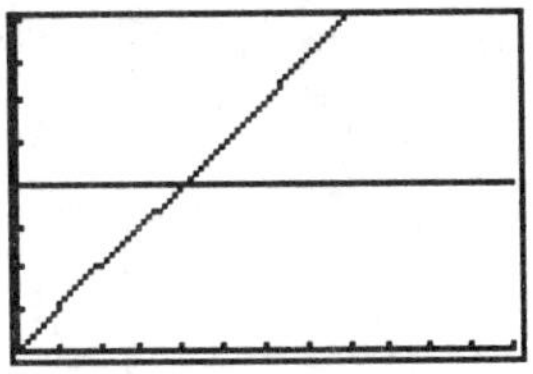

Xscl = 1   Xscl = 1

Yscl = 1   Yscl = 1

Figure 87   *Figure 88*

88 Mars: $Y_1 = 4.028$ and $Y_2 = \theta + 0.093 \sin \theta$ intersect when $\theta \approx 4.104$.

89 Earth: $Y_1 = 3.611$ and $Y_2 = \theta + 0.0167 \sin \theta$ intersect when $\theta \approx 3.619$.

$[0,\, 12]$ by $[0,\, 8]$ $[0,\, 0.3]$ by $[0,\, 0.2]$

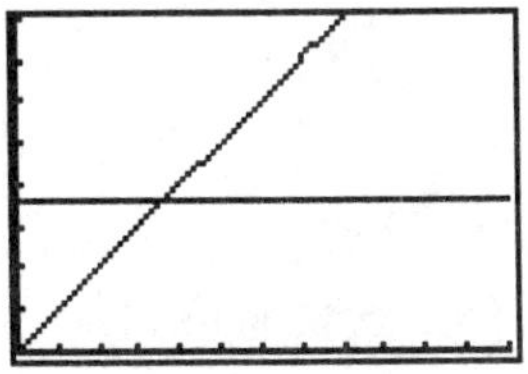

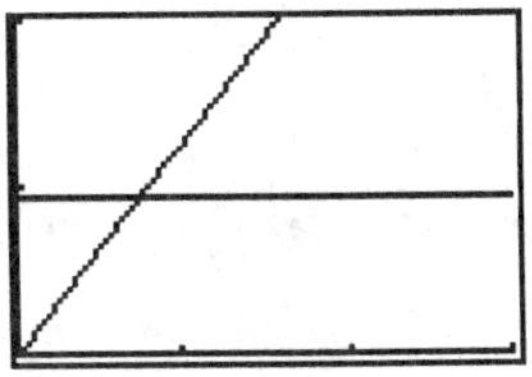

Xscl = 1   Xscl = 0.1

Yscl = 1   Yscl = 0.1

Figure 89   *Figure 90*

90 Pluto: $Y_1 = 0.09424$ and $Y_2 = \theta + 0.255 \sin \theta$ intersect when $\theta \approx 0.075$.

$\boxed{91}$ Graph $y = \sin 2x$ and $y = 2 - x^2$. From the graph, we see that there are two points

of intersection. The x-coordinates of these points are $x \approx -1.48,\ 1.08$.

$[-\pi,\ \pi]$ by $[-2.09,\ 2.09]$ $[-\pi,\ \pi]$ by $[-2.09,\ 2.09]$

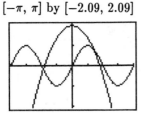
Xscl $= \pi/4$

Yscl $= 1$

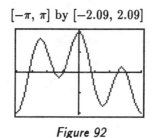
Xscl $= \pi/4$

Yscl $= 1$

Figure 91   *Figure 92*

$\boxed{92}$ Graph $y = \cos^3 x + \cos 3x - \sin^3 x$.

The graph has x-intercepts at $x \approx -2.51,\ -1.22,\ -0.79,\ 0.63,\ 1.92,\ 2.36$.

$\boxed{93}$ Graph $y = \ln(1 + \sin^2 x)$ and $y = \cos x$. From the graph, we see that there are two

points of intersection. The x-coordinates of these points are $x \approx \pm 1.00$.

$[-\pi,\ \pi]$ by $[-2.09,\ 2.09]$ $[-\pi,\ \pi]$ by $[-2.09,\ 2.09]$

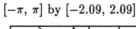
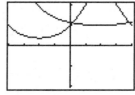
Xscl $= \pi/4$

Yscl $= 1$

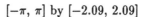
Xscl $= \pi/4$

Yscl $= 1$

Figure 93   *Figure 94*

$\boxed{94}$ Graph $y = e^{\sin x}$ and $y = \sec\left(\frac{1}{3}x - \frac{1}{2}\right)$. From the graph, we see that there are two

points of intersection. The x-coordinates of these points are $x \approx 0.11,\ 3.01$.

$\boxed{95}$ Graph $y = 3\cos^4 x - 2\cos^3 x + \cos x - 1$.

The graph has x-intercepts at $x \approx \pm 0.64,\ \pm 2.42$.

$[-\pi,\ \pi]$ by $[-2.09,\ 2.09]$ $[-\pi,\ \pi]$ by $[-2.09,\ 2.09]$

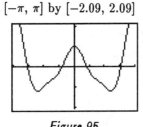
Xscl $= \pi/4$

Yscl $= 1$

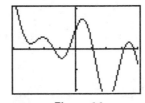
Xscl $= \pi/4$

Yscl $= 1$

Figure 95   *Figure 96*

$\boxed{96}$ Graph $y = \cos 2x + \sin 3x - \tan\frac{1}{3}x$.

The graph has x-intercepts at $x \approx -1.13,\ -0.36,\ 0.88,\ 2.45,\ 2.94$.

$\boxed{97}$ (a) $9.8 = 9.8066(1 - 0.00264\cos 2\theta) \Rightarrow 0.00264\cos 2\theta = 1 - \dfrac{9.8}{9.8066} \Rightarrow$

$\cos 2\theta = \dfrac{0.0066}{(9.8066)(0.00264)} \Rightarrow 2\theta \approx 75.2° \Rightarrow \theta \approx 37.6°$

(b) At the equator, $g_0 = 9.8066(1 - 0.00264 \cos 0°) = 9.8066(0.99736)$.

At $\theta = 0°$, $W = kg \Rightarrow 150 = kg_0 \Rightarrow k = \dfrac{150}{g_0} \Rightarrow W = \dfrac{150}{g_0} g$.

$W = 150.5 \Rightarrow 150.5 = \dfrac{150}{0.99736}(1 - 0.00264 \cos 2\theta) \Rightarrow$

$0.00264 \cos 2\theta = 1 - \dfrac{150.5(0.99736)}{150} \Rightarrow \cos 2\theta \approx -0.2593 \Rightarrow 2\theta \approx 105.0° \Rightarrow \theta \approx 52.5°$

6.3 Exercises

1. (a) $\sin 46°37' = \cos(90° - 46°37') = \cos 43°23'$

   (b) $\cos 73°12' = \sin(90° - 73°12') = \sin 16°48'$

   (c) $\tan\frac{\pi}{6} = \cot\left(\frac{\pi}{2} - \frac{\pi}{6}\right) = \cot\left(\frac{3\pi}{6} - \frac{\pi}{6}\right) = \cot\frac{2\pi}{6} = \cot\frac{\pi}{3}$

   (d) $\sec 17.28° = \csc(90° - 17.28°) = \csc 72.72°$

2. (a) $\tan 24°12' = \cot(90° - 24°12') = \cot 65°48'$

   (b) $\sin 89°41' = \cos(90° - 89°41') = \cos 0°19'$

   (c) $\cos\frac{\pi}{3} = \sin\left(\frac{\pi}{2} - \frac{\pi}{3}\right) = \sin\left(\frac{3\pi}{6} - \frac{2\pi}{6}\right) = \sin\frac{\pi}{6}$

   (d) $\cot 61.87° = \tan(90° - 61.87°) = \tan 28.13°$

3. (a) $\cos\frac{7\pi}{20} = \sin\left(\frac{\pi}{2} - \frac{7\pi}{20}\right) = \sin\frac{3\pi}{20}$ (b) $\sin\frac{1}{4} = \cos\left(\frac{\pi}{2} - \frac{1}{4}\right) = \cos\left(\frac{2\pi - 1}{4}\right)$

   (c) $\tan 1 = \cot\left(\frac{\pi}{2} - 1\right) = \cot\left(\frac{\pi - 2}{2}\right)$ (d) $\csc 0.53 = \sec\left(\frac{\pi}{2} - 0.53\right)$

4. (a) $\sin\frac{\pi}{12} = \cos\left(\frac{\pi}{2} - \frac{\pi}{12}\right) = \cos\frac{5\pi}{12}$ (b) $\cos 0.64 = \sin\left(\frac{\pi}{2} - 0.64\right)$

   (c) $\tan\sqrt{2} = \cot\left(\frac{\pi}{2} - \sqrt{2}\right)$ (d) $\sec 1.2 = \csc\left(\frac{\pi}{2} - 1.2\right)$

5. (a) $\cos\frac{\pi}{4} + \cos\frac{\pi}{6} = \frac{\sqrt{2}}{2} + \frac{\sqrt{3}}{2} = \frac{\sqrt{2} + \sqrt{3}}{2}$

   (b) $\cos\frac{5\pi}{12} = \cos\left(\frac{\pi}{4} + \frac{\pi}{6}\right) = \cos\frac{\pi}{4}\cos\frac{\pi}{6} - \sin\frac{\pi}{4}\sin\frac{\pi}{6} = \frac{\sqrt{2}}{2}\cdot\frac{\sqrt{3}}{2} - \frac{\sqrt{2}}{2}\cdot\frac{1}{2} = \frac{\sqrt{6} - \sqrt{2}}{4}$

6. (a) $\sin\frac{2\pi}{3} + \sin\frac{\pi}{4} = \frac{\sqrt{3}}{2} + \frac{\sqrt{2}}{2} = \frac{\sqrt{3} + \sqrt{2}}{2}$

   (b) $\sin\frac{11\pi}{12} = \sin\left(\frac{2\pi}{3} + \frac{\pi}{4}\right) = \sin\frac{2\pi}{3}\cos\frac{\pi}{4} + \cos\frac{2\pi}{3}\sin\frac{\pi}{4} =$

   $$\frac{\sqrt{3}}{2}\cdot\frac{\sqrt{2}}{2} + \left(-\frac{1}{2}\right)\cdot\frac{\sqrt{2}}{2} = \frac{\sqrt{6} - \sqrt{2}}{4}$$

7. (a) $\tan 60° + \tan 225° = \sqrt{3} + 1$

   (b) $\tan 285° = \tan(60° + 225°) =$

   $$\frac{\tan 60° + \tan 225°}{1 - \tan 60° \tan 225°} = \frac{\sqrt{3} + 1}{1 - (\sqrt{3})(1)} \cdot \frac{1 + \sqrt{3}}{1 + \sqrt{3}} = \frac{4 + 2\sqrt{3}}{-2} = -2 - \sqrt{3}$$

8. (a) $\cos 135° - \cos 60° = -\frac{\sqrt{2}}{2} - \frac{1}{2} = \frac{-\sqrt{2} - 1}{2}$

   (b) $\cos 75° = \cos(135° - 60°) = \cos 135°\cos 60° + \sin 135°\sin 60° =$

   $$-\frac{\sqrt{2}}{2}\cdot\frac{1}{2} + \frac{\sqrt{2}}{2}\cdot\frac{\sqrt{3}}{2} = \frac{\sqrt{6} - \sqrt{2}}{4}$$

$\boxed{9}$ (a) $\sin\frac{3\pi}{4} - \sin\frac{\pi}{6} = \frac{\sqrt{2}}{2} - \frac{1}{2} = \frac{\sqrt{2}-1}{2}$

     (b) $\sin\frac{7\pi}{12} = \sin\left(\frac{3\pi}{4} - \frac{\pi}{6}\right) = \sin\frac{3\pi}{4}\cos\frac{\pi}{6} - \cos\frac{3\pi}{4}\sin\frac{\pi}{6} = \frac{\sqrt{2}}{2}\cdot\frac{\sqrt{3}}{2} - \left(-\frac{\sqrt{2}}{2}\right)\cdot\frac{1}{2} = \frac{\sqrt{6}+\sqrt{2}}{4}$

$\boxed{10}$ (a) $\tan\frac{3\pi}{4} - \tan\frac{\pi}{6} = -1 - \frac{\sqrt{3}}{3} = \frac{-3-\sqrt{3}}{3}$

     (b) $\tan\frac{7\pi}{12} = \tan\left(\frac{3\pi}{4} - \frac{\pi}{6}\right) = \dfrac{\tan\frac{3\pi}{4} - \tan\frac{\pi}{6}}{1 + \tan\frac{3\pi}{4}\tan\frac{\pi}{6}} = \dfrac{-1 - \sqrt{3}/3}{1 + (-1)\cdot(\sqrt{3}/3)}\cdot\frac{3}{3} =$

$$\frac{-3-\sqrt{3}}{3-\sqrt{3}}\cdot\frac{3+\sqrt{3}}{3+\sqrt{3}} = \frac{-12-6\sqrt{3}}{6} = -2-\sqrt{3}$$

$\boxed{11}$ $\cos 48° \cos 23° + \sin 48° \sin 23° = \cos(48° - 23°) = \cos 25°$

$\boxed{12}$ $\cos 13° \cos 50° - \sin 13° \sin 50° = \cos(13° + 50°) = \cos 63°$

$\boxed{13}$ $\cos 10° \sin 5° - \sin 10° \cos 5° = \sin(5° - 10°) = \sin(-5°)$

$\boxed{14}$ $\sin 57° \cos 4° + \cos 57° \sin 4° = \sin(57° + 4°) = \sin 61°$

$\boxed{15}$ $\cos 3 \sin(-2) - \cos 2 \sin 3 = \sin(-2)\cos 3 - \cos(-2)\sin 3 = \sin(-2-3) = \sin(-5)$

$\boxed{16}$ $\sin(-5)\cos 2 + \cos 5 \sin(-2) = \sin(-5)\cos(-2) + \cos(-5)\sin(-2) =$

$$\sin[-2+(-5)] = \sin(-7)$$

$\boxed{17}$ (a) $\sin(\alpha+\beta) = \sin\alpha\cos\beta + \cos\alpha\sin\beta = \frac{3}{5}\cdot\frac{15}{17} + \frac{4}{5}\cdot\frac{8}{17} = \frac{77}{85}$

     (b) $\cos(\alpha+\beta) = \cos\alpha\cos\beta - \sin\alpha\sin\beta = \frac{4}{5}\cdot\frac{15}{17} - \frac{3}{5}\cdot\frac{8}{17} = \frac{36}{85}$

     (c) Since the sine and cosine of $(\alpha+\beta)$ are positive, $(\alpha+\beta)$ is in QI.

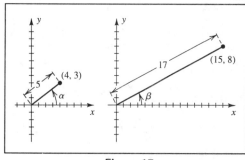

        Figure 17   *Figure 19*

$\boxed{18}$ (a) $\sin(\alpha+\beta) = \sin\alpha\cos\beta + \cos\alpha\sin\beta = \frac{12}{13}\cdot\frac{4}{5} + \frac{5}{13}\cdot\frac{3}{5} = \frac{63}{65}$

     (b) $\tan(\alpha+\beta) = \dfrac{\tan\alpha + \tan\beta}{1 - \tan\alpha\tan\beta} = \dfrac{\frac{12}{5} + \frac{3}{4}}{1 - \frac{12}{5}\cdot\frac{3}{4}}\cdot\frac{20}{20} = \frac{48+15}{20-36} = -\frac{63}{16}$

     (c) Since the sine is positive and the tangent is negative, $(\alpha+\beta)$ is in QII.

$\boxed{19}$ (a) $\sin(\alpha+\beta) = \sin\alpha\cos\beta + \cos\alpha\sin\beta = \left(-\frac{4}{5}\right)\cdot\frac{3}{5} + \left(-\frac{3}{5}\right)\cdot\frac{4}{5} = -\frac{24}{25}$

     (b) $\tan(\alpha+\beta) = \dfrac{\tan\alpha + \tan\beta}{1 - \tan\alpha\tan\beta} = \dfrac{\frac{4}{3} + \frac{4}{3}}{1 - \frac{4}{3}\cdot\frac{4}{3}}\cdot\frac{9}{9} = \frac{12+12}{9-16} = -\frac{24}{7}$

     (c) Since the sine and tangent of $(\alpha+\beta)$ are negative, $(\alpha+\beta)$ is in QIV.

$\boxed{20}$ (a) $\sin(\alpha+\beta) = \sin\alpha\cos\beta + \cos\alpha\sin\beta = \frac{7}{25}\cdot\left(-\frac{3}{5}\right) + \left(-\frac{24}{25}\right)\cdot\left(-\frac{4}{5}\right) = \frac{75}{125} = \frac{3}{5}$

     (b) $\cos(\alpha+\beta) = \cos\alpha\cos\beta - \sin\alpha\sin\beta = \left(-\frac{24}{25}\right)\cdot\left(-\frac{3}{5}\right) - \frac{7}{25}\cdot\left(-\frac{4}{5}\right) = \frac{100}{125} = \frac{4}{5}$

(c) $\tan(\alpha + \beta) = \dfrac{\sin(\alpha + \beta)}{\cos(\alpha + \beta)} = \dfrac{3/5}{4/5} = \dfrac{3}{4}$

(d) $\sin(\alpha - \beta) = \sin\alpha\cos\beta - \cos\alpha\sin\beta = \frac{7}{25}\cdot\left(-\frac{3}{5}\right) - \left(-\frac{24}{25}\right)\cdot\left(-\frac{4}{5}\right) = -\frac{117}{125}$

(e) $\cos(\alpha - \beta) = \cos\alpha\cos\beta + \sin\alpha\sin\beta = \left(-\frac{24}{25}\right)\cdot\left(-\frac{3}{5}\right) + \frac{7}{25}\cdot\left(-\frac{4}{5}\right) = \frac{44}{125}$

(f) $\tan(\alpha - \beta) = \dfrac{\sin(\alpha - \beta)}{\cos(\alpha - \beta)} = \dfrac{-117/125}{44/125} = -\dfrac{117}{44}$

$\boxed{21}$ (a) $\sin(\alpha - \beta) = \sin\alpha\cos\beta - \cos\alpha\sin\beta =$

$$\left(-\frac{\sqrt{21}}{5}\right)\cdot\left(-\frac{3}{5}\right) - \left(-\frac{2}{5}\right)\cdot\left(-\frac{4}{5}\right) = \frac{3\sqrt{21} - 8}{25} \approx 0.23$$

(b) $\cos(\alpha - \beta) = \cos\alpha\cos\beta + \sin\alpha\sin\beta =$

$$\left(-\frac{2}{5}\right)\cdot\left(-\frac{3}{5}\right) + \left(-\frac{\sqrt{21}}{5}\right)\cdot\left(-\frac{4}{5}\right) = \frac{4\sqrt{21} + 6}{25} \approx 0.97$$

(c) Since the sine and cosine of $(\alpha - \beta)$ are positive, $(\alpha - \beta)$ is in QI.

$\boxed{22}$ (a) $\sin(\alpha + \beta) = \sin\alpha\cos\beta + \cos\alpha\sin\beta =$

$$\frac{2}{3}\cdot\left(-\frac{1}{3}\right) + \left(-\frac{\sqrt{5}}{3}\right)\cdot\left(\frac{2\sqrt{2}}{3}\right) = \frac{-2 - 2\sqrt{10}}{9} \approx -0.92$$

(b) $\tan(\alpha + \beta) = \dfrac{\tan\alpha + \tan\beta}{1 - \tan\alpha\tan\beta} = \dfrac{-\dfrac{2}{\sqrt{5}} + (-2\sqrt{2})}{1 - \left(-\dfrac{2}{\sqrt{5}}\right)\cdot(-2\sqrt{2})} \cdot \dfrac{\sqrt{5}}{\sqrt{5}} = \dfrac{-2 - 2\sqrt{10}}{\sqrt{5} - 4\sqrt{2}} \approx 2.43$

(c) Since the sine is negative and the tangent is positive, $(\alpha + \beta)$ is in QIII.

$\boxed{23}$ $\sin(\theta + \pi) = \sin\theta\cos\pi + \cos\theta\sin\pi = \sin\theta(-1) + \cos\theta(0) = -\sin\theta$

$\boxed{24}$ $\sin\left(x + \frac{\pi}{2}\right) = \sin x\cos\frac{\pi}{2} + \cos x\sin\frac{\pi}{2} = \sin x(0) + \cos x(1) = \cos x$. Alternatively, we

could use the cofunction identity: $\sin\left(x + \frac{\pi}{2}\right) = \cos\left[\frac{\pi}{2} - \left(x + \frac{\pi}{2}\right)\right] = \cos(-x) = \cos x$

$\boxed{25}$ $\sin\left(x - \frac{5\pi}{2}\right) = \sin x\cos\frac{5\pi}{2} - \cos x\sin\frac{5\pi}{2} = \sin x(0) - \cos x(1) = -\cos x$

$\boxed{26}$ $\sin\left(\theta - \frac{3\pi}{2}\right) = \sin\theta\cos\frac{3\pi}{2} - \cos\theta\sin\frac{3\pi}{2} = \sin\theta(0) - \cos\theta(-1) = \cos\theta$

$\boxed{27}$ $\cos(\theta - \pi) = \cos\theta\cos\pi + \sin\theta\sin\pi = \cos\theta(-1) + \sin\theta(0) = -\cos\theta$

$\boxed{28}$ $\cos\left(x + \frac{\pi}{2}\right) = \sin\left[\frac{\pi}{2} - \left(x + \frac{\pi}{2}\right)\right] = \sin(-x) = -\sin x$

$\boxed{29}$ $\cos\left(x + \frac{3\pi}{2}\right) = \cos x\cos\frac{3\pi}{2} - \sin x\sin\frac{3\pi}{2} = \cos x(0) - \sin x(-1) = \sin x$

$\boxed{30}$ $\cos\left(\theta - \frac{5\pi}{2}\right) = \cos\theta\cos\frac{5\pi}{2} + \sin\theta\sin\frac{5\pi}{2} = \cos\theta(0) + \sin\theta(1) = \sin\theta$

$\boxed{31}$ $\tan\left(x - \frac{\pi}{2}\right) = \dfrac{\sin\left(x - \frac{\pi}{2}\right)}{\cos\left(x - \frac{\pi}{2}\right)} = \dfrac{\sin x\cos\frac{\pi}{2} - \cos x\sin\frac{\pi}{2}}{\cos x\cos\frac{\pi}{2} + \sin x\sin\frac{\pi}{2}} = \dfrac{-\cos x}{\sin x} = -\cot x$

$\boxed{32}$ $\tan(\pi - \theta) = \dfrac{\tan\pi - \tan\theta}{1 + \tan\pi\tan\theta} = \dfrac{0 - \tan\theta}{1 + (0)\tan\theta} = -\tan\theta$

$\boxed{33}$ $\tan\left(\theta + \frac{\pi}{2}\right) = \cot\left[\frac{\pi}{2} - \left(\theta + \frac{\pi}{2}\right)\right] = \cot(-\theta) = -\cot\theta$

$\boxed{34}$ $\tan(x + \pi) = \dfrac{\tan x + \tan\pi}{1 - \tan x\tan\pi} = \dfrac{\tan x + 0}{1 - (\tan x)(0)} = \tan x$

$\boxed{35}$ $\sin\left(\theta + \frac{\pi}{4}\right) = \sin\theta\cos\frac{\pi}{4} + \cos\theta\sin\frac{\pi}{4} = \frac{\sqrt{2}}{2}\sin\theta + \frac{\sqrt{2}}{2}\cos\theta = \frac{\sqrt{2}}{2}(\sin\theta + \cos\theta)$

$\boxed{36}$ $\cos\left(\theta + \frac{\pi}{4}\right) = \cos\theta\,\cos\frac{\pi}{4} - \sin\theta\,\sin\frac{\pi}{4} = \frac{\sqrt{2}}{2}\cos\theta - \frac{\sqrt{2}}{2}\sin\theta = \frac{\sqrt{2}}{2}\left(\cos\theta - \sin\theta\right)$

$\boxed{37}$ $\tan\left(u + \frac{\pi}{4}\right) = \dfrac{\tan u + \tan\frac{\pi}{4}}{1 - \tan u\,\tan\frac{\pi}{4}} = \dfrac{\tan u + 1}{1 - \tan u\,(1)} = \dfrac{1 + \tan u}{1 - \tan u}$

$\boxed{38}$ $\tan\left(x - \frac{\pi}{4}\right) = \dfrac{\tan x - \tan\frac{\pi}{4}}{1 + \tan x\,\tan\frac{\pi}{4}} = \dfrac{\tan x - 1}{1 + \tan x\,(1)} = \dfrac{\tan x - 1}{\tan x + 1}$

$\boxed{39}$ $\cos\left(u + v\right) + \cos\left(u - v\right) = (\cos u\,\cos v - \sin u\,\sin v) + (\cos u\,\cos v + \sin u\,\sin v) =$

$$2\cos u\,\cos v$$

$\boxed{40}$ $\sin\left(u + v\right) + \sin\left(u - v\right) = (\sin u\,\cos v + \cos u\,\sin v) + (\sin u\,\cos v - \cos u\,\sin v) =$

$$2\sin u\,\cos v$$

$\boxed{41}$ $\sin\left(u + v\right)\cdot\sin\left(u - v\right) = (\sin u\,\cos v + \cos u\,\sin v)\cdot(\sin u\,\cos v - \cos u\,\sin v) =$
$\sin^2 u\,\cos^2 v - \cos^2 u\,\sin^2 v = \sin^2 u\,(1 - \sin^2 v) - (1 - \sin^2 u)\,\sin^2 v =$
$$\sin^2 u - \sin^2 u\,\sin^2 v - \sin^2 v + \sin^2 u\,\sin^2 v = \sin^2 u - \sin^2 v$$

$\boxed{42}$ $\cos\left(u + v\right)\cdot\cos\left(u - v\right) = (\cos u\,\cos v - \sin u\,\sin v)\cdot(\cos u\,\cos v + \sin u\,\sin v) =$
$\cos^2 u\,\cos^2 v - \sin^2 u\,\sin^2 v = \cos^2 u\,(1 - \sin^2 v) - (1 - \cos^2 u)\,\sin^2 v =$
$$\cos^2 u - \cos^2 u\,\sin^2 v - \sin^2 v + \cos^2 u\,\sin^2 v = \cos^2 u - \sin^2 v$$

$\boxed{43}$ $\dfrac{1}{\cot\alpha - \cot\beta} = \dfrac{1}{\dfrac{\cos\alpha}{\sin\alpha} - \dfrac{\cos\beta}{\sin\beta}} = \dfrac{1}{\dfrac{\cos\alpha\,\sin\beta - \cos\beta\,\sin\alpha}{\sin\alpha\,\sin\beta}} = \dfrac{\sin\alpha\,\sin\beta}{\sin\left(\beta - \alpha\right)}$

$\boxed{44}$ $\dfrac{1}{\tan\alpha + \tan\beta} = \dfrac{1}{\dfrac{\sin\alpha}{\cos\alpha} + \dfrac{\sin\beta}{\cos\beta}} = \dfrac{1}{\dfrac{\sin\alpha\,\cos\beta + \sin\beta\,\cos\alpha}{\cos\alpha\,\cos\beta}} = \dfrac{\cos\alpha\,\cos\beta}{\sin\left(\alpha + \beta\right)}$

$\boxed{45}$ $\sin\left(u + v + w\right) = \sin\left[\left(u + v\right) + w\right]$
$\qquad = \sin\left(u + v\right)\cos w + \cos\left(u + v\right)\sin w$
$\qquad = (\sin u\,\cos v + \cos u\,\sin v)\cos w + (\cos u\,\cos v - \sin u\,\sin v)\sin w$
$\qquad = \sin u\,\cos v\,\cos w + \cos u\,\sin v\,\cos w + \cos u\,\cos v\,\sin w - \sin u\,\sin v\,\sin w$

$\boxed{46}$ $\tan\left(u + v + w\right) = \tan\left[\left(u + v\right) + w\right] = \dfrac{\tan\left(u + v\right) + \tan w}{1 - \tan\left(u + v\right)\tan w} =$

$\dfrac{\dfrac{\tan u + \tan v}{1 - \tan u\,\tan v} + \tan w}{1 - \left(\dfrac{\tan u + \tan v}{1 - \tan u\,\tan v}\right)\tan w} = \dfrac{\dfrac{\tan u + \tan v + \tan w - \tan u\,\tan v\,\tan w}{1 - \tan u\,\tan v}}{\dfrac{(1 - \tan u\,\tan v) - \tan u\,\tan w - \tan v\,\tan w}{1 - \tan u\,\tan v}} =$

$$\dfrac{\tan u + \tan v + \tan w - \tan u\,\tan v\,\tan w}{1 - (\tan u\,\tan v + \tan u\,\tan w + \tan v\,\tan w)}$$

$\boxed{47}$ $\cot\left(u + v\right) = \dfrac{\cos\left(u + v\right)}{\sin\left(u + v\right)} = \dfrac{(\cos u\,\cos v - \sin u\,\sin v)(1/\sin u\,\sin v)}{(\sin u\,\cos v + \cos u\,\sin v)(1/\sin u\,\sin v)} = \dfrac{\cot u\,\cot v - 1}{\cot v + \cot u}$

$\boxed{48}$ $\alpha + \beta = 90° \Rightarrow \alpha = 90° - \beta.\ \ \sin^2\alpha + \cos^2\alpha = 1 \Rightarrow$
$\qquad\sin^2\alpha + \cos^2(90° - \beta) = 1 \Rightarrow \sin^2\alpha + \sin^2\beta = 1$ since $\cos\left(90° - \beta\right) = \sin\beta$

$\boxed{49}$ $\sin\left(u - v\right) = \sin\left[u + (-v)\right] = \sin u\,\cos\left(-v\right) + \cos u\,\sin\left(-v\right) = \sin u\,\cos v - \cos u\,\sin v$

50 $\tan(u-v) = \tan[u+(-v)] = \dfrac{\tan u + \tan(-v)}{1-\tan u \tan(-v)} = \dfrac{\tan u - \tan v}{1+\tan u \tan v}$

51 $\dfrac{f(x+h)-f(x)}{h} = \dfrac{\cos(x+h)-\cos x}{h} = \dfrac{\cos x \cos h - \sin x \sin h - \cos x}{h} =$

$$\dfrac{\cos x \cos h - \cos x}{h} - \dfrac{\sin x \sin h}{h} = \cos x\left(\dfrac{\cos h - 1}{h}\right) - \sin x\left(\dfrac{\sin h}{h}\right)$$

52 $\dfrac{f(x+h)-f(x)}{h} = \dfrac{\tan(x+h)-\tan x}{h} = \dfrac{\dfrac{\tan x + \tan h}{1-\tan x \tan h} - \tan x}{h} =$

$$\dfrac{\tan x + \tan h - \tan x + \tan^2 x \tan h}{h(1-\tan x \tan h)} = \dfrac{\tan h (\tan^2 x + 1)}{h(1-\tan x \tan h)} =$$

$$\sec^2 x\left(\dfrac{\sin h}{h}\right)\left(\dfrac{1}{\cos h}\right)\left(\dfrac{1}{1-\tan x \tan h}\right) = \sec^2 x\left(\dfrac{\sin h}{h}\right)\dfrac{1}{\cos h - \sin h \tan x}$$

53 $\sin 4t \cos t = \sin t \cos 4t \Rightarrow \sin 4t \cos t - \sin t \cos 4t = 0 \Rightarrow \sin(4t-t) = 0 \Rightarrow$

$$\sin 3t = 0 \Rightarrow 3t = \pi n \Rightarrow t = \tfrac{\pi}{3}n. \text{ In } [0, \pi), t = 0, \tfrac{\pi}{3}, \tfrac{2\pi}{3}.$$

54 $\cos 5t \cos 3t = \tfrac{1}{2} + \sin(-5t)\sin 3t \Rightarrow \cos 5t \cos 3t + \sin 5t \sin 3t = \tfrac{1}{2} \Rightarrow$

$$\cos(5t-3t) = \tfrac{1}{2} \Rightarrow \cos 2t = \tfrac{1}{2} \Rightarrow 2t = \tfrac{\pi}{3} + 2\pi n, \tfrac{5\pi}{3} + 2\pi n \Rightarrow$$

$$t = \tfrac{\pi}{6} + \pi n, \tfrac{5\pi}{6} + \pi n. \text{ In } [0, \pi), t = \tfrac{\pi}{6}, \tfrac{5\pi}{6}.$$

55 $\cos 5t \cos 2t = -\sin 5t \sin 2t \Rightarrow \cos 5t \cos 2t + \sin 5t \sin 2t = 0 \Rightarrow$

$$\cos(5t-2t) = 0 \Rightarrow \cos 3t = 0 \Rightarrow 3t = \tfrac{\pi}{2} + \pi n \Rightarrow t = \tfrac{\pi}{6} + \tfrac{\pi}{3}n. \text{ In } [0, \pi), t = \tfrac{\pi}{6}, \tfrac{\pi}{2}, \tfrac{5\pi}{6}.$$

56 $\sin 3t \cos t + \cos 3t \sin t = -\tfrac{1}{2} \Rightarrow \sin(3t+t) = -\tfrac{1}{2} \Rightarrow \sin 4t = -\tfrac{1}{2} \Rightarrow$

$$4t = \tfrac{7\pi}{6} + 2\pi n, \tfrac{11\pi}{6} + 2\pi n \Rightarrow t = \tfrac{7\pi}{24} + \tfrac{\pi}{2}n, \tfrac{11\pi}{24} + \tfrac{\pi}{2}n. \text{ In } [0, \pi), t = \tfrac{7\pi}{24}, \tfrac{19\pi}{24}, \tfrac{11\pi}{24}, \tfrac{23\pi}{24}.$$

57 $\tan 2t + \tan t = 1 - \tan 2t \tan t \Rightarrow \dfrac{\tan 2t + \tan t}{1-\tan 2t \tan t} = 1 \Rightarrow \tan(2t+t) = 1 \Rightarrow$

$$\tan 3t = 1 \Rightarrow 3t = \tfrac{\pi}{4} + \pi n \Rightarrow t = \tfrac{\pi}{12} + \tfrac{\pi}{3}n. \text{ In } [0, \pi), t = \tfrac{\pi}{12}, \tfrac{5\pi}{12}, \tfrac{3\pi}{4}.$$

However, $\tan 2t$ is undefined if $t = \tfrac{3\pi}{4}$, so exclude this value of t.

58 $\tan t - \tan 4t = 1 + \tan 4t \tan t \Rightarrow \dfrac{\tan t - \tan 4t}{1+\tan t \tan 4t} = 1 \Rightarrow \tan(t-4t) = 1 \Rightarrow$

$$\tan(-3t) = 1 \Rightarrow -\tan 3t = 1 \Rightarrow \tan 3t = -1 \Rightarrow 3t = \tfrac{3\pi}{4} + \pi n \Rightarrow t = \tfrac{\pi}{4} + \tfrac{\pi}{3}n.$$

$$\text{In } [0, \pi), t = \tfrac{\pi}{4}, \tfrac{7\pi}{12}, \tfrac{11\pi}{12}.$$

59 (a) $f(x) = \sqrt{3}\cos 2x + \sin 2x$ • $A = \sqrt{(\sqrt{3})^2 + 1^2} = 2.$ $\tan C = \dfrac{1}{\sqrt{3}} \Rightarrow C = \tfrac{\pi}{6}.$

$$f(x) = 2\cos\left(2x - \tfrac{\pi}{6}\right) = 2\cos\left[2\left(x - \tfrac{\pi}{12}\right)\right]$$

(b) amplitude $= 2$, period $= \tfrac{2\pi}{2} = \pi$, phase shift $= \tfrac{\pi}{12}$. See *Figure 59*.

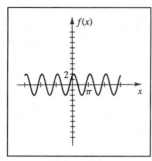

Figure 59

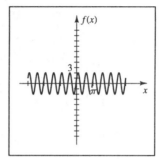

Figure 60

60 (a) $f(x) = \cos 4x + \sqrt{3}\sin 4x$ • $A = \sqrt{1^2 + (\sqrt{3})^2} = 2$. $\tan C = \dfrac{\sqrt{3}}{1} \Rightarrow C = \dfrac{\pi}{3}$.
$$f(x) = 2\cos\left(4x - \tfrac{\pi}{3}\right) = 2\cos\left[4\left(x - \tfrac{\pi}{12}\right)\right]$$

(b) amplitude $= 2$, period $= \dfrac{2\pi}{4} = \dfrac{\pi}{2}$, phase shift $= \dfrac{\pi}{12}$

61 (a) $f(x) = 2\cos 3x - 2\sin 3x$ • $A = \sqrt{2^2 + 2^2} = 2\sqrt{2}$. $\tan C = \dfrac{-2}{2} = -1 \Rightarrow$
$$C = -\tfrac{\pi}{4}.\ \ f(x) = 2\sqrt{2}\cos\left(3x + \tfrac{\pi}{4}\right) = 2\sqrt{2}\cos\left[3\left(x + \tfrac{\pi}{12}\right)\right]$$

(b) amplitude $= 2\sqrt{2}$, period $= \dfrac{2\pi}{3}$, phase shift $= -\dfrac{\pi}{12}$

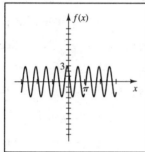

Figure 61

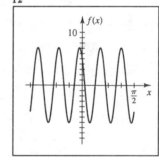

Figure 62

62 (a) $f(x) = 5\cos 10x - 5\sin 10x$ • $A = \sqrt{5^2 + (-5)^2} = 5\sqrt{2}$.
$$\tan C = \tfrac{-5}{5} = -1 \Rightarrow C = -\tfrac{\pi}{4}.\ \ f(x) = 5\sqrt{2}\cos\left(10x + \tfrac{\pi}{4}\right) = 5\sqrt{2}\cos\left[10\left(x + \tfrac{\pi}{40}\right)\right]$$

(b) amplitude $= 5\sqrt{2}$, period $= \dfrac{2\pi}{10} = \dfrac{\pi}{5}$, phase shift $= -\dfrac{\pi}{40}$

63 $y = 50\sin 60\pi t + 40\cos 60\pi t$ • $A = \sqrt{50^2 + 40^2} = 10\sqrt{41}$. $\tan C = \dfrac{50}{40} \Rightarrow$
$$C = \tan^{-1}\tfrac{5}{4} \approx 0.8961.\ \ y = 10\sqrt{41}\cos\left(60\pi t - \tan^{-1}\tfrac{5}{4}\right) \approx 10\sqrt{41}\cos\left(60\pi t - 0.8961\right).$$

64 $y = 10\sin\left(120\pi t - \tfrac{\pi}{2}\right) + 5\sin 120\pi t$ •

$\sin\left(120\pi t - \tfrac{\pi}{2}\right) = \sin 120\pi t\,\cos\tfrac{\pi}{2} - \cos 120\pi t\,\sin\tfrac{\pi}{2} = -\cos 120\pi t$.

Now, $y = -10\cos 120\pi t + 5\sin 120\pi t = -(10\cos 120\pi t - 5\sin 120\pi t)$

{ a, the coefficient of the cosine term, must be positive to apply the formula in

Example 6. }. $A = \sqrt{10^2 + (-5)^2} = 5\sqrt{5}$. $\tan C = \dfrac{-5}{10} \Rightarrow C = \tan^{-1}\left(-\tfrac{1}{2}\right) \approx -0.4636$.
$$y = -5\sqrt{5}\cos\left[120\pi t - \tan^{-1}\left(-\tfrac{1}{2}\right)\right] \approx -5\sqrt{5}\cos\left(120\pi t + 0.4636\right).$$

65 (a) $y = 2\cos t + 3\sin t$; $A = \sqrt{2^2 + 3^2} = \sqrt{13}$; $\tan C = \tfrac{3}{2} \Rightarrow C \approx 0.98$;
$$y = \sqrt{13}\cos(t - C);\ \text{amplitude} = \sqrt{13},\ \text{period} = \tfrac{2\pi}{1} = 2\pi$$

(b) $y = 0 \Rightarrow \cos(t - C) = 0 \Rightarrow$

$$t = C + \tfrac{\pi}{2} + \pi n \approx 2.5536 + \pi n \text{ for every nonnegative integer } n.$$

$\boxed{66}$ $4 = \text{amplitude} \Rightarrow 4 = \sqrt{(y_0)^2 + \left(\dfrac{v_0}{\omega}\right)^2} \Rightarrow 4 = \sqrt{1^2 + \left(\dfrac{v_0}{2}\right)^2}$ $\{y_0 = 1 \text{ and } \omega = 2\} \Rightarrow$

$$16 = 1 + \frac{v_0^2}{4} \Rightarrow v_0^2 = 60 \Rightarrow v_0 = \pm 2\sqrt{15} \text{ ft/sec}$$

$\boxed{67}$ (a) $p(t) = A \sin \omega t + B \sin(\omega t + \tau)$

$$= A \sin \omega t + B(\sin \omega t \cos \tau + \cos \omega t \sin \tau)$$

$$= (B \sin \tau) \cos \omega t + (A + B \cos \tau) \sin \omega t$$

$$= a \cos \omega t + b \sin \omega t \text{ with } a = B \sin \tau \text{ and } b = A + B \cos \tau$$

(b) $C^2 = (B \sin \tau)^2 + (A + B \cos \tau)^2$

$$= B^2 \sin^2 \tau + A^2 + 2AB \cos \tau + B^2 \cos^2 \tau$$

$$= A^2 + B^2(\sin^2 \tau + \cos^2 \tau) + 2AB \cos \tau$$

$$= A^2 + B^2 + 2AB \cos \tau$$

$\boxed{68}$ (a) Using $C^2 = A^2 + B^2 + 2AB \cos \tau$ from Exercise 67(b) and letting $A = B$ yields

$C^2 = 2A^2 + 2A^2 \cos \tau$, or $C^2 = 2A^2(1 + \cos \tau)$. If the amplitude C of p is zero,

$$\text{then } 1 + \cos \tau = 0, \text{ i.e., } \cos \tau = -1. \text{ Hence, } \tau = \pi.$$

(b) Destructive interference occurs if $C < A$. If $A, C > 0$, then $C < A \Rightarrow$

$$C^2 < A^2 \Rightarrow 2A^2(1 + \cos \tau) < A^2 \Rightarrow 1 + \cos \tau < \tfrac{1}{2} \Rightarrow \cos \tau < -\tfrac{1}{2} \Rightarrow \tfrac{2\pi}{3} < \tau < \tfrac{4\pi}{3}.$$

$\boxed{69}$ (a) $C^2 = A^2 + B^2 + 2AB \cos \tau \le A^2 + B^2 + 2AB$, since $\cos \tau \le 1$ and

$$A > 0, B > 0. \text{ Thus, } C^2 \le (A + B)^2, \text{ and hence } C \le A + B.$$

(b) $C = A + B$ if $\cos \tau = 1$, or $\tau = 0, 2\pi$.

(c) Constructive interference will occur if $C > A$. $C > A \Rightarrow C^2 > A^2 \Rightarrow$

$$A^2 + B^2 + 2AB \cos \tau > A^2 \Rightarrow B^2 + 2AB \cos \tau > 0 \Rightarrow B(B + 2A \cos \tau) > 0.$$

Since $B > 0$, the product will be positive if $B + 2A \cos \tau > 0$, i.e., $\cos \tau > -\dfrac{B}{2A}$.

$\boxed{70}$ (a) $A = B = 2$, $\omega_1 = 1$, $\omega_2 = 20$, and $\tau = 3 \Rightarrow p(t) = 2 \sin t + 2 \sin(20t + 3)$.

(b) The tone of the tuning fork with the shortest period will fade in and out at

intervals equal to the period of the tuning fork with the longest period.

$[-2\pi, 2\pi]$ by $[-4.19, 4.19]$

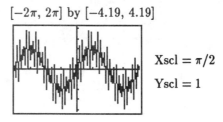

Xscl $= \pi/2$

Yscl $= 1$

Figure 70

71   Graph $y = 3\sin 2t + 2\sin(4t + 1)$. Constructive interference will occur when $y > 3$ or $y < -3$. From the graph, we see that this occurs on the intervals

$$(-2.97, -2.69), \ (-1.00, -0.37), \ (0.17, 0.46), \ \text{and} \ (2.14, 2.77).$$

$[-\pi, \pi]$ by $[-5, 5]$ $[-\pi, \pi]$ by $[-5, 5]$

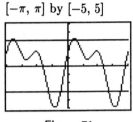   Xscl $= \pi/4$ 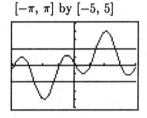   Xscl $= \pi/4$

                     Yscl $= 1$ Yscl $= 1$

              Figure 71   *Figure 72*

72   Graph $y = 2\sin t + 2\sin(3t + 3)$. Constructive interference will occur when $y > 2$ or $y < -2$. From the graph, we see that this occurs on the intervals

$$(-2.01, -1.05) \ \text{and} \ (1.13, 2.10).$$

6.4 Exercises

---

1   From *Figure 1*, $\sin\theta = \frac{4}{5}$ and $\cos\theta = \frac{3}{5}$. Thus, $\sin 2\theta = 2\sin\theta\cos\theta = 2(\frac{4}{5})(\frac{3}{5}) = \frac{24}{25}$.

$$\cos 2\theta = \cos^2\theta - \sin^2\theta = (\tfrac{3}{5})^2 - (\tfrac{4}{5})^2 = -\tfrac{7}{25}. \quad \tan 2\theta = \frac{\sin 2\theta}{\cos 2\theta} = \frac{24/25}{-7/25} = -\frac{24}{7}.$$

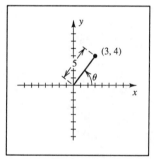   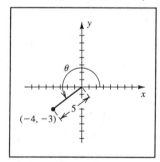

             Figure 1   *Figure 2*

2   From *Figure 2*, $\sin\theta = -\frac{3}{5}$ and $\cos\theta = -\frac{4}{5}$.

Thus, $\sin 2\theta = 2\sin\theta\cos\theta = 2(-\frac{3}{5})(-\frac{4}{5}) = \frac{24}{25}$.

$$\cos 2\theta = \cos^2\theta - \sin^2\theta = (-\tfrac{4}{5})^2 - (-\tfrac{3}{5})^2 = \tfrac{7}{25}. \quad \tan 2\theta = \frac{\sin 2\theta}{\cos 2\theta} = \frac{24/25}{7/25} = \frac{24}{7}.$$

3   From *Figure 3*, $\sin\theta = \sqrt{8}/3 = \frac{2}{3}\sqrt{2}$ and $\cos\theta = -\frac{1}{3}$.

Thus, $\sin 2\theta = 2\sin\theta\cos\theta = 2(\frac{2}{3}\sqrt{2})(-\frac{1}{3}) = -\frac{4}{9}\sqrt{2}$.

$$\cos 2\theta = \cos^2\theta - \sin^2\theta = (-\tfrac{1}{3})^2 - (\tfrac{2}{3}\sqrt{2})^2 = \tfrac{1}{9} - \tfrac{8}{9} = -\tfrac{7}{9}.$$

$$\tan 2\theta = \frac{\sin 2\theta}{\cos 2\theta} = \frac{-4\sqrt{2}/9}{-7/9} = \frac{4\sqrt{2}}{7}.$$

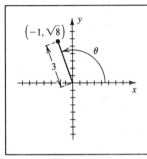

Figure 3

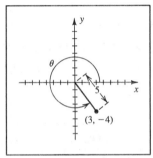

Figure 4

4 From *Figure 4*, $\sin\theta = -\frac{4}{5}$ and $\cos\theta = \frac{3}{5}$.

Thus, $\sin 2\theta = 2\sin\theta\cos\theta = 2(-\frac{4}{5})(\frac{3}{5}) = -\frac{24}{25}$.

$$\cos 2\theta = \cos^2\theta - \sin^2\theta = (\tfrac{3}{5})^2 - (-\tfrac{4}{5})^2 = -\frac{7}{25}. \quad \tan 2\theta = \frac{\sin 2\theta}{\cos 2\theta} = \frac{-24/25}{-7/25} = \frac{24}{7}.$$

5 $\sec\theta = \frac{5}{4} \Rightarrow \cos\theta = \frac{4}{5}$. θ acute implies that $\frac{\theta}{2}$ is acute, so all functions of $\frac{\theta}{2}$ are positive.

$$\sin\frac{\theta}{2} = \sqrt{\frac{1-\cos\theta}{2}} = \sqrt{\frac{1-\frac{4}{5}}{2}} = \sqrt{\frac{\frac{1}{5}}{2}} = \sqrt{\frac{1}{10}\cdot\frac{10}{10}} = \frac{\sqrt{10}}{10}.$$

$$\cos\frac{\theta}{2} = \sqrt{\frac{1+\cos\theta}{2}} = \sqrt{\frac{1+\frac{4}{5}}{2}} = \sqrt{\frac{\frac{9}{5}}{2}} = \sqrt{\frac{9}{10}\cdot\frac{10}{10}} = \frac{3\sqrt{10}}{10}.$$

$$\tan\frac{\theta}{2} = \frac{\sin\frac{\theta}{2}}{\cos\frac{\theta}{2}} = \frac{\sqrt{10}/10}{3\sqrt{10}/10} = \frac{1}{3}.$$

6 From *Figure 6*, $\cos\theta = \frac{4}{5}$ and $\frac{\theta}{2}$ is in QIV. Hence, $\sin\frac{\theta}{2} < 0$ and $\cos\frac{\theta}{2} > 0$.

$$\sin\frac{\theta}{2} = -\sqrt{\frac{1-\cos\theta}{2}} = -\sqrt{\frac{1-\frac{4}{5}}{2}} = -\sqrt{\frac{\frac{1}{5}}{2}} = -\sqrt{\frac{1}{10}\cdot\frac{10}{10}} = -\frac{\sqrt{10}}{10}.$$

$$\cos\frac{\theta}{2} = \sqrt{\frac{1+\cos\theta}{2}} = \sqrt{\frac{1+\frac{4}{5}}{2}} = \sqrt{\frac{\frac{9}{5}}{2}} = \sqrt{\frac{9}{10}\cdot\frac{10}{10}} = \frac{3\sqrt{10}}{10}.$$

$$\tan\frac{\theta}{2} = \frac{\sin\frac{\theta}{2}}{\cos\frac{\theta}{2}} = \frac{-\sqrt{10}/10}{3\sqrt{10}/10} = -\frac{1}{3}.$$

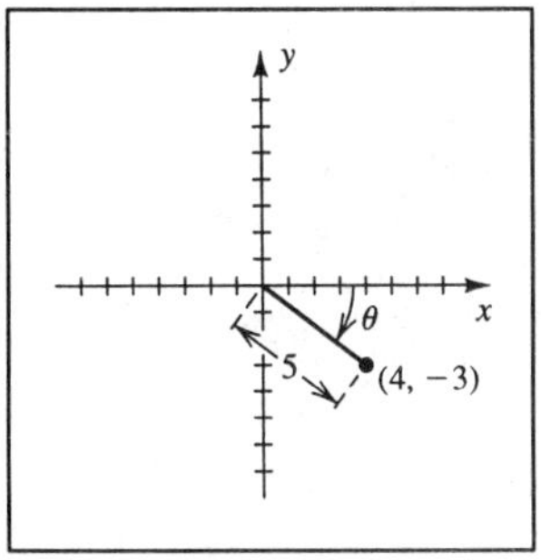

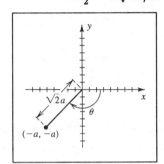

Figure 6

Figure 7

7 From *Figure 7* $(a > 0)$, $\cos\theta = -\dfrac{a}{\sqrt{2}\,a} = -\dfrac{\sqrt{2}}{2}$ and $\frac{\theta}{2}$ is in QIV.

$$\sin\frac{\theta}{2} = -\sqrt{\frac{1-\cos\theta}{2}} = -\sqrt{\frac{1+\sqrt{2}/2}{2}} = -\sqrt{\frac{2+\sqrt{2}}{4}} = -\frac{1}{2}\sqrt{2+\sqrt{2}}.$$

(cont.)

$$\cos\frac{\theta}{2} = \sqrt{\frac{1+\cos\theta}{2}} = \sqrt{\frac{1-\sqrt{2}/2}{2}} = \sqrt{\frac{2-\sqrt{2}}{4}} = \frac{1}{2}\sqrt{2-\sqrt{2}}.$$

$$\tan\frac{\theta}{2} = \frac{1-\cos\theta}{\sin\theta} = \frac{1+\sqrt{2}/2}{-\sqrt{2}/2}\cdot\frac{2}{2} = \frac{2+\sqrt{2}}{-\sqrt{2}} = -\sqrt{2}-1.$$

8 $\sec\theta = -4 \Rightarrow \cos\theta = -\frac{1}{4}.$ $180° < \theta < 270° \Rightarrow 90° < \frac{\theta}{2} < 135° \Rightarrow \frac{\theta}{2}$ is in QII.

$$\sin\frac{\theta}{2} = \sqrt{\frac{1-\cos\theta}{2}} = \sqrt{\frac{1+\frac{1}{4}}{2}} = \sqrt{\frac{\frac{5}{4}}{2}} = \sqrt{\frac{5}{8}\cdot\frac{2}{2}} = \frac{\sqrt{10}}{4}.$$

$$\cos\frac{\theta}{2} = -\sqrt{\frac{1+\cos\theta}{2}} = -\sqrt{\frac{1-\frac{1}{4}}{2}} = -\sqrt{\frac{\frac{3}{4}}{2}} = -\sqrt{\frac{3}{8}\cdot\frac{2}{2}} = -\frac{\sqrt{6}}{4}.$$

$$\tan\frac{\theta}{2} = \frac{\sin\frac{\theta}{2}}{\cos\frac{\theta}{2}} = \frac{\sqrt{10}/4}{-\sqrt{6}/4} = -\sqrt{\frac{5}{3}\cdot\frac{3}{3}} = -\frac{\sqrt{15}}{3}.$$

9 (a) $\cos 67°30' = \sqrt{\frac{1+\cos 135°}{2}} = \sqrt{\frac{1-\sqrt{2}/2}{2}} = \sqrt{\frac{2-\sqrt{2}}{4}} = \frac{1}{2}\sqrt{2-\sqrt{2}}.$

(b) $\sin 15° = \sqrt{\frac{1-\cos 30°}{2}} = \sqrt{\frac{1-\sqrt{3}/2}{2}} = \sqrt{\frac{2-\sqrt{3}}{4}} = \frac{1}{2}\sqrt{2-\sqrt{3}}.$

(c) $\tan\frac{3\pi}{8} = \frac{1-\cos\frac{3\pi}{4}}{\sin\frac{3\pi}{4}} = \frac{1+\sqrt{2}/2}{\sqrt{2}/2}\cdot\frac{2}{2} = \frac{2+\sqrt{2}}{\sqrt{2}} = \sqrt{2}+1.$

10 (a) $\cos 165° = -\sqrt{\frac{1+\cos 330°}{2}} = -\sqrt{\frac{1+\sqrt{3}/2}{2}} = -\sqrt{\frac{2+\sqrt{3}}{4}} = -\frac{1}{2}\sqrt{2+\sqrt{3}}.$

(b) $\sin 157°30' = \sqrt{\frac{1-\cos 315°}{2}} = \sqrt{\frac{1-\sqrt{2}/2}{2}} = \sqrt{\frac{2-\sqrt{2}}{4}} = \frac{1}{2}\sqrt{2-\sqrt{2}}.$

(c) $\tan\frac{\pi}{8} = \frac{1-\cos\frac{\pi}{4}}{\sin\frac{\pi}{4}} = \frac{1-\sqrt{2}/2}{\sqrt{2}/2}\cdot\frac{2}{2} = \frac{2-\sqrt{2}}{\sqrt{2}} = \sqrt{2}-1.$

11 $\sin 10\theta = \sin(2\cdot 5\theta) = 2\sin 5\theta\,\cos 5\theta$

12 $\cos^2 3x - \sin^2 3x = \cos(2\cdot 3x) = \cos 6x$

13 $4\sin\frac{x}{2}\,\cos\frac{x}{2} = 2\cdot 2\sin\frac{x}{2}\,\cos\frac{x}{2} = 2\sin\left(2\cdot\frac{x}{2}\right) = 2\sin x$

14 $\dfrac{\sin^2 2\alpha}{\sin^2\alpha} = \dfrac{(2\sin\alpha\,\cos\alpha)^2}{\sin^2\alpha} = \dfrac{4\sin^2\alpha\,\cos^2\alpha}{\sin^2\alpha} = 4\cos^2\alpha = 4(1-\sin^2\alpha) = 4 - 4\sin^2\alpha$

15 $(\sin t + \cos t)^2 = \sin^2 t + 2\sin t\,\cos t + \cos^2 t = 1 + \sin 2t$

16 $\csc 2u = \dfrac{1}{\sin 2u} = \dfrac{1}{2\sin u\,\cos u} = \dfrac{1}{2}\csc u\,\sec u$

17 $\sin 3u = \sin(2u + u) = \sin 2u\,\cos u + \cos 2u\,\sin u$

$$= (2\sin u\,\cos u)\cos u + (1 - 2\sin^2 u)\sin u = 2\sin u\,\cos^2 u + \sin u - 2\sin^3 u$$

$$= 2\sin u(1 - \sin^2 u) + \sin u - 2\sin^3 u = 2\sin u - 2\sin^3 u + \sin u - 2\sin^3 u$$

$$= 3\sin u - 4\sin^3 u = \sin u(3 - 4\sin^2 u)$$

18 $\sin 4t = \sin(2\cdot 2t) = 2\sin 2t\,\cos 2t = 2(2\sin t\,\cos t)(1 - 2\sin^2 t) =$

$$4\sin t\,\cos t\,(1 - 2\sin^2 t)$$

19 $\cos 4\theta = \cos(2 \cdot 2\theta) = 2\cos^2 2\theta - 1 = 2(2\cos^2\theta - 1)^2 - 1 =$

$$2(4\cos^4\theta - 4\cos^2\theta + 1) - 1 = 8\cos^4\theta - 8\cos^2\theta + 1$$

20 $\cos 6t = \cos(2 \cdot 3t) = 2\cos^2 3t - 1$

$$= 2(4\cos^3 t - 3\cos t)^2 - 1 \ \{\text{using Example 2}\}$$

$$= 2(16\cos^6 t - 24\cos^4 t + 9\cos^2 t) - 1$$

$$= 32\cos^6 t - 48\cos^4 t + 18\cos^2 t - 1$$

21 $\sin^4 t = (\sin^2 t)^2 = \left(\dfrac{1 - \cos 2t}{2}\right)^2 = \frac{1}{4}(1 - 2\cos 2t + \cos^2 2t) =$

$$\frac{1}{4} - \frac{1}{2}\cos 2t + \frac{1}{4}\left(\frac{1 + \cos 4t}{2}\right) = \frac{1}{4} - \frac{1}{2}\cos 2t + \frac{1}{8} + \frac{1}{8}\cos 4t = \frac{3}{8} - \frac{1}{2}\cos 2t + \frac{1}{8}\cos 4t$$

22 $\cos^4 x - \sin^4 x = (\cos^2 x + \sin^2 x)(\cos^2 x - \sin^2 x) = \cos^2 x - \sin^2 x = \cos 2x$

23 $\sec 2\theta = \dfrac{1}{\cos 2\theta} = \dfrac{1}{2\cos^2\theta - 1} = \dfrac{1}{2\left(\dfrac{1}{\sec^2\theta}\right) - 1} = \dfrac{1}{\dfrac{2 - \sec^2\theta}{\sec^2\theta}} = \dfrac{\sec^2\theta}{2 - \sec^2\theta}$

24 $\cot 2u = \dfrac{1}{\tan 2u} = \dfrac{1 - \tan^2 u}{2\tan u} = \dfrac{1 - \dfrac{1}{\cot^2 u}}{\dfrac{2}{\cot u}} \cdot \dfrac{\cot^2 u}{\cot^2 u} = \dfrac{\cot^2 u - 1}{2\cot u}$

25 $2\sin^2 2t + \cos 4t = 2\sin^2 2t + \cos(2 \cdot 2t) = 2\sin^2 2t + (1 - 2\sin^2 2t) = 1$

26 $\tan\theta + \cot\theta = \dfrac{\sin\theta}{\cos\theta} + \dfrac{\cos\theta}{\sin\theta} = \dfrac{\sin^2\theta + \cos^2\theta}{\cos\theta \sin\theta} = \dfrac{2}{2\sin\theta \cos\theta} = \dfrac{2}{\sin 2\theta} = 2\csc 2\theta$

27 $\tan 3u = \tan(2u + u) = \dfrac{\tan 2u + \tan u}{1 - \tan 2u \tan u} = \dfrac{\dfrac{2\tan u}{1 - \tan^2 u} + \tan u}{1 - \dfrac{2\tan u}{1 - \tan^2 u} \cdot \tan u} =$

$$\dfrac{\dfrac{2\tan u + \tan u - \tan^3 u}{1 - \tan^2 u}}{\dfrac{1 - \tan^2 u - 2\tan^2 u}{1 - \tan^2 u}} = \dfrac{3\tan u - \tan^3 u}{1 - 3\tan^2 u} = \dfrac{\tan u(3 - \tan^2 u)}{1 - 3\tan^2 u}$$

28 $\dfrac{1 + \sin 2v + \cos 2v}{1 + \sin 2v - \cos 2v} = \dfrac{1 + 2\sin v \cos v + 2\cos^2 v - 1}{1 + 2\sin v \cos v - 1 + 2\sin^2 v} =$

$$\dfrac{2\cos^2 v + 2\sin v \cos v}{2\sin^2 v + 2\sin v \cos v} = \dfrac{2\cos v(\cos v + \sin v)}{2\sin v(\sin v + \cos v)} = \cot v$$

29 $\cos^4 \dfrac{\theta}{2} = \left(\cos^2 \dfrac{\theta}{2}\right)^2 = \left(\dfrac{1 + \cos\theta}{2}\right)^2 = \dfrac{1 + 2\cos\theta + \cos^2\theta}{4} = \dfrac{1}{4} + \dfrac{1}{2}\cos\theta + \dfrac{1}{4}\left(\dfrac{1 + \cos 2\theta}{2}\right) =$

$$\dfrac{1}{4} + \dfrac{1}{2}\cos\theta + \dfrac{1}{8} + \dfrac{1}{8}\cos 2\theta = \dfrac{3}{8} + \dfrac{1}{2}\cos\theta + \dfrac{1}{8}\cos 2\theta$$

30 $\cos^4 2x = (\cos^2 2x)^2 = \left(\dfrac{1 + \cos 4x}{2}\right)^2 = \dfrac{1 + 2\cos 4x + \cos^2 4x}{4} =$

$$\dfrac{1}{4} + \dfrac{1}{2}\cos 4x + \dfrac{1}{4}\left(\dfrac{1 + \cos 8x}{2}\right) = \dfrac{1}{4} + \dfrac{1}{2}\cos 4x + \dfrac{1}{8} + \dfrac{1}{8}\cos 8x = \dfrac{3}{8} + \dfrac{1}{2}\cos 4x + \dfrac{1}{8}\cos 8x$$

31 $\sin^4 2x = (\sin^2 2x)^2 = \left(\dfrac{1-\cos 4x}{2}\right)^2 = \dfrac{1-2\cos 4x + \cos^2 4x}{4} =$

$\qquad \dfrac{1}{4} - \dfrac{1}{2}\cos 4x + \dfrac{1}{4}\left(\dfrac{1+\cos 8x}{2}\right) = \dfrac{1}{4} - \dfrac{1}{2}\cos 4x + \dfrac{1}{8} + \dfrac{1}{8}\cos 8x = \dfrac{3}{8} - \dfrac{1}{2}\cos 4x + \dfrac{1}{8}\cos 8x$

32 $\sin^4 \dfrac{\theta}{2} = \left(\sin^2 \dfrac{\theta}{2}\right)^2 = \left(\dfrac{1-\cos\theta}{2}\right)^2 = \dfrac{1 - 2\cos\theta + \cos^2\theta}{4} = \dfrac{1}{4} - \dfrac{1}{2}\cos\theta + \dfrac{1}{4}\left(\dfrac{1+\cos 2\theta}{2}\right) =$

$\qquad \dfrac{1}{4} - \dfrac{1}{2}\cos\theta + \dfrac{1}{8} + \dfrac{1}{8}\cos 2\theta = \dfrac{3}{8} - \dfrac{1}{2}\cos\theta + \dfrac{1}{8}\cos 2\theta$

33 $\sin 2t + \sin t = 0 \Rightarrow 2\sin t\,\cos t + \sin t = 0 \Rightarrow \sin t\,(2\cos t + 1) = 0 \Rightarrow$

$\qquad \sin t = 0 \text{ or } \cos t = -\dfrac{1}{2} \Rightarrow t = 0,\ \pi \text{ or } \dfrac{2\pi}{3},\ \dfrac{4\pi}{3}$

34 $\cos t - \sin 2t = 0 \Rightarrow \cos t - 2\sin t\,\cos t = 0 \Rightarrow \cos t\,(1 - 2\sin t) = 0 \Rightarrow$

$\qquad \cos t = 0 \text{ or } \sin t = \dfrac{1}{2} \Rightarrow t = \dfrac{\pi}{2},\ \dfrac{3\pi}{2} \text{ or } \dfrac{\pi}{6},\ \dfrac{5\pi}{6}$

35 $\cos u + \cos 2u = 0 \Rightarrow \cos u + 2\cos^2 u - 1 = 0 \Rightarrow (2\cos u - 1)(\cos u + 1) = 0 \Rightarrow$

$\qquad \cos u = \dfrac{1}{2},\ -1 \Rightarrow u = \dfrac{\pi}{3},\ \dfrac{5\pi}{3},\ \pi$

36 $\cos 2\theta - \tan\theta = 1 \Rightarrow 1 - 2\sin^2\theta - \dfrac{\sin\theta}{\cos\theta} = 1 \Rightarrow 2\sin^2\theta\,\cos\theta + \sin\theta = 0 \Rightarrow$

$\sin\theta\,(2\sin\theta\,\cos\theta + 1) = 0 \Rightarrow \sin\theta = 0 \text{ or } \sin 2\theta = -1 \Rightarrow$

$\qquad \theta = 0,\ \pi \text{ or } 2\theta = \dfrac{3\pi}{2},\ \dfrac{7\pi}{2}\ \{\text{If } \theta \in [0,\ 2\pi), \text{ then } 2\theta \in [0,\ 4\pi).\} \Rightarrow \theta = 0,\ \pi,\ \dfrac{3\pi}{4},\ \dfrac{7\pi}{4}$

37 $\tan 2x = \tan x \Rightarrow 2x = x + \pi n \Rightarrow x = \pi n \Rightarrow x = 0,\ \pi.$

$\text{Another approach is: } \tan 2x = \tan x \Rightarrow \dfrac{\sin 2x}{\cos 2x} = \dfrac{\sin x}{\cos x} \Rightarrow \sin 2x\,\cos x = \sin x\,\cos 2x \Rightarrow$

$\qquad \sin 2x\,\cos x - \sin x\,\cos 2x = 0 \Rightarrow \sin(2x - x) = 0 \Rightarrow \sin x = 0 \Rightarrow x = 0,\ \pi.$

38 $\tan 2t - 2\cos t = 0 \Rightarrow \dfrac{\sin 2t}{\cos 2t} - 2\cos t = 0 \Rightarrow$

$\dfrac{2\sin t\,\cos t}{\cos 2t} - \dfrac{(1 - 2\sin^2 t)(2\cos t)}{\cos 2t} = 0 \Rightarrow 2\sin t\,\cos t - 2\cos t + 4\cos t\,\sin^2 t = 0 \Rightarrow$

$2\cos t\,(2\sin^2 t + \sin t - 1) = 0 \Rightarrow (2\cos t)(2\sin t - 1)(\sin t + 1) \Rightarrow$

$\qquad \cos t = 0 \text{ or } \sin t = \dfrac{1}{2},\ -1 \Rightarrow t = \dfrac{\pi}{2},\ \dfrac{3\pi}{2} \text{ or } t = \dfrac{\pi}{6},\ \dfrac{5\pi}{6},\ \dfrac{3\pi}{2}$

39 $\sin\dfrac{1}{2}u + \cos u = 1 \Rightarrow \sin\dfrac{1}{2}u + (1 - 2\sin^2\dfrac{1}{2}u) = 1 \Rightarrow \sin\dfrac{1}{2}u - 2\sin^2\dfrac{1}{2}u = 0 \Rightarrow$

$\qquad \sin\dfrac{1}{2}u\,(1 - 2\sin\dfrac{1}{2}u) = 0 \Rightarrow \sin\dfrac{1}{2}u = 0,\ \dfrac{1}{2} \Rightarrow \dfrac{1}{2}u = 0,\ \dfrac{\pi}{6},\ \dfrac{5\pi}{6} \Rightarrow u = 0,\ \dfrac{\pi}{3},\ \dfrac{5\pi}{3}$

40 $2 - \cos^2 x = 4\sin^2\dfrac{1}{2}x \Rightarrow 2 - \cos^2 x = 4\left(\dfrac{1-\cos x}{2}\right) \Rightarrow 2 - \cos^2 x = 2 - 2\cos x \Rightarrow$

$\qquad \cos^2 x - 2\cos x = 0 \Rightarrow \cos x\,(\cos x - 2) = 0 \Rightarrow \cos x = 0\ \{\cos x \neq 2\} \Rightarrow x = \dfrac{\pi}{2},\ \dfrac{3\pi}{2}$

41 $\sqrt{a^2 + b^2}\,\sin(u + v) = \sqrt{a^2 + b^2}\,\sin u\,\cos v + \sqrt{a^2 + b^2}\,\cos u\,\sin v = a\,\sin u + b\,\cos u$

$\{\text{equate coefficients of } \sin u \text{ and } \cos u\} \Rightarrow a = \sqrt{a^2 + b^2}\,\cos v \text{ and } b = \sqrt{a^2 + b^2}\,\sin v$

$\Rightarrow \cos v = \dfrac{a}{\sqrt{a^2 + b^2}} \text{ and } \sin v = \dfrac{b}{\sqrt{a^2 + b^2}}. \text{ Since } 0 < u < \dfrac{\pi}{2},\ \sin u > 0 \text{ and } \cos v > 0.$

Now $a > 0$ and $b > 0$ combine with the above to imply that $\cos v > 0$ and $\sin v > 0$.

$\qquad\qquad\qquad\qquad\qquad\qquad\qquad\qquad\qquad\qquad\qquad \text{Thus, } 0 < v < \dfrac{\pi}{2}.$

42 $\sqrt{8^2 + 15^2} = 17$. $\sin v = \frac{15}{17}$ and $\cos v = \frac{8}{17} \Rightarrow v = \approx 1.08$ radians, or $v \approx 62°$.

$$8 \sin u + 15 \cos u \approx 17 \sin (u + 1.08).$$

43 (a) $\cos 2x + 2 \cos x = 0 \Rightarrow 2 \cos^2 x + 2 \cos x - 1 = 0 \Rightarrow$

$$\cos x = \frac{-2 \pm \sqrt{12}}{4} = \frac{-1 \pm \sqrt{3}}{2} \approx 0.366 \left\{ \cos x \neq \frac{-1 - \sqrt{3}}{2} \right\} \Rightarrow x \approx 1.20 \text{ and } 5.09.$$

(b) $\sin 2x + \sin x = 0 \Rightarrow 2 \sin x \cos x + \sin x = 0 \Rightarrow \sin x (2 \cos x + 1) = 0 \Rightarrow \sin x = 0$ or

$$\cos x = -\frac{1}{2} \Rightarrow x = 0, \pi, 2\pi \text{ or } \frac{2\pi}{3}, \frac{4\pi}{3}. \quad P(\frac{2\pi}{3}, -1.5), Q(\pi, -1), R(\frac{4\pi}{3}, -1.5)$$

44 (a) $\cos x - \sin 2x = 0 \Rightarrow \cos x - 2 \sin x \cos x = 0 \Rightarrow \cos x (1 - 2 \sin x) = 0 \Rightarrow$

$$\cos x = 0 \text{ or } \sin x = \frac{1}{2} \Rightarrow x = -\frac{3\pi}{2}, -\frac{\pi}{2}, \frac{\pi}{2}, \frac{3\pi}{2} \text{ or } -\frac{11\pi}{6}, -\frac{7\pi}{6}, \frac{\pi}{6}, \frac{5\pi}{6}.$$

(b) $\sin x + 2 \cos 2x = 0 \Rightarrow \sin x + 2(1 - 2 \sin^2 x) = 0 \Rightarrow$

$$4 \sin^2 x - \sin x - 2 = 0 \Rightarrow \sin x = \frac{1 \pm \sqrt{33}}{8} \approx 0.843, -0.593 \Rightarrow$$

$$x \approx 1.00, -5.28, 2.14, -4.14, -0.63, 5.65 \ 3.78, -2.51$$

45 (a) $\cos 3x - 3 \cos x = 0 \Rightarrow 4 \cos^3 x - 3 \cos x - 3 \cos x = 0 \Rightarrow$

$$4 \cos^3 x - 6 \cos x = 0 \Rightarrow 2 \cos x (2 \cos^2 x - 3) = 0 \Rightarrow \cos x = 0, \pm \sqrt{3/2} \Rightarrow$$

$$x = -\frac{3\pi}{2}, -\frac{\pi}{2}, \frac{\pi}{2}, \frac{3\pi}{2} \{ \cos x \neq \pm \sqrt{3/2} \}$$

(b) $\sin 3x - \sin x = 0 \Rightarrow 3 \sin x - 4 \sin^3 x - \sin x = 0 \Rightarrow 4 \sin^3 x - 2 \sin x = 0 \Rightarrow$

$$2 \sin x (2 \sin^2 x - 1) = 0 \Rightarrow \sin x = 0, \pm 1/\sqrt{2} \Rightarrow$$

$$x = 0, \pm \pi, \pm 2\pi, \pm \frac{\pi}{4}, \pm \frac{3\pi}{4}, \pm \frac{5\pi}{4}, \pm \frac{7\pi}{4}$$

46 $\sin 4x - 4 \sin x = 0 \Rightarrow 4 \sin x \cos x (1 - 2 \sin^2 x) - 4 \sin x = 0 \Rightarrow$

$$4 \sin x \left[\cos x (1 - 2 \sin^2 x) - 1 \right] = 0 \Rightarrow 4 \sin x \left[\cos x (2 \cos^2 x - 1) - 1 \right] = 0 \Rightarrow$$

$$4 \sin x (2 \cos^3 x - \cos x - 1) = 0 \Rightarrow 4 \sin x (\cos x - 1)(2 \cos^2 x + 2 \cos x + 1) = 0 \Rightarrow$$

$$\sin x = 0 \text{ or } \cos x = 1 \ \{ 2 \cos^2 x + 2 \cos x + 1 \neq 0 \} \Rightarrow x = 0, \pm \pi, \pm 2\pi$$

47 (a) Let $y = \overline{BC}$. Form a right triangle with hypotenuse y, side opposite θ, 20, and

side adjacent θ, x. $\sin \theta = \frac{20}{y} \Rightarrow y = \frac{20}{\sin \theta}$. $\cos \theta = \frac{x}{y} \Rightarrow x = y \cos \theta = \frac{20 \cos \theta}{\sin \theta}$.

Now $d = (40 - x) + y = 40 - \frac{20 \cos \theta}{\sin \theta} + \frac{20}{\sin \theta} = 20 \left(\frac{1 - \cos \theta}{\sin \theta} \right) + 40 = 20 \tan \frac{\theta}{2} + 40.$

(b) $50 = 20 \tan \frac{\theta}{2} + 40 \Rightarrow \tan \frac{\theta}{2} = \frac{1}{2} \Rightarrow \frac{1 - \cos \theta}{\sin \theta} = \frac{1}{2} \Rightarrow 2 - 2 \cos \theta = \sin \theta \Rightarrow$

$$4 - 8 \cos \theta + 4 \cos^2 \theta = \sin^2 \theta = 1 - \cos^2 \theta \Rightarrow 5 \cos^2 \theta - 8 \cos \theta + 3 = 0 \Rightarrow$$

$(5 \cos \theta - 3)(\cos \theta - 1) = 0 \Rightarrow \cos \theta = \frac{3}{5}, 1. \{ \cos \theta = 1 \Rightarrow \theta = 0$ and 0 is

extraneous $\}$. $\cos \theta = \frac{3}{5} \Rightarrow \sin \theta = \frac{4}{5}$ and $y = \frac{20}{4/5} = 25.$ $\cos \theta = \frac{x}{y}$ and

$\cos \theta = \frac{3}{5} \Rightarrow \frac{x}{25} = \frac{3}{5} \Rightarrow x = 15$, which means that B would be 25 miles from A.

48 $R = 150$ and $v = 80 \Rightarrow 150 = \frac{80^2}{16} \sin \theta \cos \theta \Rightarrow \frac{3}{8} = \frac{1}{2}(2 \sin \theta \cos \theta) \Rightarrow \sin 2\theta = \frac{3}{4} \Rightarrow$

$$2\theta \approx 48.59° \text{ or } 131.41° \Rightarrow \theta \approx 24.30° \text{ or } 65.70°.$$

49 (a) From Example 8, the area A of a cross section is

$$A = \tfrac{1}{2}(\text{side})^2(\text{sine of included angle}) = \tfrac{1}{2}(\tfrac{1}{2})^2 \sin \theta = \tfrac{1}{8}\sin \theta.$$

The volume $V = (\text{length of gutter})(\text{area of cross section}) = 20(\tfrac{1}{8}\sin \theta) = \tfrac{5}{2}\sin \theta.$

(b) $V = 2 \Rightarrow \tfrac{5}{2}\sin \theta = 2 \Rightarrow \sin \theta = \tfrac{4}{5} \Rightarrow \theta \approx 53.13°.$

50 (a) Let D denote the center of the circle. $\angle ACB = 180 - \phi.$

$\triangle DAC$ is a right triangle since the circle is tangent to the highway.

$$\angle DCA = \tfrac{1}{2}\angle ACB = 90° - \tfrac{\phi}{2}, \text{ so } \angle CDA = \tfrac{\phi}{2}. \quad \tan\tfrac{\phi}{2} = \tfrac{d}{R} \Rightarrow d = R\tan\tfrac{\phi}{2}.$$

(b) $20 = R\tan\tfrac{45°}{2} \Rightarrow 20 = R\left(\dfrac{1-\cos 45°}{\sin 45°}\right) \Rightarrow$

$$R = \frac{20\sin 45°}{1-\cos 45°} = \frac{20\cdot\sqrt{2}/2}{1-\sqrt{2}/2}\cdot\frac{2}{2} = \frac{20\sqrt{2}}{2-\sqrt{2}}\cdot\frac{2+\sqrt{2}}{2+\sqrt{2}} = \frac{20(2\sqrt{2}+2)}{2} =$$

$20\sqrt{2}+20 \approx 48.28$ ft. The length of the curbing can be treated as an arc length.

The radius is R and the central angle is $45°$. $s = r\theta = (20 + 20\sqrt{2})(\tfrac{\pi}{4}) \approx 37.92$ ft.

51 (a) Let $y = \overline{DB}$ and x denote the distance from D to the midpoint of $\overline{BC}$.

$$\sin\tfrac{\theta}{2} = \frac{b/2}{y} \Rightarrow y = \frac{b}{2}\cdot\frac{1}{\sin(\theta/2)} \text{ and } \tan\tfrac{\theta}{2} = \frac{b/2}{x} \Rightarrow x = \frac{b}{2}\cdot\frac{\cos(\theta/2)}{\sin(\theta/2)}.$$

$$l = (a - x) + y = a - \frac{b}{2}\cdot\frac{\cos(\theta/2)}{\sin(\theta/2)} + \frac{b}{2}\cdot\frac{1}{\sin(\theta/2)} = a + \frac{b}{2}\cdot\frac{1-\cos(\theta/2)}{\sin(\theta/2)} =$$

$$a + \frac{b}{2}\tan\left(\frac{\theta/2}{2}\right) = a + \frac{b}{2}\tan\tfrac{\theta}{4}.$$

(b) $a = 10$ mm, $b = 6$ mm, and $\theta = 156° \Rightarrow l = 10 + 3\tan 39° \approx 12.43$ mm.

52 (a) $f(t) = \sin^2 \omega t = \dfrac{1-\cos 2\omega t}{2} = \tfrac{1}{2} - \tfrac{1}{2}\cos 2\omega t.$

Now $\cos 2\omega t$ has period $\tfrac{2\pi}{2\omega} = \tfrac{\pi}{\omega}$. Since $0 \le t \le 2(\tfrac{\pi}{\omega})$, we see that f will complete

2 cycles on the given interval. Thus, the average value is $c = \tfrac{1}{2}.$

(b) $r = RI^2 = RI_0^2 \sin^2\omega t = RI_0^2(\tfrac{1}{2} - \tfrac{1}{2}\cos 2\omega t) = \tfrac{1}{2}RI_0^2 - \tfrac{1}{2}RI_0^2 \cos 2\omega t.$

Thus, the average rate at which heat is produced is $\tfrac{1}{2}RI_0^2.$

53 The graph of f appears to be that of $y = g(x) = \tan x.$

$$\frac{\sin 2x + \sin x}{\cos 2x + \cos x + 1} = \frac{2\sin x\cos x + \sin x}{(2\cos^2 x - 1) + \cos x + 1} = \frac{\sin x(2\cos x + 1)}{\cos x(2\cos x + 1)} = \frac{\sin x}{\cos x} = \tan x$$

54 The graph of f appears to be that of $y = g(x) = \cos x.$

$$\frac{\sin x(1 + \cos 2x)}{\sin 2x} = \frac{\sin x[1 + (2\cos^2 x - 1)]}{2\sin x\cos x} = \frac{2\cos^2 x}{2\cos x} = \cos x$$

55 Graph $Y_1 = \tan(0.5x + 1)$ and $Y_2 = \sin 0.5x$ on $[-2\pi,\ 2\pi]$ in Dot mode. There are two points of intersection. They occur at $x \approx -3.55,\ 5.22$.

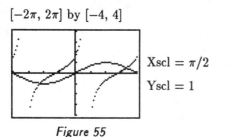

$[-2\pi,\ 2\pi]$ by $[-4,\ 4]$

Xscl $= \pi/2$
Yscl $= 1$

Figure 55

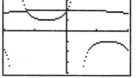

$[-\pi/2,\ \pi/2]$ by $[-4,\ 4]$

Xscl $= \pi/4$
Yscl $= 1$

Figure 56

56 Graph $Y_1 = 1/\cos(2x + 1)$ and $Y_2 = \cos(0.5x) + 1$ on $[-\pi/2,\ \pi/2]$ in Dot mode. There are two points of intersection. They occur at $x \approx -1.00,\ 0.02$.

57 Graph $Y_1 = 1/\sin(0.25x + 1)$ and $Y_2 = 1.5 - \cos 2x$ on $[-\pi,\ \pi]$. There are four points of intersection. They occur at $x \approx -2.03,\ -0.72,\ 0.58,\ 2.62$.

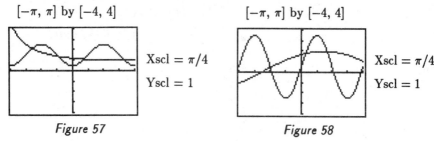

$[-\pi,\ \pi]$ by $[-4,\ 4]$

Xscl $= \pi/4$
Yscl $= 1$

Figure 57

$[-\pi,\ \pi]$ by $[-4,\ 4]$

Xscl $= \pi/4$
Yscl $= 1$

Figure 58

58 Graph $Y_1 = 3\sin(2x) + 0.5$ and $Y_2 = 2\sin(\frac{1}{2}x + 1)$ on $[-\pi,\ \pi]$. There are three points of intersection. They occur at $x \approx -1.56,\ 0.22,\ 1.31$.

59 Graph $Y_1 = 2/\tan(.25x)$ and $Y_2 = 1 - 1/\cos(.5x)$ on $[-2\pi,\ 2\pi]$ in Dot mode. There is one point of intersection. It occurs at $x \approx -2.59$.

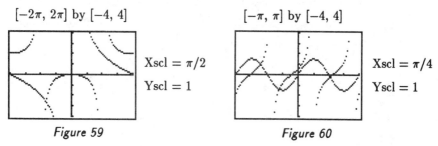

$[-2\pi,\ 2\pi]$ by $[-4,\ 4]$

Xscl $= \pi/2$
Yscl $= 1$

Figure 59

$[-\pi,\ \pi]$ by $[-4,\ 4]$

Xscl $= \pi/4$
Yscl $= 1$

Figure 60

60 Graph $Y_1 = \tan(1.5x + .5)$ and $Y_2 = 1.5\sin(2x)$ on $[-\pi,\ \pi]$ in Dot mode. There are three points of intersection. They occur at $x \approx -1.92,\ -0.97,\ 1.63$.

Note: We will reference the product-to-sum formulas as [P1]–[P4] and the sum-to-product formulas as [S1]–[S4] in the order they appear in the text. The formulas $\cos(-kx) = \cos kx$ and $\sin(-kx) = -\sin kx$ will be used without mention.

1. $\sin 7t \sin 3t = $ [P4] $\frac{1}{2}[\cos(7t - 3t) - \cos(7t + 3t)] = \frac{1}{2}\cos 4t - \frac{1}{2}\cos 10t$

2. $\sin(-4x)\cos 8x = $ [P1] $\frac{1}{2}[\sin(-4x + 8x) + \sin(-4x - 8x)] =$
$$\frac{1}{2}\sin 4x + \frac{1}{2}\sin(-12x) = \frac{1}{2}\sin 4x - \frac{1}{2}\sin 12x$$

3. $\cos 6u \cos(-4u) = $ [P3] $\frac{1}{2}\left\{\cos[6u + (-4u)] + \cos[6u - (-4u)]\right\} = \frac{1}{2}\cos 2u + \frac{1}{2}\cos 10u$

4. $\cos 4t \sin 6t = $ [P2] $\frac{1}{2}[\sin(4t + 6t) - \sin(4t - 6t)] = \frac{1}{2}\sin 10t - \frac{1}{2}\sin(-2t) =$
$$\frac{1}{2}\sin 10t + \frac{1}{2}\sin 2t$$

5. $2\sin 9\theta \cos 3\theta = $ [P1] $2 \cdot \frac{1}{2}[\sin(9\theta + 3\theta) + \sin(9\theta - 3\theta)] = \sin 12\theta + \sin 6\theta$

6. $2\sin 7\theta \sin 5\theta = $ [P4] $2 \cdot \frac{1}{2}[\cos(7\theta - 5\theta) - \cos(7\theta + 5\theta)] = \cos 2\theta - \cos 12\theta$

7. $3\cos x \sin 2x = $ [P2] $3 \cdot \frac{1}{2}[\sin(x + 2x) - \sin(x - 2x)] = \frac{3}{2}\sin 3x - \frac{3}{2}\sin(-x) =$
$$\frac{3}{2}\sin 3x + \frac{3}{2}\sin x$$

8. $5\cos u \cos 5u = $ [P3] $5 \cdot \frac{1}{2}[\cos(u + 5u) + \cos(u - 5u)] = \frac{5}{2}\cos 6u + \frac{5}{2}\cos(-4u) =$
$$\frac{5}{2}\cos 6u + \frac{5}{2}\cos 4u$$

9. $\sin 6\theta + \sin 2\theta = $ [S1] $2\sin\dfrac{6\theta + 2\theta}{2}\cos\dfrac{6\theta - 2\theta}{2} = 2\sin 4\theta \cos 2\theta$

10. $\sin 4\theta - \sin 8\theta = $ [S2] $2\cos\dfrac{4\theta + 8\theta}{2}\sin\dfrac{4\theta - 8\theta}{2} = 2\cos 6\theta \sin(-2\theta) = -2\cos 6\theta \sin 2\theta$

11. $\cos 5x - \cos 3x = $ [S4] $-2\sin\dfrac{5x + 3x}{2}\sin\dfrac{5x - 3x}{2} = -2\sin 4x \sin x$

12. $\cos 5t + \cos 6t = $ [S3] $2\cos\dfrac{5t + 6t}{2}\cos\dfrac{5t - 6t}{2} = 2\cos\frac{11}{2}t \cos(-\frac{1}{2}t) = 2\cos\frac{11}{2}t \cos\frac{1}{2}t$

13. $\sin 3t - \sin 7t = $ [S2] $2\cos\dfrac{3t + 7t}{2}\sin\dfrac{3t - 7t}{2} = 2\cos 5t \sin(-2t) = -2\cos 5t \sin 2t$

14. $\cos \theta - \cos 5\theta = $ [S4] $-2\sin\dfrac{\theta + 5\theta}{2}\sin\dfrac{\theta - 5\theta}{2} = -2\sin 3\theta \sin(-2\theta) = 2\sin 3\theta \sin 2\theta$

15. $\cos x + \cos 2x = $ [S3] $2\cos\dfrac{x + 2x}{2}\cos\dfrac{x - 2x}{2} = 2\cos\frac{3}{2}x \cos(-\frac{1}{2}x) = 2\cos\frac{3}{2}x \cos\frac{1}{2}x$

16. $\sin 8t + \sin 2t = $ [S1] $2\sin\dfrac{8t + 2t}{2}\cos\dfrac{8t - 2t}{2} = 2\sin 5t \cos 3t$

17. $\dfrac{\sin 4t + \sin 6t}{\cos 4t - \cos 6t} = \dfrac{\text{[S1] } 2\sin 5t \cos(-t)}{\text{[S4] } -2\sin 5t \sin(-t)} = \dfrac{\cos t}{\sin t} = \cot t$

18. $\dfrac{\sin \theta + \sin 3\theta}{\cos \theta + \cos 3\theta} = \dfrac{\text{[S1] } 2\sin 2\theta \cos(-\theta)}{\text{[S3] } 2\cos 2\theta \cos(-\theta)} = \dfrac{\sin 2\theta}{\cos 2\theta} = \tan 2\theta$

19. $\dfrac{\sin u + \sin v}{\cos u + \cos v} = \dfrac{\text{[S1] } 2\sin\frac{1}{2}(u + v)\cos\frac{1}{2}(u - v)}{\text{[S3] } 2\cos\frac{1}{2}(u + v)\cos\frac{1}{2}(u - v)} = \tan\frac{1}{2}(u + v)$

$\boxed{20}$ $\dfrac{\sin u - \sin v}{\cos u - \cos v} = \dfrac{[S2]\ 2\cos\frac{1}{2}(u+v)\sin\frac{1}{2}(u-v)}{[S4]\ -2\sin\frac{1}{2}(u+v)\sin\frac{1}{2}(u-v)} = -\cot\frac{1}{2}(u+v)$

$\boxed{21}$ $\dfrac{\sin u - \sin v}{\sin u + \sin v} = \dfrac{[S2]\ 2\cos\frac{1}{2}(u+v)\sin\frac{1}{2}(u-v)}{[S1]\ 2\sin\frac{1}{2}(u+v)\cos\frac{1}{2}(u-v)} = \cot\frac{1}{2}(u+v)\tan\frac{1}{2}(u-v) = \dfrac{\tan\frac{1}{2}(u-v)}{\tan\frac{1}{2}(u+v)}$

$\boxed{22}$ $\dfrac{\cos u - \cos v}{\cos u + \cos v} = \dfrac{[S4]\ -2\sin\frac{1}{2}(u+v)\sin\frac{1}{2}(u-v)}{[S3]\ 2\cos\frac{1}{2}(u+v)\cos\frac{1}{2}(u-v)} = -\tan\frac{1}{2}(u+v)\tan\frac{1}{2}(u-v)$

$\boxed{23}$ $4\cos x\cos 2x\sin 3x = 2\cos 2x\,(2\sin 3x\cos x) = 2\cos 2x\,([P1]\ \sin 4x + \sin 2x) =$

$(2\cos 2x\sin 4x) + (2\cos 2x\sin 2x) = \big[[P2]\ \sin 6x - \sin(-2x)\big] + \big([P2]\ \sin 4x - \sin 0\big) =$

$$\sin 2x + \sin 4x + \sin 6x$$

$\boxed{24}$ $\dfrac{\cos t + \cos 4t + \cos 7t}{\sin t + \sin 4t + \sin 7t} = \dfrac{\cos 4t + [S3]\ 2\cos 4t\cos(-3t)}{\sin 4t + [S1]\ 2\sin 4t\cos(-3t)} = \dfrac{\cos 4t\,(1 + 2\cos 3t)}{\sin 4t\,(1 + 2\cos 3t)} = \cot 4t$

$\boxed{25}$ $(\sin ax)(\cos bx) = [P1]\ \frac{1}{2}\big[\sin(ax+bx) + \sin(ax-bx)\big] = \frac{1}{2}\sin\big[(a+b)x\big] + \frac{1}{2}\sin\big[(a-b)x\big]$

$\boxed{26}$ $(\cos au)(\cos bu) = [P3]\ \frac{1}{2}\big[\cos(au+bu) + \cos(au-bu)\big] =$

$$\frac{1}{2}\cos\big[(a+b)u\big] + \frac{1}{2}\cos\big[(a-b)u\big]$$

$\boxed{27}$ $\sin 5t + \sin 3t = 0 \Rightarrow [S1]\ 2\sin 4t\cos t = 0 \Rightarrow \sin 4t = 0$ or $\cos t = 0 \Rightarrow$

$$4t = \pi n \text{ or } t = \tfrac{\pi}{2} + \pi n \Rightarrow t = \tfrac{\pi}{4}n\ \{\text{which includes } t = \tfrac{\pi}{2} + \pi n\}$$

$\boxed{28}$ $\sin t + \sin 3t = \sin 2t \Rightarrow [S1]\ 2\sin 2t\cos(-t) = \sin 2t \Rightarrow \sin 2t\,(2\cos t - 1) = 0 \Rightarrow$

$$\sin 2t = 0 \text{ or } \cos t = \tfrac{1}{2} \Rightarrow 2t = \pi n \text{ (i.e., } t = \tfrac{\pi}{2}n) \text{ or } t = \tfrac{\pi}{3} + 2\pi n,\ \tfrac{5\pi}{3} + 2\pi n$$

$\boxed{29}$ $\cos x = \cos 3x \Rightarrow \cos x - \cos 3x = 0 \Rightarrow [S4]\ -2\sin 2x\sin(-x) = 0 \Rightarrow$

$$\sin 2x = 0 \text{ or } \sin x = 0 \Rightarrow 2x = \pi n \text{ or } x = \pi n \Rightarrow x = \tfrac{\pi}{2}n\ \{\text{which includes } x = \pi n\}$$

$\boxed{30}$ $\cos 4x - \cos 3x = 0 \Rightarrow [S4]\ -2\sin\frac{7}{2}x\sin\frac{1}{2}x = 0 \Rightarrow \sin\frac{7}{2}x = 0$ or $\sin\frac{1}{2}x = 0 \Rightarrow$

$$\tfrac{7}{2}x = \pi n \text{ or } \tfrac{1}{2}x = \pi n \Rightarrow x = \tfrac{2\pi}{7}n \text{ or } x = 2\pi n \Rightarrow x = \tfrac{2\pi}{7}n\ \{\text{which includes } x = 2\pi n\}$$

$\boxed{31}$ $\cos 3x + \cos 5x = \cos x \Rightarrow [S3]\ 2\cos 4x\cos(-x) - \cos x = 0 \Rightarrow$

$\cos x\,(2\cos 4x - 1) = 0 \Rightarrow \cos x = 0$ or $\cos 4x = \frac{1}{2} \Rightarrow$

$$x = \tfrac{\pi}{2} + \pi n \text{ or } 4x = \tfrac{\pi}{3} + 2\pi n,\ \tfrac{5\pi}{3} + 2\pi n \Rightarrow x = \tfrac{\pi}{2} + \pi n,\ \tfrac{\pi}{12} + \tfrac{\pi}{2}n,\ \tfrac{5\pi}{12} + \tfrac{\pi}{2}n$$

$\boxed{32}$ $\cos 3x = -\cos 6x \Rightarrow \cos 3x + \cos 6x = 0 \Rightarrow [S3]\ 2\cos\frac{9}{2}x\cos(-\frac{3}{2}x) = 0 \Rightarrow$

$\frac{9}{2}x = \frac{\pi}{2} + \pi n$ or $\frac{3}{2}x = \frac{\pi}{2} + \pi n \Rightarrow x = \frac{\pi}{9} + \frac{2\pi}{9}n$ or $x = \frac{\pi}{3} + \frac{2\pi}{3}n \Rightarrow$

$$x = \tfrac{\pi}{9} + \tfrac{2\pi}{9}n\ \{\text{which includes } x = \tfrac{\pi}{3} + \tfrac{2\pi}{3}n\}$$

$\boxed{33}$ $\sin 2x - \sin 5x = 0 \Rightarrow [S2]\ 2\cos\frac{7}{2}x\sin(-\frac{3}{2}x) = 0 \Rightarrow \frac{7}{2}x = \frac{\pi}{2} + \pi n$ or $\frac{3}{2}x = \pi n \Rightarrow$

$$x = \tfrac{\pi}{7} + \tfrac{2\pi}{7}n \text{ or } x = \tfrac{2\pi}{3}n$$

$\boxed{34}$ $\sin 5x - \sin x = 2\cos 3x \Rightarrow [S2]\ 2\cos 3x\sin 2x - 2\cos 3x = 0 \Rightarrow$

$2\cos 3x\,(\sin 2x - 1) = 0 \Rightarrow \cos 3x = 0$ or $\sin 2x = 1 \Rightarrow$

$$3x = \tfrac{\pi}{2} + \pi n \text{ or } 2x = \tfrac{\pi}{2} + 2\pi n \Rightarrow x = \tfrac{\pi}{6} + \tfrac{\pi}{3}n \text{ or } x = \tfrac{\pi}{4} + \pi n$$

35 $\cos x + \cos 3x = 0 \Rightarrow$ [S3] $2\cos 2x \cos(-x) = 0 \Rightarrow \cos 2x = 0$ or $\cos x = 0 \Rightarrow$

$2x = \frac{\pi}{2} + \pi n$ or $x = \frac{\pi}{2} + \pi n \Rightarrow x = \frac{\pi}{4} + \frac{\pi}{2}n$ or $x = \frac{\pi}{2} + \pi n \Rightarrow$

$$x = \frac{\pi}{4}, \frac{3\pi}{4}, \frac{5\pi}{4}, \frac{7\pi}{4}, \frac{\pi}{2}, \frac{3\pi}{2} \text{ for } 0 \leq x \leq 2\pi$$

36 $\sin 4x - \sin x = 0 \Rightarrow$ [S2] $2\cos\frac{5}{2}x \sin\frac{3}{2}x \Rightarrow \cos\frac{5}{2}x = 0$ or $\sin\frac{3}{2}x = 0 \Rightarrow$

$\frac{5}{2}x = \frac{\pi}{2} + \pi n$ or $\frac{3}{2}x = \pi n \Rightarrow x = \frac{\pi}{5} + \frac{2\pi}{5}n$ or $x = \frac{2\pi}{3}n \Rightarrow$

$x = \frac{\pi}{5}, \frac{3\pi}{5}, \pi, \frac{7\pi}{5}, \frac{9\pi}{5}, 0, \frac{2\pi}{3}, \frac{4\pi}{3}, 2\pi$ for $0 \leq x \leq 2\pi$. *Note:* $\frac{3\pi}{5} \approx 1.88$, $\frac{2\pi}{3} \approx 2.09$,

$\frac{4\pi}{3} \approx 4.19$, and $\frac{7\pi}{5} \approx 4.40$ are the intercepts that are close together.

37 $\sin 3x - \sin x = 0 \Rightarrow$ [S2] $2\cos 2x \sin x = 0 \Rightarrow \cos 2x = 0$ or $\sin x = 0 \Rightarrow$

$2x = \frac{\pi}{2} + \pi n$ or $x = \pi n \Rightarrow x = \frac{\pi}{4} + \frac{\pi}{2}n$ or $x = \pi n \Rightarrow$

$$x = 0, \pm\pi, \pm 2\pi, \pm\frac{\pi}{4}, \pm\frac{3\pi}{4}, \pm\frac{5\pi}{4}, \pm\frac{7\pi}{4} \text{ for } -2\pi \leq x \leq 2\pi.$$

38 $\cos 4x - \cos x = 0 \Rightarrow$ [S4] $-2\sin\frac{5}{2}x \sin\frac{3}{2}x = 0 \Rightarrow \sin\frac{5}{2}x = 0$ or $\sin\frac{3}{2}x = 0 \Rightarrow$

$\frac{5}{2}x = \pi n$ or $\frac{3}{2}x = \pi n \Rightarrow x = \frac{2\pi}{5}n$ or $x = \frac{2\pi}{3}n \Rightarrow$

$$x = 0, \pm\frac{2\pi}{5}, \pm\frac{4\pi}{5}, \pm\frac{6\pi}{5}, \pm\frac{8\pi}{5}, \pm 2\pi, \pm\frac{2\pi}{3}, \pm\frac{4\pi}{3} \text{ for } -2\pi \leq x \leq 2\pi.$$

39 $f(x) = \sin\left(\frac{\pi n}{l}x\right)\cos\left(\frac{k\pi n}{l}t\right) =$ [P1] $\frac{1}{2}\left[\sin\frac{\pi n}{l}(x + kt) + \sin\frac{\pi n}{l}(x - kt)\right] =$

$$\frac{1}{2}\sin\frac{\pi n}{l}(x + kt) + \frac{1}{2}\sin\frac{\pi n}{l}(x - kt)$$

40 (a) $p(t) = a\cos\omega_1 t + a\cos\omega_2 t = a(\cos\omega_1 t + \cos\omega_2 t) =$

　　　[S3] $a \cdot 2\cos\left[\frac{1}{2}(\omega_1 + \omega_2)t\right]\cos\left[\frac{1}{2}(\omega_1 - \omega_2)t\right] = 2a\cos\frac{1}{2}(\omega_1 + \omega_2)t \cos\frac{1}{2}(\omega_1 - \omega_2)t$

(b) From part (a),

$$p(t) = \left[2a\cos\frac{1}{2}(\omega_1 - \omega_2)t\right]\cos\frac{1}{2}(\omega_1 + \omega_2)t = f(t)\cos\frac{1}{2}(\omega_1 + \omega_2)t.$$

Since $\omega_1 \approx \omega_2$, $\frac{1}{2}(\omega_1 + \omega_2) \approx \omega_1$, and the period is approximately $2\pi/\omega_1$.

　　　The maximum amplitude occurs when $\cos\frac{1}{2}(\omega_1 - \omega_2)t = 1$, i.e., $f(t) = 2a$.

(c) $p(t) = 0 \Rightarrow \cos 4.5t + \cos 3.5t = 0 \Rightarrow$ [S3] $2\cos 4t \cos\frac{1}{2}t = 0 \Rightarrow \left[2\cos\frac{1}{2}t\right]\cos 4t = 0.$

From part (b), we want to know when the amplitude is zero.

$2\cos\frac{1}{2}t = 0 \Rightarrow \frac{1}{2}t = \frac{\pi}{2} + \pi n \Rightarrow t = \pi + 2\pi n.$

　　　$A = (-\pi, 0)$ and $B = (\pi, 0)$. Near-silence occurs every 2π units of time.

(d) From the graph, we see that one-half period occurs on the interval from A to B.

$$\tfrac{1}{2}(period) = \pi - (-\pi) \Rightarrow \tfrac{1}{2}(period) = 2\pi \Rightarrow period = 4\pi.$$

41 (a) Estimating the x-intercepts, we have $x \approx 0$, ± 1.05, ± 1.57, ± 2.09, ± 3.14.

(b) $\sin 4x + \sin 2x = 2 \sin 3x \cos x = 0 \Rightarrow \sin 3x = 0$ or $\cos x = 0$.

$\sin 3x = 0 \Rightarrow 3x = \pi n \Rightarrow x = \frac{\pi}{3}n \Rightarrow x = 0$, $\pm \frac{\pi}{3}$, $\pm \frac{2\pi}{3}$, $\pm \pi$. $\cos x = 0 \Rightarrow x = \pm \frac{\pi}{2}$.

The x-intercepts are 0, $\pm \frac{\pi}{3}$, $\pm \frac{\pi}{2}$, $\pm \frac{2\pi}{3}$, $\pm \pi$.

$[-\pi, \pi]$ by $[-2.09, 2.09]$

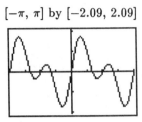

Xscl $= \pi/4$

Yscl $= 1$

Figure 41

$[-\pi, \pi]$ by $[-2.09, 2.09]$

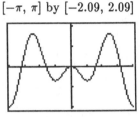

Xscl $= \pi/4$

Yscl $= 1$

Figure 42

42 (a) Estimating the x-intercepts, we have $x \approx 0$, ± 1.26, ± 2.51.

(b) $\cos 3x - \cos 2x = -2 \sin \frac{5}{2}x \sin \frac{1}{2}x = 0 \Rightarrow \sin \frac{5}{2}x = 0$ or $\sin \frac{1}{2}x = 0$.

$\sin \frac{5}{2}x = 0 \Rightarrow \frac{5}{2}x = \pi n \Rightarrow x = \frac{2\pi}{5}n \Rightarrow x = 0$, $\pm \frac{2\pi}{5}$, $\pm \frac{4\pi}{5}$. $\sin \frac{1}{2}x = 0 \Rightarrow x = 0$.

The x-intercepts are 0, $\pm \frac{2\pi}{5}$, $\pm \frac{4\pi}{5}$.

43 The graph of f appears to be that of $y = g(x) = \tan 2x$.

$$\frac{\sin x + \sin 2x + \sin 3x}{\cos x + \cos 2x + \cos 3x} = \frac{\sin 2x + (\sin 3x + \sin x)}{\cos 2x + (\cos 3x + \cos x)} = \frac{\sin 2x + 2 \sin 2x \cos x}{\cos 2x + 2 \cos 2x \cos x} =$$

$$\frac{\sin 2x (1 + 2 \cos x)}{\cos 2x (1 + 2 \cos x)} = \frac{\sin 2x}{\cos 2x} = \tan 2x$$

44 The graph of f appears to be that of $y = g(x) = \cot 2x$.

$$\frac{\cos x - \cos 2x + \cos 3x}{\sin x - \sin 2x + \sin 3x} = \frac{-\cos 2x + (\cos 3x + \cos x)}{-\sin 2x + (\sin 3x + \sin x)} = \frac{-\cos 2x + 2 \cos 2x \cos x}{-\sin 2x + 2 \sin 2x \cos x} =$$

$$\frac{\cos 2x (-1 + 2 \cos x)}{\sin 2x (-1 + 2 \cos x)} = \frac{\cos 2x}{\sin 2x} = \cot 2x$$

6.6 Exercises

1 (a) $\sin^{-1}\left(-\frac{\sqrt{2}}{2}\right) = -\frac{\pi}{4}$ (b) $\cos^{-1}\left(-\frac{1}{2}\right) = \frac{2\pi}{3}$ (c) $\tan^{-1}\left(-\sqrt{3}\right) = -\frac{\pi}{3}$

2 (a) $\sin^{-1}\left(-\frac{1}{2}\right) = -\frac{\pi}{6}$ (b) $\cos^{-1}\left(-\frac{\sqrt{2}}{2}\right) = \frac{3\pi}{4}$ (c) $\tan^{-1}(-1) = -\frac{\pi}{4}$

3 (a) $\arcsin \frac{\sqrt{3}}{2} = \frac{\pi}{3}$ (b) $\arccos \frac{\sqrt{2}}{2} = \frac{\pi}{4}$ (c) $\arctan \frac{1}{\sqrt{3}} = \frac{\pi}{6}$

4 (a) $\arcsin 0 = 0$ (b) $\arccos(-1) = \pi$ (c) $\arctan 0 = 0$

5 (a) $\sin^{-1} \frac{\pi}{3}$ is <u>not defined</u> since $\frac{\pi}{3} > 1$, i.e., $\frac{\pi}{3} \notin [-1, 1]$

(b) $\cos^{-1} \frac{\pi}{2}$ is <u>not defined</u> since $\frac{\pi}{2} > 1$, i.e., $\frac{\pi}{2} \notin [-1, 1]$ (c) $\tan^{-1} 1 = \frac{\pi}{4}$

6 (a) $\arcsin \frac{\pi}{2}$ is <u>not defined</u> since $\frac{\pi}{2} > 1$, i.e., $\frac{\pi}{2} \notin [-1, 1]$

(b) $\arccos \frac{\pi}{3}$ is <u>not defined</u> since $\frac{\pi}{3} > 1$, i.e., $\frac{\pi}{3} \notin [-1, 1]$ (c) $\arctan\left(-\frac{\sqrt{3}}{3}\right) = -\frac{\pi}{6}$

Note: Exercises 7–10 refer to the boxed properties of $\sin^{-1}$, $\cos^{-1}$, and $\tan^{-1}$.

7 (a) $\sin[\arcsin(-\tfrac{3}{10})] = -\tfrac{3}{10}$ since $-1 \le -\tfrac{3}{10} \le 1$

   (b) $\cos(\arccos\tfrac{1}{2}) = \tfrac{1}{2}$ since $-1 \le \tfrac{1}{2} \le 1$

   (c) $\tan(\arctan 14) = 14$ since $\tan(\arctan x) = x$ for every x

8 (a) $\sin(\sin^{-1}\tfrac{2}{3}) = \tfrac{2}{3}$ since $-1 \le \tfrac{2}{3} \le 1$

   (b) $\cos[\cos^{-1}(-\tfrac{1}{5})] = -\tfrac{1}{5}$ since $-1 \le -\tfrac{1}{5} \le 1$

   (c) $\tan[\tan^{-1}(-9)] = -9$ since $\tan(\arctan x) = x$ for every x

9 (a) $\sin^{-1}(\sin\tfrac{\pi}{3}) = \tfrac{\pi}{3}$ since $-\tfrac{\pi}{2} \le \tfrac{\pi}{3} \le \tfrac{\pi}{2}$ (b) $\cos^{-1}\left[\cos\left(\tfrac{5\pi}{6}\right)\right] = \tfrac{5\pi}{6}$ since $0 \le \tfrac{5\pi}{6} \le \pi$

   (c) $\tan^{-1}\left[\tan\left(-\tfrac{\pi}{6}\right)\right] = -\tfrac{\pi}{6}$ since $-\tfrac{\pi}{2} < -\tfrac{\pi}{6} < \tfrac{\pi}{2}$

10 (a) $\arcsin\left[\sin\left(-\tfrac{\pi}{2}\right)\right] = -\tfrac{\pi}{2}$ since $-\tfrac{\pi}{2} \le -\tfrac{\pi}{2} \le \tfrac{\pi}{2}$

   (b) $\arccos(\cos 0) = 0$ since $0 \le 0 \le \pi$ (c) $\arctan(\tan\tfrac{\pi}{4}) = \tfrac{\pi}{4}$ since $-\tfrac{\pi}{2} < \tfrac{\pi}{4} < \tfrac{\pi}{2}$

11 (a) $\arcsin(\sin\tfrac{5\pi}{4}) = \arcsin\left(-\tfrac{\sqrt{2}}{2}\right) = -\tfrac{\pi}{4}$

   (b) $\arccos(\cos\tfrac{5\pi}{4}) = \arccos\left(-\tfrac{\sqrt{2}}{2}\right) = \tfrac{3\pi}{4}$ (c) $\arctan(\tan\tfrac{7\pi}{4}) = \arctan(-1) = -\tfrac{\pi}{4}$

12 (a) $\sin^{-1}(\sin\tfrac{2\pi}{3}) = \sin^{-1}\tfrac{\sqrt{3}}{2} = \tfrac{\pi}{3}$ (b) $\cos^{-1}(\cos\tfrac{4\pi}{3}) = \cos^{-1}(-\tfrac{1}{2}) = \tfrac{2\pi}{3}$

   (c) $\tan^{-1}(\tan\tfrac{7\pi}{6}) = \tan^{-1}\tfrac{\sqrt{3}}{3} = \tfrac{\pi}{6}$

13 (a) $\sin[\cos^{-1}(-\tfrac{1}{2})] = \sin\tfrac{2\pi}{3} = \tfrac{\sqrt{3}}{2}$ (b) $\cos(\tan^{-1}1) = \cos\tfrac{\pi}{4} = \tfrac{\sqrt{2}}{2}$

   (c) $\tan[\sin^{-1}(-1)] = \tan(-\tfrac{\pi}{2})$, which is <u>not defined</u>.

14 (a) $\sin(\tan^{-1}\sqrt{3}) = \sin\tfrac{\pi}{3} = \tfrac{\sqrt{3}}{2}$ (b) $\cos(\sin^{-1}1) = \cos\tfrac{\pi}{2} = 0$

   (c) $\tan(\cos^{-1}0) = \tan\tfrac{\pi}{2}$, which is <u>not defined</u>.

15 (a) Let $\theta = \sin^{-1}\tfrac{2}{3}$. From *Figure 15(a)*, $\cot(\sin^{-1}\tfrac{2}{3}) = \cot\theta = \tfrac{x}{y} = \tfrac{\sqrt{5}}{2}$.

   (b) Let $\theta = \tan^{-1}(-\tfrac{3}{5})$. From *Figure 15(b)*, $\sec[\tan^{-1}(-\tfrac{3}{5})] = \sec\theta = \tfrac{r}{x} = \tfrac{\sqrt{34}}{5}$.

   (c) Let $\theta = \cos^{-1}(-\tfrac{1}{4})$. From *Figure 15(c)*, $\csc[\cos^{-1}(-\tfrac{1}{4})] = \csc\theta = \tfrac{r}{y} = \tfrac{4}{\sqrt{15}}$.

Note: Triangles could be used for the figures, and may be easier to work with in class.

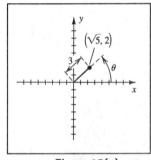

Figure 15(a)

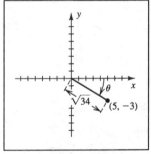

Figure 15(b)

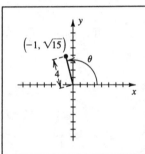

Figure 15(c)

16 (a) Let $\theta = \sin^{-1}\left(-\frac{2}{5}\right)$.

From *Figure 16(a)*, $\cot\left[\sin^{-1}\left(-\frac{2}{5}\right)\right] = \cot\theta = \frac{x}{y} = \frac{\sqrt{21}}{-2} = -\frac{\sqrt{21}}{2}$.

(b) Let $\theta = \tan^{-1}\frac{7}{4}$. From *Figure 16(b)*, $\sec\left(\tan^{-1}\frac{7}{4}\right) = \sec\theta = \frac{r}{x} = \frac{\sqrt{65}}{4}$.

(c) Let $\theta = \cos^{-1}\frac{1}{5}$. From *Figure 16(c)*, $\csc\left(\cos^{-1}\frac{1}{5}\right) = \csc\theta = \frac{r}{y} = \frac{5}{\sqrt{24}}$.

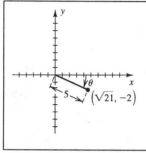

Figure 16(a)

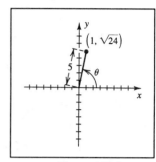

Figure 16(b)

Figure 16(c)

17 (a) $\sin\left(\arcsin\frac{1}{2} + \arccos 0\right) = \sin\left(\frac{\pi}{6} + \frac{\pi}{2}\right) = \sin\frac{2\pi}{3} = \frac{\sqrt{3}}{2}$.

(b) Let $\alpha = \arctan\left(-\frac{3}{4}\right)$ and $\beta = \arcsin\frac{4}{5}$. Using the difference identity for the cosine and figures as in Exercises 15 and 16, we have $\cos\left[\arctan\left(-\frac{3}{4}\right) - \arcsin\frac{4}{5}\right]$

$$= \cos\left(\alpha - \beta\right) = \cos\alpha\,\cos\beta + \sin\alpha\,\sin\beta = \frac{4}{5}\cdot\frac{3}{5} + \left(-\frac{3}{5}\right)\cdot\frac{4}{5} = 0.$$

(c) Let $\alpha = \arctan\frac{4}{3}$ and $\beta = \arccos\frac{8}{17}$. $\tan\left(\arctan\frac{4}{3} + \arccos\frac{8}{17}\right) =$

$$\tan\left(\alpha + \beta\right) = \frac{\tan\alpha + \tan\beta}{1 - \tan\alpha\,\tan\beta} = \frac{\frac{4}{3} + \frac{15}{8}}{1 - \frac{4}{3}\cdot\frac{15}{8}}\cdot\frac{24}{24} = \frac{32 + 45}{24 - 60} = -\frac{77}{36}.$$

18 (a) Let $\alpha = \sin^{-1}\frac{5}{13}$ and $\beta = \cos^{-1}\left(-\frac{3}{5}\right)$. $\sin\left[\sin^{-1}\frac{5}{13} - \cos^{-1}\left(-\frac{3}{5}\right)\right] =$

$$\sin\left(\alpha - \beta\right) = \sin\alpha\,\cos\beta - \cos\alpha\,\sin\beta = \frac{5}{13}\cdot\left(-\frac{3}{5}\right) - \frac{12}{13}\cdot\frac{4}{5} = -\frac{63}{65}.$$

(b) Let $\alpha = \sin^{-1}\frac{4}{5}$ and $\beta = \tan^{-1}\frac{3}{4}$. $\cos\left(\sin^{-1}\frac{4}{5} + \tan^{-1}\frac{3}{4}\right) =$

$$\cos\left(\alpha + \beta\right) = \cos\alpha\,\cos\beta - \sin\alpha\,\sin\beta = \frac{3}{5}\cdot\frac{4}{5} - \frac{4}{5}\cdot\frac{3}{5} = 0.$$

(c) $\tan\left[\cos^{-1}\frac{1}{2} - \sin^{-1}\left(-\frac{1}{2}\right)\right] = \tan\left[\frac{\pi}{3} - \left(-\frac{\pi}{6}\right)\right] = \tan\frac{\pi}{2}$, which is <u>not defined</u>.

19 (a) Let $\alpha = \arccos\left(-\frac{3}{5}\right)$. $\sin\left[2\arccos\left(-\frac{3}{5}\right)\right] = \sin 2\alpha = 2\sin\alpha\,\cos\alpha = 2\left(\frac{4}{5}\right)\left(-\frac{3}{5}\right) = -\frac{24}{25}$.

(b) Let $\alpha = \sin^{-1}\frac{15}{17}$. $\cos\left(2\sin^{-1}\frac{15}{17}\right) = \cos 2\alpha = \cos^2\alpha - \sin^2\alpha = \left(\frac{8}{17}\right)^2 - \left(\frac{15}{17}\right)^2 = -\frac{161}{289}$.

(c) Let $\alpha = \tan^{-1}\frac{3}{4}$.

$$\tan\left(2\tan^{-1}\frac{3}{4}\right) = \tan 2\alpha = \frac{2\tan\alpha}{1 - \tan^2\alpha} = \frac{2\cdot\frac{3}{4}}{1 - \left(\frac{3}{4}\right)^2}\cdot\frac{16}{16} = \frac{24}{16 - 9} = \frac{24}{7}.$$

20 (a) Let $\alpha = \tan^{-1}\frac{5}{12}$. $\sin\left(2\tan^{-1}\frac{5}{12}\right) = \sin 2\alpha = 2\sin\alpha\cos\alpha = 2\left(\frac{5}{13}\right)\left(\frac{12}{13}\right) = \frac{120}{169}$.

(b) Let $\alpha = \arccos\frac{9}{41}$.

$$\cos\left(2\arccos\frac{9}{41}\right) = \cos 2\alpha = \cos^2\alpha - \sin^2\alpha = \left(\frac{9}{41}\right)^2 - \left(\frac{40}{41}\right)^2 = -\frac{1519}{1681}.$$

(c) Let $\alpha = \arcsin\left(-\frac{8}{17}\right)$. $\tan\left[2\arcsin\left(-\frac{8}{17}\right)\right] =$

$$\tan 2\alpha = \frac{2\tan\alpha}{1-\tan^2\alpha} = \frac{2\cdot\left(-\frac{8}{15}\right)}{1-\left(-\frac{8}{15}\right)^2}\cdot\frac{225}{225} = -\frac{240}{225-64} = -\frac{240}{161}.$$

21 (a) Let $\alpha = \sin^{-1}\left(-\frac{7}{25}\right)$. $-\frac{\pi}{2} < \alpha < 0 \Rightarrow -\frac{\pi}{4} < \frac{1}{2}\alpha < 0$ and $\sin\frac{1}{2}\alpha < 0$.

$$\sin\left[\frac{1}{2}\sin^{-1}\left(-\frac{7}{25}\right)\right] = \sin\frac{1}{2}\alpha = -\sqrt{\frac{1-\cos\alpha}{2}} = -\sqrt{\frac{1-\frac{24}{25}}{2}} = -\sqrt{\frac{1}{50}\cdot\frac{2}{2}} = -\frac{1}{10}\sqrt{2}.$$

(b) Let $\alpha = \tan^{-1}\frac{8}{15}$. $0 < \alpha < \frac{\pi}{2} \Rightarrow 0 < \frac{1}{2}\alpha < \frac{\pi}{4}$ and $\cos\frac{1}{2}\alpha > 0$.

$$\cos\left(\frac{1}{2}\tan^{-1}\frac{8}{15}\right) = \cos\frac{1}{2}\alpha = \sqrt{\frac{1+\cos\alpha}{2}} = \sqrt{\frac{1+\frac{15}{17}}{2}} = \sqrt{\frac{16}{17}\cdot\frac{17}{17}} = \frac{4}{17}\sqrt{17}.$$

(c) Let $\alpha = \cos^{-1}\frac{3}{5}$. $\tan\left(\frac{1}{2}\cos^{-1}\frac{3}{5}\right) = \tan\frac{1}{2}\alpha = \frac{1-\cos\alpha}{\sin\alpha} = \frac{1-\frac{3}{5}}{\frac{4}{5}} = \frac{1}{2}.$

22 (a) Let $\alpha = \cos^{-1}\left(-\frac{3}{5}\right)$. $\frac{\pi}{2} < \alpha < \pi \Rightarrow \frac{\pi}{4} < \frac{1}{2}\alpha < \frac{\pi}{2}$ and $\sin\frac{1}{2}\alpha > 0$.

$$\sin\left[\frac{1}{2}\cos^{-1}\left(-\frac{3}{5}\right)\right] = \sin\frac{1}{2}\alpha = \sqrt{\frac{1-\cos\alpha}{2}} = \sqrt{\frac{1-\left(-\frac{3}{5}\right)}{2}} = \sqrt{\frac{4}{5}\cdot\frac{5}{5}} = \frac{2}{5}\sqrt{5}.$$

(b) Let $\alpha = \sin^{-1}\frac{12}{13}$. $0 < \alpha < \frac{\pi}{2} \Rightarrow 0 < \frac{1}{2}\alpha < \frac{\pi}{4}$ and $\cos\frac{1}{2}\alpha > 0$.

$$\cos\left(\frac{1}{2}\sin^{-1}\frac{12}{13}\right) = \cos\frac{1}{2}\alpha = \sqrt{\frac{1+\cos\alpha}{2}} = \sqrt{\frac{1+\frac{5}{13}}{2}} = \sqrt{\frac{9}{13}\cdot\frac{13}{13}} = \frac{3}{13}\sqrt{13}.$$

(c) Let $\alpha = \tan^{-1}\frac{40}{9}$. $\tan\left(\frac{1}{2}\tan^{-1}\frac{40}{9}\right) = \tan\frac{1}{2}\alpha = \frac{1-\cos\alpha}{\sin\alpha} = \frac{1-\frac{9}{41}}{\frac{40}{41}} = \frac{4}{5}.$

23 Let $\alpha = \tan^{-1}x$. From *Figure 23*, $\sin\left(\tan^{-1}x\right) = \sin\alpha = \frac{x}{\sqrt{x^2+1}}.$

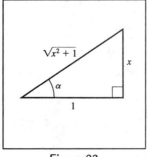

Figure 23

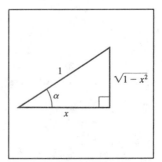

Figure 24

24 Let $\alpha = \arccos x$. From *Figure 24*, $\tan\left(\arccos x\right) = \tan\alpha = \frac{\sqrt{1-x^2}}{x}.$

25 Let $\alpha = \sin^{-1}\dfrac{x}{\sqrt{x^2+4}}$. From *Figure 25*, $\sec\left(\sin^{-1}\dfrac{x}{\sqrt{x^2+4}}\right) = \sec\alpha = \dfrac{\sqrt{x^2+4}}{2}$.

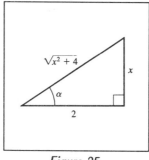

Figure 25

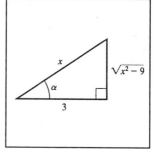

Figure 26

26 Let $\alpha = \sin^{-1}\dfrac{\sqrt{x^2-9}}{x}$. From *Figure 26*, $\cot\left(\sin^{-1}\dfrac{\sqrt{x^2-9}}{x}\right) = \cot\alpha = \dfrac{3}{\sqrt{x^2-9}}$.

27 Let $\alpha = \sin^{-1}x$. From *Figure 27*,

$$\sin(2\sin^{-1}x) = \sin 2\alpha = 2\sin\alpha\cos\alpha = 2\cdot\frac{x}{1}\cdot\frac{\sqrt{1-x^2}}{1} = 2x\sqrt{1-x^2}.$$

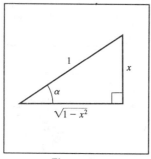

Figure 27

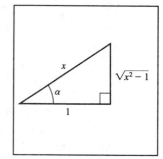

Figure 30

28 Let $\alpha = \tan^{-1}x$. See *Figure 23*. $\cos(2\tan^{-1}x) = \cos 2\alpha = \cos^2\alpha - \sin^2\alpha =$

$$\left(\frac{1}{\sqrt{x^2+1}}\right)^2 - \left(\frac{x}{\sqrt{x^2+1}}\right)^2 = \frac{1}{x^2+1} - \frac{x^2}{x^2+1} = \frac{1-x^2}{x^2+1}.$$

29 Let $\alpha = \arccos x$. See *Figure 24*. $0 \le \alpha \le \pi \Rightarrow 0 \le \frac{1}{2}\alpha \le \frac{\pi}{2}$ and $\cos\frac{1}{2}\alpha > 0$.

$$\cos(\tfrac{1}{2}\arccos x) = \cos\tfrac{1}{2}\alpha = \sqrt{\frac{1+\cos\alpha}{2}} = \sqrt{\frac{1+x}{2}}.$$

30 Let $\alpha = \cos^{-1}\frac{1}{x}$. From *Figure 30*,

$$\tan\left(\tfrac{1}{2}\cos^{-1}\tfrac{1}{x}\right) = \tan\tfrac{1}{2}\alpha = \frac{1-\cos\alpha}{\sin\alpha} = \frac{1-\frac{1}{x}}{\frac{\sqrt{x^2-1}}{x}}\cdot\frac{x}{x} = \frac{x-1}{\sqrt{x^2-1}}.$$

31 (a) See text Figure 20. As $x \to -1^+$, $\sin^{-1}x \to \underline{\;-\frac{\pi}{2}\;}$.

    (b) See text Figure 23. As $x \to 1^-$, $\cos^{-1}x \to \underline{\;0\;}$.

    (c) See text Figure 26. As $x \to \infty$, $\tan^{-1}x \to \underline{\;\frac{\pi}{2}\;}$.

32 (a) As $x \to 1^-$, $\sin^{-1}x \to \underline{\;\frac{\pi}{2}\;}$.   (b) As $x \to -1^+$, $\cos^{-1}x \to \underline{\;\pi\;}$.

    (c) As $x \to -\infty$, $\tan^{-1}x \to \underline{\;-\frac{\pi}{2}\;}$.

33 $y = \sin^{-1} 2x$ •   horizontally compress $y = \sin^{-1} x$ by a factor of 2

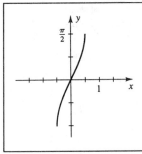

Figure 33

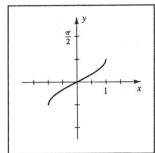

Figure 34

34 $y = \frac{1}{2}\sin^{-1} x$ •   vertically compress $y = \sin^{-1} x$ by a factor of 2

35 $y = \sin^{-1}(x+1)$ •   shift $y = \sin^{-1} x$ left 1 unit

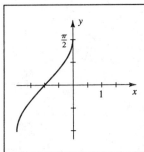

Figure 35

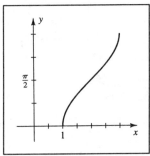

Figure 36

36 $y = \sin^{-1}(x-2) + \frac{\pi}{2}$ •   shift $y = \sin^{-1} x$ right 2 units and up $\frac{\pi}{2}$ units

37 $y = \cos^{-1}\frac{1}{2}x$ •   horizontally stretch $y = \cos^{-1} x$ by a factor of 2

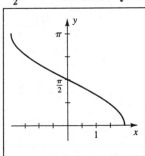

Figure 37

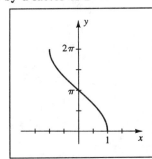

Figure 38

38 $y = 2\cos^{-1} x$ •   vertically stretch $y = \cos^{-1} x$ by a factor of 2

39 $y = 2 + \tan^{-1} x$ • shift $y = \tan^{-1} x$ up 2 units

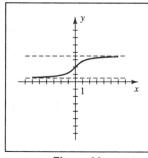

Figure 39

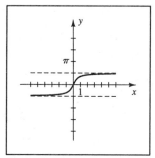

Figure 40

40 $y = \tan^{-1} 2x$ • horizontally compress $y = \tan^{-1} x$ by a factor of 2

41 If $\alpha = \arccos x$, then $\cos \alpha = x$, where $0 \le \alpha \le \pi$.

Hence, $y = \sin(\arccos x) = \sin \alpha = \sqrt{1 - \cos^2 \alpha} = \sqrt{1 - x^2}$.

Thus, we have the graph of the semicircle $y = \sqrt{1 - x^2}$ on the interval $[-1, 1]$.

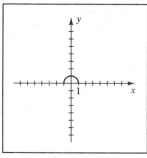

Figure 41

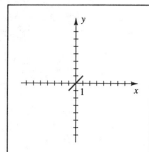

Figure 42

42 By a property of $\sin^{-1}$, $\sin(\sin^{-1} x) = x$ for $-1 \le x \le 1$.

Thus, we have the graph of the line $y = x$ on the interval $[-1, 1]$.

43 (a) $-1 \le x - 3 \le 1 \Rightarrow 2 \le x \le 4$

(b) $-\frac{\pi}{2} \le \sin^{-1}(x - 3) \le \frac{\pi}{2} \Rightarrow -\frac{\pi}{4} \le \frac{1}{2}\sin^{-1}(x - 3) \le \frac{\pi}{4} \Rightarrow -\frac{\pi}{4} \le y \le \frac{\pi}{4}$

(c) $y = \frac{1}{2}\sin^{-1}(x - 3) \Rightarrow 2y = \sin^{-1}(x - 3) \Rightarrow \sin 2y = x - 3 \Rightarrow x = \sin 2y + 3$

44 (a) Since the domain of $\tan^{-1}$ is $\mathbb{R}$, x can be any real number.

(b) $-\frac{\pi}{2} < \tan^{-1}(2x + 1) < \frac{\pi}{2} \Rightarrow -\frac{3\pi}{2} < 3\tan^{-1}(2x + 1) < \frac{3\pi}{2} \Rightarrow -\frac{3\pi}{2} < y < \frac{3\pi}{2}$

(c) $y = 3\tan^{-1}(2x + 1) \Rightarrow \frac{1}{3}y = \tan^{-1}(2x + 1) \Rightarrow \tan\frac{1}{3}y = 2x + 1 \Rightarrow$

$$2x = \tan\tfrac{1}{3}y - 1 \Rightarrow x = \tfrac{1}{2}(\tan\tfrac{1}{3}y - 1)$$

45 (a) $-1 \le \frac{2}{3}x \le 1 \Rightarrow -\frac{3}{2} \le x \le \frac{3}{2}$

(b) $0 \le \cos^{-1}\frac{2}{3}x \le \pi \Rightarrow 0 \le 4\cos^{-1}\frac{2}{3}x \le 4\pi \Rightarrow 0 \le y \le 4\pi$

(c) $y = 4\cos^{-1}\frac{2}{3}x \Rightarrow \frac{1}{4}y = \cos^{-1}\frac{2}{3}x \Rightarrow \cos\frac{1}{4}y = \frac{2}{3}x \Rightarrow x = \frac{3}{2}\cos\frac{1}{4}y$

46 (a) $-1 \le 3x - 4 \le 1 \Rightarrow 3 \le 3x \le 5 \Rightarrow 1 \le x \le \frac{5}{3}$

(b) $-\frac{\pi}{2} \le \sin^{-1}(3x - 4) \le \frac{\pi}{2} \Rightarrow -\pi \le 2\sin^{-1}(3x - 4) \le \pi \Rightarrow -\pi \le y \le \pi$

(c) $y = 2\sin^{-1}(3x - 4) \Rightarrow \frac{1}{2}y = \sin^{-1}(3x - 4) \Rightarrow \sin\frac{1}{2}y = 3x - 4 \Rightarrow$

$$3x = \sin\frac{1}{2}y + 4 \Rightarrow x = \frac{1}{3}\sin\frac{1}{2}y + \frac{4}{3}$$

$\boxed{47}$ $y = -3 - \sin x \Rightarrow y + 3 = -\sin x \Rightarrow -(y + 3) = \sin x \Rightarrow x = \sin^{-1}(-y - 3)$

$\boxed{48}$ $y = 2 + 3\sin x \Rightarrow y - 2 = 3\sin x \Rightarrow \frac{1}{3}(y - 2) = \sin x \Rightarrow x = \sin^{-1}\left[\frac{1}{3}(y - 2)\right]$

$\boxed{49}$ $y = 15 - 2\cos x \Rightarrow 2\cos x = 15 - y \Rightarrow \cos x = \frac{1}{2}(15 - y) \Rightarrow x = \cos^{-1}\left[\frac{1}{2}(15 - y)\right]$

$\boxed{50}$ $y = 6 - 3\cos x \Rightarrow 3\cos x = 6 - y \Rightarrow \cos x = \frac{1}{3}(6 - y) \Rightarrow x = \cos^{-1}\left[\frac{1}{3}(6 - y)\right]$

$\boxed{51}$ $\dfrac{\sin x}{3} = \dfrac{\sin y}{4} \Rightarrow \sin x = \frac{3}{4}\sin y.$ The reference angle for x is $x_R = \sin^{-1}\left(\frac{3}{4}\sin y\right),$

where $0 < \frac{3}{4}\sin y \le \frac{3}{4} < 1.$ If $0 < x < \frac{\pi}{2},$ then $x = x_R.$ If $\frac{\pi}{2} < x < \pi,$ then $x = \pi - x_R.$

$\boxed{52}$ $\dfrac{4}{\sin x} = \dfrac{7}{\sin y} \Rightarrow \dfrac{\sin x}{4} = \dfrac{\sin y}{7} \Rightarrow \sin x = \frac{4}{7}\sin y.$

The reference angle for x is $x_R = \sin^{-1}\left(\frac{4}{7}\sin y\right),$ where $0 < \frac{4}{7}\sin y \le \frac{4}{7} < 1.$

If $0 < x < \frac{\pi}{2},$ then $x = x_R.$ If $\frac{\pi}{2} < x < \pi,$ then $x = \pi - x_R.$

$\boxed{53}$ $\cos^2 x + 2\cos x - 1 = 0 \Rightarrow \cos x = -1 \pm \sqrt{2} \approx 0.4142, -2.4142.$

Since $-2.4142 < -1,$ $x = \cos^{-1}(-1 + \sqrt{2}) \approx 1.1437$ is one answer.

$$x = 2\pi - \cos^{-1}(-1 + \sqrt{2}) \approx 2\pi - 1.1437 \approx 5.1395 \text{ is the other.}$$

$\boxed{54}$ $\sin^2 x - \sin x - 1 = 0 \Rightarrow \sin x = \dfrac{1 \pm \sqrt{5}}{2} \approx 1.6180, -0.6180.$ Since $1.6180 > 1,$

$x_0 = \sin^{-1}\left(\dfrac{1 - \sqrt{5}}{2}\right) \approx -0.6662,$ but this is not in $[0, 2\pi).$ The reference angle is

$x_R = -x_0 \approx 0.6662.$ Since the sine is negative in quadrants III and IV,

the values are $\pi + x_R \approx 3.8078$ and $2\pi - x_R \approx 5.6170.$

$\boxed{55}$ $2\tan^2 t + 9\tan t + 3 = 0 \Rightarrow \tan t = \dfrac{-9 \pm \sqrt{81 - 24}}{4} \Rightarrow t = \tan^{-1}\frac{1}{4}(-9 \pm \sqrt{57})$

$$\tan^{-1}\tfrac{1}{4}(-9 + \sqrt{57}) \approx -0.3478, \ \tan^{-1}\tfrac{1}{4}(-9 - \sqrt{57}) \approx -1.3337$$

$\boxed{56}$ $3\sin^2 t + 7\sin t + 3 = 0 \Rightarrow \sin t = \dfrac{-7 \pm \sqrt{49 - 36}}{6} \Rightarrow$

$t = \sin^{-1}\frac{1}{6}(-7 + \sqrt{13}) \ \{\sin t \ne \frac{1}{6}(-7 - \sqrt{13}) < -1\}; \ \sin^{-1}\frac{1}{6}(-7 + \sqrt{13}) \approx -0.6013$

$\boxed{57}$ $15\cos^4 x - 14\cos^2 x + 3 = 0 \Rightarrow (5\cos^2 x - 3)(3\cos^2 x - 1) = 0 \Rightarrow \cos^2 x = \frac{3}{5}, \frac{1}{3} \Rightarrow$

$\cos x = \pm\frac{1}{5}\sqrt{15}, \ \pm\frac{1}{3}\sqrt{3} \Rightarrow x = \cos^{-1}(\pm\frac{1}{5}\sqrt{15}), \ \cos^{-1}(\pm\frac{1}{3}\sqrt{3}).$

$\cos^{-1}\frac{1}{5}\sqrt{15} \approx 0.6847, \ \cos^{-1}(-\frac{1}{5}\sqrt{15}) \approx 2.4569,$

$$\cos^{-1}\tfrac{1}{3}\sqrt{3} \approx 0.9553, \ \cos^{-1}(-\tfrac{1}{3}\sqrt{3}) \approx 2.1863$$

$\boxed{58}$ $3\tan^4\theta - 19\tan^2\theta + 2 = 0 \Rightarrow \tan^2\theta = \dfrac{19 \pm \sqrt{361 - 24}}{6} \Rightarrow$

$\theta = \tan^{-1}\left(\pm\sqrt{\frac{1}{6}(19 \pm \sqrt{337})}\right).$

$$\tan^{-1}\left(\pm\sqrt{\tfrac{1}{6}(19 + \sqrt{337})}\right) \approx \pm1.1896, \ \tan^{-1}\left(\pm\sqrt{\tfrac{1}{6}(19 - \sqrt{337})}\right) \approx \pm0.3162$$

59 $6\sin^3\theta + 18\sin^2\theta - 5\sin\theta - 15 = 0 \Rightarrow 6\sin^2\theta(\sin\theta + 3) - 5(\sin\theta + 3) = 0 \Rightarrow$

$(6\sin^2\theta - 5)(\sin\theta + 3) = 0 \Rightarrow \sin\theta = \pm\frac{1}{6}\sqrt{30} \Rightarrow \theta = \sin^{-1}(\pm\frac{1}{6}\sqrt{30}) \approx \pm 1.1503$

60 (a) $6\sin 2x - 8\cos x + 9\sin x - 6 = 0 \Rightarrow 12\sin x\cos x - 8\cos x + 9\sin x - 6 = 0 \Rightarrow$

$4\cos x(3\sin x - 2) + 3(3\sin x - 2) = 0 \Rightarrow (4\cos x + 3)(3\sin x - 2) = 0 \Rightarrow x =$

$\cos^{-1}(-\frac{3}{4})$, $\sin^{-1}\frac{2}{3} \approx 0.7297$. However, $\cos^{-1}(-\frac{3}{4})$ is in $(\frac{\pi}{2}, \pi)$, and <u>not</u> in $(-\frac{\pi}{2}, \frac{\pi}{2})$.

61 $(\cos x)(15\cos x + 4) = 3 \Rightarrow 15\cos^2 x + 4\cos x - 3 = 0 \Rightarrow (5\cos x + 3)(3\cos x - 1) =$

$0 \Rightarrow \cos x = -\frac{3}{5}, \frac{1}{3} \Rightarrow x = \cos^{-1}(-\frac{3}{5}) \approx 2.2143$, $\cos^{-1}\frac{1}{3} \approx 1.2310$.

In $[0, 2\pi)$, we also have $2\pi - \cos^{-1}(-\frac{3}{5}) \approx 4.0689$ and $2\pi - \cos^{-1}\frac{1}{3} \approx 5.0522$.

62 $6\sin^2 x = \sin x + 2 \Rightarrow 6\sin^2 x - \sin x - 2 = 0 \Rightarrow (3\sin x - 2)(2\sin x + 1) = 0 \Rightarrow$

$\sin x = \frac{2}{3}, -\frac{1}{2} \Rightarrow x = \sin^{-1}\frac{2}{3} \approx 0.7297$, $\pi - \sin^{-1}\frac{2}{3} \approx 2.4119$, $\frac{7\pi}{6} \approx 3.6652$, $\frac{11\pi}{6} \approx 5.7596$.

63 $3\cos 2x - 7\cos x + 5 = 0 \Rightarrow 3(2\cos^2 x - 1) - 7\cos x + 5 = 0 \Rightarrow$

$6\cos^2 x - 7\cos x + 2 = 0 \Rightarrow (3\cos x - 2)(2\cos x - 1) = 0 \Rightarrow \cos x = \frac{2}{3}, \frac{1}{2} \Rightarrow$

$x = \cos^{-1}\frac{2}{3} \approx 0.8411$, $2\pi - \cos^{-1}\frac{2}{3} \approx 5.4421$, $\frac{\pi}{3} \approx 1.0472$, $\frac{5\pi}{3} \approx 5.2360$.

64 $\sin 2x = -1.5\cos x \Rightarrow \sin 2x + 1.5\cos x = 0 \Rightarrow 2\sin x\cos x + 1.5\cos x = 0 \Rightarrow$

$(\cos x)(2\sin x + 1.5) = 0 \Rightarrow \cos x = 0$ or $\sin x = -\frac{3}{4} \Rightarrow x = \frac{\pi}{2} \approx 1.5708$, $\frac{3\pi}{2} \approx 4.7124$,

$\sin^{-1}(-\frac{3}{4})$ { not in $[0, 2\pi)$ }, $2\pi + \sin^{-1}(-\frac{3}{4}) \approx 5.4351$, $\pi - \sin^{-1}(-\frac{3}{4}) \approx 3.9897$.

65 (a) $S = 4$, $D = 3.5$, $d = 1 \Rightarrow M = \frac{S}{2}\left(1 - \frac{2}{\pi}\tan^{-1}\frac{d}{D}\right) = \frac{4}{2}\left(1 - \frac{2}{\pi}\tan^{-1}\frac{1}{3.5}\right) \approx 1.65$ m

(b) $d = 4 \Rightarrow M = \frac{S}{2}\left(1 - \frac{2}{\pi}\tan^{-1}\frac{d}{D}\right) = \frac{4}{2}\left(1 - \frac{2}{\pi}\tan^{-1}\frac{4}{3.5}\right) \approx 0.92$ m

(c) $d = 10 \Rightarrow M = \frac{S}{2}\left(1 - \frac{2}{\pi}\tan^{-1}\frac{d}{D}\right) = \frac{4}{2}\left(1 - \frac{2}{\pi}\tan^{-1}\frac{10}{3.5}\right) \approx 0.43$ m

66 $M = \frac{S}{2}\left(1 - \frac{2}{\pi}\tan^{-1}\frac{d}{D}\right) \Rightarrow \frac{2}{\pi}\tan^{-1}\frac{d}{D} = 1 - \frac{2M}{S} \Rightarrow \tan^{-1}\frac{d}{D} = \frac{\pi}{2}\left(1 - \frac{2M}{S}\right) \Rightarrow$

$\frac{d}{D} = \tan\left[\frac{\pi}{2}\left(1 - \frac{2M}{S}\right)\right] \Rightarrow D = d\cot\left[\frac{\pi}{2}\left(1 - \frac{2M}{S}\right)\right] = 5\cot\left[\frac{\pi}{2}\left(1 - \frac{2(0.6)}{3}\right)\right] \approx 3.63$ km

67 opp $= \frac{1}{2}(30)$ and hyp $= 280 \Rightarrow \sin\theta = \frac{15}{280} \Rightarrow \theta = \sin^{-1}\frac{15}{280} \approx 3.07°$

68 $\tan\alpha = \frac{4'}{11'10''} \Rightarrow \alpha = \tan^{-1}\frac{48}{142} \approx 18.7°$. $\alpha + \beta = 90° \Rightarrow \beta \approx 71.3°$.

69 (a) Let β denote the angle by the sailboat with opposite side d and hypotenuse k.

Now $\sin\beta = \frac{d}{k} \Rightarrow \beta = \sin^{-1}\frac{d}{k}$. Using alternate interior angles,

we see that $\alpha + \beta = \theta$. Thus, $\alpha = \theta - \beta = \theta - \sin^{-1}\frac{d}{k}$.

(b) $d = 50$, $k = 210$, and $\theta = 53.4° \Rightarrow \alpha = 53.4° - \sin^{-1}\frac{50}{210} \approx 39.63°$, or $40°$.

70 (a) Draw a line from the art critic's eyes to the painting. This forms two right

triangles with opposite sides 8 { upper $\triangle$ } and 2 { lower $\triangle$ } and adjacent side x.

Let α be the angle of elevation to the top of the painting and β be the angle of

depression to the bottom of the painting.

Since $\tan\alpha = \frac{8}{x}$ and $\tan\beta = \frac{2}{x}$, $\theta = \alpha + \beta = \tan^{-1}\frac{8}{x} + \tan^{-1}\frac{2}{x}$.

(b) $\tan \theta = \tan (\alpha + \beta) = \dfrac{\tan \alpha + \tan \beta}{1 - \tan \alpha \tan \beta} = \dfrac{8/x + 2/x}{1 - (8/x)(2/x)} \cdot \dfrac{x^2}{x^2} = \dfrac{8x + 2x}{x^2 - 16} = \dfrac{10x}{x^2 - 16} \Rightarrow$

$\theta = \tan^{-1}\left(\dfrac{10x}{x^2 - 16}\right)$. Note that if $0 < x < 4$, $\dfrac{10x}{x^2 - 16} < 0$ and $90° < \theta < 180°$,

not $-90° < \theta < 0°$ since $0° < \theta < 180°$ in any triangle.

If $x = 4$, $\dfrac{10x}{x^2 - 16}$ is undefined and $\theta = 90°$. If $x > 4$, $\dfrac{10x}{x^2 - 16} > 0$ and $0 < \theta < 90°$.

(c) $45° = \tan^{-1}\left(\dfrac{10x}{x^2 - 16}\right) \Rightarrow \tan 45° = \dfrac{10x}{x^2 - 16} \Rightarrow (1)(x^2 - 16) = 10x \Rightarrow$

$$x^2 - 10x - 16 = 0 \Rightarrow x = \dfrac{10 \pm \sqrt{164}}{2} = \{x > 0\}\ x = 5 + \sqrt{41} \approx 11.4 \text{ ft.}$$

Note: The following is a general outline that can be used for verifying trigonometric identities involving inverse trigonometric functions.

    (1) Define angles and their ranges—make sure the range of values for one side of the equation is equal to the range of values for the other side.

    (2) Choose a trigonometric function T that is one-to-one on the range of values listed in part (1).

    (3) Show that $T(\text{LS}) = T(\text{RS})$. Note that $T(\text{LS}) = T(\text{RS}) \not\Rightarrow \text{LS} = \text{RS}$.

    (4) Conclude that since T is one-to-one on the range of values, $\text{LS} = \text{RS}$.

71 Let $\alpha = \sin^{-1} x$ and $\beta = \tan^{-1}\dfrac{x}{\sqrt{1 - x^2}}$ with $-\frac{\pi}{2} < \alpha < \frac{\pi}{2}$ and $-\frac{\pi}{2} < \beta < \frac{\pi}{2}$.

Thus, $\sin \alpha = x$ and $\sin \beta = x$.

    Since the sine function is one-to-one on $\left(-\frac{\pi}{2}, \frac{\pi}{2}\right)$, we have $\alpha = \beta$.

72 Let $\alpha = \arccos x$ and $\beta = \arccos \sqrt{1 - x^2}$.

Since $0 \le x \le 1$, we have $0 \le \alpha \le \frac{\pi}{2}$ and $0 \le \beta \le \frac{\pi}{2}$, and hence $0 \le \alpha + \beta \le \pi$.

Thus, $\cos (\alpha + \beta) = \cos \alpha \cos \beta - \sin \alpha \sin \beta = x \cdot \sqrt{1 - x^2} - \sqrt{1 - x^2} \cdot x = 0$.

    Since the cosine function is one-to-one on $[0, \pi]$, we have $\alpha + \beta = \frac{\pi}{2}$.

73 Let $\alpha = \arcsin (-x)$ and $\beta = \arcsin x$ with $-\frac{\pi}{2} \le \alpha \le \frac{\pi}{2}$ and $-\frac{\pi}{2} \le \beta \le \frac{\pi}{2}$.

Thus, $\sin \alpha = -x$ and $\sin \beta = x$. Consequently, $\sin \alpha = -\sin \beta = \sin (-\beta)$.

    Since the sine function is one-to-one on $\left[-\frac{\pi}{2}, \frac{\pi}{2}\right]$, we have $\alpha = -\beta$.

74 Let $\alpha = \arccos (-x)$ and $\beta = \pi - \arccos x$ with $0 \le \alpha \le \pi$ and $0 \le \beta \le \pi$ since

$0 \le \arccos x \le \pi \Rightarrow 0 \ge -\arccos x \ge -\pi \Rightarrow \pi \ge \pi - \arccos x \ge 0$.

Thus, $\cos \alpha = -x$ and $\cos \beta = \cos (\pi - \arccos x) = \cos \pi \cdot x + \sin \pi \cdot \sin (\arccos x) = -x$.

    Since the cosine function is one-to-one on $[0, \pi]$, we have $\alpha = \beta$.

75 Let $\alpha = \arctan x$ and $\beta = \arctan(1/x)$.

Since $x > 0$, we have $0 < \alpha < \frac{\pi}{2}$ and $0 < \beta < \frac{\pi}{2}$, and hence $0 < \alpha + \beta < \pi$.

Thus, $\tan(\alpha + \beta) = \dfrac{\tan \alpha + \tan \beta}{1 - \tan \alpha \tan \beta} = \dfrac{x + (1/x)}{1 - x \cdot (1/x)} = \dfrac{x + (1/x)}{0}$.

Since the denominator is 0, $\tan(\alpha + \beta)$ is undefined and hence $\alpha + \beta = \frac{\pi}{2}$.

76 Let $\alpha = \cos^{-1} x$ and $\beta = \cos^{-1}(2x^2 - 1)$. Since $0 \le x \le 1$, $0 \le \alpha \le \frac{\pi}{2}$ and $0 \le 2\alpha \le \pi$.

Also, $0 \le x \le 1 \Rightarrow 0 \le 2x^2 \le 2 \Rightarrow -1 \le 2x^2 - 1 \le 1$ and $0 \le \beta \le \pi$.

Thus, $\cos 2\alpha = \cos^2 \alpha - \sin^2 \alpha = (x)^2 - (\sqrt{1 - x^2})^2 = x^2 - (1 - x^2) = 2x^2 - 1$ and

$\cos \beta = 2x^2 - 1$. Since the cosine function is one-to-one on $[0, \pi]$, we have $2\alpha = \beta$.

77 The domain of $\sin^{-1}(x - 1)$ is $[0, 2]$ and the domain of $\cos^{-1}\frac{1}{2}x$ is $[-2, 2]$.

The domain of f is the intersection of $[0, 2]$ and $[-2, 2]$, i.e., $[0, 2]$.

From the graph, we see that the function is increasing and its range is $[-\frac{\pi}{2}, \pi]$.

$[-3, 6]$ by $[-2, 4]$ $[-3, 12]$ by $[-4, 6]$

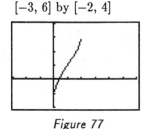
Xscl $= 1$
Yscl $= 1$

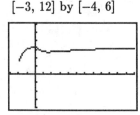
Xscl $= 1$
Yscl $= 1$

Figure 77   *Figure 78*

78 The domain of $\frac{1}{2}\tan^{-1}(1 - 2x)$ is $(-\infty, \infty)$ and the domain of $3\tan^{-1}\sqrt{x + 2}$ is $[-2, \infty)$. The domain of f is $[-2, \infty)$. The minimum value of approximately $\frac{1}{2}\tan^{-1} 5 \approx 0.69$ occurs at $x = -2$. The maximum value of the function does not occur at $x \approx -0.13$. Rather for large x, $\frac{1}{2}\tan^{-1}(1 - 2x)$ approaches $-\frac{\pi}{4}$ and $3\tan^{-1}\sqrt{x + 2}$ approaches $\frac{3\pi}{2}$. Thus, the function increases asymptotically to $\frac{5\pi}{4} \approx 3.93$. The range of the function is $[\frac{1}{2}\tan^{-1} 5, \frac{5\pi}{4})$.

79 Graph $y = \sin^{-1} 2x$ and $y = \tan^{-1}(1 - x)$.

From the graph, we see that there is one solution at $x \approx 0.29$.

$[-3, 3]$ by $[-2, 2]$ $[-6, 6]$ by $[-4.5, 4.5]$

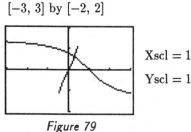
Xscl $= 1$
Yscl $= 1$

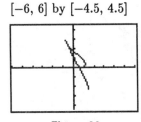
Xscl $= 1$
Yscl $= 1$

Figure 79   *Figure 80*

80 Graph $y = \cos^{-1}(x - \frac{1}{5})$ and $y = 2\sin^{-1}(\frac{1}{2} - x)$.

From the graph, we see that there is one solution at $x \approx -0.39$.

⑧① From the graph, we see that when $f(\theta) = 0.2$, $\theta \approx 1.25$, or approximately $72°$.

$[0, \pi/2]$ by $[0, 1.05]$ $[-\pi/2, \pi/2]$ by $[-1.05, 1.05]$

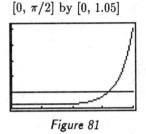

Xscl $= 0.2$

Yscl $= 0.2$

Figure 81

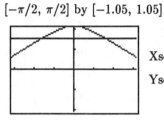

Xscl $= 0.5$

Yscl $= 0.5$

Figure 82

⑧② (a) $\phi = \sin^{-1}(\sin 23.5° \sin 51.7° + \cos 23.5° \cos 51.7° \cos H)$

(b) From *Figure 82*, we find that $\phi = 45° = \frac{\pi}{4} \approx 0.785398$ at $H \approx \pm 0.8044$. Since 6

hours corresponds to $\frac{\pi}{2}$, 1 hour corresponds to $\frac{\pi}{12}$. $\pm 0.8044 \div \frac{\pi}{12} \approx \pm 3.07$ hr $\approx$

± 3 hr and 4 min. The times are approximately 8:56 A.M. and 3:04 P.M.

⑧③ Actual distance between x-ticks is equal to $x_A = \frac{3 \text{ units}}{3 \text{ ticks}} = 1$ unit between ticks.

Actual distance between y-ticks is equal to $y_A = \frac{2 \text{ units}}{2 \text{ ticks}} = 1$ unit between ticks.

The ratio is $m_A = \frac{y_A}{x_A} = \frac{1}{1} = 1$. The graph will make an angle of $\theta = \tan^{-1} 1 = 45°$.

$[0, 3]$ by $[0, 2]$ $[0, 6]$ by $[0, 2]$

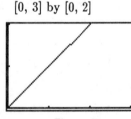

Xscl $= 1$

Yscl $= 1$

Figure 83

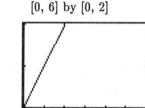

Xscl $= 1$

Yscl $= 1$

Figure 84

⑧④ $x_A = \frac{3 \text{ units}}{6 \text{ ticks}} = \frac{1}{2}$, $y_A = \frac{2 \text{ units}}{2 \text{ ticks}} = 1 \Rightarrow m_A = \frac{1}{1/2} = 2 \Rightarrow \theta = \tan^{-1} 2 \approx 63.4°$.

⑧⑤ $x_A = \frac{3 \text{ units}}{3 \text{ ticks}} = 1$, $y_A = \frac{2 \text{ units}}{4 \text{ ticks}} = \frac{1}{2} \Rightarrow m_A = \frac{1/2}{1} = \frac{1}{2} \Rightarrow \theta = \tan^{-1}\frac{1}{2} \approx 26.6°$.

$[0, 3]$ by $[0, 4]$ $[0, 2]$ by $[0, 2]$

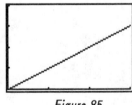

Xscl $= 1$

Yscl $= 1$

Figure 85

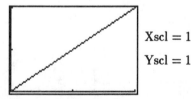

Xscl $= 1$

Yscl $= 1$

Figure 86

⑧⑥ $x_A = \frac{3 \text{ units}}{2 \text{ ticks}} = \frac{3}{2}$, $y_A = \frac{2 \text{ units}}{2 \text{ ticks}} = 1 \Rightarrow m_A = \frac{1}{3/2} = \frac{2}{3} \Rightarrow \theta = \tan^{-1}\frac{2}{3} \approx 33.7°$.

Chapter 6 Review Exercises

1 $(\cot^2 x + 1)(1 - \cos^2 x) = (\csc^2 x)(\sin^2 x) = 1$

2 $\cos\theta + \sin\theta\tan\theta = \cos\theta + \sin\theta \cdot \dfrac{\sin\theta}{\cos\theta} = \dfrac{\cos^2\theta + \sin^2\theta}{\cos\theta} = \dfrac{1}{\cos\theta} = \sec\theta$

3 $\dfrac{(\sec^2\theta - 1)\cot\theta}{\tan\theta\sin\theta + \cos\theta} = \dfrac{(\tan^2\theta)\cot\theta}{\dfrac{\sin\theta}{\cos\theta}\cdot\sin\theta + \cos\theta} = \dfrac{\tan\theta}{\dfrac{\sin^2\theta + \cos^2\theta}{\cos\theta}} = \dfrac{\sin\theta/\cos\theta}{1/\cos\theta} = \sin\theta$

4 $(\tan x + \cot x)^2 = \left(\dfrac{\sin x}{\cos x} + \dfrac{\cos x}{\sin x}\right)^2 = \left(\dfrac{\sin^2 x + \cos^2 x}{\cos x\sin x}\right)^2 = \dfrac{1}{\cos^2 x\sin^2 x} = \sec^2 x\,\csc^2 x$

5 $\dfrac{1}{1 + \sin t}\cdot\dfrac{1 - \sin t}{1 - \sin t} = \dfrac{1 - \sin t}{1 - \sin^2 t} = \dfrac{1 - \sin t}{\cos^2 t} = \dfrac{1 - \sin t}{\cos t}\cdot\dfrac{1}{\cos t} =$

$$\left(\dfrac{1}{\cos t} - \dfrac{\sin t}{\cos t}\right)\cdot\sec t = (\sec t - \tan t)\sec t$$

6 $\dfrac{\sin(\alpha - \beta)}{\cos(\alpha + \beta)} = \dfrac{(\sin\alpha\cos\beta - \cos\alpha\sin\beta)\,/\,\cos\alpha\cos\beta}{(\cos\alpha\cos\beta - \sin\alpha\sin\beta)\,/\,\cos\alpha\cos\beta} = \dfrac{\tan\alpha - \tan\beta}{1 - \tan\alpha\tan\beta}$

7 $\tan 2u = \dfrac{2\tan u}{1 - \tan^2 u} = \dfrac{2\cdot\dfrac{1}{\cot u}}{1 - \dfrac{1}{\cot^2 u}} = \dfrac{\dfrac{2}{\cot u}}{\dfrac{\cot^2 u - 1}{\cot^2 u}} = \dfrac{2\cot u}{\cot^2 u - 1} = \dfrac{2\cot u}{(\csc^2 u - 1) - 1} =$

$$\dfrac{2\cot u}{\csc^2 u - 2}$$

8 $\cos^2\dfrac{v}{2} = \dfrac{1 + \cos v}{2} = \dfrac{1 + \dfrac{1}{\sec v}}{2} = \dfrac{\dfrac{\sec v + 1}{\sec v}}{2} = \dfrac{1 + \sec v}{2\sec v}$

9 $\dfrac{\tan^3\phi - \cot^3\phi}{\tan^2\phi + \csc^2\phi} = \dfrac{(\tan\phi - \cot\phi)[(\tan^2\phi + \tan\phi\cot\phi + \cot^2\phi)]}{[\tan^2\phi + (1 + \cot^2\phi)]} = \tan\phi - \cot\phi$

10 $\text{LS} = \dfrac{\sin u + \sin v}{\csc u + \csc v} = \dfrac{\sin u + \sin v}{\dfrac{1}{\sin u} + \dfrac{1}{\sin v}} = \dfrac{\sin u + \sin v}{\dfrac{\sin v + \sin u}{\sin u\sin v}} = \sin u\sin v$

$$\text{RS} = \dfrac{1 - \sin u\sin v}{-1 + \csc u\csc v} = \dfrac{1 - \sin u\sin v}{-1 + \dfrac{1}{\sin u\sin v}} = \dfrac{1 - \sin u\sin v}{\dfrac{1 - \sin u\sin v}{\sin u\sin v}} = \sin u\sin v$$

Since the LS and RS equal the same expression and the steps are reversible,

the identity is verified.

11 $\left(\dfrac{\sin^2 x}{\tan^4 x}\right)^3\left(\dfrac{\csc^3 x}{\cot^6 x}\right)^2 = \left(\dfrac{\sin^6 x}{\tan^{12} x}\right)\left(\dfrac{\csc^6 x}{\cot^{12} x}\right) = \dfrac{(\sin x\csc x)^6}{(\tan x\cot x)^{12}} = \dfrac{(1)^6}{(1)^{12}} = 1$

12 $\dfrac{\cos\gamma}{1 - \tan\gamma} + \dfrac{\sin\gamma}{1 - \cot\gamma} = \dfrac{\cos\gamma}{\dfrac{\cos\gamma - \sin\gamma}{\cos\gamma}} + \dfrac{\sin\gamma}{\dfrac{\sin\gamma - \cos\gamma}{\sin\gamma}} = \dfrac{\cos^2\gamma}{\cos\gamma - \sin\gamma} + \dfrac{\sin^2\gamma}{\sin\gamma - \cos\gamma} =$

$$\dfrac{\cos^2\gamma - \sin^2\gamma}{\cos\gamma - \sin\gamma} = \dfrac{(\cos\gamma + \sin\gamma)(\cos\gamma - \sin\gamma)}{\cos\gamma - \sin\gamma} = \cos\gamma + \sin\gamma$$

13 $\dfrac{\cos(-t)}{\sec(-t)+\tan(-t)} = \dfrac{\cos t}{\sec t - \tan t} = \dfrac{\cos t}{\dfrac{1}{\cos t} - \dfrac{\sin t}{\cos t}} = \dfrac{\cos t}{\dfrac{1-\sin t}{\cos t}} = \dfrac{\cos^2 t}{1-\sin t} =$

$$\dfrac{1-\sin^2 t}{1-\sin t} = \dfrac{(1-\sin t)(1+\sin t)}{1-\sin t} = 1+\sin t$$

14 $\dfrac{\cot(-t)+\csc(-t)}{\sin(-t)} = \dfrac{-\cot t - \csc t}{-\sin t} = \dfrac{\dfrac{\cos t}{\sin t}+\dfrac{1}{\sin t}}{\sin t} = \dfrac{\cos t + 1}{\sin^2 t} =$

$$\dfrac{\cos t + 1}{1-\cos^2 t} = \dfrac{\cos t + 1}{(1-\cos t)(1+\cos t)} = \dfrac{1}{1-\cos t}$$

15 $\sqrt{\dfrac{1-\cos t}{1+\cos t}} = \sqrt{\dfrac{(1-\cos t)}{(1+\cos t)}\cdot\dfrac{(1-\cos t)}{(1-\cos t)}} = \sqrt{\dfrac{(1-\cos t)^2}{1-\cos^2 t}} = \sqrt{\dfrac{(1-\cos t)^2}{\sin^2 t}} =$

$$\dfrac{|1-\cos t|}{|\sin t|} = \dfrac{1-\cos t}{|\sin t|}, \text{ since } (1-\cos t) \geq 0.$$

16 $\sqrt{\dfrac{1-\sin\theta}{1+\sin\theta}} = \sqrt{\dfrac{(1-\sin\theta)}{(1+\sin\theta)}\cdot\dfrac{(1+\sin\theta)}{(1+\sin\theta)}} = \sqrt{\dfrac{1-\sin^2\theta}{(1+\sin\theta)^2}} = \sqrt{\dfrac{\cos^2\theta}{(1+\sin\theta)^2}} =$

$$\dfrac{|\cos\theta|}{|1+\sin\theta|} = \dfrac{|\cos\theta|}{1+\sin\theta}, \text{ since } (1+\sin\theta) \geq 0.$$

17 $\cos\left(x - \tfrac{5\pi}{2}\right) = \cos x \cos\tfrac{5\pi}{2} + \sin x \sin\tfrac{5\pi}{2} = \cos x\,(0) + \sin x\,(1) = \sin x$

18 $\tan\left(x + \tfrac{3\pi}{4}\right) = \dfrac{\tan x + \tan\tfrac{3\pi}{4}}{1 - \tan x \tan\tfrac{3\pi}{4}} = \dfrac{\tan x - 1}{1 + \tan x}$

19 $\tfrac{1}{4}\sin 4\beta = \tfrac{1}{4}\sin(2\cdot 2\beta) = \tfrac{1}{4}(2\sin 2\beta\,\cos 2\beta) = \tfrac{1}{2}(2\sin\beta\,\cos\beta)(\cos^2\beta - \sin^2\beta) =$

$$\sin\beta\,\cos^3\beta - \cos\beta\,\sin^3\beta$$

20 $\tan\tfrac{1}{2}\theta = \dfrac{1-\cos\theta}{\sin\theta} = \dfrac{1}{\sin\theta} - \dfrac{\cos\theta}{\sin\theta} = \csc\theta - \cot\theta$

21 $\sin 8\theta = 2\sin 4\theta\,\cos 4\theta = 2\,(2\sin 2\theta\,\cos 2\theta)(1 - 2\sin^2 2\theta)$

$= 8\sin\theta\,\cos\theta\,(1 - 2\sin^2\theta)[1 - 2\,(2\sin\theta\,\cos\theta)^2]$

$= 8\sin\theta\,\cos\theta\,(1 - 2\sin^2\theta)(1 - 8\sin^2\theta\,\cos^2\theta)$

22 Let $\alpha = \arctan x$ and $\beta = \arctan\dfrac{2x}{1-x^2}$. Because $-1 < x < 1$, $-\tfrac{\pi}{4} < \alpha < \tfrac{\pi}{4}$.

Thus, $\tan\alpha = x$ and $\tan\beta = \dfrac{2x}{1-x^2} = \dfrac{2\tan\alpha}{1-\tan^2\alpha} = \tan 2\alpha$. Since the tangent function

is one-to-one on $\left(-\tfrac{\pi}{2}, \tfrac{\pi}{2}\right)$, we have $\beta = 2\alpha$ or, equivalently, $\alpha = \tfrac{1}{2}\beta$.

23 $2\cos^3\theta - \cos\theta = 0 \Rightarrow \cos\theta\,(2\cos^2\theta - 1) = 0 \Rightarrow \cos\theta = 0,\ \pm\dfrac{\sqrt{2}}{2} \Rightarrow$

$$\theta = \tfrac{\pi}{2}, \tfrac{3\pi}{2}, \tfrac{\pi}{4}, \tfrac{7\pi}{4}, \tfrac{3\pi}{4}, \tfrac{5\pi}{4}$$

24 $2\cos\alpha + \tan\alpha = \sec\alpha \Rightarrow \{\text{multiply by }\cos\alpha\}\ 2\cos^2\alpha + \sin\alpha = 1 \Rightarrow$

$2(1-\sin^2\alpha) + \sin\alpha = 1 \Rightarrow 2\sin^2\alpha - \sin\alpha - 1 = 0 \Rightarrow$

$(2\sin\alpha + 1)(\sin\alpha - 1) = 0 \Rightarrow \sin\alpha = -\tfrac{1}{2},\ 1 \Rightarrow \alpha = \tfrac{7\pi}{6}, \tfrac{11\pi}{6}, \tfrac{\pi}{2}.$

However, $\tan\tfrac{\pi}{2}$ is undefined so exclude $\tfrac{\pi}{2}$ and $\alpha = \tfrac{7\pi}{6}, \tfrac{11\pi}{6}$.

25 $\sin\theta = \tan\theta \Rightarrow \sin\theta - \dfrac{\sin\theta}{\cos\theta} = 0 \Rightarrow \sin\theta\left(1 - \dfrac{1}{\cos\theta}\right) = 0 \Rightarrow$

$$\sin\theta = 0 \text{ or } \cos\theta = 1 \Rightarrow \theta = 0,\ \pi \text{ or } \theta = 0 \Rightarrow \theta = 0,\ \pi$$

26 $\csc^5\theta - 4\csc\theta = 0 \Rightarrow \csc\theta\,(\csc^4\theta - 4) = 0 \Rightarrow$

$$\csc^2\theta = 2 \ \{\csc\theta \neq 0,\ \csc^2\theta \neq -2\} \Rightarrow \csc\theta = \pm\sqrt{2} \Rightarrow \theta = \tfrac{\pi}{4}, \tfrac{3\pi}{4}, \tfrac{5\pi}{4}, \tfrac{7\pi}{4}$$

27 $2\cos^3 t + \cos^2 t - 2\cos t - 1 = 0 \Rightarrow \cos^2 t\,(2\cos t + 1) - 1(2\cos t + 1) = 0 \Rightarrow$

$$(\cos^2 t - 1)(2\cos t + 1) = 0 \Rightarrow \cos t = \pm 1,\ -\tfrac{1}{2} \Rightarrow t = 0,\ \pi,\ \tfrac{2\pi}{3}, \tfrac{4\pi}{3}$$

28 $\cos x\,\cot^2 x = \cos x \Rightarrow \cos x\,\cot^2 x - \cos x = 0 \Rightarrow \cos x\,(\cot^2 x - 1) = 0 \Rightarrow$

$$\cos x = 0 \text{ or } \cot x = \pm 1 \Rightarrow x = \tfrac{\pi}{2}, \tfrac{3\pi}{2}, \tfrac{\pi}{4}, \tfrac{5\pi}{4}, \tfrac{3\pi}{4}, \tfrac{7\pi}{4}$$

29 $\sin\beta + 2\cos^2\beta = 1 \Rightarrow \sin\beta + 2(1 - \sin^2\beta) = 1 \Rightarrow 2\sin^2\beta - \sin\beta - 1 = 0 \Rightarrow$

$$(2\sin\beta + 1)(\sin\beta - 1) = 0 \Rightarrow \sin\beta = -\tfrac{1}{2},\ 1 \Rightarrow \beta = \tfrac{7\pi}{6}, \tfrac{11\pi}{6}, \tfrac{\pi}{2}$$

30 $\cos 2x + 3\cos x + 2 = 0 \Rightarrow 2\cos^2 x + 3\cos x + 1 = 0 \Rightarrow$

$$(2\cos x + 1)(\cos x + 1) = 0 \Rightarrow \cos x = -\tfrac{1}{2},\ -1 \Rightarrow x = \tfrac{2\pi}{3}, \tfrac{4\pi}{3},\ \pi$$

31 $2\sec u\,\sin u + 2 = 4\sin u + \sec u \Rightarrow 2\sec u\,\sin u - 4\sin u - \sec u + 2 = 0 \Rightarrow$

$2\sin u\,(\sec u - 2) - 1(\sec u - 2) = 0 \Rightarrow (2\sin u - 1)(\sec u - 2) = 0 \Rightarrow$

$$\sin u = \tfrac{1}{2} \text{ or } \sec u = 2 \Rightarrow u = \tfrac{\pi}{6}, \tfrac{5\pi}{6}, \tfrac{\pi}{3}, \tfrac{5\pi}{3}$$

32 $\tan 2x\,\cos 2x = \sin 2x \Rightarrow \sin 2x = \sin 2x$. This is an identity and is true for all values of x in $[0, 2\pi)$ except those that make $\tan 2x$ undefined, or, equivalently, those that make $\cos 2x$ equal to 0. $\cos 2x = 0 \Rightarrow 2x = \tfrac{\pi}{2} + \pi n \Rightarrow x = \tfrac{\pi}{4} + \tfrac{\pi}{2}n$.

Hence, the solutions are all x in $[0, 2\pi)$ except $\tfrac{\pi}{4}, \tfrac{3\pi}{4}, \tfrac{5\pi}{4}, \tfrac{7\pi}{4}$.

33 $2\cos 3x\,\cos 2x = 1 - 2\sin 3x\,\sin 2x \Rightarrow 2\cos 3x\,\cos 2x + 2\sin 3x\,\sin 2x = 1 \Rightarrow$

$$2(\cos 3x\,\cos 2x + \sin 3x\,\sin 2x) = 1 \Rightarrow \cos(3x - 2x) = \tfrac{1}{2} \Rightarrow \cos x = \tfrac{1}{2} \Rightarrow x = \tfrac{\pi}{3}, \tfrac{5\pi}{3}$$

34 $\sin x\,\cos 2x + \cos x\,\sin 2x = 0 \Rightarrow \sin(x + 2x) = 0 \Rightarrow \sin 3x = 0 \Rightarrow 3x = \pi n \Rightarrow$

$$x = \tfrac{\pi}{3}n \Rightarrow x = 0,\ \tfrac{\pi}{3}, \tfrac{2\pi}{3},\ \pi,\ \tfrac{4\pi}{3}, \tfrac{5\pi}{3}$$

35 $\cos\pi x + \sin\pi x = 0 \Rightarrow \sin\pi x = -\cos\pi x \Rightarrow \tan\pi x = -1 \Rightarrow \pi x = \tfrac{3\pi}{4} + \pi n \Rightarrow$

$$x = \tfrac{3}{4} + n \Rightarrow x = \tfrac{3}{4}, \tfrac{7}{4}, \tfrac{11}{4}, \tfrac{15}{4}, \tfrac{19}{4}, \tfrac{23}{4}$$

36 $\sin 2u = \sin u \Rightarrow 2\sin u\,\cos u = \sin u \Rightarrow 2\sin u\,\cos u - \sin u = 0 \Rightarrow$

$$\sin u\,(2\cos u - 1) = 0 \Rightarrow \sin u = 0 \text{ or } \cos u = \tfrac{1}{2} \Rightarrow u = 0,\ \pi,\ \tfrac{\pi}{3}, \tfrac{5\pi}{3}$$

37 $2\cos^2\tfrac{1}{2}\theta - 3\cos\theta = 0 \Rightarrow 2\left(\dfrac{1 + \cos\theta}{2}\right) - 3\cos\theta = 0 \Rightarrow$

$$(1 + \cos\theta) - 3\cos\theta = 0 \Rightarrow 1 - 2\cos\theta = 0 \Rightarrow \cos\theta = \tfrac{1}{2} \Rightarrow \theta = \tfrac{\pi}{3}, \tfrac{5\pi}{3}$$

38 $\sec 2x\,\csc 2x = 2\csc 2x \Rightarrow \sec 2x\,\csc 2x - 2\csc 2x = 0 \Rightarrow \csc 2x\,(\sec 2x - 2) = 0 \Rightarrow$

$$\cos 2x = \tfrac{1}{2} \ \{\csc 2x \neq 0\} \Rightarrow 2x = \tfrac{\pi}{3}, \tfrac{5\pi}{3}, \tfrac{7\pi}{3}, \tfrac{11\pi}{3} \Rightarrow x = \tfrac{\pi}{6}, \tfrac{5\pi}{6}, \tfrac{7\pi}{6}, \tfrac{11\pi}{6}$$

39 $\sin 5x = \sin 3x \Rightarrow \sin 5x - \sin 3x = 0 \Rightarrow 2 \cos \dfrac{5x + 3x}{2} \sin \dfrac{5x - 3x}{2} = 0 \Rightarrow$

$\cos 4x \sin x = 0 \Rightarrow 4x = \frac{\pi}{2} + \pi n$ or $x = \pi n \Rightarrow x = \frac{\pi}{8} + \frac{\pi}{4}n$ or $x = 0, \pi \Rightarrow$

$$x = 0, \tfrac{\pi}{8}, \tfrac{3\pi}{8}, \tfrac{5\pi}{8}, \tfrac{7\pi}{8}, \pi, \tfrac{9\pi}{8}, \tfrac{11\pi}{8}, \tfrac{13\pi}{8}, \tfrac{15\pi}{8}$$

40 $\cos 3x = -\cos 2x \Rightarrow \cos 3x + \cos 2x = 0 \Rightarrow 2 \cos \dfrac{3x + 2x}{2} \cos \dfrac{3x - 2x}{2} = 0 \Rightarrow$

$\cos \frac{5}{2}x \cos \frac{1}{2}x = 0 \Rightarrow \frac{5}{2}x = \frac{\pi}{2} + \pi n$ or $\frac{1}{2}x = \frac{\pi}{2} + \pi n \Rightarrow x = \frac{\pi}{5} + \frac{2\pi}{5}n$ or $x = \pi + 2\pi n \Rightarrow$

$$x = \tfrac{\pi}{5}, \tfrac{3\pi}{5}, \pi, \tfrac{7\pi}{5}, \tfrac{9\pi}{5}$$

41 $\cos 75° = \cos(45° + 30°) = \cos 45° \cos 30° - \sin 45° \sin 30° = \dfrac{\sqrt{2}}{2} \cdot \dfrac{\sqrt{3}}{2} - \dfrac{\sqrt{2}}{2} \cdot \dfrac{1}{2} = \dfrac{\sqrt{6} - \sqrt{2}}{4}$

42 $\tan 285° = \tan(225° + 60°) =$

$$\dfrac{\tan 225° + \tan 60°}{1 - \tan 225° \tan 60°} = \dfrac{1 + \sqrt{3}}{1 - \sqrt{3}} \cdot \dfrac{1 + \sqrt{3}}{1 + \sqrt{3}} = \dfrac{4 + 2\sqrt{3}}{-2} = -2 - \sqrt{3}$$

43 $\sin 195° = \sin(135° + 60°)$

$$= \sin 135° \cos 60° + \cos 135° \sin 60° = \dfrac{\sqrt{2}}{2} \cdot \dfrac{1}{2} + \left(-\dfrac{\sqrt{2}}{2}\right) \cdot \dfrac{\sqrt{3}}{2} = \dfrac{\sqrt{2} - \sqrt{6}}{4}$$

44 $\csc \dfrac{\pi}{8} = \dfrac{1}{\sin\left(\frac{1}{2} \cdot \frac{\pi}{4}\right)} = \dfrac{1}{\sqrt{\dfrac{1 - \cos \frac{\pi}{4}}{2}}} = \dfrac{1}{\sqrt{\dfrac{1 - \sqrt{2}/2}{2}}} = \dfrac{1}{\sqrt{\dfrac{2 - \sqrt{2}}{4}}} = \dfrac{2}{\sqrt{2 - \sqrt{2}}}$

45 $\sin(\theta + \phi) = \sin\theta \cos\phi + \cos\theta \sin\phi = \frac{3}{5} \cdot \frac{8}{17} + \frac{4}{5} \cdot \frac{15}{17} = \frac{84}{85}$

46 $\cos(\theta + \phi) = \cos\theta \cos\phi - \sin\theta \sin\phi = \frac{4}{5} \cdot \frac{8}{17} - \frac{3}{5} \cdot \frac{15}{17} = -\frac{13}{85}$

47 $\tan(\phi + \theta) = \tan(\theta + \phi) = \dfrac{\sin(\theta + \phi)}{\cos(\theta + \phi)} = \dfrac{84/85}{-13/85} = -\dfrac{84}{13}$

48 $\tan(\theta - \phi) = \dfrac{\tan\theta - \tan\phi}{1 + \tan\theta \tan\phi} = \dfrac{\frac{3}{4} - \frac{15}{8}}{1 + \frac{3}{4} \cdot \frac{15}{8}} \cdot \dfrac{32}{32} = \dfrac{24 - 60}{32 + 45} = -\dfrac{36}{77}$

49 $\sin(\phi - \theta) = \sin\phi \cos\theta - \cos\phi \sin\theta = \frac{15}{17} \cdot \frac{4}{5} - \frac{8}{17} \cdot \frac{3}{5} = \frac{36}{85}$

50 First recognize the relationship to Exercise 49.

$$\sin(\theta - \phi) = \sin\left[-(\phi - \theta)\right] = -\sin(\phi - \theta) = -\tfrac{36}{85}$$

51 $\sin 2\phi = 2 \sin\phi \cos\phi = 2 \cdot \frac{15}{17} \cdot \frac{8}{17} = \frac{240}{289}$

52 $\cos 2\phi = \cos^2\phi - \sin^2\phi = \left(\frac{8}{17}\right)^2 - \left(\frac{15}{17}\right)^2 = -\frac{161}{289}$

53 $\tan 2\theta = \dfrac{2 \tan\theta}{1 - \tan^2\theta} = \dfrac{2 \cdot \frac{3}{4}}{1 - \left(\frac{3}{4}\right)^2} \cdot \dfrac{16}{16} = \dfrac{24}{16 - 9} = \dfrac{24}{7}$

54 $\sin \frac{1}{2}\theta = \sqrt{\dfrac{1 - \cos\theta}{2}} = \sqrt{\dfrac{1 - \frac{4}{5}}{2}} = \sqrt{\dfrac{\frac{1}{5}}{2}} = \sqrt{\dfrac{1}{10} \cdot \dfrac{10}{10}} = \dfrac{1}{10}\sqrt{10}$

55 $\tan \frac{1}{2}\theta = \dfrac{1 - \cos\theta}{\sin\theta} = \dfrac{1 - \frac{4}{5}}{\frac{3}{5}} = \dfrac{\frac{1}{5}}{\frac{3}{5}} = \dfrac{1}{3}$

56 $\cos \frac{1}{2}\phi = \sqrt{\dfrac{1 + \cos\phi}{2}} = \sqrt{\dfrac{1 + \frac{8}{17}}{2}} = \sqrt{\dfrac{\frac{25}{17}}{2}} = \sqrt{\dfrac{25}{34} \cdot \dfrac{34}{34}} = \dfrac{5}{34}\sqrt{34}$

[57] (a) $\sin 7t \sin 4t = [\text{P4}] \; \frac{1}{2}[\cos(7t-4t) - \cos(7t+4t)] = \frac{1}{2}\cos 3t - \frac{1}{2}\cos 11t$

(b) $\cos\frac{1}{4}u \cos\left(-\frac{1}{6}u\right) = [\text{P3}] \; \frac{1}{2}\left\{ \cos\left[\frac{1}{4}u + \left(-\frac{1}{6}u\right)\right] + \cos\left[\frac{1}{4}u - \left(-\frac{1}{6}u\right)\right]\right\} =$

$$\frac{1}{2}\left(\cos\frac{2}{24}u + \cos\frac{10}{24}u\right) = \frac{1}{2}\cos\frac{1}{12}u + \frac{1}{2}\cos\frac{5}{12}u$$

(c) $6\cos 5x \sin 3x = [\text{P2}] \; 6 \cdot \frac{1}{2}[\sin(5x+3x) - \sin(5x-3x)] = 3\sin 8x - 3\sin 2x$

(d) $4\sin 3\theta \cos 7\theta = [\text{P1}] \; 4 \cdot \frac{1}{2}[\sin(3\theta+7\theta) + \sin(3\theta-7\theta)] = 2\sin 10\theta - 2\sin 4\theta$

[58] (a) $\sin 8u + \sin 2u = [\text{S1}] \; 2\sin\dfrac{8u+2u}{2} \cos\dfrac{8u-2u}{2} = 2\sin 5u \cos 3u$

(b) $\cos 3\theta - \cos 8\theta = [\text{S4}] \; -2\sin\dfrac{3\theta+8\theta}{2} \sin\dfrac{3\theta-8\theta}{2} = -2\sin\frac{11}{2}\theta \sin\left(-\frac{5}{2}\theta\right) =$

$$2\sin\tfrac{11}{2}\theta \sin\tfrac{5}{2}\theta$$

(c) $\sin\frac{1}{4}t - \sin\frac{1}{5}t = [\text{S2}] \; 2\cos\dfrac{\frac{1}{4}t+\frac{1}{5}t}{2} \sin\dfrac{\frac{1}{4}t-\frac{1}{5}t}{2} = 2\cos\frac{9}{40}t \sin\frac{1}{40}t$

(d) $3\cos 2x + 3\cos 6x = [\text{S3}] \; 3 \cdot 2\cos\dfrac{2x+6x}{2} \cos\dfrac{2x-6x}{2} = 6\cos 4x \cos(-2x) =$

$$6\cos 4x \cos 2x$$

[59] $\cos^{-1}\left(\dfrac{\sqrt{3}}{2}\right) = \frac{\pi}{6}$ [60] $\arcsin\left(\dfrac{\sqrt{2}}{2}\right) = \frac{\pi}{4}$

[61] $\arctan\sqrt{3} = \frac{\pi}{3}$ [62] $\arccos\left(\tan\frac{3\pi}{4}\right) = \arccos(-1) = \pi$

[63] $\arcsin\left(\sin\frac{5\pi}{4}\right) = \arcsin\left(-\dfrac{\sqrt{2}}{2}\right) = -\frac{\pi}{4}$ [64] $\cos^{-1}\left(\cos\frac{5\pi}{4}\right) = \cos^{-1}\left(-\dfrac{\sqrt{2}}{2}\right) = \frac{3\pi}{4}$

[65] $\sin\left[\arccos\left(-\dfrac{\sqrt{3}}{2}\right)\right] = \sin\frac{5\pi}{6} = \frac{1}{2}$

[66] $\tan(\tan^{-1} 2) = 2$ since $\tan(\arctan x) = x$ for every x

[67] $\sec(\sin^{-1}\frac{3}{2})$ is not defined since $\frac{3}{2} > 1$ [68] $\cos^{-1}(\sin 0) = \cos^{-1} 0 = \frac{\pi}{2}$.

[69] Let $\alpha = \sin^{-1}\frac{15}{17}$ and $\beta = \sin^{-1}\frac{8}{17}$.

$\cos\left(\sin^{-1}\frac{15}{17} - \sin^{-1}\frac{8}{17}\right) = \cos(\alpha - \beta) = \cos\alpha \cos\beta + \sin\alpha \sin\beta = \frac{8}{17}\cdot\frac{15}{17} + \frac{15}{17}\cdot\frac{8}{17} = \frac{240}{289}$.

[70] Let $\alpha = \sin^{-1}\frac{4}{5}$. $\cos\left(2\sin^{-1}\frac{4}{5}\right) = \cos(2\alpha) = \cos^2\alpha - \sin^2\alpha = \left(\frac{3}{5}\right)^2 - \left(\frac{4}{5}\right)^2 = -\frac{7}{25}$.

[71] $y = \cos^{-1} 3x$ •   horizontally compress $y = \cos^{-1} x$ by a factor of 3

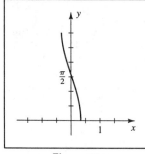

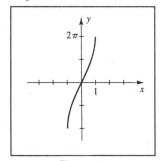

Figure 71   Figure 72

[72] $y = 4\sin^{-1} x$ •   vertically stretch $y = \sin^{-1} x$ by a factor of 4

73 $y = 1 - \sin^{-1} x = -\sin^{-1} x + 1$ •

reflect $y = \sin^{-1} x$ through the x-axis and shift it up 1 unit.

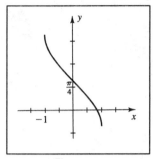

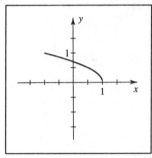

Figure 73   Figure 74

74 If $\alpha = \cos^{-1} x$, then $\cos \alpha = x$, where $0 \le \alpha \le \pi$.

Hence, $y = \sin\left(\frac{1}{2}\cos^{-1} x\right) = \sin \frac{1}{2}\alpha = \sqrt{\frac{1 - \cos \alpha}{2}} = \sqrt{\frac{1 - x}{2}}$.

Thus, we have the graph of the half-parabola $y = \sqrt{\frac{1}{2}(1 - x)}$ on the interval $[-1, 1]$.

75 $\cos(\alpha + \beta + \gamma) = \cos[(\alpha + \beta) + \gamma] = \cos(\alpha + \beta)\cos\gamma - \sin(\alpha + \beta)\sin\gamma =$

$(\cos\alpha\cos\beta - \sin\alpha\sin\beta)\cos\gamma - (\sin\alpha\cos\beta + \cos\alpha\sin\beta)\sin\gamma =$

$\cos\alpha\cos\beta\cos\gamma - \sin\alpha\sin\beta\cos\gamma - \sin\alpha\cos\beta\sin\gamma - \cos\alpha\sin\beta\sin\gamma$

76 (a) $t = -\frac{\pi}{2b} \Rightarrow F = A\left[\cos\left(-\frac{\pi}{2}\right) - a\cos\left(-\frac{3\pi}{2}\right)\right] = A(0 - a \cdot 0) = 0$

$t = \frac{\pi}{2b} \Rightarrow F = A\left(\cos\frac{\pi}{2} - a\cos\frac{3\pi}{2}\right) = A(0 - a \cdot 0) = 0$

(b) $a = \frac{1}{3} \Rightarrow \sin 3bt = \sin bt \Rightarrow \sin 3bt - \sin bt = 0 \Rightarrow$

[S2] $2\cos\frac{3bt + bt}{2}\sin\frac{3bt - bt}{2} = 0 \Rightarrow \cos 2bt \sin bt = 0 \Rightarrow$

$\cos 2bt = 0$ or $\sin bt = 0 \Rightarrow 2bt = \frac{\pi}{2} + \pi n$ or $bt = \pi n \Rightarrow$

$t = \frac{\pi}{4b} + \frac{\pi}{2b}n$ or $t = \frac{\pi}{b}n$. Since $-\frac{\pi}{2b} < t < \frac{\pi}{2b}$, $t = \pm\frac{\pi}{4b}$, 0.

(c) Using the values from part (b), $t = 0 \Rightarrow F = A\left(\cos 0 - \frac{1}{3}\cos 0\right) = A\left(1 - \frac{1}{3}\right) = \frac{2}{3}A$.

$t = \pm\frac{\pi}{4b} \Rightarrow F = A\left[\cos\left(\pm\frac{\pi}{4}\right) - \frac{1}{3}\cos\left(\pm\frac{3\pi}{4}\right)\right] = A\left(\frac{\sqrt{2}}{2} + \frac{\sqrt{2}}{6}\right) = \frac{4\sqrt{2}}{6}A = \frac{2}{3}\sqrt{2}\,A.$

The second value is $\sqrt{2}$ times the first, hence $\frac{2}{3}\sqrt{2}\,A$ is the maximum force.

77 $\cos x - \cos 2x + \cos 3x = 0 \Rightarrow (\cos x + \cos 3x) - \cos 2x \Rightarrow$

[S3] $2\cos\frac{x + 3x}{2}\cos\frac{x - 3x}{2} - \cos 2x = 0 \Rightarrow 2\cos 2x \cos x - \cos 2x = 0 \Rightarrow$

$\cos 2x(2\cos x - 1) = 0 \Rightarrow \cos 2x = 0$ or $\cos x = \frac{1}{2} \Rightarrow$

$2x = \frac{\pi}{2} + \pi n$ (or $x = \frac{\pi}{4} + \frac{\pi}{2}n$) or $x = \frac{\pi}{3} + 2\pi n$, $\frac{5\pi}{3} + 2\pi n$.

In the figure on $[-2\pi, 2\pi]$, $x = \pm\frac{\pi}{4}$, $\pm\frac{3\pi}{4}$, $\pm\frac{5\pi}{4}$, $\pm\frac{7\pi}{4}$, $\pm\frac{\pi}{3}$, $\pm\frac{5\pi}{3}$.

$\boxed{78}$ (a) Bisect θ to form two right triangles. $\tan\frac{1}{2}\theta = \dfrac{\frac{1}{2}x}{d} \Rightarrow x = 2d\tan\frac{1}{2}\theta$.

(b) Using part (a) with $x = 0.5$ ft and $\theta = 0.0005$ radian,

$$\text{we have } d = \frac{x}{2\tan\frac{1}{2}\theta} \approx 1000 \text{ ft, so } d \le 1000 \text{ ft.}$$

$\boxed{79}$ (a) Bisect θ to form two right triangles.

$$\cos\frac{1}{2}\theta = \frac{r}{d+r} \Rightarrow d+r = \frac{r}{\cos\frac{1}{2}\theta} \Rightarrow d = r\sec\frac{1}{2}\theta - r = r\left(\sec\frac{1}{2}\theta - 1\right).$$

(b) $d = 300$ and $r = 4000 \Rightarrow \cos\frac{1}{2}\theta = \frac{r}{d+r} = \frac{4000}{4300} \Rightarrow \frac{1}{2}\theta \approx 21.5° \Rightarrow \theta \approx 43°$.

$\boxed{80}$ (a) $\tan\theta = \frac{h}{w} = \frac{400}{80} = 5 \Rightarrow \theta = \tan^{-1}5 \approx 78.7°$

(b) $\tan\theta = \frac{h}{w} = \frac{55}{30} = \frac{11}{6} \Rightarrow \theta = \tan^{-1}\frac{11}{6} \approx 61.4°$

Chapter 6 Discussion Exercises

$\boxed{1}$ $\dfrac{\tan x}{1-\cot x} + \dfrac{\cot x}{1-\tan x} = \dfrac{\frac{\sin x}{\cos x}}{1 - \frac{\cos x}{\sin x}} + \dfrac{\frac{\cos x}{\sin x}}{1 - \frac{\sin x}{\cos x}} =$

$\dfrac{\sin^2 x}{\cos x\,(\sin x - \cos x)} + \dfrac{\cos^2 x}{\sin x\,(\cos x - \sin x)} = \dfrac{\sin^2 x}{\cos x\,(\sin x - \cos x)} - \dfrac{\cos^2 x}{\sin x\,(\sin x - \cos x)} =$

$\dfrac{\sin^3 x - \cos^3 x}{\cos x\,\sin x\,(\sin x - \cos x)} = \dfrac{(\sin x - \cos x)(\sin^2 x + \sin x\,\cos x + \cos^2 x)}{\cos x\,\sin x\,(\sin x - \cos x)} =$

$\dfrac{1 + \sin x\,\cos x}{\cos x\,\sin x} = \dfrac{1}{\cos x\,\sin x} + 1 = 1 + \sec x\,\csc x$

$\boxed{2}$ $\sqrt{a^2 - x^2} = \begin{cases} a\cos\theta & \text{if } 0 \le \theta \le \pi/2 \text{ or } 3\pi/2 \le \theta < 2\pi \\ -a\cos\theta & \text{if } \pi/2 < \theta < 3\pi/2 \end{cases}$

$\boxed{3}$ *Note:* Graphing on a TI-82/83 doesn't really help to solve this problem.

$3\cos 45x + 4\sin 45x = 5 \Rightarrow \{\text{ by Example 6 in Section 6.3}\}$

$5\cos\left(45x - \tan^{-1}\frac{4}{3}\right) = 5 \Rightarrow \cos\left(45x - \tan^{-1}\frac{4}{3}\right) = 1 \Rightarrow 45x - \tan^{-1}\frac{4}{3} = 2\pi n \Rightarrow$

$45x = 2\pi n + \tan^{-1}\frac{4}{3} \Rightarrow x = \dfrac{2\pi n + \tan^{-1}\frac{4}{3}}{45}.$ $n = 0, 1, \ldots, 44$ will yield x values in

$[0, 2\pi)$. *Note:* After using Example 6, you might notice that this is a function with period $2\pi/45$, and it will obtain 45 maximums on an interval of length 2π. The largest value of x is approximately 6.164 {when $n = 44$}.

$\boxed{4}$ The difference quotient for the sine function appears to be the cosine function.

$$\frac{f(x+h) - f(x)}{h} = \frac{\sin(x+h) - \sin x}{h}$$

$$= \frac{\sin x\,\cos h + \cos x\,\sin h - \sin x}{h}$$

$$= \sin x\left(\frac{\cos h - 1}{h}\right) + \cos x\left(\frac{\sin h}{h}\right)$$

5   Let $\alpha = \tan^{-1}\left(\frac{1}{239}\right)$ and $\theta = \tan^{-1}\left(\frac{1}{5}\right)$. $\frac{\pi}{4} = 4\theta - \alpha \Rightarrow \frac{\pi}{4} + \alpha = 4\theta$. Both sides are acute angles, and we will show that the tangent of each side is equal to the same value, hence proving the identity.

$$\text{LS} = \tan\left(\frac{\pi}{4} + \alpha\right) = \frac{\tan\frac{\pi}{4} + \tan\alpha}{1 - \tan\frac{\pi}{4}\tan\alpha} = \frac{1 + \frac{1}{239}}{1 - 1 \cdot \frac{1}{239}} = \frac{\frac{240}{239}}{\frac{238}{239}} = \frac{240}{238} = \frac{120}{119}.$$

$$\text{RS} = \tan 4\theta =$$

$$\frac{2\tan 2\theta}{1 - \tan^2(2\theta)} = \frac{2 \cdot \dfrac{2\tan\theta}{1 - \tan^2\theta}}{1 - \left(\dfrac{2\tan\theta}{1 - \tan^2\theta}\right)^2} = \frac{2 \cdot \dfrac{\frac{2}{5}}{1 - \frac{1}{25}}}{1 - \left(\dfrac{\frac{2}{5}}{1 - \frac{1}{25}}\right)^2} = \frac{\dfrac{\frac{4}{5}}{\frac{24}{25}}}{1 - \dfrac{\frac{4}{25}}{\frac{24 \cdot 24}{25 \cdot 25}}} = \frac{\frac{5}{6}}{\frac{119}{144}} = \frac{120}{119}.$$

Similarly, for the second relationship, we could write $\frac{\pi}{4} = \alpha + \beta + \gamma$ and show that $\tan\left(\frac{\pi}{4} - \alpha\right) = \tan(\beta + \gamma) = \frac{1}{3}$.

6   (a) The **inverse sawtooth function**, denoted by saw^{-1} or arcsaw, is defined by
$$y = \text{saw}^{-1} x \text{ iff } x = \text{saw } y \text{ for } -2 \le x \le 2 \text{ and } -1 \le y \le 1.$$

(b) $\text{arcsaw}(1.7) = 0.85$ since $\text{saw}(0.85) = 1.7$

     $\text{arcsaw}(-0.8) = -0.4$ since $\text{saw}(-0.4) = -0.8$

(c) $\text{saw}\left(\text{saw}^{-1}x\right) = \text{saw}(\text{arcsaw } x) = x$ if $-2 \le x \le 2$

     $\text{saw}^{-1}(\text{saw } y) = \text{arcsaw}(\text{saw } y) = y$ if $-1 \le y \le 1$

(d)

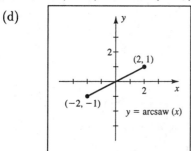

Figure 6

Chapter 7: Applications of Trigonometry

$\boxed{1}$ $\beta = 180° - \alpha - \gamma = 180° - 41° - 77° = 62°.$

$$\frac{b}{\sin \beta} = \frac{a}{\sin \alpha} \Rightarrow b = \frac{a \sin \beta}{\sin \alpha} = \frac{10.5 \sin 62°}{\sin 41°} \approx 14.1.$$

$$\frac{c}{\sin \gamma} = \frac{a}{\sin \alpha} \Rightarrow c = \frac{a \sin \gamma}{\sin \alpha} = \frac{10.5 \sin 77°}{\sin 41°} \approx 15.6.$$

$\boxed{2}$ $\alpha = 180° - \beta - \gamma = 180° - 20° - 31° = 129°.$

$$\frac{a}{\sin \alpha} = \frac{b}{\sin \beta} \Rightarrow a = \frac{b \sin \alpha}{\sin \beta} = \frac{210 \sin 129°}{\sin 20°} \approx 477, \text{ or 480 to 2 significant figures.}$$

$$\frac{c}{\sin \gamma} = \frac{b}{\sin \beta} \Rightarrow c = \frac{b \sin \gamma}{\sin \beta} = \frac{210 \sin 31°}{\sin 20°} \approx 316, \text{ or 320.}$$

$\boxed{3}$ $\gamma = 180° - \alpha - \beta = 180° - 27°40' - 52°10' = 100°10'.$

$$\frac{b}{\sin \beta} = \frac{a}{\sin \alpha} \Rightarrow b = \frac{a \sin \beta}{\sin \alpha} = \frac{32.4 \sin 52°10'}{\sin 27°40'} \approx 55.1.$$

$$\frac{c}{\sin \gamma} = \frac{a}{\sin \alpha} \Rightarrow c = \frac{a \sin \gamma}{\sin \alpha} = \frac{32.4 \sin 100°10'}{\sin 27°40'} \approx 68.7.$$

$\boxed{4}$ $\alpha = 180° - \beta - \gamma = 180° - 50°50' - 70°30' = 58°40'.$

$$\frac{a}{\sin \alpha} = \frac{c}{\sin \gamma} \Rightarrow a = \frac{c \sin \alpha}{\sin \gamma} = \frac{537 \sin 58°40'}{\sin 70°30'} \approx 487.$$

$$\frac{b}{\sin \beta} = \frac{c}{\sin \gamma} \Rightarrow b = \frac{c \sin \beta}{\sin \gamma} = \frac{537 \sin 50°50'}{\sin 70°30'} \approx 442.$$

$\boxed{5}$ $\beta = 180° - \alpha - \gamma = 180° - 42°10' - 61°20' = 76°30'.$

$$\frac{a}{\sin \alpha} = \frac{b}{\sin \beta} \Rightarrow a = \frac{b \sin \alpha}{\sin \beta} = \frac{19.7 \sin 42°10'}{\sin 76°30'} \approx 13.6.$$

$$\frac{c}{\sin \gamma} = \frac{b}{\sin \beta} \Rightarrow c = \frac{b \sin \gamma}{\sin \beta} = \frac{19.7 \sin 61°20'}{\sin 76°30'} \approx 17.8.$$

$\boxed{6}$ $\beta = 180° - \alpha - \gamma = 180° - 103.45° - 27.19° = 49.36°.$

$$\frac{a}{\sin \alpha} = \frac{b}{\sin \beta} \Rightarrow a = \frac{b \sin \alpha}{\sin \beta} = \frac{38.84 \sin 103.45°}{\sin 49.36°} \approx 49.78.$$

$$\frac{c}{\sin \gamma} = \frac{b}{\sin \beta} \Rightarrow c = \frac{b \sin \gamma}{\sin \beta} = \frac{38.84 \sin 27.19°}{\sin 49.36°} \approx 23.39.$$

$\boxed{7}$ $\dfrac{\sin \beta}{b} = \dfrac{\sin \gamma}{c} \Rightarrow \beta = \sin^{-1}\left(\dfrac{b \sin \gamma}{c}\right) = \sin^{-1}\left(\dfrac{12 \sin 81°}{11}\right) \approx \sin^{-1}(1.0775).$ Since 1.0775 is

not in the domain of the inverse sine function, which is $[-1, 1]$, *no triangle exists.*

$\boxed{8}$ $\dfrac{\sin \gamma}{c} = \dfrac{\sin \alpha}{a} \Rightarrow \gamma = \sin^{-1}\left(\dfrac{c \sin \alpha}{a}\right) = \sin^{-1}\left(\dfrac{574.3 \sin 32.32°}{263.6}\right) \approx \sin^{-1}(1.1648).$

Since 1.1648 is not in the domain of the inverse sine function, which is $[-1, 1]$,

no triangle exists.

9 $\frac{\sin\alpha}{a}=\frac{\sin\gamma}{c} \Rightarrow \alpha=\sin^{-1}\!\left(\frac{a\sin\gamma}{c}\right)=\sin^{-1}\!\left(\frac{140\sin 53°20'}{115}\right)\approx\sin^{-1}(0.9765)\approx$

$77°30'$ or $102°30'$ {rounded to the nearest 10 minutes}.

There are two triangles possible since in either case $\alpha+\gamma<180°$.

$\beta=(180°-\gamma)-\alpha\approx(180°-53°20')-(77°30'\text{ or }102°30')=49°10'\text{ or }24°10'$.

$$\frac{b}{\sin\beta}=\frac{c}{\sin\gamma} \Rightarrow b=\frac{c\sin\beta}{\sin\gamma}\approx\frac{115\sin(49°10'\text{ or }24°10')}{\sin 53°20'}\approx 108\text{ or }58.7.$$

10 $\frac{\sin\gamma}{c}=\frac{\sin\alpha}{a} \Rightarrow \gamma=\sin^{-1}\!\left(\frac{c\sin\alpha}{a}\right)=\sin^{-1}\!\left(\frac{52.8\sin 27°30'}{28.1}\right)\approx\sin^{-1}(0.8676)\approx$

$60°10'$ or $119°50'$ {rounded to the nearest 10 minutes}.

There are two triangles possible since in either case $\alpha+\gamma<180°$.

$\beta=(180°-\alpha)-\gamma\approx(180°-27°30')-(60°10'\text{ or }119°50')=92°20'\text{ or }32°40'$.

$$\frac{b}{\sin\beta}=\frac{a}{\sin\alpha} \Rightarrow b=\frac{a\sin\beta}{\sin\alpha}\approx\frac{28.1\sin(92°20'\text{ or }32°40')}{\sin 27°30'}\approx 60.8\text{ or }32.8.$$

11 $\frac{\sin\alpha}{a}=\frac{\sin\gamma}{c} \Rightarrow \alpha=\sin^{-1}\!\left(\frac{a\sin\gamma}{c}\right)=\sin^{-1}\!\left(\frac{131.08\sin 47.74°}{97.84}\right)\approx\sin^{-1}(0.9915)\approx$

$82.54°$ or $97.46°$. There are two triangles possible since in either case $\alpha+\gamma<180°$.

$\beta=(180°-\gamma)-\alpha\approx(180°-47.74°)-(82.54°\text{ or }97.46°)=49.72°\text{ or }34.80°$.

$$\frac{b}{\sin\beta}=\frac{c}{\sin\gamma} \Rightarrow b=\frac{c\sin\beta}{\sin\gamma}\approx\frac{97.84\sin(49.72°\text{ or }34.80°)}{\sin 47.74°}\approx 100.85\text{ or }75.45.$$

12 $\frac{\sin\beta}{b}=\frac{\sin\alpha}{a} \Rightarrow \beta=\sin^{-1}\!\left(\frac{b\sin\alpha}{a}\right)=\sin^{-1}\!\left(\frac{6.12\sin 42.17°}{5.01}\right)\approx\sin^{-1}(0.8201)\approx$

$55.09°$ or $124.91°$. There are two triangles possible since in either case $\alpha+\beta<180°$.

$\gamma=(180°-\alpha)-\beta\approx(180°-42.17°)-(55.09°\text{ or }124.91°)=82.74°\text{ or }12.92°$.

$$\frac{c}{\sin\gamma}=\frac{a}{\sin\alpha} \Rightarrow c=\frac{a\sin\gamma}{\sin\alpha}\approx\frac{5.01\sin(82.74°\text{ or }12.92°)}{\sin 42.17°}\approx 7.40\text{ or }1.67.$$

13 $\frac{\sin\beta}{b}=\frac{\sin\alpha}{a} \Rightarrow \beta=\sin^{-1}\!\left(\frac{b\sin\alpha}{a}\right)=\sin^{-1}\!\left(\frac{18.9\sin 65°10'}{21.3}\right)\approx\sin^{-1}(0.8053)\approx$

$53°40'$ or $126°20'$ {rounded to the nearest 10 minutes}. Reject $126°20'$ because then

$\alpha+\beta\geq 180°$. $\gamma=180°-\alpha-\beta\approx 180°-65°10'-53°40'=61°10'$.

$$\frac{c}{\sin\gamma}=\frac{a}{\sin\alpha} \Rightarrow c=\frac{a\sin\gamma}{\sin\alpha}\approx\frac{21.3\sin 61°10'}{\sin 65°10'}\approx 20.6.$$

14 $\frac{\sin\gamma}{c}=\frac{\sin\beta}{b} \Rightarrow \gamma=\sin^{-1}\!\left(\frac{c\sin\beta}{b}\right)=\sin^{-1}\!\left(\frac{195\sin 113°10'}{248}\right)\approx\sin^{-1}(0.7229)\approx$

$46°20'$ or $133°40'$ {rounded to the nearest 10 minutes}. Reject $133°40'$ because then

$\beta+\gamma\geq 180°$. $\alpha=180°-\beta-\gamma\approx 180°-113°10'-46°20'=20°30'$.

$$\frac{a}{\sin\alpha}=\frac{b}{\sin\beta} \Rightarrow a=\frac{b\sin\alpha}{\sin\beta}\approx\frac{248\sin 20°30'}{\sin 113°10'}\approx 94.5.$$

15 $\dfrac{\sin\gamma}{c}=\dfrac{\sin\beta}{b}\Rightarrow\gamma=\sin^{-1}\!\left(\dfrac{c\sin\beta}{b}\right)=\sin^{-1}\!\left(\dfrac{0.178\sin 121.624°}{0.283}\right)\approx\sin^{-1}(0.5356)\approx$

32.383° or 147.617°. Reject 147.617° because then $\beta+\gamma\ge 180°$.

$\alpha=180°-\beta-\gamma\approx 180°-121.624°-32.383°=25.993°.$

$$\dfrac{a}{\sin\alpha}=\dfrac{b}{\sin\beta}\Rightarrow a=\dfrac{b\sin\alpha}{\sin\beta}\approx\dfrac{0.283\sin 25.993°}{\sin 121.624°}\approx 0.146.$$

16 $\dfrac{\sin\alpha}{a}=\dfrac{\sin\gamma}{c}\Rightarrow\alpha=\sin^{-1}\!\left(\dfrac{a\sin\gamma}{c}\right)=\sin^{-1}\!\left(\dfrac{17.31\sin 73.01°}{20.24}\right)\approx\sin^{-1}(0.8179)\approx$

54.88° or 125.12°. Reject 125.12° because then $\alpha+\gamma\ge 180°$.

$\beta=180°-\gamma-\alpha\approx 180°-73.01°-54.88°=52.11°.$

$$\dfrac{b}{\sin\beta}=\dfrac{c}{\sin\gamma}\Rightarrow b=\dfrac{c\sin\beta}{\sin\gamma}\approx\dfrac{20.24\sin 52.11°}{\sin 73.01°}\approx 16.70.$$

17 $\angle ABC=180°-54°10'-63°20'=62°30'.\quad\dfrac{\overline{AB}}{\sin 54°10'}=\dfrac{240}{\sin 62°30'}\Rightarrow\overline{AB}\approx 219.36$ yd

18 $\dfrac{\sin\angle ABC}{375}=\dfrac{\sin 49°30'}{530}\Rightarrow\angle ABC\approx 32°30'.$

$\angle ACB\approx 180°-49°30'-32°30'=98°.$

$\dfrac{\overline{AB}}{\sin 98°}=\dfrac{530}{\sin 49°30'}\Rightarrow\overline{AB}\approx 690$ yards.

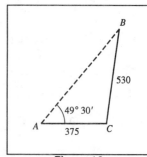

Figure 18

19 (a) $\angle ABP=180°-65°=115°.\quad\angle APB=180°-21°-115°=44°.$

$$\dfrac{\overline{AP}}{\sin 115°}=\dfrac{1.2}{\sin 44°}\Rightarrow\overline{AP}\approx 1.57,\text{ or }1.6\text{ mi.}$$

(b) $\sin 21°=\dfrac{\text{height of }P}{\overline{AP}}\Rightarrow\text{height of }P=\dfrac{1.2\sin 115°\sin 21°}{\sin 44°}\ \{\text{from part (a)}\}\approx 0.56,$

or 0.6 mi.

20 The angle between the road and the dashed line to the sun is $57°-15°=42°.$

The angle between the road and the pole is $90°+15°=105°.$

Hence, the angle between the pole and the dashed line is $180°-42°-105°=33°.$

Let l denote the length of the pole. $\dfrac{l}{\sin 42°}=\dfrac{75}{\sin 33°}\Rightarrow l=\dfrac{75\sin 42°}{\sin 33°}\approx 92.14$ ft.

21 Let C denote the base of the balloon and P its projection on the ground.

$\angle ACB=180°-24°10'-47°40'=108°10'.\quad\dfrac{\overline{AC}}{\sin 47°40'}=\dfrac{8.4}{\sin 108°10'}\Rightarrow\overline{AC}\approx 6.5$ mi.

$$\sin 24°10'=\dfrac{\overline{PC}}{\overline{AC}}\Rightarrow\overline{PC}=\dfrac{8.4\sin 47°40'\sin 24°10'}{\sin 108°10'}\approx 2.7\text{ mi.}$$

$\boxed{22}$ The angle between the panel and the roof is $45° - 25° = 20°$.

The angle between the brace and the roof is $90° + 25° = 115°$.

$$\frac{d}{\sin 20°} = \frac{10}{\sin 115°} \Rightarrow d = \frac{10 \sin 20°}{\sin 115°} \approx 3.77 \text{ ft.}$$

$\boxed{23}$ $\angle APQ = 57° - 22° = 35°$. $\angle AQP = 180° - (63° - 22°) = 139°$.

$$\angle PAQ = 180° - 139° - 35° = 6°. \quad \frac{\overline{AP}}{\sin 139°} = \frac{100}{\sin 6°} \Rightarrow \overline{AP} = \frac{100 \sin 139°}{\sin 6°} \approx 628 \text{ m.}$$

$\boxed{24}$ Let $\gamma = \angle BCA$. $\angle BAC = 63° - 38° = 25°$. $\frac{\sin \gamma}{239} = \frac{\sin 25°}{374} \Rightarrow \gamma \approx 15°40'$.

$$\angle ABC \approx 180° - 15°40' - 25° = 139°20'. \quad \frac{\overline{AC}}{\sin 139°20'} = \frac{374}{\sin 25°} \Rightarrow \overline{AC} \approx 577 \text{ yards.}$$

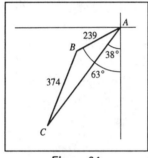

Figure 24

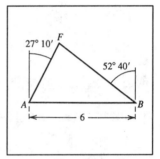

Figure 25

$\boxed{25}$ $\angle FAB = 90° - 27°10' = 62°50'$. $\angle FBA = 90° - 52°40' = 37°20'$.

$$\angle AFB = 180° - 62°50' - 37°20' = 79°50'. \quad \frac{\overline{AF}}{\sin 37°20'} = \frac{6}{\sin 79°50'} \Rightarrow \overline{AF} \approx 3.70 \text{ mi.}$$

$$\frac{\overline{BF}}{\sin 62°50'} = \frac{6}{\sin 79°50'} \Rightarrow \overline{BF} \approx 5.42 \text{ mi.}$$

$\boxed{26}$ (a) Label the base of the tower A, the top of the tower B, and the observation point

C. Let $\alpha = \angle BAC$ and $\beta = \angle ABC$. $\frac{\sin \beta}{150} = \frac{\sin 53.3°}{179} \Rightarrow \beta \approx 42.2°$.

$$\alpha \approx 180° - 42.2° - 53.3° = 84.5°. \quad \theta = 90° - \alpha \approx 5.5°.$$

(b) $\sin \theta = \frac{d}{179} \Rightarrow d \approx 17.2 \text{ ft.}$

$\boxed{27}$ Let A denote the base of the hill, B the base of the cathedral, and C the top of the

spire. The angle at the base of the hill is $180° - 48° = 132°$. The angle at the top

of the spire is $180° - 132° - 41° = 7°$. $\frac{\overline{AC}}{\sin 41°} = \frac{200}{\sin 7°} \Rightarrow \overline{AC} = \frac{200 \sin 41°}{\sin 7°} \approx 1077 \text{ ft.}$

$\angle BAC = 48° - 32° = 16°$. $\angle ACB = 90° - 48° = 42°$. $\angle ABC = 180° - 42° - 16° = 122°$.

$$\frac{\overline{BC}}{\sin 16°} = \frac{\overline{AC}}{\sin 122°} \Rightarrow \overline{BC} = \frac{200 \sin 41° \sin 16°}{\sin 7° \sin 122°} \approx 350 \text{ ft.}$$

28 (a) Let A denote the shorter mountain peak, B the higher mountain peak, and C the helicopter. $\angle BAC = 90° - 18° = 72°$. $\angle ACB = 90° - 43° = 47°$.

$\angle ABC = 180° - 72° - 47° = 61°$. $\dfrac{\overline{AB}}{\sin 47°} = \dfrac{1000}{\sin 61°} \Rightarrow \overline{AB} = \dfrac{1000\sin 47°}{\sin 61°} \approx 836$ ft.

(b) Let h denote the height that B is above the 5210 foot level.

$\sin 18° = \dfrac{h}{\overline{AB}} \Rightarrow h \approx 258$ ft, so the height of B is $5210 + 258 = 5468$ ft.

29 (a) In the triangle that forms the base, the third angle is $180° - 103° - 52° = 25°$.

Let l denote the length of the dashed line. $\dfrac{l}{\sin 103°} = \dfrac{12.0}{\sin 25°} \Rightarrow l \approx 27.7$ units.

Now $\tan 34° = \dfrac{h}{l} \Rightarrow h \approx 18.7$ units.

(b) Draw a line from the $103°$ angle that is perpendicular to l and call it d.

$\sin 52° = \dfrac{d}{12} \Rightarrow d \approx 9.5$ units. The area of the triangular base is $B = \frac{1}{2}ld$.

The volume V is $\frac{1}{3}(\frac{1}{2}ld)h = 288\sin 52° \sin^2 103° \tan 34° \csc^2 25° \approx 814$ cubic units.

30 (a) $\angle CBA = 180° - 153° = 27°$. $\dfrac{\sin \angle BAC}{35.9} = \dfrac{\sin 27°}{16.7} \Rightarrow \angle BAC \approx 77.4°$.

$\phi = 180° - \angle BAC \approx 102.6°$.

(b) Let h denote the perpendicular distance from $\overline{BA}$ to C.

$\sin \angle BAC = \dfrac{h}{16.7} \Rightarrow h \approx 16.30$ ft. The wing span CC' is $2h + 4.80 \approx 37.4$ ft.

(c) $\angle BCA \approx 180° - 27° - 77.4° = 75.6°$. $\dfrac{\overline{BA}}{\sin 75.6°} = \dfrac{16.7}{\sin 27°} \Rightarrow \overline{BA} \approx 35.6$ ft.

The area of $\triangle ABC$ is then $\frac{1}{2}(\overline{BA})h \approx 290.3$ ft^2.

31 Draw a line through P perpendicular to the x-axis. Locate points A and B on this line so that $\angle PAQ = \angle PBR = 90°$. $\overline{AP} = 5127.5 - 3452.8 = 1674.7$,

$\overline{AQ} = 3145.8 - 1487.7 = 1658.1$, and $\tan \angle APQ = \frac{1658.1}{1674.7} \Rightarrow \angle APQ \approx 44°43'$.

Thus, $\angle BPR \approx 180° - 55°50' - 44°43' = 79°27'$.

By the distance formula, $\overline{PQ} \approx \sqrt{(1674.7)^2 + (1658.1)^2} \approx 2356.7$.

Now $\dfrac{\overline{PR}}{\sin 65°22'} = \dfrac{\overline{PQ}}{\sin(180° - 55°50' - 65°22')} \Rightarrow \overline{PR} = \dfrac{2356.7\sin 65°22'}{\sin 58°48'} \approx 2504.5$.

$\sin \angle BPR = \dfrac{\overline{BR}}{\overline{PR}} \Rightarrow \overline{BR} \approx (2504.5)(\sin 79°27') \approx 2462.2$. $\cos \angle BPR = \dfrac{\overline{BP}}{\overline{PR}} \Rightarrow$

$\overline{BP} \approx (2504.5)(\cos 79°27') \approx 458.6$. Using the coordinates of P, we see that

$$R(x, y) \approx (1487.7 + 2462.2, 3452.8 - 458.6) = (3949.9, 2994.2).$$

Note: These formulas will be used to solve problems that involve the law of cosines.

(1) $a^2 = b^2 + c^2 - 2bc \cos \alpha \Rightarrow a = \sqrt{b^2 + c^2 - 2bc \cos \alpha}$

(Similar formulas are used for b and c.)

(2) $a^2 = b^2 + c^2 - 2bc \cos \alpha \Rightarrow 2bc \cos \alpha = b^2 + c^2 - a^2 \Rightarrow$

$$\cos \alpha = \left(\frac{b^2 + c^2 - a^2}{2bc} \right) \Rightarrow \alpha = \cos^{-1}\left(\frac{b^2 + c^2 - a^2}{2bc} \right)$$

(Similar formulas are used for β and γ.)

$\boxed{1}$ $a = \sqrt{b^2 + c^2 - 2bc \cos \alpha} = \sqrt{20^2 + 30^2 - 2(20)(30) \cos 60°} = \sqrt{700} \approx 26.$

$\beta = \cos^{-1}\left(\frac{a^2 + c^2 - b^2}{2ac} \right) = \cos^{-1}\left(\frac{700 + 30^2 - 20^2}{2(\sqrt{700})(30)} \right) \approx \cos^{-1}(0.7559) \approx 41°.$

$\gamma = 180° - \alpha - \beta \approx 180° - 60° - 41° = 79°.$

$\boxed{2}$ $c = \sqrt{a^2 + b^2 - 2ab \cos \gamma} = \sqrt{325 - 150\sqrt{2}} \approx 10.6.$

$\alpha = \cos^{-1}\left(\frac{b^2 + c^2 - a^2}{2bc} \right) \approx \cos^{-1}(-0.0571) \approx 93°20'.$

$\beta = 180° - \alpha - \gamma \approx 180° - 93°20' - 45° = 41°40'.$

$\boxed{3}$ $b = \sqrt{a^2 + c^2 - 2ac \cos \beta} = \sqrt{23{,}400 + 4500\sqrt{3}} \approx 177$, or 180.

$\alpha = \cos^{-1}\left(\frac{b^2 + c^2 - a^2}{2bc} \right) \approx \cos^{-1}(0.9054) \approx 25°10'$, or 25°.

$\gamma = 180° - \alpha - \beta \approx 180° - 25°10' - 150° = 4°50'$, or 5°.

$\boxed{4}$ $b = \sqrt{a^2 + c^2 - 2ac \cos \beta} \approx \sqrt{7086.74} \approx 84.2.$

$\alpha = \cos^{-1}\left(\frac{b^2 + c^2 - a^2}{2bc} \right) \approx \cos^{-1}(-0.1214) \approx 97°00'.$

$\gamma = 180° - \alpha - \beta \approx 180° - 97° - 73°50' = 9°10'.$

$\boxed{5}$ $c = \sqrt{a^2 + b^2 - 2ab \cos \gamma} \approx \sqrt{7.58} \approx 2.75.$

$\alpha = \cos^{-1}\left(\frac{b^2 + c^2 - a^2}{2bc} \right) \approx \cos^{-1}(0.9324) \approx 21°10'.$

$\beta = 180° - \alpha - \gamma \approx 180° - 21°10' - 115°10' = 43°40'.$

$\boxed{6}$ $a = \sqrt{b^2 + c^2 - 2bc \cos \alpha} \approx \sqrt{4367} \approx 66.1.$

$\beta = \cos^{-1}\left(\frac{a^2 + c^2 - b^2}{2ac} \right) \approx \cos^{-1}(-0.9051) \approx 154°50'.$

$\gamma = 180° - \alpha - \beta \approx 180° - 23°40' - 154°50' = 1°30'.$

$\boxed{7}$ $\alpha = \cos^{-1}\left(\frac{b^2 + c^2 - a^2}{2bc} \right) = \cos^{-1}(0.875) \approx 29°.$

$\beta = \cos^{-1}\left(\frac{a^2 + c^2 - b^2}{2ac} \right) = \cos^{-1}(0.6875) \approx 47°.$

$\gamma = 180° - \alpha - \beta \approx 180° - 29° - 47° = 104°.$

$\boxed{8}$ $\alpha = \cos^{-1}\left(\dfrac{b^2 + c^2 - a^2}{2bc}\right) \approx \cos^{-1}(0.7472) \approx 41°40'$, or $42°$.

$\quad \beta = \cos^{-1}\left(\dfrac{a^2 + c^2 - b^2}{2ac}\right) \approx \cos^{-1}(0.0792) \approx 85°30'$, or $85°$.

$\qquad\qquad\qquad \gamma = 180° - \alpha - \beta \approx 180° - 41°40' - 85°30' = 52°50'$, or $53°$.

$\boxed{9}$ $\alpha = \cos^{-1}\left(\dfrac{b^2 + c^2 - a^2}{2bc}\right) \approx \cos^{-1}(0.9766) \approx 12°30'$.

$\quad \beta = \cos^{-1}\left(\dfrac{a^2 + c^2 - b^2}{2ac}\right) = \cos^{-1}(-0.725) \approx 136°30'$.

$\qquad\qquad\qquad \gamma = 180° - \alpha - \beta \approx 180° - 12°30' - 136°30' = 31°00'$.

$\boxed{10}$ $\alpha = \cos^{-1}\left(\dfrac{b^2 + c^2 - a^2}{2bc}\right) = \cos^{-1}(0.25) \approx 75°30'$. $\;\; \beta = \alpha$ since $b = a$.

$\qquad\qquad\qquad \gamma = 180° - \alpha - \beta \approx 180° - 75°30' - 75°30' = 29°00'$.

$\boxed{11}$ Third side $= \sqrt{175^2 + 150^2 - 2(175)(150)\cos 73°40'} \approx 196$ feet.

$\boxed{12}$ $\overline{AB} = \sqrt{420^2 + 540^2 - 2(420)(540)\cos 63°10'} \approx 513$ yards.

$\boxed{13}$ 20 minutes $= \frac{1}{3}$ hour $\Rightarrow$ the cars have traveled $60(\frac{1}{3}) = 20$ miles and $45(\frac{1}{3}) = 15$ miles,

$\quad$ respectively. The distance d apart is $d = \sqrt{20^2 + 15^2 - 2(20)(15)\cos 84°} \approx 24$ miles.

$\boxed{14}$ The smallest angle α between the sides is the angle opposite the shortest side (180 ft).

$$\alpha = \cos^{-1}\left(\frac{420^2 + 350^2 - 180^2}{2(420)(350)}\right) \approx \cos^{-1}(0.9065) \approx 25°.$$

$\boxed{15}$ The first ship travels $(24)(2) = 48$ miles in two hours. The second ship travels

$\quad (18)(1\frac{1}{2}) = 27$ miles in $1\frac{1}{2}$ hours. The angle between the paths is $20° + 35° = 55°$.

$$\overline{AB} = \sqrt{27^2 + 48^2 - 2(27)(48)\cos 55°} \approx 39 \text{ miles.}$$

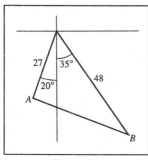

Figure 15

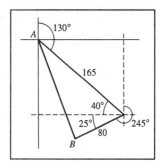

Figure 16

$\boxed{16}$ The angle between the two paths is $40° + 25° = 65°$.

$$\overline{AB} = \sqrt{165^2 + 80^2 - 2(165)(80)\cos 65°} \approx 150 \text{ miles.}$$

17 $\angle ABC = 40° + 20° = 60°$.

$$\overline{AB} = \left(\frac{1 \text{ mile}}{8 \text{ min}} \cdot 20 \text{ min}\right) = 2.5 \text{ miles and } \overline{BC} = \left(\frac{1 \text{ mile}}{8 \text{ min}} \cdot 16 \text{ min}\right) = 2 \text{ miles.}$$

$$\overline{AC} = \sqrt{2.5^2 + 2^2 - 2(2)(2.5)\cos 60°} = \sqrt{5.25} \approx 2.3 \text{ miles.}$$

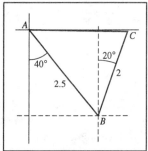

Figure 17

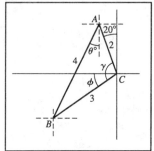

Figure 19

18 $PQ = \sqrt{300^2 + 438^2 - 2(300)(438)\cos 37°40'} \approx 271.7$, or 272 feet

19 $\gamma = \cos^{-1}\left(\dfrac{2^2 + 3^2 - 4^2}{2 \cdot 2 \cdot 3}\right) = \cos^{-1}(-0.25) \approx 104°29'$.　$\phi \approx 104°29' - 70° = 34°29'$.

The direction that the third side was traversed is approximately

$$\text{N}(90° - 34°29')\text{E} = \text{N}55°31'\text{ E.}$$

20 The length of the diagonal in the base is $\sqrt{6^2 + 8^2} = \sqrt{100} = 10$ inches.

The length of the diagonal of the $6'' \times 4''$ side is $\sqrt{6^2 + 4^2} = \sqrt{52}$ inches.

The length of the diagonal of the $8'' \times 4''$ side is $\sqrt{8^2 + 4^2} = \sqrt{80}$ inches, and it is the

side opposite angle θ.　$\theta = \cos^{-1}\left(\dfrac{100 + 52 - 80}{2(10)\sqrt{52}}\right) \approx \cos^{-1}(0.4992) \approx 60.05°$, or 60°.

21 Let H denote home plate, M the mound, F first base, S second base, and T third

base.　$\overline{HS} = \sqrt{90^2 + 90^2} = 90\sqrt{2} \approx 127.3$ ft.　$\overline{MS} = 90\sqrt{2} - 60.5 \approx 66.8$ ft.

$\angle MHF = 45°$ so $\overline{MF} = \sqrt{60.5^2 + 90^2 - 2(60.5)(90)\cos 45°} \approx 63.7$ ft.

$$\overline{MT} = \overline{MF} \text{ by the symmetry of the field.}$$

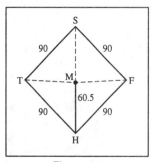

Figure 21

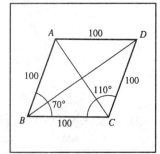

Figure 22

22 $\overline{AC} = \sqrt{100^2 + 100^2 - 2(100)(100)\cos 70°} \approx 114.7$.

$$\overline{BD} = \sqrt{100^2 + 100^2 - 2(100)(100)\cos 110°} \approx 163.8.$$

23 $\angle RTP = 21°$ and $\angle RSP = 37°$. $\sin \angle RSP = \dfrac{10,000}{\overline{SP}} \Rightarrow \overline{SP} = 10,000 \csc 37° \approx$

16,616 ft. $\sin \angle RTP = \dfrac{10,000}{\overline{TP}} \Rightarrow \overline{TP} = 10,000 \csc 21° \approx 27,904$ ft.

$$\overline{ST} = \sqrt{\overline{SP}^2 + \overline{TP}^2 - 2(\overline{SP})(\overline{TP}) \cos 110°} \approx 37,039 \text{ ft} \approx 7 \text{ miles.}$$

24 (a) The angle between the ship's path and its intended
path is 14°. Let d denote the distance from P to the
port. $d = \sqrt{80^2 + 150^2 - 2(80)(150) \cos 14°} \approx 74.9$ mi.

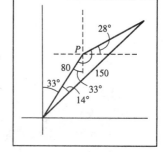

(b) $\angle P = \cos^{-1}\left(\dfrac{80^2 + d^2 - 150^2}{2(80)d}\right) \approx \cos^{-1}(-0.8749)$
$\approx 151°.$

From *Figure 24*, $\angle P = 33° + 90° + 28°$ { $= 151°$ }.

The angle that should then be taken is $N(90° - 28°)E$,
or N62°E.

Figure 24

25 Let $d = \overline{ES}$. $d^2 = R^2 + R^2 - 2RR \cos \theta \Rightarrow d^2 = 2R^2(1 - \cos \theta) \Rightarrow$

$d^2 = 4R^2\left(\dfrac{1 - \cos \theta}{2}\right) \Rightarrow d = 2R\sqrt{\dfrac{1 - \cos \theta}{2}} \Rightarrow d = 2R \sin\dfrac{\theta}{2}.$

Since $d = vt$, $t = \dfrac{d}{v} = \dfrac{2R}{v} \sin\dfrac{\theta}{2}.$

26 (a) In $\triangle CBD$,
$$\angle CBD = \cos^{-1}\left(\dfrac{\overline{BC}^2 + \overline{BD}^2 - \overline{CD}^2}{2(\overline{BC})(\overline{BD})}\right) = \cos^{-1}\left(\dfrac{184^2 + 102^2 - 236^2}{2(184)(102)}\right) \approx 107.74°.$$

In $\triangle BCE$,
$$\angle BCE = \cos^{-1}\left(\dfrac{\overline{BC}^2 + \overline{CE}^2 - \overline{BE}^2}{2(\overline{BC})(\overline{CE})}\right) = \cos^{-1}\left(\dfrac{184^2 + 80^2 - 218^2}{2(184)(80)}\right) \approx 104.29°.$$

In $\triangle ABC$, $\angle BCA = 180° - \angle BCE \approx 75.71°$, $\angle CBA = 180° - \angle CBD \approx 72.26°$,
and $\angle BAC = 180° - \angle BCA - \angle CBA \approx 32.03°$. We now use the law of sines to

find $\overline{AB}$ and $\overline{AC}$. $\dfrac{\overline{AB}}{\sin \angle BCA} = \dfrac{\overline{BC}}{\sin \angle BAC} \Rightarrow \overline{AB} = \dfrac{184 \sin 75.71°}{\sin 32.03°} \approx 336.2$ ft.

$\dfrac{\overline{AC}}{\sin \angle CBA} = \dfrac{\overline{BC}}{\sin \angle BAC} \Rightarrow \overline{AC} = \dfrac{184 \sin 72.26°}{\sin 32.03°} \approx 330.4$ ft.

(b) Let h denote the perpendicular distance from A to $\overline{BC}$.
$$\sin \angle BCA = \dfrac{h}{\overline{AC}} \Rightarrow h \approx (330.4)(\sin 75.71°) \approx 320.2 \text{ ft.}$$

27 (a) $\angle BCP = \frac{1}{2}(\angle BCD) = \frac{1}{2}(72°) = 36°$. $\triangle BPC$ is isosceles so
$\angle BPC = \angle PBC$ and $2\angle BPC = 180° - 36° \Rightarrow \underline{\angle BPC = 72°}.$
$\underline{\angle APB} = 180° - \angle BPC = 180° - 72° = \underline{108°}.$
$\underline{\angle ABP} = 180° - \angle APB - \angle BAP = 180° - 108° - 36° = \underline{36°}.$

(b) $\overline{BP} = \sqrt{\overline{BC}^2 + \overline{PC}^2 - 2(\overline{BC})(\overline{PC}) \cos 36°} = \sqrt{1^2 + 1^2 - 2(1)(1) \cos 36°} \approx 0.62.$

(c) $\text{Area}_{\text{kite}} = 2(\text{Area of } \triangle BPC) = 2 \cdot \frac{1}{2}(\overline{CB})(\overline{CP}) \sin \angle BCP = \sin 36° \approx 0.59.$

$\text{Area}_{\text{dart}} = 2(\text{Area of } \triangle ABP) = 2 \cdot \frac{1}{2}(\overline{AB})(\overline{BP}) \sin \angle ABP = \overline{BP} \sin 36° \approx 0.36.$

$\{\overline{BP} \text{ was found in part (b)}\}$

[28] Note that $\triangle TPQ$ is similar to $\triangle THB$. $\frac{TQ}{TB} = \frac{PQ}{HB} \Rightarrow \frac{TQ}{42} = \frac{24}{32} \Rightarrow \overline{TQ} = 31.5$ in.

$\overline{TP} = \sqrt{\overline{TQ}^2 + \overline{PQ}^2 - 2(\overline{TQ})(\overline{PQ}) \cos \angle TQP} =$

$$\sqrt{31.5^2 + 24^2 - 2(31.5)(24) \cos(90° - 26°)} \approx 30.1 \text{ in.}$$

Note: Exer. 29–36: $\mathcal{A}$ (the area) is measured in square units.

[29] Since α is the angle between sides b and c, we may apply the area of a triangle

formula listed in this section. $\mathcal{A} = \frac{1}{2}bc \sin \alpha = \frac{1}{2}(20)(30) \sin 60° = 300(\sqrt{3}/2) \approx 260.$

[30] $\mathcal{A} = \frac{1}{2}ab \sin \gamma = \frac{1}{2}(15.0)(10.0) \sin 45° = 75(\sqrt{2}/2) \approx 53.0.$

[31] $\gamma = 180° - \alpha - \beta = 180° - 40.3° - 62.9° = 76.8°.$

$$\frac{a}{\sin \alpha} = \frac{b}{\sin \beta} \Rightarrow a = \frac{b \sin \alpha}{\sin \beta} = \frac{5.63 \sin 40.3°}{\sin 62.9°}. \quad \mathcal{A} = \frac{1}{2}ab \sin \gamma \approx 11.21.$$

[32] $\beta = 180° - \alpha - \gamma = 180° - 35.7° - 105.2° = 39.1°.$

$$\frac{a}{\sin \alpha} = \frac{b}{\sin \beta} \Rightarrow a = \frac{b \sin \alpha}{\sin \beta} = \frac{17.2 \sin 35.7°}{\sin 39.1°}. \quad \mathcal{A} = \frac{1}{2}ab \sin \gamma \approx 132.1.$$

[33] $\frac{\sin \beta}{b} = \frac{\sin \alpha}{a} \Rightarrow \sin \beta = \frac{b \sin \alpha}{a} = \frac{3.4 \sin 80.1°}{8.0} \approx 0.4187 \Rightarrow \beta \approx 24.8°$ or $155.2°.$

Reject $155.2°$ because then $\alpha + \beta = 235.3° \geq 180°.$ $\gamma \approx 180° - 80.1° - 24.8° = 75.1°.$

$$\mathcal{A} = \frac{1}{2}ab \sin \gamma = \frac{1}{2}(8.0)(3.4) \sin 75.1° \approx 13.1.$$

[34] $\frac{\sin \alpha}{a} = \frac{\sin \gamma}{c} \Rightarrow \sin \alpha = \frac{a \sin \gamma}{c} = \frac{14.6 \sin 32.1°}{15.8} \approx 0.4910 \Rightarrow \alpha \approx 29.4°$ or $150.6°.$

Reject $150.6°$ because then $\alpha + \gamma = 182.7° \geq 180°.$ $\beta \approx 180° - 29.4° - 32.1° = 118.5°.$

$$\mathcal{A} = \frac{1}{2}ac \sin \beta = \frac{1}{2}(14.6)(15.8) \sin 118.5° \approx 101.4.$$

[35] $s = \frac{1}{2}(a + b + c) = \frac{1}{2}(25.0 + 80.0 + 60.0) = 82.5.$

$$\mathcal{A} = \sqrt{s(s-a)(s-b)(s-c)} = \sqrt{(82.5)(57.5)(2.5)(22.5)} \approx 516.56, \text{ or } 517.0.$$

[36] $s = \frac{1}{2}(a + b + c) = \frac{1}{2}(20.0 + 20.0 + 10.0) = 25.$

$$\mathcal{A} = \sqrt{s(s-a)(s-b)(s-c)} = \sqrt{(25)(5)(5)(15)} \approx 96.8.$$

[37] $s = \frac{1}{2}(a + b + c) = \frac{1}{2}(115 + 140 + 200) = 227.5.$ $\mathcal{A} = \sqrt{s(s-a)(s-b)(s-c)} =$

$$\sqrt{(227.5)(112.5)(87.5)(27.5)} \approx 7847.6 \text{ yd}^2, \text{ or } \mathcal{A}/4840 \approx 1.62 \text{ acres.}$$

[38] $s = \frac{1}{2}(a + b + c) = \frac{1}{2}(320 + 350 + 500) = 585.$ $\mathcal{A} = \sqrt{s(s-a)(s-b)(s-c)} =$

$$\sqrt{(585)(265)(235)(85)} \approx 55,647.3 \text{ yd}^2, \text{ or } \mathcal{A}/4840 \approx 11.5 \text{ acres.}$$

[39] The area of the parallelogram is twice the area of the triangle formed by the two

sides and the included angle. $\mathcal{A} = 2(\frac{1}{2})(12.0)(16.0) \sin 40° \approx 123.4 \text{ ft}^2.$

[40] As in Exercise 39, $\mathcal{A} = 2(\frac{1}{2})(40.3)(52.6) \sin 100° \approx 2087.6 \text{ ft}^2.$

7.3 Exercises

1 $|3-4i| = \sqrt{3^2 + (-4)^2} = \sqrt{25} = 5$ **2** $|5+8i| = \sqrt{5^2 + 8^2} = \sqrt{89}$

3 $|-6-7i| = \sqrt{(-6)^2 + (-7)^2} = \sqrt{85}$ **4** $|1-i| = \sqrt{1^2 + (-1)^2} = \sqrt{2}$

5 $|8i| = |0+8i| = \sqrt{0^2 + 8^2} = \sqrt{64} = 8$

6 $|i^7| = |i^4 \cdot i^2 \cdot i| = |(1)(-1)(i)| = |-i| = |0-i| = \sqrt{0^2 + (-1)^2} = \sqrt{1} = 1$

   Note: $|i^m| = 1$ for any integer m.

7 $|i^{500}| = |(i^4)^{125}| = |(1)^{125}| = |1| = |1+0i| = \sqrt{1^2 + 0^2} = \sqrt{1} = 1$

8 $|-15i| = |0-15i| = \sqrt{0^2 + (-15)^2} = \sqrt{225} = 15$

9 $|0| = |0+0i| = \sqrt{0^2 + 0^2} = \sqrt{0} = 0$

10 $|-15| = |-15+0i| = \sqrt{(-15)^2 + 0^2} = \sqrt{225} = 15$

11 $4+2i$ **12** $-5+3i$ **13** $3-5i$ **14** $-2-6i$ **15** $-(3-6i) = -3+6i$

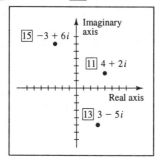

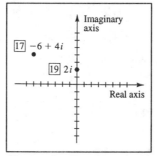

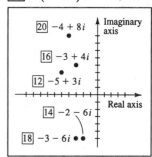

Figures for Exercises 11–20

16 $(1+2i)^2 = 1 + 2(1)(2i) + (2i)^2 = 1 + 4i - 4 = -3 + 4i$

17 $2i(2+3i) = 4i + 6i^2 = 4i - 6 = -6 + 4i$

18 $(-3i)(2-i) = -6i + 3i^2 = -6i - 3 = -3 - 6i$

19 $(1+i)^2 = 1 + 2(1)(i) + i^2 = 1 + 2i - 1 = 2i$

20 $4(-1+2i) = -4 + 8i$

21 $z = 1 - i \Rightarrow r = \sqrt{1 + (-1)^2} = \sqrt{2}$. $\tan\theta = \frac{-1}{1} = -1$ and θ in QIV $\Rightarrow \theta = \frac{7\pi}{4}$.

   Thus, $z = 1 - i = \sqrt{2}\left(\cos\frac{7\pi}{4} + i\sin\frac{7\pi}{4}\right)$, or simply $\sqrt{2}\,\mathrm{cis}\,\frac{7\pi}{4}$.

22 $z = \sqrt{3} + i \Rightarrow r = \sqrt{(\sqrt{3})^2 + 1^2} = \sqrt{4} = 2$. $\tan\theta = \frac{1}{\sqrt{3}}$ and θ in QI $\Rightarrow \theta = \frac{\pi}{6}$.

   $z = 2\,\mathrm{cis}\,\frac{\pi}{6}$.

23 $z = -4\sqrt{3} + 4i \Rightarrow r = \sqrt{(-4\sqrt{3})^2 + 4^2} = \sqrt{64} = 8$.

   $\tan\theta = \frac{4}{-4\sqrt{3}} = -\frac{1}{\sqrt{3}}$ and θ in QII $\Rightarrow \theta = \frac{5\pi}{6}$. $z = 8\,\mathrm{cis}\,\frac{5\pi}{6}$.

24 $z = -2 - 2i \Rightarrow r = \sqrt{(-2)^2 + (-2)^2} = \sqrt{8} = 2\sqrt{2}.$

$\tan\theta = \frac{-2}{-2} = 1$ and θ in QIII $\Rightarrow \theta = \frac{5\pi}{4}.$ $z = 2\sqrt{2}\operatorname{cis}\frac{5\pi}{4}.$

25 $z = 2\sqrt{3} + 2i \Rightarrow r = \sqrt{(2\sqrt{3})^2 + 2^2} = \sqrt{16} = 4.$

$\tan\theta = \frac{2}{2\sqrt{3}} = \frac{1}{\sqrt{3}}$ and θ in QI $\Rightarrow \theta = \frac{\pi}{6}.$ $z = 4\operatorname{cis}\frac{\pi}{6}.$

26 $z = 3 - 3\sqrt{3}i \Rightarrow r = \sqrt{3^2 + (-3\sqrt{3})^2} = \sqrt{36} = 6.$

$\tan\theta = \frac{-3\sqrt{3}}{3} = -\sqrt{3}$ and θ in QIV $\Rightarrow \theta = \frac{5\pi}{3}.$ $z = 6\operatorname{cis}\frac{5\pi}{3}.$

27 $z = -4 - 4i \Rightarrow r = \sqrt{(-4)^2 + (-4)^2} = \sqrt{32} = 4\sqrt{2}.$

$\tan\theta = \frac{-4}{-4} = 1$ and θ in QIII $\Rightarrow \theta = \frac{5\pi}{4}.$ $z = 4\sqrt{2}\operatorname{cis}\frac{5\pi}{4}.$

28 $z = -10 + 10i \Rightarrow r = \sqrt{(-10)^2 + 10^2} = \sqrt{200} = 10\sqrt{2}.$

$\tan\theta = \frac{10}{-10} = -1$ and θ in QII $\Rightarrow \theta = \frac{3\pi}{4}.$ $z = 10\sqrt{2}\operatorname{cis}\frac{3\pi}{4}.$

29 $z = -20i \Rightarrow r = 20.$ θ on the negative y-axis $\Rightarrow \theta = \frac{3\pi}{2}.$ $z = 20\operatorname{cis}\frac{3\pi}{2}.$

30 $z = -6i \Rightarrow r = 6.$ θ on the negative y-axis $\Rightarrow \theta = \frac{3\pi}{2}.$ $z = 6\operatorname{cis}\frac{3\pi}{2}.$

31 $z = 12 \Rightarrow r = 12.$ θ on the positive x-axis $\Rightarrow \theta = 0.$ $z = 12\operatorname{cis}0.$

32 $z = 15 \Rightarrow r = 15.$ θ on the positive x-axis $\Rightarrow \theta = 0.$ $z = 15\operatorname{cis}0.$

33 $z = -7 \Rightarrow r = 7.$ θ on the negative x-axis $\Rightarrow \theta = \pi.$ $z = 7\operatorname{cis}\pi.$

34 $z = -5 \Rightarrow r = 5.$ θ on the negative x-axis $\Rightarrow \theta = \pi.$ $z = 5\operatorname{cis}\pi.$

35 $z = 6i \Rightarrow r = 6.$ θ on the positive y-axis $\Rightarrow \theta = \frac{\pi}{2}.$ $z = 6\operatorname{cis}\frac{\pi}{2}.$

36 $z = 4i \Rightarrow r = 4.$ θ on the positive y-axis $\Rightarrow \theta = \frac{\pi}{2}.$ $z = 4\operatorname{cis}\frac{\pi}{2}.$

37 $z = -5 - 5\sqrt{3}i \Rightarrow r = \sqrt{(-5)^2 + (-5\sqrt{3})^2} = \sqrt{100} = 10.$

$\tan\theta = \frac{-5\sqrt{3}}{-5} = \sqrt{3}$ and θ in QIII $\Rightarrow \theta = \frac{4\pi}{3}.$ $z = 10\operatorname{cis}\frac{4\pi}{3}.$

38 $z = \sqrt{3} - i \Rightarrow r = \sqrt{(\sqrt{3})^2 + (-1)^2} = \sqrt{4} = 2.$ $\tan\theta = \frac{-1}{\sqrt{3}}$ and θ in QIV $\Rightarrow \theta = \frac{11\pi}{6}.$

$z = 2\operatorname{cis}\frac{11\pi}{6}.$

39 $z = 2 + i \Rightarrow r = \sqrt{2^2 + 1^2} = \sqrt{5}.$ $\tan\theta = \frac{1}{2}$ and θ in QI $\Rightarrow \theta = \tan^{-1}\frac{1}{2}.$

$z = \sqrt{5}\operatorname{cis}\left(\tan^{-1}\frac{1}{2}\right).$

40 $z = 3 + 2i \Rightarrow r = \sqrt{3^2 + 2^2} = \sqrt{13}.$ $\tan\theta = \frac{2}{3}$ and θ in QI $\Rightarrow \theta = \tan^{-1}\frac{2}{3}.$

$z = \sqrt{13}\operatorname{cis}\left(\tan^{-1}\frac{2}{3}\right).$

41 $z = -3 + i \Rightarrow r = \sqrt{(-3)^2 + 1^2} = \sqrt{10}.$

$\tan\theta = \frac{1}{-3}$ and θ in QII $\Rightarrow \theta = \tan^{-1}\left(-\frac{1}{3}\right) + \pi.$ We must add π to $\tan^{-1}\left(-\frac{1}{3}\right)$

because $-\frac{\pi}{2} < \tan^{-1}\left(-\frac{1}{3}\right) < 0$ and we want θ to be in the interval $\left(\frac{\pi}{2}, \pi\right).$

$z = \sqrt{10}\operatorname{cis}\left[\tan^{-1}\left(-\frac{1}{3}\right) + \pi\right].$

42 $z = -4 + 2i \Rightarrow r = \sqrt{(-4)^2 + 2^2} = \sqrt{20} = 2\sqrt{5}.$ $\tan\theta = \frac{2}{-4} = -\frac{1}{2}$ and θ in QII $\Rightarrow$

$\theta = \tan^{-1}\left(-\frac{1}{2}\right) + \pi.$ $z = 2\sqrt{5}\operatorname{cis}\left[\tan^{-1}\left(-\frac{1}{2}\right) + \pi\right].$

43 $z = -5 - 3i \Rightarrow r = \sqrt{(-5)^2 + (-3)^2} = \sqrt{34}.$ $\tan\theta = \frac{-3}{-5} = \frac{3}{5}$ and

θ in QIII $\Rightarrow \theta = \tan^{-1}\frac{3}{5} + \pi.$ We must add π to $\tan^{-1}\frac{3}{5}$ because $0 < \tan^{-1}\frac{3}{5} < \frac{\pi}{2}$ and

we want θ to be in the interval $(\pi, \frac{3\pi}{2}).$ $z = \sqrt{34}\,\mathrm{cis}\left(\tan^{-1}\frac{3}{5} + \pi\right).$

44 $z = -2 - 7i \Rightarrow r = \sqrt{(-2)^2 + (-7)^2} = \sqrt{53}.$

$\tan\theta = \frac{-7}{-2} = \frac{7}{2}$ and θ in QIII $\Rightarrow \theta = \tan^{-1}\frac{7}{2} + \pi.$ $z = \sqrt{53}\,\mathrm{cis}\left(\tan^{-1}\frac{7}{2} + \pi\right).$

45 $z = 4 - 3i \Rightarrow r = \sqrt{4^2 + (-3)^2} = \sqrt{25} = 5.$

$\tan\theta = \frac{-3}{4}$ and θ in QIV $\Rightarrow \theta = \tan^{-1}\left(-\frac{3}{4}\right) + 2\pi.$ We must add 2π to $\tan^{-1}\left(-\frac{3}{4}\right)$

because $-\frac{\pi}{2} < \tan^{-1}\left(-\frac{3}{4}\right) < 0$ and we want θ to be in the interval $(\frac{3\pi}{2}, 2\pi).$

$$z = 5\,\mathrm{cis}\left[\tan^{-1}\left(-\tfrac{3}{4}\right) + 2\pi\right].$$

46 $z = 1 - 3i \Rightarrow r = \sqrt{1^2 + (-3)^2} = \sqrt{10}.$

$\tan\theta = \frac{-3}{1} = -3$ and θ in QIV $\Rightarrow \theta = \tan^{-1}(-3) + 2\pi.$ $z = \sqrt{10}\,\mathrm{cis}\left[\tan^{-1}(-3) + 2\pi\right].$

47 $4\left(\cos\frac{\pi}{4} + i\sin\frac{\pi}{4}\right) = 4\left(\frac{\sqrt{2}}{2} + \frac{\sqrt{2}}{2}i\right) = 2\sqrt{2} + 2\sqrt{2}i$

48 $8\left(\cos\frac{7\pi}{4} + i\sin\frac{7\pi}{4}\right) = 8\left(\frac{\sqrt{2}}{2} - \frac{\sqrt{2}}{2}i\right) = 4\sqrt{2} - 4\sqrt{2}i$

49 $6\left(\cos\frac{2\pi}{3} + i\sin\frac{2\pi}{3}\right) = 6\left(-\frac{1}{2} + \frac{\sqrt{3}}{2}i\right) = -3 + 3\sqrt{3}i$

50 $12\left(\cos\frac{4\pi}{3} + i\sin\frac{4\pi}{3}\right) = 12\left(-\frac{1}{2} - \frac{\sqrt{3}}{2}i\right) = -6 - 6\sqrt{3}i$

51 $5\left(\cos\pi + i\sin\pi\right) = 5\left(-1 + 0i\right) = -5$

52 $3\left(\cos\frac{3\pi}{2} + i\sin\frac{3\pi}{2}\right) = 3\left(0 - 1i\right) = -3i$

53 $\sqrt{34}\,\mathrm{cis}\left(\tan^{-1}\frac{3}{5}\right) = \sqrt{34}\left[\cos\left(\tan^{-1}\frac{3}{5}\right) + i\sin\left(\tan^{-1}\frac{3}{5}\right)\right] = \sqrt{34}\left(\frac{5}{\sqrt{34}} + \frac{3}{\sqrt{34}}i\right) = 5 + 3i$

54 $\sqrt{53}\,\mathrm{cis}\left[\tan^{-1}\left(-\frac{2}{7}\right)\right] = \sqrt{53}\left\{\cos\left[\tan^{-1}\left(-\frac{2}{7}\right)\right] + i\sin\left[\tan^{-1}\left(-\frac{2}{7}\right)\right]\right\} =$

$$\sqrt{53}\left(\frac{7}{\sqrt{53}} - \frac{2}{\sqrt{53}}i\right) = 7 - 2i$$

55 $\sqrt{5}\,\mathrm{cis}\left[\tan^{-1}\left(-\frac{1}{2}\right)\right] = \sqrt{5}\left\{\cos\left[\tan^{-1}\left(-\frac{1}{2}\right)\right] + i\sin\left[\tan^{-1}\left(-\frac{1}{2}\right)\right]\right\} =$

$$\sqrt{5}\left(\frac{2}{\sqrt{5}} - \frac{1}{\sqrt{5}}i\right) = 2 - i$$

56 $\sqrt{10}\,\mathrm{cis}\left(\tan^{-1}3\right) = \sqrt{10}\left[\cos\left(\tan^{-1}3\right) + i\sin\left(\tan^{-1}3\right)\right] =$

$$\sqrt{10}\left(\frac{1}{\sqrt{10}} + \frac{3}{\sqrt{10}}i\right) = 1 + 3i$$

57 $z_1 = \sqrt{2}\,\mathrm{cis}\frac{3\pi}{4}$ and $z_2 = \sqrt{2}\,\mathrm{cis}\frac{\pi}{4}.$ $z_1 z_2 = \sqrt{2}\cdot\sqrt{2}\,\mathrm{cis}\left(\frac{3\pi}{4} + \frac{\pi}{4}\right) = 2\,\mathrm{cis}\,\pi = -2 + 0i.$

$$\frac{z_1}{z_2} = \frac{\sqrt{2}}{\sqrt{2}}\,\mathrm{cis}\left(\frac{3\pi}{4} - \frac{\pi}{4}\right) = 1\,\mathrm{cis}\frac{\pi}{2} = 0 + i$$

58 $z_1 = 2 \operatorname{cis} \frac{11\pi}{6}$ and $z_2 = 2 \operatorname{cis} \frac{7\pi}{6}$. $z_1 z_2 = 2 \cdot 2 \operatorname{cis} \left(\frac{11\pi}{6} + \frac{7\pi}{6} \right) = 4 \operatorname{cis} 3\pi = -4 + 0i$.

$$\frac{z_1}{z_2} = \frac{2}{2} \operatorname{cis} \left(\frac{11\pi}{6} - \frac{7\pi}{6} \right) = 1 \operatorname{cis} \frac{2\pi}{3} = -\frac{1}{2} + \frac{\sqrt{3}}{2} i.$$

59 $z_1 = 4 \operatorname{cis} \frac{4\pi}{3}$ and $z_2 = 5 \operatorname{cis} \frac{\pi}{2}$. $z_1 z_2 = 4 \cdot 5 \operatorname{cis} \left(\frac{4\pi}{3} + \frac{\pi}{2} \right) = 20 \operatorname{cis} \frac{11\pi}{6} = 10\sqrt{3} - 10i$.

$$\frac{z_1}{z_2} = \frac{4}{5} \operatorname{cis} \left(\frac{4\pi}{3} - \frac{\pi}{2} \right) = \frac{4}{5} \operatorname{cis} \frac{5\pi}{6} = -\frac{2}{5}\sqrt{3} + \frac{2}{5} i.$$

60 $z_1 = 5\sqrt{2} \operatorname{cis} \frac{3\pi}{4}$ and $z_2 = 3 \operatorname{cis} \frac{3\pi}{2}$. $z_1 z_2 = 5\sqrt{2} \cdot 3 \operatorname{cis} \left(\frac{3\pi}{4} + \frac{3\pi}{2} \right) = 15\sqrt{2} \operatorname{cis} \frac{9\pi}{4} =$

$$15 + 15i. \quad \frac{z_1}{z_2} = \frac{5\sqrt{2}}{3} \operatorname{cis} \left(\frac{3\pi}{4} - \frac{3\pi}{2} \right) = \frac{5\sqrt{2}}{3} \operatorname{cis} \left(-\frac{3\pi}{4} \right) = -\frac{5}{3} - \frac{5}{3} i.$$

61 $z_1 = 10 \operatorname{cis} \pi$ and $z_2 = 4 \operatorname{cis} \pi$. $z_1 z_2 = 10 \cdot 4 \operatorname{cis} (\pi + \pi) = 40 \operatorname{cis} 2\pi = 40 + 0i$.

$$\frac{z_1}{z_2} = \frac{10}{4} \operatorname{cis} (\pi - \pi) = \frac{5}{2} \operatorname{cis} 0 = \frac{5}{2} + 0i.$$

62 $z_1 = 2 \operatorname{cis} \frac{\pi}{2}$ and $z_2 = 3 \operatorname{cis} \frac{3\pi}{2}$. $z_1 z_2 = 2 \cdot 3 \operatorname{cis} \left(\frac{\pi}{2} + \frac{3\pi}{2} \right) = 6 \operatorname{cis} 2\pi = 6 + 0i$.

$$\frac{z_1}{z_2} = \frac{2}{3} \operatorname{cis} \left(\frac{\pi}{2} - \frac{3\pi}{2} \right) = \frac{2}{3} \operatorname{cis} (-\pi) = -\frac{2}{3} + 0i.$$

63 $z_1 = 4 \operatorname{cis} 0$ and $z_2 = \sqrt{5} \operatorname{cis} \left[\tan^{-1} \left(-\frac{1}{2} \right) \right]$. Let $\theta = \tan^{-1} \left(-\frac{1}{2} \right)$.

$$z_1 z_2 = 4 \cdot \sqrt{5} \operatorname{cis} (0 + \theta) = 4\sqrt{5} (\cos \theta + i \sin \theta) = 4\sqrt{5} \left(\frac{2}{\sqrt{5}} + \frac{-1}{\sqrt{5}} i \right) = 8 - 4i.$$

$$\frac{z_1}{z_2} = \frac{4}{\sqrt{5}} \operatorname{cis} (0 - \theta) = \frac{4}{\sqrt{5}} [\cos (-\theta) + i \sin (-\theta)] = \frac{4}{\sqrt{5}} \left(\frac{2}{\sqrt{5}} + \frac{1}{\sqrt{5}} i \right) = \frac{8}{5} + \frac{4}{5} i.$$

64 $z_1 = 3 \operatorname{cis} \pi$ and $z_2 = \sqrt{29} \operatorname{cis} \left(\tan^{-1} \frac{2}{5} \right)$. Let $\theta = \tan^{-1} \frac{2}{5}$. $z_1 z_2 = 3 \cdot \sqrt{29} \operatorname{cis} (\pi + \theta) =$

$$3\sqrt{29} [\cos (\pi + \theta) + i \sin (\pi + \theta)] = 3\sqrt{29} \left(\frac{-5}{\sqrt{29}} + \frac{-2}{\sqrt{29}} i \right) = -15 - 6i.$$

We simplify the above using the addition formulas for the sine and cosine as follows:

$$\cos (\pi + \theta) = \cos \pi \cos \theta - \sin \pi \sin \theta = -\cos \theta = \frac{-5}{\sqrt{29}}$$

and $\qquad \sin (\pi + \theta) = \sin \pi \cos \theta + \cos \pi \sin \theta = -\sin \theta = \frac{-2}{\sqrt{29}}$

$$\frac{z_1}{z_2} = \frac{3}{\sqrt{29}} \operatorname{cis} (\pi - \theta) = \frac{3}{\sqrt{29}} \left(\frac{-5}{\sqrt{29}} + \frac{2}{\sqrt{29}} i \right)$$

$$\{ \text{since } \cos (\pi - \theta) = -\cos \theta \text{ and } \sin (\pi - \theta) = \sin \theta \} = -\frac{15}{29} + \frac{6}{29} i.$$

65 Let $z_1 = r_1 \operatorname{cis} \theta_1$ and $z_2 = r_2 \operatorname{cis} \theta_2$.

$$\frac{z_1}{z_2} = \frac{r_1 \operatorname{cis} \theta_1}{r_2 \operatorname{cis} \theta_2} = \frac{r_1 (\cos \theta_1 + i \sin \theta_1)(\cos \theta_2 - i \sin \theta_2)}{r_2 (\cos \theta_2 + i \sin \theta_2)(\cos \theta_2 - i \sin \theta_2)}$$

$$\{ \text{multiplying by the conjugate of the denominator} \}$$

$$= \frac{r_1 [(\cos \theta_1 \cos \theta_2 + \sin \theta_1 \sin \theta_2) + i (\sin \theta_1 \cos \theta_2 - \sin \theta_2 \cos \theta_1)]}{r_2 [(\cos^2 \theta_2 + \sin^2 \theta_2) + i (\sin \theta_2 \cos \theta_2 - \cos \theta_2 \sin \theta_2)]}$$

$$= \frac{r_1 [\cos (\theta_1 - \theta_2) + i \sin (\theta_1 - \theta_2)]}{r_2 (1 + 0i)} = \frac{r_1}{r_2} \operatorname{cis} (\theta_1 - \theta_2).$$

66 (a) Let $z_1 = r_1 \operatorname{cis}\theta_1$, $z_2 = r_2 \operatorname{cis}\theta_2$, and $z_3 = r_3 \operatorname{cis}\theta_3$.

Then $z_1 z_2 z_3 = (z_1 z_2) z_3 = \left[r_1 r_2 \operatorname{cis}(\theta_1 + \theta_2) \right](r_3 \operatorname{cis}\theta_3) =$
$$\left[(r_1 r_2) r_3 \right] \operatorname{cis}\left[(\theta_1 + \theta_2) + \theta_3 \right] = (r_1 r_2 r_3) \operatorname{cis}(\theta_1 + \theta_2 + \theta_3).$$

(b) The generalization is $z_1 z_2 \cdots z_n = (r_1 r_2 \cdots r_n) \operatorname{cis}(\theta_1 + \theta_2 + \cdots + \theta_n)$.

67 The unknown quantity is V: $I = V/Z \Rightarrow$
$$V = IZ = (10 \operatorname{cis}35°)(3 \operatorname{cis}20°) = (10 \times 3) \operatorname{cis}(35° + 20°) = 30 \operatorname{cis}55° \approx 17.21 + 24.57i.$$

68 The unknown quantity is V: $I = V/Z \Rightarrow V = IZ =$
$$(12 \operatorname{cis}5°)(100 \operatorname{cis}90°) = (12 \times 100) \operatorname{cis}(5° + 90°) = 1200 \operatorname{cis}95° \approx -104.59 + 1195.43i$$

69 The unknown quantity is Z:
$$I = \frac{V}{Z} \Rightarrow Z = \frac{V}{I} = \frac{115 \operatorname{cis}45°}{8 \operatorname{cis}5°} = (115 \div 8) \operatorname{cis}(45° - 5°) = 14.375 \operatorname{cis}40° \approx 11.01 + 9.24i$$

70 The unknown quantity is I:
$$I = \frac{V}{Z} = \frac{163 \operatorname{cis}17°}{78 \operatorname{cis}61°} = (163 \div 78) \operatorname{cis}(17° - 61°) = \frac{163}{78} \operatorname{cis}(-44°) \approx 1.50 - 1.45i$$

71 $Z = 14 - 13i \Rightarrow |Z| = \sqrt{14^2 + (-13)^2} = \sqrt{365} \approx 19.1$ ohms

72 $I = \dfrac{V}{Z} \Rightarrow Z = \dfrac{V}{I} = \dfrac{220 \operatorname{cis}34°}{5 \operatorname{cis}90°} = 44 \operatorname{cis}(-56°) \approx 24.60 - 36.48i.$

The resistance is 24.60 ohms and the reactance is 36.48 ohms.

73 $I = \dfrac{V}{Z} \Rightarrow V = IZ = (4 \operatorname{cis}90°)[18 \operatorname{cis}(-78°)] = 72 \operatorname{cis}12° \approx 70.43 + 14.97i$

74 $I = \dfrac{V}{Z} = \dfrac{163 \operatorname{cis}43°}{100 \operatorname{cis}17°} = 1.63 \operatorname{cis}26° \approx 1.47 + 0.71i$

7.4 Exercises

1 $(3 + 3i)^5 = (3\sqrt{2} \operatorname{cis}\frac{\pi}{4})^5 = (3\sqrt{2})^5 \operatorname{cis}\frac{5\pi}{4} = 972\sqrt{2}\left(-\frac{\sqrt{2}}{2} - \frac{\sqrt{2}}{2}i \right) = -972 - 972i$

2 $(1 + i)^{12} = (\sqrt{2} \operatorname{cis}\frac{\pi}{4})^{12} = (\sqrt{2})^{12} \operatorname{cis}3\pi = 64 \operatorname{cis}\pi = 64(-1 + 0i) = -64$

3 $(1 - i)^{10} = (\sqrt{2} \operatorname{cis}\frac{7\pi}{4})^{10} = (\sqrt{2})^{10} \operatorname{cis}\frac{35\pi}{2} = 32 \operatorname{cis}\frac{3\pi}{2} = 32(0 - i) = -32i$

4 $(-1 + i)^8 = (\sqrt{2} \operatorname{cis}\frac{3\pi}{4})^8 = (\sqrt{2})^8 \operatorname{cis}6\pi = 16 \operatorname{cis}0 = 16(1 + 0i) = 16$

5 $(1 - \sqrt{3}\,i)^3 = (2 \operatorname{cis}\frac{5\pi}{3})^3 = 2^3 \operatorname{cis}5\pi = 8 \operatorname{cis}\pi = 8(-1 + 0i) = -8$

6 $(1 - \sqrt{3}\,i)^5 = (2 \operatorname{cis}\frac{5\pi}{3})^5 = 2^5 \operatorname{cis}\frac{25\pi}{3} = 32 \operatorname{cis}\frac{\pi}{3} = 32\left(\frac{1}{2} + \frac{\sqrt{3}}{2}i \right) = 16 + 16\sqrt{3}\,i$

7 $\left(-\frac{\sqrt{2}}{2} + \frac{\sqrt{2}}{2}i \right)^{15} = (1 \operatorname{cis}\frac{3\pi}{4})^{15} = 1^{15} \operatorname{cis}\frac{45\pi}{4} = \operatorname{cis}\frac{5\pi}{4} = -\frac{\sqrt{2}}{2} - \frac{\sqrt{2}}{2}i$

8 $\left(\frac{\sqrt{2}}{2} + \frac{\sqrt{2}}{2}i \right)^{25} = (1 \operatorname{cis}\frac{\pi}{4})^{25} = 1^{25} \operatorname{cis}\frac{25\pi}{4} = \operatorname{cis}\frac{\pi}{4} = \frac{\sqrt{2}}{2} + \frac{\sqrt{2}}{2}i$

9 $\left(-\dfrac{\sqrt{3}}{2}-\dfrac{1}{2}i\right)^{20} = (1\operatorname{cis}\dfrac{7\pi}{6})^{20} = 1^{20}\operatorname{cis}\dfrac{70\pi}{3} = \operatorname{cis}\dfrac{4\pi}{3} = -\dfrac{1}{2}-\dfrac{\sqrt{3}}{2}i$

10 $\left(-\dfrac{\sqrt{3}}{2}-\dfrac{1}{2}i\right)^{50} = (1\operatorname{cis}\dfrac{7\pi}{6})^{50} = 1^{50}\operatorname{cis}\dfrac{175\pi}{3} = \operatorname{cis}\dfrac{\pi}{3} = \dfrac{1}{2}+\dfrac{\sqrt{3}}{2}i$

11 $(\sqrt{3}+i)^{7} = (2\operatorname{cis}\dfrac{\pi}{6})^{7} = 2^{7}\operatorname{cis}\dfrac{7\pi}{6} = 128\left(-\dfrac{\sqrt{3}}{2}-\dfrac{1}{2}i\right) = -64\sqrt{3}-64i$

12 $(-2-2i)^{10} = (2\sqrt{2}\operatorname{cis}\dfrac{5\pi}{4})^{10} = (2\sqrt{2})^{10}\operatorname{cis}\dfrac{25\pi}{2} = 32{,}768\operatorname{cis}\dfrac{\pi}{2} = 32{,}768(0+i) = 32{,}768i$

13 $1+\sqrt{3}i = 2\operatorname{cis}60°.$ $w_k = \sqrt{2}\operatorname{cis}\left(\dfrac{60°+360°k}{2}\right)$ for $k = 0, 1.$

$$w_0 = \sqrt{2}\operatorname{cis}30° = \sqrt{2}\left(\dfrac{\sqrt{3}}{2}+\dfrac{1}{2}i\right) = \dfrac{\sqrt{6}}{2}+\dfrac{\sqrt{2}}{2}i.$$

$$w_1 = \sqrt{2}\operatorname{cis}210° = \sqrt{2}\left(-\dfrac{\sqrt{3}}{2}-\dfrac{1}{2}i\right) = -\dfrac{\sqrt{6}}{2}-\dfrac{\sqrt{2}}{2}i.$$

14 $-9i = 9\operatorname{cis}270°.$ $w_k = \sqrt{9}\operatorname{cis}\left(\dfrac{270°+360°k}{2}\right)$ for $k = 0, 1.$

$$w_0 = 3\operatorname{cis}135° = 3\left(-\dfrac{\sqrt{2}}{2}+\dfrac{\sqrt{2}}{2}i\right) = -\dfrac{3\sqrt{2}}{2}+\dfrac{3\sqrt{2}}{2}i.$$

$$w_1 = 3\operatorname{cis}315° = 3\left(\dfrac{\sqrt{2}}{2}-\dfrac{\sqrt{2}}{2}i\right) = \dfrac{3\sqrt{2}}{2}-\dfrac{3\sqrt{2}}{2}i.$$

15 $-1-\sqrt{3}i = 2\operatorname{cis}240°.$ $w_k = \sqrt[4]{2}\operatorname{cis}\left(\dfrac{240°+360°k}{4}\right)$ for $k = 0, 1, 2, 3.$

$$w_0 = \sqrt[4]{2}\operatorname{cis}60° = \sqrt[4]{2}\left(\dfrac{1}{2}+\dfrac{\sqrt{3}}{2}i\right) = \dfrac{\sqrt[4]{2}}{2}+\dfrac{\sqrt[4]{18}}{2}i.$$

$$\{\text{since } \sqrt[4]{2}\cdot\sqrt{3} = \sqrt[4]{2}\cdot\sqrt[4]{9} = \sqrt[4]{18}\}$$

$$w_1 = \sqrt[4]{2}\operatorname{cis}150° = \sqrt[4]{2}\left(-\dfrac{\sqrt{3}}{2}+\dfrac{1}{2}i\right) = -\dfrac{\sqrt[4]{18}}{2}+\dfrac{\sqrt[4]{2}}{2}i.$$

$$w_2 = \sqrt[4]{2}\operatorname{cis}240° = \sqrt[4]{2}\left(-\dfrac{1}{2}-\dfrac{\sqrt{3}}{2}i\right) = -\dfrac{\sqrt[4]{2}}{2}-\dfrac{\sqrt[4]{18}}{2}i.$$

$$w_3 = \sqrt[4]{2}\operatorname{cis}330° = \sqrt[4]{2}\left(\dfrac{\sqrt{3}}{2}-\dfrac{1}{2}i\right) = \dfrac{\sqrt[4]{18}}{2}-\dfrac{\sqrt[4]{2}}{2}i.$$

16 $-8+8\sqrt{3}i = 16\operatorname{cis}120°.$ $w_k = \sqrt[4]{16}\operatorname{cis}\left(\dfrac{120°+360°k}{4}\right)$ for $k = 0, 1, 2, 3.$

$$w_0 = 2\operatorname{cis}30° = 2\left(\dfrac{\sqrt{3}}{2}+\dfrac{1}{2}i\right) = \sqrt{3}+i.$$

$$w_1 = 2\operatorname{cis}120° = 2\left(-\dfrac{1}{2}+\dfrac{\sqrt{3}}{2}i\right) = -1+\sqrt{3}i.$$

$$w_2 = 2\operatorname{cis}210° = 2\left(-\dfrac{\sqrt{3}}{2}-\dfrac{1}{2}i\right) = -\sqrt{3}-i.$$

$$w_3 = 2\operatorname{cis}300° = 2\left(\dfrac{1}{2}-\dfrac{\sqrt{3}}{2}i\right) = 1-\sqrt{3}i.$$

$\boxed{17}$ $-27i = 27\operatorname{cis}270°$. $w_k = \sqrt[3]{27}\operatorname{cis}\left(\dfrac{270° + 360°k}{3}\right)$ for $k = 0, 1, 2$.

$$w_0 = 3\operatorname{cis}90° = 3(0 + i) = 3i.$$

$$w_1 = 3\operatorname{cis}210° = 3\left(-\frac{\sqrt{3}}{2} - \frac{1}{2}i\right) = -\frac{3\sqrt{3}}{2} - \frac{3}{2}i.$$

$$w_2 = 3\operatorname{cis}330° = 3\left(\frac{\sqrt{3}}{2} - \frac{1}{2}i\right) = \frac{3\sqrt{3}}{2} - \frac{3}{2}i.$$

$\boxed{18}$ $64i = 64\operatorname{cis}90°$. $w_k = \sqrt[3]{64}\operatorname{cis}\left(\dfrac{90° + 360°k}{3}\right)$ for $k = 0, 1, 2$.

$$w_0 = 4\operatorname{cis}30° = 4\left(\frac{\sqrt{3}}{2} + \frac{1}{2}i\right) = 2\sqrt{3} + 2i.$$

$$w_1 = 4\operatorname{cis}150° = 4\left(-\frac{\sqrt{3}}{2} + \frac{1}{2}i\right) = -2\sqrt{3} + 2i.$$

$$w_2 = 4\operatorname{cis}270° = 4(0 - i) = -4i.$$

$\boxed{19}$ $1 = 1\operatorname{cis}0°$. $w_k = \sqrt[6]{1}\operatorname{cis}\left(\dfrac{0° + 360°k}{6}\right)$ for $k = 0, 1, 2, 3, 4, 5$.

$$w_0 = 1\operatorname{cis}0° = 1 + 0i. \qquad w_1 = 1\operatorname{cis}60° = \frac{1}{2} + \frac{\sqrt{3}}{2}i.$$

$$w_2 = 1\operatorname{cis}120° = -\frac{1}{2} + \frac{\sqrt{3}}{2}i. \qquad w_3 = 1\operatorname{cis}180° = -1 + 0i.$$

$$w_4 = 1\operatorname{cis}240° = -\frac{1}{2} - \frac{\sqrt{3}}{2}i. \qquad w_5 = 1\operatorname{cis}300° = \frac{1}{2} - \frac{\sqrt{3}}{2}i.$$

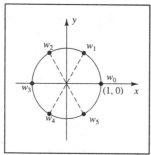

Figure 19

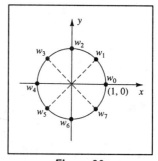

Figure 20

$\boxed{20}$ $1 = 1\operatorname{cis}0°$. $w_k = \sqrt[8]{1}\operatorname{cis}\left(\dfrac{0° + 360°k}{8}\right)$ for $k = 0, 1, 2, 3, 4, 5, 6, 7$.

$$w_0 = 1\operatorname{cis}0° = 1 + 0i. \qquad w_1 = 1\operatorname{cis}45° = \frac{\sqrt{2}}{2} + \frac{\sqrt{2}}{2}i.$$

$$w_2 = 1\operatorname{cis}90° = 0 + i. \qquad w_3 = 1\operatorname{cis}135° = -\frac{\sqrt{2}}{2} + \frac{\sqrt{2}}{2}i.$$

$$w_4 = 1\operatorname{cis}180° = -1 + 0i. \qquad w_5 = 1\operatorname{cis}225° = -\frac{\sqrt{2}}{2} - \frac{\sqrt{2}}{2}i.$$

$$w_6 = 1\operatorname{cis}270° = 0 - i. \qquad w_7 = 1\operatorname{cis}315° = \frac{\sqrt{2}}{2} - \frac{\sqrt{2}}{2}i.$$

21 $1 + i = \sqrt{2} \operatorname{cis} 45°$. $w_k = \sqrt{\sqrt[5]{2}} \operatorname{cis}\left(\dfrac{45° + 360°k}{5}\right)$ for $k = 0, 1, 2, 3, 4$.

$$w_k = \sqrt[10]{2} \operatorname{cis} \theta \text{ with } \theta = 9°, 81°, 153°, 225°, 297°.$$

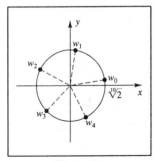

Figure 21

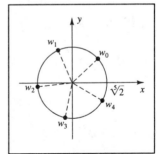

Figure 22

22 $-\sqrt{3} - i = 2 \operatorname{cis} 210°$. $w_k = \sqrt[5]{2} \operatorname{cis}\left(\dfrac{210° + 360°k}{5}\right)$ for $k = 0, 1, 2, 3, 4$.

$$w_k = \sqrt[5]{2} \operatorname{cis} \theta \text{ with } \theta = 42°, 114°, 186°, 258°, 330°.$$

23 $x^4 - 16 = 0 \Rightarrow x^4 = 16$. The problem is now to find the 4 fourth roots of 16.

$16 = 16 + 0i = 16 \operatorname{cis} 0°$. $w_k = \sqrt[4]{16} \operatorname{cis}\left(\dfrac{0° + 360°k}{4}\right)$ for $k = 0, 1, 2, 3$.

$w_0 = 2 \operatorname{cis} 0° = 2(1 + 0i) = 2$. $w_1 = 2 \operatorname{cis} 90° = 2(0 + i) = 2i$.

$w_2 = 2 \operatorname{cis} 180° = 2(-1 + 0i) = -2$. $w_3 = 2 \operatorname{cis} 270° = 2(0 - i) = -2i$.

24 $x^6 - 64 = 0 \Rightarrow x^6 = 64$. The problem is now to find the 6 sixth roots of 64.

$64 = 64 + 0i = 64 \operatorname{cis} 0°$. $w_k = \sqrt[6]{64} \operatorname{cis}\left(\dfrac{0° + 360°k}{6}\right)$ for $k = 0, 1, 2, 3, 4, 5$.

$w_0 = 2 \operatorname{cis} 0° = 2(1 + 0i) = 2$.

$w_1 = 2 \operatorname{cis} 60° = 2\left(\dfrac{1}{2} + \dfrac{\sqrt{3}}{2}i\right) = 1 + \sqrt{3}\,i$.

$w_2 = 2 \operatorname{cis} 120° = 2\left(-\dfrac{1}{2} + \dfrac{\sqrt{3}}{2}i\right) = -1 + \sqrt{3}\,i$.

$w_3 = 2 \operatorname{cis} 180° = 2(-1 + 0i) = -2$.

$w_4 = 2 \operatorname{cis} 240° = 2\left(-\dfrac{1}{2} - \dfrac{\sqrt{3}}{2}i\right) = -1 - \sqrt{3}\,i$.

$w_5 = 2 \operatorname{cis} 300° = 2\left(\dfrac{1}{2} - \dfrac{\sqrt{3}}{2}i\right) = 1 - \sqrt{3}\,i$.

25 $x^6 + 64 = 0 \Rightarrow x^6 = -64$. The problem is now to find the 6 sixth roots of -64.

$-64 = -64 + 0i = 64 \operatorname{cis} 180°$. $w_k = \sqrt[6]{64} \operatorname{cis}\left(\dfrac{180° + 360°k}{6}\right)$ for $k = 0, 1, \ldots, 5$.

$w_0 = 2 \operatorname{cis} 30° = 2\left(\dfrac{\sqrt{3}}{2} + \dfrac{1}{2}i\right) = \sqrt{3} + i$.

$w_1 = 2 \operatorname{cis} 90° = 2(0 + i) = 2i$.

$w_2 = 2 \operatorname{cis} 150° = 2\left(-\dfrac{\sqrt{3}}{2} + \dfrac{1}{2}i\right) = -\sqrt{3} + i$.   (continued)

$w_3 = 2\operatorname{cis}210° = 2\left(-\dfrac{\sqrt{3}}{2} - \dfrac{1}{2}i\right) = -\sqrt{3} - i.$

$w_4 = 2\operatorname{cis}270° = 2(0 - i) = -2i.$

$w_5 = 2\operatorname{cis}330° = 2\left(\dfrac{\sqrt{3}}{2} - \dfrac{1}{2}i\right) = \sqrt{3} - i.$

26 $x^5 + 1 = 0 \Rightarrow x^5 = -1.$ The problem is now to find the 5 fifth roots of -1.

$-1 = -1 + 0i = 1\operatorname{cis}180°.$ $w_k = \sqrt[5]{1}\operatorname{cis}\left(\dfrac{180° + 360°k}{5}\right)$ for $k = 0, 1, 2, 3, 4.$

$w_k = 1\operatorname{cis}\theta$ with $\theta = 36°, 108°, 180°, 252°, 324°.$

27 $x^3 + 8i = 0 \Rightarrow x^3 = -8i.$ The problem is now to find the 3 cube roots of $-8i$.

$-8i = 0 - 8i = 8\operatorname{cis}270°.$ $w_k = \sqrt[3]{8}\operatorname{cis}\left(\dfrac{270° + 360°k}{3}\right)$ for $k = 0, 1, 2.$

$w_0 = 2\operatorname{cis}90° = 2(0 + i) = 2i.$

$w_1 = 2\operatorname{cis}210° = 2\left(-\dfrac{\sqrt{3}}{2} - \dfrac{1}{2}i\right) = -\sqrt{3} - i.$

$w_2 = 2\operatorname{cis}330° = 2\left(\dfrac{\sqrt{3}}{2} - \dfrac{1}{2}i\right) = \sqrt{3} - i.$

28 $x^3 - 64i = 0 \Rightarrow x^3 = 64i.$ The problem is now to find the 3 cube roots of $64i$.

$64i = 0 + 64i = 64\operatorname{cis}90°.$ $w_k = \sqrt[3]{64}\operatorname{cis}\left(\dfrac{90° + 360°k}{3}\right)$ for $k = 0, 1, 2.$

$w_0 = 4\operatorname{cis}30° = 4\left(\dfrac{\sqrt{3}}{2} + \dfrac{1}{2}i\right) = 2\sqrt{3} + 2i.$

$w_1 = 4\operatorname{cis}150° = 4\left(-\dfrac{\sqrt{3}}{2} + \dfrac{1}{2}i\right) = -2\sqrt{3} + 2i.$

$w_2 = 4\operatorname{cis}270° = 4(0 - i) = -4i.$

29 $x^5 - 243 = 0 \Rightarrow x^5 = 243.$ The problem is now to find the 5 fifth roots of 243.

$243 = 243 + 0i = 243\operatorname{cis}0°.$ $w_k = \sqrt[5]{243}\operatorname{cis}\left(\dfrac{0° + 360°k}{5}\right)$ for $k = 0, 1, 2, 3, 4.$

$w_k = 3\operatorname{cis}\theta$ with $\theta = 0°, 72°, 144°, 216°, 288°.$

30 $x^4 + 81 = 0 \Rightarrow x^4 = -81.$ The problem is now to find the 4 fourth roots of -81.

$-81 = -81 + 0i = 81\operatorname{cis}180°.$ $w_k = \sqrt[4]{81}\operatorname{cis}\left(\dfrac{180° + 360°k}{4}\right)$ for $k = 0, 1, 2, 3.$

$w_0 = 3\operatorname{cis}45° = 3\left(\dfrac{\sqrt{2}}{2} + \dfrac{\sqrt{2}}{2}i\right) = \dfrac{3\sqrt{2}}{2} + \dfrac{3\sqrt{2}}{2}i.$

$w_1 = 3\operatorname{cis}135° = 3\left(-\dfrac{\sqrt{2}}{2} + \dfrac{\sqrt{2}}{2}i\right) = -\dfrac{3\sqrt{2}}{2} + \dfrac{3\sqrt{2}}{2}i.$

$w_2 = 3\operatorname{cis}225° = 3\left(-\dfrac{\sqrt{2}}{2} - \dfrac{\sqrt{2}}{2}i\right) = -\dfrac{3\sqrt{2}}{2} - \dfrac{3\sqrt{2}}{2}i.$

$w_3 = 3\operatorname{cis}315° = 3\left(\dfrac{\sqrt{2}}{2} - \dfrac{\sqrt{2}}{2}i\right) = \dfrac{3\sqrt{2}}{2} - \dfrac{3\sqrt{2}}{2}i.$

7.5 Exercises

1 $\mathbf{a} + \mathbf{b} = \langle 2, -3 \rangle + \langle 1, 4 \rangle = \langle 2 + 1, -3 + 4 \rangle = \langle 3, 1 \rangle$.

$\mathbf{a} - \mathbf{b} = \langle 2, -3 \rangle - \langle 1, 4 \rangle = \langle 2 - 1, -3 - 4 \rangle = \langle 1, -7 \rangle$.

$4\mathbf{a} + 5\mathbf{b} = 4\langle 2, -3 \rangle + 5\langle 1, 4 \rangle = \langle 8, -12 \rangle + \langle 5, 20 \rangle = \langle 8 + 5, -12 + 20 \rangle = \langle 13, 8 \rangle$

$4\mathbf{a} - 5\mathbf{b} = 4\langle 2, -3 \rangle - 5\langle 1, 4 \rangle = \langle 8, -12 \rangle - \langle 5, 20 \rangle = \langle 8 - 5, -12 - 20 \rangle = \langle 3, -32 \rangle$

Note: For Exercises 2–6, the answers are given in the following order:

$\mathbf{a} + \mathbf{b}$,	$\mathbf{a} - \mathbf{b}$,	$4\mathbf{a} + 5\mathbf{b}$, and	$4\mathbf{a} - 5\mathbf{b}$.

2 $\langle 0, 9 \rangle$, $\langle -4, 3 \rangle$, $\langle 2, 39 \rangle$, $\langle -18, 9 \rangle$

3 $\langle -15, 6 \rangle$, $\langle 1, -2 \rangle$, $\langle -68, 28 \rangle$, $\langle 12, -12 \rangle$

4 $\langle 4, -8 \rangle$, $\langle 16, -8 \rangle$, $\langle 10, -32 \rangle$, $\langle 70, -32 \rangle$

5 $4\mathbf{i} - 3\mathbf{j}$, $-2\mathbf{i} + 7\mathbf{j}$, $19\mathbf{i} - 17\mathbf{j}$, $-11\mathbf{i} + 33\mathbf{j}$

6 $-6\mathbf{i} + 2\mathbf{j}$, $0\mathbf{i} + 0\mathbf{j}$, $-27\mathbf{i} + 9\mathbf{j}$, $3\mathbf{i} - \mathbf{j}$

7 $\mathbf{a} = 3\mathbf{i} + 2\mathbf{j}$ and $\mathbf{b} = -\mathbf{i} + 5\mathbf{j} \Rightarrow \mathbf{a} + \mathbf{b} = 2\mathbf{i} + 7\mathbf{j}$, $2\mathbf{a} = 6\mathbf{i} + 4\mathbf{j}$, and $-3\mathbf{b} = 3\mathbf{i} - 15\mathbf{j}$.

Terminal points of the vectors are $(3, 2)$, $(-1, 5)$, $(2, 7)$, $(6, 4)$, and $(3, -15)$.

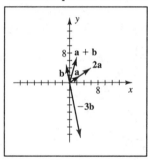

Figure 7

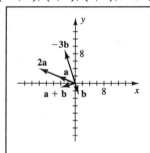

Figure 8

8 $\mathbf{a} = -5\mathbf{i} + 2\mathbf{j}$ and $\mathbf{b} = \mathbf{i} - 3\mathbf{j} \Rightarrow \mathbf{a} + \mathbf{b} = -4\mathbf{i} - \mathbf{j}$, $2\mathbf{a} = -10\mathbf{i} + 4\mathbf{j}$, and $-3\mathbf{b} = -3\mathbf{i} + 9\mathbf{j}$.

Terminal points of the vectors are $(-5, 2)$, $(1, -3)$, $(-4, -1)$, $(-10, 4)$, and $(-3, 9)$.

9 $\mathbf{a} = \langle -4, 6 \rangle$ and $\mathbf{b} = \langle -2, 3 \rangle \Rightarrow \mathbf{a} + \mathbf{b} = \langle -6, 9 \rangle$, $2\mathbf{a} = \langle -8, 12 \rangle$, and $-3\mathbf{b} = \langle 6, -9 \rangle$.

Terminal points of the vectors are $(-4, 6)$, $(-2, 3)$, $(-6, 9)$, $(-8, 12)$, and $(6, -9)$.

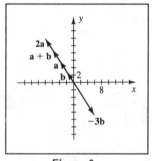

Figure 9

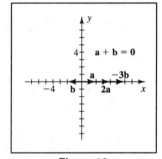

Figure 10

10 $\mathbf{a} = \langle 2, 0 \rangle$ and $\mathbf{b} = \langle -2, 0 \rangle \Rightarrow \mathbf{a} + \mathbf{b} = \langle 0, 0 \rangle$, $2\mathbf{a} = \langle 4, 0 \rangle$, and $-3\mathbf{b} = \langle 6, 0 \rangle$.

Terminal points of the vectors are $(2, 0)$, $(-2, 0)$, $(0, 0)$, $(4, 0)$, and $(6, 0)$.

$\boxed{11}$ $\mathbf{a} + \mathbf{b} = \langle 2, 0 \rangle + \langle -1, 0 \rangle = \langle 1, 0 \rangle = -\langle -1, 0 \rangle = -\mathbf{b}$

$\boxed{12}$ $\mathbf{c} - \mathbf{d} = \langle 0, 2 \rangle - \langle 0, -1 \rangle = \langle 0, 3 \rangle = -3\langle 0, -1 \rangle = -3\mathbf{d}$

$\boxed{13}$ $\mathbf{b} + \mathbf{e} = \langle -1, 0 \rangle + \langle 2, 2 \rangle = \langle 1, 2 \rangle = \mathbf{f}$

$\boxed{14}$ $\mathbf{f} - \mathbf{b} = \langle 1, 2 \rangle - \langle -1, 0 \rangle = \langle 2, 2 \rangle = \mathbf{e}$

$\boxed{15}$ $\mathbf{b} + \mathbf{d} = \langle -1, 0 \rangle + \langle 0, -1 \rangle = \langle -1, -1 \rangle = -\frac{1}{2}\langle 2, 2 \rangle = -\frac{1}{2}\mathbf{e}$

$\boxed{16}$ $\mathbf{e} + \mathbf{c} = \langle 2, 2 \rangle + \langle 0, 2 \rangle = \langle 2, 4 \rangle = 2\langle 1, 2 \rangle = 2\mathbf{f}$

$\boxed{17}$
$$\begin{aligned}
\mathbf{a} + (\mathbf{b} + \mathbf{c}) &= \langle a_1, a_2 \rangle + (\langle b_1, b_2 \rangle + \langle c_1, c_2 \rangle) \\
&= \langle a_1, a_2 \rangle + \langle b_1 + c_1, b_2 + c_2 \rangle \\
&= \langle a_1 + b_1 + c_1, a_2 + b_2 + c_2 \rangle \\
&= \langle a_1 + b_1, a_2 + b_2 \rangle + \langle c_1, c_2 \rangle \\
&= (\langle a_1, a_2 \rangle + \langle b_1, b_2 \rangle) + \langle c_1, c_2 \rangle = (\mathbf{a} + \mathbf{b}) + \mathbf{c}
\end{aligned}$$

$\boxed{18}$ $\mathbf{a} + \mathbf{0} = \langle a_1, a_2 \rangle + \langle 0, 0 \rangle = \langle a_1 + 0, a_2 + 0 \rangle = \langle a_1, a_2 \rangle = \mathbf{a}$

$\boxed{19}$
$$\begin{aligned}
\mathbf{a} + (-\mathbf{a}) &= \langle a_1, a_2 \rangle + (-\langle a_1, a_2 \rangle) \\
&= \langle a_1, a_2 \rangle + \langle -a_1, -a_2 \rangle \\
&= \langle a_1 - a_1, a_2 - a_2 \rangle \\
&= \langle 0, 0 \rangle = \mathbf{0}
\end{aligned}$$

$\boxed{20}$
$$\begin{aligned}
(m + n)\mathbf{a} &= (m + n)\langle a_1, a_2 \rangle \\
&= \langle (m + n)a_1, (m + n)a_2 \rangle \\
&= \langle ma_1 + na_1, ma_2 + na_2 \rangle \\
&= \langle ma_1, ma_2 \rangle + \langle na_1, na_2 \rangle \\
&= m\langle a_1, a_2 \rangle + n\langle a_1, a_2 \rangle = m\mathbf{a} + n\mathbf{a}
\end{aligned}$$

$\boxed{21}$
$$\begin{aligned}
(mn)\mathbf{a} &= (mn)\langle a_1, a_2 \rangle \\
&= \langle (mn)a_1, (mn)a_2 \rangle \\
&= \langle mna_1, mna_2 \rangle \\
&= m\langle na_1, na_2 \rangle && \text{or } n\langle ma_1, ma_2 \rangle \\
&= m(n\langle a_1, a_2 \rangle) && \text{or } n(m\langle a_1, a_2 \rangle) \\
&= m(n\mathbf{a}) && \text{or } n(m\mathbf{a})
\end{aligned}$$

$\boxed{22}$ $1\mathbf{a} = 1\langle a_1, a_2 \rangle = \langle 1a_1, 1a_2 \rangle = \langle a_1, a_2 \rangle = \mathbf{a}$

$\boxed{23}$ $0\mathbf{a} = 0\langle a_1, a_2 \rangle = \langle 0a_1, 0a_2 \rangle = \langle 0, 0 \rangle = \mathbf{0}.$

Also, $m\mathbf{0} = m\langle 0, 0 \rangle = \langle m0, m0 \rangle = \langle 0, 0 \rangle = \mathbf{0}.$

24 $(-m)\mathbf{a} = (-m)\langle a_1, a_2 \rangle$

$\qquad = \langle (-m)a_1, (-m)a_2 \rangle$

$\qquad = \langle -(ma_1), -(ma_2) \rangle$

$\qquad = -(\langle ma_1, ma_2 \rangle)$

$\qquad = -(m\langle a_1, a_2 \rangle)$

$\qquad = -m\langle a_1, a_2 \rangle = -m\mathbf{a}$

25 $-(\mathbf{a}+\mathbf{b}) = -(\langle a_1, a_2 \rangle + \langle b_1, b_2 \rangle)$

$\qquad = -(\langle a_1+b_1, a_2+b_2 \rangle)$

$\qquad = \langle -(a_1+b_1), -(a_2+b_2) \rangle$

$\qquad = \langle -a_1-b_1, -a_2-b_2 \rangle$

$\qquad = \langle -a_1, -a_2 \rangle + \langle -b_1, -b_2 \rangle$

$\qquad = -\mathbf{a}+(-\mathbf{b}) = -\mathbf{a}-\mathbf{b}$

26 $m(\mathbf{a}-\mathbf{b}) = m(\langle a_1, a_2 \rangle - \langle b_1, b_2 \rangle)$

$\qquad = m\langle a_1-b_1, a_2-b_2 \rangle$

$\qquad = \langle m(a_1-b_1), m(a_2-b_2) \rangle$

$\qquad = \langle ma_1-mb_1, ma_2-mb_2 \rangle$

$\qquad = \langle ma_1, ma_2 \rangle + \langle -mb_1, -mb_2 \rangle$

$\qquad = m\langle a_1, a_2 \rangle + (-m)\langle b_1, b_2 \rangle = m\mathbf{a}-m\mathbf{b}$

27 $\|2\mathbf{v}\| = \|2\langle a, b \rangle\| = \|\langle 2a, 2b \rangle\| = \sqrt{(2a)^2+(2b)^2} = \sqrt{4a^2+4b^2} =$

$\qquad\qquad\qquad\qquad\qquad 2\sqrt{a^2+b^2} = 2\|\langle a, b \rangle\| = 2\|\mathbf{v}\|$

28 $\|k\mathbf{v}\| = \|k\langle a, b \rangle\| = \|\langle ka, kb \rangle\| = \sqrt{(ka)^2+(kb)^2} = \sqrt{k^2a^2+k^2b^2} =$

$\qquad\qquad\qquad\qquad \sqrt{k^2}\sqrt{a^2+b^2} = |k|\,\|\langle a, b \rangle\| = |k|\,\|\mathbf{v}\|$

29 $\|\mathbf{a}\| = \sqrt{3^2+(-3)^2} = \sqrt{18} = 3\sqrt{2}. \ \tan\theta = \frac{-3}{3} = -1$ and θ in QIV $\Rightarrow \theta = \frac{7\pi}{4}$.

30 $\|\mathbf{a}\| = \sqrt{(-2)^2+(-2\sqrt{3})^2} = \sqrt{16} = 4. \ \tan\theta = \frac{-2\sqrt{3}}{-2} = \sqrt{3}$ and θ in QIII $\Rightarrow \theta = \frac{4\pi}{3}$.

31 $\|\mathbf{a}\| = 5.$ The terminal side of θ is on the negative x-axis $\Rightarrow \theta = \pi$.

32 $\|\mathbf{a}\| = 10.$ The terminal side of θ is on the positive y-axis $\Rightarrow \theta = \frac{\pi}{2}$.

33 $\|\mathbf{a}\| = \sqrt{41}. \ \tan\theta = \frac{5}{-4}$ and θ in QII $\Rightarrow \theta = \tan^{-1}\left(-\frac{5}{4}\right) + \pi$.

34 $\|\mathbf{a}\| = 10\sqrt{2}. \ \tan\theta = \frac{-10}{10} = -1$ and θ in QIV $\Rightarrow \theta = \frac{7\pi}{4}$.

35 $\|\mathbf{a}\| = 18.$ The terminal side of θ is on the negative y-axis $\Rightarrow \theta = \frac{3\pi}{2}$.

36 $\|\mathbf{a}\| = \sqrt{13}. \ \tan\theta = \frac{-3}{2}$ and θ in QIV $\Rightarrow \theta = \tan^{-1}\left(-\frac{3}{2}\right) + 2\pi$.

Note: Exercises 37–42: Each resultant force is found by completing the parallelogram and

then applying the law of cosines.

[37] $\|\mathbf{r}\| = \sqrt{40^2 + 70^2 - 2(40)(70)\cos 135°} = \sqrt{6500 + 2800\sqrt{2}} \approx 102.3$, or 102 lb.

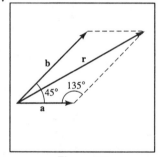

Figure 37

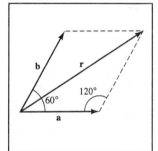

Figure 38

[38] $\|\mathbf{r}\| = \sqrt{5.5^2 + 6.2^2 - 2(5.5)(6.2)\cos 120°} = \sqrt{102.79} \approx 10.1$ lb.

[39] $\|\mathbf{r}\| = \sqrt{2^2 + 8^2 - 2(2)(8)\cos 60°} = \sqrt{52} \approx 7.2$ kg.

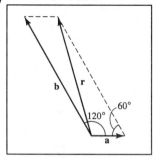

Figure 39

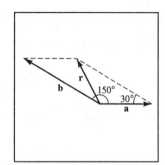

Figure 40

[40] $\|\mathbf{r}\| = \sqrt{30^2 + 50^2 - 2(30)(50)\cos 30°} = \sqrt{3400 - 1500\sqrt{3}} \approx 28.3$, or 28 kg.

[41] $\|\mathbf{r}\| = \sqrt{90^2 + 60^2 - 2(90)(60)\cos 70°} \approx 89.48$, or 89 kg.

Using the law of cosines, $\alpha = \cos^{-1}\left(\dfrac{90^2 + \|\mathbf{r}\|^2 - 60^2}{2(90)(\|\mathbf{r}\|)}\right) \approx \cos^{-1}(0.7765) \approx 39°$,

which is 24° under the negative x-axis. This angle is 204°, or S66°W.

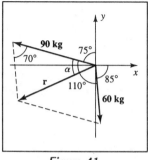

Figure 41

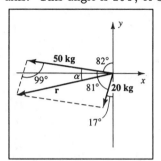

Figure 42

[42] $\|\mathbf{r}\| = \sqrt{50^2 + 20^2 - 2(50)(20)\cos 99°} \approx 56.68$, or 57 kg.

Using the law of cosines, $\alpha = \cos^{-1}\left(\dfrac{50^2 + \|\mathbf{r}\|^2 - 20^2}{2(50)(\|\mathbf{r}\|)}\right) \approx \cos^{-1}(0.9373) \approx 20°$,

which is 12° under the negative x-axis. This angle is 192°, or S78°W.

Note: Exercises 43–44: We will use a component approach for these problems.

43 (a) $= \langle 6\cos 110°, \ 6\sin 110° \rangle \approx \langle -2.05, \ 5.64 \rangle$.

(b) $= \langle 2\cos 215°, \ 2\sin 215° \rangle \approx \langle -1.64, \ -1.15 \rangle$.

$\mathbf{a} + \mathbf{b} \approx \langle -3.69, \ 4.49 \rangle$ and $\|\mathbf{a} + \mathbf{b}\| \approx 5.8$ lb. $\tan\theta \approx \frac{4.49}{-3.69} \Rightarrow \theta \approx 129°$ since θ is in QII.

44 (a) $= \langle 70\cos 320°, \ 70\sin 320° \rangle \approx \langle 53.62, \ -45.00 \rangle$.

(b) $= \langle 40\cos 30°, \ 40\sin 30° \rangle \approx \langle 34.64, \ 20 \rangle$.

$\mathbf{a} + \mathbf{b} \approx \langle 88.26, \ -25.00 \rangle$ and $\|\mathbf{a} + \mathbf{b}\| \approx 91.73$, or 92 lb.

$$\tan\theta \approx \frac{-25.00}{88.26} \Rightarrow \theta \approx 344° \text{ since } \theta \text{ is in QIV.}$$

45 Horizontal $= 50\cos 35° \approx 40.96$. Vertical $= 50\sin 35° \approx 28.68$.

46 Horizontal $= 20\cos 40° \approx 15.32$. Vertical $= 20\sin 40° \approx 12.86$.

47 Horizontal $= 20\cos 108° \approx -6.18$. Vertical $= 20\sin 108° \approx 19.02$.

48 Horizontal $= 160\cos 7.5° \approx 158.63$. Vertical $= 160\sin 7.5° \approx 20.88$.

49 (a) $\mathbf{F} = \mathbf{F_1} + \mathbf{F_2} + \mathbf{F_3} = \langle 4, \ 3 \rangle + \langle -2, \ -3 \rangle + \langle 5, \ 2 \rangle = \langle 7, \ 2 \rangle$.

(b) $\mathbf{F} + \mathbf{G} = \mathbf{0} \Rightarrow \mathbf{G} = -\mathbf{F} = \langle -7, \ -2 \rangle$.

50 (a) $\mathbf{F} = \mathbf{F_1} + \mathbf{F_2} + \mathbf{F_3} = \langle -3, \ -1 \rangle + \langle 0, \ -3 \rangle + \langle 3, \ 4 \rangle = \langle 0, \ 0 \rangle$.

(b) No additional force is needed since the system is in equilibrium.

51 (a) $\mathbf{F} = \mathbf{F_1} + \mathbf{F_2} = \langle 6\cos 130°, \ 6\sin 130° \rangle + \langle 4\cos(-120°), \ 4\sin(-120°) \rangle \approx \langle -5.86, \ 1.13 \rangle$.

(b) $\mathbf{F} + \mathbf{G} = \mathbf{0} \Rightarrow \mathbf{G} = -\mathbf{F} \approx \langle 5.86, \ -1.13 \rangle$.

52 (a) $\mathbf{F} = \mathbf{F_1} + \mathbf{F_2} + \mathbf{F_3} =$

$\langle 8\cos 50°, \ 8\sin 50° \rangle + \langle 7\cos 130°, \ 7\sin 130° \rangle + \langle 5\cos 200°, \ 5\sin 200° \rangle \approx \langle -4.06, \ 9.78 \rangle$.

(b) $\mathbf{F} + \mathbf{G} = \mathbf{0} \Rightarrow \mathbf{G} = -\mathbf{F} \approx \langle 4.06, \ -9.78 \rangle$.

53 The vertical components of the forces must add up to zero for the large ship to move along the line segment AB. The vertical component of the smaller tug is $3200\sin(-30°) = -1600$. The vertical component of the larger tug is $4000\sin\theta$.

$$4000\sin\theta = 1600 \Rightarrow \theta = \sin^{-1}\left(\frac{1600}{4000}\right) = \sin^{-1}(0.4) \approx 23.6°.$$

54 (a) Consider the force of 160 pounds to be the resultant vector of two vectors whose initial point is at the astronaut's feet, one along the positive x-axis and the other along the negative y-axis. The angle formed by the resultant vector and the positive x-axis is the complement of θ, $90° - \theta$.

Now $\qquad \cos(90° - \theta) = \dfrac{x\text{-component}}{160} \Rightarrow x\text{-component} = 160\sin\theta$

and $\qquad \sin(90° - \theta) = \dfrac{y\text{-component}}{160} \Rightarrow y\text{-component} = 160\cos\theta$.

(b) $27 = 160\cos\theta \Rightarrow \theta = \cos^{-1}\left(\frac{27}{160}\right) \approx 80.28°$ on the moon.

$60 = 160\cos\theta \Rightarrow \theta = \cos^{-1}\left(\frac{60}{160}\right) = \cos^{-1}\left(\frac{3}{8}\right) \approx 67.98°$ on Mars.

Note: Exercises 55–60: Measure angles from the positive x-axis.

[55] $\mathbf{p} = \langle 200 \cos 40°,\ 200 \sin 40° \rangle \approx \langle 153.21,\ 128.56 \rangle$. $\mathbf{w} = \langle 40 \cos 0°,\ 40 \sin 0° \rangle = \langle 40,\ 0 \rangle$.

$\mathbf{p} + \mathbf{w} \approx \langle 193.21,\ 128.56 \rangle$ and $\| \mathbf{p} + \mathbf{w} \| \approx 232.07$, or 232 mi/hr.

$$\tan \theta \approx \tfrac{128.56}{193.21} \Rightarrow \theta \approx 34°. \quad \text{The true course is then N}(90° - 34°)\text{E, or N56°E.}$$

[56] $\mathbf{p} = \langle 500 \cos 310°,\ 500 \sin 310° \rangle \approx \langle 321.39,\ -383.02 \rangle$.

$\mathbf{w} = \langle 30 \cos 25°,\ 30 \sin 25° \rangle \approx \langle 27.19,\ 12.68 \rangle$.

$\mathbf{p} + \mathbf{w} \approx \langle 348.58,\ -370.34 \rangle$ and $\| \mathbf{p} + \mathbf{w} \| \approx 508.59$,

or 509 mi/hr.

$\tan \theta \approx \tfrac{-370.34}{348.58} \Rightarrow \theta \approx -46.7°$, or $-47°$, or,

equivalently, 137°.

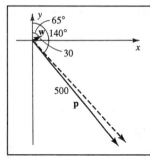

Figure 56

[57] $\mathbf{w} = \langle 50 \cos 90°,\ 50 \sin 90° \rangle = \langle 0,\ 50 \rangle$.

$\mathbf{r} = \langle 400 \cos 200°,\ 400 \sin 200° \rangle \approx \langle -375.88,\ -136.81 \rangle$, where $\mathbf{r}$ is the desired resultant of

$\mathbf{p} + \mathbf{w}$. Since $\mathbf{r} = \mathbf{p} + \mathbf{w}$, $\mathbf{p} = \mathbf{r} - \mathbf{w} \approx \langle -375.88,\ -186.81 \rangle$. $\| \mathbf{p} \| \approx 419.74$, or 420 mi/hr.

$\tan \theta \approx \tfrac{-186.81}{-375.88}$ and θ is in QIII $\Rightarrow \theta \approx 206°$ from the positive x-axis,

or 244° using the directional form.

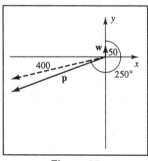

Figure 57

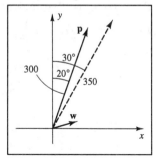

Figure 58

[58] $\mathbf{p} = \langle 300 \cos 70°,\ 300 \sin 70° \rangle \approx \langle 102.61,\ 281.91 \rangle$.

$\mathbf{r} = \langle 350 \cos 60°,\ 350 \sin 60° \rangle \approx \langle 175,\ 303.11 \rangle$.

$\mathbf{w} = \mathbf{r} - \mathbf{p} \approx \langle 72.39,\ 21.20 \rangle$ and $\| \mathbf{w} \| \approx 75.43$, or 75 mi/hr.

$$\tan \theta \approx \tfrac{21.20}{72.39} \Rightarrow \theta \approx 16°, \quad \text{or in the direction of } 74°.$$

$\boxed{59}$ Let the vectors **c**, **b**, and **r** denote the current, the boat, and the resultant, respectively. $\mathbf{c} = \langle 1.5\cos 0°,\ 1.5\sin 0°\rangle = \langle 1.5,\ 0\rangle$. $\mathbf{r} = \langle s\cos 90°,\ s\sin 90°\rangle = \langle 0,\ s\rangle$, where s is the resulting speed. $\mathbf{b} = \langle 4\cos\theta,\ 4\sin\theta\rangle$. Also, $\mathbf{b} = \mathbf{r} - \mathbf{c} = \langle -1.5,\ s\rangle$.

$$4\cos\theta = -1.5 \Rightarrow \theta \approx 112°,\ \text{or N22°W.}$$

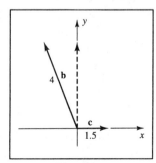

Figure 59

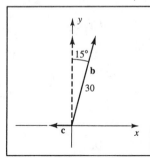

Figure 60

$\boxed{60}$ Let the vectors **c**, **b**, and **r** denote the current, the boat, and the resultant, respectively. Let s denote the rate of the current and t the resulting speed.

$\mathbf{b} = \langle 30\cos 75°,\ 30\sin 75°\rangle \approx \langle 7.76,\ 28.98\rangle$.

$\mathbf{c} = \langle s\cos 180°,\ s\sin 180°\rangle = \langle -s,\ 0\rangle$. $\mathbf{r} = \langle t\cos 90°,\ t\sin 90°\rangle = \langle 0,\ t\rangle$.

Since $\mathbf{c} = \mathbf{r} - \mathbf{b}$, we have $-s = 0 - 7.76 \Rightarrow s = 7.76$, or 8 mi/hr.

$\boxed{61}$ From the figure, we see that

$$\mathbf{v}_1 = \|\mathbf{v}_1\|\sin\theta_1\,\mathbf{i} - \|\mathbf{v}_1\|\cos\theta_1\,\mathbf{j} = 8.2(\tfrac{1}{2})\mathbf{i} - 8.2(\sqrt{3}/2)\mathbf{j} = 4.1\mathbf{i} - 4.1\sqrt{3}\,\mathbf{j} \approx 4.1\mathbf{i} - 7.10\mathbf{j}.$$

$$\frac{\|\mathbf{v}_1\|}{\|\mathbf{v}_2\|} = \frac{\tan\theta_1}{\tan\theta_2} \Rightarrow \tan\theta_2 = \frac{\|\mathbf{v}_2\|}{\|\mathbf{v}_1\|}\tan\theta_1 = \frac{3.8}{8.2} \times \frac{1}{\sqrt{3}} \Rightarrow \tan\theta_2 \approx 0.2676 \Rightarrow \theta_2 \approx 14.98°.$$

It follows that $\mathbf{v}_2 = \|\mathbf{v}_2\|\sin\theta_2\,\mathbf{i} - \|\mathbf{v}_2\|\cos\theta_2\,\mathbf{j} \approx 0.98\mathbf{i} - 3.67\mathbf{j}.$

$\boxed{62}$ Since θ_1 is an acute angle, $\mathbf{v}_1 = 20\mathbf{i} - 82\mathbf{j} \Rightarrow \tan\theta_1 = \frac{20}{82} \Rightarrow \theta_1 \approx 13.71°.$

$$\|\mathbf{v}_1\| = \sqrt{20^2 + (-82)^2} = \sqrt{7124} \approx 84.40\ \text{cm/day.}$$

$$\frac{\|\mathbf{v}_1\|}{\|\mathbf{v}_2\|} = \frac{\tan\theta_1}{\tan\theta_2} \Rightarrow \tan\theta_2 = \frac{\|\mathbf{v}_2\|}{\|\mathbf{v}_1\|}\tan\theta_1 \approx \frac{725}{\sqrt{7124}}\left(\tfrac{20}{82}\right) \approx 2.095 \Rightarrow \theta_2 \approx 64.48°.$$

$\boxed{63}$ (a) $\mathbf{a} = 15\cos 40°\mathbf{i} + 15\sin 40°\mathbf{j} \approx 11.49\mathbf{i} + 9.64\mathbf{j}.$

    $\mathbf{b} = 17\cos 40°\mathbf{i} + 17\sin 40°\mathbf{j} \approx 13.02\mathbf{i} + 10.93\mathbf{j}.$

$$\overrightarrow{PR} = \mathbf{a} + \mathbf{b} \approx 24.51\mathbf{i} + 20.57\mathbf{j} \Rightarrow R \approx (24.51,\ 20.57).$$

  (b) $\mathbf{c} = 15\cos(40° + 85°)\mathbf{i} + 15\sin 125°\mathbf{j} \approx -8.60\mathbf{i} + 12.29\mathbf{j}.$

    $\mathbf{d} = 17\cos(40° + 85° + 35°)\mathbf{i} + 17\sin 160°\mathbf{j} \approx -15.97\mathbf{i} + 5.81\mathbf{j}.$

$$\overrightarrow{PR} = \mathbf{c} + \mathbf{d} \approx -24.57\mathbf{i} + 18.10\mathbf{j} \Rightarrow R \approx (-24.57,\ 18.10).$$

$\boxed{64}$ (a) $\mathbf{a} = 15\cos(-50°)\mathbf{i} + 15\sin(-50°)\mathbf{j} \approx 9.64\mathbf{i} - 11.49\mathbf{j}$.

$\mathbf{b} = 10\cos(-50°)\mathbf{i} + 10\sin(-50°)\mathbf{j} \approx 6.43\mathbf{i} - 7.66\mathbf{j}$.

$\mathbf{c} = 7\cos(-50°)\mathbf{i} + 7\sin(-50°)\mathbf{j} \approx 4.50\mathbf{i} - 5.36\mathbf{j}$.

$$\overrightarrow{PR} = \mathbf{a} + \mathbf{b} + \mathbf{c} \approx 20.57\mathbf{i} - 24.51\mathbf{j} \Rightarrow R \approx (20.57, -24.51).$$

(b) $\mathbf{d} = 15\cos(-50° + 75°)\mathbf{i} + 15\sin 25°\mathbf{j} \approx 13.59\mathbf{i} + 6.34\mathbf{j}$.

$\mathbf{e} = 10\cos(-50° + 75° - 80°)\mathbf{i} + 10\sin(-55°)\mathbf{j} \approx 5.74\mathbf{i} - 8.19\mathbf{j}$.

$\mathbf{f} = 7\cos(-50° + 75° - 80° + 40°)\mathbf{i} + 7\sin(-15°)\mathbf{j} \approx 6.76\mathbf{i} - 1.81\mathbf{j}$.

$$\overrightarrow{PR} = \mathbf{d} + \mathbf{e} + \mathbf{f} \approx 26.09\mathbf{i} - 3.66\mathbf{j} \Rightarrow R \approx (26.09, -3.66).$$

$\boxed{65}$ Break the force into a horizontal and a vertical component. The people had to contribute a force equal to the vertical component up the ramp. The vertical component is $99{,}000\sin 9° \approx 15{,}487$ lb. $\dfrac{15{,}487}{550} \approx 28.2$ lb/person. (The actual would have been more since friction was ignored.)

7.6 Exercises

$\boxed{1}$ (a) $\langle -2, 5\rangle \cdot \langle 3, 6\rangle = (-2)(3) + (5)(6) = -6 + 30 = 24$

(b) $\theta = \cos^{-1}\left(\dfrac{\langle -2, 5\rangle \cdot \langle 3, 6\rangle}{\|\langle -2, 5\rangle\|\|\langle 3, 6\rangle\|}\right) = \cos^{-1}\left(\dfrac{24}{\sqrt{29}\sqrt{45}}\right) \approx 48°22'$

$\boxed{2}$ (a) $\langle 4, -7\rangle \cdot \langle -2, 3\rangle = (4)(-2) + (-7)(3) = -8 - 21 = -29$

(b) $\theta = \cos^{-1}\left(\dfrac{\langle 4, -7\rangle \cdot \langle -2, 3\rangle}{\|\langle 4, -7\rangle\|\|\langle -2, 3\rangle\|}\right) = \cos^{-1}\left(\dfrac{-29}{\sqrt{65}\sqrt{13}}\right) \approx 176°3'$

$\boxed{3}$ (a) $(4\mathbf{i} - \mathbf{j}) \cdot (-3\mathbf{i} + 2\mathbf{j}) = (4)(-3) + (-1)(2) = -12 - 2 = -14$

(b) $\theta = \cos^{-1}\left(\dfrac{(4\mathbf{i} - \mathbf{j}) \cdot (-3\mathbf{i} + 2\mathbf{j})}{\|4\mathbf{i} - \mathbf{j}\|\|-3\mathbf{i} + 2\mathbf{j}\|}\right) = \cos^{-1}\left(\dfrac{-14}{\sqrt{17}\sqrt{13}}\right) \approx 160°21'$

$\boxed{4}$ (a) $(8\mathbf{i} - 3\mathbf{j}) \cdot (2\mathbf{i} - 7\mathbf{j}) = (8)(2) + (-3)(-7) = 16 + 21 = 37$

(b) $\theta = \cos^{-1}\left(\dfrac{(8\mathbf{i} - 3\mathbf{j}) \cdot (2\mathbf{i} - 7\mathbf{j})}{\|8\mathbf{i} - 3\mathbf{j}\|\|2\mathbf{i} - 7\mathbf{j}\|}\right) = \cos^{-1}\left(\dfrac{37}{\sqrt{73}\sqrt{53}}\right) \approx 53°30'$

$\boxed{5}$ (a) $(9\mathbf{i}) \cdot (5\mathbf{i} + 4\mathbf{j}) = (9)(5) + (0)(4) = 45 + 0 = 45$

(b) $\theta = \cos^{-1}\left(\dfrac{(9\mathbf{i}) \cdot (5\mathbf{i} + 4\mathbf{j})}{\|9\mathbf{i}\|\|5\mathbf{i} + 4\mathbf{j}\|}\right) = \cos^{-1}\left(\dfrac{45}{\sqrt{81}\sqrt{41}}\right) \approx 38°40'$

$\boxed{6}$ (a) $(6\mathbf{j}) \cdot (-4\mathbf{i}) = (0)(-4) + (6)(0) = 0 + 0 = 0$

(b) $\theta = \cos^{-1}\left(\dfrac{(6\mathbf{j}) \cdot (-4\mathbf{i})}{\|6\mathbf{j}\|\|-4\mathbf{i}\|}\right) = \cos^{-1}\left(\dfrac{0}{\sqrt{36}\sqrt{16}}\right) = \cos^{-1}(0) = 90°$

7 (a) $\langle 10, 7\rangle \cdot \langle -2, -\frac{7}{5}\rangle = (10)(-2) + (7)(-\frac{7}{5}) = -\frac{149}{5}$

(b) $\theta = \cos^{-1}\left(\dfrac{\langle 10, 7\rangle \cdot \langle -2, -\frac{7}{5}\rangle}{\|\langle 10, 7\rangle\|\,\|\langle -2, -\frac{7}{5}\rangle\|}\right) = \cos^{-1}\left(\dfrac{-149/5}{\sqrt{149}\,\sqrt{149/25}}\right) = \cos^{-1}(-1) = 180°$

8 (a) $\langle -3, 6\rangle \cdot \langle -1, 2\rangle = (-3)(-1) + (6)(2) = 15$

(b) $\theta = \cos^{-1}\left(\dfrac{\langle -3, 6\rangle \cdot \langle -1, 2\rangle}{\|\langle -3, 6\rangle\|\,\|\langle -1, 2\rangle\|}\right) = \cos^{-1}\left(\dfrac{15}{\sqrt{45}\,\sqrt{5}}\right) = \cos^{-1}(1) = 0°$

9 $\langle 4, -1\rangle \cdot \langle 2, 8\rangle = 8 - 8 = 0 \Rightarrow$ vectors are orthogonal.

10 $\langle 3, 6\rangle \cdot \langle 4, -2\rangle = 12 - 12 = 0 \Rightarrow$ vectors are orthogonal.

11 $(-4\mathbf{j}) \cdot (-7\mathbf{i}) = 0 + 0 = 0 \Rightarrow$ vectors are orthogonal.

12 $(8\mathbf{i} - 4\mathbf{j}) \cdot (-6\mathbf{i} - 12\mathbf{j}) = -48 + 48 = 0 \Rightarrow$ vectors are orthogonal.

13 $\cos\theta = \dfrac{\mathbf{a} \cdot \mathbf{b}}{\|\mathbf{a}\|\|\mathbf{b}\|} = \dfrac{(3)(-\frac{12}{7}) + (-5)(\frac{20}{7})}{\sqrt{9 + 25}\,\sqrt{\frac{144}{49} + \frac{400}{49}}} = \dfrac{-\frac{136}{7}}{\sqrt{\frac{18,496}{49}}} = \dfrac{-\frac{136}{7}}{\frac{136}{7}} = -1 \Rightarrow$

$\theta = \cos^{-1}(-1) = \pi.$ $\mathbf{b} = m\mathbf{a} \Rightarrow -\frac{12}{7}\mathbf{i} + \frac{20}{7}\mathbf{j} = 3m\mathbf{i} - 5m\mathbf{j} \Rightarrow$

$3m = -\frac{12}{7}$ and $-5m = \frac{20}{7} \Rightarrow m = -\frac{4}{7} < 0 \Rightarrow$ **a** and **b** have the opposite direction.

14 $\cos\theta = \dfrac{\mathbf{a} \cdot \mathbf{b}}{\|\mathbf{a}\|\|\mathbf{b}\|} = \dfrac{(-\frac{5}{2})(-10) + (6)(24)}{\sqrt{\frac{25}{4} + 36}\,\sqrt{100 + 576}} = \dfrac{169}{\sqrt{\frac{169}{4}}\cdot 24} = 1 \Rightarrow \theta = \cos^{-1}1 = 0.$

$\mathbf{b} = m\mathbf{a} \Rightarrow -10\mathbf{i} + 24\mathbf{j} = -\frac{5}{2}m\mathbf{i} + 6m\mathbf{j} \Rightarrow -\frac{5}{2}m = -10$ and $6m = 24 \Rightarrow m = 4 > 0 \Rightarrow$

a and **b** have the same direction.

15 $\cos\theta = \dfrac{\mathbf{a} \cdot \mathbf{b}}{\|\mathbf{a}\|\|\mathbf{b}\|} = \dfrac{(\frac{2}{3})(8) + (\frac{1}{2})(6)}{\sqrt{\frac{4}{9} + \frac{1}{4}}\,\sqrt{64 + 36}} = \dfrac{\frac{25}{3}}{\sqrt{\frac{25}{36}}\cdot 10} = 1 \Rightarrow \theta = \cos^{-1}1 = 0.$

$\mathbf{b} = m\mathbf{a} \Rightarrow 8\mathbf{i} + 6\mathbf{j} = \frac{2}{3}m\mathbf{i} + \frac{1}{2}m\mathbf{j} \Rightarrow 8 = \frac{2}{3}m$ and $6 = \frac{1}{2}m \Rightarrow m = 12 > 0 \Rightarrow$

a and **b** have the same direction.

16 $\cos\theta = \dfrac{\mathbf{a} \cdot \mathbf{b}}{\|\mathbf{a}\|\|\mathbf{b}\|} = \dfrac{(6)(-4) + (18)(-12)}{\sqrt{36 + 324}\,\sqrt{16 + 144}} = \dfrac{-240}{\sqrt{57,600}} = -1 \Rightarrow \theta = \cos^{-1}(-1) = \pi.$

$\mathbf{b} = m\mathbf{a} \Rightarrow -4\mathbf{i} - 12\mathbf{j} = 6m\mathbf{i} + 18m\mathbf{j} \Rightarrow 6m = -4$ and $18m = -12 \Rightarrow m = -\frac{2}{3} < 0 \Rightarrow$

a and **b** have the opposite direction.

17 We need to have the dot product of the two vectors equal 0.

$$(3\mathbf{i} - 2\mathbf{j}) \cdot (4\mathbf{i} + 5m\mathbf{j}) = 0 \Rightarrow 12 - 10m = 0 \Rightarrow m = \frac{6}{5}.$$

18 $(4m\mathbf{i} + \mathbf{j}) \cdot (9m\mathbf{i} - 25\mathbf{j}) = 0 \Rightarrow 36m^2 - 25 = 0 \Rightarrow m^2 = \frac{25}{36} \Rightarrow m = \pm\frac{5}{6}.$

19 $(9\mathbf{i} - 16m\mathbf{j}) \cdot (\mathbf{i} + 4m\mathbf{j}) = 0 \Rightarrow 9 - 64m^2 = 0 \Rightarrow m^2 = \frac{9}{64} \Rightarrow m = \pm\frac{3}{8}.$

20 $(5m\mathbf{i} + 3\mathbf{j}) \cdot (2\mathbf{i} + 7\mathbf{j}) = 0 \Rightarrow 10m + 21 = 0 \Rightarrow m = -\frac{21}{10}.$

21 (a) $\mathbf{a} \cdot (\mathbf{b} + \mathbf{c}) = \langle 2, -3\rangle \cdot (\langle 3, 4\rangle + \langle -1, 5\rangle) = \langle 2, -3\rangle \cdot \langle 2, 9\rangle = 4 - 27 = -23$

(b) $\mathbf{a} \cdot \mathbf{b} + \mathbf{a} \cdot \mathbf{c} = \langle 2, -3\rangle \cdot \langle 3, 4\rangle + \langle 2, -3\rangle \cdot \langle -1, 5\rangle = (6 - 12) + (-2 - 15) = -23$

22 (a) $\mathbf{b} \cdot (\mathbf{a} - \mathbf{c}) = \langle 3, 4 \rangle \cdot (\langle 2, -3 \rangle - \langle -1, 5 \rangle) = \langle 3, 4 \rangle \cdot \langle 3, -8 \rangle = 9 - 32 = -23$

(b) $\mathbf{b} \cdot \mathbf{a} - \mathbf{b} \cdot \mathbf{c} = \langle 3, 4 \rangle \cdot \langle 2, -3 \rangle - \langle 3, 4 \rangle \cdot \langle -1, 5 \rangle = (6 - 12) - (-3 + 20) = -23$

23 $(2\mathbf{a} + \mathbf{b}) \cdot (3\mathbf{c}) = (2\langle 2, -3 \rangle + \langle 3, 4 \rangle) \cdot (3\langle -1, 5 \rangle)$

$$= (\langle 4, -6 \rangle + \langle 3, 4 \rangle) \cdot \langle -3, 15 \rangle$$

$$= \langle 7, -2 \rangle \cdot \langle -3, 15 \rangle = -21 - 30 = -51$$

24 $(\mathbf{a} - \mathbf{b}) \cdot (\mathbf{b} + \mathbf{c}) = (\langle 2, -3 \rangle - \langle 3, 4 \rangle) \cdot (\langle 3, 4 \rangle + \langle -1, 5 \rangle)$

$$= \langle -1, -7 \rangle \cdot \langle 2, 9 \rangle = -2 - 63 = -65$$

25 $\text{comp}_{\mathbf{c}} \mathbf{b} = \dfrac{\mathbf{b} \cdot \mathbf{c}}{\|\mathbf{c}\|} = \dfrac{\langle 3, 4 \rangle \cdot \langle -1, 5 \rangle}{\|\langle -1, 5 \rangle\|} = \dfrac{17}{\sqrt{26}} \approx 3.33$

26 $\text{comp}_{\mathbf{b}} \mathbf{c} = \dfrac{\mathbf{c} \cdot \mathbf{b}}{\|\mathbf{b}\|} = \dfrac{\langle -1, 5 \rangle \cdot \langle 3, 4 \rangle}{\|\langle 3, 4 \rangle\|} = \dfrac{17}{5} = 3.4$

27 $\text{comp}_{\mathbf{b}}(\mathbf{a} + \mathbf{c}) = \dfrac{(\mathbf{a} + \mathbf{c}) \cdot \mathbf{b}}{\|\mathbf{b}\|} = \dfrac{(\langle 2, -3 \rangle + \langle -1, 5 \rangle) \cdot \langle 3, 4 \rangle}{\|\langle 3, 4 \rangle\|} = \dfrac{\langle 1, 2 \rangle \cdot \langle 3, 4 \rangle}{5} = \dfrac{11}{5} = 2.2$

28 $\text{comp}_{\mathbf{c}} \mathbf{c} = \dfrac{\mathbf{c} \cdot \mathbf{c}}{\|\mathbf{c}\|} = \dfrac{\langle -1, 5 \rangle \cdot \langle -1, 5 \rangle}{\|\langle -1, 5 \rangle\|} = \dfrac{26}{\sqrt{26}} = \sqrt{26} \approx 5.10$. Note that, in general,

the component of a vector along itself is just the magnitude of the vector.

29 $\mathbf{c} \cdot \overrightarrow{PQ} = \langle 3, 4 \rangle \cdot \langle 5, -2 \rangle = 15 - 8 = 7$.

30 $\mathbf{c} \cdot \overrightarrow{PQ} = \langle -10, 12 \rangle \cdot \langle 4, 7 \rangle = -40 + 84 = 44$.

31 We want a vector with initial point at the origin and terminal point located so that this vector has the same magnitude and direction as $\overrightarrow{PQ}$. Following the hint in the text, $\mathbf{b} = \overrightarrow{PQ} \Rightarrow \langle b_1, b_2 \rangle = \langle 4 - 2, 3 - (-1) \rangle \Rightarrow \langle b_1, b_2 \rangle = \langle 2, 4 \rangle$.

$$\mathbf{c} \cdot \mathbf{b} = \langle 6, 4 \rangle \cdot \langle 2, 4 \rangle = 12 + 16 = 28.$$

32 As in Exercise 31, $\mathbf{c} \cdot \overrightarrow{PQ} = \langle -1, 7 \rangle \cdot \langle 6 - (-2), 1 - 5 \rangle = -36$.

33 The force is described by the vector $\langle 0, 4 \rangle$.

$$\text{The work done is } \langle 0, 4 \rangle \cdot \langle 8, 3 \rangle = 0 + 12 = 12.$$

34 The force is described by the vector $\langle -10, 0 \rangle$.

$$\text{The work done is } \langle -10, 0 \rangle \cdot \langle 1 - 0, 0 - 1 \rangle = -10 + 0 = -10.$$

35 $\mathbf{a} \cdot \mathbf{a} = \langle a_1, a_2 \rangle \cdot \langle a_1, a_2 \rangle = a_1^2 + a_2^2 = \left(\sqrt{a_1^2 + a_2^2}\right)^2 = \|\mathbf{a}\|^2$

36 $\mathbf{a} \cdot \mathbf{b} = \langle a_1, a_2 \rangle \cdot \langle b_1, b_2 \rangle = a_1 b_1 + a_2 b_2 = b_1 a_1 + b_2 a_2 = \langle b_1, b_2 \rangle \cdot \langle a_1, a_2 \rangle = \mathbf{b} \cdot \mathbf{a}$

37 $(m\mathbf{a}) \cdot \mathbf{b} = (m\langle a_1, a_2 \rangle) \cdot \langle b_1, b_2 \rangle$

$$= \langle ma_1, ma_2 \rangle \cdot \langle b_1, b_2 \rangle$$

$$= ma_1 b_1 + ma_2 b_2$$

$$= m(a_1 b_1 + a_2 b_2) = m(\mathbf{a} \cdot \mathbf{b})$$

38 $m(\mathbf{a}\cdot\mathbf{b}) = m(\langle a_1, a_2\rangle \cdot \langle b_1, b_2\rangle)$

$= m(a_1 b_1 + a_2 b_2)$

$= ma_1 b_1 + ma_2 b_2$

$= a_1(mb_1) + a_2(mb_2)$

$= \langle a_1, a_2\rangle \cdot \langle mb_1, mb_2\rangle$

$= \mathbf{a}\cdot(m\langle b_1, b_2\rangle) = \mathbf{a}\cdot(m\mathbf{b})$

39 $\mathbf{0}\cdot\mathbf{a} = \langle 0, 0\rangle \cdot \langle a_1, a_2\rangle = 0(a_1) + 0(a_2) = 0 + 0 = 0$

40 $(\mathbf{a}+\mathbf{b})\cdot(\mathbf{a}-\mathbf{b}) = (\langle a_1, a_2\rangle + \langle b_1, b_2\rangle)\cdot(\langle a_1, a_2\rangle - \langle b_1, b_2\rangle)$

$= \langle a_1 + b_1, a_2 + b_2\rangle \cdot \langle a_1 - b_1, a_2 - b_2\rangle$

$= (a_1 + b_1)(a_1 - b_1) + (a_2 + b_2)(a_2 - b_2)$

$= a_1^2 - b_1^2 + a_2^2 - b_2^2$

$= (a_1^2 + a_2^2) - (b_1^2 + b_2^2)$

$= (\langle a_1, a_2\rangle \cdot \langle a_1, a_2\rangle) - (\langle b_1, b_2\rangle \cdot \langle b_1, b_2\rangle) = \mathbf{a}\cdot\mathbf{a} - \mathbf{b}\cdot\mathbf{b}$

41 Using the horizontal and vertical components of a vector from Section 7.5,

we have the force vector as $\langle 20\cos 30°, 20\sin 30°\rangle = \langle 10\sqrt{3}, 10\rangle$.

The distance (direction vector) can be described by the vector $\langle 100, 0\rangle$.

The work done is $\langle 10\sqrt{3}, 10\rangle \cdot \langle 100, 0\rangle = 1000\sqrt{3} \approx 1732$ ft-lb.

42 The force vector is now $\langle 20\cos 60°, 20\sin 60°\rangle = \langle 10, 10\sqrt{3}\rangle$.

The direction vector is $\langle 100\cos 30°, 100\sin 30°\rangle = \langle 50\sqrt{3}, 50\rangle$. The work done is

$\langle 10, 10\sqrt{3}\rangle \cdot \langle 50\sqrt{3}, 50\rangle = 500\sqrt{3} + 500\sqrt{3} = 1000\sqrt{3} \approx 1732$ ft-lb. Note that the

force in relation to the direction of movement is exactly the same as in Exercise 41.

43 (a) The horizontal component has magnitude 93×10^6 and

the vertical component has magnitude 0.432×10^6.

Thus, $\mathbf{v} = (93\times 10^6)\mathbf{i} + (0.432\times 10^6)\mathbf{j}$ and $\mathbf{w} = (93\times 10^6)\mathbf{i} - (0.432\times 10^6)\mathbf{j}$.

(b) $\cos\theta = \dfrac{\mathbf{v}\cdot\mathbf{w}}{\|\mathbf{v}\|\|\mathbf{w}\|} \approx 0.99995684 \Rightarrow \theta \approx 0.53°$

44 Let the vector $\mathbf{I}$ represent the magnitude and direction of the sun's rays and $\mathbf{h}$ a

horizontal vector. Then, $\text{comp}_\mathbf{h}\mathbf{I} = \|\mathbf{I}\|\cos\phi = I\cos\phi = $

$978\,e^{-0.136/\sin 30°}\cos 30° \approx 645$ watts/m^2. The total amount of radiation striking the

wall is approximately $160\times 645 = 103{,}200$ watts.

45 $\mathbf{R} = 2(\mathbf{N}\cdot\mathbf{L})\mathbf{N} - \mathbf{L} = 2(\langle 0, 1\rangle \cdot \langle -\frac{4}{5}, \frac{3}{5}\rangle)\langle 0, 1\rangle - \langle -\frac{4}{5}, \frac{3}{5}\rangle = 2(\frac{3}{5})\langle 0, 1\rangle - \langle -\frac{4}{5}, \frac{3}{5}\rangle =$

$\langle 0, \frac{6}{5}\rangle - \langle -\frac{4}{5}, \frac{3}{5}\rangle = \langle \frac{4}{5}, \frac{3}{5}\rangle$

46 $\mathbf{R} = 2(\mathbf{N}\cdot\mathbf{L})\mathbf{N} - \mathbf{L} = 2(\langle \frac{1}{2}\sqrt{2}, \frac{1}{2}\sqrt{2}\rangle \cdot \langle \frac{12}{13}, -\frac{5}{13}\rangle)\langle \frac{1}{2}\sqrt{2}, \frac{1}{2}\sqrt{2}\rangle - \langle \frac{12}{13}, -\frac{5}{13}\rangle =$

$(\frac{7}{13}\sqrt{2})\langle \frac{1}{2}\sqrt{2}, \frac{1}{2}\sqrt{2}\rangle - \langle \frac{12}{13}, -\frac{5}{13}\rangle = \langle \frac{7}{13}, \frac{7}{13}\rangle - \langle \frac{12}{13}, -\frac{5}{13}\rangle = \langle -\frac{5}{13}, \frac{12}{13}\rangle$

47 Let horizontal ground be represented by $\mathbf{b} = \langle 1, 0 \rangle$ (it could be any $\langle a, 0 \rangle$).

$$\text{comp}_{\mathbf{b}}\, \mathbf{a} = \frac{\mathbf{a} \cdot \mathbf{b}}{\|\mathbf{b}\|} = \frac{\langle 2.6, 4.5 \rangle \cdot \langle 1, 0 \rangle}{\|\langle 1, 0 \rangle\|} = \frac{2.6}{1} = 2.6 \Rightarrow |\text{comp}_{\mathbf{b}}\, \mathbf{a}| = 2.6$$

48 Let horizontal ground be represented by $\mathbf{b} = \langle 1, 0 \rangle$.

$$\text{comp}_{\mathbf{b}}\, \mathbf{a} = \frac{\mathbf{a} \cdot \mathbf{b}}{\|\mathbf{b}\|} = \frac{\langle -3.1, 7.9 \rangle \cdot \langle 1, 0 \rangle}{\|\langle 1, 0 \rangle\|} = \frac{-3.1}{1} = -3.1 \Rightarrow |\text{comp}_{\mathbf{b}}\, \mathbf{a}| = 3.1$$

49 Let the direction of the ground be represented by $\mathbf{b} = \langle \cos\theta, \sin\theta \rangle = \langle \cos 12°, \sin 12° \rangle$.

$$\text{comp}_{\mathbf{b}}\, \mathbf{a} = \frac{\mathbf{a} \cdot \mathbf{b}}{\|\mathbf{b}\|} = \frac{\langle 25.7, -3.9 \rangle \cdot \langle \cos 12°, \sin 12° \rangle}{\|\langle \cos 12°, \sin 12° \rangle\|} \approx \frac{24.33}{1} = 24.33 \Rightarrow |\text{comp}_{\mathbf{b}}\, \mathbf{a}| = 24.33$$

50 Let the direction of the ground be represented by
$$\mathbf{b} = \langle \cos\theta, \sin\theta \rangle = \langle \cos(-17°), \sin(-17°) \rangle.$$

$$\text{comp}_{\mathbf{b}}\, \mathbf{a} = \frac{\mathbf{a} \cdot \mathbf{b}}{\|\mathbf{b}\|} = \frac{\langle -13.8, 19.4 \rangle \cdot \langle \cos(-17°), \sin(-17°) \rangle}{\|\langle \cos(-17°), \sin(-17°) \rangle\|} \approx \frac{-18.87}{1} = -18.87 \Rightarrow$$
$$|\text{comp}_{\mathbf{b}}\, \mathbf{a}| = 18.87$$

51 $P = \frac{1}{550}(\mathbf{F} \cdot \mathbf{v}) = \frac{1}{550}\|\mathbf{F}\|\,\|\mathbf{v}\|\cos\theta = \frac{1}{550}(2200)(8)\cos 30° = 16\sqrt{3} \approx 27.7$ horsepower.

Chapter 7 Review Exercises

1 $a = \sqrt{b^2 + c^2 - 2bc\cos\alpha} = \sqrt{6^2 + 7^2 - 2(6)(7)\cos 60°} = \sqrt{43}.$

$$\beta = \cos^{-1}\left(\frac{a^2 + c^2 - b^2}{2ac}\right) = \cos^{-1}\left(\frac{43 + 49 - 36}{2\sqrt{43}\,(7)}\right) = \cos^{-1}\left(\frac{4}{\sqrt{43}}\right).$$

$$\gamma = \cos^{-1}\left(\frac{a^2 + b^2 - c^2}{2ab}\right) = \cos^{-1}\left(\frac{43 + 36 - 49}{2\sqrt{43}\,(6)}\right) = \cos^{-1}\left(\frac{5}{2\sqrt{43}}\right).$$

2 $\frac{\sin\alpha}{a} = \frac{\sin\gamma}{c} \Rightarrow \alpha = \sin^{-1}\left(\frac{a\sin\gamma}{c}\right) = \sin^{-1}\left(\frac{2\sqrt{3}\cdot\frac{1}{2}}{2}\right) = \sin^{-1}\left(\frac{\sqrt{3}}{2}\right) = 60°$ or $120°$.

There are two triangles possible since in either case $\alpha + \gamma < 180°$.

$\beta = (180° - \gamma) - \alpha = (180° - 30°) - (60°\text{ or }120°) = 90°$ or $30°$.

$$\frac{b}{\sin\beta} = \frac{c}{\sin\gamma} \Rightarrow b = \frac{c\sin\beta}{\sin\gamma} = \frac{2\sin(90°\text{ or }30°)}{\sin 30°} = 4 \text{ or } 2.$$

3 $\gamma = 180° - \alpha - \beta = 180° - 60° - 45° = 75°.$

$$\frac{a}{\sin\alpha} = \frac{b}{\sin\beta} \Rightarrow a = \frac{b\sin\alpha}{\sin\beta} = \frac{100\sin 60°}{\sin 45°} = \frac{100\cdot(\sqrt{3}/2)}{\sqrt{2}/2}\cdot\frac{\sqrt{2}}{\sqrt{2}} = 50\sqrt{6}.$$

$$\frac{c}{\sin\gamma} = \frac{b}{\sin\beta} \Rightarrow c = \frac{b\sin\gamma}{\sin\beta} = \frac{100\sin(45° + 30°)}{\sqrt{2}/2} =$$

$$100\sqrt{2}\,(\sin 45°\cos 30° + \cos 45°\sin 30°) = 100\sqrt{2}\left(\frac{\sqrt{2}}{2}\cdot\frac{\sqrt{3}}{2} + \frac{\sqrt{2}}{2}\cdot\frac{1}{2}\right) =$$

$$\frac{100}{4}\sqrt{2}\,(\sqrt{6} + \sqrt{2}) = 25(2\sqrt{3} + 2) = 50(1 + \sqrt{3}).$$

4 $\alpha = \cos^{-1}\left(\dfrac{b^2 + c^2 - a^2}{2bc}\right) = \cos^{-1}\left(\dfrac{9 + 16 - 4}{2(3)(4)}\right) = \cos^{-1}\left(\dfrac{7}{8}\right).$

$\beta = \cos^{-1}\left(\dfrac{a^2 + c^2 - b^2}{2ac}\right) = \cos^{-1}\left(\dfrac{4 + 16 - 9}{2(2)(4)}\right) = \cos^{-1}\left(\dfrac{11}{16}\right).$

$\gamma = \cos^{-1}\left(\dfrac{a^2 + b^2 - c^2}{2ab}\right) = \cos^{-1}\left(\dfrac{4 + 9 - 16}{2(2)(3)}\right) = \cos^{-1}\left(-\dfrac{1}{4}\right).$

5 $\alpha = 180° - \beta - \gamma = 180° - 67° - 75° = 38°.$

$\dfrac{a}{\sin \alpha} = \dfrac{b}{\sin \beta} \Rightarrow a = \dfrac{b \sin \alpha}{\sin \beta} = \dfrac{12 \sin 38°}{\sin 67°} \approx 8.0.$

$\dfrac{c}{\sin \gamma} = \dfrac{b}{\sin \beta} \Rightarrow c = \dfrac{b \sin \gamma}{\sin \beta} = \dfrac{12 \sin 75°}{\sin 67°} \approx 12.6,\ \text{or } 13.$

6 $\dfrac{\sin \gamma}{c} = \dfrac{\sin \alpha}{a} \Rightarrow \gamma = \sin^{-1}\left(\dfrac{c \sin \alpha}{a}\right) = \sin^{-1}\left(\dfrac{125 \sin 23°30'}{152}\right) \approx \sin^{-1}(0.3279) \approx$

19°10' or 160°50' { rounded to the nearest 10 minutes }.   Reject 160°50' because then

$\alpha + \gamma \geq 180°.$ $\beta = 180° - \alpha - \gamma \approx 180° - 23°30' - 19°10' = 137°20'.$

$\dfrac{b}{\sin \beta} = \dfrac{a}{\sin \alpha} \Rightarrow b = \dfrac{a \sin \beta}{\sin \alpha} = \dfrac{152 \sin 137°20'}{\sin 23°30'} \approx 258.3,\ \text{or } 258.$

7 $b = \sqrt{a^2 + c^2 - 2ac \cos \beta} \approx \sqrt{102.8} \approx 10.1.$

$\alpha = \cos^{-1}\left(\dfrac{b^2 + c^2 - a^2}{2bc}\right) \approx \cos^{-1}(0.9116) \approx 24°.$

$\gamma = 180° - \alpha - \beta \approx 180° - 24° - 115° = 41°.$

8 $\alpha = \cos^{-1}\left(\dfrac{b^2 + c^2 - a^2}{2bc}\right) \approx \cos^{-1}(0.7410) \approx 42°.$

$\beta = \cos^{-1}\left(\dfrac{a^2 + c^2 - b^2}{2ac}\right) \approx \cos^{-1}(0.0607) \approx 87°.$

$\gamma = 180° - \alpha - \beta \approx 180° - 42° - 87° = 51°.$

9 $\mathcal{A} = \frac{1}{2}bc \sin \alpha = \frac{1}{2}(20)(30) \sin 75° \approx 289.8,\ \text{or } 290 \text{ square units.}$

10 $s = \frac{1}{2}(a + b + c) = \frac{1}{2}(4 + 7 + 10) = 10.5.$

$\mathcal{A} = \sqrt{s(s - a)(s - b)(s - c)} = \sqrt{(10.5)(6.5)(3.5)(0.5)} \approx 10.9 \text{ square units.}$

11 $z = -10 + 10i \Rightarrow r = \sqrt{(-10)^2 + 10^2} = \sqrt{200} = 10\sqrt{2}.$

$\tan \theta = \dfrac{10}{-10} = -1 \text{ and } \theta \text{ in QII} \Rightarrow \theta = \dfrac{3\pi}{4}.\ \ z = 10\sqrt{2}\,\mathrm{cis}\,\dfrac{3\pi}{4}.$

12 $z = 2 - 2\sqrt{3}i \Rightarrow r = \sqrt{2^2 + (-2\sqrt{3})^2} = \sqrt{16} = 4.$

$\tan \theta = \dfrac{-2\sqrt{3}}{2} = -\sqrt{3} \text{ and } \theta \text{ in QIV} \Rightarrow \theta = \dfrac{5\pi}{3}.\ \ z = 4\,\mathrm{cis}\,\dfrac{5\pi}{3}.$

13 $z = -17 \Rightarrow r = 17.$ θ on the negative x-axis $\Rightarrow \theta = \pi.$ $z = 17\,\mathrm{cis}\,\pi.$

14 $z = -12i \Rightarrow r = 12.$ θ on the negative y-axis $\Rightarrow \theta = \dfrac{3\pi}{2}.$ $z = 12\,\mathrm{cis}\,\dfrac{3\pi}{2}.$

15 $z = -5\sqrt{3} - 5i \Rightarrow r = \sqrt{(-5\sqrt{3})^2 + (-5)^2} = \sqrt{100} = 10.$

$\tan \theta = \dfrac{-5}{-5\sqrt{3}} = \dfrac{1}{\sqrt{3}} \text{ and } \theta \text{ in QIII} \Rightarrow \theta = \dfrac{7\pi}{6}.\ \ z = 10\,\mathrm{cis}\,\dfrac{7\pi}{6}.$

$\boxed{16}$ $z = 4 + 5i \Rightarrow r = \sqrt{4^2 + 5^2} = \sqrt{41}.$ $\tan\theta = \frac{5}{4}$ and θ in QI $\Rightarrow \theta = \tan^{-1}\frac{5}{4}.$

$$z = \sqrt{41}\,\text{cis}\,(\tan^{-1}\tfrac{5}{4}).$$

$\boxed{17}$ $20\,(\cos\frac{11\pi}{6} + i\sin\frac{11\pi}{6}) = 20\left(\frac{\sqrt{3}}{2} - \frac{1}{2}i\right) = 10\sqrt{3} - 10i$

$\boxed{18}$ $13\,\text{cis}\,(\tan^{-1}\frac{5}{12}) = 13\left[\cos(\tan^{-1}\frac{5}{12}) + i\sin(\tan^{-1}\frac{5}{12})\right] = 13\,(\frac{12}{13} + \frac{5}{13}i) = 12 + 5i$

$\boxed{19}$ $z_1 = -3\sqrt{3} - 3i = 6\,\text{cis}\,\frac{7\pi}{6}$ and $z_2 = 2\sqrt{3} + 2i = 4\,\text{cis}\,\frac{\pi}{6}.$

$z_1 z_2 = 6 \cdot 4\,\text{cis}\,(\frac{7\pi}{6} + \frac{\pi}{6}) = 24\,\text{cis}\,\frac{4\pi}{3} = 24\left(-\frac{1}{2} - \frac{\sqrt{3}}{2}i\right) = -12 - 12\sqrt{3}\,i.$

$\frac{z_1}{z_2} = \frac{6}{4}\,\text{cis}\,(\frac{7\pi}{6} - \frac{\pi}{6}) = \frac{3}{2}\,\text{cis}\,\pi = \frac{3}{2}(-1 + 0i) = -\frac{3}{2}.$

$\boxed{20}$ $z_1 = 2\sqrt{2} + 2\sqrt{2}i = 4\,\text{cis}\,\frac{\pi}{4}$ and $z_2 = -1 - i = \sqrt{2}\,\text{cis}\,\frac{5\pi}{4}.$

$z_1 z_2 = 4 \cdot \sqrt{2}\,\text{cis}\,(\frac{\pi}{4} + \frac{5\pi}{4}) = 4\sqrt{2}\,\text{cis}\,\frac{3\pi}{2} = 4\sqrt{2}\,(0 - i) = -4\sqrt{2}\,i.$

$\frac{z_1}{z_2} = \frac{4}{\sqrt{2}}\,\text{cis}\,(\frac{\pi}{4} - \frac{5\pi}{4}) = 2\sqrt{2}\,\text{cis}\,(-\pi) = 2\sqrt{2}\,(-1 + 0i) = -2\sqrt{2}.$

$\boxed{21}$ $(-\sqrt{3} + i)^9 = (2\,\text{cis}\,\frac{5\pi}{6})^9 = 2^9\,\text{cis}\,\frac{15\pi}{2} = 512\,\text{cis}\,\frac{3\pi}{2} = 512(0 - i) = -512i$

$\boxed{22}$ $\left(\frac{\sqrt{2}}{2} - \frac{\sqrt{2}}{2}i\right)^{30} = (1\,\text{cis}\,\frac{7\pi}{4})^{30} = 1^{30}\,\text{cis}\,\frac{105\pi}{2} = \text{cis}\,\frac{\pi}{2} = 0 + i$

$\boxed{23}$ $(3 - 3i)^5 = (3\sqrt{2}\,\text{cis}\,\frac{7\pi}{4})^5 = (3\sqrt{2})^5\,\text{cis}\,\frac{35\pi}{4} = 972\sqrt{2}\,\text{cis}\,\frac{3\pi}{4} = 972\sqrt{2}\left(-\frac{\sqrt{2}}{2} + \frac{\sqrt{2}}{2}i\right) =$

$$-972 + 972i$$

$\boxed{24}$ $(2 + 2\sqrt{3}\,i)^{10} = (4\,\text{cis}\,\frac{\pi}{3})^{10} = 4^{10}\,\text{cis}\,\frac{10\pi}{3} = 2^{20}\,\text{cis}\,\frac{4\pi}{3} = 2^{20}\left(-\frac{1}{2} - \frac{\sqrt{3}}{2}i\right) =$

$$-2^{19} - 2^{19}\sqrt{3}\,i$$

$\boxed{25}$ $-27 + 0i = 27\,\text{cis}\,180°.$ $w_k = \sqrt[3]{27}\,\text{cis}\left(\frac{180° + 360°k}{3}\right)$ for $k = 0,\,1,\,2.$

$w_0 = 3\,\text{cis}\,60° = 3\left(\frac{1}{2} + \frac{\sqrt{3}}{2}i\right) = \frac{3}{2} + \frac{3\sqrt{3}}{2}i.$

$w_1 = 3\,\text{cis}\,180° = 3(-1 + 0i) = -3.$

$w_2 = 3\,\text{cis}\,300° = 3\left(\frac{1}{2} - \frac{\sqrt{3}}{2}i\right) = \frac{3}{2} - \frac{3\sqrt{3}}{2}i.$

$\boxed{26}$ (a) $z^{24} = (1 - \sqrt{3}\,i)^{24} = (2\,\text{cis}\,\frac{5\pi}{3})^{24} = 2^{24}\,\text{cis}\,40\pi = 2^{24}(1 + 0i) = 2^{24}$

(b) $1 - \sqrt{3}\,i = 2\,\text{cis}\,300°.$ $w_k = \sqrt[3]{2}\,\text{cis}\left(\frac{300° + 360°k}{3}\right)$ for $k = 0,\,1,\,2.$

$$w_k = \sqrt[3]{2}\,\text{cis}\,\theta \text{ with } \theta = 100°,\,220°,\,340°.$$

$\boxed{27}$ $x^5 - 32 = 0 \Rightarrow x^5 = 32.$ The problem is now to find the 5 fifth roots of 32.

$32 = 32 + 0i = 32\,\text{cis}\,0°.$ $w_k = \sqrt[5]{32}\,\text{cis}\left(\frac{0° + 360°k}{5}\right)$ for $k = 0,\,1,\,2,\,3,\,4.$

$$w_k = 2\,\text{cis}\,\theta \text{ with } \theta = 0°,\,72°,\,144°,\,216°,\,288°.$$

28 (a) $\mathbf{a} = \langle -4, 5 \rangle$ and $\mathbf{b} = \langle 2, -8 \rangle \Rightarrow$

$\mathbf{a} + \mathbf{b} = \langle -4 + 2, 5 + (-8) \rangle = \langle -2, -3 \rangle.$

(b) $\mathbf{a} - \mathbf{b} = \langle -4 - 2, 5 - (-8) \rangle = \langle -6, 13 \rangle.$

(c) $2\mathbf{a} = 2\langle -4, 5 \rangle = \langle -8, 10 \rangle.$

(d) $-\frac{1}{2}\mathbf{b} = -\frac{1}{2}\langle 2, -8 \rangle = \langle -1, 4 \rangle.$

Terminal points are $(-2, -3)$, $(-6, 13)$, $(-8, 10)$, $(-1, 4)$.

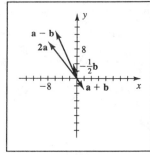

Figure 28

29 (a) $4\mathbf{a} + \mathbf{b} = 4(2\mathbf{i} + 5\mathbf{j}) + (4\mathbf{i} - \mathbf{j}) = 8\mathbf{i} + 20\mathbf{j} + 4\mathbf{i} - \mathbf{j} = 12\mathbf{i} + 19\mathbf{j}.$

(b) $2\mathbf{a} - 3\mathbf{b} = 2(2\mathbf{i} + 5\mathbf{j}) - 3(4\mathbf{i} - \mathbf{j}) = 4\mathbf{i} + 10\mathbf{j} - 12\mathbf{i} + 3\mathbf{j} = -8\mathbf{i} + 13\mathbf{j}.$

(c) $\| \mathbf{a} - \mathbf{b} \| = \| (2\mathbf{i} + 5\mathbf{j}) - (4\mathbf{i} - \mathbf{j}) \| = \| -2\mathbf{i} + 6\mathbf{j} \| = \sqrt{40} = 2\sqrt{10} \approx 6.32.$

(d) $\| \mathbf{a} \| - \| \mathbf{b} \| = \| 2\mathbf{i} + 5\mathbf{j} \| - \| 4\mathbf{i} - \mathbf{j} \| = \sqrt{29} - \sqrt{17} \approx 1.26.$

30 $\| \mathbf{r} - \mathbf{a} \| = c \Rightarrow \| \langle x - a_1, y - a_2 \rangle \| = c \Rightarrow \sqrt{(x - a_1)^2 + (y - a_2)^2} = c \Rightarrow$

$(x - a_1)^2 + (y - a_2)^2 = c^2.$ This is a circle with center (a_1, a_2) and radius c.

31 The vectors $\mathbf{a}$, $\mathbf{b}$, and $\mathbf{a} - \mathbf{b}$ form a triangle with the vector $\mathbf{a} - \mathbf{b}$ opposite angle θ.

The conclusion is a direct application of the law of cosines with sides $\| \mathbf{a} \|$, $\| \mathbf{b} \|$, and

$\| \mathbf{a} - \mathbf{b} \|$.

32 S50°E is the same as 320°, or −40°, on the xy-plane.

$$\langle 14 \cos(-40°), 14 \sin(-40°) \rangle = \langle 14 \cos 40°, -14 \sin 40° \rangle \approx \langle 10.72, -9.00 \rangle.$$

33 S60°E is equivalent to 330° and N74°E is equivalent to 16°.

$$\langle 72 \cos 330°, 72 \sin 330° \rangle + \langle 46 \cos 16°, 46 \sin 16° \rangle = \mathbf{r} \approx \langle 106.57, -23.32 \rangle.$$

$$\| \mathbf{r} \| \approx 109 \text{ kg.} \quad \tan \theta \approx \tfrac{-23.32}{106.57} \Rightarrow \theta \approx -12°, \text{ or equivalently, S78°E.}$$

34 $\mathbf{p} = \langle 400 \cos 10°, 400 \sin 10° \rangle \approx \langle 393.92, 69.46 \rangle.$

$\mathbf{r} = \langle 390 \cos 0°, 390 \sin 0° \rangle = \langle 390, 0 \rangle.$

$\mathbf{w} = \mathbf{r} - \mathbf{p} \approx \langle -3.92, -69.46 \rangle$ and $\| \mathbf{w} \| \approx 69.57$, or 70 mi/hr.

$\tan \theta \approx \tfrac{-69.46}{-3.92} \Rightarrow \theta \approx 267°$, or in the direction of 183°.

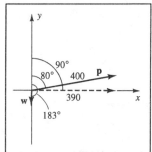

Figure 34

35 (a) $\mathbf{a} \cdot \mathbf{b} = \langle 2, -3 \rangle \cdot \langle -1, -4 \rangle = (2)(-1) + (-3)(-4) = -2 + 12 = 10$

(b) The angle between $\mathbf{a}$ and $\mathbf{b}$ is $\theta = \cos^{-1}\left(\dfrac{\mathbf{a} \cdot \mathbf{b}}{\| \mathbf{a} \| \| \mathbf{b} \|} \right) = \cos^{-1}\left(\dfrac{10}{\sqrt{13}\sqrt{17}} \right) \approx 47°44'.$

(c) $\text{comp}_{\mathbf{a}} \mathbf{b} = \dfrac{\mathbf{b} \cdot \mathbf{a}}{\| \mathbf{a} \|} = \dfrac{10}{\sqrt{13}} \approx 2.77$

36 (a) $(2\mathbf{a} - 3\mathbf{b}) \cdot \mathbf{a} = [2(6\mathbf{i} - 2\mathbf{j}) - 3(\mathbf{i} + 3\mathbf{j})] \cdot (6\mathbf{i} - 2\mathbf{j})$

$= (9\mathbf{i} - 13\mathbf{j}) \cdot (6\mathbf{i} - 2\mathbf{j}) = 54 + 26 = 80.$

(b) $\mathbf{c} = \mathbf{a} + \mathbf{b} = (6\mathbf{i} - 2\mathbf{j}) + (\mathbf{i} + 3\mathbf{j}) = 7\mathbf{i} + \mathbf{j}.$ The angle between $\mathbf{a}$ and $\mathbf{c}$ is

$$\theta = \cos^{-1}\left(\frac{\mathbf{a} \cdot \mathbf{c}}{\|\mathbf{a}\|\|\mathbf{c}\|}\right) = \cos^{-1}\left(\frac{(6\mathbf{i} - 2\mathbf{j}) \cdot (7\mathbf{i} + \mathbf{j})}{\|6\mathbf{i} - 2\mathbf{j}\|\|7\mathbf{i} + \mathbf{j}\|}\right) = \cos^{-1}\left(\frac{40}{\sqrt{40}\sqrt{50}}\right) \approx 26°34'.$$

(c) $\text{comp}_{\mathbf{a}}(\mathbf{a} + \mathbf{b}) = \text{comp}_{\mathbf{a}}\mathbf{c} = \frac{\mathbf{c} \cdot \mathbf{a}}{\|\mathbf{a}\|} = \frac{40}{\sqrt{40}} = \sqrt{40} = 2\sqrt{10} \approx 6.32.$

37 $\mathbf{a} \cdot \overrightarrow{PQ} = \langle 7, 4 \rangle \cdot \langle 3 - (-5), 0 - 0 \rangle = 56 + 0 = 56.$

38 $\dfrac{\sin \gamma}{150} = \dfrac{\sin 27.4°}{200} \Rightarrow$

$\gamma = \sin^{-1}\left(\dfrac{150 \sin 27.4°}{200}\right) \approx \sin^{-1}(0.3451) \approx 20.2°.$

$\beta = 180° - \alpha - \beta \approx 180° - 27.4° - 20.2° = 132.4°.$

The angle between the hill and the horizontal is then

$180° - 132.4° = 47.6°.$

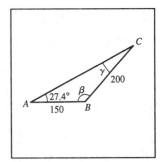

Figure 38

39 Let a be the Earth–Venus distance, b be the Earth–sun distance, and c be the Venus–sun distance. Then, by the law of cosines (with a, b, and c in millions),

$a^2 = b^2 + c^2 - 2bc \cos \alpha = 93^2 + 67^2 - 2(93)(67) \cos 34° \approx 2807 \Rightarrow$

$a \approx 53$—that is, 53,000,000 miles.

40 Let P denote the point at the base of the shorter building, S the point at the top of the shorter building, T the point at the top of the skyscraper, Q the point 50 feet up the side of the skyscraper, and h the height of the skyscraper.

(a) $\angle SPT = 90° - 62° = 28°.$ $\angle PST = 90° + 59° = 149°.$

Thus, $\angle STP = 180° - 28° - 149° = 3°.$ $\dfrac{\overline{ST}}{\sin 28°} = \dfrac{50}{\sin 3°} \Rightarrow \overline{ST} \approx 448.52,$ or 449 ft.

(b) $h = \overline{QT} + 50 = \overline{ST} \sin 59° + 50 \approx 434.45,$ or 434 ft.

41 (a) $\angle LAS = 180° - 47.2° - 66.4° = 66.4°.$ $\dfrac{\overline{AL}}{\sin 47.2°} = \dfrac{41}{\sin 66.4°} \Rightarrow$

$\overline{AL} = \dfrac{41 \sin 47.2°}{\sin 66.4°} \approx 32.83,$ or 33 miles. $\overline{AS} = \overline{LS} = 41$ since $\triangle LAS$ is isosceles.

(b) Let $\overline{AP}$ be perpendicular to $\overline{LS}.$ $\sin 47.2° = \dfrac{\overline{AP}}{\overline{AS}} \Rightarrow \overline{AP} \approx 30.08,$ or 30 miles.

$\boxed{42}$ Let E denote the middle point. $\angle CDA = \angle BDC - \angle BDA = 125° - 100° = 25°$.

In $\triangle CAD$, $\angle CAD = 180° - \angle ACD - \angle CDA = 180° - 115° - 25° = 40°$.

$\dfrac{\overline{AD}}{\sin 115°} = \dfrac{120}{\sin 40°} \Rightarrow \overline{AD} \approx 169.20$. $\angle DCB = \angle ACD - \angle ACB = 115° - 92° = 23°$.

In $\triangle DBC$, $\angle DBC = 180° - \angle BDC - \angle DCB = 180° - 125° - 23° = 32°$.

$\dfrac{\overline{BD}}{\sin 23°} = \dfrac{120}{\sin 32°} \Rightarrow \overline{BD} \approx 88.48$.

In $\triangle ADB$, $\overline{AB}^2 = \overline{AD}^2 + \overline{BD}^2 - 2(\overline{AD})(\overline{BD})\cos \angle BDA \Rightarrow$

$$\overline{AB} \approx \sqrt{(169.20)^2 + (88.48)^2 - 2(169.20)(88.48)\cos 100°} \approx 204.1, \text{ or } 204 \text{ ft.}$$

$\boxed{43}$ If d denotes the distance each girl walks before losing contact with each other,

then $d = 5t$, where t is in hours. Using the law of cosines,

$10^2 = d^2 + d^2 - 2(d)(d)\cos 105° \Rightarrow 100 = 2d^2(1 - \cos 105°) \Rightarrow d \approx 6.30 \Rightarrow$

$$t = d/5 \approx 1.26 \text{ hours, or } 1 \text{ hour and } 16 \text{ minutes.}$$

$\boxed{44}$ (a) Draw a vertical line l through C and label its x-intercept D. Since we have

alternate interior angles, $\angle ACD = \theta_1$. $\angle DCP = 180° - \theta_2$.

$$\text{Thus } \angle ACP = \angle ACD + \angle DCP = \theta_1 + (180° - \theta_2) = 180° - (\theta_2 - \theta_1).$$

(b) Let $k = d(A, P)$. $k^2 = 17^2 + 17^2 - 2(17)(17)\cos\big[180° - (\theta_2 - \theta_1)\big]$.

Since $\cos(180° - \alpha) = \cos 180° \cos \alpha + \sin 180° \sin \alpha = -\cos \alpha$, we have

$k^2 = 578 + 578\cos(\theta_2 - \theta_1) = 578\big[1 + \cos(\theta_2 - \theta_1)\big]$. Using the distance

formula with the points $A(0, 26)$ and $P(x, y)$, we also have $k^2 = x^2 + (y - 26)^2$.

Hence, $578\big[1 + \cos(\theta_2 - \theta_1)\big] = x^2 + (y - 26)^2 \Rightarrow 1 + \cos(\theta_2 - \theta_1) = \dfrac{x^2 + (y - 26)^2}{578}$.

(c) If $x = 25$, $y = 4$, and $\theta_1 = 135°$, then $1 + \cos(\theta_2 - 135°) = \dfrac{25^2 + (-22)^2}{578} = \dfrac{1109}{578} \Rightarrow$

$$\cos(\theta_2 - 135°) = \tfrac{531}{578} \Rightarrow \theta_2 - 135° \approx 23.3° \Rightarrow \theta_2 \approx 158.3°, \text{ or } 158°.$$

$\boxed{45}$ (a) Let d denote the length of the rescue tunnel. Using the law of cosines,

$d^2 = 45^2 + 50^2 - 2(45)(50)\cos 78° \Rightarrow d \approx 59.91$ ft. Now using the law of sines,

$$\frac{\sin \theta}{45} = \frac{\sin 78°}{d} \Rightarrow \theta = \sin^{-1}\left(\frac{45 \sin 78°}{d}\right) \approx 47.28°, \text{ or } 47°.$$

(b) If x denotes the number of hours needed, then

$$d \text{ ft} = (3 \text{ ft/hr})(x \text{ hr}) \Rightarrow x = \tfrac{1}{3}d = \tfrac{1}{3}(59.91) \approx 20 \text{ hr.}$$

46 (a) $\angle CBA = 180° - 136° = 44°$ and

$$d = \overline{AC} = \sqrt{22.9^2 + 17.2^2 - 2(22.9)(17.2)\cos 44°} \approx 15.9. \text{ Let } \alpha = \angle BAC.$$

Using the law of sines, $\dfrac{\sin\alpha}{22.9} = \dfrac{\sin 44°}{d} \Rightarrow \alpha = \sin^{-1}\left(\dfrac{22.9\sin 44°}{d}\right) \approx 87.4°.$

Let $\beta = \angle CAD$. Using the law of cosines, $5.7^2 = d^2 + 16^2 - 2(d)(16)\cos\beta \Rightarrow$

$$\beta = \cos^{-1}\left(\frac{d^2 + 16^2 - 5.7^2}{2(d)(16)}\right) \approx 20.6°. \quad \phi \approx 180° - 87.4° - 20.6° = 72°.$$

(b) The area of $ABCD$ is the sum of the areas of $\triangle CBA$ and $\triangle ADC$.

$$\begin{aligned}
\text{Area } &= \tfrac{1}{2}(\text{base } \overline{BC})(\text{height to } A) + \tfrac{1}{2}(\text{base } \overline{AC})(\text{height to } D) \\
&= \tfrac{1}{2}(\overline{BC})(\overline{BA})\sin\angle CBA + \tfrac{1}{2}(\overline{AC})(\overline{AD})\sin\angle CAD \\
&= \tfrac{1}{2}(22.9)(17.2)\sin 44° + \tfrac{1}{2}(15.9)(16)\sin 20.6° \approx 136.8 + 44.8 = 181.6 \text{ ft}^2.
\end{aligned}$$

(c) Let h denote the perpendicular distance from $\overline{BA}$ to C.

$$\sin 44° = \frac{h}{22.9} \Rightarrow h \approx 15.9. \text{ The wing span } \overline{CC'} \text{ is } 2h + 5.8 \approx 37.6 \text{ ft.}$$

Chapter 7 Discussion Exercises

1 (a) $\dfrac{a}{\sin\alpha} = \dfrac{c}{\sin\gamma} \Rightarrow \dfrac{a}{c} = \dfrac{\sin\alpha}{\sin\gamma}$ and $\dfrac{b}{\sin\beta} = \dfrac{c}{\sin\gamma} \Rightarrow \dfrac{b}{c} = \dfrac{\sin\beta}{\sin\gamma}$.

Adding the equations yields $\dfrac{a}{c} + \dfrac{b}{c} = \dfrac{\sin\alpha}{\sin\gamma} + \dfrac{\sin\beta}{\sin\gamma} \Rightarrow \dfrac{a+b}{c} = \dfrac{\sin\alpha + \sin\beta}{\sin\gamma}.$

(b) $\dfrac{a+b}{c} = \dfrac{\sin\alpha + \sin\beta}{\sin\gamma} \Rightarrow \dfrac{a+b}{c} = \dfrac{\text{[S1]} \; 2\sin\frac{1}{2}(\alpha+\beta)\cos\frac{1}{2}(\alpha-\beta)}{2\sin\frac{1}{2}\gamma\cos\frac{1}{2}\gamma}.$

Now $\gamma = 180° - (\alpha+\beta) \Rightarrow \frac{1}{2}\gamma = \left[90° - \frac{1}{2}(\alpha+\beta)\right]$ and

$$\sin\tfrac{1}{2}(\alpha+\beta) = \cos\left[90° - \tfrac{1}{2}(\alpha+\beta)\right] = \cos\tfrac{1}{2}\gamma. \text{ Thus, } \frac{a+b}{c} = \frac{\cos\frac{1}{2}(\alpha-\beta)}{\sin\frac{1}{2}\gamma}.$$

Note: This is an interesting result and gives an answer to the question "How can I check these triangle problems?" Some of my students have written programs for their graphing calculators to utilize this check.

2 $z^{-n} = r^{-n}\left[\cos(-n\theta) + i\sin(-n\theta)\right] = \dfrac{\cos n\theta - i\sin n\theta}{r^n}$ { cos is even, sin is odd } $=$

$$\frac{(\cos n\theta - i\sin n\theta)(\cos n\theta + i\sin n\theta)}{r^n(\cos n\theta + i\sin n\theta)} = \frac{\cos^2 n\theta - i^2\sin^2 n\theta}{r^n(\cos n\theta + i\sin n\theta)} = \frac{\cos^2 n\theta + \sin^2 n\theta}{r^n(\cos n\theta + i\sin n\theta)} =$$

$$\frac{1}{r^n(\cos n\theta + i\sin n\theta)} = \frac{1}{z^n}$$

3 Algebraic: $\sqrt[3]{a}, \; \sqrt[3]{a}\operatorname{cis}\frac{2\pi}{3}, \; \sqrt[3]{a}\operatorname{cis}\frac{4\pi}{3}$

Geometric: All roots lie on a circle of radius $\sqrt[3]{a}$, they are all 120° apart,

one is on the real axis, one is on $\theta = \frac{2\pi}{3}$, and one is on $\theta = \frac{4\pi}{3}$

4 (a) The vector $\mathbf{v} - \mathbf{w}$ is the vector that would need to be added to $\mathbf{w}$ to equal $\mathbf{v}$. That is, if the initial point of $\mathbf{v} - \mathbf{w}$ (assuming $\mathbf{v}$ and $\mathbf{w}$ have the same initial point) is placed on the terminal point of $\mathbf{w}$, the terminal point of $\mathbf{v} - \mathbf{w}$ would coincide with the terminal point of $\mathbf{v}$ and "complete the triangle."

   (b) Use the law of cosines to obtain
$$\| \mathbf{v} - \mathbf{w} \| = \sqrt{\| \mathbf{v} \|^2 + \| \mathbf{w} \|^2 - 2 \| \mathbf{v} \| \| \mathbf{w} \| \cos \theta}.$$

5 (a) $\mathbf{c} = \mathbf{b} + \mathbf{a} = (\| \mathbf{b} \| \cos \alpha \, \mathbf{i} + \| \mathbf{b} \| \sin \alpha \, \mathbf{j}) + (\| \mathbf{a} \| \cos (-\beta) \, \mathbf{i} + \| \mathbf{a} \| \sin (-\beta) \, \mathbf{j})$
$$= \| \mathbf{b} \| \cos \alpha \, \mathbf{i} + \| \mathbf{b} \| \sin \alpha \, \mathbf{j} + \| \mathbf{a} \| \cos \beta \, \mathbf{i} - \| \mathbf{a} \| \sin \beta \, \mathbf{j}$$
$$= (\| \mathbf{b} \| \cos \alpha + \| \mathbf{a} \| \cos \beta) \mathbf{i} + (\| \mathbf{b} \| \sin \alpha - \| \mathbf{a} \| \sin \beta) \mathbf{j}$$

   (b) $\| \mathbf{c} \|^2 = (\| \mathbf{b} \| \cos \alpha + \| \mathbf{a} \| \cos \beta)^2 + (\| \mathbf{b} \| \sin \alpha - \| \mathbf{a} \| \sin \beta)^2$
$$= \| \mathbf{b} \|^2 \cos^2 \alpha + 2 \| \mathbf{a} \| \| \mathbf{b} \| \cos \alpha \cos \beta + \| \mathbf{a} \|^2 \cos^2 \beta +$$
$$\| \mathbf{b} \|^2 \sin^2 \alpha - 2 \| \mathbf{a} \| \| \mathbf{b} \| \sin \alpha \sin \beta + \| \mathbf{a} \|^2 \sin^2 \beta$$
$$= (\| \mathbf{b} \|^2 \cos^2 \alpha + \| \mathbf{b} \|^2 \sin^2 \alpha) + (\| \mathbf{a} \|^2 \cos^2 \beta + \| \mathbf{a} \|^2 \sin^2 \beta) +$$
$$2 \| \mathbf{a} \| \| \mathbf{b} \| \cos \alpha \cos \beta - 2 \| \mathbf{a} \| \| \mathbf{b} \| \sin \alpha \sin \beta$$
$$= \| \mathbf{b} \|^2 + \| \mathbf{a} \|^2 + 2 \| \mathbf{a} \| \| \mathbf{b} \| (\cos \alpha \cos \beta - \sin \alpha \sin \beta)$$
$$= \| \mathbf{a} \|^2 + \| \mathbf{b} \|^2 + 2 \| \mathbf{a} \| \| \mathbf{b} \| \cos (\alpha + \beta)$$
$$= \| \mathbf{a} \|^2 + \| \mathbf{b} \|^2 + 2 \| \mathbf{a} \| \| \mathbf{b} \| \cos (\pi - \gamma) \; \{ \alpha + \beta + \gamma = \pi \}$$
$$= \| \mathbf{a} \|^2 + \| \mathbf{b} \|^2 - 2 \| \mathbf{a} \| \| \mathbf{b} \| \cos \gamma \; \{ \cos (\pi - \gamma) = -\cos \gamma \}$$

   (c) From part (a), we let $(\| \mathbf{b} \| \sin \alpha - \| \mathbf{a} \| \sin \beta) = 0$.
$$\text{Thus,} \; \| \mathbf{b} \| \sin \alpha = \| \mathbf{a} \| \sin \beta, \text{ and } \frac{\sin \alpha}{\| \mathbf{a} \|} = \frac{\sin \beta}{\| \mathbf{b} \|}.$$

6 (a) $e^{2\pi i} = \cos 2\pi + i \sin 2\pi = 1 + i \cdot 0 = 1$

   (b) $\mathrm{LN} \, (-1) = \mathrm{LN} \, (-1 + 0i) = \ln | -1 + 0i | + i(\pi + 2\pi \cdot 0) =$
$$\ln \sqrt{(-1)^2 + 0^2} + i(\pi) = \ln 1 + \pi i = 0 + \pi i = \pi i$$
$\mathrm{LN} \, i = \mathrm{LN} \, (0 + i) = \ln | 0 + i | + i(\frac{\pi}{2} + 2\pi \cdot 0) = \ln \sqrt{0^2 + 1^2} + i(\frac{\pi}{2}) =$
$$\ln 1 + \tfrac{\pi}{2} i = 0 + \tfrac{\pi}{2} i = \tfrac{\pi}{2} i$$

   (c) $\sqrt{i} = i^{1/2} = e^{(1/2) \mathrm{LN} \, i} = e^{(1/2) (\ln 1 + i(\pi/2))} = e^{(1/2) (i(\pi/2))} = e^{(\pi/4) i} =$
$$\cos \tfrac{\pi}{4} + i \sin \tfrac{\pi}{4} = \frac{\sqrt{2}}{2} + \frac{\sqrt{2}}{2} i$$
$i^i = e^{i \mathrm{LN} \, i} = e^{i \, (\ln 1 + i(\pi/2))} = e^{i(i(\pi/2))} = e^{-\pi/2} \approx 0.2079 \; \{ \text{a real number!} \}$

Chapter 8: Systems of Equations and Inequalities

Note: The notation E_1 and E_2 refers to the first equation and the second equation.

1. Substituting y in E_2 into E_1 yields $2x - 1 = x^2 - 4 \Rightarrow x^2 - 2x - 3 = 0 \Rightarrow$

   $(x - 3)(x + 1) = 0 \Rightarrow x = 3, -1; \ y = 5, -3.$ $\star$ $(3, 5), (-1, -3)$

2. Substituting y in E_1 into E_2 yields $x + x^2 + 1 = 3 \Rightarrow x^2 + x - 2 = 0 \Rightarrow$

   $(x + 2)(x - 1) = 0 \Rightarrow x = -2, 1; \ y = 5, 2.$ $\star$ $(-2, 5), (1, 2)$

3. Solving E_2 for x and substituting into E_1 yields $y^2 = 1 - (1 - 2y) \Rightarrow$

   $y^2 - 2y = 0 \Rightarrow y(y - 2) = 0 \Rightarrow y = 0, 2; \ x = 1, -3.$ $\star$ $(1, 0), (-3, 2)$

4. Solving E_2 for x and substituting into E_1 yields $y^2 = -2y - 3 \Rightarrow$

   $$y^2 + 2y + 3 = 0 \Rightarrow y = -1 \pm \sqrt{2}\,i. \text{ There are \textit{no real solutions}.}$$

5. Substituting y in E_2 into E_1 yields $8x^3 = x^2 \Rightarrow x^2(8x - 1) = 0 \Rightarrow$

   $x = 0, \frac{1}{8}; \ y = 0, \frac{1}{128}.$ $\star$ $(0, 0), (\frac{1}{8}, \frac{1}{128})$

6. Solving E_1 for x and substituting into E_2 yields $2(y^3 + 1) = 9y^2 + 2 \Rightarrow$

   $2y^3 - 9y^2 = 0 \Rightarrow y^2(2y - 9) = 0 \Rightarrow y = 0, \frac{9}{2}; \ x = 1, \frac{737}{8}.$ $\star$ $(1, 0), (\frac{737}{8}, \frac{9}{2})$

7. Solving E_1 for x and substituting into E_2 yields $2(-2y - 1) - 3y = 12 \Rightarrow$

   $-7y = 14 \Rightarrow y = -2; \ x = 3.$ $\star$ $(3, -2)$

8. Solving E_2 for y and substituting into E_1 yields

   $3x - 4(-4 - \frac{3}{2}x) + 20 = 0 \Rightarrow 9x = -36 \Rightarrow x = -4; \ y = 2.$ $\star$ $(-4, 2)$

9. Solving E_1 for x and substituting into E_2 yields $-6(\frac{1}{2} + \frac{3}{2}y) + 9y = 4 \Rightarrow -3 = 4.$

   There are *no solutions*.

10. Solving E_1 for x and substituting into E_2 yields $8(\frac{1}{2} + \frac{5}{4}y) - 10y = -5 \Rightarrow 4 = -5.$

    There are *no solutions*.

11. Solving E_1 for x and substituting into E_2 yields $(5 - 3y)^2 + y^2 = 25 \Rightarrow$

    $10y^2 - 30y = 0 \Rightarrow 10y(y - 3) = 0 \Rightarrow y = 0, 3; \ x = 5, -4.$ $\star$ $(-4, 3), (5, 0)$

12 Solving E_1 for x and substituting into E_2 yields $(\frac{25}{3} + \frac{4}{3}y)^2 + y^2 = 25 \Rightarrow$

$\frac{25}{9}y^2 + \frac{200}{9}y + \frac{400}{9} = 0 \Rightarrow y^2 + 8y + 16 = 0 \Rightarrow$

$(y + 4)^2 = 0 \Rightarrow y = -4;\ x = 3.$　　　　　　　　★ $(3, -4)$

13 Solving E_2 for y and substituting into E_1 yields $x^2 + (x + 4)^2 = 8 \Rightarrow$

$2x^2 + 8x + 8 = 0 \Rightarrow 2(x + 2)^2 = 0 \Rightarrow x = -2;\ y = 2.$　　　　★ $(-2, 2)$

14 Solving E_2 for x and substituting into E_1 yields

$(-\frac{4}{3}y - \frac{25}{3})^2 + y^2 = 25 \Rightarrow \frac{25}{9}y^2 + \frac{200}{9}y + \frac{400}{9} = 0 \Rightarrow$

$y^2 + 8y + 16 = 0 \Rightarrow (y + 4)^2 = 0 \Rightarrow y = -4;\ x = -3.$　　　★ $(-3, -4)$

15 Solving E_2 for y and substituting into E_1 yields

$x^2 + (3x + 2)^2 = 9 \Rightarrow 10x^2 + 12x - 5 = 0 \Rightarrow x = \dfrac{-6 \pm \sqrt{86}}{10} = -\frac{3}{5} \pm \frac{1}{10}\sqrt{86}.$

$y = 3\left(\dfrac{-6 \pm \sqrt{86}}{10}\right) + 2 = \dfrac{-18 \pm 3\sqrt{86}}{10} + \frac{20}{10} = \dfrac{2 \pm 3\sqrt{86}}{10} = \frac{1}{5} \pm \frac{3}{10}\sqrt{86}.$

★ $(-\frac{3}{5} + \frac{1}{10}\sqrt{86}, \frac{1}{5} + \frac{3}{10}\sqrt{86}),\ (-\frac{3}{5} - \frac{1}{10}\sqrt{86}, \frac{1}{5} - \frac{3}{10}\sqrt{86})$

16 Solving E_2 for y and substituting into E_1 yields $x^2 + (-2x - 1)^2 = 16 \Rightarrow$

$5x^2 + 4x - 15 = 0 \Rightarrow x = -\frac{2}{5} \pm \frac{1}{5}\sqrt{79};\ y = -2(-\frac{2}{5} \pm \frac{1}{5}\sqrt{79}) - 1 =$

$\frac{4}{5} \mp \frac{2}{5}\sqrt{79} - \frac{5}{5} = -\frac{1}{5} \mp \frac{2}{5}\sqrt{79}.$　　　★ $(-\frac{2}{5} \pm \frac{1}{5}\sqrt{79},\ -\frac{1}{5} \mp \frac{2}{5}\sqrt{79})$

17 Solving E_2 for x and substituting into E_1 yields $(2y - 4)^2 + y^2 = 16 \Rightarrow$

$5y^2 - 16y = 0 \Rightarrow y(5y - 16) = 0 \Rightarrow y = 0,\ \frac{16}{5};\ x = -4,\ \frac{12}{5}.$　　★ $(-4, 0),\ (\frac{12}{5}, \frac{16}{5})$

18 Solving E_2 for y and substituting into E_1 yields $x^2 + (-2x - 3)^2 = 1 \Rightarrow$

$5x^2 + 12x + 8 = 0 \Rightarrow x = -\frac{6}{5} \pm \frac{2}{5}i.$　There are *no real solutions*.

19 Solving E_2 for x and substituting into E_1 yields

$(1 - y - 1)^2 + (y + 2)^2 = 10 \Rightarrow 2y^2 + 4y - 6 = 0 \Rightarrow$

$2(y + 3)(y - 1) = 0 \Rightarrow y = -3,\ 1;\ x = 4,\ 0.$　　　　★ $(0, 1),\ (4, -3)$

20 Solving E_1 for y and substituting into E_2 yields $3x - \frac{2}{x} + 5 = 0 \Rightarrow 3x^2 + 5x - 2 = 0 \Rightarrow$

$(3x - 1)(x + 2) = 0 \Rightarrow x = \frac{1}{3},\ -2;\ y = 6,\ -1.$　　　★ $(\frac{1}{3}, 6),\ (-2, -1)$

21 Substituting y in E_1 into E_2 yields $20/x^2 = 9 - x^2 \Rightarrow x^4 - 9x^2 + 20 = 0 \Rightarrow$

$(x^2 - 4)(x^2 - 5) = 0 \Rightarrow x = \pm 2, \pm\sqrt{5}; y = 5, 4.$ $\star (\pm 2, 5), (\pm\sqrt{5}, 4)$

22 Solving E_2 for x and substituting into E_1 yields $y + 1 = y^2 - 4y + 5 \Rightarrow$

$y^2 - 5y + 4 = 0 \Rightarrow (y - 1)(y - 4) = 0 \Rightarrow y = 1, 4; x = 2, 5.$ $\star (2, 1), (5, 4)$

23 Solving E_1 for y^2 and substituting into E_2 yields $9(4x^2 + 4) + 16x^2 = 140 \Rightarrow$

$52x^2 = 104 \Rightarrow x = \pm\sqrt{2}; y = \pm 2\sqrt{3}.$ $\star (\sqrt{2}, \pm 2\sqrt{3}), (-\sqrt{2}, \pm 2\sqrt{3})$

24 Solving E_2 for x^2 and substituting into E_1 yields $25y^2 - 16(\frac{9}{4}y^2 - 9) = 400 \Rightarrow$

$$-11y^2 = 256 \Rightarrow y^2 = -\tfrac{256}{11}. \text{ There are } \textit{no real solutions.}$$

25 Solving E_1 for x^2 and substituting into E_2 yields $(y^2 + 4) + y^2 = 12 \Rightarrow 2y^2 = 8 \Rightarrow$

$y = \pm 2; x = \pm 2\sqrt{2}.$ $\star (2\sqrt{2}, \pm 2), (-2\sqrt{2}, \pm 2)$

26 Solving E_1 for y^3 and substituting into E_2 yields $3x^3 + 4(6x^3 - 1) = 5 \Rightarrow$

$27x^3 = 9 \Rightarrow x^3 = \frac{1}{3} \Rightarrow x = \sqrt[3]{\frac{1}{3}}$ or $\frac{1}{3}\sqrt[3]{9}; y = 1.$ $\star (\frac{1}{3}\sqrt[3]{9}, 1)$

27 Solving E_2 for y and substituting into E_1 and E_3 yields

$$\begin{cases} x + 2(2x + z - 9) - z &= -1 \\ x + 3(2x + z - 9) + 3z &= 6 \end{cases} \Rightarrow \begin{cases} 5x + z &= 17 \quad (E_4) \\ 7x + 6z &= 33 \quad (E_5) \end{cases}$$

Solving E_4 for z and substituting into E_5 yields

$7x + 6(17 - 5x) = 33 \Rightarrow -23x = -69 \Rightarrow x = 3.$

Now $z = 17 - 5x = 2$ and $y = 2x + z - 9 = -1.$ $\star (3, -1, 2)$

28 Solving E_2 for z^2 and substituting into E_1 yields $\begin{cases} x - 2y &= 1 \quad (E_4) \\ x^2 - xy &= 0 \quad (E_3) \end{cases}$

Now solve E_4 for x and substitute into E_3 yielding

$(2y + 1)^2 - (2y + 1)y = 0 \Rightarrow 2y^2 + 3y + 1 = 0 \Rightarrow (2y + 1)(y + 1) = 0 \Rightarrow y = -\frac{1}{2}, -1.$

$x = 2y + 1 = 0, -1; z^2 = x - y + 1 = \frac{3}{2}, 1 \Rightarrow$

$z = \pm\sqrt{\frac{3}{2}}, \pm 1.$ $\star (0, -\frac{1}{2}, \pm\sqrt{\frac{3}{2}}), (-1, -1, \pm 1)$

29 Solving E_3 for y and substituting into E_2 yields $\begin{cases} x^2 + z^2 &= 5 \quad (E_1) \\ 2x - z &= 0 \quad (E_4) \end{cases}$

Now solve E_4 for z and substitute into E_1 yielding $x^2 + (2x)^2 = 5 \Rightarrow 5x^2 = 5 \Rightarrow$

$x = \pm 1; z = 2x = \pm 2; y = 1 - z = -1, 3.$ $\star (1, -1, 2), (-1, 3, -2)$

30 Solving E_2 for z and substituting into E_1 and E_3 yields $\begin{cases} x + 4y & = 9 & (E_4) \\ xy(2y - 4) & = 0 & (E_5) \end{cases}$

Now solve E_4 for x and substitute into E_5 yielding

$(9 - 4y)y(2y - 4) = 0 \Rightarrow y = \frac{9}{4}, 0, 2; \ x = 9 - 4y = 0, 9, 1;$

$z = 2y - 4 = \frac{1}{2}, -4, 0.$ ★ $(0, \frac{9}{4}, \frac{1}{2}), (9, 0, -4), (1, 2, 0)$

31 Using $P = 40 = 2l + 2w$ and $A = 96 = lw$, we have $\begin{cases} 2l + 2w & = 40 & (E_1) \\ lw & = 96 & (E_2) \end{cases}$

Solving E_1 for l and substituting into E_2 yields $(20 - w)w = 96 \Rightarrow$

$w^2 - 20w + 96 = 0 \Rightarrow (w - 8)(w - 12) = 0 \Rightarrow w = 8, 12; \ l = 12, 8.$

The rectangle is 12 in × 8 in.

32 Substituting $y = x + b$ into $x^2 + y^2 = 4$ yields $x^2 + (x + b)^2 = 4 \Rightarrow$

$2x^2 + 2bx + (b^2 - 4) = 0 \Rightarrow x = \dfrac{-2b \pm \sqrt{4b^2 - 8(b^2 - 4)}}{4} = \dfrac{-b \pm \sqrt{8 - b^2}}{2}.$

For x to have 1, 2, or no values, the discriminant $8 - b^2$ must be equal to zero, greater than zero, or less than zero, respectively. Graphically, the line would be (a) tangent to the circle, (b) intersect the circle in two points, and (c) not intersect the circle.

(a) $8 - b^2 = 0 \Rightarrow b = \pm\sqrt{8} = \pm 2\sqrt{2}.$

(b) $8 - b^2 > 0 \Rightarrow b^2 < 8 \Rightarrow |b| < 2\sqrt{2} \Rightarrow -2\sqrt{2} < b < 2\sqrt{2}.$

(c) $8 - b^2 < 0 \Rightarrow b > 2\sqrt{2}$ or $b < -2\sqrt{2}$ from parts (a) and (b).

33 From the graph, it is clear that there is a point of intersection and therefore a single solution between 0 and 1.

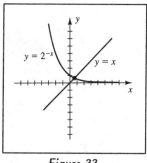

Figure 33

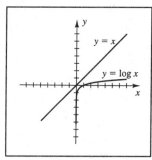

Figure 34

34 From the graph, it is clear that there are no intersection points of the two graphs, and therefore there are no solutions.

35 $A = 200 = (2\pi r)h \Rightarrow \pi rh = 100. \ V = 200 = \pi r^2 h \Rightarrow h = 200/(\pi r^2).$

Substituting h into $\pi rh = 100$ yields $200/r = 100 \Rightarrow r = 2$ in; $h = 50/\pi \approx 15.9$ in.

$\boxed{36}$ The equation of the line is $y - 1 = m(x - 1)$, or $y = mx + (1 - m)$. Setting this

expression equal to x^2 yields $x^2 - mx + m - 1 = 0 \Rightarrow x = \dfrac{m \pm \sqrt{m^2 - 4m + 4}}{2}$.

For there to be only one value of x, the discriminant $m^2 - 4m + 4 = (m - 2)^2$ must be

zero, i.e., $m = 2$. This line, $y = 2x - 1$, is tangent to the parabola.

$\boxed{37}$ (a) Let $S = 40,000$ and $R = 60,000$ for the data for 1995 and 1996.

Then let $S = 60,000$ and $R = 72,000$ for the data for 1996 and 1997.

$$\begin{cases} 60,000 = (40,000a)/(40,000 + b) \\ 72,000 = (60,000a)/(60,000 + b) \end{cases} \Rightarrow \begin{cases} 120,000 + 3b = 2a \quad (E_1) \\ 360,000 + 6b = 5a \quad (E_2) \end{cases}$$

Solving E_1 for a and substituting into E_2 yields

$$360,000 + 6b = 5(60,000 + \tfrac{3}{2}b) \Rightarrow 60,000 = \tfrac{3}{2}b \Rightarrow b = 40,000; \ a = 120,000.$$

(b) Now let $S = 72,000$ and thus $R = \dfrac{(120,000)(72,000)}{72,000 + 40,000} = \dfrac{540,000}{7} \approx 77,143.$

$\boxed{38}$ Follow the outline of the solution in Exercise 37.

(a) $\begin{cases} 60,000 = a(40,000)e^{(-b)(40,000)} \\ 72,000 = a(60,000)e^{(-b)(60,000)} \end{cases} \Rightarrow \begin{cases} 3 = 2ae^{-40,000b} \\ 6 = 5ae^{-60,000b} \end{cases}$

$\Rightarrow 6 = 5\left(\dfrac{3}{2e^{-40,000b}}\right)e^{-60,000b} \Rightarrow 0.8 = e^{-20,000b} \Rightarrow -20,000b = \ln 0.8 \Rightarrow$

$b = \dfrac{\ln 0.8}{-20,000} \approx 0.00001116; \ a = \dfrac{3}{2e^{-40,000\,[\ln 0.8/(-20,000)]}} = \dfrac{3}{2(e^{\ln 0.8})^2} = \dfrac{75}{32}$

(b) $R = \tfrac{75}{32}(72,000)e^{-[\ln 0.8/(-20,000)](72,000)}$

$= 168,750(e^{\ln 0.8})^{3.6} = 168,750(0.8)^{3.6} \approx 75,573$

$\boxed{39}$ Let R_1 and R_2 equal 0. The system is then $\begin{cases} 0 = x(50 - x - y) \\ 0 = y(100 - y - \tfrac{1}{2}x) \end{cases}$

A solution is $x = 0$ and $y = 0$, or $(0, 0)$.

A second solution is $x = 0$ and $100 - y - \tfrac{1}{2}x = 0$ $\{y = 100\}$, or $(0, 100)$.

A third solution is $y = 0$ and $50 - x - y = 0$ $\{x = 50\}$, or $(50, 0)$.

A fourth solution occurs if $50 - x - y = 0$ and $100 - y - \tfrac{1}{2}x = 0$.

Solve the first equation for y $\{y = 50 - x\}$ and substitute into the second

equation: $100 - (50 - x) - \tfrac{1}{2}x = 0 \Rightarrow 50 = -\tfrac{1}{2}x \Rightarrow x = -100; \ y = 150.$

This solution is meaningless for this problem.

40 Let l be the length of the side opposite the river and w the length of the other two

sides. $\{10 \text{ acres} = 435{,}600 \text{ ft}^2\}$ $\qquad \begin{cases} l + 2w &= 2420 & \text{(E}_1) \\ lw &= 435{,}600 & \text{(E}_2) \end{cases}$

Solve E_1 for l and substitute into E_2. $(2420 - 2w)w = 435{,}600 \Rightarrow$

$2w^2 - 2420w + 435{,}600 = 0 \Rightarrow w^2 - 1210w + 217{,}800 = 0 \Rightarrow$

$\qquad\qquad (w - 990)(w - 220) = 0 \Rightarrow w = 990 \text{ or } 220; \ l = 2420 - 2w = 440 \text{ or } 1980.$

41 $\begin{cases} x^2 y = 2 & \textit{Volume} \\ 2x^2 + 3xy = 8 & \textit{Surface Area} \end{cases}$ $\qquad$ Solving E_1 for y and substituting into

E_2 yields $2x^2 + 3x(2/x^2) = 8 \Rightarrow 2x^3 - 8x + 6 = 0 \Rightarrow 2(x - 1)(x^2 + x - 3) = 0 \Rightarrow$

$\{x > 0\} \ x = 1, \dfrac{-1 + \sqrt{13}}{2}.$ There are two solutions: 1 ft $\times$ 1 ft $\times$ 2 ft or

$\qquad\qquad \dfrac{\sqrt{13} - 1}{2} \text{ ft} \times \dfrac{\sqrt{13} - 1}{2} \text{ ft} \times \dfrac{8}{(\sqrt{13} - 1)^2} \text{ ft} \approx 1.30 \text{ ft} \times 1.30 \text{ ft} \times 1.18 \text{ ft.}$

42 Let r denote the radius of a circle, and l and w the length and width of a rectangle.

If the rectangle and circle have equal perimeters and areas, then

$\begin{cases} 2l + 2w = 2\pi r & \textit{Perimeter} \\ lw = \pi r^2 & \textit{Area} \end{cases}$ $\qquad$ Solve E_1 for l and substitute into E_2.

$(\pi r - w)w = \pi r^2 \Rightarrow w^2 - \pi r w + \pi r^2 = 0 \Rightarrow$

$w = \dfrac{\pi r \pm \sqrt{\pi^2 r^2 - 4\pi r^2}}{2} = \dfrac{\pi r \pm r\sqrt{\pi(\pi - 4)}}{2}.$

$\qquad\qquad$ Since the discriminant is negative, there are no real roots.

43 We eliminate n from the equations to determine all intersection points.

(a) $x^2 + y^2 = n^2$ and $y = n - 1 \Rightarrow x^2 + y^2 = (y + 1)^2 \Rightarrow x^2 = 2y + 1 \Rightarrow y = \frac{1}{2}x^2 - \frac{1}{2}.$

$\qquad\qquad$ The points are on the parabola $y = \frac{1}{2}x^2 - \frac{1}{2}.$

(b) $x^2 + y^2 = (y + 2)^2 \Rightarrow x^2 = 4y + 4 \Rightarrow y = \frac{1}{4}x^2 - 1$

44 (a) $\begin{cases} \frac{4}{3}\pi(\frac{1}{2})^3 &= \pi r^2 h & \textit{Volume} \\ 2\left[4\pi(\frac{1}{2})^2\right] &= 2\pi r h + 2\pi r^2 & \textit{S.A.} \end{cases} \Rightarrow \begin{cases} 1 = 6r^2 h & \text{(E}_1) \\ 1 = r^2 + rh & \text{(E}_2) \end{cases}$

$\qquad$ Solve E_1 for h and substitute into E_2. $r^2 + r\left(\dfrac{1}{6r^2}\right) = 1 \Rightarrow 6r^3 - 6r + 1 = 0.$

(b) $r = 0.172 \Rightarrow h \approx 5.63$ (unreasonable) and $r = 0.903 \Rightarrow h \approx 0.204$ (reasonable).

45 (a) The slope of the line from $(-4, -3)$ to the origin is $\frac{3}{4}$ so the slope of the tangent

line (which is perpendicular to the line to the origin) is $-\frac{4}{3}$. The line through

$\qquad (-4, -3)$ is $y + 3 = -\frac{4}{3}(x + 4)$, or $4x + 3y = -25$. Letting $y = -50$, $x = 31.25.$

(b) The slope of the line from (x, y) to the origin is $\frac{y}{x}$ so the slope of the tangent line

is $-\frac{x}{y}$. The line through $(0, -50)$ is $y + 50 = \left(-\frac{x}{y}\right)(x - 0)$, or $y^2 + 50y = -x^2$.

Substituting $x^2 = 25 - y^2$ and solving for y,

$$\text{we have } y = -\tfrac{1}{2} \text{ and } x = -\tfrac{3}{2}\sqrt{11} \approx -4.975.$$

46 (a) Since $y = -\frac{3}{4}x$ is a line that describes the slope, and $x^2 + y^2 = 50^2$, the point

where the ball hits the ground can be found by solving $(x)^2 + \left(-\frac{3}{4}x\right)^2 = 50^2$ for x.

The point is $(40, -30)$.

$$c \text{ is } 0, \text{ so substitute } (40, -30) \text{ for } (x, y) \text{ in } y = ax^2 + x \text{ to give } a = -\tfrac{7}{160}.$$

(b) The maximum height *off the ground* is found when the difference d between the

parabola and the line is greatest. $d = \left(-\frac{7}{160}x^2 + x\right) - \left(-\frac{3}{4}x\right) = -\frac{7}{160}x^2 + \frac{7}{4}x.$

d will be a maximum when $x = \dfrac{-b}{2a} = \dfrac{-7/4}{2(-7/160)} = 20.$ $x = 20 \Rightarrow d = 17.5$ ft.

$$\text{Note that the vertex } \textit{of the parabola} \text{ is } \left(\tfrac{80}{7}, \tfrac{40}{7}\right) \approx (11.4, 5.7).$$

47 Graphically: $x^2 + y^2 = 4 \Rightarrow y = \pm\sqrt{4 - x^2}$ and $x + y = 1 \Rightarrow y = 1 - x$.

Graph $Y_1 = \sqrt{4 - x^2}$, $Y_2 = -Y_1$, and $Y_3 = 1 - x$. There are two points of

intersection at approximately $(-0.82, 1.82)$ and $(1.82, -0.82)$.

Algebraically: $y = 1 - x$ and $x^2 + y^2 = 4 \Rightarrow x^2 + (1 - x)^2 = 4 \Rightarrow 2x^2 - 2x - 3 = 0.$

Using the quadratic formula, $x = \dfrac{2 \pm \sqrt{4 - 4(2)(-3)}}{4} = \dfrac{1 \pm \sqrt{7}}{2}.$ $y = 1 - x \Rightarrow$

$y = 1 - \dfrac{1 \pm \sqrt{7}}{2} = \dfrac{1 \mp \sqrt{7}}{2}.$ The points of intersection are $\left(\tfrac{1}{2} \pm \tfrac{\sqrt{7}}{2}, \tfrac{1}{2} \mp \tfrac{\sqrt{7}}{2}\right).$

The graphical solution approximates the algebraic solution.

[−6, 6] by [−4, 4]   [−9, 9] by [−6, 6]

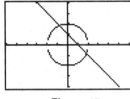

Xscl = 1
Yscl = 1

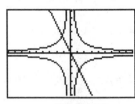

Xscl = 1
Yscl = 1

Figure 47   *Figure 48*

48 Graphically: $x^2 y^2 = 9 \Rightarrow y = \pm\frac{3}{x}$ and $2x + y = 0 \Rightarrow y = -2x.$

Graph $Y_1 = \frac{3}{x}$, $Y_2 = -Y_1$, and $Y_3 = -2x$. There are two points of intersection

at approximately $(-1.22, 2.45)$ and $(1.22, -2.45)$.

Algebraically: $y = -2x$, $x^2 y^2 = 9 \Rightarrow x^2(-2x)^2 = 9 \Rightarrow 4x^4 = 9 \Rightarrow x = \pm\sqrt{\frac{3}{2}} = \pm\frac{1}{2}\sqrt{6}.$

$y = -2x = \mp\sqrt{6}.$ The points of intersection are $\left(\pm\frac{1}{2}\sqrt{6}, \mp\sqrt{6}\right).$

The graphical solution approximates the algebraic solution.

49 After zooming-in near the region of interest in the second quadrant, we see that the cubic intersects the circle twice. Due to the symmetry, we know there are two more points of intersection in the fourth quadrant. Thus, the six points of intersection are approximately (∓ 0.56, ± 1.92), (∓ 0.63, ± 1.90), and (± 1.14, ± 1.65).

$[-6, 6]$ by $[-4, 4]$

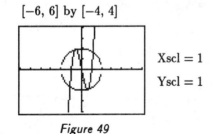

Xscl = 1

Yscl = 1

Figure 49

$[-6, 6]$ by $[-4, 4]$

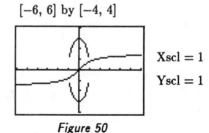

Xscl = 1

Yscl = 1

Figure 50

50 From the graph, there are two points of intersection.

They are approximately (± 0.97, ± 0.77).

51 $|x + \ln |x|| - y^2 = 0 \Rightarrow y = \pm \sqrt{|x + \ln |x||}$ and $\dfrac{x^2}{4} + \dfrac{y^2}{2.25} = 1 \Rightarrow$

$y = \pm 1.5\sqrt{1 - x^2/4}$. The graph is symmetric with respect to x-axis.

There are 8 points of intersection. Their coordinates are approximately

$(-1.44, \pm 1.04)$, $(-0.12, \pm 1.50)$, $(0.10, \pm 1.50)$, and $(1.22, \pm 1.19)$.

$[-3, 3]$ by $[-2, 2]$

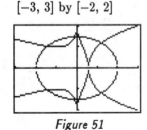

Xscl = 1

Yscl = 1

Figure 51

$[-3, 3]$ by $[-1.8, 2.2]$

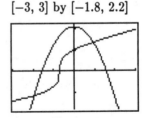

Xscl = 1

Yscl = 1

Figure 52

52 $y^3 - e^{x/2} = x \Rightarrow y = (x + e^{x/2})^{1/3}$ and $y + 0.85x^2 = 2.1 \Rightarrow y = 2.1 - 0.85x^2$.

There are 2 points of intersection.

Their coordinates are approximately $(-1.96, -1.17)$ and $(0.93, 1.36)$.

53 When $x = 1$, $f(1) = ae^{-b} = 0.80487 \Rightarrow a = 0.80487e^{b}$. When $x = 2$, $f(2) = ae^{-2b} = 0.53930 \Rightarrow a = 0.53930e^{2b}$. Let $a = y$ and $b = x$ and then graph $Y_1 = 0.80487e^{x}$ and $Y_2 = 0.53930e^{2x}$. The graphs intersect at approximately $(0.4004, 1.2012) = (b, a)$. Thus, $a \approx 1.2012$, $b \approx 0.4004$, and $f(x) = 1.2012e^{-0.4004x}$. The function f is also accurate at $x = 3, 4$.

[0, 3] by [0, 2]

[1, 13] by [−7, 1]

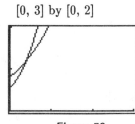

Xscl = 1

Yscl = 1

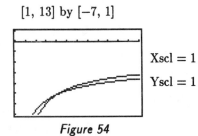

Xscl = 1

Yscl = 1

Figure 53

Figure 54

54 When $x = 1$, $f(1) = a \ln b = -8.208 \Rightarrow a = \dfrac{-8.208}{\ln b}$. When $x = 2$, $f(2) = a \ln 2b = -11.74 \Rightarrow a = \dfrac{-11.74}{\ln 2b}$. Graph $Y_1 = \dfrac{-8.208}{\ln x}$ and $Y_2 = \dfrac{-11.74}{\ln 2x}$. The graphs intersect at approximately $(5.0068, -5.0956)$. Thus, $a \approx -5.0956$, $b \approx 5.0068$, and $f(x) = -5.0956 \ln (5.0068x)$. The function f is also accurate at $x = 3, 4$.

55 When $x = 2$, $f(2) = 4a + e^{2b} = 17.2597 \Rightarrow a = \dfrac{17.2597 - e^{2b}}{4}$. When $x = 3$, $f(3) = 9a + e^{3b} = 40.1058 \Rightarrow a = \dfrac{40.1058 - e^{3b}}{9}$. Graph $Y_1 = \dfrac{17.2597 - e^{2x}}{4}$ and $Y_2 = \dfrac{40.1058 - e^{3x}}{9}$. The graphs intersect at approximately $(0.9002, 2.8019)$. Thus, $a \approx 2.8019$, $b \approx 0.9002$, and $f(x) = 2.8019x^2 + e^{0.9002x}$. The function f is also accurate at $x = 4$.

[0, 4] by [0, 4]

[0, 12] by [0, 8]

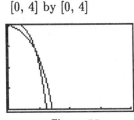

Xscl = 1

Yscl = 1

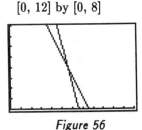

Xscl = 1

Yscl = 1

Figure 55

Figure 56

56 When $x = 2$, $f(2) = \sqrt{2a + b} = 3.8859 \Rightarrow 2a + b = (3.8859)^2 \Rightarrow b = (3.8859)^2 - 2a$. When $x = 4$, $f(4) = \sqrt{4a + b} = 5.1284 \Rightarrow 4a + b = (5.1284)^2 \Rightarrow b = (5.1284)^2 - 4a$. Graph $Y_1 = (3.8859)^2 - 2x$ and $Y_2 = (5.1284)^2 - 4x$. The graphs intersect at approximately $(5.6001, 3.9000)$. Thus, $a \approx 5.6001$, $b \approx 3.9000$, and $f(x) = \sqrt{5.6001x + 3.9000}$. The function f is also accurate at $x = 6$.

$\boxed{1}$ $-2\,E_2 + E_1 \Rightarrow 7y = -14 \Rightarrow y = -2;\ x = 4$ $\qquad\qquad$ ★ $(4,\,-2)$

$\boxed{2}$ $-5\,E_2 + E_1 \Rightarrow -11x = 33 \Rightarrow x = -3;\ y = 5$ $\qquad\qquad$ ★ $(-3,\,5)$

$\boxed{3}$ $3\,E_1 - 2\,E_2 \Rightarrow 29y = 0 \Rightarrow y = 0;\ x = 8$ $\qquad\qquad$ ★ $(8,\,0)$

$\boxed{4}$ $4\,E_1 - 7\,E_2 \Rightarrow -53y = 106 \Rightarrow y = -2;\ x = -1$ $\qquad\qquad$ ★ $(-1,\,-2)$

$\boxed{5}$ $2\,E_2 + E_1 \Rightarrow 5r = -5 \Rightarrow r = -1;\ s = \frac{3}{2}$ $\qquad\qquad$ ★ $(-1,\,\frac{3}{2})$

$\boxed{6}$ $-3\,E_2 + E_1 \Rightarrow 17v = -51 \Rightarrow v = -3;\ u = \frac{2}{3}$ $\qquad\qquad$ ★ $(\frac{2}{3},\,-3)$

$\boxed{7}$ $3\,E_1 - 5\,E_2 \Rightarrow -53y = -28 \Rightarrow y = \frac{28}{53};$

Instead of substituting into one of the equations to find the value of the other variable, it is usually easier to pick different multipliers and re-solve the system for the other variable. $7\,E_1 + 6\,E_2 \Rightarrow 53x = 76 \Rightarrow x = \frac{76}{53}$ $\qquad\qquad$ ★ $(\frac{76}{53},\,\frac{28}{53})$

$\boxed{8}$ $3\,E_1 - 2\,E_2 \Rightarrow 34y = 13 \Rightarrow y = \frac{13}{34};\ 5\,E_1 + 8\,E_2 \Rightarrow 34x = 67 \Rightarrow x = \frac{67}{34}$ $\qquad$ ★ $(\frac{67}{34},\,\frac{13}{34})$

$\boxed{9}$ $\begin{cases} 6\,E_1 \\ 3\,E_2 \end{cases} \Rightarrow \begin{cases} 2c + 3d = 30 & (E_3) \\ 3c - 2d = -3 & (E_4) \end{cases}$ $\quad 3\,E_3 - 2\,E_4 \Rightarrow 13d = 96 \Rightarrow d = \frac{96}{13};$

$2\,E_3 + 3\,E_4 \Rightarrow 13c = 51 \Rightarrow c = \frac{51}{13}$ $\qquad\qquad$ ★ $(\frac{51}{13},\,\frac{96}{13})$

$\boxed{10}$ $\begin{cases} 10\,E_1 \\ 12\,E_2 \end{cases} \Rightarrow \begin{cases} 5t - 2v = 15 & (E_3) \\ 8t + 3v = 5 & (E_4) \end{cases}$ $\quad 8\,E_3 - 5\,E_4 \Rightarrow -31v = 95 \Rightarrow v = -\frac{95}{31};$

$3\,E_3 + 2\,E_4 \Rightarrow 31t = 55 \Rightarrow t = \frac{55}{31}$ $\qquad\qquad$ ★ $(\frac{55}{31},\,-\frac{95}{31})$

$\boxed{11}$ $\sqrt{3}\,E_1 + \sqrt{2}\,E_2 \Rightarrow 7x = 8 \Rightarrow x = \frac{8}{7};$

$2\sqrt{2}\,E_1 - \sqrt{3}\,E_2 \Rightarrow -7y = 3\sqrt{6} \Rightarrow y = -\frac{3}{7}\sqrt{6}$ $\qquad\qquad$ ★ $(\frac{8}{7},\,-\frac{3}{7}\sqrt{6})$

$\boxed{12}$ $\begin{cases} 100\,E_1 \\ 100\,E_2 \end{cases} \Rightarrow \begin{cases} 11x - 3y = 25 & (E_3) \\ 12x + 5y = 70 & (E_4) \end{cases}$

$12\,E_3 - 11\,E_4 \Rightarrow -91y = -470 \Rightarrow y = \frac{470}{91};$

$5\,E_3 + 3\,E_4 \Rightarrow 91x = 335 \Rightarrow x = \frac{335}{91}$ $\qquad\qquad$ ★ $(\frac{335}{91},\,\frac{470}{91})$

$\boxed{13}$ $3\,E_1 + E_2 \Rightarrow 0 = 27;$ *no solution.* $\qquad$ $\boxed{14}$ $4\,E_1 + E_2 \Rightarrow 0 = 31;$ *no solution.*

$\boxed{15}$ $2\,E_1 + E_2 \Rightarrow 0 = 0;$ all ordered pairs $(m,\,n)$ such that $3m - 4n = 2$.

$\boxed{16}$ $-3\,E_1 + E_2 \Rightarrow 0 = 0;$ all ordered pairs $(x,\,y)$ such that $x - 5y = 2$.

$\boxed{17}$ $3\,E_1 - 2\,E_2 \Rightarrow -23x = 0 \Rightarrow x = 0;\ y = 0$ $\qquad\qquad$ ★ $(0,\,0)$

$\boxed{18}$ $-7\,E_2 + E_1 \Rightarrow 3x = -26 \Rightarrow x = -\frac{26}{3};\ y = 5$ $\qquad\qquad$ ★ $(-\frac{26}{3},\,5)$

$\boxed{19}$ Using the hint, the system is $\begin{cases} 2u + 3v = -2 & (E_3) \\ 4u - 5v = 1 & (E_4) \end{cases}$

$-2\,E_3 + E_4 \Rightarrow -11v = 5 \Rightarrow v = -\frac{5}{11};\ 5\,E_3 + 3\,E_4 \Rightarrow 22u = -7 \Rightarrow u = -\frac{7}{22};$

Resubstituting, we have $x = -\frac{22}{7}$ and $y = -\frac{11}{5}$. $\qquad\qquad$ ★ $(-\frac{22}{7},\,-\frac{11}{5})$

20 Let $u = \dfrac{1}{x-1}$ and $v = \dfrac{1}{y+2}$. $\begin{cases} 3u + 4v &= 2 \quad (E_3) \\ 6u - 7v &= -3 \quad (E_4) \end{cases}$

$-2\,E_3 + E_4 \Rightarrow -15v = -7 \Rightarrow v = \frac{7}{15}; \ 7\,E_3 + 4\,E_4 \Rightarrow 45u = 2 \Rightarrow u = \frac{2}{45};$

$x = \frac{1}{u} + 1 = \frac{47}{2}; \ y = \frac{1}{v} - 2 = \frac{1}{7}$ $\bigstar \ \left(\frac{47}{2}, \frac{1}{7}\right)$

21 $\begin{cases} a e^{3x} + b e^{-3x} &= 0 \quad (E_1) \\ a(3e^{3x}) + b(-3e^{-3x}) &= e^{3x} \quad (E_2) \end{cases}$

$-3\,E_1 + E_2 \Rightarrow -3b\,e^{-3x} - 3b\,e^{-3x} = e^{3x} \Rightarrow -6b\,e^{-3x} = e^{3x} \Rightarrow b = -\frac{1}{6}e^{6x}.$

Substituting back into E_1 yields $a e^{3x} + (-\frac{1}{6}e^{6x})e^{-3x} = 0 \Rightarrow a e^{3x} = \frac{1}{6}e^{3x} \Rightarrow a = \frac{1}{6}.$

22 $\begin{cases} a e^{-x} + b e^{4x} &= 0 \quad (E_1) \\ -a e^{-x} + b(4e^{4x}) &= 2 \quad (E_2) \end{cases}$

$E_1 + E_2 \Rightarrow b e^{4x} + 4b\,e^{4x} = 2 \Rightarrow 5b\,e^{4x} = 2 \Rightarrow b = \frac{2}{5}e^{-4x}.$ Substituting back into E_1

yields $a e^{-x} + (\frac{2}{5}e^{-4x})e^{4x} = 0 \Rightarrow a e^{-x} + \frac{2}{5} = 0 \Rightarrow a e^{-x} = -\frac{2}{5} \Rightarrow a = -\frac{2}{5}e^{x}.$

23 $\begin{cases} a \cos x + b \sin x &= 0 \quad (E_1) \\ -a \sin x + b \cos x &= \tan x \quad (E_2) \end{cases}$

$\sin x \ (E_1)$ and $\cos x \ (E_2)$ yield $\begin{cases} a \sin x \cos x + b \sin^2 x &= 0 \quad (E_3) \\ -a \sin x \cos x + b \cos^2 x &= \sin x \quad (E_4) \end{cases}$

$E_3 + E_4 \Rightarrow b \sin^2 x + b \cos^2 x = \sin x \Rightarrow b(\sin^2 x + \cos^2 x) = \sin x \Rightarrow b(1) = \sin x \Rightarrow$

$b = \sin x.$ Substituting back into E_1 yields $a \cos x + \sin^2 x = 0 \Rightarrow$

$$a = -\frac{\sin^2 x}{\cos x} = -\frac{1 - \cos^2 x}{\cos x} = -\frac{1}{\cos x} + \frac{\cos^2 x}{\cos x} = -\sec x + \cos x = \cos x - \sec x.$$

24 $\begin{cases} a \cos x + b \sin x &= 0 \quad (E_1) \\ -a \sin x + b \cos x &= \sin x \quad (E_2) \end{cases}$

$\sin x \ (E_1)$ and $\cos x \ (E_2)$ yield $\begin{cases} a \sin x \cos x + b \sin^2 x &= 0 \quad (E_3) \\ -a \sin x \cos x + b \cos^2 x &= \sin x \cos x \quad (E_4) \end{cases}$

$E_3 + E_4 \Rightarrow b \sin^2 x + b \cos^2 x = \sin x \cos x \Rightarrow b = \sin x \cos x.$

Substituting back into E_1 yields $a \cos x = -\sin^2 x \cos x \Rightarrow a = -\sin^2 x.$

25 Let x denote the number of \$1.50 tickets and y the number of \$2.25 tickets.

$\begin{cases} x + y = 450 & \textit{quantity} \\ 1.50x + 2.25y = 777.75 & \textit{value} \end{cases}$ $100\,E_2 - 150\,E_1 \Rightarrow 75y = 10{,}275 \Rightarrow$
$y = 137; \ x = 313$

26 Let x denote the number of passengers that purchased a ticket to Phoenix and y the number of passengers that purchased a ticket to Albuquerque.

$\begin{cases} x + y = 185 & \textit{quantity} \\ 45x + 60y = 10{,}500 & \textit{value} \end{cases}$ $E_2 - 45\,E_1 \Rightarrow 15y = 2175 \Rightarrow y = 145; \ x = 40$

27 The radius is $\frac{1}{2}$ cm. $\begin{cases} x + y = 8 & \text{length} \\ \pi(\frac{1}{2})^2 x + \frac{1}{3}\pi(\frac{1}{2})^2 y = 5 & \text{volume} \end{cases}$

Solving E_1 for y and substituting into E_2 yields $\frac{\pi}{4}x + \frac{\pi}{12}(8 - x) = 5 \Rightarrow$

$$\frac{\pi}{6}x = \frac{15 - 2\pi}{3} \Rightarrow x = \frac{30 - 4\pi}{\pi} = \frac{30}{\pi} - 4 \approx 5.55 \text{ cm};$$

$$y = 8 - \left(\frac{30 - 4\pi}{\pi}\right) = \frac{12\pi - 30}{\pi} = 12 - \frac{30}{\pi} \approx 2.45 \text{ cm}$$

28 Let x denote the rate at which he can row in still water and y the speed of the

current. $D = RT \begin{cases} 500 = (x - y)10 & \text{upstream} \\ 300 = (x + y)5 & \text{downstream} \end{cases} \Rightarrow \begin{cases} 50 = x - y \\ 60 = x + y \end{cases}$

$$E_1 + E_2 \Rightarrow 2x = 110 \Rightarrow x = 55 \text{ ft/min}; \; y = 5 \text{ ft/min}$$

29 $\begin{cases} 2l + 2\pi(\frac{1}{2}w) = 40 & \text{perimeter} \\ lw = 2\left[\pi(\frac{1}{2}w)^2\right] & \text{area} \end{cases}$ Solving E_1 for l and substituting into E_2

yields $\left(\frac{40 - \pi w}{2}\right)w = \frac{\pi w^2}{2} \Rightarrow 40w = 2\pi w^2 \Rightarrow 2w(\pi w - 20) = 0 \Rightarrow w = 0, \frac{20}{\pi};$

$$w = 20/\pi \approx 6.37 \text{ ft}, \; l = 10 \text{ ft}$$

30 Let x denote the amount invested in the 6% fund and y the amount in the 8% fund.

$\begin{cases} x + y = 15{,}000 & \text{amount} \\ 0.06x + 0.08y = 1000 & \text{interest} \end{cases}$

$$100\,E_2 - 6\,E_1 \Rightarrow 2y = 10{,}000 \Rightarrow y = \$5000; \; x = \$10{,}000$$

31 Let x denote the number of adults and y the number of kittens. Thus,

$(\frac{1}{2}x)$ is the number of adult females. $\begin{cases} x + y = 6000 & \text{total} \\ y = 3(\frac{1}{2}x) & \text{3 kittens per adult female} \end{cases}$

Substituting y from E_2 into E_1 yields $x + \frac{3}{2}x = 6000 \Rightarrow x = 2400; \; y = 3600$

32 Let x denote the flow rate of the inlet pipe and y the flow rate of one of the outlet

pipes. $\{\text{(inlet rate} - \text{outlet rate)(hours)} = \text{gallons}\}$

$\begin{cases} (x - 2y)5 = 300 & \text{both open} \\ (x - y)3 = 300 & \text{one closed} \end{cases} \Rightarrow \begin{cases} x - 2y = 60 \\ x - y = 100 \end{cases}$

$$E_2 - E_1 \Rightarrow y = 40 \text{ gal/hr}; \; x = 140 \text{ gal/hr}$$

33 Let x denote the number of grams of the 35% alloy and y the number of grams of the

60% alloy. $\begin{cases} x + y = 100 & \text{quantity} \\ 0.35x + 0.60y = (0.50)(100) & \text{quality} \end{cases}$

$$100\,E_2 - 35\,E_1 \Rightarrow 25y = 1500 \Rightarrow y = 60; \; x = 40$$

34 Let x denote the number of pounds of peanuts used and y the number of pounds of cashews used.

$$\begin{cases} x + y = 60 & \text{\textit{quantity}} \\ 3x + 8y = 5(60) & \text{\textit{quality}} \end{cases}$$

$$E_2 - 3\,E_1 \Rightarrow 5y = 120 \Rightarrow y = 24; \ x = 36$$

35 Let x denote the speed of the plane and y the speed of the wind. $D = RT$

$$\begin{cases} 1200 = (x+y)(2) & \text{\textit{with the wind}} \\ 1200 = (x-y)(2\tfrac{1}{2}) & \text{\textit{against the wind}} \end{cases} \Rightarrow \begin{cases} 600 = x+y \\ 480 = x-y \end{cases}$$

$$E_1 + E_2 \Rightarrow 2x = 1080 \Rightarrow x = 540 \text{ mi/hr}; \ y = 60 \text{ mi/hr}$$

36 Let x denote the number of \$0.50 notebooks and y the number of \$0.70 notebooks.

$$\begin{cases} x + y = 500 & \text{\textit{quantity}} \\ 0.50x + 0.70y = 286 & \text{\textit{value}} \end{cases}$$

$$10\,E_2 - 5\,E_1 \Rightarrow 2y = 360 \Rightarrow y = 180; \ x = 320$$

37 $v(2) = 16 \Rightarrow 16 = v_0 + 2a; \ (E_1)$

$v(5) = 25 \Rightarrow 25 = v_0 + 5a; \ (E_2)$ $\qquad\qquad E_2 - E_1 \Rightarrow 9 = 3a \Rightarrow a = 3; \ v_0 = 10$

38 $s(1) = 84 \Rightarrow 84 = -16 + v_0 + s_0; \ (E_1)$

$s(2) = 116 \Rightarrow 116 = -64 + 2v_0 + s_0; \ (E_2)$ $\qquad E_2 - E_1 \Rightarrow v_0 = 80; \ s_0 = 20$

39 Let x denote the number of sofas produced and y the number of recliners produced.

$$\begin{cases} 8x + 6y = 340 & \text{\textit{labor hours}} \\ 60x + 35y = 2250 & \text{\textit{cost of materials}} \end{cases}$$

$$6\,E_2 - 35\,E_1 \Rightarrow 80x = 1600 \Rightarrow x = 20; \ y = 30$$

40 Let x denote the number of ounces of oats used and y the number of ounces of cornmeal used.

$$\begin{cases} 4x + 3y = 200 & \text{\textit{protein}} \\ 18x + 24y = 1320 & \text{\textit{carbohydrates}} \end{cases}$$

$$E_2 - 8\,E_1 \Rightarrow -14x = -280 \Rightarrow x = 20; \ y = 40$$

41 (a) $6x + 5y$ represents the total bill for the plumber's business. This should equal the plumber's income, i.e., $(6+4)\,x$. $4x + 6y$ represents the total bill for the electrician's business. This should equal the electrician's income, i.e., $(5+6)\,y$.

$$\begin{cases} 6x + 5y = 10x \\ 4x + 6y = 11y \end{cases} \Rightarrow \begin{cases} 5y = 4x \\ 4x = 5y \end{cases} \Rightarrow y = \tfrac{4}{5}x, \text{ or } y = 0.80x$$

(b) The electrician should charge 80% of what the plumber charges.

80% of \$20 per hour is \$16 per hour.

42 We want the equations of the 3 lines that are perpendicular to a side and pass through the opposite vertex. $m_{AB} = \frac{1}{4}$; the equation of the line through C with a slope of -4 is $y + 8 = -4(x - 3) \Leftrightarrow \underline{4x + y = 4}$ (E_1). Similarly, the other two altitudes are: $m_{BC} = 6$; $y - 2 = -\frac{1}{6}(x + 3) \Leftrightarrow \underline{x + 6y = 9}$ (E_2)

$m_{AC} = -\frac{5}{3}$; $y - 4 = \frac{3}{5}(x - 5) \Leftrightarrow \underline{3x - 5y = -5}$ (E_3)

Finding the intersection of E_1 and E_2, we have

$$E_1 - 4E_2 \Rightarrow -23y = -32 \Rightarrow y = \tfrac{32}{23}; \; x = \tfrac{15}{23}. \; \left(\tfrac{15}{23}, \tfrac{32}{23}\right) \text{ also lies on } E_3.$$

43 Let $t = 0$ correspond to the year 1891. The average daily maximum can then be approximated by the equation $y_1 = 0.011t + 15.1$ and the average daily minimum by the equation $y_2 = 0.019t + 5.8$. We must determine t when y_1 and y_2 differ by 9.

$y_1 - y_2 = 9 \Rightarrow (0.011t + 15.1) - (0.019t + 5.8) = 9 \Rightarrow -0.008t = -0.3 \Rightarrow t = 37.5$.

$1891 + 37.5 = 1928.5$ or during 1928.

$$t = 37.5 \Rightarrow y_1 = 0.011(37.5) + 15.1 = 15.5125 \approx 15.5 \,°C.$$

44 (a) Let x denote the cost of the first minute and y the cost of each additional minute. $\begin{cases} x + 35y = 7.27 & 36 \text{ minute call} \\ x + 12y = 2.67 & 13 \text{ minute call} \end{cases}$

$$E_1 - E_2 \Rightarrow 23y = 4.60 \Rightarrow y = \$0.20; \; x = \$0.27$$

(b) If C denotes the cost of an n minute phone call, then $C = 0.27 + 0.20(n - 1)$.

The total cost of the call is

$T = (\text{cost}) + (\text{federal tax}) + (\text{state tax}) = C + 0.032C + 0.072C = 1.104C$.

$T = 5.00 \Rightarrow 5.00 = 1.104C \Rightarrow \frac{5.00}{1.104} = C \Rightarrow \frac{5.00}{1.104} = 0.27 + 0.20(n - 1) \Rightarrow$

$$n \approx 22.29 \text{ min, or } 22 \text{ min.}$$

45 (a) Model this as a line through the two points $(10, 1{,}000{,}000)$ and $(11, 900{,}000)$.

$$Q - 1{,}000{,}000 = \tfrac{900{,}000 - 1{,}000{,}000}{11 - 10}(p - 10) \Rightarrow Q = -100{,}000p + 2{,}000{,}000$$

(b) $K - 2{,}000{,}000 = \frac{150{,}000}{1}(p - 15) \Rightarrow K = 150{,}000p - 250{,}000$

(c) $Q = K \Rightarrow -100{,}000p + 2{,}000{,}000 = 150{,}000p - 250{,}000 \Rightarrow$

$$250{,}000p = 2{,}250{,}000 \Rightarrow p = \$9.00$$

8.3 Exercises

Note: Some equations are interchanged to obtain the matrix in the first step. Most systems are solved using the back substitution method. The solution for Exercise 18 uses the reduced echelon method. To avoid fractions, many solutions include linear combinations of rows.

$\boxed{1}$ $\begin{bmatrix} 1 & -2 & -3 & -1 \\ 2 & 1 & 1 & 6 \\ 1 & 3 & -2 & 13 \end{bmatrix}$ $\begin{array}{l} R_2 - 2R_1 \rightarrow R_2 \\ R_3 - R_1 \rightarrow R_3 \end{array}$

$\begin{bmatrix} 1 & -2 & -3 & -1 \\ 0 & 5 & 7 & 8 \\ 0 & 5 & 1 & 14 \end{bmatrix}$ $R_3 - R_2 \rightarrow R_3$

$\begin{bmatrix} 1 & -2 & -3 & -1 \\ 0 & 5 & 7 & 8 \\ 0 & 0 & -6 & 6 \end{bmatrix}$ $-\frac{1}{6}R_3 \rightarrow R_3$

R_3: $z = -1$
R_2: $5y + 7z = 8 \Rightarrow y = 3$ $\star$ $(2, 3, -1)$
R_1: $x - 2y - 3z = -1 \Rightarrow x = 2$

$\boxed{2}$ $\begin{bmatrix} 1 & 3 & -1 & -3 \\ 3 & -1 & 2 & 1 \\ 2 & -1 & 1 & -1 \end{bmatrix}$ $\begin{array}{l} R_2 - 3R_1 \rightarrow R_2 \\ R_3 - 2R_1 \rightarrow R_3 \end{array}$

$\begin{bmatrix} 1 & 3 & -1 & -3 \\ 0 & -10 & 5 & 10 \\ 0 & -7 & 3 & 5 \end{bmatrix}$ $2R_2 - 3R_3 \rightarrow R_2$

$\begin{bmatrix} 1 & 3 & -1 & -3 \\ 0 & 1 & 1 & 5 \\ 0 & -7 & 3 & 5 \end{bmatrix}$ $R_3 + 7R_2 \rightarrow R_3$

$\begin{bmatrix} 1 & 3 & -1 & -3 \\ 0 & 1 & 1 & 5 \\ 0 & 0 & 10 & 40 \end{bmatrix}$ $\frac{1}{10}R_3 \rightarrow R_3$

R_3: $z = 4$
R_2: $y + z = 5 \Rightarrow y = 1$ $\star$ $(-2, 1, 4)$
R_1: $x + 3y - z = -3 \Rightarrow x = -2$

$\boxed{3}$ $\begin{bmatrix} 1 & -2 & 2 & 0 \\ 5 & 2 & -1 & -7 \\ 0 & 3 & 1 & 17 \end{bmatrix}$ $R_2 - 5R_1 \rightarrow R_2$

$\begin{bmatrix} 1 & -2 & 2 & 0 \\ 0 & 12 & -11 & -7 \\ 0 & 3 & 1 & 17 \end{bmatrix}$ $4R_3 - R_2 \rightarrow R_3$

$\begin{bmatrix} 1 & -2 & 2 & 0 \\ 0 & 12 & -11 & -7 \\ 0 & 0 & 15 & 75 \end{bmatrix}$ $\frac{1}{15}R_3 \rightarrow R_3$

R_3: $z = 5$
R_2: $12y - 11z = -7 \Rightarrow y = 4$ $\star$ $(-2, 4, 5)$
R_1: $x - 2y + 2z = 0 \Rightarrow x = -2$

4
$$\begin{bmatrix} 4 & -1 & 3 & 6 \\ -8 & 3 & -5 & -6 \\ 5 & -4 & 0 & -9 \end{bmatrix} \quad R_3 - R_1 \to R_3$$

$$\begin{bmatrix} 4 & -1 & 3 & 6 \\ -8 & 3 & -5 & -6 \\ 1 & -3 & -3 & -15 \end{bmatrix} \quad \begin{matrix} R_1 - 4R_3 \to R_1 \\ R_2 + 8R_3 \to R_2 \end{matrix}$$

$$\begin{bmatrix} 0 & 11 & 15 & 66 \\ 0 & -21 & -29 & -126 \\ 1 & -3 & -3 & -15 \end{bmatrix} \quad R_2 + 2R_1 \to R_2$$

$$\begin{bmatrix} 0 & 11 & 15 & 66 \\ 0 & 1 & 1 & 6 \\ 1 & -3 & -3 & -15 \end{bmatrix} \quad R_1 - 11R_2 \to R_1$$

$$\begin{bmatrix} 0 & 0 & 4 & 0 \\ 0 & 1 & 1 & 6 \\ 1 & -3 & -3 & -15 \end{bmatrix} \quad \tfrac{1}{4}R_1 \to R_1$$

R_1: $z = 0$
R_2: $y + z = 6 \Rightarrow y = 6$
R_3: $x - 3y - 3z = -15 \Rightarrow x = 3$

★ (3, 6, 0)

5
$$\begin{bmatrix} 1 & 3 & -2 & 4 \\ 2 & 6 & -4 & 1 \\ 2 & 1 & -3 & -7 \end{bmatrix} \quad \begin{matrix} R_2 - 2R_1 \to R_2 \\ R_3 - 2R_1 \to R_3 \end{matrix}$$

$$\begin{bmatrix} 1 & 3 & -2 & 4 \\ 0 & 0 & 0 & -7 \\ 0 & -5 & 1 & -15 \end{bmatrix}$$

The second row, $0x + 0y + 0z = -7$, has *no solution.*

6
$$\begin{bmatrix} 1 & 3 & -3 & -5 \\ 2 & -1 & 1 & -3 \\ -6 & 3 & -3 & 4 \end{bmatrix} \quad \begin{matrix} R_2 - 2R_1 \to R_2 \\ R_3 + 6R_1 \to R_3 \end{matrix}$$

$$\begin{bmatrix} 1 & 3 & -3 & -5 \\ 0 & -7 & 7 & 7 \\ 0 & 21 & -21 & -26 \end{bmatrix} \quad -\tfrac{1}{7}R_2 \to R_2$$

$$\begin{bmatrix} 1 & 3 & -3 & -5 \\ 0 & 1 & -1 & -1 \\ 0 & 21 & -21 & -26 \end{bmatrix} \quad R_3 - 21R_2 \to R_3$$

$$\begin{bmatrix} 1 & 3 & -3 & -5 \\ 0 & 1 & -1 & -1 \\ 0 & 0 & 0 & -5 \end{bmatrix}$$

The third row, $0x + 0y + 0z = -5$, has *no solution.*

7 $\begin{bmatrix} -3 & 2 & 1 & 1 \\ 4 & 1 & -3 & 4 \\ 2 & -3 & 2 & -3 \end{bmatrix}$ $R_1 + R_2 \rightarrow R_1$

$\begin{bmatrix} 1 & 3 & -2 & 5 \\ 4 & 1 & -3 & 4 \\ 2 & -3 & 2 & -3 \end{bmatrix}$ $\begin{matrix} R_2 - 4R_1 \rightarrow R_2 \\ R_3 - 2R_1 \rightarrow R_3 \end{matrix}$

$\begin{bmatrix} 1 & 3 & -2 & 5 \\ 0 & -11 & 5 & -16 \\ 0 & -9 & 6 & -13 \end{bmatrix}$ $4R_2 - 5R_3 \rightarrow R_2$

$\begin{bmatrix} 1 & 3 & -2 & 5 \\ 0 & 1 & -10 & 1 \\ 0 & -9 & 6 & -13 \end{bmatrix}$ $R_3 + 9R_2 \rightarrow R_3$

$\begin{bmatrix} 1 & 3 & -2 & 5 \\ 0 & 1 & -10 & 1 \\ 0 & 0 & -84 & -4 \end{bmatrix}$ $-\frac{1}{84}R_3 \rightarrow R_3$

R_3: $z = \frac{1}{21}$
R_2: $y - 10z = 1 \Rightarrow y = \frac{31}{21}$
R_1: $x + 3y - 2z = 5 \Rightarrow x = \frac{14}{21} = \frac{2}{3}$

★ $\left(\frac{2}{3}, \frac{31}{21}, \frac{1}{21} \right)$

8 $\begin{bmatrix} 2 & -3 & 1 & 2 \\ 3 & 2 & -1 & -5 \\ 5 & -2 & 1 & 0 \end{bmatrix}$ $-R_1 + R_2 \rightarrow R_1$

$\begin{bmatrix} 1 & 5 & -2 & -7 \\ 3 & 2 & -1 & -5 \\ 5 & -2 & 1 & 0 \end{bmatrix}$ $\begin{matrix} R_2 - 3R_1 \rightarrow R_2 \\ R_3 - 5R_1 \rightarrow R_3 \end{matrix}$

$\begin{bmatrix} 1 & 5 & -2 & -7 \\ 0 & -13 & 5 & 16 \\ 0 & -27 & 11 & 35 \end{bmatrix}$ $2R_2 - R_3 \rightarrow R_2$

$\begin{bmatrix} 1 & 5 & -2 & -7 \\ 0 & 1 & -1 & -3 \\ 0 & -27 & 11 & 35 \end{bmatrix}$ $R_3 + 27R_2 \rightarrow R_3$

$\begin{bmatrix} 1 & 5 & -2 & -7 \\ 0 & 1 & -1 & -3 \\ 0 & 0 & -16 & -46 \end{bmatrix}$ $-\frac{1}{16}R_3 \rightarrow R_3$

R_3: $z = \frac{23}{8}$
R_2: $y - z = -3 \Rightarrow y = -\frac{1}{8}$
R_1: $x + 5y - 2z = -7 \Rightarrow x = -\frac{5}{8}$

★ $\left(-\frac{5}{8}, -\frac{1}{8}, \frac{23}{8} \right)$

Note: Exer. 9–16: There are other forms for the answers; c is any real number.

9
$$\begin{bmatrix} 1 & 3 & 1 & 0 \\ 1 & 1 & -1 & 0 \\ 1 & -2 & -4 & 0 \end{bmatrix} \quad \begin{matrix} R_2 - R_1 \to R_2 \\ R_3 - R_1 \to R_3 \end{matrix}$$

$$\begin{bmatrix} 1 & 3 & 1 & 0 \\ 0 & -2 & -2 & 0 \\ 0 & -5 & -5 & 0 \end{bmatrix} \quad \begin{matrix} -\frac{1}{2} R_2 \to R_2 \\ \\ -\frac{1}{5} R_3 \to R_3 \end{matrix}$$

$$\begin{bmatrix} 1 & 3 & 1 & 0 \\ 0 & 1 & 1 & 0 \\ 0 & 1 & 1 & 0 \end{bmatrix} \quad \begin{matrix} R_1 - 3 R_2 \to R_1 \\ \\ R_3 - R_2 \to R_3 \end{matrix}$$

$$\begin{bmatrix} 1 & 0 & -2 & 0 \\ 0 & 1 & 1 & 0 \\ 0 & 0 & 0 & 0 \end{bmatrix}$$

R_1: $x - 2z = 0 \Rightarrow x = 2z$
R_2: $y + z = 0 \Rightarrow y = -z$ ★ $(2c, -c, c)$

10
$$\begin{bmatrix} 1 & -1 & -2 & 0 \\ 2 & -1 & 1 & 0 \\ 2 & -3 & -1 & 0 \end{bmatrix} \quad \begin{matrix} R_2 - 2 R_1 \to R_2 \\ R_3 - 2 R_1 \to R_3 \end{matrix}$$

$$\begin{bmatrix} 1 & -1 & -2 & 0 \\ 0 & 1 & 5 & 0 \\ 0 & -1 & 3 & 0 \end{bmatrix} \quad \begin{matrix} \\ \\ R_3 + R_2 \to R_3 \end{matrix}$$

$$\begin{bmatrix} 1 & -1 & -2 & 0 \\ 0 & 1 & 5 & 0 \\ 0 & 0 & 8 & 0 \end{bmatrix} \quad \begin{matrix} \\ \\ \frac{1}{8} R_3 \to R_3 \end{matrix}$$

R_3: $z = 0$
R_2: $y + 5z = 0 \Rightarrow y = 0$ ★ $(0, 0, 0)$
R_1: $x - y - 2z = 0 \Rightarrow x = 0$

11
$$\begin{bmatrix} 1 & -2 & -2 & 0 \\ 2 & 1 & 1 & 0 \\ 1 & 1 & 1 & 0 \end{bmatrix} \quad \begin{matrix} R_2 - 2 R_1 \to R_2 \\ R_3 - R_1 \to R_3 \end{matrix}$$

$$\begin{bmatrix} 1 & -2 & -2 & 0 \\ 0 & 5 & 5 & 0 \\ 0 & 3 & 3 & 0 \end{bmatrix} \quad \begin{matrix} \frac{1}{5} R_2 \to R_2 \\ \\ \frac{1}{3} R_3 \to R_3 \end{matrix}$$

$$\begin{bmatrix} 1 & -2 & -2 & 0 \\ 0 & 1 & 1 & 0 \\ 0 & 1 & 1 & 0 \end{bmatrix} \quad \begin{matrix} R_1 + 2 R_2 \to R_1 \\ \\ R_3 - R_2 \to R_3 \end{matrix}$$

$$\begin{bmatrix} 1 & 0 & 0 & 0 \\ 0 & 1 & 1 & 0 \\ 0 & 0 & 0 & 0 \end{bmatrix}$$

R_1: $x = 0$
R_2: $y + z = 0 \Rightarrow y = -z$ ★ $(0, -c, c)$

12. $\begin{bmatrix} 1 & 1 & -2 & 0 \\ 1 & -1 & -4 & 0 \\ 0 & 1 & 1 & 0 \end{bmatrix}$ $R_2 - R_1 \to R_2$

$\begin{bmatrix} 1 & 1 & -2 & 0 \\ 0 & -2 & -2 & 0 \\ 0 & 1 & 1 & 0 \end{bmatrix}$ $-\frac{1}{2}R_2 \to R_2$

$\begin{bmatrix} 1 & 1 & -2 & 0 \\ 0 & 1 & 1 & 0 \\ 0 & 1 & 1 & 0 \end{bmatrix}$ $\begin{array}{l} R_1 - R_2 \to R_1 \\ \\ R_3 - R_2 \to R_3 \end{array}$

$\begin{bmatrix} 1 & 0 & -3 & 0 \\ 0 & 1 & 1 & 0 \\ 0 & 0 & 0 & 0 \end{bmatrix}$

R_1: $x - 3z = 0 \Rightarrow x = 3z$
R_2: $y + z = 0 \Rightarrow y = -z$ $\qquad\qquad$ ★ $(3c, -c, c)$

13. $\begin{bmatrix} 1 & 4 & -1 & -2 \\ 3 & -2 & 5 & 7 \end{bmatrix}$ $R_2 - 3R_1 \to R_2$

$\begin{bmatrix} 1 & 4 & -1 & -2 \\ 0 & -14 & 8 & 13 \end{bmatrix}$

R_2: $-14y + 8z = 13 \Rightarrow y = \frac{4}{7}z - \frac{13}{14}$

R_1: $x + 4y - z = -2 \Rightarrow x = -4\left(\frac{4}{7}z - \frac{13}{14}\right) + z - 2 = -\frac{9}{7}z + \frac{12}{7}$ $\qquad$ ★ $\left(\frac{12}{7} - \frac{9}{7}c, \frac{4}{7}c - \frac{13}{14}, c\right)$

14. $\begin{bmatrix} 2 & -1 & 4 & 8 \\ -3 & 1 & -2 & 5 \end{bmatrix}$ $-R_1 - R_2 \to R_1$

$\begin{bmatrix} 1 & 0 & -2 & -13 \\ -3 & 1 & -2 & 5 \end{bmatrix}$ $R_2 + 3R_1 \to R_2$

$\begin{bmatrix} 1 & 0 & -2 & -13 \\ 0 & 1 & -8 & -34 \end{bmatrix}$

R_2: $y - 8z = -34 \Rightarrow y = 8z - 34$
R_1: $x - 2z = -13 \Rightarrow x = 2z - 13$ $\qquad\qquad$ ★ $(2c - 13, 8c - 34, c)$

15. $\begin{bmatrix} 4 & -2 & 1 & 5 \\ 3 & 1 & -4 & 0 \end{bmatrix}$ $R_1 - R_2 \to R_1$

$\begin{bmatrix} 1 & -3 & 5 & 5 \\ 3 & 1 & -4 & 0 \end{bmatrix}$ $R_2 - 3R_1 \to R_2$

$\begin{bmatrix} 1 & -3 & 5 & 5 \\ 0 & 10 & -19 & -15 \end{bmatrix}$

R_2: $10y - 19z = -15 \Rightarrow y = \frac{19}{10}z - \frac{3}{2}$

R_1: $x - 3y + 5z = 5 \Rightarrow x = 3\left(\frac{19}{10}z - \frac{3}{2}\right) - 5z + 5 = \frac{7}{10}z + \frac{1}{2}$ $\qquad$ ★ $\left(\frac{7}{10}c + \frac{1}{2}, \frac{19}{10}c - \frac{3}{2}, c\right)$

16. $\begin{bmatrix} 5 & 2 & -1 & 10 \\ 0 & 1 & 1 & -3 \end{bmatrix}$

R_2: $y + z = -3 \Rightarrow y = -z - 3$

R_1: $5x + 2y - z = 10 \Rightarrow x = -\frac{2}{5}(-z - 3) + \frac{1}{5}z + 2 = \frac{3}{5}z + \frac{16}{5}$ $\qquad$ ★ $\left(\frac{3}{5}c + \frac{16}{5}, -c - 3, c\right)$

$\boxed{17}$
$\begin{bmatrix} 5 & 0 & 2 & 1 \\ 0 & 1 & -3 & 2 \\ 2 & 1 & 0 & 3 \end{bmatrix}$ $R_1 - 2R_3 \rightarrow R_1$

$\begin{bmatrix} 1 & -2 & 2 & -5 \\ 0 & 1 & -3 & 2 \\ 2 & 1 & 0 & 3 \end{bmatrix}$ $R_3 - 2R_1 \rightarrow R_3$

$\begin{bmatrix} 1 & -2 & 2 & -5 \\ 0 & 1 & -3 & 2 \\ 0 & 5 & -4 & 13 \end{bmatrix}$ $R_3 - 5R_2 \rightarrow R_3$

$\begin{bmatrix} 1 & -2 & 2 & -5 \\ 0 & 1 & -3 & 2 \\ 0 & 0 & 11 & 3 \end{bmatrix}$ $\frac{1}{11}R_3 \rightarrow R_3$

R_3: $z = \frac{3}{11}$

R_2: $y - 3z = 2 \Rightarrow y = \frac{31}{11}$

R_1: $x - 2y + 2z = -5 \Rightarrow x = \frac{1}{11}$ $\star \left(\frac{1}{11}, \frac{31}{11}, \frac{3}{11} \right)$

$\boxed{18}$
$\begin{bmatrix} 2 & -3 & 0 & 12 \\ 0 & 3 & 1 & -2 \\ 5 & 0 & -3 & 3 \end{bmatrix}$ $3R_1 - R_3 \rightarrow R_1$

$\begin{bmatrix} 1 & -9 & 3 & 33 \\ 0 & 3 & 1 & -2 \\ 5 & 0 & -3 & 3 \end{bmatrix}$ $R_3 - 5R_1 \rightarrow R_3$

$\begin{bmatrix} 1 & -9 & 3 & 33 \\ 0 & 3 & 1 & -2 \\ 0 & 45 & -18 & -162 \end{bmatrix}$ $\frac{1}{9}R_3 \rightarrow R_3$

$\begin{bmatrix} 1 & -9 & 3 & 33 \\ 0 & 3 & 1 & -2 \\ 0 & 5 & -2 & -18 \end{bmatrix}$ $2R_2 - R_3 \rightarrow R_2$

$\begin{bmatrix} 1 & -9 & 3 & 33 \\ 0 & 1 & 4 & 14 \\ 0 & 5 & -2 & -18 \end{bmatrix}$ $\begin{array}{l} R_1 + 9R_2 \rightarrow R_1 \\ R_3 - 5R_2 \rightarrow R_3 \end{array}$

$\begin{bmatrix} 1 & 0 & 39 & 159 \\ 0 & 1 & 4 & 14 \\ 0 & 0 & -22 & -88 \end{bmatrix}$ $-\frac{1}{22}R_3 \rightarrow R_3$

$\begin{bmatrix} 1 & 0 & 39 & 159 \\ 0 & 1 & 4 & 14 \\ 0 & 0 & 1 & 4 \end{bmatrix}$ $\begin{array}{l} R_1 - 39R_3 \rightarrow R_1 \\ R_2 - 4R_3 \rightarrow R_2 \end{array}$

$\begin{bmatrix} 1 & 0 & 0 & 3 \\ 0 & 1 & 0 & -2 \\ 0 & 0 & 1 & 4 \end{bmatrix}$ $\star (3, -2, 4)$

$\boxed{19}$ $\begin{bmatrix} 4 & -3 & 1 \\ 2 & 1 & -7 \\ -1 & 1 & -1 \end{bmatrix}$ $R_1 + 3R_3 \rightarrow R_1$

$\begin{bmatrix} 1 & 0 & -2 \\ 2 & 1 & -7 \\ -1 & 1 & -1 \end{bmatrix}$ $\begin{aligned} R_2 - 2R_1 &\rightarrow R_2 \\ R_3 + R_1 &\rightarrow R_3 \end{aligned}$

$\begin{bmatrix} 1 & 0 & -2 \\ 0 & 1 & -3 \\ 0 & 1 & -3 \end{bmatrix}$ $R_3 - R_2 \rightarrow R_3$

$\begin{bmatrix} 1 & 0 & -2 \\ 0 & 1 & -3 \\ 0 & 0 & 0 \end{bmatrix}$ $R_2: y = -3;\ R_1: x = -2$ $\quad\star\ (-2, -3)$

$\boxed{20}$ $\begin{bmatrix} 1 & 1 & 1 \\ 2 & 3 & -2 \\ 1 & -2 & 13 \end{bmatrix}$ $\begin{aligned} R_2 - 2R_1 &\rightarrow R_2 \\ R_3 - R_1 &\rightarrow R_3 \end{aligned}$

$\begin{bmatrix} 1 & 1 & 1 \\ 0 & 1 & -4 \\ 0 & -3 & 12 \end{bmatrix}$ $\begin{aligned} R_1 - R_2 &\rightarrow R_1 \\ R_3 + 3R_2 &\rightarrow R_3 \end{aligned}$

$\begin{bmatrix} 1 & 0 & 5 \\ 0 & 1 & -4 \\ 0 & 0 & 0 \end{bmatrix}$ $R_2: y = -4;\ R_1: x = 5$ $\quad\star\ (5, -4)$

$\boxed{21}$ $\begin{bmatrix} 1 & -3 & 4 \\ 2 & 3 & 5 \\ 1 & 1 & -2 \end{bmatrix}$ $\begin{aligned} R_2 - 2R_1 &\rightarrow R_2 \\ R_3 - R_1 &\rightarrow R_3 \end{aligned}$

$\begin{bmatrix} 1 & -3 & 4 \\ 0 & 9 & -3 \\ 0 & 4 & -6 \end{bmatrix}$ $R_2 - 2R_3 \rightarrow R_2$

$\begin{bmatrix} 1 & -3 & 4 \\ 0 & 1 & 9 \\ 0 & 4 & -6 \end{bmatrix}$ $\begin{aligned} R_1 + 3R_2 &\rightarrow R_1 \\ R_3 - 4R_2 &\rightarrow R_3 \end{aligned}$

$\begin{bmatrix} 1 & 0 & 31 \\ 0 & 1 & 9 \\ 0 & 0 & -42 \end{bmatrix}$

There is a contradiction in row 3, therefore there is *no solution*.

$\boxed{22}$ $\begin{bmatrix} 4 & -1 & 2 \\ 2 & 2 & 1 \\ 4 & -5 & 3 \end{bmatrix}$ $\begin{aligned} 2R_2 - R_1 &\rightarrow R_2 \\ R_3 - R_1 &\rightarrow R_3 \end{aligned}$

$\begin{bmatrix} 4 & -1 & 2 \\ 0 & 5 & 0 \\ 0 & -4 & 1 \end{bmatrix}$

$R_2 \Rightarrow y = 0$ and $R_3 \Rightarrow y = -\frac{1}{4}$, a contradiction, there is *no solution*.

23 Let x, y, and z denote the number of liters of the 10% acid, 30% acid, and 50% acid.

$$\begin{cases} x + y + z = 50 & \quad \textit{quantity} & (E_1) \\ 0.10x + 0.30y + 0.50z = (0.32)(50) & \quad \textit{quality} & (E_2) \\ z = 2y & \quad \textit{constraint} & (E_3) \end{cases}$$

Substitute $z = 2y$ into E_1 and $100\,E_2$ to obtain

$$\begin{cases} x + 3y & = 50 & (E_4) \\ 10x + 130y & = 1600 & (E_5) \end{cases}$$

$$E_5 - 10\,E_4 \Rightarrow 100y = 1100 \Rightarrow y = 11;\ x = 17;\ z = 22$$

24 Let z denote the number of hours it takes for pipe C to fill the pool alone.

By adding the hourly rates, i.e., how much of the pool each pipe fills in one hour, we have $\frac{1}{8} + \frac{1}{z} = \frac{1}{6} \Rightarrow z = 24$. Let y denote the number of hours it takes for pipe B to fill the pool alone. $\frac{1}{y} + \frac{1}{24} = \frac{1}{10} \Rightarrow y = \frac{120}{7}$. Let x denote the number of hours it takes for all three pipes to fill the pool. $\frac{1}{8} + \frac{7}{120} + \frac{1}{24} = \frac{1}{x} \Rightarrow x = \frac{120}{27} = \frac{40}{9}$.

25 Let x, y, and z denote the number of hours needed for A, B, and C, respectively, to produce 1000 items. In one hour, A, B, and C produce $\frac{1000}{x}$, $\frac{1000}{y}$, and $\frac{1000}{z}$ items, respectively. In 6 hours, A and B produce $\frac{6000}{x}$ and $\frac{6000}{y}$ items. From the table, this sum must equal 4500. The system of equations is then:

$$\begin{cases} \dfrac{6000}{x} + \dfrac{6000}{y} & = & 4500 \\[2mm] \dfrac{8000}{x} + \dfrac{8000}{z} & = & 3600 \\[2mm] \dfrac{7000}{y} + \dfrac{7000}{z} & = & 4900 \end{cases}$$

To simplify, let $a = 1/x$, $b = 1/y$, $c = 1/z$ and divide each equation by its greatest common factor $\{1500,\ 400,\ \text{and}\ 700\}$.

$$\begin{cases} 4a + 4b & = 3 & (E_1) \\ 20a + \ + 20c & = 9 & (E_2) \\ 10b + 10c & = 7 & (E_3) \end{cases}$$

$E_2 - 5\,E_1 \Rightarrow 20c - 20b = -6 \quad (E_4)$

$E_4 + 2\,E_3 \Rightarrow 40c = 8 \Rightarrow c = \frac{1}{5};\ b = \frac{1}{2};\ a = \frac{1}{4}$. Resubstituting, $x = 4$, $y = 2$, and $z = 5$.

26
$$\begin{cases} \dfrac{1}{A} + \dfrac{1}{B} & = \dfrac{1}{48} \\[2mm] \dfrac{1}{B} + \dfrac{1}{C} & = \dfrac{1}{80} \\[2mm] \dfrac{1}{A} + \dfrac{1}{C} & = \dfrac{1}{60} \end{cases} \Rightarrow \begin{cases} 48x + 48y & = 1 & (E_1) \\ 80y + 80z & = 1 & (E_2) \\ 60x + 60z & = 1 & (E_3) \end{cases}$$

where $x = 1/A$, $y = 1/B$, and $z = 1/C$. $5\,E_1 - 4\,E_3 \Rightarrow 240y - 240z = 1 \quad (E_4)$

$E_4 + 3\,E_2 \Rightarrow 480y = 4 \Rightarrow y = \frac{1}{120};\ z = \frac{1}{240};\ x = \frac{1}{80}$.

Resubstituting, $A = 80$, $B = 120$, and $C = 240$.

27 Let x, y, and z denote the amounts of G_1, G_2, and G_3, respectively.

$$\begin{cases} x + y + z = 600 & \textit{quantity} & (E_1) \\ 0.30x + 0.20y + 0.15z = (0.25)(600) & \textit{quality} & (E_2) \\ z = 100 + y & \textit{constraint} & (E_3) \end{cases}$$

Substitute $z = 100 + y$ into E_1 and $100\,E_2$ to obtain

$$\begin{cases} x + 2y = 500 & (E_4) \\ 30x + 35y = 13{,}500 & (E_5) \end{cases}$$

$$E_5 - 30\,E_4 \Rightarrow -25y = -1500 \Rightarrow y = 60; \ z = 160; \ x = 380$$

28 $s\left(\frac{1}{2}\right) = 7 \qquad\qquad 7 = \frac{1}{8}a + \frac{1}{2}v_0 + s_0 \qquad (E_1)$

$s(1) = 11 \quad \Rightarrow \quad 11 = \frac{1}{2}a + v_0 + s_0 \qquad (E_2)$

$s\left(\frac{3}{2}\right) = 17 \qquad\qquad 17 = \frac{9}{8}a + \frac{3}{2}v_0 + s_0 \qquad (E_3)$

Solving E_2 for s_0 and substituting into E_1 and E_3 yields

$$\begin{cases} -4 = -\frac{3}{8}a - \frac{1}{2}v_0 & (E_4) \\ 6 = \frac{5}{8}a + \frac{1}{2}v_0 & (E_5) \end{cases} \qquad E_4 + E_5 \Rightarrow 2 = \frac{1}{4}a \Rightarrow a = 8; \ v_0 = 2; \ s_0 = 5.$$

29 (a) $I_1 - I_2 + I_3 = 0 \qquad\qquad I_1 = I_2 - I_3 \qquad (E_1)$

$ \ 3I_1 + 3I_2 = 6 \qquad \Rightarrow \qquad I_1 + I_2 = 2 \qquad (E_2)$

$ \ 3I_2 + 3I_3 = 12 \qquad\qquad I_2 + I_3 = 4 \qquad (E_3)$

Substitute I_1 in E_1 into E_2 to obtain $2I_2 - I_3 = 2$ (E_4).

$$E_4 + E_3 \Rightarrow 3I_2 = 6 \Rightarrow I_2 = 2; \ I_3 = 2; \ I_1 = 0.$$

(b) $I_1 = I_2 - I_3 \qquad (E_1)$

$ \ 4I_1 + I_2 = 6 \qquad (E_2)$

$ \ I_2 + 4I_3 = 12 \qquad (E_3)$

Substitute I_1 in E_1 into E_2 to obtain $5I_2 - 4I_3 = 6$ (E_4).

$$E_4 + E_3 \Rightarrow 6I_2 = 18 \Rightarrow I_2 = 3; \ I_3 = \frac{9}{4}; \ I_1 = \frac{3}{4}.$$

30 Let x, y, and z denote the number of birds on island A, B, and C, respectively.

$$\begin{cases} x + y + z = 35{,}000 & \textit{quantity} & (E_1) \\ x - 0.10x + 0.05z = x & \textit{island A} & (E_2) \\ y - 0.20y + 0.10x = y & \textit{island B} & (E_3) \\ z - 0.05z + 0.20y = z & \textit{island C} & (E_4) \end{cases}$$

Solve E_2 for z $\{z = 2x\}$, E_3 for y $\{y = \frac{1}{2}x\}$, and substitute both expressions into E_1

to obtain $x + \frac{1}{2}x + 2x = 35{,}000 \Rightarrow \frac{7}{2}x = 35{,}000 \Rightarrow x = 10{,}000; \ y = 5000; \ z = 20{,}000.$

31 Let x, y, and z denote the amount of Colombian, Brazilian, and Kenyan coffee used, respectively.

$$\begin{cases} x + y + z = 1 & \text{\textit{quantity}} & (E_1) \\ 10x + 6y + 8z = (8.50)(1) & \text{\textit{quality}} & (E_2) \\ x = 3y & \text{\textit{constraint}} & (E_3) \end{cases}$$

Substitute $x = 3y$ into E_1 and E_2 to obtain

$$\begin{cases} 4y + z = 1 & (E_4) \\ 36y + 8z = 8.5 & (E_5) \end{cases} \quad E_5 - 8\,E_4 \Rightarrow 4y = \tfrac{1}{2} \Rightarrow y = \tfrac{1}{8};\ z = \tfrac{1}{2};\ x = \tfrac{3}{8}.$$

32 (a) Number of $Adults$ = surviving adults + surviving yearlings

$$= (0.90)(400) + (0.80)(150) = \underline{480}$$

Number of $Yearlings$ = surviving calves

$$= (0.75)(200) = \underline{150}$$

Number of $Calves$ = number of female adults

$$= (0.50)(480) = \underline{240}$$

(b) 75% of last spring's calves equal the number of this year's yearlings (150),

thus the number of $calves$ is $\underline{200}$.

The number of calves is equal to the number of adult females and this is one-half

of the number of adults, thus the number of $adults$ is $\underline{400}$.

90% of these (360) are part of the 400 adults this year. The other 40 adults

represent 80% of last year's yearlings, thus the number of $yearlings$ is $\underline{50}$.

33 (a) A: $x_1 + x_4 = 75$, B: $x_1 + x_2 = 150$, C: $x_2 + x_3 = 225$, D: $x_3 + x_4 = 150$

(b) From C, $x_3 = 100 \Rightarrow x_2 = 125$. From D, $x_3 = 100 \Rightarrow x_4 = 50$.

From A, $x_4 = 50 \Rightarrow x_1 = 25$.

(c) From D, $x_3 = 150 - x_4 \Rightarrow x_3 \le 150$ since $x_4 \ge 0$. From C,

$$x_3 = 225 - x_2 = 225 - (150 - x_1)\ \{\text{from B}\} = 75 + x_1 \Rightarrow x_3 \ge 75 \text{ since } x_1 \ge 0.$$

34 $\begin{cases} f(-3) = -12 \\ f(-1) = 22 \\ f(2) = 13 \end{cases} \Rightarrow \begin{cases} -27a - 3b + c = -12 & (E_1) \\ -a - b + c = 22 & (E_2) \\ 8a + 2b + c = 13 & (E_3) \end{cases}$

Solving E_2 for c and substituting into E_1 and E_3 yields

$$\begin{cases} -13a - b = -17 & (E_4) \\ 3a + b = -3 & (E_5) \end{cases} \quad E_4 + E_5 \Rightarrow -10a = -20 \Rightarrow a = 2;\ b = -9;\ c = 15.$$

35 $t = 2070 - 1990 = 80$. $rt = (0.025)(80) = 2$ for E_1, $(0.015)(80) = 1.2$ for E_2,

and $(0.01)(0) = 0$ for E_3. Summarizing as a system, we have:

$$\begin{cases} a + 80c + e^2k = 800 & (E_1) \\ a + 80c + e^{1.2}k = 560 & (E_2) \\ a \phantom{{}+80c} + k = 340 & (E_3) \end{cases}$$

We want to find t when $A = 2(340)$. First we find c and k.

$E_1 - E_2 \Rightarrow e^2k - e^{1.2}k = 240 \Rightarrow k = \dfrac{240}{e^2 - e^{1.2}} \approx 58.98$.

Substituting into E_3 gives $a = 340 - k \approx 281.02$.

Substituting into E_1 gives $c = \dfrac{800 - a - e^2k}{80} \approx \dfrac{800 - 281.02 - (58.98)e^2}{80} \approx 1.04$.

Thus, $A = 281.02 + 1.04t + 58.98e^{rt}$. If $A = 680$ and $r = 0.01$, then

$680 = 281.02 + 1.04t + 58.98e^{0.01t} \Rightarrow 1.04t + 58.98e^{0.01t} - 398.98 = 0$. Graphing

$y = 1.04t + 58.98e^{0.01t} - 398.98$, we see there is an x-intercept at $x \approx 144.08$.

 $1990 + 144.08 = 2134.08$, or during the year 2134.

[0, 1050] by [−350, 350]

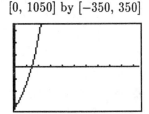

Xscl = 100

Yscl = 100

Figure 35

[0, 1050] by [−350, 350]

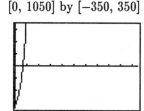

Xscl = 100

Yscl = 100

Figure 36

36 $\quad \begin{cases} a + 40c + e^{0.8}k = 455 & (E_1) \\ a + 40c + e^{0.6}k = 430 & (E_2) \\ a \phantom{{}+40c} + k = 340 & (E_3) \end{cases}$

$E_1 - E_2 \Rightarrow e^{0.8}k - e^{0.6}k = 25 \Rightarrow k = \dfrac{25}{e^{0.8} - e^{0.6}} \approx 61.97$.

Substituting into E_3 gives $a = 340 - k \approx 278.03$.

Substituting into E_1 gives $c = \dfrac{455 - a - ke^{0.8}}{40} \approx \dfrac{455 - 278.03 - (61.97)e^{0.8}}{40} \approx 0.98$.

Thus, $A = 278.03 + 0.98t + 61.97e^{rt}$. If $A = 680$ and $r = 0.025$, then

$680 = 278.03 + 0.98t + 61.97e^{rt} \Rightarrow 0.98t + 61.97e^{0.025t} - 401.97 = 0$. Graphing

$y = 0.98t + 61.97e^{0.025t} - 401.97$, we see there is an x-intercept at $x \approx 67.59$.

 $1990 + 67.59 = 2057.59$, or during the year 2057.

37 The circle has an equation of the form $x^2 + y^2 + ax + by + c = 0$.

Substituting the x and y values of $P, Q,$ and R into this equation yields:

$$\begin{cases} 2a + b + c = -5 & P \quad (E_1) \\ -a - 4b + c = -17 & Q \quad (E_2) \\ 3a + c = -9 & R \quad (E_3) \end{cases}$$

Solving E_3 for c $\{c = -9 - 3a\}$ and substituting into E_1 and E_2 yields:

$$\begin{cases} -a + b = 4 & (E_4) \\ -4a - 4b = -8 & (E_5) \end{cases} \Rightarrow \begin{cases} -a + b = 4 & (E_6) \\ a + b = 2 & (E_7) \end{cases}$$

$E_6 + E_7 \Rightarrow 2b = 6 \Rightarrow b = 3; a = -1; c = -6.$ The equation is $x^2 + y^2 - x + 3y - 6 = 0$.

38 As in Exercise 37, the circle has an equation of the form $x^2 + y^2 + ax + by + c = 0$.

Substituting the x and y values of $P, Q,$ and R into this equation yields:

$$\begin{cases} -5a + 5b + c = -50 & P \quad (E_1) \\ -2a - 4b + c = -20 & Q \quad (E_2) \\ 2a + 4b + c = -20 & R \quad (E_3) \end{cases}$$

Solving E_2 for c $\{c = 2a + 4b - 20\}$ and substituting into E_1 and E_3 yields:

$$\begin{cases} -3a + 9b = -30 & (E_4) \\ 4a + 8b = 0 & (E_5) \end{cases} \Rightarrow \begin{cases} -a + 3b = -10 & (E_6) \\ a + 2b = 0 & (E_7) \end{cases}$$

$E_6 + E_7 \Rightarrow 5b = -10 \Rightarrow b = -2; a = 4; c = -20.$

The equation is $x^2 + y^2 + 4x - 2y - 20 = 0$.

39 For $y = f(x) = ax^3 + bx^2 + cx + d$ and the points $(-1, 2), (0.5, 2), (1, 3),$ and $(2, 4.5)$, we obtain the system:

$$\begin{cases} -a + b - c + d = 2 & (-1, 2) \\ 0.125a + 0.25b + 0.5c + d = 2 & (0.5, 2) \\ a + b + c + d = 3 & (1, 3) \\ 8a + 4b + 2c + d = 4.5 & (2, 4.5) \end{cases}$$

Solving the system yields $a = -\frac{4}{9}, b = \frac{11}{9}, c = \frac{17}{18},$ and $d = \frac{23}{18}$.

40 For $y = f(x) = ax^4 + bx^3 + cx^2 + dx + e$ and the points $(-2, 1.5), (-1, -2), (1, -3),$ $(2, -3.5),$ and $(3, -4.8)$, we obtain the system:

$$\begin{cases} 16a - 8b + 4c - 2d + e = 1.5 & (-2, 1.5) \\ a - b + c - d + e = -2 & (-1, -2) \\ a + b + c + d + e = -3 & (1, -3) \\ 16a + 8b + 4c + 2d + e = -3.5 & (2, -3.5) \\ 81a + 27b + 9c + 3d + e = -4.8 & (3, -4.8) \end{cases}$$

Solving the system yields $a = 0.03, b = -0.25, c = 0.35, d = -0.25,$ and $e = -2.88$.

Note: The general outline for the solutions in this section is as follows:

1st line)   The expression is shown on the left side of the equation and its decomposition is on the right side.

2nd line)   The equation in the first line is multiplied by its least common denominator and left in factored form.

3rd line and beyond)   Values are substituted into the equation in the second line and the coefficients are found by solving the resulting equations. It will be stated when the method of equating coefficients is used.

1. $\dfrac{8x-1}{(x-2)(x+3)} = \dfrac{A}{x-2} + \dfrac{B}{x+3}$

$8x - 1 = A(x+3) + B(x-2)$

$x = -3:\ -25 = -5B \Rightarrow B = 5$

$x = 2:\ 15 = 5A \Rightarrow A = 3$

$\bigstar\ \dfrac{3}{x-2} + \dfrac{5}{x+3}$

2. $\dfrac{x-29}{(x-4)(x+1)} = \dfrac{A}{x-4} + \dfrac{B}{x+1}$

$x - 29 = A(x+1) + B(x-4)$

$x = -1:\ -30 = -5B \Rightarrow B = 6$

$x = 4:\ -25 = 5A \Rightarrow A = -5$

$\bigstar\ -\dfrac{5}{x-4} + \dfrac{6}{x+1}$

3. $\dfrac{x+34}{(x-6)(x+2)} = \dfrac{A}{x-6} + \dfrac{B}{x+2}$

$x + 34 = A(x+2) + B(x-6)$

$x = -2:\ 32 = -8B \Rightarrow B = -4$

$x = 6:\ 40 = 8A \Rightarrow A = 5$

$\bigstar\ \dfrac{5}{x-6} - \dfrac{4}{x+2}$

4. $\dfrac{5x-12}{x(x-4)} = \dfrac{A}{x} + \dfrac{B}{x-4}$

$5x - 12 = A(x-4) + Bx$

$x = 4:\ 8 = 4B \Rightarrow B = 2$

$x = 0:\ -12 = -4A \Rightarrow A = 3$

$\bigstar\ \dfrac{3}{x} + \dfrac{2}{x-4}$

5. $\dfrac{4x^2 - 15x - 1}{(x-1)(x+2)(x-3)} = \dfrac{A}{x-1} + \dfrac{B}{x+2} + \dfrac{C}{x-3}$

$4x^2 - 15x - 1 = A(x+2)(x-3) + B(x-1)(x-3) + C(x-1)(x+2)$

$x = -2$: $45 = 15B \Rightarrow B = 3$

$x = 1$: $-12 = -6A \Rightarrow A = 2$ $\qquad\qquad$ ★ $\dfrac{2}{x-1} + \dfrac{3}{x+2} - \dfrac{1}{x-3}$

$x = 3$: $-10 = 10C \Rightarrow C = -1$

6. $\dfrac{x^2 + 19x + 20}{x(x+2)(x-5)} = \dfrac{A}{x} + \dfrac{B}{x+2} + \dfrac{C}{x-5}$

$x^2 + 19x + 20 = A(x+2)(x-5) + Bx(x-5) + Cx(x+2)$

$x = -2$: $-14 = 14B \Rightarrow B = -1$

$x = 5$: $140 = 35C \Rightarrow C = 4$ $\qquad\qquad$ ★ $-\dfrac{2}{x} - \dfrac{1}{x+2} + \dfrac{4}{x-5}$

$x = 0$: $20 = -10A \Rightarrow A = -2$

7. $\dfrac{4x^2 - 5x - 15}{x(x-5)(x+1)} = \dfrac{A}{x} + \dfrac{B}{x-5} + \dfrac{C}{x+1}$

$4x^2 - 5x - 15 = A(x-5)(x+1) + Bx(x+1) + Cx(x-5)$

$x = -1$: $-6 = 6C \Rightarrow C = -1$

$x = 0$: $-15 = -5A \Rightarrow A = 3$ $\qquad\qquad$ ★ $\dfrac{3}{x} + \dfrac{2}{x-5} - \dfrac{1}{x+1}$

$x = 5$: $60 = 30B \Rightarrow B = 2$

8. $\dfrac{37 - 11x}{(x+1)(x-2)(x-3)} = \dfrac{A}{x+1} + \dfrac{B}{x-2} + \dfrac{C}{x-3}$

$37 - 11x = A(x-2)(x-3) + B(x+1)(x-3) + C(x+1)(x-2)$

$x = -1$: $48 = 12A \Rightarrow A = 4$

$x = 2$: $15 = -3B \Rightarrow B = -5$ $\qquad\qquad$ ★ $\dfrac{4}{x+1} - \dfrac{5}{x-2} + \dfrac{1}{x-3}$

$x = 3$: $4 = 4C \Rightarrow C = 1$

9. $\dfrac{2x + 3}{(x-1)^2} = \dfrac{A}{x-1} + \dfrac{B}{(x-1)^2}$

$2x + 3 = A(x-1) + B$

$x = 1$: $5 = B$ $\qquad\qquad$ ★ $\dfrac{2}{x-1} + \dfrac{5}{(x-1)^2}$

$x = 0$: $3 = -A + B \Rightarrow A = 2$

10 $\dfrac{5x^2-4}{x^2(x+2)}=\dfrac{A}{x}+\dfrac{B}{x^2}+\dfrac{C}{x+2}$

$5x^2-4=Ax(x+2)+B(x+2)+Cx^2$

$x=-2$: $16=4C\Rightarrow C=4$

$x=0$: $-4=2B\Rightarrow B=-2$

$x=1$: $1=3A+3B+C\Rightarrow A=1$

$\bigstar\ \dfrac{1}{x}-\dfrac{2}{x^2}+\dfrac{4}{x+2}$

11 $\dfrac{19x^2+50x-25}{x^2(3x-5)}=\dfrac{A}{x}+\dfrac{B}{x^2}+\dfrac{C}{3x-5}$

$19x^2+50x-25=Ax(3x-5)+B(3x-5)+Cx^2$

$x=\frac{5}{3}$: $\frac{1000}{9}=\frac{25}{9}C\Rightarrow C=40$

$x=0$: $-25=-5B\Rightarrow B=5$

$x=1$: $44=-2A-2B+C\Rightarrow A=-7$

$\bigstar\ -\dfrac{7}{x}+\dfrac{5}{x^2}+\dfrac{40}{3x-5}$

12 $\dfrac{10-x}{(x+5)^2}=\dfrac{A}{x+5}+\dfrac{B}{(x+5)^2}$

$10-x=A(x+5)+B$

$x=-5$: $15=B$

$x=0$: $10=5A+B\Rightarrow A=-1$

$\bigstar\ -\dfrac{1}{x+5}+\dfrac{15}{(x+5)^2}$

13 $\dfrac{x^2-6}{(x+2)^2(2x-1)}=\dfrac{A}{x+2}+\dfrac{B}{(x+2)^2}+\dfrac{C}{2x-1}$

$x^2-6=A(x+2)(2x-1)+B(2x-1)+C(x+2)^2$

$x=-2$: $-2=-5B\Rightarrow B=\frac{2}{5}$

$x=\frac{1}{2}$: $-\frac{23}{4}=\frac{25}{4}C\Rightarrow C=-\frac{23}{25}$

$x=1$: $-5=3A+B+9C\Rightarrow A=\frac{24}{25}$

$\bigstar\ \dfrac{\frac{24}{25}}{x+2}+\dfrac{\frac{2}{5}}{(x+2)^2}-\dfrac{\frac{23}{25}}{2x-1}$

14 $\dfrac{2x^2+x}{(x-1)^2(x+1)^2}=\dfrac{A}{x-1}+\dfrac{B}{(x-1)^2}+\dfrac{C}{x+1}+\dfrac{D}{(x+1)^2}$

$2x^2+x=A(x-1)(x+1)^2+B(x+1)^2+C(x+1)(x-1)^2+D(x-1)^2$

$x=-1$: $1=4D\Rightarrow D=\frac{1}{4}$

$x=1$: $3=4B\Rightarrow B=\frac{3}{4}$

$x=0$: $0=-A+B+C+D$ (E_1)

$x=2$: $10=9A+9B+3C+D$ (E_2)

Substituting the values for B and D into E_1 and E_2 yields

$\begin{cases}-A+C=-1\\9A+3C=3\end{cases}\Rightarrow\begin{cases}A-C=1 & (\text{E}_3)\\3A+C=1 & (\text{E}_4)\end{cases}$ $\bigstar\ \dfrac{\frac{1}{2}}{x-1}+\dfrac{\frac{3}{4}}{(x-1)^2}-\dfrac{\frac{1}{2}}{x+1}+\dfrac{\frac{1}{4}}{(x+1)^2}$

$\text{E}_3+\text{E}_4\Rightarrow 4A=2\Rightarrow A=\frac{1}{2};\ C=-\frac{1}{2}$

15 $\dfrac{3x^3 + 11x^2 + 16x + 5}{x(x+1)^3} = \dfrac{A}{x} + \dfrac{B}{x+1} + \dfrac{C}{(x+1)^2} + \dfrac{D}{(x+1)^3}$

$3x^3 + 11x^2 + 16x + 5 = A(x+1)^3 + Bx(x+1)^2 + Cx(x+1) + Dx$

$x = -1: \ -3 = -D \Rightarrow D = 3$

$x = 0: \ 5 = A$

$x = 1: \ 35 = 8A + 4B + 2C + D \quad (E_1)$

$x = -2: \ -7 = -A - 2B + 2C - 2D \quad (E_2)$

Substituting the values for A and D into E_1 and E_2 yields

$\begin{cases} 4B + 2C &= -8 \\ -2B + 2C &= 4 \end{cases} \Rightarrow \begin{cases} 2B + C &= -4 \quad (E_3) \\ -B + C &= 2 \quad (E_4) \end{cases}$ $\star \ \dfrac{5}{x} - \dfrac{2}{x+1} + \dfrac{3}{(x+1)^3}$

$E_3 + 2E_4 \Rightarrow 3C = 0 \Rightarrow C = 0; \ B = -2$

16 $\dfrac{4x^3 + 3x^2 + 5x - 2}{x^3(x+2)} = \dfrac{A}{x} + \dfrac{B}{x^2} + \dfrac{C}{x^3} + \dfrac{D}{x+2}$

$4x^3 + 3x^2 + 5x - 2 = Ax^2(x+2) + Bx(x+2) + C(x+2) + Dx^3$

$x = -2: \ -32 = -8D \Rightarrow D = 4$

$x = 0: \ -2 = 2C \Rightarrow C = -1$

$x = -1: \ -8 = A - B + C - D \quad (E_1)$

$x = 1: \ 10 = 3A + 3B + 3C + D \quad (E_2)$

Substituting the values for C and D into E_1 and E_2 yields

$\begin{cases} A - B &= -3 \\ 3A + 3B &= 9 \end{cases} \Rightarrow \begin{cases} A - B &= -3 \quad (E_3) \\ A + B &= 3 \quad (E_4) \end{cases}$ $\star \ \dfrac{3}{x^2} - \dfrac{1}{x^3} + \dfrac{4}{x+2}$

$E_3 + E_4 \Rightarrow 2A = 0 \Rightarrow A = 0; \ B = 3$

17 $\dfrac{x^2 + x - 6}{(x^2+1)(x-1)} = \dfrac{Ax + B}{x^2+1} + \dfrac{C}{x-1}$

$x^2 + x - 6 = (Ax + B)(x - 1) + C(x^2 + 1)$

$x = 1: \ -4 = 2C \Rightarrow C = -2$

$x = 0: \ -6 = -B + C \Rightarrow B = 4$ $\star \ -\dfrac{2}{x-1} + \dfrac{3x+4}{x^2+1}$

$x = 2: \ 0 = 2A + B + 5C \Rightarrow A = 3$

[18] $\dfrac{x^2 - x - 21}{(x^2 + 4)(2x - 1)} = \dfrac{Ax + B}{x^2 + 4} + \dfrac{C}{2x - 1}$

$x^2 - x - 21 = (Ax + B)(2x - 1) + C(x^2 + 4)$

$x = \frac{1}{2}: \; -\frac{85}{4} = \frac{17}{4}C \Rightarrow C = -5$

$x = 0: \; -21 = -B + 4C \Rightarrow B = 1$

$x = 1: \; -21 = A + B + 5C \Rightarrow A = 3$

$\bigstar \; -\dfrac{5}{2x - 1} + \dfrac{3x + 1}{x^2 + 4}$

[19] $\dfrac{9x^2 - 3x + 8}{x(x^2 + 2)} = \dfrac{A}{x} + \dfrac{Bx + C}{x^2 + 2}$

$9x^2 - 3x + 8 = A(x^2 + 2) + (Bx + C)x$

$x = 0: \; 8 = 2A \Rightarrow A = 4$

$x = 1: \; 14 = 3A + B + C \quad (E_1)$

$x = -1: \; 20 = 3A + B - C \quad (E_2)$

$E_1 - E_2 \Rightarrow -6 = 2C \Rightarrow C = -3; \; B = 5$

$\bigstar \; \dfrac{4}{x} + \dfrac{5x - 3}{x^2 + 2}$

[20] $\dfrac{2x^3 + 2x^2 + 4x - 3}{x^2(x^2 + 1)} = \dfrac{A}{x} + \dfrac{B}{x^2} + \dfrac{Cx + D}{x^2 + 1}$

$\begin{aligned} 2x^3 + 2x^2 + 4x - 3 &= Ax(x^2 + 1) + B(x^2 + 1) + (Cx + D)x^2 \\ &= (A + C)x^3 + (B + D)x^2 + Ax + B \end{aligned}$

Equating coefficients, we have the following:

$\quad$ constant $\quad : B = -3$

$\quad x \qquad\quad : A = 4$

$\quad x^2 \qquad\quad : B + D = 2 \Rightarrow D = 5$

$\quad x^3 \qquad\quad : A + C = 2 \Rightarrow C = -2$

$\bigstar \; \dfrac{4}{x} - \dfrac{3}{x^2} + \dfrac{-2x + 5}{x^2 + 1}$

[21] $\dfrac{4x^3 - x^2 + 4x + 2}{(x^2 + 1)^2} = \dfrac{Ax + B}{x^2 + 1} + \dfrac{Cx + D}{(x^2 + 1)^2}$

$\begin{aligned} 4x^3 - x^2 + 4x + 2 &= (Ax + B)(x^2 + 1) + Cx + D \\ &= Ax^3 + Bx^2 + (A + C)x + (B + D) \end{aligned}$

Equating coefficients, we have the following:

$\quad x^3 \qquad\quad : A = 4$

$\quad x^2 \qquad\quad : B = -1$

$\quad x \qquad\quad : A + C = 4 \Rightarrow C = 0$

$\quad$ constant $\quad : B + D = 2 \Rightarrow D = 3$

$\bigstar \; \dfrac{4x - 1}{x^2 + 1} + \dfrac{3}{(x^2 + 1)^2}$

$\boxed{22}$ $\dfrac{3x^3 + 13x - 1}{(x^2 + 4)^2} = \dfrac{Ax + B}{x^2 + 4} + \dfrac{Cx + D}{(x^2 + 4)^2}$

$\quad 3x^3 + 13x - 1 = (Ax + B)(x^2 + 4) + Cx + D$

$\qquad\qquad\qquad\;\; = Ax^3 + Bx^2 + (4A + C)x + (4B + D)$

Equating coefficients, we have the following:

$\quad x^3 \qquad\quad : A = 3$

$\quad x^2 \qquad\quad : B = 0$

$\quad x \qquad\qquad : 4A + C = 13 \Rightarrow C = 1$

$\quad$ constant $\;\; : 4B + D = -1 \Rightarrow D = -1$

$\star\ \dfrac{3x}{x^2 + 4} + \dfrac{x - 1}{(x^2 + 4)^2}$

$\boxed{23}$ By first dividing and then factoring, we have the following:

$\quad 2x + \dfrac{4x^2 - 3x + 1}{(x^2 + 1)(x - 1)} = 2x + \dfrac{Ax + B}{x^2 + 1} + \dfrac{C}{x - 1}$

$\quad 4x^2 - 3x + 1 = (Ax + B)(x - 1) + C(x^2 + 1)$

$\quad x = 1 \colon 2 = 2C \Rightarrow C = 1$

$\quad x = 0 \colon 1 = -B + C \Rightarrow B = 0$

$\quad x = -1 \colon 8 = 2A - 2B + 2C \Rightarrow A = 3$

$\star\ 2x + \dfrac{1}{x - 1} + \dfrac{3x}{x^2 + 1}$

$\boxed{24}$ By first dividing and then factoring, we have the following:

$\quad 1 + \dfrac{3x^2 - 9x + 27}{(x^2 + 9)(x - 3)} = 1 + \dfrac{Ax + B}{x^2 + 9} + \dfrac{C}{x - 3}$

$\quad 3x^2 - 9x + 27 = (Ax + B)(x - 3) + C(x^2 + 9)$

$\quad x = 3 \colon 27 = 18C \Rightarrow C = \frac{3}{2}$

$\quad x = 0 \colon 27 = -3B + 9C \Rightarrow B = -\frac{9}{2}$

$\quad x = 2 \colon 21 = -2A - B + 13C \Rightarrow A = \frac{3}{2}$

$\star\ 1 + \dfrac{\frac{3}{2}}{x - 3} + \dfrac{\frac{3}{2}x - \frac{9}{2}}{x^2 + 9}$

$\boxed{25}$ By first dividing and then factoring, we have the following:

$\quad 3 + \dfrac{12x - 16}{x(x - 4)} = 3 + \dfrac{A}{x} + \dfrac{B}{x - 4}$

$\quad 12x - 16 = A(x - 4) + Bx$

$\quad x = 0 \colon -16 = -4A \Rightarrow A = 4$

$\quad x = 4 \colon 32 = 4B \Rightarrow B = 8$

$\star\ 3 + \dfrac{4}{x} + \dfrac{8}{x - 4}$

$\boxed{26}$ By first dividing and then factoring, we have the following:

$$2 + \frac{-5x - 18}{(x+3)^2} = 2 + \frac{A}{x+3} + \frac{B}{(x+3)^2}$$

$$-5x - 18 = A(x+3) + B$$

$x = -3:\ -3 = B \Rightarrow B = -3$

$\bigstar\ 2 - \dfrac{5}{x+3} - \dfrac{3}{(x+3)^2}$

Equating coefficients of x, we see that $A = -5$.

$\boxed{27}$ By first dividing and then factoring, we have the following:

$$2x + 3 + \frac{x+5}{(2x+1)(x-1)} = 2x + 3 + \frac{A}{2x+1} + \frac{B}{x-1}$$

$$x + 5 = A(x-1) + B(2x+1)$$

$x = 1:\ 6 = 3B \Rightarrow B = 2$

$x = -\frac{1}{2}:\ \frac{9}{2} = -\frac{3}{2}A \Rightarrow A = -3$

$\bigstar\ 2x + 3 + \dfrac{2}{x-1} - \dfrac{3}{2x+1}$

$\boxed{28}$ By first dividing and then factoring, we have the following:

$$x^2 - 2x + 1 + \frac{2x^2 - 4x + 12}{x^2(x-3)} = x^2 - 2x + 1 + \frac{A}{x} + \frac{B}{x^2} + \frac{C}{x-3}$$

$$2x^2 - 4x + 12 = Ax(x-3) + B(x-3) + Cx^2$$

$x = 3:\ 18 = 9C \Rightarrow C = 2$

$x = 0:\ 12 = -3B \Rightarrow B = -4$

$\bigstar\ x^2 - 2x + 1 - \dfrac{4}{x^2} + \dfrac{2}{x-3}$

$x = 1:\ 10 = -2A - 2B + C \Rightarrow A = 0$

8.5 Exercises

$\boxed{1}$ $3x - 2y < 6 \Leftrightarrow y > \frac{3}{2}x - 3$; test point $(0, 0) \rightarrow$ True

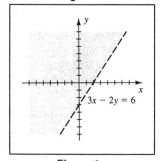

Figure 1

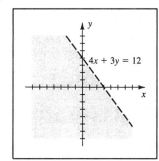

Figure 2

$\boxed{2}$ $4x + 3y < 12 \Leftrightarrow y < -\frac{4}{3}x + 4$; test point $(0, 0) \rightarrow$ True

$\boxed{3}$ $2x + 3y \geq 2y + 1 \Leftrightarrow y \geq -2x + 1$; test point $(0,\,0) \rightarrow$ False

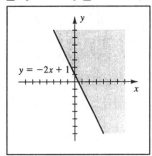

Figure 3

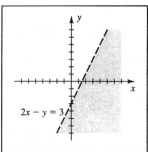

Figure 4

$\boxed{4}$ $2x - y > 3 \Leftrightarrow y < 2x - 3$; test point $(0;\,0) \rightarrow$ False

$\boxed{5}$ $y + 2 < x^2 \Leftrightarrow y < x^2 - 2$; test point $(0,\,0) \rightarrow$ False

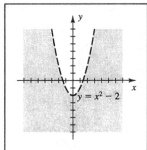

Figure 5

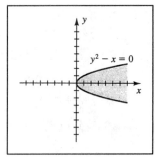

Figure 6

$\boxed{6}$ $y^2 - x \leq 0 \Leftrightarrow x \geq y^2$; test point $(1,\,0) \rightarrow$ True

$\boxed{7}$ $x^2 + 1 \leq y \Leftrightarrow y \geq x^2 + 1$; test point $(0,\,0) \rightarrow$ False

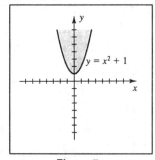

Figure 7

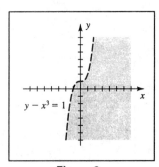

Figure 8

$\boxed{8}$ $y - x^3 < 1 \Leftrightarrow y < x^3 + 1$; test point $(0,\,0) \rightarrow$ True

9 $yx^2 \geq 1 \Leftrightarrow y \geq 1/x^2 \ \{x \neq 0\}$; test point $(1, 0) \to$ False

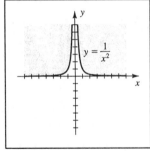

Figure 9

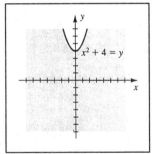

Figure 10

10 $x^2 + 4 \geq y \Leftrightarrow y \leq x^2 + 4$; test point $(0, 0) \to$ True

Note: The notation $V @ (a, b), (c, d), \ldots$ is used to denote the intersection point(s)

of the solution region of the graph.

11 $\begin{cases} 3x + y < 3 \\ 4 - y < 2x \end{cases} \Leftrightarrow \begin{cases} y < -3x + 3 \\ y > -2x + 4 \end{cases}$ $V @ (-1, 6)$

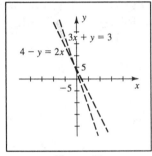

Figure 11

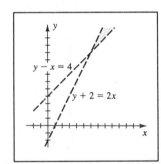

Figure 12

12 $\begin{cases} y + 2 < 2x \\ y - x > 4 \end{cases} \Leftrightarrow \begin{cases} y < 2x - 2 \\ y > x + 4 \end{cases}$ $V @ (6, 10)$

13 $\begin{cases} y - x < 0 \\ 2x + 5y < 10 \end{cases} \Leftrightarrow \begin{cases} y < x \\ y < -\frac{2}{5}x + 2 \end{cases}$ $V @ (\frac{10}{7}, \frac{10}{7})$

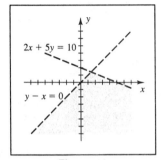

Figure 13

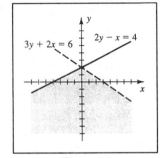

Figure 14

14 $\begin{cases} 2y - x \leq 4 \\ 3y + 2x < 6 \end{cases} \Leftrightarrow \begin{cases} y \leq \frac{1}{2}x + 2 \\ y < -\frac{2}{3}x + 2 \end{cases}$ $V @ (0, 2)$

15 $\begin{cases} 3x + y \le 6 \\ y - 2x \ge 1 \\ x \ge -2 \\ y \le 4 \end{cases}$ $\Leftrightarrow$ $\begin{cases} y \le -3x + 6 \\ y \ge 2x + 1 \\ x \ge -2 \\ y \le 4 \end{cases}$ $V @ (-2, -3), (-2, 4), (\frac{2}{3}, 4), (1, 3)$

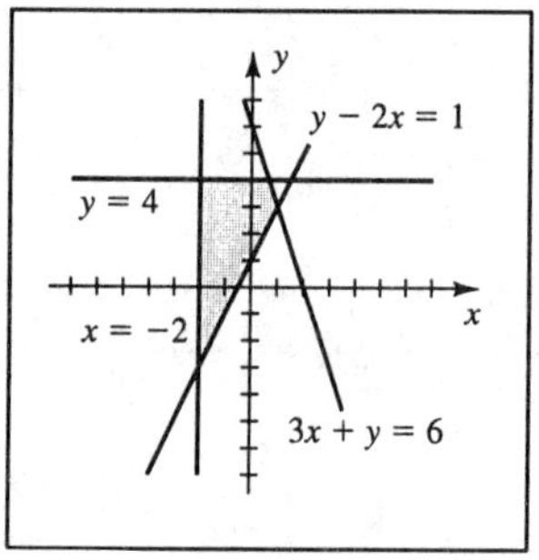

Figure 15

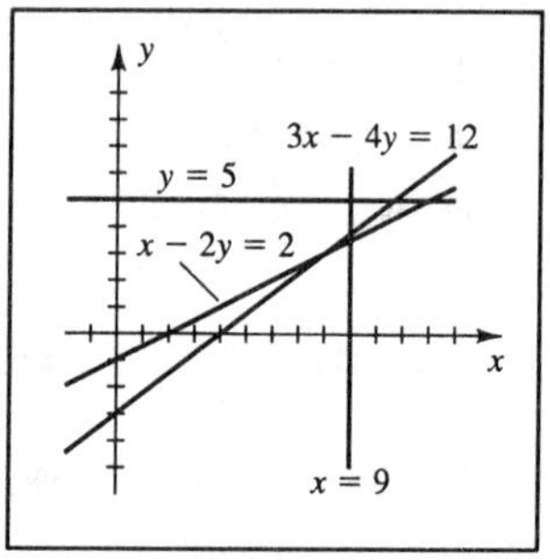

Figure 16

16 $\begin{cases} 3x - 4y \ge 12 \\ x - 2y \le 2 \\ x \ge 9 \\ y \le 5 \end{cases}$ $\Leftrightarrow$ $\begin{cases} y \le \frac{3}{4}x - 3 \\ y \ge \frac{1}{2}x - 1 \\ x \ge 9 \\ y \le 5 \end{cases}$ $V @ (9, \frac{7}{2}), (9, \frac{15}{4}), (\frac{32}{3}, 5), (12, 5)$

17 $\begin{cases} x + 2y \le 8 \\ 0 \le x \le 4 \\ 0 \le y \le 3 \end{cases}$

18 $\begin{cases} 2x + 3y \ge 6 \\ 0 \le x \le 5 \\ 0 \le y \le 4 \end{cases}$

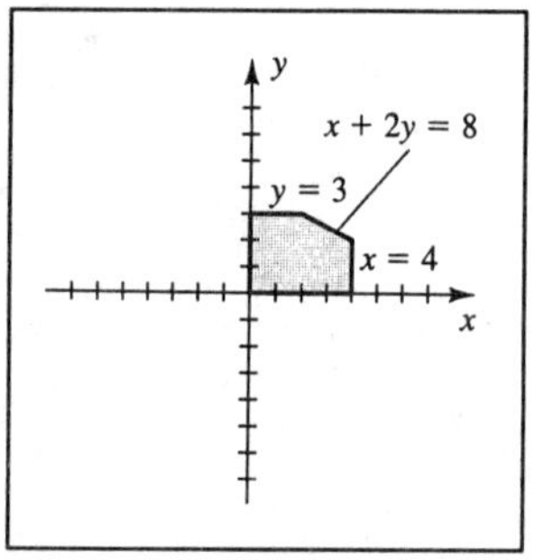

Figure 17

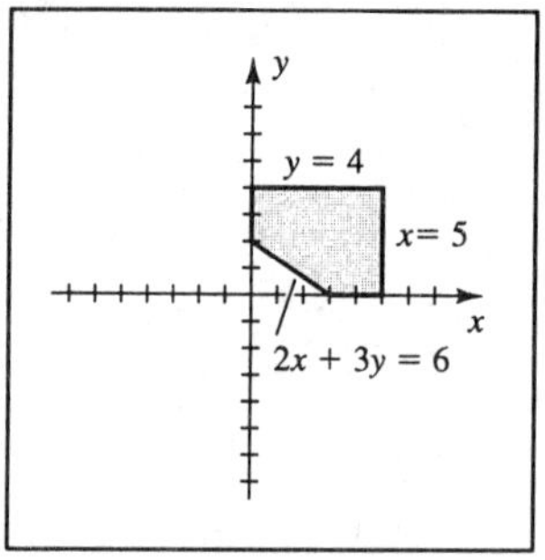

Figure 18

19   $|x| \ge 2 \Leftrightarrow x \ge 2$ or $x \le -2$; $|y| < 3 \Leftrightarrow -3 < y < 3$

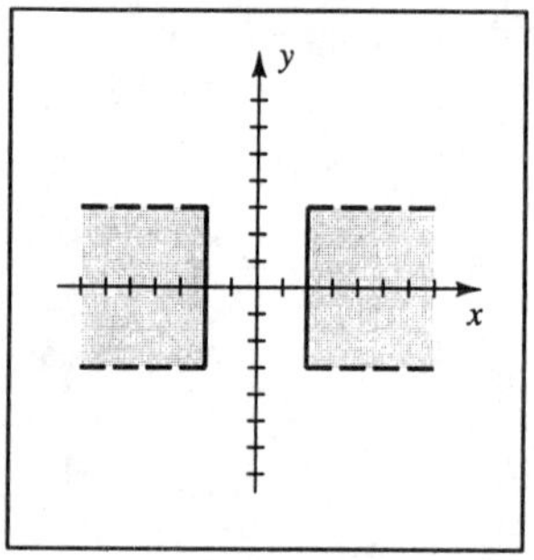

Figure 19

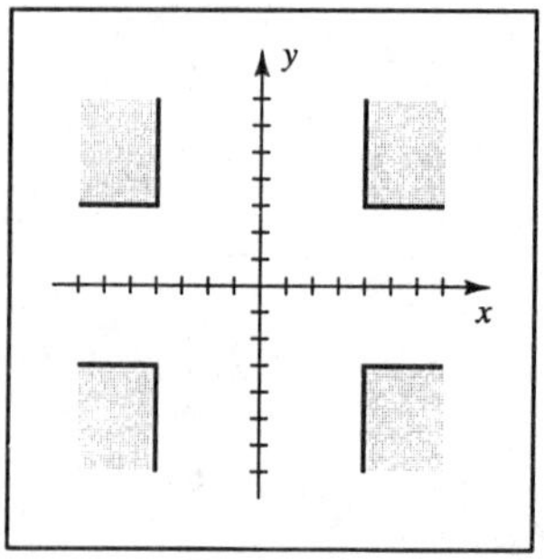

Figure 20

20   $|x| \ge 4 \Leftrightarrow x \ge 4$ or $x \le -4$; $|y| \ge 3 \Leftrightarrow y \ge 3$ or $y \le -3$

21. $|x+2| \leq 1 \Leftrightarrow -1 \leq x+2 \leq 1 \Leftrightarrow -3 \leq x \leq -1;$

$|y-3| < 5 \Leftrightarrow -5 < y-3 < 5 \Leftrightarrow -2 < y < 8$

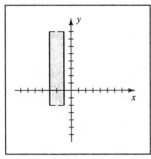

Figure 21

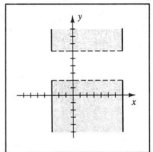

Figure 22

22. $|x-2| \leq 5 \Leftrightarrow -5 \leq x-2 \leq 5 \Leftrightarrow -3 \leq x \leq 7;$

$|y-4| > 2 \Leftrightarrow y-4 > 2$ or $y-4 < -2 \Leftrightarrow y > 6$ or $y < 2$

23. $\begin{cases} x^2+y^2 \leq 4 \\ x+y \geq 1 \end{cases} \Leftrightarrow \begin{cases} x^2+y^2 \leq 2^2 \\ y \geq -x+1 \end{cases}$ $V @ (\frac{1}{2} \mp \frac{1}{2}\sqrt{7}, \frac{1}{2} \pm \frac{1}{2}\sqrt{7})$

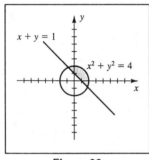

Figure 23

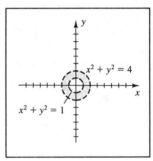

Figure 24

24. $\begin{cases} x^2+y^2 > 1 \\ x^2+y^2 < 4 \end{cases}$

25. $\begin{cases} x^2 \leq 1-y \\ x \geq 1+y \end{cases} \Leftrightarrow \begin{cases} y \leq -x^2+1 \\ y \leq x-1 \end{cases}$ $V @ (-2, -3), (1, 0)$

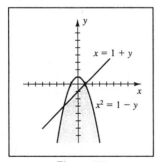

Figure 25

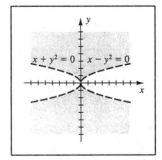

Figure 26

26. $\begin{cases} x-y^2 < 0 \\ x+y^2 > 0 \end{cases} \Leftrightarrow \begin{cases} x < y^2 \\ x > -y^2 \end{cases}$

27 $\begin{cases} 0 \le x < 3 \\ y < -x + 4 \\ y \ge x - 4 \end{cases}$ slope between $(0, 4)$ and $(4, 0)$ is -1, y-intercept is 4
  slope between $(0, -4)$ and $(4, 0)$ is 1, y-intercept is -4

28 $\begin{cases} x^2 + y^2 \le 9 \\ (x - 1)^2 + y^2 < 9 \end{cases}$ center is $(0, 0)$, radius is 3
  center is $(1, 0)$, radius is 3

29 $\begin{cases} x^2 + y^2 \le 9 \\ y > -2x + 4 \end{cases}$ center is $(0, 0)$, radius is 3
  slope between $(0, 4)$ and $(2, 0)$ is -2, y-intercept is 4

30 $\begin{cases} 0 \le y \le 3 \\ x \ge 0 \\ y < -x + 4 \\ y \ge \frac{3}{2}x - 3 \end{cases}$ slope between $(0, 4)$ and $(4, 0)$ is -1, y-intercept is 4
  slope between $(0, -3)$ and $(2, 0)$ is $\frac{3}{2}$, y-intercept is -3

31 $\begin{cases} y < x \\ y \le -x + 4 \\ (x - 2)^2 + (y - 2)^2 \le 8 \end{cases}$ slope between $(0, 4)$ and $(4, 0)$ is -1, y-intercept is 4
  center is $(2, 2)$, radius is $\sqrt{8}$

32 $\begin{cases} y < x^2 \\ x^2 + y^2 \le 9 \end{cases}$ center is $(0, 0)$, radius is 3

33 $\begin{cases} y > \frac{1}{8}x + \frac{1}{2} \\ y \le x + 4 \\ y \le -\frac{3}{4}x + 4 \end{cases}$ slope between $(-4, 0)$ and $(4, 1)$ is $\frac{1}{8}$, y-intercept is $\frac{1}{2}$
  slope between $(-4, 0)$ and $(0, 4)$ is 1, y-intercept is 4
  slope between $(0, 4)$ and $(4, 1)$ is $-\frac{3}{4}$, y-intercept is 4

34 $\begin{cases} y < \frac{4}{3}x + 4 \\ y \le -x + 2 \end{cases}$ slope between $(-3, 0)$ and $(0, 4)$ is $\frac{4}{3}$, y-intercept is 4
  slope between $(2, 0)$ and $(0, 2)$ is -1, y-intercept is 2

35 If x and y denote the number of sets of brand A and brand B, respectively, then a system is $x \ge 20$, $y \ge 10$, $x \ge 2y$, $x + y \le 100$. The graph is the region bounded by the triangle with vertices $(20, 10)$, $(90, 10)$, $(\frac{200}{3}, \frac{100}{3})$.

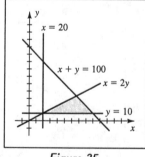

Figure 35

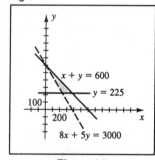

Figure 36

36 If x and y denote the number of \$8.00 and \$5.00 seats, respectively, then a system is $x + y \le 600$, $y \ge 225$, $8x + 5y \ge 3000$. The graph is the region bounded by the triangle with vertices $(0, 600)$, $(375, 225)$, $(\frac{1875}{8} \{ = 234.375 \}, 225)$.

37 If x and y denote the amount placed in the high-risk and low-risk investment, respectively, then a system is $x \geq 2000$, $y \geq 3x$, $x + y \leq 15,000$. The graph is the region bounded by the triangle with vertices $(2000, 6000)$, $(2000, 13,000)$, and $(3750, 11,250)$.

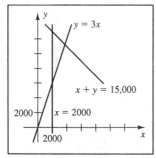
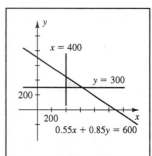

Figure 37   *Figure 38*

38 If x and y denote the number of $0.55 and $0.85 notebooks, respectively, then a system is $0.55x + 0.85y \leq 600$, $y \geq 300$, $x \geq 400$.

The graph is the region bounded by the triangle with

vertices $(400, 300)$, $(400, \frac{7600}{17} \{ \approx 447.1 \})$, $(\frac{6900}{11} \{ \approx 627.3 \}, 300)$.

39 A system is $x + y \leq 9$, $y \geq x$, $x \geq 1$. To justify the condition $y \geq x$, start with

$$\frac{\text{cylinder volume}}{\text{total volume}} \geq 0.75 \Rightarrow \frac{\pi r^2 y}{\pi r^2 y + \frac{1}{3}\pi r^2 x} \geq \frac{3}{4} \Rightarrow 4\pi r^2 y \geq 3\pi r^2 y + \pi r^2 x \Rightarrow$$

$\pi r^2 y \geq \pi r^2 x \Rightarrow y \geq x$. The graph is the region bounded by the triangle with vertices $(1, 1)$, $(1, 8)$, $(\frac{9}{2}, \frac{9}{2})$.

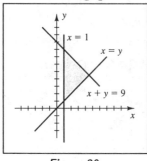
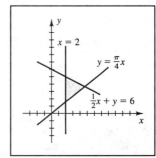

Figure 39   *Figure 40*

40 If ℓ denotes the length of the rectangle (the height of the rectangular portion of the window), then a system is $\frac{1}{2}d + \ell \leq 6$, $\ell \geq \frac{\pi}{4}d$, $d \geq 2$. To justify the condition $\ell \geq \frac{\pi}{4}d$, start with (area of rectangle) ≥ 2 (area of semicircle) $\Rightarrow$

$d\ell \geq 2\left[\frac{1}{2}\pi(\frac{1}{2}d)^2\right] \Rightarrow d\ell \geq \frac{\pi}{4}d^2 \Rightarrow \ell \geq \frac{\pi}{4}d$. The graph is the region bounded by the

triangle with vertices $(2, 5)$, $(2, \frac{\pi}{2})$, $\left(\frac{24}{\pi + 2}, \frac{6\pi}{\pi + 2}\right) \approx (4.67, 3.67)$.

41 If the plant is located at (x, y), then a system is $(60)^2 \leq x^2 + y^2 \leq (100)^2$,

$(60)^2 \leq (x - 100)^2 + y^2 \leq (100)^2$, $y \geq 0$. The graph is the region in the first

quadrant that lies between the two concentric circles with center $(0, 0)$ and radii 60

and 100, and also between the two concentric circles with center $(100, 0)$ and radii 60

and 100. Equating the different circle equations, we obtain the vertices of the

solution region $(50, 50\sqrt{3})$, $(50, 10\sqrt{11})$, $(18, 6\sqrt{91})$, $(82, 6\sqrt{91})$.

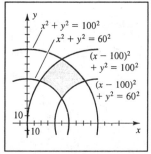   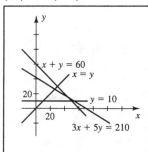

      Figure 41   Figure 42

42 If x and y denote the depths of the patio and pool areas, respectively, then a system

is $y \geq 10$, $x + y \leq 60$ {sum of depths cannot exceed 60},

$x \geq y$ {patio area $\geq$ pool area}, $3x + 5y \leq 210$ { $3(50x) + 5(50y) \leq 10,500$ }.

The graph is the region bounded by the quadrilateral with vertices

$(10, 10)$, $(26\frac{1}{4}, 26\frac{1}{4})$, $(45, 15)$, $(50, 10)$.

43 $64y^3 - x^3 \leq e^{1 - 2x} \Rightarrow y \leq \frac{1}{4}(e^{1 - 2x} + x^3)^{1/3}$ Graph $y = \frac{1}{4}(e^{1 - 2x} + x^3)^{1/3}$ { Y_1 }.

The solution includes the graph and the region below the graph.

Shading was obtained by using the command Shade(Ymin, Y_1, 1, Xmin, Xmax).

$[-3.5, 4]$ by $[-1, 4]$ $[-3.5, 4]$ by $[-1, 4]$

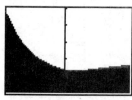   Xscl $= 1$ 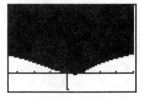   Xscl $= 1$
                         Yscl $= 1$ Yscl $= 1$

      Figure 43   Figure 44

44 $e^{5y} - e^{-x} \geq x^4 \Rightarrow e^{5y} \geq x^4 + e^{-x} \Rightarrow y \geq \frac{1}{5}\ln(x^4 + e^{-x})$. Graph $y = \frac{1}{5}\ln(x^4 + e^{-x})$

{ Y_1 }. The solution includes the graph and the region above the graph.

Shading was obtained by using the command Shade(Y_1, Ymax, 1, Xmin, Xmax).

[45] $5^{1-y} \geq x^4 + x^2 + 1 \Rightarrow 1 - y \geq \log_5 (x^4 + x^2 + 1) \Rightarrow y \leq 1 - \log_5 (x^4 + x^2 + 1)$.

$x + 3y \geq x^{5/3} \Rightarrow y \geq \frac{1}{3}(x^{5/3} - x)$. Graph $y = 1 - \log_5 (x^4 + x^2 + 1)$ $\{Y_1\}$ and

$y = \frac{1}{3}(x^{5/3} - x)$ $\{Y_2\}$. The graphs intersect at approximately (1.21, 0.05) and

(−1.32, −0.09). The solution is located between the points of intersection. It

includes the graphs and the region below the first graph and above the second graph.

Shading was obtained by using the command Shade(Y_2, Y_1, 1, −1.32, 1.21).

[−1.5, 1.5] by [−1, 1]

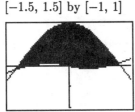

Xscl = 0.5

Yscl = 0.5

[−3, 3] by [−2, 2]

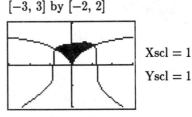

Xscl = 1

Yscl = 1

Figure 45

Figure 46

[46] $x^4 + y^5 < 2^x \Rightarrow y < (2^x - x^4)^{1/5}$. $y^3 > \ln(x^2 + 1) \Rightarrow y > [\ln(x^2 + 1)]^{1/3}$.

Graph $y = (2^x - x^4)^{1/5}$ and $y = [\ln(x^2 + 1)]^{1/3}$. The graphs intersect at

approximately (−0.76, 0.77) and (1.10, 0.93). The solution does not include the

graphs. It includes the region located between the points of intersection that is below

the first graph and above the second graph.

[47] $x^4 - 2x < 3y \Rightarrow y > \frac{1}{3}(x^4 - 2x)$. $x + 2y < x^3 - 5 \Rightarrow y < \frac{1}{2}(x^3 - x - 5)$.

Graph $y = \frac{1}{3}(x^4 - 2x)$ and $y = \frac{1}{2}(x^3 - x - 5)$. The graphs do not intersect.

The solution must be above the first graph and below the second graph.

Since the regions do not intersect, there is no solution.

[−4.5, 4.5] by [−3, 3]

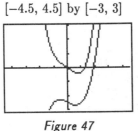

Xscl = 1

Yscl = 1

[0, 9] by [−3, 3]

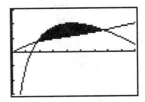

Xscl = 1

Yscl = 1

Figure 47

Figure 48

[48] $e^x + x^2 \leq 2^{x+2y} \Rightarrow \log_2 (e^x + x^2) \leq x + 2y \Rightarrow y \geq \frac{1}{2}\left[\log_2 (e^x + x^2) - x\right]$.

$2^{x+2y} \leq x^3 2^y \Rightarrow x + 2y \leq \log_2 (x^3 2^y) \Rightarrow 2y \leq \log_2 x^3 + \log_2 2^y - x \Rightarrow y \leq 3\log_2 x - x$.

Graph $y = \frac{1}{2}\left[\log_2 (e^x + x^2) - x\right]$ and $y = 3\log_2 x - x$. The graphs intersect at

approximately (1.77, 0.70) and (6.72, 1.53). The solution is located between the

points of intersection. It includes the graphs and the region above the first graph and

below the second graph.

49 (a) $29T - 39P < 450 \Rightarrow 29(37) - 39(21.2) < 450 \Rightarrow 246.2 < 450$ (true).

                                            Yes, forests can grow.

(b) $29T - 39P < 450 \Rightarrow -39P < -29T + 450 \Rightarrow P > \frac{29}{39}T - \frac{150}{13}$.

                                    Graph $Y_1 = \frac{29}{39}x - \frac{150}{13}$.

(c) Forests can grow whenever the point (T, P) lies above the line $P = \frac{29}{39}T - \frac{150}{13}$.

     [33, 80] by [0, 50]   [33, 80] by [0, 50]

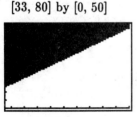   Xscl = 5   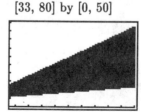   Xscl = 5

               Yscl = 5   Yscl = 5

         Figure 49   *Figure 50*

50 (a) $22P - 3T > 33 \Rightarrow 22(7.8) - 3(70) > 33 \Rightarrow -38.4 > 33$ (false).

                                No, grasslands will not grow.

(b) $22P - 3T > 33 \Rightarrow 22P > 3T + 33 \Rightarrow P > \frac{3}{22}T + \frac{3}{2}$.   Graph $Y_2 = \frac{3}{22}x + \frac{3}{2}$ together with the line $Y_1 = \frac{29}{39}x - \frac{150}{13}$ from the previous exercise.

(c) Grasslands can grow, but not forests, whenever the point (T, P) is located between the two lines.

8.6 Exercises

1

(x, y)	(0, 2)	(0, 4)	(3, 5)	(6, 2)	(5, 0)	(2, 0)
C	9 ■	13	24	27 ■	20	11

$C = 3x + 2y + 5$; maximum of 27 at (6, 2); minimum of 9 at (0, 2)

2

(x, y)	(1, 3)	(0, 5)	(2, 5)	(6, 2)	(6, 0)	(3, 1)
C	26	38	42 ■	29	15 ■	16

$C = 2x + 7y + 3$; maximum of 42 at (2, 5); minimum of 15 at (6, 0)

3

(x, y)	(0, 0)	(0, 3)	(4, 6)	(6, 3)	(5, 0)
C	0	3	18	21 ■	15

$C = 3x + y$;

maximum of 21 at (6, 3)

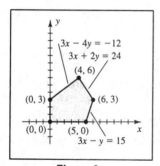

Figure 3

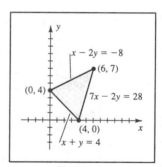

Figure 4

4

(x, y)	(0, 4)	(6, 7)	(4, 0)
C	−8	10	16 ■

$C = 4x - 2y$;

maximum of 16 at (4, 0); see *Figure 4*

5

(x, y)	(8, 0)	(3, 2)	(0, 4)
C	24	21 ■	24

$C = 3x + 6y$;

minimum of 21 at (3, 2)

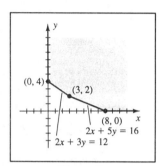

Figure 5

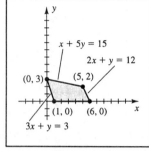

Figure 6

6

(x, y)	(0, 3)	(5, 2)	(6, 0)	(1, 0)
C	3 ■	32	36	6

$C = 6x + y$;

minimum of 3 at (0, 3)

7

(x, y)	(0, 0)	(0, 4)	(2, 5)	(6, 3)	(8, 0)
C	0	16	24 ■	24 ■	16

$C = 2x + 4y$;

C has the maximum value 24 for any point on the line segment from (2, 5) to (6, 3).

$C = 2x + 4y = 2x + 4(6 - \frac{1}{2}x) = 2x + 24 - 2x = 24.$

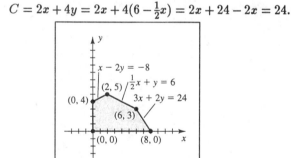

Figure 7

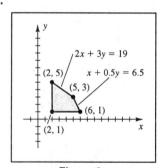

Figure 8

8

(x, y)	(2, 1)	(2, 5)	(5, 3)	(6, 1)
C	15	27	39 ■	39 ■

$C = 6x + 3y$;

C has the maximum value 39 for any point on the line segment from (6, 1) to (5, 3).

$C = 6x + 3y = 6(6.5 - 0.5y) + 3y = 39 - 3y + 3y = 39.$

9 Let x and y denote the number of oversized and standard rackets, respectively.

Profit function: $P = 15x + 8y$; see *Figure 9*

(x, y)	(10, 30)	(30, 30)	(30, 50)	(10, 70)
P	390	690	850 ■	710

$\begin{cases} 30 \le y \le 80 \\ 10 \le x \le 30 \\ x + y \le 80 \end{cases}$

The maximum profit of $850 per day occurs when 30 oversized rackets and 50 standard rackets are manufactured.

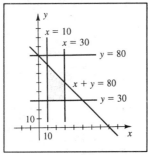

Figure 9

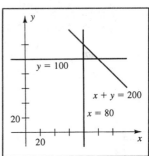

Figure 10

10 Let x and y denote the number of deluxe and standard model CB radios, respectively.

Profit function: $P = 25x + 30y$

$$\begin{cases} x + y \le 200 \\ x \ge 80 \\ y \ge 100 \end{cases}$$

(x, y)	(80, 100)	(100, 100)	(80, 120)
P	5000	5500	5600 ■

The maximum profit of $5,600 per day occurs when 80 deluxe models and 120 standard models are produced.

11 Let x and y denote the number of pounds of S and T, respectively.

Cost function: $C = 3x + 4y$

$$\begin{cases} 2x + 2y \ge 9 & \text{amount of I} \\ 4x + 6y \ge 20 & \text{amount of G} \\ x \ge 0 \\ y \ge 0 \end{cases}$$

(x, y)	(0, 4.5)	(3.5, 1)	(5, 0)
C	18	14.5 ■	15

The minimum cost of $14.50 occurs when 3.5 pounds of S and 1 pound of T are used.

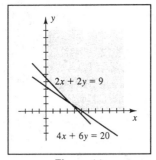

Figure 11

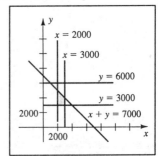

Figure 12

12 Let x and y denote the number of deluxe and regular notebooks, respectively.

Difference function: $D = 0.25x + 0.15y$

$$\begin{cases} 2000 \le x \le 3000 \\ 3000 \le y \le 6000 \\ x + y \le 7000 \end{cases}$$

(x, y)	(2000, 3000)	(3000, 3000)	(3000, 4000)	(2000, 5000)
D	950	1200	1350 ■	1250

The maximum difference of $1350 occurs when 3000 deluxe notebooks and 4000 regular notebooks are produced.

13. Let x and y denote the number of units sent to A and B, respectively, from W_1.

Cost function: $C = 12x + 10(35 - x) + 16y + 12(60 - y) = \underline{2x + 4y + 1070}$

The points are the same as those in Example 4.

$$\begin{cases} 0 \le x \le 35 \\ 0 \le y \le 60 \\ x + y \le 80 \\ x + y \ge 25 \end{cases}$$

(x, y)	(0, 25)	(0, 60)	(20, 60)	(35, 45)	(35, 0)	(25, 0)
C	1170	1310	1350	1320	1140	1120 ■

To minimize the shipping costs, send 25 units from W_1 to A and 0 from W_1 to B.

Send 10 { 35 − 25 } units from W_2 to A and 60 { 60 − 0 } units from W_2 to B.

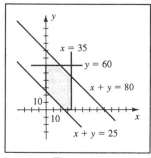

Figure 13

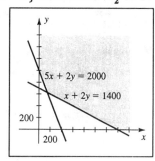

Figure 14

14. Let x and y denote the number of tons purchased from supplier A and B, respectively. Cost function: $C = 125x + 200y$

$$\begin{cases} 0.20x + 0.40y \ge 280 & premium\ grade \\ 0.50x + 0.20y \ge 200 & regular\ grade \\ x \ge 0 \\ y \ge 0 \end{cases} \Rightarrow \begin{cases} x + 2y \ge 1400 \\ 5x + 2y \ge 2000 \\ x \ge 0 \\ y \ge 0 \end{cases}$$

(x, y)	(0, 1000)	(150, 625)	(1400, 0)
C	200,000	143,750 ■	175,000

The minimum cost of \$143,750 occurs when 150 tons are purchased from supplier A and 625 tons are purchased from supplier B.

15. Let x and y denote the number of acres planted with alfalfa and corn, respectively.

Profit function: $P = 110x - 4x - 20x + 150y - 6y - 10y = \underline{86x + 134y}$

$$\begin{cases} 4x + 6y \le 480 & seed\ cost \\ 20x + 10y \le 1400 & labor\ cost \\ x + y \le 90 & area \\ x,\ y \ge 0 \end{cases}$$

(x, y)	(70, 0)	(50, 40)	(30, 60)	(0, 80)	(0, 0)
P	6020	9660	10,620	10,720 ■	0

The maximum profit of \$10,720 occurs when

0 acres of alfalfa are planted and 80 acres of corn are planted. See *Figure 15*.

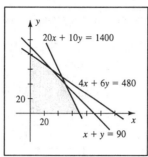

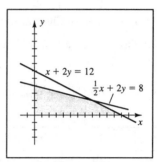

Figure 15

Figure 16

16 Let x and y denote the number of bookshelves and desks manufactured, respectively.

Profit function: $P = 20x + 50y$

(x, y)	$(12, 0)$	$(8, 2)$	$(0, 4)$	$(0, 0)$
P	240	260	200	0

$$\begin{cases} 1x + 2y \le 12 & \textit{router use} \\ \frac{1}{2}x + 2y \le 8 & \textit{saw use} \\ x, y \ge 0 \end{cases}$$

The maximum profit of $260 occurs when 8 bookshelves and 2 desks are manufactured daily.

17 Let x, y, and z denote the number of ounces of X, Y, and Z, respectively.

Cost function: $C = 0.25x + 0.35y + 0.50z$

$$= 0.25x + 0.35y + 0.50(20 - x - y) = \underline{10 - 0.25x - 0.15y}$$

$$\begin{cases} 0.20x + 0.20y + 0.10z \ge 0.14(20) & \textit{amount of A} \\ 0.10x + 0.40y + 0.20z \ge 0.16(20) & \textit{amount of B} \\ 0.25x + 0.15y + 0.25z \ge 0.20(20) & \textit{amount of C} \end{cases} \Rightarrow \begin{cases} x + y \ge 8 \\ x - 2y \le 8 \\ y \le 10 \\ x + y \le 20 \\ 0 \le x, y \le 20 \end{cases}$$

The new restrictions are found by substituting $z = 20 - x - y$ into the 3 inequalities, simplifying, and adding the last 2 inequalities.

(x, y)	$(8, 0)$	$(16, 4)$	$(10, 10)$	$(0, 10)$	$(0, 8)$
C	8.00	5.40 ■	6.00	8.50	8.80 ■■

The minimum cost of $5.40 requires 16 oz of X, 4 oz of Y, and 0 oz of Z.

The maximum cost of $8.80 requires 0 oz of X, 8 oz of Y, and 12 oz of Z.

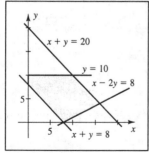

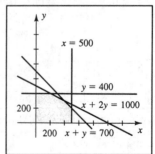

Figure 17

Figure 18

18 Let x and y denote the number of bags of peanuts and candy, respectively.

Profit function: $P = 0.60x + 0.80y$

$$\begin{cases} 0.40x + 0.80y \leq 400 & purchase \\ x + y \leq 700 & sell \\ 0 \leq x \leq 500 \\ 0 \leq y \leq 400 \end{cases} \Rightarrow \begin{cases} x + 2y \leq 1000 \\ x + y \leq 700 \\ 0 \leq x \leq 500 \\ 0 \leq y \leq 400 \end{cases}$$ See *Figure 18.*

(x, y)	(500, 0)	(500, 200)	(400, 300)	(200, 400)	(0, 400)	(0, 0)
P	300	460	480 ■	440	320	0

The maximum profit of \$480 occurs when he sells 400 bags of peanuts and 300 bags

of candy.

19 Let x and y denote the number of vans and buses purchased, respectively.

$$\begin{cases} 10,000x + 20,000y \leq 100,000 & purchase \\ 100x + 75y \leq 500 & maintenance \\ x \geq 0 \\ y \geq 0 \end{cases} \Rightarrow \begin{cases} x + 2y \leq 10 \\ 4x + 3y \leq 20 \\ x \geq 0 \\ y \geq 0 \end{cases}$$

(x, y)	(5, 0)	(2, 4)	(0, 5)	(0, 0)
P	75	130 ■	125	0

Passenger capacity function: $P = 15x + 25y$

The maximum passenger capacity of 130 would occur if the community purchases 2

vans and 4 buses.

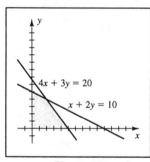

Figure 19

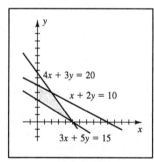

Figure 20

20 Let x and y denote the number of vans and buses purchased, respectively.

$$\begin{cases} 10,000x + 20,000y \leq 100,000 & purchase \\ 100x + 75y \leq 500 & maintenance \\ 15x + 25y \geq 75 & passengers \\ x, y \geq 0 \end{cases} \Rightarrow \begin{cases} x + 2y \leq 10 \\ 4x + 3y \leq 20 \\ 3x + 5y \geq 15 \\ x, y \geq 0 \end{cases}$$

(x, y)	(5, 0)	(2, 4)	(0, 5)	(0, 3)
C	2750	4500	4250	2550 ■

Cost function: $C = 550x + 850y$

The minimum cost of \$2550 per month would occur if the community purchased

3 buses and no vans.

21 Let x and y denote the number of trout and bass, respectively.

Pound function: $P = 3x + 4y$

$$\begin{cases} x + y \le 5000 & number\ of\ fish \\ 0.50x + 0.75y \le 3000 & cost \\ x \ge 0 \\ y \ge 0 \end{cases} \Rightarrow \begin{cases} x + y \le 5000 \\ 2x + 3y \le 12{,}000 \\ x \ge 0 \\ y \ge 0 \end{cases}$$

(x, y)	$(5000, 0)$	$(3000, 2000)$	$(0, 4000)$	$(0, 0)$
P	$15{,}000$	$17{,}000$ ■	$16{,}000$	0

The total number of pounds of fish will be a maximum of 17,000 if 3000 trout and 2000 bass are purchased.

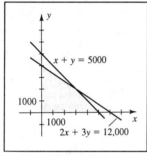

Figure 21

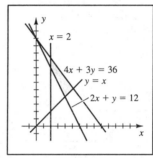

Figure 22

22 Let x and y denote the number of ounces of corn and squash, respectively.

$$\begin{cases} \frac{1}{2}x + \frac{1}{4}y \ge 3 & protein \\ 4x + 3y \le 36 & cost \\ x \ge 2 & corn \\ y \ge x & ratio \end{cases} \Rightarrow \begin{cases} 2x + y \ge 12 \\ 4x + 3y \le 36 \\ x \ge 2 \\ y \ge x \end{cases}$$

(x, y)	$(4, 4)$	$\left(\frac{36}{7}, \frac{36}{7}\right)$	$\left(2, \frac{28}{3}\right)$	$(2, 8)$
W	8 ■	$10\frac{2}{7}$	$11\frac{1}{3}$	10

Weight function: $W = x + y$

The weight is a minimum of 8 ounces when 4 ounces of each are used.

23 Let x and y denote the number of basic and deluxe units constructed, respectively.

$$\begin{cases} 300x + 600y \le 30{,}000 & cost \\ x \ge 2y & ratio \\ 80x + 120y \le 7200 & area \\ x, y \ge 0 \end{cases} \Rightarrow \begin{cases} x + 2y \le 100 \\ y \le \frac{1}{2}x \\ 2x + 3y \le 180 \\ x, y \ge 0 \end{cases}$$

(x, y)	$(90, 0)$	$(60, 20)$	$(50, 25)$	$(0, 0)$
R	3600	3900 ■	3875	0

See *Figure 23.*

Revenue function: $R = 40x + 75y$

The maximum monthly revenue of $3900 occurs if 60 basic units and 20 deluxe units are constructed.

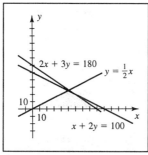

Figure 23

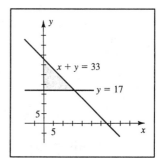

Figure 24

24 Let x and y denote the number of kg of tree leaves and aquatic plants, respectively.

Energy function: $E = 4x + y$

$$\begin{cases} x + y \le 33 \\ y \ge 17 \\ x \ge 0 \end{cases}$$

(x, y)	$(0, 17)$	$(0, 33)$	$(16, 17)$
E	17	33	81

The maximum daily energy intake of 81 units occurs if the moose eats 16 kg of tree leaves and 17 kg of aquatic plants.

8.7 Exercises

1 $A + B = \begin{bmatrix} 5 & -2 \\ 1 & 3 \end{bmatrix} + \begin{bmatrix} 4 & 1 \\ -3 & 2 \end{bmatrix} = \begin{bmatrix} 9 & -1 \\ -2 & 5 \end{bmatrix}$,

$A - B = \begin{bmatrix} 1 & -3 \\ 4 & 1 \end{bmatrix}$, $2A = \begin{bmatrix} 10 & -4 \\ 2 & 6 \end{bmatrix}$, $-3B = \begin{bmatrix} -12 & -3 \\ 9 & -6 \end{bmatrix}$

2 $A + B = \begin{bmatrix} 3 & 0 \\ -1 & 2 \end{bmatrix} + \begin{bmatrix} 3 & -4 \\ 1 & 1 \end{bmatrix} = \begin{bmatrix} 6 & -4 \\ 0 & 3 \end{bmatrix}$,

$A - B = \begin{bmatrix} 0 & 4 \\ -2 & 1 \end{bmatrix}$, $2A = \begin{bmatrix} 6 & 0 \\ -2 & 4 \end{bmatrix}$, $-3B = \begin{bmatrix} -9 & 12 \\ -3 & -3 \end{bmatrix}$

3 $A + B = \begin{bmatrix} 6 & -1 \\ 2 & 0 \\ -3 & 4 \end{bmatrix} + \begin{bmatrix} 3 & 1 \\ -1 & 5 \\ 6 & 0 \end{bmatrix} = \begin{bmatrix} 9 & 0 \\ 1 & 5 \\ 3 & 4 \end{bmatrix}$,

$A - B = \begin{bmatrix} 3 & -2 \\ 3 & -5 \\ -9 & 4 \end{bmatrix}$, $2A = \begin{bmatrix} 12 & -2 \\ 4 & 0 \\ -6 & 8 \end{bmatrix}$, $-3B = \begin{bmatrix} -9 & -3 \\ 3 & -15 \\ -18 & 0 \end{bmatrix}$

4 $A + B = \begin{bmatrix} 0 & -2 & 7 \\ 5 & 4 & -3 \end{bmatrix} + \begin{bmatrix} 8 & 4 & 0 \\ 0 & 1 & 4 \end{bmatrix} = \begin{bmatrix} 8 & 2 & 7 \\ 5 & 5 & 1 \end{bmatrix}$,

$A - B = \begin{bmatrix} -8 & -6 & 7 \\ 5 & 3 & -7 \end{bmatrix}$, $2A = \begin{bmatrix} 0 & -4 & 14 \\ 10 & 8 & -6 \end{bmatrix}$, $-3B = \begin{bmatrix} -24 & -12 & 0 \\ 0 & -3 & -12 \end{bmatrix}$

5 $A + B = \begin{bmatrix} 4 & -3 & 2 \end{bmatrix} + \begin{bmatrix} 7 & 0 & -5 \end{bmatrix} = \begin{bmatrix} 11 & -3 & -3 \end{bmatrix}$,

$A - B = \begin{bmatrix} -3 & -3 & 7 \end{bmatrix}$, $2A = \begin{bmatrix} 8 & -6 & 4 \end{bmatrix}$, $-3B = \begin{bmatrix} -21 & 0 & 15 \end{bmatrix}$

6 $A + B = \begin{bmatrix} 7 \\ -16 \end{bmatrix} + \begin{bmatrix} -11 \\ 9 \end{bmatrix} = \begin{bmatrix} -4 \\ -7 \end{bmatrix}$, $A - B = \begin{bmatrix} 18 \\ -25 \end{bmatrix}$, $2A = \begin{bmatrix} 14 \\ -32 \end{bmatrix}$, $-3B = \begin{bmatrix} 33 \\ -27 \end{bmatrix}$

7 $A + B$ and $A - B$ are not possible since A and B are different sizes.

$$2A = 2\begin{bmatrix} 3 & -2 & 2 \\ 0 & 1 & -4 \\ -3 & 2 & -1 \end{bmatrix} = \begin{bmatrix} 6 & -4 & 4 \\ 0 & 2 & -8 \\ -6 & 4 & -2 \end{bmatrix}, \quad -3B = -3\begin{bmatrix} 4 & 0 \\ 2 & -1 \\ -1 & 3 \end{bmatrix} = \begin{bmatrix} -12 & 0 \\ -6 & 3 \\ 3 & -9 \end{bmatrix}$$

8 $A + B$ and $A - B$ are not possible since A and B are different sizes.

$$2A = 2\begin{bmatrix} 2 & 1 \end{bmatrix} = \begin{bmatrix} 4 & 2 \end{bmatrix}, \quad -3B = -3\begin{bmatrix} 3 & -1 & 5 \end{bmatrix} = \begin{bmatrix} -9 & 3 & -15 \end{bmatrix}$$

9 To find c_{21} in Exercise 15, use the second row of A and the first column of B.

$$c_{21} = (-5)(2) + (2)(0) + (2)(-4) = -10 + 0 - 8 = -18.$$

10 To find c_{23} in Exercise 16, use the second row of A and the third column of B.

$$c_{23} = (3)(1) + (-2)(0) + (0)(4) + (5)(3) = 3 + 0 + 0 + 15 = 18.$$

11 $AB = \begin{bmatrix} 2 & 6 \\ 3 & -4 \end{bmatrix}\begin{bmatrix} 5 & -2 \\ 1 & 7 \end{bmatrix} = \begin{bmatrix} 16 & 38 \\ 11 & -34 \end{bmatrix}, \quad BA = \begin{bmatrix} 4 & 38 \\ 23 & -22 \end{bmatrix}$

12 $AB = \begin{bmatrix} 4 & -2 \\ -2 & 1 \end{bmatrix}\begin{bmatrix} 2 & 1 \\ 4 & 2 \end{bmatrix} = \begin{bmatrix} 0 & 0 \\ 0 & 0 \end{bmatrix}, \quad BA = \begin{bmatrix} 6 & -3 \\ 12 & -6 \end{bmatrix}$

13 $AB = \begin{bmatrix} 3 & 0 & -1 \\ 0 & 4 & 2 \\ 5 & -3 & 1 \end{bmatrix}\begin{bmatrix} 1 & -5 & 0 \\ 4 & 1 & -2 \\ 0 & -1 & 3 \end{bmatrix} = \begin{bmatrix} 3 & -14 & -3 \\ 16 & 2 & -2 \\ -7 & -29 & 9 \end{bmatrix},$

$$BA = \begin{bmatrix} 3 & -20 & -11 \\ 2 & 10 & -4 \\ 15 & -13 & 1 \end{bmatrix}$$

14 $AB = \begin{bmatrix} 5 & 0 & 0 \\ 0 & -3 & 0 \\ 0 & 0 & 2 \end{bmatrix}\begin{bmatrix} 3 & 0 & 0 \\ 0 & 4 & 0 \\ 0 & 0 & -2 \end{bmatrix} = \begin{bmatrix} 15 & 0 & 0 \\ 0 & -12 & 0 \\ 0 & 0 & -4 \end{bmatrix},$

$$BA = \begin{bmatrix} 15 & 0 & 0 \\ 0 & -12 & 0 \\ 0 & 0 & -4 \end{bmatrix}$$

15 $AB = \begin{bmatrix} 4 & -3 & 1 \\ -5 & 2 & 2 \end{bmatrix}\begin{bmatrix} 2 & 1 \\ 0 & 1 \\ -4 & 7 \end{bmatrix} = \begin{bmatrix} 4 & 8 \\ -18 & 11 \end{bmatrix}, \quad BA = \begin{bmatrix} 3 & -4 & 4 \\ -5 & 2 & 2 \\ -51 & 26 & 10 \end{bmatrix}$

16 $AB = \begin{bmatrix} 2 & 1 & -1 & 0 \\ 3 & -2 & 0 & 5 \\ -2 & 1 & 4 & 2 \end{bmatrix}\begin{bmatrix} 5 & -3 & 1 \\ 1 & 2 & 0 \\ -1 & 0 & 4 \\ 0 & -2 & 3 \end{bmatrix} = \begin{bmatrix} 12 & -4 & -2 \\ 13 & -23 & 18 \\ -13 & 4 & 20 \end{bmatrix},$

$$BA = \begin{bmatrix} -1 & 12 & -1 & -13 \\ 8 & -3 & -1 & 10 \\ -10 & 3 & 17 & 8 \\ -12 & 7 & 12 & -4 \end{bmatrix}$$

17 $AB = \begin{bmatrix} 1 & 2 & 3 \\ 4 & 5 & 6 \\ 7 & 8 & 9 \end{bmatrix}\begin{bmatrix} 1 & 0 & 0 \\ 0 & 1 & 0 \\ 0 & 0 & 1 \end{bmatrix} = \begin{bmatrix} 1 & 2 & 3 \\ 4 & 5 & 6 \\ 7 & 8 & 9 \end{bmatrix}, \quad BA = \begin{bmatrix} 1 & 2 & 3 \\ 4 & 5 & 6 \\ 7 & 8 & 9 \end{bmatrix}$

18 $AB = \begin{bmatrix} 1 & 2 & 3 \\ 2 & 3 & 1 \\ 3 & 1 & 2 \end{bmatrix} \begin{bmatrix} 2 & 0 & 0 \\ 0 & 2 & 0 \\ 0 & 0 & 2 \end{bmatrix} = \begin{bmatrix} 2 & 4 & 6 \\ 4 & 6 & 2 \\ 6 & 2 & 4 \end{bmatrix}, BA = \begin{bmatrix} 2 & 4 & 6 \\ 4 & 6 & 2 \\ 6 & 2 & 4 \end{bmatrix}$

19 $AB = \begin{bmatrix} -3 & 7 & 2 \end{bmatrix} \begin{bmatrix} 1 \\ 4 \\ -5 \end{bmatrix} = \begin{bmatrix} 15 \end{bmatrix}, BA = \begin{bmatrix} -3 & 7 & 2 \\ -12 & 28 & 8 \\ 15 & -35 & -10 \end{bmatrix}$

20 $AB = \begin{bmatrix} 4 & 8 \end{bmatrix} \begin{bmatrix} -3 \\ 2 \end{bmatrix} = \begin{bmatrix} 4 \end{bmatrix}, BA = \begin{bmatrix} -12 & -24 \\ 8 & 16 \end{bmatrix}$

21 $AB = \begin{bmatrix} 2 & 0 & 1 \\ -1 & 2 & 0 \end{bmatrix} \begin{bmatrix} 1 & -1 & 2 \\ 3 & 1 & 0 \\ 0 & 2 & 1 \end{bmatrix} = \begin{bmatrix} 2 & 0 & 5 \\ 5 & 3 & -2 \end{bmatrix}, BA$ is not possible since the

number of columns of B, 3, and the number of rows of A, 2, are not equal.

22 AB is not possible, $BA = \begin{bmatrix} -2 \\ 5 \end{bmatrix} \begin{bmatrix} 3 & -1 & 4 \end{bmatrix} = \begin{bmatrix} -6 & 2 & -8 \\ 15 & -5 & 20 \end{bmatrix}$

23 $AB = \begin{bmatrix} 4 & -2 \\ 0 & 3 \\ -7 & 5 \end{bmatrix} \begin{bmatrix} 3 \\ 4 \end{bmatrix} = \begin{bmatrix} 4 \\ 12 \\ -1 \end{bmatrix}$ **24** $AB = \begin{bmatrix} 4 \\ -3 \\ 2 \end{bmatrix} \begin{bmatrix} 5 & 1 \end{bmatrix} = \begin{bmatrix} 20 & 4 \\ -15 & -3 \\ 10 & 2 \end{bmatrix}$

25 $AB = \begin{bmatrix} 2 & 1 & 0 & -3 \\ -7 & 0 & -2 & 4 \end{bmatrix} \begin{bmatrix} 4 & -2 & 0 \\ 1 & 1 & -2 \\ 0 & 0 & 5 \\ -3 & -1 & 0 \end{bmatrix} = \begin{bmatrix} 18 & 0 & -2 \\ -40 & 10 & -10 \end{bmatrix}$

26 $AB = \begin{bmatrix} 1 & 2 & -3 \\ 4 & -5 & 6 \end{bmatrix} \begin{bmatrix} 1 & -1 & 0 & 2 \\ -2 & 3 & 1 & 0 \\ 0 & 4 & 0 & -3 \end{bmatrix} = \begin{bmatrix} -3 & -7 & 2 & 11 \\ 14 & 5 & -5 & -10 \end{bmatrix}$

27 $(A + B)(A - B) = \begin{bmatrix} 3 & 1 \\ 3 & -2 \end{bmatrix} \begin{bmatrix} -1 & 3 \\ -3 & -4 \end{bmatrix} = \begin{bmatrix} -6 & 5 \\ 3 & 17 \end{bmatrix};$

$A^2 - B^2 = \begin{bmatrix} 1 & -4 \\ 0 & 9 \end{bmatrix} - \begin{bmatrix} 1 & -3 \\ 9 & -2 \end{bmatrix} = \begin{bmatrix} 0 & -1 \\ -9 & 11 \end{bmatrix}; (A + B)(A - B) \neq A^2 - B^2$

28 $(A + B)(A + B) = \begin{bmatrix} 3 & 1 \\ 3 & -2 \end{bmatrix} \begin{bmatrix} 3 & 1 \\ 3 & -2 \end{bmatrix} = \begin{bmatrix} 12 & 1 \\ 3 & 7 \end{bmatrix};$

$A^2 + 2AB + B^2 = \begin{bmatrix} 1 & -4 \\ 0 & 9 \end{bmatrix} + \begin{bmatrix} 16 & 2 \\ -18 & -6 \end{bmatrix} + \begin{bmatrix} 1 & -3 \\ 9 & -2 \end{bmatrix} = \begin{bmatrix} 18 & -5 \\ -9 & 1 \end{bmatrix}$

29 $A(B + C) = \begin{bmatrix} 1 & 2 \\ 0 & -3 \end{bmatrix} \begin{bmatrix} 5 & 0 \\ 1 & 1 \end{bmatrix} = \begin{bmatrix} 7 & 2 \\ -3 & -3 \end{bmatrix};$

$AB + AC = \begin{bmatrix} 8 & 1 \\ -9 & -3 \end{bmatrix} + \begin{bmatrix} -1 & 1 \\ 6 & 0 \end{bmatrix} = \begin{bmatrix} 7 & 2 \\ -3 & -3 \end{bmatrix}$

30 $A(BC) = \begin{bmatrix} 1 & 2 \\ 0 & -3 \end{bmatrix} \begin{bmatrix} 8 & 2 \\ 7 & 3 \end{bmatrix} = \begin{bmatrix} 22 & 8 \\ -21 & -9 \end{bmatrix};$

$(AB)C = \begin{bmatrix} 8 & 1 \\ -9 & -3 \end{bmatrix} \begin{bmatrix} 3 & 1 \\ -2 & 0 \end{bmatrix} = \begin{bmatrix} 22 & 8 \\ -21 & -9 \end{bmatrix}$

31 $m(A+B)$ $= m\begin{bmatrix} a+p & b+q \\ c+r & d+s \end{bmatrix} = \begin{bmatrix} m(a+p) & m(b+q) \\ m(c+r) & m(d+s) \end{bmatrix}$

$= \begin{bmatrix} ma+mp & mb+mq \\ mc+mr & md+ms \end{bmatrix} = \begin{bmatrix} ma & mb \\ mc & md \end{bmatrix} + \begin{bmatrix} mp & mq \\ mr & ms \end{bmatrix}$

$= m\begin{bmatrix} a & b \\ c & d \end{bmatrix} + m\begin{bmatrix} p & q \\ r & s \end{bmatrix} = mA + mB$

32 $(m+n)A$ $= (m+n)\begin{bmatrix} a & b \\ c & d \end{bmatrix} = \begin{bmatrix} (m+n)a & (m+n)b \\ (m+n)c & (m+n)d \end{bmatrix}$

$= \begin{bmatrix} ma+na & mb+nb \\ mc+nc & md+nd \end{bmatrix} = \begin{bmatrix} ma & mb \\ mc & md \end{bmatrix} + \begin{bmatrix} na & nb \\ nc & nd \end{bmatrix}$

$= m\begin{bmatrix} a & b \\ c & d \end{bmatrix} + n\begin{bmatrix} a & b \\ c & d \end{bmatrix} = mA + nA$

33 $A(B+C)$ $= \begin{bmatrix} a & b \\ c & d \end{bmatrix}\begin{bmatrix} p+w & q+x \\ r+y & s+z \end{bmatrix}$

$= \begin{bmatrix} a(p+w)+b(r+y) & a(q+x)+b(s+z) \\ c(p+w)+d(r+y) & c(q+x)+d(s+z) \end{bmatrix}$

$= \begin{bmatrix} ap+aw+br+by & aq+ax+bs+bz \\ cp+cw+dr+dy & cq+cx+ds+dz \end{bmatrix}$

$= \begin{bmatrix} ap+br & aq+bs \\ cp+dr & cq+ds \end{bmatrix} + \begin{bmatrix} aw+by & ax+bz \\ cw+dy & cx+dz \end{bmatrix}$

$= \begin{bmatrix} a & b \\ c & d \end{bmatrix}\begin{bmatrix} p & q \\ r & s \end{bmatrix} + \begin{bmatrix} a & b \\ c & d \end{bmatrix}\begin{bmatrix} w & x \\ y & z \end{bmatrix} = AB + AC$

34 $A(BC) = \begin{bmatrix} a & b \\ c & d \end{bmatrix}\left(\begin{bmatrix} p & q \\ r & s \end{bmatrix}\begin{bmatrix} w & x \\ y & z \end{bmatrix}\right) = \begin{bmatrix} a & b \\ c & d \end{bmatrix}\begin{bmatrix} pw+qy & px+qz \\ rw+sy & rx+sz \end{bmatrix}$

$= \begin{bmatrix} a(pw+qy)+b(rw+sy) & a(px+qz)+b(rx+sz) \\ c(pw+qy)+d(rw+sy) & c(px+qz)+d(rx+sz) \end{bmatrix}$

$= \begin{bmatrix} apw+aqy+brw+bsy & apx+aqz+brx+bsz \\ cpw+cqy+drw+dsy & cpx+cqz+drx+dsz \end{bmatrix}$

$= \begin{bmatrix} (ap+br)w+(aq+bs)y & (ap+br)x+(aq+bs)z \\ (cp+dr)w+(cq+ds)y & (cp+dr)x+(cq+ds)z \end{bmatrix}$

$= \begin{bmatrix} ap+br & aq+bs \\ cp+dr & cq+ds \end{bmatrix}\begin{bmatrix} w & x \\ y & z \end{bmatrix}$

$= \left(\begin{bmatrix} a & b \\ c & d \end{bmatrix}\begin{bmatrix} p & q \\ r & s \end{bmatrix}\right)\begin{bmatrix} w & x \\ y & z \end{bmatrix} = (AB)C$

Note: For Exercises 35–38, $A = \begin{bmatrix} 3 & -3 & 7 \\ 2 & 6 & -2 \\ 4 & 2 & 5 \end{bmatrix}$ and $B = \begin{bmatrix} -9 & 5 & -8 \\ 3 & -7 & 1 \\ -1 & 2 & 6 \end{bmatrix}$.

35 $A^2 + B^2 = \begin{bmatrix} 31 & -13 & 62 \\ 10 & 26 & -8 \\ 36 & 10 & 49 \end{bmatrix} + \begin{bmatrix} 104 & -96 & 29 \\ -49 & 66 & -25 \\ 9 & -7 & 46 \end{bmatrix} = \begin{bmatrix} 135 & -109 & 91 \\ -39 & 92 & -33 \\ 45 & 3 & 95 \end{bmatrix}$

36 $3A - BA = \begin{bmatrix} 9 & -9 & 21 \\ 6 & 18 & -6 \\ 12 & 6 & 15 \end{bmatrix} - \begin{bmatrix} -49 & 41 & -113 \\ -1 & -49 & 40 \\ 25 & 27 & 19 \end{bmatrix} = \begin{bmatrix} 58 & -50 & 134 \\ 7 & 67 & -46 \\ -13 & -21 & -4 \end{bmatrix}$

37 $A^2 - 5B = \begin{bmatrix} 31 & -13 & 62 \\ 10 & 26 & -8 \\ 36 & 10 & 49 \end{bmatrix} - \begin{bmatrix} -45 & 25 & -40 \\ 15 & -35 & 5 \\ -5 & 10 & 30 \end{bmatrix} = \begin{bmatrix} 76 & -38 & 102 \\ -5 & 61 & -13 \\ 41 & 0 & 19 \end{bmatrix}$

38 $A + A^2 + B + B^2 = \begin{bmatrix} 3 & -3 & 7 \\ 2 & 6 & -2 \\ 4 & 2 & 5 \end{bmatrix} + \begin{bmatrix} 31 & -13 & 62 \\ 10 & 26 & -8 \\ 36 & 10 & 49 \end{bmatrix} + \begin{bmatrix} -9 & 5 & -8 \\ 3 & -7 & 1 \\ -1 & 2 & 6 \end{bmatrix} +$

$\begin{bmatrix} 104 & -96 & 29 \\ -49 & 66 & -25 \\ 9 & -7 & 46 \end{bmatrix} = \begin{bmatrix} 129 & -107 & 90 \\ -34 & 91 & -34 \\ 48 & 7 & 106 \end{bmatrix}$

39 (a) For the inventory matrix, we have 5 colors and 3 kinds of disks, and for each kind of disk, we have 1 price. We choose a 5×3 matrix A and a 3×1 matrix B.

$$\text{inventory matrix } A = \begin{bmatrix} 400 & 550 & 500 \\ 400 & 450 & 500 \\ 300 & 500 & 600 \\ 250 & 200 & 300 \\ 100 & 100 & 200 \end{bmatrix}, \text{ price matrix } B = \begin{bmatrix} \$0.22 \\ \$0.25 \\ \$0.28 \end{bmatrix}$$

(b) $C = AB = \begin{bmatrix} 400 & 550 & 500 \\ 400 & 450 & 500 \\ 300 & 500 & 600 \\ 250 & 200 & 300 \\ 100 & 100 & 200 \end{bmatrix} \begin{bmatrix} \$0.22 \\ \$0.25 \\ \$0.28 \end{bmatrix} = \begin{bmatrix} \$365.50 \\ \$340.50 \\ \$359.00 \\ \$189.00 \\ \$103.00 \end{bmatrix}$

(c) The \$103.00 represents the amount the store would receive if all the yellow disks were sold.

40 (a) For the cost matrix, we have 3 sizes and 2 types of cost, and for the order matrix, we have 3 quantities. We choose a 1×3 matrix A and a 3×2 matrix B.

$$\text{order matrix } A = \begin{bmatrix} 4 & 10 & 6 \end{bmatrix}, \text{ cost matrix } B = \begin{bmatrix} 34 & 50 \\ 40 & 60 \\ 43 & 67 \end{bmatrix}$$

(b) $C = AB = \begin{bmatrix} 4 & 10 & 6 \end{bmatrix} \begin{bmatrix} 34 & 50 \\ 40 & 60 \\ 43 & 67 \end{bmatrix} = \begin{bmatrix} 794 & 1202 \end{bmatrix}$

(c) The \$794,000 represents the amount needed for labor and the \$1,202,000

represents the amount needed for materials.

8.8 Exercises

Note: Exer. 1–10: Let A denote the given matrix.

1 $\begin{bmatrix} 2 & -4 & | & 1 & 0 \\ 1 & 3 & | & 0 & 1 \end{bmatrix} R_1 - R_2 \rightarrow R_1 \Rightarrow \begin{bmatrix} 1 & -7 & | & 1 & -1 \\ 1 & 3 & | & 0 & 1 \end{bmatrix} R_2 - R_1 \rightarrow R_2$

$\begin{bmatrix} 1 & -7 & | & 1 & -1 \\ 0 & 10 & | & -1 & 2 \end{bmatrix} \frac{1}{10} R_2 \rightarrow R_2 \Rightarrow \begin{bmatrix} 1 & -7 & | & 1 & -1 \\ 0 & 1 & | & -\frac{1}{10} & \frac{2}{10} \end{bmatrix} R_1 + 7 R_2 \rightarrow R_1$

$\begin{bmatrix} 1 & 0 & | & \frac{3}{10} & \frac{4}{10} \\ 0 & 1 & | & -\frac{1}{10} & \frac{2}{10} \end{bmatrix} \Rightarrow A^{-1} = \frac{1}{10} \begin{bmatrix} 3 & 4 \\ -1 & 2 \end{bmatrix}$

2 $\begin{bmatrix} 3 & 2 & | & 1 & 0 \\ 4 & 5 & | & 0 & 1 \end{bmatrix} -R_1 + R_2 \rightarrow R_1 \Rightarrow \begin{bmatrix} 1 & 3 & | & -1 & 1 \\ 4 & 5 & | & 0 & 1 \end{bmatrix} R_2 - 4 R_1 \rightarrow R_2$

$\begin{bmatrix} 1 & 3 & | & -1 & 1 \\ 0 & -7 & | & 4 & -3 \end{bmatrix} -\frac{1}{7} R_2 \rightarrow R_2 \Rightarrow \begin{bmatrix} 1 & 3 & | & -1 & 1 \\ 0 & 1 & | & -\frac{4}{7} & \frac{3}{7} \end{bmatrix} R_1 - 3 R_2 \rightarrow R_1$

$\begin{bmatrix} 1 & 0 & | & \frac{5}{7} & -\frac{2}{7} \\ 0 & 1 & | & -\frac{4}{7} & \frac{3}{7} \end{bmatrix} \Rightarrow A^{-1} = \frac{1}{7} \begin{bmatrix} 5 & -2 \\ -4 & 3 \end{bmatrix}$

3 $\begin{bmatrix} 2 & 4 & | & 1 & 0 \\ 4 & 8 & | & 0 & 1 \end{bmatrix} \frac{1}{2} R_1 \rightarrow R_1 \Rightarrow \begin{bmatrix} 1 & 2 & | & \frac{1}{2} & 0 \\ 4 & 8 & | & 0 & 1 \end{bmatrix} R_2 - 4 R_1 \rightarrow R_2$

$\begin{bmatrix} 1 & 2 & | & \frac{1}{2} & 0 \\ 0 & 0 & | & -2 & 1 \end{bmatrix}$

Since the identity matrix cannot be obtained on the left, *no inverse exists.*

4 $\begin{bmatrix} 3 & -1 & | & 1 & 0 \\ 6 & -2 & | & 0 & 1 \end{bmatrix} R_2 - 2 R_1 \rightarrow R_2 \Rightarrow \begin{bmatrix} 3 & -1 & | & 1 & 0 \\ 0 & 0 & | & -2 & 1 \end{bmatrix}$

Since the identity matrix cannot be obtained on the left, *no inverse exists.*

5 $\begin{bmatrix} 3 & -1 & 0 & | & 1 & 0 & 0 \\ 2 & 2 & 0 & | & 0 & 1 & 0 \\ 0 & 0 & 4 & | & 0 & 0 & 1 \end{bmatrix} R_1 - R_2 \rightarrow R_1$

$\begin{bmatrix} 1 & -3 & 0 & | & 1 & -1 & 0 \\ 2 & 2 & 0 & | & 0 & 1 & 0 \\ 0 & 0 & 4 & | & 0 & 0 & 1 \end{bmatrix} R_2 - 2 R_1 \rightarrow R_2$

$\begin{bmatrix} 1 & -3 & 0 & | & 1 & -1 & 0 \\ 0 & 8 & 0 & | & -2 & 3 & 0 \\ 0 & 0 & 4 & | & 0 & 0 & 1 \end{bmatrix} \begin{matrix} (1/8) R_2 \rightarrow R_2 \\ (1/4) R_3 \rightarrow R_3 \end{matrix}$

$\begin{bmatrix} 1 & -3 & 0 & | & 1 & -1 & 0 \\ 0 & 1 & 0 & | & -\frac{2}{8} & \frac{3}{8} & 0 \\ 0 & 0 & 1 & | & 0 & 0 & \frac{1}{4} \end{bmatrix} R_1 + 3 R_2 \rightarrow R_1$

(continued)

$$\begin{bmatrix} 1 & 0 & 0 & \frac{2}{8} & \frac{1}{8} & 0 \\ 0 & 1 & 0 & -\frac{2}{8} & \frac{3}{8} & 0 \\ 0 & 0 & 1 & 0 & 0 & \frac{2}{8} \end{bmatrix}$$

$$A^{-1} = \frac{1}{8}\begin{bmatrix} 2 & 1 & 0 \\ -2 & 3 & 0 \\ 0 & 0 & 2 \end{bmatrix}$$

6 $\begin{bmatrix} 3 & 0 & 2 & 1 & 0 & 0 \\ 0 & 1 & 0 & 0 & 1 & 0 \\ -4 & 0 & 2 & 0 & 0 & 1 \end{bmatrix}$ $-R_1 - R_3 \to R_1$

$$\begin{bmatrix} 1 & 0 & -4 & -1 & 0 & -1 \\ 0 & 1 & 0 & 0 & 1 & 0 \\ -4 & 0 & 2 & 0 & 0 & 1 \end{bmatrix} \quad R_3 + 4R_1 \to R_3$$

$$\begin{bmatrix} 1 & 0 & -4 & -1 & 0 & -1 \\ 0 & 1 & 0 & 0 & 1 & 0 \\ 0 & 0 & -14 & -4 & 0 & -3 \end{bmatrix} \quad -\frac{1}{14}R_3 \to R_3$$

$$\begin{bmatrix} 1 & 0 & -4 & -1 & 0 & -1 \\ 0 & 1 & 0 & 0 & 1 & 0 \\ 0 & 0 & 1 & \frac{4}{14} & 0 & \frac{3}{14} \end{bmatrix} \quad R_1 + 4R_3 \to R_1$$

$$\begin{bmatrix} 1 & 0 & 0 & \frac{2}{14} & 0 & -\frac{2}{14} \\ 0 & 1 & 0 & 0 & 1 & 0 \\ 0 & 0 & 1 & \frac{4}{14} & 0 & \frac{3}{14} \end{bmatrix}$$

$$A^{-1} = \frac{1}{14}\begin{bmatrix} 2 & 0 & -2 \\ 0 & 14 & 0 \\ 4 & 0 & 3 \end{bmatrix}$$

7 $\begin{bmatrix} -2 & 2 & 3 & 1 & 0 & 0 \\ 1 & -1 & 0 & 0 & 1 & 0 \\ 0 & 1 & 4 & 0 & 0 & 1 \end{bmatrix}$ $R_1 + 2R_2 \leftrightarrow R_2$

$$\begin{bmatrix} 1 & -1 & 0 & 0 & 1 & 0 \\ 0 & 0 & 3 & 1 & 2 & 0 \\ 0 & 1 & 4 & 0 & 0 & 1 \end{bmatrix} \quad R_1 + R_3 \to R_1$$

$$\begin{bmatrix} 1 & 0 & 4 & 0 & 1 & 1 \\ 0 & 0 & 3 & 1 & 2 & 0 \\ 0 & 1 & 4 & 0 & 0 & 1 \end{bmatrix} \quad \frac{1}{3}R_2 \leftrightarrow R_3$$

$$\begin{bmatrix} 1 & 0 & 4 & 0 & 1 & 1 \\ 0 & 1 & 4 & 0 & 0 & 1 \\ 0 & 0 & 1 & \frac{1}{3} & \frac{2}{3} & 0 \end{bmatrix} \quad \begin{matrix} R_1 - 4R_3 \to R_1 \\ R_2 - 4R_3 \to R_2 \end{matrix}$$

$$\begin{bmatrix} 1 & 0 & 0 & -\frac{4}{3} & -\frac{5}{3} & 1 \\ 0 & 1 & 0 & -\frac{4}{3} & -\frac{8}{3} & 1 \\ 0 & 0 & 1 & \frac{1}{3} & \frac{2}{3} & 0 \end{bmatrix}$$

$$A^{-1} = \frac{1}{3}\begin{bmatrix} -4 & -5 & 3 \\ -4 & -8 & 3 \\ 1 & 2 & 0 \end{bmatrix}$$

8 $\begin{bmatrix} 1 & 2 & 3 & | & 1 & 0 & 0 \\ -2 & 1 & 0 & | & 0 & 1 & 0 \\ 3 & -1 & 1 & | & 0 & 0 & 1 \end{bmatrix}$ $\begin{matrix} R_2 + 2R_1 \to R_2 \\ R_3 - 3R_1 \to R_3 \end{matrix}$

$\begin{bmatrix} 1 & 2 & 3 & | & 1 & 0 & 0 \\ 0 & 5 & 6 & | & 2 & 1 & 0 \\ 0 & -7 & -8 & | & -3 & 0 & 1 \end{bmatrix}$ $3R_2 + 2R_3 \to R_2$

$\begin{bmatrix} 1 & 2 & 3 & | & 1 & 0 & 0 \\ 0 & 1 & 2 & | & 0 & 3 & 2 \\ 0 & -7 & -8 & | & -3 & 0 & 1 \end{bmatrix}$ $\begin{matrix} R_1 - 2R_2 \to R_1 \\ \\ R_3 + 7R_2 \to R_3 \end{matrix}$

$\begin{bmatrix} 1 & 0 & -1 & | & 1 & -6 & -4 \\ 0 & 1 & 2 & | & 0 & 3 & 2 \\ 0 & 0 & 6 & | & -3 & 21 & 15 \end{bmatrix}$ $\frac{1}{6}R_3 \to R_3$

$\begin{bmatrix} 1 & 0 & -1 & | & 1 & -6 & -4 \\ 0 & 1 & 2 & | & 0 & 3 & 2 \\ 0 & 0 & 1 & | & -\frac{1}{2} & \frac{7}{2} & \frac{5}{2} \end{bmatrix}$ $\begin{matrix} R_1 + R_3 \to R_1 \\ R_2 - 2R_3 \to R_2 \end{matrix}$

$\begin{bmatrix} 1 & 0 & 0 & | & \frac{1}{2} & -\frac{5}{2} & -\frac{3}{2} \\ 0 & 1 & 0 & | & 1 & -4 & -3 \\ 0 & 0 & 1 & | & -\frac{1}{2} & \frac{7}{2} & \frac{5}{2} \end{bmatrix}$ $A^{-1} = \frac{1}{2}\begin{bmatrix} 1 & -5 & -3 \\ 2 & -8 & -6 \\ -1 & 7 & 5 \end{bmatrix}$

9 $\begin{bmatrix} 2 & 0 & 0 & | & 1 & 0 & 0 \\ 0 & 4 & 0 & | & 0 & 1 & 0 \\ 0 & 0 & 6 & | & 0 & 0 & 1 \end{bmatrix}$ $\begin{matrix} (1/2)R_1 \to R_1 \\ (1/4)R_2 \to R_2 \\ (1/6)R_3 \to R_3 \end{matrix}$

$\begin{bmatrix} 1 & 0 & 0 & | & \frac{1}{2} & 0 & 0 \\ 0 & 1 & 0 & | & 0 & \frac{1}{4} & 0 \\ 0 & 0 & 1 & | & 0 & 0 & \frac{1}{6} \end{bmatrix}$ $A^{-1} = \frac{1}{12}\begin{bmatrix} 6 & 0 & 0 \\ 0 & 3 & 0 \\ 0 & 0 & 2 \end{bmatrix}$

10 $\begin{bmatrix} 1 & 1 & 1 & | & 1 & 0 & 0 \\ 2 & 2 & 2 & | & 0 & 1 & 0 \\ 3 & 3 & 3 & | & 0 & 0 & 1 \end{bmatrix}$ $\begin{matrix} R_2 - 2R_1 \to R_2 \\ R_3 - 3R_1 \to R_3 \end{matrix}$

$\begin{bmatrix} 1 & 1 & 1 & | & 1 & 0 & 0 \\ 0 & 0 & 0 & | & -2 & 1 & 0 \\ 0 & 0 & 0 & | & -3 & 0 & 1 \end{bmatrix}$ *No inverse exists.*

11 $\begin{bmatrix} a & 0 & | & 1 & 0 \\ 0 & b & | & 0 & 1 \end{bmatrix}$ $\begin{matrix} (1/a)R_1 \to R_1 \\ (1/b)R_2 \to R_2 \end{matrix}$ $\Rightarrow \begin{bmatrix} 1 & 0 & | & 1/a & 0 \\ 0 & 1 & | & 0 & 1/b \end{bmatrix}$

The inverse is the matrix with main diagonal elements $(1/a)$ and $(1/b)$.

The required conditions are that a and b are nonzero to avoid division by zero.

12 Refer to Exercise 11. Generalizing, we have the inverse $\begin{bmatrix} 1/a & 0 & 0 \\ 0 & 1/b & 0 \\ 0 & 0 & 1/c \end{bmatrix}$.

13 $AI_3 = \begin{bmatrix} a_{11} & a_{12} & a_{13} \\ a_{21} & a_{22} & a_{23} \\ a_{31} & a_{32} & a_{33} \end{bmatrix} \begin{bmatrix} 1 & 0 & 0 \\ 0 & 1 & 0 \\ 0 & 0 & 1 \end{bmatrix} = \begin{bmatrix} a_{11} & a_{12} & a_{13} \\ a_{21} & a_{22} & a_{23} \\ a_{31} & a_{32} & a_{33} \end{bmatrix} = A$

$I_3A = \begin{bmatrix} 1 & 0 & 0 \\ 0 & 1 & 0 \\ 0 & 0 & 1 \end{bmatrix} \begin{bmatrix} a_{11} & a_{12} & a_{13} \\ a_{21} & a_{22} & a_{23} \\ a_{31} & a_{32} & a_{33} \end{bmatrix} = \begin{bmatrix} a_{11} & a_{12} & a_{13} \\ a_{21} & a_{22} & a_{23} \\ a_{31} & a_{32} & a_{33} \end{bmatrix} = A$

14 Show that the same conditions in Exercise 13 hold using a square matrix of order 4.

15 (a) $X = A^{-1}B = \frac{1}{10} \begin{bmatrix} 3 & 4 \\ -1 & 2 \end{bmatrix} \begin{bmatrix} 3 \\ 1 \end{bmatrix} = \frac{1}{10} \begin{bmatrix} 13 \\ -1 \end{bmatrix}; \quad (\frac{13}{10}, -\frac{1}{10})$

(b) $X = A^{-1}B = \frac{1}{10} \begin{bmatrix} 3 & 4 \\ -1 & 2 \end{bmatrix} \begin{bmatrix} -2 \\ 5 \end{bmatrix} = \frac{1}{10} \begin{bmatrix} 14 \\ 12 \end{bmatrix}; \quad (\frac{7}{5}, \frac{6}{5})$

16 (a) $X = A^{-1}B = \frac{1}{7} \begin{bmatrix} 5 & -2 \\ -4 & 3 \end{bmatrix} \begin{bmatrix} -1 \\ 1 \end{bmatrix} = \frac{1}{7} \begin{bmatrix} -7 \\ 7 \end{bmatrix}; \quad (-1, 1)$

(b) $X = A^{-1}B = \frac{1}{7} \begin{bmatrix} 5 & -2 \\ -4 & 3 \end{bmatrix} \begin{bmatrix} 4 \\ 3 \end{bmatrix} = \frac{1}{7} \begin{bmatrix} 14 \\ -7 \end{bmatrix}; \quad (2, -1)$

17 (a) $X = A^{-1}B = \frac{1}{3} \begin{bmatrix} -4 & -5 & 3 \\ -4 & -8 & 3 \\ 1 & 2 & 0 \end{bmatrix} \begin{bmatrix} 1 \\ 3 \\ -2 \end{bmatrix} = \frac{1}{3} \begin{bmatrix} -25 \\ -34 \\ 7 \end{bmatrix}; \quad (-\frac{25}{3}, -\frac{34}{3}, \frac{7}{3})$

(b) $X = A^{-1}B = \frac{1}{3} \begin{bmatrix} -4 & -5 & 3 \\ -4 & -8 & 3 \\ 1 & 2 & 0 \end{bmatrix} \begin{bmatrix} -1 \\ 0 \\ 4 \end{bmatrix} = \frac{1}{3} \begin{bmatrix} 16 \\ 16 \\ -1 \end{bmatrix}; \quad (\frac{16}{3}, \frac{16}{3}, -\frac{1}{3})$

18 (a) $X = A^{-1}B = \frac{1}{2} \begin{bmatrix} 1 & -5 & -3 \\ 2 & -8 & -6 \\ -1 & 7 & 5 \end{bmatrix} \begin{bmatrix} -1 \\ 4 \\ 2 \end{bmatrix} = \frac{1}{2} \begin{bmatrix} -27 \\ -46 \\ 39 \end{bmatrix}; \quad (-\frac{27}{2}, -23, \frac{39}{2})$

(b) $X = A^{-1}B = \frac{1}{2} \begin{bmatrix} 1 & -5 & -3 \\ 2 & -8 & -6 \\ -1 & 7 & 5 \end{bmatrix} \begin{bmatrix} -3 \\ -2 \\ 1 \end{bmatrix} = \frac{1}{2} \begin{bmatrix} 4 \\ 4 \\ -6 \end{bmatrix}; \quad (2, 2, -3)$

19 $A = \begin{bmatrix} 2 & -5 & 8 \\ 3 & 7 & -1 \\ 0 & 2 & 1 \end{bmatrix} \Rightarrow A^{-1} \approx \begin{bmatrix} 0.11111 & 0.25926 & -0.62963 \\ -0.03704 & 0.02469 & 0.32099 \\ 0.07407 & -0.04938 & 0.35802 \end{bmatrix}$

20 $A = \begin{bmatrix} 0 & 1.2 & 4.1 \\ -1 & 0 & -1 \\ 5.9 & 2 & 0 \end{bmatrix} \Rightarrow A^{-1} \approx \begin{bmatrix} -0.13089 & -0.53665 & 0.07853 \\ 0.38613 & 1.58312 & 0.26832 \\ 0.13089 & -0.46335 & -0.07853 \end{bmatrix}$

21 $A = \begin{bmatrix} 2 & -1 & 1 & 4 \\ 7 & 1.2 & -8 & 0 \\ 2.5 & 0 & 1.9 & 7.9 \\ 1 & -1 & 3 & 1 \end{bmatrix} \Rightarrow A^{-1} \approx \begin{bmatrix} -0.22278 & 0.12932 & 0.06496 & 0.37796 \\ -1.17767 & 0.09503 & 0.55936 & 0.29171 \\ -0.37159 & 0.00241 & 0.14074 & 0.37447 \\ 0.15987 & -0.04150 & 0.07218 & -0.20967 \end{bmatrix}$

22 $A = \begin{bmatrix} -3 & -7 & 4 & 0 \\ -7 & 0 & 5.5 & 9 \\ 3 & 1 & 0 & 0 \\ 9 & -11 & 4 & 1 \end{bmatrix} \Rightarrow A^{-1} \approx \begin{bmatrix} -0.03078 & -0.00404 & 0.18416 & 0.03633 \\ 0.09233 & 0.01211 & 0.44753 & -0.10898 \\ 0.38850 & 0.01816 & 0.92129 & -0.16347 \\ -0.26135 & 0.09687 & -0.41978 & 0.12815 \end{bmatrix}$

23 (a) $AX = B \Leftrightarrow \begin{bmatrix} 4.0 & 7.1 \\ 2.2 & -4.9 \end{bmatrix} \begin{bmatrix} x \\ y \end{bmatrix} = \begin{bmatrix} 6.2 \\ 2.9 \end{bmatrix}$

   (b) $A^{-1} \approx \begin{bmatrix} 0.1391 & 0.2016 \\ 0.0625 & -0.1136 \end{bmatrix}$

   (c) $X = A^{-1}B \approx \begin{bmatrix} 0.1391 & 0.2016 \\ 0.0625 & -0.1136 \end{bmatrix} \begin{bmatrix} 6.2 \\ 2.9 \end{bmatrix} \approx \begin{bmatrix} 1.4472 \\ 0.0579 \end{bmatrix}$.

24 (a) $AX = B \Leftrightarrow \begin{bmatrix} 5.1 & 8.7 & 2.5 \\ 9.9 & 15 & 12 \\ -4.3 & -2.2 & -1 \end{bmatrix} \begin{bmatrix} x \\ y \\ z \end{bmatrix} = \begin{bmatrix} 1.1 \\ 3.8 \\ -7.1 \end{bmatrix}$

   (b) $A^{-1} \approx \begin{bmatrix} -0.0576 & -0.0162 & -0.3381 \\ 0.2108 & -0.0286 & 0.1842 \\ -0.2159 & 0.1324 & 0.0487 \end{bmatrix}$

   (c) $X = A^{-1}B \approx \begin{bmatrix} -0.0576 & -0.0162 & -0.3381 \\ 0.2108 & -0.0286 & 0.1842 \\ -0.2159 & 0.1324 & 0.0487 \end{bmatrix} \begin{bmatrix} 1.1 \\ 3.8 \\ -7.1 \end{bmatrix} = \begin{bmatrix} 2.2759 \\ -1.1847 \\ -0.0801 \end{bmatrix}$.

25 (a) $AX = B \Leftrightarrow \begin{bmatrix} 3.1 & 6.7 & -8.7 \\ 4.1 & -5.1 & 0.2 \\ 0.6 & 1.1 & -7.4 \end{bmatrix} \begin{bmatrix} x \\ y \\ z \end{bmatrix} = \begin{bmatrix} 1.5 \\ 2.1 \\ 3.9 \end{bmatrix}$

   (b) $A^{-1} \approx \begin{bmatrix} 0.1474 & 0.1572 & -0.1691 \\ 0.1197 & -0.0696 & -0.1426 \\ 0.0297 & 0.0024 & -0.1700 \end{bmatrix}$

   (c) $X = A^{-1}B \approx \begin{bmatrix} 0.1474 & 0.1572 & -0.1691 \\ 0.1197 & -0.0696 & -0.1426 \\ 0.0297 & 0.0024 & -0.1700 \end{bmatrix} \begin{bmatrix} 1.5 \\ 2.1 \\ 3.9 \end{bmatrix} \approx \begin{bmatrix} -0.1081 \\ -0.5227 \\ -0.6135 \end{bmatrix}$

26 (a) $AX = B \Leftrightarrow \begin{bmatrix} 5.6 & 8.4 & -7.2 & 4.2 \\ 8.4 & 9.2 & -6.1 & -6.2 \\ -7.2 & -6.1 & 9.2 & 4.5 \\ 4.2 & -6.2 & -4.5 & 5.8 \end{bmatrix} \begin{bmatrix} x \\ y \\ z \\ w \end{bmatrix} = \begin{bmatrix} 8.1 \\ 5.3 \\ 0.4 \\ 2.7 \end{bmatrix}$

(b) $A^{-1} \approx \begin{bmatrix} -0.0295 & 0.2513 & 0.2069 & 0.1294 \\ 0.0784 & 0.0139 & 0.0363 & -0.0701 \\ -0.0163 & 0.2085 & 0.2530 & 0.0384 \\ 0.0925 & -0.0054 & 0.0852 & 0.0335 \end{bmatrix}$

(c) $X = A^{-1}B \approx \begin{bmatrix} -0.0295 & 0.2513 & 0.2069 & 0.1294 \\ 0.0784 & 0.0139 & 0.0363 & -0.0701 \\ -0.0163 & 0.2085 & 0.2530 & 0.0384 \\ 0.0925 & -0.0054 & 0.0852 & 0.0335 \end{bmatrix} \begin{bmatrix} 8.1 \\ 5.3 \\ 0.4 \\ 2.7 \end{bmatrix} \approx \begin{bmatrix} 1.5255 \\ 0.5341 \\ 1.1778 \\ 0.8456 \end{bmatrix}$

27 (a) $f(2) = 4a + 2b + c = 19$; $f(8) = 64a + 8b + c = 59$; $f(11) = 121a + 11b + c = 26$

Solve the 3×3 linear system using the inverse method.

$$\begin{bmatrix} 4 & 2 & 1 \\ 64 & 8 & 1 \\ 121 & 11 & 1 \end{bmatrix} \begin{bmatrix} a \\ b \\ c \end{bmatrix} = \begin{bmatrix} 19 \\ 59 \\ 26 \end{bmatrix} \Rightarrow \begin{bmatrix} a \\ b \\ c \end{bmatrix} \approx \begin{bmatrix} -1.9630 \\ 26.2963 \\ -25.7407 \end{bmatrix}$$

Thus, let $f(x) \doteq -1.9630x^2 + 26.2963x - 25.7407$.

(c) For June, $f(6) \approx 61\,°F$ and for October, $f(10) \approx 41\,°F$.

[1, 12] by [−15, 70]   [1, 12] by [−15, 70]

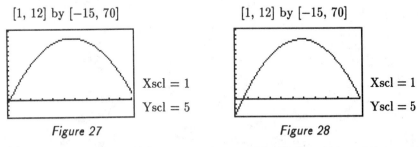

Xscl = 1   Xscl = 1

Yscl = 5   Yscl = 5

Figure 27   *Figure 28*

28 (a) $f(2) = 4a + 2b + c = 9$; $f(7) = 49a + 7b + c = 60$; $f(11) = 121a + 11b + c = 21$

Solve the 3×3 linear system using the inverse method.

$$\begin{bmatrix} 4 & 2 & 1 \\ 49 & 7 & 1 \\ 121 & 11 & 1 \end{bmatrix} \begin{bmatrix} a \\ b \\ c \end{bmatrix} = \begin{bmatrix} 9 \\ 60 \\ 21 \end{bmatrix} \Rightarrow \begin{bmatrix} a \\ b \\ c \end{bmatrix} \approx \begin{bmatrix} -2.2167 \\ 30.1500 \\ -42.4333 \end{bmatrix}$$

Thus, let $f(x) = -2.2167x^2 + 30.15x - 42.4333$.

(c) For June, $f(6) \approx 59\,°F$ and for October, $f(10) \approx 37\,°F$.

1 $M_{11} = 0 = A_{11}$; $M_{12} = 5$ and $A_{12} = -5$; $M_{21} = -1$ and $A_{21} = 1$; $M_{22} = 7 = A_{22}$

2 $M_{11} = 2 = A_{11}$; $M_{12} = 3$ and $A_{12} = -3$; $M_{21} = 4$ and $A_{21} = -4$; $M_{22} = -6 = A_{22}$

3 $M_{11} = \begin{vmatrix} 3 & 2 \\ 7 & 0 \end{vmatrix} = -14 = A_{11}$; $M_{12} = \begin{vmatrix} 0 & 2 \\ -5 & 0 \end{vmatrix} = 10$; $A_{12} = -10$;

$M_{13} = \begin{vmatrix} 0 & 3 \\ -5 & 7 \end{vmatrix} = 15 = A_{13}$; $M_{21} = \begin{vmatrix} 4 & -1 \\ 7 & 0 \end{vmatrix} = 7$; $A_{21} = -7$;

$M_{22} = \begin{vmatrix} 2 & -1 \\ -5 & 0 \end{vmatrix} = -5 = A_{22}$; $M_{23} = \begin{vmatrix} 2 & 4 \\ -5 & 7 \end{vmatrix} = 34$; $A_{23} = -34$;

$M_{31} = \begin{vmatrix} 4 & -1 \\ 3 & 2 \end{vmatrix} = 11 = A_{31}$; $M_{32} = \begin{vmatrix} 2 & -1 \\ 0 & 2 \end{vmatrix} = 4$; $A_{32} = -4$;

$M_{33} = \begin{vmatrix} 2 & 4 \\ 0 & 3 \end{vmatrix} = 6 = A_{33}$;

4 $M_{11} = \begin{vmatrix} 7 & 0 \\ 4 & -1 \end{vmatrix} = -7 = A_{11}$; $M_{12} = \begin{vmatrix} 4 & 0 \\ -3 & -1 \end{vmatrix} = -4$; $A_{12} = 4$;

$M_{13} = \begin{vmatrix} 4 & 7 \\ -3 & 4 \end{vmatrix} = 37 = A_{13}$; $M_{21} = \begin{vmatrix} -2 & 1 \\ 4 & -1 \end{vmatrix} = -2$; $A_{21} = 2$;

$M_{22} = \begin{vmatrix} 5 & 1 \\ -3 & -1 \end{vmatrix} = -2 = A_{22}$; $M_{23} = \begin{vmatrix} 5 & -2 \\ -3 & 4 \end{vmatrix} = 14$; $A_{23} = -14$;

$M_{31} = \begin{vmatrix} -2 & 1 \\ 7 & 0 \end{vmatrix} = -7 = A_{31}$; $M_{32} = \begin{vmatrix} 5 & 1 \\ 4 & 0 \end{vmatrix} = -4$; $A_{32} = 4$;

$M_{33} = \begin{vmatrix} 5 & -2 \\ 4 & 7 \end{vmatrix} = 43 = A_{33}$;

Note: Exer. 5–20: Let A denote the given matrix.

5 $\begin{vmatrix} 7 & -1 \\ 5 & 0 \end{vmatrix} = (7)(0) - (-1)(5) = 0 + 5 = 5$

6 $\begin{vmatrix} -6 & 4 \\ 3 & 2 \end{vmatrix} = (-6)(2) - (4)(3) = -12 - 12 = -24$

7 Expand by the first column.

$|A| = a_{11}A_{11} + a_{21}A_{21} + a_{31}A_{31} = 2(-14) + 0(A_{21}) - 5(11) = -83$

8 Expand by the third column.

$|A| = a_{13}A_{13} + a_{23}A_{23} + a_{33}A_{33} = 1(37) + 0(A_{23}) - 1(43) = -6$

9 $|A| = (-5)(2) - (4)(-3) = -10 + 12 = 2$

10 $|A| = (6)(2) - (4)(-3) = 12 + 12 = 24$

11 $|A| = (a)(-b) - (-a)(b) = -ab + ab = 0$

12 $|A| = (c)(c) - (d)(-d) = c^2 + d^2$

13 Expand by the first row.

$$|A| = a_{11}A_{11} + a_{12}A_{12} + a_{13}A_{13} = 3(-17) + 1(-26) - 2(24) = -125$$

14 Expand by the first row.

$$|A| = a_{11}A_{11} + a_{12}A_{12} + a_{13}A_{13} = 2(15) - 5(33) + 1(2) = -133$$

15 Expand by the third row.

$$|A| = a_{31}A_{31} + a_{32}A_{32} + a_{33}A_{33} = 2(30) + 0(A_{32}) + 6(-2) = 48$$

16 Expand by the second row.

$$|A| = a_{21}A_{21} + a_{22}A_{22} + a_{23}A_{23} = 1(17) + 0(A_{22}) + 4(30) = 137$$

17 Expand $|A|$ by the third row. $|A| = 6A_{32} = -6M_{32} = -6 \begin{vmatrix} 3 & 2 & 0 \\ 4 & -3 & 5 \\ 1 & -4 & 2 \end{vmatrix}$.

Expand M_{32} by the first row.

$$M_{32} = 3(14) + 2(-3) + 0(-13) = 36 \Rightarrow |A| = -6(36) = -216.$$

18 Expand $|A|$ by the fourth column. $|A| = 6A_{34} = -6M_{34} = -6 \begin{vmatrix} 2 & 5 & 1 \\ -4 & 0 & -3 \\ -1 & 4 & 2 \end{vmatrix}$.

Expand M_{34} by the second column.

$$5(11) + 0(5) + 4(2) = 63, \therefore |A| = -6(63) = -378$$

19 Expand by the first row. $|A| = -b \begin{vmatrix} 0 & c & 0 \\ a & 0 & 0 \\ 0 & 0 & d \end{vmatrix}$.

Expand again by the first row. $|A| = (-b)(-c) \begin{vmatrix} a & 0 \\ 0 & d \end{vmatrix} = abcd.$

20 Expand by the first column. $|A| = a \begin{vmatrix} b & x & y \\ 0 & c & z \\ 0 & 0 & d \end{vmatrix}$.

Expand again by the first column. $|A| = (ab) \begin{vmatrix} c & z \\ 0 & d \end{vmatrix} = abcd.$

21 LS $= ad - bc$; RS $= -(bc - ad) = ad - bc$

22 LS $= ad - bc$; RS $= -(bc - ad) = ad - bc$

23 LS $= adk - bck$; RS $= k(ad - bc) = adk - bck$

24 LS $= adk - bck$; RS $= k(ad - bc) = adk - bck$

25 LS $= ad - bc$; RS $= abk + ad - abk - bc = ad - bc$

26 LS $= ad - bc$; RS $= ack + ad - ack - bc = ad - bc$

27 LS $= ad - bc + af - ce$; RS $= ad + af - bc - ce$

28 LS $= ad - bc + af - be$; RS $= ad + af - bc - be$

29 All elements in A above the main diagonal are zero. Similar to Exercise 20,

we can evaluate the determinant using n expansions by the first row.

[30] $\begin{bmatrix} a_{11} & a_{12} & | & 1 & 0 \\ a_{21} & a_{22} & | & 0 & 1 \end{bmatrix} \frac{1}{a_{11}} R_1 \to R_1$ $\{a_{11}$ or a_{21} must be nonzero since $|A| \neq 0.\}$
$\{$ The rows could be swapped. $\}$

$\begin{bmatrix} 1 & a_{12}/a_{11} & | & 1/a_{11} & 0 \\ a_{21} & a_{22} & | & 0 & 1 \end{bmatrix} R_2 - a_{21} R_1 \to R_2$

$\begin{bmatrix} 1 & a_{12}/a_{11} & | & 1/a_{11} & 0 \\ 0 & (a_{11}a_{22} - a_{12}a_{21})/a_{11} & | & -a_{21}/a_{11} & 1 \end{bmatrix} (a_{11}/|A|) R_2 \to R_2,$

where $|A| = a_{11}a_{22} - a_{12}a_{21}$

$\begin{bmatrix} 1 & a_{12}/a_{11} & | & 1/a_{11} & 0 \\ 0 & 1 & | & -a_{21}/|A| & a_{11}/|A| \end{bmatrix} R_1 - (a_{12}/a_{11}) R_2 \to R_1$

$\begin{bmatrix} 1 & 0 & | & 1/a_{11} + (a_{12}a_{21})/(a_{11}|A|) & -a_{12}/|A| \\ 0 & 1 & | & -a_{21}/|A| & a_{11}/|A| \end{bmatrix}$

$= \begin{bmatrix} 1 & 0 & | & (|A| + a_{12}a_{21})/(a_{11}|A|) & -a_{12}/|A| \\ 0 & 1 & | & -a_{21}/|A| & a_{11}/|A| \end{bmatrix}$

$\{$ Use the definition of $|A|$ above. $\}$

$= \begin{bmatrix} 1 & 0 & | & a_{22}/|A| & -a_{12}/|A| \\ 0 & 1 & | & -a_{21}/|A| & a_{11}/|A| \end{bmatrix}$ $A^{-1} = \frac{1}{|A|} \begin{bmatrix} a_{22} & -a_{12} \\ -a_{21} & a_{11} \end{bmatrix}$

[31] (a) $A - xI = \begin{bmatrix} 1 & 2 \\ 3 & 2 \end{bmatrix} - x \begin{bmatrix} 1 & 0 \\ 0 & 1 \end{bmatrix} = \begin{bmatrix} 1-x & 2 \\ 3 & 2-x \end{bmatrix}.$

$$f(x) = |A - xI| = \begin{vmatrix} 1-x & 2 \\ 3 & 2-x \end{vmatrix} = x^2 - 3x - 4.$$

(b) $(x - 4)(x + 1) = 0 \Rightarrow x = -1, 4$

[32] (a) $f(x) = |A - xI| = \begin{vmatrix} 3-x & 1 \\ 2 & 2-x \end{vmatrix} = x^2 - 5x + 4$

(b) $(x - 1)(x - 4) = 0 \Rightarrow x = 1, 4$

[33] (a) $f(x) = |A - xI| = \begin{vmatrix} -3-x & -2 \\ 2 & 2-x \end{vmatrix} = x^2 + x - 2$

(b) $(x + 2)(x - 1) = 0 \Rightarrow x = -2, 1$

[34] (a) $f(x) = |A - xI| = \begin{vmatrix} 2-x & -4 \\ -3 & 5-x \end{vmatrix} = x^2 - 7x - 2$

(b) $x^2 - 7x - 2 = 0 \Rightarrow x = \dfrac{7 \pm \sqrt{49 + 8}}{2} = \dfrac{7 \pm \sqrt{57}}{2} \approx 7.27, -0.27$

35 (a) $f(x) = \begin{vmatrix} 1-x & 0 & 0 \\ 1 & 0-x & -2 \\ -1 & 1 & -3-x \end{vmatrix}$ 　$\{$ Expand by the first row. $\}$

$$= (1-x)[(-x)(-3-x)-(-2)]$$
$$= (1-x)(x^2+3x+2)$$
$$= (1-x)(x+1)(x+2) \text{ or}$$
$$(-x^3-2x^2+x+2)$$

(b) $x = -2, -1, 1$

36 (a) $f(x) = \begin{vmatrix} 2-x & 1 & 0 \\ -1 & 0-x & 0 \\ 1 & 3 & 2-x \end{vmatrix}$ 　$\{$ Expand by the third column. $\}$

$$= (2-x)[(2-x)(-x)-(-1)]$$
$$= (2-x)(x^2-2x+1)$$
$$= (2-x)(x-1)^2 \text{ or } (-x^3+4x^2-5x+2)$$

(b) $x = 1, 2$

37 (a) $f(x) = \begin{vmatrix} 0-x & 2 & -2 \\ -1 & 3-x & 1 \\ -3 & 3 & 1-x \end{vmatrix}$ 　$\{$ Expand by the first row. $\}$

$$= (-x)[(3-x)(1-x)-3]-2[(x-1)+3]-2[-3+3(3-x)]$$
$$= -x^3+4x^2+4x-16 = (x-2)(-x^2+2x+8) = (x+2)(x-2)(-x+4)$$

(b) $x = -2, 2, 4$

38 (a) $f(x) = \begin{vmatrix} 3-x & 2 & 2 \\ 1 & 0-x & 2 \\ -1 & -1 & 0-x \end{vmatrix}$ 　$\{$ Expand by the first row. $\}$

$$= (3-x)(x^2+2)-2(-x+2)+2(-1-x)$$
$$= -x^3+3x^2-2x = (-x)(x^2-3x+2) = (-x)(x-1)(x-2)$$

(b) $x = 0, 1, 2$

Note: Exer. 39–42: Expand by the first row.

39 $\begin{vmatrix} i & j & k \\ 2 & -1 & 6 \\ -3 & 5 & 1 \end{vmatrix} = i\begin{vmatrix} -1 & 6 \\ 5 & 1 \end{vmatrix} - j\begin{vmatrix} 2 & 6 \\ -3 & 1 \end{vmatrix} + k\begin{vmatrix} 2 & -1 \\ -3 & 5 \end{vmatrix} = -31i - 20j + 7k$

40 $\begin{vmatrix} i & j & k \\ 1 & -2 & 3 \\ 2 & 1 & -4 \end{vmatrix} = i\begin{vmatrix} -2 & 3 \\ 1 & -4 \end{vmatrix} - j\begin{vmatrix} 1 & 3 \\ 2 & -4 \end{vmatrix} + k\begin{vmatrix} 1 & -2 \\ 2 & 1 \end{vmatrix} = 5i + 10j + 5k$

41 $\begin{vmatrix} i & j & k \\ 5 & -6 & -1 \\ 3 & 0 & 1 \end{vmatrix} = i\begin{vmatrix} -6 & -1 \\ 0 & 1 \end{vmatrix} - j\begin{vmatrix} 5 & -1 \\ 3 & 1 \end{vmatrix} + k\begin{vmatrix} 5 & -6 \\ 3 & 0 \end{vmatrix} = -6i - 8j + 18k$

42 $\begin{vmatrix} i & j & k \\ 4 & -6 & 2 \\ -2 & 3 & -1 \end{vmatrix} = i\begin{vmatrix} -6 & 2 \\ 3 & -1 \end{vmatrix} - j\begin{vmatrix} 4 & 2 \\ -2 & -1 \end{vmatrix} + k\begin{vmatrix} 4 & -6 \\ -2 & 3 \end{vmatrix} = 0i + 0j + 0k$

43 $A = \begin{bmatrix} 29 & -17 & 90 \\ -34 & 91 & -34 \\ 48 & 7 & 10 \end{bmatrix} \Rightarrow |A| = -359{,}284.$

44 $A = \begin{bmatrix} -2 & 5.5 & 8 \\ -0.3 & 8.5 & 7 \\ 4.9 & 6.7 & 11 \end{bmatrix} \Rightarrow |A| = -235.68.$

45 $A = \begin{bmatrix} 4 & -7 & -3 & 13 \\ -17 & -0.8 & 5 & 0.9 \\ 1.1 & 0.2 & 10 & -4 \\ 3 & -6 & 2 & 1 \end{bmatrix} \Rightarrow |A| = 10{,}739.92.$

46 $A = \begin{bmatrix} 4.2 & 1.7 & -2 & -4 \\ -7 & 0.1 & 4.6 & 2.7 \\ 4.1 & -7 & 12 & 6.8 \\ 4.6 & 2 & 3.2 & 1.2 \end{bmatrix} \Rightarrow |A| = 1323.1608.$

47 (a) $f(x) = |A - xI| = \begin{vmatrix} 1-x & 0 & 1 \\ 0 & 2-x & 1 \\ 1 & 1 & -2-x \end{vmatrix} = -x^3 + x^2 + 6x - 7$

(b) The characteristic values of A are equal to the zeros of f. From the graph,

we see that the zeros are approximately -2.51, 1.22, and 2.29.

[−10, 11] by [−12, 2]

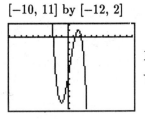

Xscl = 1

Yscl = 1

Figure 47

[−15, 15] by [−10, 10]

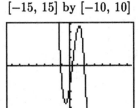

Xscl = 2

Yscl = 2

Figure 48

48 (a) $f(x) = |A - xI| = \begin{vmatrix} 3-x & -1 & -1 \\ -1 & 1-x & 0 \\ -1 & 0 & -2-x \end{vmatrix} = -x^3 + 2x^2 + 7x - 5$

(b) The characteristic values of A are equal to the zeros of f. From the graph,

we see that the zeros are approximately -2.20, 0.64, and 3.57.

8.10 Exercises

1 $R_2 \leftrightarrow R_3$

2 $C_2 \leftrightarrow C_3$

3 $-R_1 + R_3 \rightarrow R_3$

4 $-R_2 + R_1 \rightarrow R_1$

5 2 is a common factor of R_1 and R_3

6 2 is a common factor of C_1 and 3 is a common factor of C_3

7 R_1 and R_3 are identical

8 C_1 and C_3 are identical

9 -1 is a common factor of R_2

10 -1 is a common factor of R_1

$\boxed{11}$ Every number in C_2 is 0 $\boxed{12}$ Every number in R_2 is 0

$\boxed{13}$ $2C_1 + C_3 \rightarrow C_3$ $\boxed{14}$ $C_1 \leftrightarrow C_3$

Note: The notation $\{R_i\,(C_i)\}$ means expand the determinant by the ith row (column).

$\boxed{15}$ $\begin{vmatrix} 3 & 1 & 0 \\ -2 & 0 & 1 \\ 1 & 3 & -1 \end{vmatrix}$ $R_3 - 3R_1 \rightarrow R_3 = $ $\begin{vmatrix} 3 & 1 & 0 \\ -2 & 0 & 1 \\ -8 & 0 & -1 \end{vmatrix}$ $\{C_2\} = (-1)\begin{vmatrix} -2 & 1 \\ -8 & -1 \end{vmatrix} = $

$$(-1)(2+8) = -10$$

$\boxed{16}$ $\begin{vmatrix} -3 & 0 & 4 \\ 1 & 2 & 0 \\ 4 & 1 & -1 \end{vmatrix}$ $R_2 - 2R_3 \rightarrow R_2 = $ $\begin{vmatrix} -3 & 0 & 4 \\ -7 & 0 & 2 \\ 4 & 1 & -1 \end{vmatrix}$ $\{C_2\} = (-1)\begin{vmatrix} -3 & 4 \\ -7 & 2 \end{vmatrix} = $

$$(-1)(-6+28) = -22$$

$\boxed{17}$ $\begin{vmatrix} 5 & 4 & 3 \\ -3 & 2 & 1 \\ 0 & 7 & -2 \end{vmatrix}$ $\begin{matrix} R_1 - 3R_2 \rightarrow R_1 \\ \\ R_3 + 2R_2 \rightarrow R_3 \end{matrix}$ $= \begin{vmatrix} 14 & -2 & 0 \\ -3 & 2 & 1 \\ -6 & 11 & 0 \end{vmatrix}$ $\{C_3\} = (-1)\begin{vmatrix} 14 & -2 \\ -6 & 11 \end{vmatrix} = $

$$(-1)(154-12) = -142$$

$\boxed{18}$ $\begin{vmatrix} 0 & 2 & -6 \\ 5 & 1 & -3 \\ 6 & -2 & 5 \end{vmatrix}$ $\begin{matrix} R_1 - 2R_2 \rightarrow R_1 \\ \\ R_3 + 2R_2 \rightarrow R_3 \end{matrix}$ $= \begin{vmatrix} -10 & 0 & 0 \\ 5 & 1 & -3 \\ 16 & 0 & -1 \end{vmatrix}$ $\{C_2\} = (1)\begin{vmatrix} -10 & 0 \\ 16 & -1 \end{vmatrix} = $

$$(1)(10-0) = 10$$

$\boxed{19}$ $\begin{vmatrix} 2 & 2 & -3 \\ 3 & 6 & 9 \\ -2 & 5 & 4 \end{vmatrix}$ $\{3 \text{ is a common factor of } R_2\} = (3)\begin{vmatrix} 2 & 2 & -3 \\ 1 & 2 & 3 \\ -2 & 5 & 4 \end{vmatrix}$ $\begin{matrix} R_1 - 2R_2 \rightarrow R_1 \\ \\ R_3 + 2R_2 \rightarrow R_3 \end{matrix}$

$= (3)\begin{vmatrix} 0 & -2 & -9 \\ 1 & 2 & 3 \\ 0 & 9 & 10 \end{vmatrix}$ $\{C_1\} = (3)(-1)\begin{vmatrix} -2 & -9 \\ 9 & 10 \end{vmatrix} = (-3)(-20+81) = -183$

$\boxed{20}$ $\begin{vmatrix} 3 & 8 & 5 \\ 5 & 3 & -6 \\ 2 & 4 & -2 \end{vmatrix}$ $\{2 \text{ is a common factor of } R_3\} = (2)\begin{vmatrix} 3 & 8 & 5 \\ 5 & 3 & -6 \\ 1 & 2 & -1 \end{vmatrix}$ $\begin{matrix} R_1 - 3R_3 \rightarrow R_1 \\ \\ R_2 - 5R_3 \rightarrow R_2 \end{matrix}$

$= (2)\begin{vmatrix} 0 & 2 & 8 \\ 0 & -7 & -1 \\ 1 & 2 & -1 \end{vmatrix}$ $\{C_1\} = (2)(1)\begin{vmatrix} 2 & 8 \\ -7 & -1 \end{vmatrix} = (2)(-2+56) = 108$

$\boxed{21}$ $\begin{vmatrix} 3 & 1 & -2 & 2 \\ 2 & 0 & 1 & 4 \\ 0 & 1 & 3 & 5 \\ -1 & 2 & 0 & -3 \end{vmatrix}$ $\begin{matrix} \\ \\ R_3 - R_1 \rightarrow R_3 \\ R_4 - 2R_1 \rightarrow R_4 \end{matrix}$ $= \begin{vmatrix} 3 & 1 & -2 & 2 \\ 2 & 0 & 1 & 4 \\ -3 & 0 & 5 & 3 \\ -7 & 0 & 4 & -7 \end{vmatrix}$ $\{C_2\}$

$= (-1)\begin{vmatrix} 2 & 1 & 4 \\ -3 & 5 & 3 \\ -7 & 4 & -7 \end{vmatrix}$ $\begin{matrix} \\ R_2 - 5R_1 \rightarrow R_2 \\ R_3 - 4R_1 \rightarrow R_3 \end{matrix}$ $= (-1)\begin{vmatrix} 2 & 1 & 4 \\ -13 & 0 & -17 \\ -15 & 0 & -23 \end{vmatrix}$ $\{C_2\}$

$= (-1)(-1)\begin{vmatrix} -13 & -17 \\ -15 & -23 \end{vmatrix} = (1)(299-255) = 44$

22
$$\begin{vmatrix} 3 & 2 & 0 & 4 \\ -2 & 0 & 5 & 0 \\ 4 & -3 & 1 & 6 \\ 2 & -1 & 2 & 0 \end{vmatrix} \begin{array}{l} R_2 - 5R_3 \to R_2 \\ \\ R_4 - 2R_3 \to R_4 \end{array} = \begin{vmatrix} 3 & 2 & 0 & 4 \\ -22 & 15 & 0 & -30 \\ 4 & -3 & 1 & 6 \\ -6 & 5 & 0 & -12 \end{vmatrix} \{C_3\}$$

$$= (1) \begin{vmatrix} 3 & 2 & 4 \\ -22 & 15 & -30 \\ -6 & 5 & -12 \end{vmatrix} \begin{array}{l} C_1 - C_2 \to C_1 \end{array} = \begin{vmatrix} 1 & 2 & 4 \\ -37 & 15 & -30 \\ -11 & 5 & -12 \end{vmatrix} \begin{array}{l} R_2 + 37R_1 \to R_2 \\ R_3 + 11R_1 \to R_3 \end{array}$$

$$= \begin{vmatrix} 1 & 2 & 4 \\ 0 & 89 & 118 \\ 0 & 27 & 32 \end{vmatrix} \{C_1\} = (1) \begin{vmatrix} 89 & 118 \\ 27 & 32 \end{vmatrix} = (1)(2848 - 3186) = -338$$

23
$$\begin{vmatrix} 2 & -2 & 0 & 0 & -3 \\ 3 & 0 & 3 & 2 & -1 \\ 0 & 1 & -2 & 0 & 2 \\ -1 & 2 & 0 & 3 & 0 \\ 0 & 4 & 1 & 0 & 0 \end{vmatrix} \begin{array}{l} C_2 - 4C_3 \to C_2 \end{array} = \begin{vmatrix} 2 & -2 & 0 & 0 & -3 \\ 3 & -12 & 3 & 2 & -1 \\ 0 & 9 & -2 & 0 & 2 \\ -1 & 2 & 0 & 3 & 0 \\ 0 & 0 & 1 & 0 & 0 \end{vmatrix} \{R_5\}$$

$$= (1) \begin{vmatrix} 2 & -2 & 0 & -3 \\ 3 & -12 & 2 & -1 \\ 0 & 9 & 0 & 2 \\ -1 & 2 & 3 & 0 \end{vmatrix} \begin{array}{l} R_1 + 2R_4 \to R_1 \\ R_2 + 3R_4 \to R_2 \end{array} = \begin{vmatrix} 0 & 2 & 6 & -3 \\ 0 & -6 & 11 & -1 \\ 0 & 9 & 0 & 2 \\ -1 & 2 & 3 & 0 \end{vmatrix} \{C_1\}$$

$$= (1) \begin{vmatrix} 2 & 6 & -3 \\ -6 & 11 & -1 \\ 9 & 0 & 2 \end{vmatrix} \begin{array}{l} R_1 - 3R_2 \to R_1 \\ \\ R_3 + 2R_2 \to R_3 \end{array} = \begin{vmatrix} 20 & -27 & 0 \\ -6 & 11 & -1 \\ -3 & 22 & 0 \end{vmatrix} \{C_3\}$$

$$= (1) \begin{vmatrix} 20 & -27 \\ -3 & 22 \end{vmatrix} = (1)(440 - 81) = 359$$

24
$$\begin{vmatrix} 2 & 0 & -1 & 0 & 2 \\ 1 & 3 & 0 & 0 & 1 \\ 0 & 4 & 3 & 0 & -1 \\ -1 & 2 & 0 & -2 & 0 \\ 0 & 1 & 5 & 0 & -4 \end{vmatrix} \{C_4\} = (-2) \begin{vmatrix} 2 & 0 & -1 & 2 \\ 1 & 3 & 0 & 1 \\ 0 & 4 & 3 & -1 \\ 0 & 1 & 5 & -4 \end{vmatrix} \begin{array}{l} R_1 - 2R_2 \to R_1 \end{array}$$

$$= (-2) \begin{vmatrix} 0 & -6 & -1 & 0 \\ 1 & 3 & 0 & 1 \\ 0 & 4 & 3 & -1 \\ 0 & 1 & 5 & -4 \end{vmatrix} \{C_1\} = (-2)(-1) \begin{vmatrix} -6 & -1 & 0 \\ 4 & 3 & -1 \\ 1 & 5 & -4 \end{vmatrix} \begin{array}{l} R_1 + 6R_3 \to R_1 \\ R_2 - 4R_3 \to R_2 \end{array}$$

$$= (2) \begin{vmatrix} 0 & 29 & -24 \\ 0 & -17 & 15 \\ 1 & 5 & -4 \end{vmatrix} \{C_1\} = (2)(1) \begin{vmatrix} 29 & -24 \\ -17 & 15 \end{vmatrix} = (2)(435 - 408) = 54$$

25
$$\begin{vmatrix} 1 & 1 & 1 \\ a & b & c \\ a^2 & b^2 & c^2 \end{vmatrix} \begin{array}{l} C_1 - C_2 \rightarrow C_1 \\ \\ C_3 - C_2 \rightarrow C_3 \end{array}$$

$$= \begin{vmatrix} 0 & 1 & 0 \\ a-b & b & c-b \\ a^2-b^2 & b^2 & c^2-b^2 \end{vmatrix} \begin{array}{l} a-b \text{ is a common factor of } C_1 \\ \\ c-b \text{ is a common factor of } C_3 \end{array}$$

$$= (a-b)(c-b) \begin{vmatrix} 0 & 1 & 0 \\ 1 & b & 1 \\ a+b & b^2 & c+b \end{vmatrix} \{ `R_1 \}$$

$$= (a-b)(c-b)(-1) \begin{vmatrix} 1 & 1 \\ a+b & c+b \end{vmatrix}$$

$$= (a-b)(b-c)(c+b-a-b) = \underline{(a-b)(b-c)(c-a)}$$

26
$$\begin{vmatrix} 1 & 1 & 1 \\ a & b & c \\ a^3 & b^3 & c^3 \end{vmatrix} \begin{array}{l} R_2 - aR_1 \rightarrow R_2 \\ \\ R_3 - a^3 R_1 \rightarrow R_3 \end{array} = \begin{vmatrix} 1 & 1 & 1 \\ 0 & b-a & c-a \\ 0 & b^3-a^3 & c^3-a^3 \end{vmatrix} \{ C_1 \}$$

$$= (1) \begin{vmatrix} b-a & c-a \\ b^3-a^3 & c^3-a^3 \end{vmatrix}$$

$$= (b-a)(c^3-a^3) - (c-a)(b^3-a^3)$$

$$= (b-a)(c-a)(c^2+ac+a^2) - (c-a)(b-a)(b^2+ab+a^2)$$

$$= (b-a)(c-a)(c^2+ac+a^2-b^2-ab-a^2)$$

$$= (b-a)(c-a)(c^2+ac-b^2-ab)$$

$$= (b-a)(c-a)[(c-b)(c+b)+a(c-b)]$$

$$= (b-a)(c-a)[(c-b)(c+b+a)]$$

$$= (a-b)(b-c)(c-a)(a+b+c)$$

27
$$\begin{vmatrix} a_{11} & a_{12} & a_{13} & a_{14} \\ 0 & a_{22} & a_{23} & a_{24} \\ 0 & 0 & a_{33} & a_{34} \\ 0 & 0 & 0 & a_{44} \end{vmatrix} \{ C_1 \} = (a_{11}) \begin{vmatrix} a_{22} & a_{23} & a_{24} \\ 0 & a_{33} & a_{34} \\ 0 & 0 & a_{44} \end{vmatrix} \{ C_1 \}$$

$$= (a_{11})(a_{22}) \begin{vmatrix} a_{33} & a_{34} \\ 0 & a_{44} \end{vmatrix} = (a_{11}a_{22})(a_{33}a_{44}-0) = a_{11}a_{22}a_{33}a_{44}$$

28 $|A| = \begin{vmatrix} a & b & 0 & 0 \\ c & d & 0 & 0 \\ 0 & 0 & e & f \\ 0 & 0 & g & h \end{vmatrix} \{ C_1 \}$

$$= a \begin{vmatrix} d & 0 & 0 \\ 0 & e & f \\ 0 & g & h \end{vmatrix} - c \begin{vmatrix} b & 0 & 0 \\ 0 & e & f \\ 0 & g & h \end{vmatrix} \{ R_1 \text{ for both determinants} \}$$

$$= ad \begin{vmatrix} e & f \\ g & h \end{vmatrix} - cb \begin{vmatrix} e & f \\ g & h \end{vmatrix} = (ad-bc) \begin{vmatrix} e & f \\ g & h \end{vmatrix} = \begin{vmatrix} a & b \\ c & d \end{vmatrix} \begin{vmatrix} e & f \\ g & h \end{vmatrix}$$

29 $|AB| = \begin{vmatrix} a_{11}b_{11} + a_{12}b_{21} & a_{11}b_{12} + a_{12}b_{22} \\ a_{21}b_{11} + a_{22}b_{21} & a_{21}b_{12} + a_{22}b_{22} \end{vmatrix}$

$\quad = (a_{11}b_{11} + a_{12}b_{21})(a_{21}b_{12} + a_{22}b_{22}) - (a_{11}b_{12} + a_{12}b_{22})(a_{21}b_{11} + a_{22}b_{21})$

$\quad = \quad a_{11}b_{11}a_{21}b_{12} + a_{11}b_{11}a_{22}b_{22} + a_{12}b_{21}a_{21}b_{12} + a_{12}b_{21}a_{22}b_{22}$

$\qquad - a_{11}b_{12}a_{21}b_{11} - a_{11}b_{12}a_{22}b_{21} - a_{12}b_{22}a_{21}b_{11} - a_{12}b_{22}a_{22}b_{21}$

$\quad = a_{11}a_{22}b_{11}b_{22} - a_{11}a_{22}b_{21}b_{12} - a_{21}a_{12}b_{11}b_{22} + a_{21}a_{12}b_{21}b_{12}$

$\quad = (a_{11}a_{22} - a_{21}a_{12})(b_{11}b_{22} - b_{21}b_{12}) = |A| |B|$

30 Let $B = kA$. Since k is a factor of each of the n rows of A, n repeated applications of property (2) of the theorem on row and column transformations of a determinant yields $|B| = k^n |A|$.

31 Expanding by the first row yields $Ax + By + C = 0$ {an equation of a line} where A, B, and C are constants. To show that the line contains (x_1, y_1) and (x_2, y_2), we must show that these points are solutions of the equation. Substituting x_1 for x and y_1 for y, we obtain two identical rows and the determinant is zero. Hence, (x_1, y_1) is a solution of the equation and a similar argument can be made for (x_2, y_2).

32 Expanding by the first row yields $A(x^2 + y^2) + Bx + Cy + D = 0$ {an equation of a circle} where A, B, C, and D are constants. To show that the circle contains (x_1, y_1), (x_2, y_2), and (x_3, y_3) we must show that these points are solutions of the equation. Substituting x_1 for x and y_1 for y, we obtain two identical rows and the determinant is zero. Hence, (x_1, y_1) is a solution of the equation and similar arguments can be made for (x_2, y_2) and (x_3, y_3).

33 For the system $\begin{cases} 2x + 3y = 2 \\ x - 2y = 8 \end{cases}$, $|D| = \begin{vmatrix} 2 & 3 \\ 1 & -2 \end{vmatrix} = -4 - 3 = -7.$

Since $|D| = -7 \neq 0$, we may solve the system using Cramer's rule.

$|D_x| = \begin{vmatrix} 2 & 3 \\ 8 & -2 \end{vmatrix} = -4 - 24 = -28.$ $|D_y| = \begin{vmatrix} 2 & 2 \\ 1 & 8 \end{vmatrix} = 16 - 2 = 14.$

$x = \dfrac{|D_x|}{|D|} = \dfrac{-28}{-7} = 4.$ $y = \dfrac{|D_y|}{|D|} = \dfrac{14}{-7} = -2.$ $\bigstar (4, -2)$

34 $|D_x| = 33$, $|D_y| = -55$, $|D| = -11$; $x = -3$, $y = 5$

35 $|D_x| = -232$, $|D_y| = 0$, $|D| = -29$; $x = 8$, $y = 0$

36 $|D_x| = -53$, $|D_y| = -106$, $|D| = 53$; $x = -1$, $y = -2$

37 $|D| = 18 - 18 = 0$, so Cramer's rule cannot be used.

38 $|D| = 12 - 12 = 0$, so Cramer's rule cannot be used.

39 $|D_x| = -60$, $|D_y| = -90$, $|D_z| = 30$, $|D| = -30$;

$x = 2$, $y = 3$, $z = -1$

$\boxed{40}$ $|D_x| = -10,$ $\quad |D_y| = 5,$ $\quad |D_z| = 20,$ $\quad |D| = 5;$

$x = -2,$ $\qquad y = 1,$ $\qquad z = 4$

$\boxed{41}$ $|D_x| = 90,$ $\quad |D_y| = -180,$ $\quad |D_z| = -225,$ $\quad |D| = -45;$

$x = -2,$ $\qquad y = 4,$ $\qquad z = 5$

$\boxed{42}$ $|D_x| = -12,$ $\quad |D_y| = -24,$ $\quad |D_z| = 0,$ $\quad |D| = -4;$

$x = 3,$ $\qquad y = 6,$ $\qquad z = 0$

Chapter 8 Review Exercises

$\boxed{1}$ $4\,E_1 + 3\,E_2 \Rightarrow 23x = 19 \Rightarrow x = \frac{19}{23}; -5\,E_1 + 2\,E_2 \Rightarrow 23y = -18 \Rightarrow y = -\frac{18}{23}$

$\bigstar \left(\frac{19}{23}, -\frac{18}{23}\right)$

$\boxed{2}$ $2\,E_1 + E_2 \Rightarrow 0 = 10;$ *no solution.*

$\boxed{3}$ Solve E_2 for y $\{y = -2x - 1\}$ and substitute into E_1 to yield $x^2 + 2x - 3 = 0 \Rightarrow$

$(x + 3)(x - 1) = 0 \Rightarrow x = -3, 1$ and $y = 5, -3.$ $\qquad \bigstar (-3, 5), (1, -3)$

$\boxed{4}$ Solve E_2 for x $\{x = y + 7\}$ and substitute into E_1 to yield $y^2 + 7y + 12 = 0 \Rightarrow$

$(y + 3)(y + 4) = 0 \Rightarrow y = -3, -4$ and $x = 4, 3.$ $\qquad \bigstar (4, -3), (3, -4)$

$\boxed{5}$ $4\,E_2 + E_1 \Rightarrow 13x^2 = 156 \Rightarrow x = \pm 2\sqrt{3}$ and $y = \pm\sqrt{2}.$

There are four solutions: $(2\sqrt{3}, \pm\sqrt{2}), (-2\sqrt{3}, \pm\sqrt{2}).$

$\boxed{6}$ From E_3, $x^2 - xz = 0 \Rightarrow x(x - z) = 0 \Rightarrow x = 0$ or $x = z.$

If $x = 0$, E_1 is $0 = y^2 + 3z$ and E_2 is $z = 1 - y^2.$ Substituting z into E_1 yields

$2y^2 = 3$ or $y = \pm\frac{1}{2}\sqrt{6}$ and z is $-\frac{1}{2}$ for both values of $y.$

If $x = z$, E_1 is $0 = y^2 + z$ and E_2 is $y^2 = 1.$

Thus, $y = \pm 1$ and in either case, $x = z = -1.$

There are four solutions: $(-1, \pm 1, -1), (0, \pm\frac{1}{2}\sqrt{6}, -\frac{1}{2}).$

$\boxed{7}$ $-4\,E_1 + E_2 \Rightarrow -14/y = -27 \Rightarrow y = \frac{14}{27}; 2\,E_1 + 3\,E_2 \Rightarrow 14/x = 17 \Rightarrow x = \frac{14}{17};$ $\quad \bigstar \left(\frac{14}{17}, \frac{14}{27}\right)$

$\boxed{8}$ Treat 3^{y+1} as $3 \cdot 3^y$ and 2^{x+1} as $2 \cdot 2^x.$ Now $E_1 + 3\,E_2 \Rightarrow 7 \cdot 2^x = 25 \Rightarrow$

$2^x = \frac{25}{7} \Rightarrow x = \log_2 \frac{25}{7}.$ Resolving the original system for y;

$-2\,E_1 + E_2 \Rightarrow -7 \cdot 3^y = -15 \Rightarrow 3^y = \frac{15}{7} \Rightarrow y = \log_3 \frac{15}{7}.$ $\qquad \bigstar \left(\log_2 \frac{25}{7}, \log_3 \frac{15}{7}\right)$

$\boxed{9}$ Solve E_3 for z and substitute into E_1 and E_2 to yield

$\begin{cases} 3x + y - 2(4x + 5y + 2) = -1 \\ 2x - 3y + (4x + 5y + 2) = 4 \end{cases} \Rightarrow \begin{cases} -5x - 9y = 3 & (E_4) \\ 6x + 2y = 2 & (E_5) \end{cases}$

$6\,E_4 + 5\,E_5 \Rightarrow -44y = 28 \Rightarrow y = -\frac{7}{11};$

$2\,E_4 + 9\,E_5 \Rightarrow 44x = 24 \Rightarrow x = \frac{6}{11}; z = 1$ $\qquad \bigstar \left(\frac{6}{11}, -\frac{7}{11}, 1\right)$

10 Solve E_1 for x $\{x = -3y\}$ and substitute into E_3 to yield

$$\begin{cases} y - 5z = 3 & (E_2) \\ -6y + z = -1 & (E_4) \end{cases}$$

$6\,E_2 + E_4 \Rightarrow -29z = 17 \Rightarrow z = -\frac{17}{29};$

$E_2 + 5\,E_4 \Rightarrow -29y = -2 \Rightarrow y = \frac{2}{29};\ x = -\frac{6}{29}$ $\star \left(-\frac{6}{29}, \frac{2}{29}, -\frac{17}{29}\right)$

11 Solve E_2 for x and substitute into E_1 and E_3 to yield

$$\begin{cases} 4(y+z) - 3y - z = 0 \\ 3(y+z) - y + 3z = 0 \end{cases} \Rightarrow \begin{cases} y + 3z = 0 & (E_4) \\ 2y + 6z = 0 & (E_5) \end{cases}$$

Now E_5 is $2\,E_4$, hence $y = -3z$ and $x = y + z = -3z + z = -2z.$

The general solution is $(-2c, -3c, c)$ for any real number c.

12 Solve E_2 for x and substitute into E_1 and E_3 to yield

$$\begin{cases} 2(2y - z) + y - z = 0 \\ 3(2y - z) + 3y + 2z = 0 \end{cases} \Rightarrow \begin{cases} 5y - 3z = 0 & (E_4) \\ 9y - z = 0 & (E_5) \end{cases}$$

$E_4 - 3\,E_5 \Rightarrow -22y = 0 \Rightarrow y = 0,\ z = 0,\ x = 0;$ $\star (0, 0, 0)$

13 $E_1 - E_2 \Rightarrow x - 5z = -1 \Rightarrow x = 5z - 1;$

Substitute this value into E_1 to obtain $y = \dfrac{-19z + 5}{2};\ \left(5c - 1, \dfrac{-19c + 5}{2}, c\right)$ is

the general solution, where c is any real number.

14 $3\,E_1 + E_2 \Rightarrow 7x = 35 \Rightarrow x = 5$ and $y = -4$. This solution also satisfies E_3. $\star (5, -4)$

15 Let $a = 1/x$, $b = 1/y$, and $c = 1/z$ to obtain the system

$$\begin{cases} 4a + b + 2c = 4 & (E_1) \\ 2a + 3b - c = 1 & (E_2) \\ a + b + c = 4 & (E_3) \end{cases}$$

Solving E_2 for c and substituting into E_1 and E_3 yields

$$\begin{cases} 4a + b + 2(2a + 3b - 1) = 4 \\ a + b + (2a + 3b - 1) = 4 \end{cases} \Rightarrow \begin{cases} 8a + 7b = 6 & (E_4) \\ 3a + 4b = 5 & (E_5) \end{cases}$$

$3\,E_4 - 8\,E_5 \Rightarrow -11b = -22 \Rightarrow b = 2$

$4\,E_4 - 7\,E_5 \Rightarrow 11a = -11 \Rightarrow a = -1,\ c = 3;\ (x, y, z) = \left(-1, \frac{1}{2}, \frac{1}{3}\right)$

$\boxed{16}$ Solve E_1 for w and substitute into E_2, E_3, and E_4 to obtain

$$\begin{cases} 5x + y + 2z = 10 & (E_5) \\ -3x - y - 5z = 2 & (E_6) \\ 5x - 2y + 13z = -9 & (E_7) \end{cases}$$

Solve E_6 for y and substitute into E_5 and E_7 to obtain

$$\begin{cases} 2x - 3z = 12 & (E_8) \\ 11x + 23z = -13 & (E_9) \end{cases}$$

$11\,E_8 - 2\,E_9 \Rightarrow -79z = 158 \Rightarrow z = -2$

$23\,E_8 + 3\,E_9 \Rightarrow 79x = 237 \Rightarrow x = 3,\ y = -1,\ w = 4$ $\bigstar\ (3, -1, -2, 4)$

$\boxed{17}$ $\dfrac{4x^2 + 54x + 134}{(x+3)(x^2 + 4x - 5)} = \dfrac{A}{x+3} + \dfrac{B}{x+5} + \dfrac{C}{x-1}$

$4x^2 + 54x + 134 = A(x+5)(x-1) + B(x+3)(x-1) + C(x+3)(x+5)$

$x = 1:\ 192 = 24C \Rightarrow C = 8$

$x = -3:\ 8 = -8A \Rightarrow A = -1$ $\bigstar\ \dfrac{8}{x-1} - \dfrac{3}{x+5} - \dfrac{1}{x+3}$

$x = -5:\ -36 = 12B \Rightarrow B = -3$

$\boxed{18}$ By first dividing and then factoring, we have the following:

$\dfrac{2x^2 + 7x + 9}{x^2 + 2x + 1} = 2 + \dfrac{3x + 7}{(x+1)^2} = 2 + \dfrac{A}{x+1} + \dfrac{B}{(x+1)^2}$

$3x + 7 = A(x+1) + B$

$x = -1:\ 4 = B \Rightarrow B = 4$ $\bigstar\ 2 + \dfrac{3}{x+1} + \dfrac{4}{(x+1)^2}$

$x = 0:\ 7 = A + B \Rightarrow A = 3$

$\boxed{19}$ $\dfrac{x^2 + 14x - 13}{x^3 + 5x^2 + 4x + 20} = \dfrac{A}{x+5} + \dfrac{Bx + C}{x^2 + 4}$

$x^2 + 14x - 13 = A(x^2 + 4) + (Bx + C)(x + 5)$

$x = -5:\ -58 = 29A \Rightarrow A = -2$

$x = 0:\ -13 = 4A + 5C \Rightarrow C = -1$ $\bigstar\ -\dfrac{2}{x+5} + \dfrac{3x - 1}{x^2 + 4}$

$x = 1:\ 2 = 5A + 6B + 6C \Rightarrow B = 3$

$\boxed{20}$ $\dfrac{x^3 + 2x^2 + 2x + 16}{x^4 + 7x^2 + 10} = \dfrac{Ax + B}{x^2 + 2} + \dfrac{Cx + D}{x^2 + 5}$

$\begin{aligned} x^3 + 2x^2 + 2x + 16 &= (Ax + B)(x^2 + 5) + (Cx + D)(x^2 + 2) \\ &= (A + C)x^3 + (B + D)x^2 + (5A + 2C)x + (5B + 2D) \end{aligned}$

Equating coefficients, we have the following:

$x^3 \qquad : A + C = 1$

$x^2 \qquad : B + D = 2$ $\bigstar\ \dfrac{4}{x^2 + 2} + \dfrac{x - 2}{x^2 + 5}$

$x \qquad\ \ : 5A + 2C = 2\ \{A + C = 1\} \Rightarrow A = 0\ \text{and}\ C = 1$

constant $\ : 5B + 2D = 16\ \{B + D = 2\} \Rightarrow 3B = 12 \Rightarrow B = 4\ \text{and}\ D = -2$

21 $\begin{cases} x^2 + y^2 < 16 \\ y - x^2 > 0 \end{cases} \Leftrightarrow \begin{cases} x^2 + y^2 < 4^2 \\ y > x^2 \end{cases}$

$$V @ \left(\pm\sqrt{-\tfrac{1}{2} + \tfrac{1}{2}\sqrt{65}}, \; -\tfrac{1}{2} + \tfrac{1}{2}\sqrt{65} \right) \approx (\pm 1.88, \, 3.53)$$

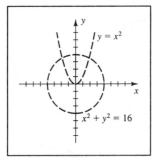

Figure 21

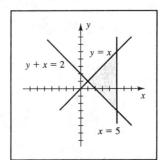

Figure 22

22 $\begin{cases} y - x \le 0 \\ y + x \ge 2 \\ x \le 5 \end{cases} \Leftrightarrow \begin{cases} y \le x \\ y \ge -x + 2 \\ x \le 5 \end{cases}$ $V @ (1, 1), (5, 5), (5, -3)$

23 $\begin{cases} x - 2y \le 2 \\ y - 3x \le 4 \\ 2x + y \le 4 \end{cases} \Leftrightarrow \begin{cases} y \ge \tfrac{1}{2}x - 1 \\ y \le 3x + 4 \\ y \le -2x + 4 \end{cases}$ $V @ (-2, -2), (0, 4), (2, 0)$

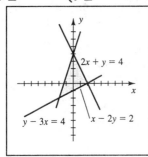

Figure 23

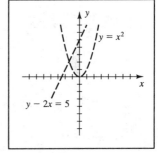

Figure 24

24 $\begin{cases} x^2 - y < 0 \\ y - 2x < 5 \\ xy < 0 \end{cases} \Leftrightarrow \begin{cases} y > x^2 \\ y < 2x + 5 \\ xy < 0 \end{cases}$

$$V @ (1 - \sqrt{6}, \, 7 - 2\sqrt{6}) \approx (-1.45, \, 2.10), \, (0, 5), \, (0, 0)$$

25 $\begin{bmatrix} 2 & -1 & 0 \\ 3 & 0 & -2 \end{bmatrix} \begin{bmatrix} 2 & -1 & 3 \\ 0 & 3 & 0 \\ 1 & 4 & 2 \end{bmatrix} = \begin{bmatrix} 4 & -5 & 6 \\ 4 & -11 & 5 \end{bmatrix}$

26 $\begin{bmatrix} 4 & 2 \\ 5 & -3 \end{bmatrix} \begin{bmatrix} 3 \\ 7 \end{bmatrix} = \begin{bmatrix} 26 \\ -6 \end{bmatrix}$

27 $\begin{bmatrix} 2 & 0 \\ 1 & 4 \\ -2 & 3 \end{bmatrix} \begin{bmatrix} 0 & 2 & -3 \\ 4 & 5 & 1 \end{bmatrix} = \begin{bmatrix} 0 & 4 & -6 \\ 16 & 22 & 1 \\ 12 & 11 & 9 \end{bmatrix}$

28 $\begin{bmatrix} 0 & -2 & 3 \\ 4 & 1 & 2 \end{bmatrix} \begin{bmatrix} 2 & 0 \\ 3 & 8 \\ 2 & -7 \end{bmatrix} = \begin{bmatrix} 0 & -37 \\ 15 & -6 \end{bmatrix}$

$\boxed{29}$ $2\begin{bmatrix} 0 & -1 & -4 \\ 3 & 2 & 1 \end{bmatrix} - 3\begin{bmatrix} 4 & -2 & 1 \\ 0 & 5 & -1 \end{bmatrix} =$

$$\begin{bmatrix} 0 & -2 & -8 \\ 6 & 4 & 2 \end{bmatrix} + \begin{bmatrix} -12 & 6 & -3 \\ 0 & -15 & 3 \end{bmatrix} = \begin{bmatrix} -12 & 4 & -11 \\ 6 & -11 & 5 \end{bmatrix}$$

$\boxed{30}$ $\begin{bmatrix} 1 & 3 \\ 2 & 4 \end{bmatrix}\begin{bmatrix} a & 0 \\ 0 & a \end{bmatrix} = \begin{bmatrix} a & 3a \\ 2a & 4a \end{bmatrix}$

$\boxed{31}$ $\begin{bmatrix} a & 0 \\ 0 & b \end{bmatrix}\begin{bmatrix} 1 & 3 \\ 2 & 4 \end{bmatrix} = \begin{bmatrix} a & 3a \\ 2b & 4b \end{bmatrix}$ $\boxed{32}$ $\begin{bmatrix} 3 & 2 \\ 0 & 0 \end{bmatrix}\begin{bmatrix} -2 & 0 \\ 3 & 0 \end{bmatrix} = \begin{bmatrix} 0 & 0 \\ 0 & 0 \end{bmatrix}$

$\boxed{33}$ $\begin{bmatrix} 1 & 2 \\ 3 & 4 \end{bmatrix}\left\{\begin{bmatrix} 2 & -4 \\ 3 & 7 \end{bmatrix} + \begin{bmatrix} 1 & 5 \\ -2 & -3 \end{bmatrix}\right\} = \begin{bmatrix} 1 & 2 \\ 3 & 4 \end{bmatrix}\begin{bmatrix} 3 & 1 \\ 1 & 4 \end{bmatrix} = \begin{bmatrix} 5 & 9 \\ 13 & 19 \end{bmatrix}$

$\boxed{34}$ $A A^{-1} = I_3$

Note: Let A denote each of the matrices in Exercises 35–50.

$\boxed{35}$ $\left[\begin{array}{cc|cc} 5 & -4 & 1 & 0 \\ -3 & 2 & 0 & 1 \end{array}\right] 2R_1 + 3R_2 \to R_1 \Rightarrow \left[\begin{array}{cc|cc} 1 & -2 & 2 & 3 \\ -3 & 2 & 0 & 1 \end{array}\right] R_2 + 3R_1 \to R_2$

$\left[\begin{array}{cc|cc} 1 & -2 & 2 & 3 \\ 0 & -4 & 6 & 10 \end{array}\right] -\frac{1}{4}R_2 \to R_2 \quad \Rightarrow \left[\begin{array}{cc|cc} 1 & -2 & 2 & 3 \\ 0 & 1 & -\frac{3}{2} & -\frac{5}{2} \end{array}\right] R_1 + 2R_2 \to R_1$

$\left[\begin{array}{cc|cc} 1 & 0 & -1 & -2 \\ 0 & 1 & -\frac{3}{2} & -\frac{5}{2} \end{array}\right]$ $\qquad\qquad A^{-1} = -\frac{1}{2}\begin{bmatrix} 2 & 4 \\ 3 & 5 \end{bmatrix}$

$\boxed{36}$ $\left[\begin{array}{ccc|ccc} 2 & -1 & 0 & 1 & 0 & 0 \\ 1 & 4 & 2 & 0 & 1 & 0 \\ 3 & -2 & 1 & 0 & 0 & 1 \end{array}\right] \begin{array}{l} R_1 - 2R_2 \leftrightarrow R_2 \\ \\ R_3 - 3R_2 \to R_3 \end{array}$

$\left[\begin{array}{ccc|ccc} 1 & 4 & 2 & 0 & 1 & 0 \\ 0 & -9 & -4 & 1 & -2 & 0 \\ 0 & -14 & -5 & 0 & -3 & 1 \end{array}\right] 3R_2 - 2R_3 \to R_2$

$\left[\begin{array}{ccc|ccc} 1 & 4 & 2 & 0 & 1 & 0 \\ 0 & 1 & -2 & 3 & 0 & -2 \\ 0 & -14 & -5 & 0 & -3 & 1 \end{array}\right] \begin{array}{l} R_1 - 4R_2 \to R_1 \\ \\ R_3 + 14R_2 \to R_3 \end{array}$

$\left[\begin{array}{ccc|ccc} 1 & 0 & 10 & -12 & 1 & 8 \\ 0 & 1 & -2 & 3 & 0 & -2 \\ 0 & 0 & -33 & 42 & -3 & -27 \end{array}\right] -\frac{1}{33}R_3 \to R_3$

$\left[\begin{array}{ccc|ccc} 1 & 0 & 10 & -12 & 1 & 8 \\ 0 & 1 & -2 & 3 & 0 & -2 \\ 0 & 0 & 1 & -\frac{14}{11} & \frac{1}{11} & \frac{9}{11} \end{array}\right] \begin{array}{l} R_1 - 10R_3 \to R_1 \\ R_2 + 2R_3 \to R_2 \end{array}$

$\left[\begin{array}{ccc|ccc} 1 & 0 & 0 & \frac{8}{11} & \frac{1}{11} & -\frac{2}{11} \\ 0 & 1 & 0 & \frac{5}{11} & \frac{2}{11} & -\frac{4}{11} \\ 0 & 0 & 1 & -\frac{14}{11} & \frac{1}{11} & \frac{9}{11} \end{array}\right] \qquad A^{-1} = \frac{1}{11}\begin{bmatrix} 8 & 1 & -2 \\ 5 & 2 & -4 \\ -14 & 1 & 9 \end{bmatrix}$

37
$$\left[\begin{array}{ccc|ccc} 1 & 0 & 0 & 1 & 0 & 0 \\ 0 & 4 & 7 & 0 & 1 & 0 \\ 0 & 1 & 2 & 0 & 0 & 1 \end{array}\right] R_3 \leftrightarrow R_2$$

$$\left[\begin{array}{ccc|ccc} 1 & 0 & 0 & 1 & 0 & 0 \\ 0 & 1 & 2 & 0 & 0 & 1 \\ 0 & 4 & 7 & 0 & 1 & 0 \end{array}\right] R_3 - 4R_2 \to R_3$$

$$\left[\begin{array}{ccc|ccc} 1 & 0 & 0 & 1 & 0 & 0 \\ 0 & 1 & 2 & 0 & 0 & 1 \\ 0 & 0 & -1 & 0 & 1 & -4 \end{array}\right] -R_3 \to R_3$$

$$\left[\begin{array}{ccc|ccc} 1 & 0 & 0 & 1 & 0 & 0 \\ 0 & 1 & 2 & 0 & 0 & 1 \\ 0 & 0 & 1 & 0 & -1 & 4 \end{array}\right] R_2 - 2R_3 \to R_2$$

$$\left[\begin{array}{ccc|ccc} 1 & 0 & 0 & 1 & 0 & 0 \\ 0 & 1 & 0 & 0 & 2 & -7 \\ 0 & 0 & 1 & 0 & -1 & 4 \end{array}\right] \qquad A^{-1} = \left[\begin{array}{ccc} 1 & 0 & 0 \\ 0 & 2 & -7 \\ 0 & -1 & 4 \end{array}\right]$$

38
$$\left[\begin{array}{ccc|ccc} 2 & 0 & 5 & 1 & 0 & 0 \\ 0 & 3 & -1 & 0 & 1 & 0 \\ 3 & 4 & 0 & 0 & 0 & 1 \end{array}\right] R_3 - R_1 \leftrightarrow R_1$$

$$\left[\begin{array}{ccc|ccc} 1 & 4 & -5 & -1 & 0 & 1 \\ 0 & 3 & -1 & 0 & 1 & 0 \\ 2 & 0 & 5 & 1 & 0 & 0 \end{array}\right] R_3 - 2R_1 \to R_3$$

$$\left[\begin{array}{ccc|ccc} 1 & 4 & -5 & -1 & 0 & 1 \\ 0 & 3 & -1 & 0 & 1 & 0 \\ 0 & -8 & 15 & 3 & 0 & -2 \end{array}\right] 3R_2 + R_3 \to R_2$$

$$\left[\begin{array}{ccc|ccc} 1 & 4 & -5 & -1 & 0 & 1 \\ 0 & 1 & 12 & 3 & 3 & -2 \\ 0 & -8 & 15 & 3 & 0 & -2 \end{array}\right] \begin{array}{l} R_1 - 4R_2 \to R_1 \\ R_3 + 8R_2 \to R_3 \end{array}$$

$$\left[\begin{array}{ccc|ccc} 1 & 0 & -53 & -13 & -12 & 9 \\ 0 & 1 & 12 & 3 & 3 & -2 \\ 0 & 0 & 111 & 27 & 24 & -18 \end{array}\right] \frac{1}{111} R_3 \to R_3$$

$$\left[\begin{array}{ccc|ccc} 1 & 0 & -53 & -13 & -12 & 9 \\ 0 & 1 & 12 & 3 & 3 & -2 \\ 0 & 0 & 1 & \frac{9}{37} & \frac{8}{37} & -\frac{6}{37} \end{array}\right] \begin{array}{l} R_1 + 53R_3 \to R_1 \\ R_2 - 12R_3 \to R_2 \end{array}$$

$$\left[\begin{array}{ccc|ccc} 1 & 0 & 0 & -\frac{4}{37} & -\frac{20}{37} & \frac{15}{37} \\ 0 & 1 & 0 & \frac{3}{37} & \frac{15}{37} & -\frac{2}{37} \\ 0 & 0 & 1 & \frac{9}{37} & \frac{8}{37} & -\frac{6}{37} \end{array}\right] \qquad A^{-1} = \frac{1}{37}\left[\begin{array}{ccc} -4 & -20 & 15 \\ 3 & 15 & -2 \\ 9 & 8 & -6 \end{array}\right]$$

39 $X = A^{-1}B = -\frac{1}{2}\begin{bmatrix} 2 & 4 \\ 3 & 5 \end{bmatrix}\begin{bmatrix} 30 \\ -16 \end{bmatrix} = -\frac{1}{2}\begin{bmatrix} -4 \\ 10 \end{bmatrix} = \begin{bmatrix} 2 \\ -5 \end{bmatrix}; \ (x, y) = (2, -5)$

40 $X = A^{-1}B = \frac{1}{11}\begin{bmatrix} 8 & 1 & -2 \\ 5 & 2 & -4 \\ -14 & 1 & 9 \end{bmatrix}\begin{bmatrix} -5 \\ 15 \\ -7 \end{bmatrix} = \frac{1}{11}\begin{bmatrix} -11 \\ 33 \\ 22 \end{bmatrix} = \begin{bmatrix} -1 \\ 3 \\ 2 \end{bmatrix};$

$$(x, y, z) = (-1, 3, 2)$$

41 $A = \begin{bmatrix} -6 \end{bmatrix} \Rightarrow |A| = -6.$

42 $|A| = -15 - (-24) = 9$

43 $|A| = 24 - (-24) = 48$

44 $\{R_1\} \ |A| = 0(A_{11}) - 4(20) - 3(2) = -86$

45 $\{R_1\} \ |A| = 2(-7) + 3(-5) + 5(-11) = -84$

46 $\{R_1\} \ |A| = 3(0) - 1(58) - 2(-29) = 0$

47 From Exercise 29 of §8.9, $|A| = (5)(-3)(-4)(2) = 120$

48 $\begin{vmatrix} 1 & 2 & 0 & 3 & 1 \\ -2 & -1 & 4 & 1 & 2 \\ 3 & 0 & -1 & 0 & -1 \\ 2 & -3 & 2 & -4 & 2 \\ -1 & 1 & 0 & 1 & 3 \end{vmatrix} \begin{array}{l} R_2 + 4R_3 \to R_2 \\ \\ R_4 + 2R_3 \to R_4 \end{array} = \begin{vmatrix} 1 & 2 & 0 & 3 & 1 \\ 10 & -1 & 0 & 1 & -2 \\ 3 & 0 & -1 & 0 & -1 \\ 8 & -3 & 0 & -4 & 0 \\ -1 & 1 & 0 & 1 & 3 \end{vmatrix} \{C_3\}$

$= (-1)\begin{vmatrix} 1 & 2 & 3 & 1 \\ 10 & -1 & 1 & -2 \\ 8 & -3 & -4 & 0 \\ -1 & 1 & 1 & 3 \end{vmatrix} \begin{array}{l} R_2 + 2R_1 \to R_2 \\ \\ R_4 - 3R_1 \to R_4 \end{array} = (-1)\begin{vmatrix} 1 & 2 & 3 & 1 \\ 12 & 3 & 7 & 0 \\ 8 & -3 & -4 & 0 \\ -4 & -5 & -8 & 0 \end{vmatrix} \{C_4\}$

$= (-1)(-1)\begin{vmatrix} 12 & 3 & 7 \\ 8 & -3 & -4 \\ -4 & -5 & -8 \end{vmatrix} \{4 \text{ is a common factor of } C_1 \text{ and } -1 \text{ of } R_3\}$

$= (-4)\begin{vmatrix} 3 & 3 & 7 \\ 2 & -3 & -4 \\ 1 & 5 & 8 \end{vmatrix} \begin{array}{l} R_1 - 3R_3 \to R_1 \\ R_2 - 2R_3 \to R_2 \end{array} = (-4)\begin{vmatrix} 0 & -12 & -17 \\ 0 & -13 & -20 \\ 1 & 5 & 8 \end{vmatrix} \{C_1\}$

$= (-4)\begin{vmatrix} -12 & -17 \\ -13 & -20 \end{vmatrix} = (-4)(240 - 221) = -76$

49 C_2 and C_4 are equal, so $|A| = 0.$

50 As in Exercise 28 of §8.10, $|A| = \begin{vmatrix} 1 & 2 \\ 3 & 4 \end{vmatrix}\begin{vmatrix} 1 & 2 & 3 \\ 2 & -1 & 1 \\ 1 & 3 & -1 \end{vmatrix}.$

Expand the 3×3 by R_1.

$|A| = (-2)\big[1(-2) - 2(-3) + 3(7)\big] = -50$

51 $\begin{vmatrix} 2 - x & 3 \\ 1 & -4 - x \end{vmatrix} = 0 \Rightarrow (2 - x)(-4 - x) - 3 = 0 \Rightarrow$

$$x^2 + 2x - 11 = 0 \Rightarrow x = \frac{-2 \pm \sqrt{4 + 44}}{2} = -1 \pm 2\sqrt{3}$$

[52] $\begin{vmatrix} 2-x & -1 & 3 \\ 0 & 4-x & 0 \\ 1 & 0 & -2-x \end{vmatrix} = 0 \Rightarrow \{C_1\}$

$(2-x)(4-x)(-2-x) - 3(4-x) = 0 \Rightarrow$

$$(4-x)[(2-x)(-2-x) - 3] = 0 \Rightarrow (4-x)(x^2 - 7) = 0 \Rightarrow x = 4, \pm\sqrt{7}$$

[53] 2 is a common factor of R_1, 2 is a common factor of C_2,

and 3 is a common factor of C_3.

[54] Interchange R_1 with R_2 and then R_2 with R_3 to obtain the determinant on the right.

The effect is to multiply by -1 twice.

[55] This is an extension of Exercise 29 of §8.9. Expanding by C_1, only a_{11} is not 0.

Expanding by the new C_1 again, only a_{22} is not 0. Repeating this process yields

$$|A| = a_{11}a_{22}a_{33}\cdots a_{nn}, \text{ the product of the main diagonal elements.}$$

[56] $\begin{vmatrix} 1 & a & b+c \\ 1 & b & a+c \\ 1 & c & a+b \end{vmatrix}$ $C_3 + C_2 \rightarrow C_2$

$= \begin{vmatrix} 1 & a & a+b+c \\ 1 & b & a+b+c \\ 1 & c & a+b+c \end{vmatrix}$ $C_3 - (a+b+c)C_1 \rightarrow C_3$

$= \begin{vmatrix} 1 & a & 0 \\ 1 & b & 0 \\ 1 & c & 0 \end{vmatrix} = 0$, since C_3 consists of all zeros.

[57] $|D_x| = 76$, $\quad |D_y| = 28$, $\quad |D| = 53$; $\quad x = \frac{76}{53}$, $\quad y = \frac{28}{53}$

[58] $|D_x| = -14$, $\quad |D_y| = -31$, $\quad |D_z| = -1$, $\quad |D| = -21$;

$x = \frac{2}{3}$, $\qquad y = \frac{31}{21}$, $\qquad z = \frac{1}{21}$

[59] Let x and y denote the length and width, respectively, of the rectangle.

$\begin{cases} xy = 4000 & \quad area & (E_1) \\ x^2 + y^2 = 100^2 & \quad diagonal & (E_2) \end{cases}$

Solve E_1 for y $\{y = 4000/x\}$ and substitute into E_2.

$x^2 + \dfrac{4000^2}{x^2} = 100^2 \Rightarrow x^4 - 10{,}000x^2 + 16{,}000{,}000 = 0 \Rightarrow$

$(x^2 - 2000)(x^2 - 8000) = 0 \Rightarrow x = 20\sqrt{5}, 40\sqrt{5}$ and $y = 40\sqrt{5}, 20\sqrt{5}$.

The dimensions are $20\sqrt{5}$ ft $\times 40\sqrt{5}$ ft.

60 Following the hint, we have $x^2 + (mx + 3)^2 = 1 \Rightarrow$

$$(m^2 + 1)x^2 + (6m)x + (8) = 0 \Rightarrow x = \frac{-6m \pm \sqrt{36m^2 - 32m^2 - 32}}{2(m^2 + 1)}.$$

If there is to be only one solution to the system, i.e., one point of intersection
between the circle and the line, then the discriminant must equal 0.

$$4m^2 - 32 = 0 \Rightarrow m = \pm 2\sqrt{2} \text{ and the equations of the lines are } y = \pm 2\sqrt{2}\,x + 3.$$

61 Let x and y denote the total amount of taxes paid and bonus money, respectively.

$$\begin{cases} x = 0.40(50{,}000 - y) \quad taxes \\ y = 0.10(50{,}000 - x) \quad bonuses \end{cases} \Rightarrow \begin{cases} 10x + 4y = 200{,}000 \quad (E_1) \\ x + 10y = 50{,}000 \quad (E_2) \end{cases}$$

$$E_1 - 10\,E_2 \Rightarrow -96y = -300{,}000 \Rightarrow y = \$3{,}125; \ x = \$18{,}750$$

62 Let r_1 and r_2 denote the inside radius and the outside radius, respectively.

Inside distance $= 90\% \,(\text{outside distance}) \Rightarrow 2\pi r_1 = 0.90\,(2\pi r_2) \Rightarrow$

$$r_1 = 0.90\,(r_1 + 10)\ \{\text{since } r_2 = r_1 + 10\} \Rightarrow 0.1r_1 = 9 \Rightarrow r_1 = 90 \text{ ft and } r_2 = 100 \text{ ft}$$

63 Let x, y, and z denote the number of ft^3/hr flowing through pipes A, B, and C,
respectively.

$$\begin{cases} 10x + 10y + 10z = 1000 \quad all\ 3\ working \\ 20x + 20y \quad\quad = 1000 \quad A\ and\ B\ only \\ 12.5x \quad\quad + 12.5z = 1000 \quad A\ and\ C\ only \end{cases} \Rightarrow \begin{cases} x + y + z = 100 \ (E_1) \\ x + y \quad\;\; = 50 \ (E_2) \\ x + \quad z = 80 \ (E_3) \end{cases}$$

$$E_1 - E_2 \Rightarrow z = 50; \ E_1 - E_3 \Rightarrow y = 20; \ \text{from } E_2, \ x = 30.$$

64 Let x and y denote the number of desks shipped from the western warehouse and the
eastern warehouse, respectively.

$$\begin{cases} x + y = 150 \quad quantity \\ 24x + 35y = 4205 \quad price \end{cases} \quad E_2 - 24\,E_1 \Rightarrow 11y = 605 \Rightarrow y = 55; \ x = 95$$

65 If x and y denote the length and the width, respectively, then a system is
$x \le 12$, $y \le 8$, $y \ge \frac{1}{2}x$. The graph is the region bounded by the quadrilateral with
vertices $(0, 0)$, $(0, 8)$, $(12, 8)$, $(12, 6)$.

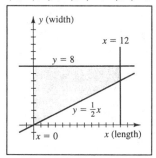

Figure 65

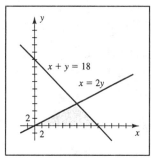

Figure 66

$\boxed{66}$ The number of hours spent resting is $24 - x - y$.

A system is $24 - x - y \geq 6$ {hours resting}, $x \geq 2y$, $x \geq 0$, $y \geq 0$.

The first inequality is $x + y \leq 18$. See *Figure 66.*

The graph is the region bounded by the triangle with vertices $(0, 0)$, $(18, 0)$, $(12, 6)$.

$\boxed{67}$ Let x and y denote the number of lawn mowers and edgers produced, respectively.

Profit function: $P = 100x + 80y$
$$\begin{cases} 6x + 4y \leq 600 & \text{\textit{machining}} \\ 2x + 3y \leq 300 & \text{\textit{welding}} \\ 5x + 5y \leq 550 & \text{\textit{assembly}} \\ x, y \geq 0 \end{cases}$$

(x, y)	$(100, 0)$	$(80, 30)$	$(30, 80)$	$(0, 100)$	$(0, 0)$
P	10,000	10,400 ■	9400	8000	0

The maximum weekly profit of $10,400 occurs when **80 lawn mowers and 30 edgers are produced.**

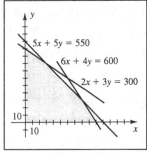

Figure 67

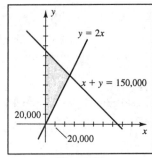

Figure 68

$\boxed{68}$ Let x and y denote the amount in the high- and low-risk investments, respectively.

The amount in bonds is $150,000 - x - y$.

Profit function: $P = 0.15x + 0.10y + 0.08(150,000 - x - y) = 12,000 + 0.07x + 0.02y$

(x, y)	$(0, 0)$	$(0, 150,000)$	$(50,000, 100,000)$
P	12,000	15,000	17,500 ■

$$\begin{cases} x + y \leq 150,000 \\ y \geq 2x \\ x, y \geq 0 \end{cases}$$

The maximum return of $17,500 occurs when

$50,000 is invested in the high-risk investment,

$100,000 is invested in the low-risk investment, and $0 is invested in bonds.

1 (a) For $b = 1.99$, we get $x = 204$ and $y = -100$. For $b = 1.999$, we get $x = 2004$ and $y = -1000$.

   (b) Solving $\begin{cases} x + 2y = 4 \\ x + by = 5 \end{cases}$ for y gives us $y = \dfrac{1}{b-2}$ and then solving for x we

   obtain $x = \dfrac{4b - 10}{b - 2}$. Both x and y are rational functions of b and as $b \to 2^-$,

   $x \to \infty$ and $y \to -\infty$.

   (c) If b gets very large, (x, y) gets close to $(4, 0)$.

2 (a) $D = \begin{bmatrix} 12{,}000 & 9000 & 14{,}000 \end{bmatrix}$; $E = \begin{bmatrix} 0.90 & 0.10 & 0.00 \\ 0.00 & 0.80 & 0.20 \\ 0.05 & 0.00 & 0.95 \end{bmatrix}$

   (b) $F = DE = \begin{bmatrix} 12{,}000 & 9000 & 14{,}000 \end{bmatrix} \begin{bmatrix} 0.90 & 0.10 & 0.00 \\ 0.00 & 0.80 & 0.20 \\ 0.05 & 0.00 & 0.95 \end{bmatrix} = \begin{bmatrix} 11{,}500 & 8400 & 15{,}100 \end{bmatrix}$.

   The elements of F represent the populations on islands A, B, and C, respectively, after one year.

   (c) After repeated multiplications of the population matrix by the proportion matrix, we obtain the matrix $G = \begin{bmatrix} 10{,}000 & 5000 & 20{,}000 \end{bmatrix}$. Our conclusion is that the population stabilizes with 10,000 birds on A, 5000 birds on B, and 20,000 birds on C.

   (d) If we begin with $D = \begin{bmatrix} 34{,}000 & 500 & 500 \end{bmatrix}$, multiply by E, and continue to multiply the result by E, we eventually get the values in G. Our conclusion is that regardless of the initial population distribution of the 35,000 birds, the populations tend toward the distribution described in part (c).

3 If we let A be an $m \times n$ matrix $(m \neq n)$, then B would have to be an $n \times m$ matrix so that AB and BA are both defined. But then $AB = I_m$ and $BA = I_n$, different orders of the identity matrix, which we can't have (they must be the same).

4 $AX = B \Leftrightarrow \begin{bmatrix} 0.5 & 0.4 & 0.1 \\ 0.3 & 0.2 & 0.5 \\ 0.2 & 0.4 & 0.4 \end{bmatrix} \begin{bmatrix} x \\ y \\ z \end{bmatrix} = \begin{bmatrix} 0.34 \\ 0.33 \\ 0.33 \end{bmatrix} \Rightarrow X = A^{-1}B = \begin{bmatrix} 0.35 \\ 0.3\overline{3} \\ 0.31\overline{6} \end{bmatrix}$.

   Give 35% to the AD, $33\frac{1}{3}$% to the DS, and $31\frac{2}{3}$% to the SP.

⑤ Synthetically dividing $x^4 + ax^2 + bx + c$ by $x + 1$, $x - 2$, and $x - 3$ yields the remainders $a - b + c + 1$, $4a + 2b + c + 16$, and $9a + 3b + c + 81$, respectively. Setting each of the remainders equal to 0 gives us the following system of equations in matrix form.

$$AX = B \Leftrightarrow \begin{bmatrix} 1 & -1 & 1 \\ 4 & 2 & 1 \\ 9 & 3 & 1 \end{bmatrix} \begin{bmatrix} a \\ b \\ c \end{bmatrix} = \begin{bmatrix} -1 \\ -16 \\ -81 \end{bmatrix} \Rightarrow X = A^{-1}B = \begin{bmatrix} -15 \\ 10 \\ 24 \end{bmatrix}.$$

Hence, $a = -15$, $b = 10$, $c = 24$, and we graph $Y_1 = x^4 - 15x^2 + 10x + 24$.

The roots of Y_1 are -1, 2, 3, and -4.

⑥ With $y = ax^3 + bx^2 + cx + d$ and the points $(-6, -6)$, $(-4, 3)$, $(2, 2)$, and $(6, 6)$, we have

$$AX = B \Leftrightarrow \begin{bmatrix} -216 & 36 & -6 & 1 \\ 8 & 4 & 2 & 1 \\ 216 & 36 & 6 & 1 \\ -64 & 16 & -4 & 1 \end{bmatrix} \begin{bmatrix} a \\ b \\ c \\ d \end{bmatrix} = \begin{bmatrix} -6 \\ 2 \\ 6 \\ 3 \end{bmatrix} \Rightarrow X = A^{-1}B = \begin{bmatrix} 0.058\overline{3} \\ -0.11\overline{6} \\ -1.1 \\ 4.2 \end{bmatrix}.$$

So the equation is $y = 0.058\overline{3}x^3 - 0.11\overline{6}x^2 - 1.1x + 4.2$. As y gets large positive, the values of a and d get larger positively and the values of b and c get larger negatively. As y gets large negative, the values of a and d get larger negatively and the values of b and c get larger positively. In either case, changing the y-value for $(-4, y)$ makes the graph appear nearly vertical through the other three points.

Chapter 9: Sequences, Series, and Probability

Note: For Exercises 1–16, the answers are listed in the order a_1, a_2, a_3, a_4; and a_8.

☐1 $a_n = 12 - 3n$ ★ 9, 6, 3, 0; -12

☐2 $a_n = \dfrac{3}{5n-2}$ ★ $1, \frac{3}{8}, \frac{3}{13}, \frac{1}{6}; \frac{3}{38}$

☐3 $a_n = \dfrac{3n-2}{n^2+1}$ ★ $\frac{1}{2}, \frac{4}{5}, \frac{7}{10}, \frac{10}{17}; \frac{22}{65}$

☐4 $a_n = 10 + \dfrac{1}{n}$ ★ $11, \frac{21}{2}, \frac{31}{3}, \frac{41}{4}; \frac{81}{8}$

☐5 $a_n = 9$ ★ 9, 9, 9, 9; 9

☐6 $a_n = \sqrt{2}$ ★ $\sqrt{2}, \sqrt{2}, \sqrt{2}, \sqrt{2}; \sqrt{2}$

☐7 $a_n = 2 + (-0.1)^n$ ★ 1.9, 2.01, 1.999, 2.0001; 2.00000001

☐8 $a_n = 4 + (0.1)^n$ ★ 4.1, 4.01, 4.001, 4.0001; 4.00000001

☐9 $a_n = (-1)^{n-1} \dfrac{n+7}{2n}$ ★ $4, -\frac{9}{4}, \frac{5}{3}, -\frac{11}{8}; -\frac{15}{16}$

☐10 $a_n = (-1)^n \dfrac{6-2n}{\sqrt{n+1}}$ ★ $-2\sqrt{2}, \frac{2}{3}\sqrt{3}, 0, -\frac{2}{5}\sqrt{5}; -\frac{10}{3}$

☐11 $a_n = 1 + (-1)^{n+1}$ ★ 2, 0, 2, 0; 0

☐12 $a_n = (-1)^{n+1} + (0.1)^{n-1}$ ★ 2, -0.9, 1.01, -0.999; -0.9999999

☐13 $a_n = \dfrac{2^n}{n^2+2}$ ★ $\frac{2}{3}, \frac{2}{3}, \frac{8}{11}, \frac{8}{9}; \frac{128}{33}$

☐14 $a_n = (n-1)(n-2)(n-3)$ ★ 0, 0, 0, 6; 210

☐15 a_n is the number of decimal places in $(0.1)^n$.   ★ 1, 2, 3, 4; 8

☐16 a_n is the number of positive integers less than n^3.   ★ 0, 7, 26, 63; 511

Note: For Exercises 17–24, the answers are listed in the order a_1, a_2, a_3, a_4, a_5.

☐17 $a_2 = 3a_1 - 5 = 3(2) - 5 = 1,$ $a_3 = 3a_2 - 5 = 3(1) - 5 = -2,$

     $a_4 = 3a_3 - 5 = 3(-2) - 5 = -11,$ $a_5 = 3a_4 - 5 = 3(-11) - 5 = -38$

☐18 $a_1 = 5,$ $a_{k+1} = 7 - 2a_k$ ●   ★ 5, -3, 13, -19, 45

☐19 $a_1 = -3,$ $a_{k+1} = a_k^2$ ●   ★ -3, 3^2, 3^4, 3^8, 3^{16}

☐20 $a_1 = 128,$ $a_{k+1} = \frac{1}{4}a_k$ ●   ★ 128, 32, 8, 2, $\frac{1}{2}$

☐21 $a_1 = 5,$ $a_{k+1} = ka_k$ ●   ★ 5, 5, 10, 30, 120

☐22 $a_2 = 1/a_1 = \frac{1}{3}, a_3 = 1/a_2 = 1/(\frac{1}{3}) = 3, a_4 = 1/a_3 = \frac{1}{3}, a_5 = 1/a_4 = 1/(\frac{1}{3}) = 3$

☐23 $a_1 = 2,$ $a_{k+1} = (a_k)^k$ ●   ★ 2, 2, 4, 4^3, 4^{12}

☐24 $a_1 = 2,$ $a_{k+1} = (a_k)^{1/k}$ ○   ★ 2, 2, $2^{1/2}$, $2^{1/6}$, $2^{1/24}$

☐25 $S_1 = a_1 = 3 + \frac{1}{2} = \frac{7}{2}.\ \ S_2 = S_1 + a_2 = \frac{7}{2} + 4 = \frac{15}{2}.\ \ S_3 = S_2 + a_3 = \frac{15}{2} + \frac{9}{2} = 12.$

$$S_4 = S_3 + a_4 = 12 + 5 = 17.$$

26 $S_1 = a_1 = 1$. $S_2 = S_1 + a_2 = 1 + \frac{1}{4} = \frac{5}{4}$. $S_3 = S_2 + a_3 = \frac{5}{4} + \frac{1}{9} = \frac{49}{36}$.

$$S_4 = S_3 + a_4 = \frac{49}{36} + \frac{1}{16} = \frac{205}{144}.$$

27 $S_1 = a_1 = -1$. $S_2 = S_1 + a_2 = -1 + 1/\sqrt{2}$. $S_3 = S_2 + a_3 = -1 + 1/\sqrt{2} - 1/\sqrt{3}$.

$$S_4 = S_3 + a_4 = -1 + 1/\sqrt{2} - 1/\sqrt{3} + \tfrac{1}{2} = -\tfrac{1}{2} + 1/\sqrt{2} - 1/\sqrt{3}.$$

28 $S_1 = a_1 = -\frac{1}{2}$. $S_2 = S_1 + a_2 = -\frac{1}{2} + \frac{1}{4} = -\frac{1}{4}$. $S_3 = S_2 + a_3 = -\frac{1}{4} - \frac{1}{8} = -\frac{3}{8}$.

$$S_4 = S_3 + a_4 = -\tfrac{3}{8} + \tfrac{1}{16} = -\tfrac{5}{16}.$$

29 $\displaystyle\sum_{k=1}^{5} (2k-7) = (-5) + (-3) + (-1) + 1 + 3 = -5$

30 $\displaystyle\sum_{k=1}^{6} (10-3k) = 7 + 4 + 1 + (-2) + (-5) + (-8) = -3$

31 $\displaystyle\sum_{k=1}^{4} (k^2 - 5) = (-4) + (-1) + 4 + 11 = 10$

32 $\displaystyle\sum_{k=1}^{10} \left[1 + (-1)^k\right] = 0 + 2 + 0 + 2 + 0 + 2 + 0 + 2 + 0 + 2 = 10$

33 $\displaystyle\sum_{k=0}^{5} k(k-2) = 0 + (-1) + 0 + 3 + 8 + 15 = 25$

34 $\displaystyle\sum_{k=0}^{4} (k-1)(k-3) = 3 + 0 + (-1) + 0 + 3 = 5$

35 $\displaystyle\sum_{k=3}^{6} \frac{k-5}{k-1} = (-1) + (-\tfrac{1}{3}) + 0 + \tfrac{1}{5} = -\frac{17}{15}$ **36** $\displaystyle\sum_{k=1}^{6} \frac{3}{k+1} = \frac{3}{2} + 1 + \frac{3}{4} + \frac{3}{5} + \frac{1}{2} + \frac{3}{7} = \frac{669}{140}$

37 $\displaystyle\sum_{k=1}^{5} (-3)^{k-1} = 1 + (-3) + 9 + (-27) + 81 = 61$

38 $\displaystyle\sum_{k=0}^{4} 3(2^k) = 3 + 6 + 12 + 24 + 48 = 93$

39 $\displaystyle\sum_{k=1}^{100} 100 = 100(100) = 10{,}000$ **40** $\displaystyle\sum_{k=1}^{1000} 5 = 1000(5) = 5000$

41 $\displaystyle\sum_{k=253}^{571} \frac{1}{3} = (571 - 253 + 1)(\tfrac{1}{3}) = 319(\tfrac{1}{3}) = \frac{319}{3}$

42 $\displaystyle\sum_{k=137}^{428} 2.1 = (428 - 137 + 1)(2.1) = 292(2.1) = 613.2$

43 $\displaystyle\sum_{j=1}^{7} \tfrac{1}{2}k^2 = 7(\tfrac{1}{2}k^2) = \tfrac{7}{2}k^2$ { note that j, not k, is the summation variable }

44 $\displaystyle\sum_{k=0}^{5} (3j+2) = 6(3j+2) = 18j + 12$ { note that k, not j, is the summation variable }

45 $\displaystyle\sum_{k=1}^{n} (a_k - b_k) = (a_1 - b_1) + (a_2 - b_2) + \cdots + (a_n - b_n)$

$$= (a_1 + a_2 + \cdots + a_n) + (-b_1 - b_2 - \cdots - b_n)$$

$$= (a_1 + a_2 + \cdots + a_n) - (b_1 + b_2 + \cdots + b_n)$$

$$= \sum_{k=1}^{n} a_k - \sum_{k=1}^{n} b_k$$

46 $\displaystyle\sum_{k=1}^{n}(a_k+b_k+c_k) = \sum_{k=1}^{n}[(a_k+b_k)+c_k]$

$$= \sum_{k=1}^{n}(a_k+b_k) + \sum_{k=1}^{n}c_k$$

$$= \sum_{k=1}^{n}a_k + \sum_{k=1}^{n}b_k + \sum_{k=1}^{n}c_k$$

47 As k increases, the terms approach 1.

48 (a) 3, 3.142546543, 3.141592653, 3.141592654, 3.141592654

(b) When $x_1 = 6$, the terms of the sequence approach 2π.

49 $a_k = 0.1(3 \cdot 2^{k-2} + 4) \Rightarrow a_2 = 0.1(3 \cdot 2^{2-2} + 4) = 0.1(7) = 0.7$ ★ 0.4, 0.7, 1, 1.6, 2.8

50 (a) After one day, 1000; two days, 2000; three days, 4000.

(b) After n days, $a_n = 500(2)^n$.

51 (a) 1, 1, 2, 3, 5, 8, 13, 21, 34, 55

(b) $r_1 = \frac{1}{1} = 1$, $r_2 = \frac{2}{1} = 2$, $r_3 = \frac{3}{2} = 1.5$, $r_4 = \frac{5}{3} = 1.\overline{6}$, $r_5 = \frac{8}{5} = 1.6$,

$r_6 = \frac{13}{8} = 1.625$, $r_7 = \frac{21}{13} \approx 1.6153846$, $r_8 = \frac{34}{21} \approx 1.6190476$,

$r_9 = \frac{55}{34} \approx 1.6176471$, and $r_{10} = \frac{89}{55} \approx 1.6181818$.

52 $a_1 = \dfrac{1}{\sqrt{5}}\left(\dfrac{1+\sqrt{5}}{2}\right)^1 - \dfrac{1}{\sqrt{5}}\left(\dfrac{1-\sqrt{5}}{2}\right)^1 = \dfrac{1}{2\sqrt{5}} + \dfrac{1}{2} - \dfrac{1}{2\sqrt{5}} + \dfrac{1}{2} = 1.$

Similarly, $a_2 = 1$, $a_3 = 2$, $a_4 = 3$, $a_5 = 5$, $a_6 = 8$, $a_7 = 13$, and $a_8 = 21$.

53 (a) Since the amount of chlorine decreases by a factor of 0.20 each day, $a_n = 0.8a_{n-1}$, where a_0 is the initial amount of chlorine in the pool.

(b) Let $a_0 = 7$ and $a_n = 0.8a_{n-1}$.

Day (n)	0	1	2	3	4	5
Chlorine (a_n)	7.00	5.60	4.48	3.58	2.87	2.29

The chlorine level will drop below 3 ppm during the fourth day.

54 (a) $a_0 = 2$, $a_1 = 0.8a_0 + 0.5 = 2.1$, $a_2 = 0.8a_1 + 0.5 = 2.18$, $a_3 = 0.8a_2 + 0.5 = 2.244$, $a_4 = 0.8a_3 + 0.5 = 2.2952$. In general, the next value can be calculated by multiplying the previous value by 0.8 and adding 0.5. Thus, $a_n = 0.8a_{n-1} + 0.5$.

(b) Using the table, $a_{15} \approx 2.482$. By continuing to calculate a_n for larger and larger n, the amount of chlorine appears to level off at 2.5 ppm.

n	a_n	n	a_n	n	a_n
1	2.100	6	2.369	11	2.457
2	2.180	7	2.395	12	2.466
3	2.244	8	2.416	13	2.473
4	2.295	9	2.433	14	2.478
5	2.336	10	2.446	15	2.482

(c) Since we are retaining 80% each day, we are replacing 20%. Because the target amount is 1.5 ppm, we must replace 20% of 1.5 ppm, or equivalently, 0.3 ppm. *Note:* You could also solve this part by trial and error—from part (b) we know 0.5 is too large, so decrease that amount until you arrive at 0.3.

$\boxed{55}$ $N = 5$ and $x_1 = \frac{5}{2} \Rightarrow x_2 = \frac{1}{2}\left(x_1 + \frac{N}{x_1}\right) = \frac{1}{2}\left(2.5 + \frac{5}{2.5}\right) = 2.25 \Rightarrow$

$x_3 = \frac{1}{2}\left(2.25 + \frac{5}{2.25}\right) \approx 2.236111 \Rightarrow x_4 \approx 2.236068 \Rightarrow x_5 \approx 2.236068.$

Thus, $\sqrt{5} \approx 2.236068.$

$\boxed{56}$ $N = 18$ and $x_1 = \frac{18}{2} = 9 \Rightarrow x_2 = \frac{1}{2}\left(x_1 + \frac{N}{x_1}\right) = \frac{1}{2}\left(9 + \frac{18}{9}\right) = 5.5 \Rightarrow$

$x_3 \approx 4.386364 \Rightarrow x_4 \approx 4.244995 \Rightarrow x_5 \approx 4.242641 \Rightarrow x_6 \approx 4.242641.$

Thus, $\sqrt{18} \approx 4.242641.$

$\boxed{57}$ $x_1 = 2$ and $x_2 = \frac{1}{3}\sqrt[3]{x_1} + 2 \Rightarrow x_2 \approx 2.419974 \Rightarrow x_3 \approx 2.447523 \Rightarrow x_4 \approx 2.449215 \Rightarrow$

$x_5 \approx 2.449319 \Rightarrow x_6 \approx 2.449325.$ The root is approximately 2.4493.

$\boxed{58}$ $2x + \dfrac{1}{x^4 + x + 2} = 0 \Rightarrow x = -\dfrac{1}{2(x^4 + x + 2)} \Rightarrow x_2 = -\dfrac{1}{2(x_1^4 + x_1 + 2)}.$

$x_1 = 0 \Rightarrow x_2 = -0.25 \Rightarrow x_3 \approx -0.285078 \Rightarrow x_4 \approx -0.290440 \Rightarrow x_5 \approx -0.291261 \Rightarrow$

$x_6 \approx -0.291386 \Rightarrow x_7 \approx -0.291405.$ The root is approximately $-0.2914.$

$\boxed{59}$ (a) $f(1) = -1 < 0$ and $f(2) \approx 0.30 > 0.$

Thus, f assumes both positive and negative values on $[1, 2].$

(b) $\log x + x - 2 = 0 \Rightarrow x = 2 - \log x.$

$x_1 = 1.5 \Rightarrow x_2 = 2 - \log x_1 = 2 - \log 1.5 \approx 1.823909 \Rightarrow x_3 \approx 1.738997 \Rightarrow$

$x_4 \approx 1.759701 \Rightarrow x_5 \approx 1.754561 \Rightarrow x_6 \approx 1.755832 \Rightarrow x_7 \approx 1.755517.$

The zero is approximately 1.76.

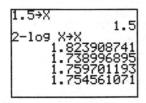

Figure 59

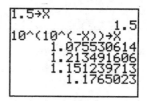

Figure 60

$\boxed{60}$ (a) $f(1) = -0.1 < 0$ and $f(2) \approx 0.29 > 0.$

Thus, f assumes both positive and negative values on $[1, 2].$

(b) $\log x - 10^{-x} = 0 \Rightarrow \log x = 10^{-x} \Rightarrow x = (10)^{10^{-x}}.$

$x_1 = 1.5 \Rightarrow x_2 = (10)^{10^{-x_1}} = (10)^{10^{-1.5}} \approx 1.075531 \Rightarrow x_3 \approx 1.213492 \Rightarrow$

$x_4 \approx 1.151240 \Rightarrow x_5 \approx 1.176502 \Rightarrow x_6 \approx 1.165745 \Rightarrow x_7 \approx 1.170237.$

The zero is approximately 1.17.

61 Graph $y = \left(1 + \frac{1}{x} + \frac{1}{2x^2}\right)^x$ on the interval $[1, 100]$.

The graph approaches the horizontal asymptote $y \approx 2.718 \approx e$.

For increasing values of n, the terms of the sequence appear to approximate e.

[1, 100] by [0, 3]

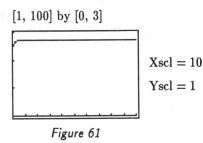

Xscl = 10

Yscl = 1

Figure 61

[1, 100] by [0, 3]

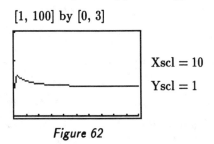

Xscl = 10

Yscl = 1

Figure 62

62 Graph $y = x^{1/x}$ on the interval $[1, 100]$.

The graph approaches the horizontal asymptote $y \approx 1$ from above.

For increasing values of n, the terms of the sequence appear to approximate 1.

63 Graph $y = \left(\frac{1}{x}\right)^{1/x}$ on the interval $[1, 100]$.

The graph approaches the horizontal asymptote $y \approx 1$ from below.

For increasing values of n, the terms of the sequence appear to approximate 1.

[1, 100] by [0, 3]

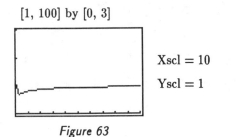

Xscl = 10

Yscl = 1

Figure 63

[1, 100] by [0, 5]

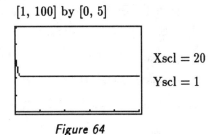

Xscl = 20

Yscl = 1

Figure 64

64 Graph $y = (2.1^x + 1)^{1/x}$ on the interval $[1, 100]$.

The graph approaches the horizontal asymptote $y \approx 2.1$.

For increasing values of n, the terms of the sequence appear to approximate 2.1.

65 By tracing the graph we see that $a_9 \approx 66.55$ and $a_{10} \approx 113.64$. Thus, $k = 10$.

[0, 20] by [0, 125]

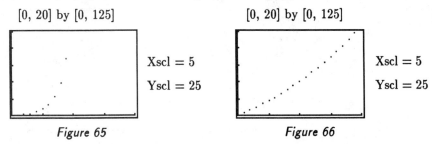

Xscl = 5

Yscl = 25

Figure 65

[0, 20] by [0, 125]

Xscl = 5

Yscl = 25

Figure 66

66 By tracing the graph we see that $a_{16} \approx 98.79$ and $a_{17} \approx 107.73$. Thus, $k = 17$.

67 By tracing the graph we see that $a_{18} \approx 50.39$ and $a_{19} \approx 255.96$. Thus, $k = 19$.

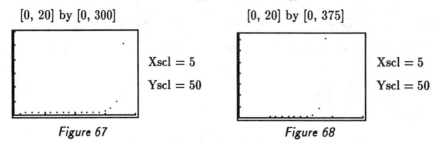

[0, 20] by [0, 300]		[0, 20] by [0, 375]	
	Xscl = 5		Xscl = 5
	Yscl = 50		Yscl = 50

Figure 67   Figure 68

68 By tracing the graph we see that $a_{14} \approx 42.12$ and $a_{15} \approx 356.37$. Thus, $k = 15$.

69 (a) Since $c = 0.5$, let the sequence be defined by $a_{k+1} = 0.5a_k(1 - a_k)$. Then, $a_1 = 0.25$, $a_2 = 0.5a_1(1 - a_1) = 0.5(0.25)(1 - 0.25) = 0.09375$. In a similar manner, $a_3 \approx 0.04248$, $a_4 \approx 0.02034$, ... , $a_{10} \approx 0.00031$, $a_{11} \approx 0.00015$, $a_{12} \approx 0.00008$. The insect population is initially $1000a_1 = 1000(0.25) = 250$. It then becomes approximately 94, 42, 20, and so on, until the population decreases to zero.

(b) The sequence determined is $a_1 = 0.25$, $a_2 \approx 0.28125$, $a_3 \approx 0.30322$, $a_4 \approx 0.31692$, ... , $a_{18} \approx 0.33333$, $a_{19} \approx 0.33333$, $a_{20} \approx 0.33333$. The insect population is initially 250. It then becomes approximately 281, 303, 317, and so on, until the population stabilizes at 333.

(c) The sequence determined is $a_1 = 0.25$, $a_2 \approx 0.51563$, $a_3 \approx 0.68683$, $a_4 \approx 0.59151$, ... , $a_{40} \approx 0.63636$, $a_{41} \approx 0.63636$, $a_{42} \approx 0.63636$. The insect population is initially 250. It then becomes approximately 516, 687, 592, and so on, until the population stabilizes at 636.

70 (a) One conjecture is that the population will decrease to zero as in part (a) of the previous exercise.

(b) Whenever $0 < c < 1$, the insect population decreases to zero.

9.2 Exercises

1 To show that the given sequence, $-6, -2, 2, \ldots, 4n - 10, \ldots$, is arithmetic, we must show that $a_{k+1} - a_k$ is equal to some constant, which is the common difference.

$a_n = 4n - 10 \Rightarrow a_{k+1} - a_k = [4(k+1) - 10] - [4(k) - 10] = 4k + 4 - 10 - 4k + 10 = 4$

2 $53, 48, 43, \ldots, 58 - 5n, \ldots$ ●

$a_n = 58 - 5n \Rightarrow a_{k+1} - a_k = [58 - 5(k+1)] - [58 - 5k] = 58 - 5k - 5 - 58 + 5k = -5$

3 $d = 6 - 2 = 4$; $a_n = 2 + (n-1)(4) = 4n - 2$; $a_5 = 18$; $a_{10} = 38$

4 $d = 13 - 16 = -3$; $a_n = 16 + (n-1)(-3) = -3n + 19$; $a_5 = 4$; $a_{10} = -11$

5 $d = 2.7 - 3 = -0.3$; $a_n = 3 + (n-1)(-0.3) = -0.3n + 3.3$; $a_5 = 1.8$; $a_{10} = 0.3$

6 $d = -4.5 - (-6) = 1.5$; $a_n = -6 + (n-1)(1.5) = 1.5n - 7.5$; $a_5 = 0$; $a_{10} = 7.5$

7 $d = -3.9 - (-7) = 3.1$; $a_n = -7 + (n-1)(3.1) = 3.1n - 10.1$; $a_5 = 5.4$; $a_{10} = 20.9$

8 $d = (x-3) - (x-8) = 5$;

$$a_n = x - 8 + (n-1)(5) = x + 5n - 13; \quad a_5 = x + 12; \quad a_{10} = x + 37$$

9 An equivalent sequence is $\ln 3$, $2\ln 3$, $3\ln 3$, $4\ln 3$, ...; $d = 2\ln 3 - \ln 3 = \ln 3$;

$$a_n = \ln 3 + (n-1)(\ln 3) = n\ln 3 \text{ or } \ln 3^n; \quad a_5 = 5\ln 3 \text{ or } \ln 3^5; \quad a_{10} = 10\ln 3 \text{ or } \ln 3^{10}$$

10 An equivalent sequence is 3, 2, 1, 0, ...; $d = 2 - 3 = -1$;

$$a_n = 3 + (n-1)(-1) = -n + 4; \quad a_5 = -1; \quad a_{10} = -6$$

11 $a_6 = a_1 + 5d$ and $a_2 = a_1 + d \Rightarrow a_6 - a_2 = 4d$. But $a_6 - a_2 = -11 - 21 = -32$.

Hence, $4d = -32$ and $d = -8$.

12 $a_{11} = a_1 + 10d$ and $a_4 = a_1 + 3d \Rightarrow a_{11} - a_4 = 7d$. But $a_{11} - a_4 = 35 - 14 = 21$.

Hence, $7d = 21$ and $d = 3$.

13 $d = a_2 - a_1 = 7.5 - 9.1 = -1.6$. $a_{12} = 9.1 + (11)(-1.6) = -8.5$

14 $d = 1 - \sqrt{2}$; $a_{11} = (2 + \sqrt{2}) + (10)(1 - \sqrt{2}) = 12 - 9\sqrt{2}$

15 $d = 2.5$; $a_6 = a_1 + 5d \Rightarrow 2.7 = a_1 + 12.5 \Rightarrow a_1 = -9.8$

16 $a_9 = 53$ and $a_8 = 47 \Rightarrow d = 6$. $a_8 = a_1 + 7d \Rightarrow 47 = a_1 + 7(6) \Rightarrow a_1 = 5$

17 $a_3 = 7$ and $a_{20} = 43 \Rightarrow 17d = 36 \Rightarrow d = \frac{36}{17}$. $a_{15} = a_3 + 12d = 7 + 12(\frac{36}{17}) = \frac{551}{17}$.

18 $a_2 = 1$ and $a_{18} = 49 \Rightarrow 16d = 49 - 1 \Rightarrow d = 3$. $a_{10} = a_2 + 8d = 1 + 8(3) = 25$.

Note: In Exercises 19–26,

$$S_n = \frac{n}{2}[2a_1 + (n-1)(d)] \text{ and } S_n = \frac{n}{2}(a_1 + a_n) \text{ are used to find the sum.}$$

19 $S_{30} = \frac{30}{2}[2(40) + (29)(-3)] = -105$ **20** $S_{40} = \frac{40}{2}[2(5) + (39)(0.1)] = 278$

21 $S_{10} = \frac{10}{2}(-9 + 15) = 30$

22 $a_7 = a_1 + 6d \Rightarrow \frac{7}{3} = a_1 + 6(-\frac{2}{3}) \Rightarrow a_1 = \frac{19}{3}$. $S_{15} = \frac{15}{2}[2(\frac{19}{3}) + (14)(-\frac{2}{3})] = 25$

23 $\displaystyle\sum_{k=1}^{20} (3k - 5)$ • $S_{20} = \frac{20}{2}(-2 + 55) = 530$

24 $\displaystyle\sum_{k=1}^{12} (7 - 4k)$ • $S_{12} = \frac{12}{2}[3 + (-41)] = -228$

25 $\displaystyle\sum_{k=1}^{18} (\frac{1}{2}k + 7)$ • $S_{18} = \frac{18}{2}(\frac{15}{2} + 16) = \frac{423}{2}$

26 $\displaystyle\sum_{k=1}^{10} (\frac{1}{4}k + 3)$ • $S_{10} = \frac{10}{2}(\frac{13}{4} + \frac{11}{2}) = \frac{175}{4}$

27 $1 + 3 + 5 + 7$. Since the difference in terms is 2, the general term is

$$1 + (n-1)2 = 2n - 1. \quad \sum_{n=1}^{4} (2n - 1)$$

28 $2 + 4 + 6 + 8 + 10$. Since the difference in terms is 2, the general term is

$$2 + (n-1)2 = 2n. \qquad \sum_{n=1}^{5} 2n$$

29 $1 + 3 + 5 + \cdots + 73$. From Exercise 27, the general term is $2n - 1$ with

$$n \text{ starting at } 1. \quad 2n - 1 = 73 \Rightarrow n = 37, \text{ the largest value.} \quad \sum_{n=1}^{37} (2n - 1)$$

30 $2 + 4 + 6 + \cdots + 150$. From Exercise 28, the general term is $2n$ with

$$n \text{ starting at } 1. \quad 2n = 150 \Rightarrow n = 75, \text{ the largest value.} \quad \sum_{n=1}^{75} 2n$$

31 $\frac{3}{7} + \frac{6}{11} + \frac{9}{15} + \frac{12}{19} + \frac{15}{23} + \frac{18}{27}$. The numerators increase by 3, the denominators increase

by 4. The general terms are $3 + (n-1)3 = 3n$ and $7 + (n-1)4 = 4n + 3$. $\quad \displaystyle\sum_{n=1}^{6} \frac{3n}{4n+3}$

32 $\frac{5}{13} + \frac{10}{11} + \frac{15}{9} + \frac{20}{7}$. The numerators increase by 5, the denominators decrease by 2.

The general terms are $5 + (n-1)5 = 5n$ and $13 + (n-1)(-2) = 15 - 2n$. $\quad \displaystyle\sum_{n=1}^{4} \frac{5n}{15-2n}$

33 $S_n = \frac{n}{2}\left[2a_1 + (n-1)(d)\right] \Rightarrow 21 = \frac{n}{2}\left[2(-2) + (n-1)(\frac{1}{4})\right] \Rightarrow$

$$42 = n\left(\tfrac{1}{4}n - \tfrac{17}{4}\right) \Rightarrow 168 = n^2 - 17n \Rightarrow (n-24)(n+7) = 0 \Rightarrow n = 24$$

34 $a_6 = a_1 + 5d \Rightarrow -3 = a_1 + 1 \Rightarrow a_1 = -4;$

$$S_n = \frac{n}{2}\left[2a_1 + (n-1)(d)\right] \Rightarrow -33 = \frac{n}{2}\left[2(-4) + (n-1)(0.2)\right] \Rightarrow -66 = n(0.2n - 8.2) \Rightarrow$$

$$2n^2 - 82n + 660 = 0 \Rightarrow n^2 - 41n + 330 = 0 \Rightarrow (n-11)(n-30) = 0 \Rightarrow n = 11, 30.$$

There are two sequences that satisfy the given conditions.

35 Five arithmetic means $\Rightarrow 6d = 10 - 2 \Rightarrow d = \frac{4}{3}$. The terms are $2, \frac{10}{3}, \frac{14}{3}, 6, \frac{22}{3}, \frac{26}{3}, 10$.

36 Three arithmetic means $\Rightarrow 4d = -5 - 3 \Rightarrow d = -2$. The terms are $3, 1, -1, -3, -5$.

37 (a) The first integer greater than 32 that is divisible by 6 is 36 $\{6 \cdot 6\}$

and the last integer less than 395 that is divisible by 6 is 390 $\{65 \cdot 6\}$.

The number of terms is then $65 - 6 + 1 = 60$.

(b) The sum is $S_{60} = \frac{60}{2}(36 + 390) = 12{,}780$.

38 (a) The first integer greater than -500 that is divisible by 33 is -495 $\{-15 \cdot 33\}$.

There are 15 negative integers greater than -500 that are divisible by 33.

(b) The sum is $S_{15} = \frac{15}{2}\left[-495 + (-33)\right] = -3960$.

39 There are $(24 - 10 + 1) = 15$ layers. Model this problem as an arithmetic sequence

with $a_1 = 10$ and $a_{15} = 24$. $S_{15} = \frac{15}{2}(10 + 24) = 255$.

40 Model this problem as an arithmetic sequence with $a_1 = 30$ and $d = 2$.

$S_{10} = \frac{10}{2}\left[2(30) + (10-1)(2)\right] = 390$. The last ten rows $\{11\text{th to }20\text{th}\}$ each have

$10(50) = 500$ seats so that the total is 890 seats.

41 This is similar to inserting 9 arithmetic means between 4 and 24.

$10d = 20 \Rightarrow d = 2$. The circumference of each ring is πD with $D = 4, 6, 8, \ldots, 24$.

$$S_{11} = \tfrac{11}{2}(4\pi + 24\pi) = 154\pi \text{ ft.}$$

42 The sequence of feet traveled each second is $4, 9, 14, \ldots$.

$$S_{11} = \tfrac{11}{2}\big[2(4) + (11 - 1)(5)\big] = 319 \text{ ft.}$$

43 $n = 5$, $S_5 = 5000$, $d = -100 \Rightarrow$

$$5000 = \tfrac{5}{2}\big[2a_1 + 4(-100)\big] \Rightarrow 2000 = 2a_1 - 400 \Rightarrow a_1 = \$1200$$

44 $n = 10$, $S_{10} = 46{,}000$, $a_1 = 1000 \Rightarrow 46{,}000 = \tfrac{10}{2}\big[2(1000) + 9d\big] \Rightarrow$

$7200 = 9d \Rightarrow d = 800$. The bonuses { from 10th to 1st } are:

$$\$1000, \$1800, \$2600, \$3400, \$4200, \$5000, \$5800, \$6600, \$7400, \text{ and } \$8200.$$

45 The sequence $16, 48, 80, 112, \ldots$, is an arithmetic sequence with $a_1 = 16$ and

$d = 48 - 16 = 32$. The total distance traveled in n seconds is

$$a_1 + a_2 + \cdots + a_n = \tfrac{n}{2}\big[2a_1 + (n-1)d\big] = \tfrac{n}{2}\big[2(16) + (n-1)(32)\big] = \tfrac{n}{2}(32n) = 16n^2.$$

46 Let f be the linear function $f(n) = a(n) + b$.

The difference between the $(n + 1)$st term and the nth term is

$$f(n + 1) - f(n) = \big[a(n + 1) + b\big] - \big[a(n) + b\big] = an + a + b - an - b = a.$$

∴ successive terms differ by the same real number and the sequence is arithmetic.

47 If the nth term is $\frac{1}{x_n}$ and $x_{n+1} = \frac{x_n}{1 + x_n}$, then the $(n + 1)$st term is

$\dfrac{1}{x_{n+1}} = \dfrac{1}{\frac{x_n}{1 + x_n}} = 1 + \dfrac{1}{x_n}$, which is 1 greater than the nth term and therefore the

sequence is arithmetic.

48 The sequence of the lengths is 2–1 inch lengths, 2–2 in, 2–3 in, $\ldots$, 2–16 in.

This sequence is the same as $2, 4, 6, \ldots, 32$, and has sum $S_{16} = \tfrac{16}{2}(2 + 32) = 272$ in.

If the width is 32, then the sequence is $2, 4, 6, \ldots, 64$,

$$\text{and the sum is } S_{32} = \tfrac{32}{2}(2 + 64) = 1056 \text{ in.}$$

49 (a) $T_8 = 1 + 2 + \cdots + 8 = 36$. $A_1 = \dfrac{8 - 1 + 1}{36} = \dfrac{8}{36}$.

$$A_2 = \tfrac{7}{36}, \; A_3 = \tfrac{6}{36}, \; A_4 = \tfrac{5}{36}, \; A_5 = \tfrac{4}{36}, \; A_6 = \tfrac{3}{36}, \; A_7 = \tfrac{2}{36}, \; A_8 = \tfrac{1}{36}.$$

(b) $d = A_{k+1} - A_k = -\tfrac{1}{36}$ for $k = 1, 2, \ldots, 7$. $S_8 = \displaystyle\sum_{k=1}^{8} A_k = \tfrac{8}{36} + \tfrac{7}{36} + \cdots + \tfrac{1}{36} = 1$.

(c) $\$1000\left(\tfrac{8}{36} + \tfrac{7}{36} + \tfrac{6}{36} + \tfrac{5}{36}\right) \approx \$722.22$

50 (a) $A_1 = \dfrac{n - 1 + 1}{T_n} = \dfrac{n}{T_n}$. $A_2, A_3, \ldots, A_n = \dfrac{n-1}{T_n}, \dfrac{n-2}{T_n}, \ldots, \dfrac{1}{T_n}$.

(b) $d = A_{k+1} - A_k = \dfrac{n - (k + 1) + 1}{T_n} - \dfrac{n - k + 1}{T_n} = -\dfrac{1}{T_n}$.

$$S_n = \sum_{k=1}^{n} A_k = \tfrac{1}{T_n} + \tfrac{2}{T_n} + \cdots + \tfrac{n}{T_n} = \dfrac{1 + 2 + \cdots + n}{T_n} = \dfrac{1 + 2 + \cdots + n}{1 + 2 + \cdots + n} = 1.$$

1 To show that the given sequence, $5, -\frac{5}{4}, \frac{5}{16}, \ldots, 5(-\frac{1}{4})^{n-1}, \ldots$, is geometric,

we must show that $\frac{a_{k+1}}{a_k}$ is equal to some constant, which is the common ratio.

$$a_n = 5(-\tfrac{1}{4})^{n-1} \Rightarrow \frac{a_{k+1}}{a_k} = \frac{5(-\tfrac{1}{4})^{(k+1)-1}}{5(-\tfrac{1}{4})^{k-1}} = -\frac{1}{4}$$

2 $\frac{1}{7}, \frac{3}{7}, \frac{9}{7}, \ldots, \frac{1}{7}(3)^{n-1}, \ldots$ • $a_n = \frac{1}{7}(3)^{n-1} \Rightarrow \frac{a_{k+1}}{a_k} = \frac{\frac{1}{7}(3)^{(k+1)-1}}{\frac{1}{7}(3)^{k-1}} = 3$

3 $r = \frac{4}{8} = \frac{1}{2}; \; a_n = 8(\frac{1}{2})^{n-1} = 2^3(2^{-1})^{n-1} = 2^{4-n}; \; a_5 = 2^{-1} = \frac{1}{2}; \; a_8 = 2^{-4} = \frac{1}{16}$

4 $r = \frac{1.2}{4} = 0.3; \; a_n = 4(0.3)^{n-1}; \; a_5 = 4(0.3)^4 = 0.0324; \; a_8 = 4(0.3)^7 = 0.0008748$

5 $r = \frac{-30}{300} = -0.1; \; a_n = 300(-0.1)^{n-1};$

$$a_5 = 300(-0.1)^4 = 0.03; \; a_8 = 300(-0.1)^7 = -0.00003$$

6 $r = \frac{-\sqrt{3}}{1} = -\sqrt{3}; \; a_n = 1(-\sqrt{3})^{n-1}; \; a_5 = (-\sqrt{3})^4 = 9; \; a_8 = (-\sqrt{3})^7 = -27\sqrt{3}$

7 $r = \frac{25}{5} = 5; \; a_n = 5(5)^{n-1} = 5^n; \; a_5 = 5^5 = 3125; \; a_8 = 5^8 = 390{,}625$

8 $r = \frac{6}{2} = 3; \; a_n = 2(3)^{n-1}; \; a_5 = 2 \cdot 3^4 = 162; \; a_8 = 2 \cdot 3^7 = 4374$

9 $r = \frac{-6}{4} = -1.5; \; a_n = 4(-1.5)^{n-1}; \; a_5 = 4(-1.5)^4 = 20.25; \; a_8 = 4(-1.5)^7 = -68.34375$

10 $r = \frac{-54}{162} = -\frac{1}{3}; \; a_n = 162(-\frac{1}{3})^{n-1}; \; a_5 = 162(-\frac{1}{3})^4 = 2; \; a_8 = 162(-\frac{1}{3})^7 = -\frac{2}{27}$

11 $r = \frac{-x^2}{1} = -x^2; \; a_n = 1(-x^2)^{n-1} = (-1)^{n-1}x^{2n-2}; \; a_5 = x^8; \; a_8 = -x^{14}$

12 $r = \frac{-\frac{x}{3}}{1} = -\frac{x}{3}; \; a_n = 1(-\frac{x}{3})^{n-1} = (-1)^{n-1}(\frac{x}{3})^{n-1}; \; a_5 = \frac{x^4}{81}; \; a_8 = -\frac{x^7}{2187}$

13 $r = \frac{2^{x+1}}{2} = 2^x; \; a_n = 2(2^x)^{n-1} = 2^{(n-1)x+1}; \; a_5 = 2^{4x+1}; \; a_8 = 2^{7x+1}$

14 $r = \frac{10^{2x-1}}{10} = 10^{2x-2}; \; a_n = 10(10^{2x-2})^{n-1} = 10^{2(n-1)x+(3-2n)};$

$$a_5 = 10^{8x-7}; \; a_8 = 10^{14x-13}$$

15 $\frac{a_6}{a_4} = \frac{9}{3} = 3$ and $\frac{a_6}{a_4} = \frac{a_1 r^5}{a_1 r^3} = r^2$. Hence, $r^2 = 3$ and $r = \pm\sqrt{3}$.

16 $\frac{a_7}{a_3} = \frac{1/4}{4} = \frac{1}{16}$ and $\frac{a_7}{a_3} = \frac{a_1 r^6}{a_1 r^2} = r^4$. Hence, $r^4 = \frac{1}{16}$ and $r = \pm\frac{1}{2}$.

17 $r = \frac{6}{4} = \frac{3}{2}; \; a_6 = 4(\frac{3}{2})^5 = \frac{243}{8}$

18 $r = \frac{-\sqrt{2}}{2} = -\frac{1}{\sqrt{2}}; \; a_1 = \frac{a_2}{r} = -2\sqrt{2}; \; a_7 = -2\sqrt{2}\left(-\frac{1}{\sqrt{2}}\right)^6 = -\frac{\sqrt{2}}{4}$

$\boxed{19}$ $a_4 = 4$ and $a_7 = 12 \Rightarrow r^3 = \frac{12}{4} = 3 \Rightarrow r = \sqrt[3]{3}$. $a_{10} = a_7 r^3 = 12(3) = 36$.

$\boxed{20}$ $a_2 = 3$ and $a_5 = -81 \Rightarrow r^3 = \frac{-81}{3} = -27 \Rightarrow r = -3$. $a_9 = a_5 r^4 = (-81)(-3)^4 = -6561$.

$\boxed{21}$ $\displaystyle\sum_{k=1}^{10} 3^k = 3 \cdot \frac{1 - 3^{10}}{1 - 3} = 3 \cdot \frac{-59{,}048}{-2} = 88{,}572$

$\boxed{22}$ $\displaystyle\sum_{k=1}^{9} (-\sqrt{5})^k = -\sqrt{5} \cdot \frac{1 - (-\sqrt{5})^9}{1 - (-\sqrt{5})} = \frac{(-\sqrt{5})(1 + 625\sqrt{5})}{1 + \sqrt{5}} \cdot \frac{1 - \sqrt{5}}{1 - \sqrt{5}} = \frac{3124\sqrt{5} - 3120}{-4}$
$$= 780 - 781\sqrt{5}$$

$\boxed{23}$ $\displaystyle\sum_{k=0}^{9} (-\tfrac{1}{2})^{k+1} = \sum_{k=1}^{10} (-\tfrac{1}{2})^k = -\frac{1}{2} \cdot \frac{1 - (-\frac{1}{2})^{10}}{1 - (-\frac{1}{2})} = -\frac{1}{2} \cdot \frac{\frac{1023}{1024}}{\frac{3}{2}} = -\frac{1023}{3072}$

$\boxed{24}$ $\displaystyle\sum_{k=1}^{7} (3^{-k}) = \sum_{k=1}^{7} (\tfrac{1}{3})^k = \frac{1}{3} \cdot \frac{1 - (\frac{1}{3})^7}{1 - \frac{1}{3}} = \frac{1}{3} \cdot \frac{\frac{2186}{2187}}{\frac{2}{3}} = \frac{1093}{2187}$

$\boxed{25}$ $2 + 4 + 8 + 16 + 32 + 64 + 128 = 2^1 + 2^2 + 2^3 + 2^4 + 2^5 + 2^6 + 2^7 = \displaystyle\sum_{n=1}^{7} 2^n$

$\boxed{26}$ $2 - 4 + 8 - 16 + 32 - 64 = 2^1 - 2^2 + 2^3 - 2^4 + 2^5 - 2^6$.

The terms have alternating signs and are doubling. $\displaystyle\sum_{n=1}^{6} (-1)^{n+1}(2)^n$

$\boxed{27}$ $\frac{1}{4} - \frac{1}{12} + \frac{1}{36} - \frac{1}{108} = \frac{1}{4} - \frac{1}{4} \cdot \frac{1}{3^1} + \frac{1}{4} \cdot \frac{1}{3^2} - \frac{1}{4} \cdot \frac{1}{3^3} = \displaystyle\sum_{n=1}^{4} (-1)^{n+1} \frac{1}{4}(\tfrac{1}{3})^{n-1}$

$\boxed{28}$ $3 + \frac{3}{5} + \frac{3}{25} + \frac{3}{125} + \frac{3}{625} = 3 + 3(\tfrac{1}{5})^1 + 3(\tfrac{1}{5})^2 + 3(\tfrac{1}{5})^3 + 3(\tfrac{1}{5})^4 = \displaystyle\sum_{n=1}^{5} 3(\tfrac{1}{5})^{n-1}$

$\boxed{29}$ $1 - \frac{1}{2} + \frac{1}{4} - \frac{1}{8} + \cdots$ • $a_1 = 1$, $r = -\frac{1}{2}$, $S = \frac{1}{1 + \frac{1}{2}} = \frac{2}{3}$

$\boxed{30}$ $2 + \frac{2}{3} + \frac{2}{9} + \frac{2}{27} + \cdots$ • $a_1 = 2$, $r = \frac{1}{3}$, $S = \frac{2}{1 - \frac{1}{3}} = 3$

$\boxed{31}$ $1.5 + 0.015 + 0.00015 + \cdots$ • $a_1 = 1.5$, $r = 0.01$, $S = \frac{1.5}{1 - 0.01} = \frac{50}{33}$

$\boxed{32}$ $1 - 0.1 + 0.01 - 0.001 + \cdots$ • $a_1 = 1$, $r = -0.1$, $S = \frac{1}{1 + 0.1} = \frac{10}{11}$

$\boxed{33}$ $\sqrt{2} - 2 + \sqrt{8} - 4 + \cdots$ • ★ Since $|r| = \sqrt{2} > 1$, the sum does not exist.

$\boxed{34}$ $1 + \frac{3}{2} + \frac{9}{4} + \frac{27}{8} + \cdots$ • ★ Since $|r| = \frac{3}{2} > 1$, the sum does not exist.

$\boxed{35}$ $256 + 192 + 144 + 108 + \cdots$ • $a_1 = 256$, $r = \frac{192}{256} = \frac{3}{4}$, $S = \frac{256}{1 - \frac{3}{4}} = 1024$

$\boxed{36}$ $250 - 100 + 40 - 16 + \cdots$ • $a_1 = 250$, $r = -\frac{2}{5}$, $S = \frac{250}{1 + \frac{2}{5}} = \frac{1250}{7}$

$\boxed{37}$ $0.\overline{23}$ • $a_1 = 0.23$, $r = 0.01$, $S = \frac{0.23}{1 - 0.01} = \frac{23}{99}$

$\boxed{38}$ $0.0\overline{71}$ • $a_1 = 0.071$, $r = 0.01$, $S = \frac{0.071}{1 - 0.01} = \frac{71}{990}$

$\boxed{39}$ $2.4\overline{17}$ • $a_1 = 0.017$, $r = 0.01$, $S = \frac{0.017}{1 - 0.01} = \frac{17}{990}$; $2.4\overline{17} = 2.4 + \frac{17}{990} = \frac{2393}{990}$

$\boxed{40}$ $10.\overline{5}$ • $a_1 = 0.5$, $r = 0.1$, $S = \frac{0.5}{1 - 0.1} = \frac{5}{9}$; $10.\overline{5} = 10 + \frac{5}{9} = \frac{95}{9}$

$\boxed{41}$ $5.\overline{146}$ • $a_1 = 0.146$, $r = 0.001$, $S = \dfrac{0.146}{1-0.001} = \dfrac{146}{999}$; $5.\overline{146} = 5 + \dfrac{146}{999} = \dfrac{5141}{999}$

$\boxed{42}$ $3.2\overline{394}$ • $a_1 = 0.0394$, $r = 0.001$, $S = \dfrac{0.0394}{1-0.001} = \dfrac{394}{9990}$;

$$3.2\overline{394} = 3.2 + \frac{394}{9990} = \frac{32{,}362}{9990} = \frac{16{,}181}{4995}$$

$\boxed{43}$ $1.\overline{6124}$ • $a_1 = 0.6124$, $r = 0.0001$, $S = \dfrac{0.6124}{1-0.0001} = \dfrac{6124}{9999}$;

$$1.\overline{6124} = 1 + \frac{6124}{9999} = \frac{16{,}123}{9999}$$

$\boxed{44}$ $123.61\overline{83}$ • $a_1 = 0.0083$, $r = 0.01$, $S = \dfrac{0.0083}{1-0.01} = \dfrac{83}{9900}$;

$$123.61\overline{83} = 123.61 + \frac{83}{9900} = \frac{1{,}223{,}822}{9900} = \frac{611{,}911}{4950}$$

$\boxed{45}$ The geometric mean of 12 and 48 is $\sqrt{12\cdot 48} = \sqrt{576} = 24$.

$\boxed{46}$ The geometric mean of 20 and 25 is $\sqrt{20\cdot 25} = \sqrt{500} = 10\sqrt{5}$.

$\boxed{47}$ 2 geometric means $\Rightarrow 4\cdot r^{2+1} = 500 \Rightarrow r^3 = \dfrac{500}{4} = 125 \Rightarrow r = 5$.

The terms are 4, 20, 100, and 500.

$\boxed{48}$ 3 geometric means $\Rightarrow 2\cdot r^{3+1} = 512 \Rightarrow r^4 = \dfrac{512}{2} = 256 \Rightarrow r = 4 \; \{r > 0\}$.

The terms are 2, 8, 32, 128, and 512.

$\boxed{49}$ Let $a_1 = x$ and $r = \frac{1}{2}$. $a_{11} = x\left(\frac{1}{2}\right)^{10} = \frac{1}{1024}x$.

This is $\left(\frac{1}{1024}\cdot 100\right)\%$ or $\frac{25}{256}\%$ or approximately 0.1% of x.

$\boxed{50}$ Let $a_1 = 20{,}000$ and $r = 1 - \frac{1}{4} = \frac{3}{4}$ { since the value at the end of the year is 75%

of its value at the beginning of the year }. $a_7 = 20{,}000\left(\frac{3}{4}\right)^6 \approx \$3559.57$

$\boxed{51}$ Let $a_1 = 10{,}000$ and $r = 1.2$, i.e., 120% every hour.

(a) $N(1) = a_2 = 10{,}000(1.2)^1$, $N(2) = a_3 = 10{,}000(1.2)^2$, $\ldots$,

$$N(t) = a_{t+1} = 10{,}000(1.2)^t$$

(b) $N(10) = a_{11} = 10{,}000(1.2)^{10} \approx 61{,}917$.

$\boxed{52}$ The sequence of terms is P, $P + P\cdot\dfrac{r}{4} = P\left(1 + \dfrac{r}{4}\right)^1$,

$$P\left(1 + \frac{r}{4}\right) + P\left(1 + \frac{r}{4}\right)\cdot\frac{r}{4} = P\left(1 + \frac{r}{4}\right)\left(1 + \frac{r}{4}\right) = P\left(1 + \frac{r}{4}\right)^2, \ldots.$$

In n years, there will be $4n$ compounding periods. $a_{4n} = P\left(1 + \dfrac{r}{4}\right)^{4n}$

$\boxed{53}$ Distance$_{\text{total}}$ = Distance$_{\text{down}}$ + Distance$_{\text{up}}$

$$= \left[60 + 60\left(\tfrac{2}{3}\right) + 60\left(\tfrac{2}{3}\right)^2 + \cdots\right] + \left[60\left(\tfrac{2}{3}\right) + 60\left(\tfrac{2}{3}\right)^2 + \cdots\right]$$

$$= 60 + 2\left[60\left(\tfrac{2}{3}\right) + 60\left(\tfrac{2}{3}\right)^2 + \cdots\right] = 60 + 2\left(\frac{60\left(\tfrac{2}{3}\right)}{1 - \tfrac{2}{3}}\right) = 300 \text{ ft.}$$

$\boxed{54}$ The pendulum travels $24 + 24\left(\tfrac{5}{6}\right) + 24\left(\tfrac{5}{6}\right)^2 + \cdots = \dfrac{24}{1 - \tfrac{5}{6}} = 144$ cm.

$\boxed{55}$ Spending $= 2{,}000{,}000(0.60) + 2{,}000{,}000(0.60)^2 + \cdots = \dfrac{1{,}200{,}000}{1 - 0.60} = \$3{,}000{,}000$

56 (a) The number of flies after n days for one group of flies is $a_n = N(0.9)^{n-1}$.

Since N flies are released each day, the number of flies on the nth day is

$$\sum_{k=1}^{n} a_k = \sum_{k=1}^{n} N(0.9)^{k-1} = N + (0.9)N + (0.9)^2 N + \cdots + (0.9)^{n-1} N.$$

(b) $r = 0.9 < 1$. For a long-range goal, the sum of an infinite geometric series

may be used with $S = 20{,}000$ and $a_1 = N$. $S = \dfrac{a_1}{1-r} \Rightarrow 20{,}000 = \dfrac{N}{1-0.9} \Rightarrow$

$N = 2000$ flies per day. Alternatively, since 10% of the flies *do not* survive a

given day, we need to replace 10% of 20,000, or 2000 flies per day.

57 (a) A half-life of 2 hours means there will be $(\frac{1}{2})(\frac{1}{2}D) = \frac{1}{4}D$ after 4 hours. The

amount remaining after n doses { not hours } for a given dose is $a_n = D(\frac{1}{4})^{n-1}$.

Since D mg are administered every 4 hours, the amount of the drug in the

bloodstream after n doses is $\displaystyle\sum_{k=1}^{n} a_k = \sum_{k=1}^{n} D(\frac{1}{4})^{k-1} = D + \frac{1}{4}D + \cdots + (\frac{1}{4})^{n-1}D$.

Since $r = \frac{1}{4} < 1$, S_n may be approximated by

$$S = \frac{a_1}{1-r} \text{ for large } n. \quad S = \frac{D}{1-\frac{1}{4}} = \frac{4}{3}D.$$

(b) $\frac{4}{3}D \leq 500 \Rightarrow D \leq 375$ mg.

58 From the figure we see that 2 prior generations yields 4 grandparents, 3 prior

generations yields 8 grandparents, and in general n prior generations yields 2^n

grandparents for $n \geq 2$. Going back 10 generations, there would be 2^{10} { 1024 }

grandparents and the total would be $\displaystyle\sum_{k=2}^{10} 2^k = \sum_{k=1}^{9} 2^{k+1} = 4 \cdot \frac{1 - 2^9}{1 - 2} = 2044$.

59 (a) From the figure we see that $(\frac{1}{4}a_k)^2 + (\frac{3}{4}a_k)^2 = (a_{k+1})^2 \Rightarrow$

$$\frac{10}{16}a_k^2 = a_{k+1}^2 \Rightarrow a_{k+1} = \frac{1}{4}\sqrt{10}\, a_k.$$

(b) From part (a), $a_n = a_1(\frac{1}{4}\sqrt{10})^{n-1}$.

$A_{k+1} = a_{k+1}^2 = \frac{10}{16}a_k^2 = \frac{5}{8}A_k$, hence $A_n = (\frac{5}{8})^{n-1}A_1$.

$P_{k+1} = 4a_{k+1} = 4 \cdot \frac{1}{4}\sqrt{10}\, a_k = \sqrt{10}\, a_k = \sqrt{10}(\frac{1}{4}P_k)$, hence $P_n = (\frac{1}{4}\sqrt{10})^{n-1}P_1$.

(c) $\displaystyle\sum_{n=1}^{\infty} P_n$ is an infinite geometric series with first term P_1 and $r = \frac{1}{4}\sqrt{10}$.

$$S = \frac{P_1}{1 - \frac{1}{4}\sqrt{10}} = \frac{4P_1}{4 - \sqrt{10}} = \frac{16a_1}{4 - \sqrt{10}}.$$

60 (a) Let s_n denote the length of a side of the nth square and $\frac{1}{2}s_n$ the length of the

radius of the inscribed circle. Now $C_n = \pi(\frac{1}{2}s_n)^2 = \frac{\pi}{4}s_n^2 = \frac{\pi}{4}S_n$, i.e.,

$S_n = \frac{4}{\pi}C_n$. Let r_n be the radius of the nth circle. The inscribed square will

have a side of length $s_{n+1} = \sqrt{r_n^2 + r_n^2} = \sqrt{2}\, r_n$.

Thus, $C_n = \pi r_n^2$ and $S_{n+1} = s_{n+1}^2 = 2r_n^2 \Rightarrow C_n = \frac{\pi}{2}S_{n+1}$.

(b) The shaded region has area $(S_1 - C_1) + (S_2 - C_2) + (S_3 - C_3) + \cdots =$

$$\sum_{n=1}^{\infty} S_n - \sum_{n=1}^{\infty} C_n = \sum_{n=1}^{\infty} S_n - \sum_{n=1}^{\infty} \tfrac{\pi}{4} S_n = \tfrac{4-\pi}{4} \sum_{n=1}^{\infty} S_n. \text{ From part (a),}$$

$$S_{n+1} = \tfrac{2}{\pi}(\tfrac{\pi}{4} S_n) = \tfrac{1}{2} S_n. \text{ Hence, } \sum_{n=1}^{\infty} S_n = S_1 + \tfrac{1}{2} S_1 + \tfrac{1}{4} S_1 + \cdots = \frac{S_1}{1 - \tfrac{1}{2}} =$$

$2 S_1$. Thus, the area is $\tfrac{4-\pi}{4}(2 S_1) = \tfrac{4-\pi}{2} S_1$ or approximately 43% of S_1.

61 (a) The sequence is 1, 3, 9, 27, 81, ... Thus, $a_k = 3^{k-1}$ for $k = 1, 2, 3, \ldots$.

(b) $a_{15} = 3^{14} = 4{,}782{,}969$

(c) The area of the triangle removed first is $\tfrac{1}{4}$. During the next step, 3 triangles with an area of $\tfrac{1}{16}$ are removed. Then, 9 triangles with an area of $\tfrac{1}{64}$ are removed. At each step the number of triangles increase by a factor of 3, while the area of each triangle decreases by a factor of 4. Thus, $b_k = \dfrac{3^{k-1}}{4^k} = \dfrac{1}{4}\left(\dfrac{3}{4}\right)^{k-1}$.

(d) $b_7 = \tfrac{1}{4}\left(\tfrac{3}{4}\right)^6 = \tfrac{729}{16{,}384} \approx 0.0445 = 4.45\%$.

62 (a) From the previous exercise, $\displaystyle\sum_{k=1}^{n} a_k = \sum_{k=1}^{n} 3^{k-1}$.

(b) $\displaystyle\sum_{k=1}^{12} 3^{k-1} = 3^0 + 3^1 + 3^2 + 3^3 + \cdots + 3^{11} = 1 \cdot \dfrac{1 - 3^{12}}{1 - 3} = 265{,}720$

(c) From the previous exercise, $\displaystyle\sum_{k=1}^{n} b_k = \sum_{k=1}^{n} \tfrac{1}{4}\left(\tfrac{3}{4}\right)^{k-1}$.

(d) $\displaystyle\sum_{k=1}^{12} \tfrac{1}{4}\left(\tfrac{3}{4}\right)^{k-1} = \tfrac{1}{4} + \tfrac{1}{4}\left(\tfrac{3}{4}\right) + \tfrac{1}{4}\left(\tfrac{3}{4}\right)^2 + \tfrac{1}{4}\left(\tfrac{3}{4}\right)^3 + \cdots + \tfrac{1}{4}\left(\tfrac{3}{4}\right)^{11} = \left(\tfrac{1}{4}\right)\dfrac{1 - \left(\tfrac{3}{4}\right)^{12}}{1 - \tfrac{3}{4}} \approx$

$$0.96832 \approx 97\%$$

63 Let $a_k = 100\left(1 + \tfrac{0.06}{12}\right)^k = 100(1.005)^k$, where k represents the number of compounding periods for each deposit. For the first deposit, $k = 18 \cdot 12 = 216$. For the last deposit, $k = 1$. $\quad S_{216} = a_1 + a_2 + \cdots + a_{216}$

$$= 100(1.005)^1 + 100(1.005)^2 + \cdots + 100(1.005)^{216}$$

$$= 100(1.005)\left(\frac{1 - (1.005)^{216}}{1 - (1.005)}\right) \approx \$38{,}929.00$$

64 $A = P\left(1 + \tfrac{r}{12}\right)^1 + P\left(1 + \tfrac{r}{12}\right)^2 + \cdots + P\left(1 + \tfrac{r}{12}\right)^n$

$$= P\left(1 + \tfrac{r}{12}\right)\left(\frac{1 - (1 + \tfrac{r}{12})^n}{1 - (1 + \tfrac{r}{12})}\right) = P\left(1 + \tfrac{r}{12}\right)\left(\frac{1 - (1 + \tfrac{r}{12})^n}{-\tfrac{r}{12}}\right) = P\left(\tfrac{12}{r} + 1\right)\left[(1 + \tfrac{r}{12})^n - 1\right]$$

65 $A = 100\left(\tfrac{12}{0.08} + 1\right)\left[\left(1 + \tfrac{0.08}{12}\right)^{60} - 1\right] \approx \$7396.67$

66 First, solve for n. $A = P\left(\frac{12}{r}+1\right)\left[\left(1+\frac{r}{12}\right)^n - 1\right] \Rightarrow \left(1+\frac{r}{12}\right)^n - 1 = \frac{Ar}{P(12+r)} \Rightarrow$

$$\left(1+\frac{r}{12}\right)^n = \frac{Ar}{P(12+r)} + 1 \Rightarrow n\ln\left(1+\frac{r}{12}\right) = \ln\left(\frac{Ar}{P(12+r)}+1\right) \Rightarrow$$

$$n = \ln\left(\frac{Ar}{P(12+r)}+1\right)\Big/ \ln\left(1+\frac{r}{12}\right)$$

(a) $A = 100{,}000$, $r = 0.10$, and $P = 100 \Rightarrow n \approx 268.25$ mo, or, 22.35 yr.

(b) $A = 100{,}000$, $r = 0.10$, and $P = 200 \Rightarrow n \approx 197.08$ mo, or, 16.42 yr.

67 (a) $A_1 = \frac{2}{5}\left(1-\frac{2}{5}\right)^{1-1} = \frac{2}{5}\left(\frac{3}{5}\right)^0 = \frac{2}{5}$.

$$A_2 = \frac{2}{5}\left(\frac{3}{5}\right)^1 = \frac{6}{25}, \; A_3 = \frac{2}{5}\left(\frac{3}{5}\right)^2 = \frac{18}{125}, \; A_4 = \frac{2}{5}\left(\frac{3}{5}\right)^3 = \frac{54}{625}, \; A_5 = \frac{2}{5}\left(\frac{3}{5}\right)^4 = \frac{162}{3125}.$$

(b) $r = A_{k+1}/A_k = \frac{3}{5}$ for $k = 1, 2, 3, 4$.

$$S_5 = \sum_{k=1}^{5} A_k = A_1 + A_2 + A_3 + A_4 + A_5 = \frac{2}{5}\cdot\frac{1-\left(\frac{3}{5}\right)^5}{1-\frac{3}{5}} = 1-\left(\frac{3}{5}\right)^5 = \frac{2882}{3125} = 0.92224.$$

(c) $\$25{,}000\left(\frac{2}{5}+\frac{6}{25}\right) = \$25{,}000\left(\frac{16}{25}\right) = \$16{,}000$

68 (a) $A_1 = \frac{2}{n}\left(1-\frac{2}{n}\right)^{1-1} = \frac{2}{n}\left(1-\frac{2}{n}\right)^0 = \frac{2}{n}$.

$$A_2, A_3, \ldots, A_n = \frac{2}{n}\left(1-\frac{2}{n}\right)^1, \frac{2}{n}\left(1-\frac{2}{n}\right)^2, \ldots, \frac{2}{n}\left(1-\frac{2}{n}\right)^{n-1}.$$

(b) $r = \dfrac{A_{k+1}}{A_k} = \dfrac{\frac{2}{n}\left(1-\frac{2}{n}\right)^{(k+1)-1}}{\frac{2}{n}\left(1-\frac{2}{n}\right)^{k-1}} = \left(1-\frac{2}{n}\right)^{k-(k-1)} = 1-\frac{2}{n}$.

$$S_n = \sum_{k=1}^{n} A_k = A_1 \frac{1-r^n}{1-r} = \frac{2}{n}\cdot\left[\frac{1-\left(1-\frac{2}{n}\right)^n}{1-\left(1-\frac{2}{n}\right)}\right] = 1-\left(1-\frac{2}{n}\right)^n.$$

9.4 Exercises

1 (1) P_1 is true, since $2(1) = 1(1+1) = 2$.

(2) Assume P_k is true:

$$2 + 4 + 6 + \cdots + 2k = k(k+1). \text{ Hence,}$$

$$2 + 4 + 6 + \cdots + 2k + 2(k+1) = k(k+1) + 2(k+1)$$

$$= (k+1)(k+2)$$

$$= (k+1)(k+1+1).$$

Thus, P_{k+1} is true, and the proof is complete.

2   (1) P_1 is true, since $3(1) - 2 = \dfrac{1[3(1) - 1]}{2} = 1.$

(2)   Assume P_k is true:

$$1 + 4 + 7 + \cdots + (3k - 2) = \frac{k(3k - 1)}{2}. \quad \text{Hence,}$$

$$
\begin{aligned}
1 + 4 + 7 + \cdots + (3k - 2) + 3(k + 1) - 2 &= \frac{k(3k - 1)}{2} + 3(k + 1) - 2 \\
&= \frac{3k^2 + 5k + 2}{2} \\
&= \frac{(k + 1)(3k + 2)}{2} \\
&= \frac{(k + 1)[3(k + 1) - 1]}{2}.
\end{aligned}
$$

Thus, P_{k+1} is true, and the proof is complete.

3   (1) P_1 is true, since $2(1) - 1 = (1)^2 = 1.$

(2)   Assume P_k is true:

$$1 + 3 + 5 + \cdots + (2k - 1) = k^2. \quad \text{Hence,}$$

$$
\begin{aligned}
1 + 3 + 5 + \cdots + (2k - 1) + 2(k + 1) - 1 &= k^2 + 2(k + 1) - 1 \\
&= k^2 + 2k + 1 \\
&= (k + 1)^2.
\end{aligned}
$$

Thus, P_{k+1} is true, and the proof is complete.

4   (1) P_1 is true, since $6(1) - 3 = 3(1)^2 = 3.$

(2)   Assume P_k is true:

$$3 + 9 + 15 + \cdots + (6k - 3) = 3k^2. \quad \text{Hence,}$$

$$
\begin{aligned}
3 + 9 + 15 + \cdots + (6k - 3) + 6(k + 1) - 3 &= 3k^2 + 6(k + 1) - 3 \\
&= 3k^2 + 6k + 3 \\
&= 3(k^2 + 2k + 1) \\
&= 3(k + 1)^2.
\end{aligned}
$$

Thus, P_{k+1} is true, and the proof is complete.

5   (1) P_1 is true, since $5(1) - 3 = \frac{1}{2}(1)[5(1) - 1] = 2.$

(2)   Assume P_k is true:

$$2 + 7 + 12 + \cdots + (5k - 3) = \tfrac{1}{2}k(5k - 1). \quad \text{Hence,}$$

$$
\begin{aligned}
2 + 7 + 12 + \cdots + (5k - 3) + 5(k + 1) - 3 &= \tfrac{1}{2}k(5k - 1) + 5(k + 1) - 3 \\
&= \tfrac{5}{2}k^2 + \tfrac{9}{2}k + 2 \\
&= \tfrac{1}{2}(5k^2 + 9k + 4) \\
&= \tfrac{1}{2}(k + 1)(5k + 4) \\
&= \tfrac{1}{2}(k + 1)[5(k + 1) - 1].
\end{aligned}
$$

Thus, P_{k+1} is true, and the proof is complete.

$\boxed{6}$ (1) P_1 is true, since $2 \cdot 3^{1-1} = 3^1 - 1 = 2$.

(2) Assume P_k is true:

$$2 + 6 + 18 + \cdots + 2 \cdot 3^{k-1} = 3^k - 1. \text{ Hence,}$$

$$\begin{aligned}
2 + 6 + 18 + \cdots + 2 \cdot 3^{k-1} + 2 \cdot 3^k &= 3^k - 1 + 2 \cdot 3^k \\
&= 1 \cdot 3^k + 2 \cdot 3^k - 1 \\
&= 3^1 \cdot 3^k - 1 \\
&= 3^{k+1} - 1.
\end{aligned}$$

Thus, P_{k+1} is true, and the proof is complete.

$\boxed{7}$ (1) P_1 is true, since $1 \cdot 2^{1-1} = 1 + (1-1) \cdot 2^1 = 1$.

(2) Assume P_k is true:

$$1 + 2 \cdot 2 + 3 \cdot 2^2 + \cdots + k \cdot 2^{k-1} = 1 + (k-1) \cdot 2^k. \text{ Hence,}$$

$$\begin{aligned}
1 + 2 \cdot 2 + 3 \cdot 2^2 + \cdots + k \cdot 2^{k-1} + (k+1) \cdot 2^k &= 1 + (k-1) \cdot 2^k + (k+1) \cdot 2^k \\
&= 1 + k \cdot 2^k - 2^k + k \cdot 2^k + 2^k \\
&= 1 + k \cdot 2^1 \cdot 2^k \\
&= 1 + \left[(k+1) - 1\right] \cdot 2^{k+1}.
\end{aligned}$$

Thus, P_{k+1} is true, and the proof is complete.

$\boxed{8}$ (1) P_1 is true, since $(-1)^1 = \dfrac{(-1)^1 - 1}{2} = -1$.

(2) Assume P_k is true:

$$(-1)^1 + (-1)^2 + (-1)^3 + \cdots + (-1)^k = \frac{(-1)^k - 1}{2}. \text{ Hence,}$$

$$\begin{aligned}
(-1)^1 + (-1)^2 + (-1)^3 + \cdots + (-1)^k + (-1)^{k+1} &= \frac{(-1)^k - 1}{2} + (-1)^{k+1} \\
&= \frac{1(-1)^k}{2} - \frac{1}{2} - \frac{2(-1)^k}{2} \\
&= \frac{(-1)^k \cdot (-1) - 1}{2} \\
&= \frac{(-1)^{k+1} - 1}{2}.
\end{aligned}$$

Thus, P_{k+1} is true, and the proof is complete.

9 (1) P_1 is true, since $(1)^1 = \dfrac{1(1+1)[2(1)+1]}{6} = 1$.

(2) Assume P_k is true:

$$1^2 + 2^2 + 3^2 + \cdots + k^2 = \frac{k(k+1)(2k+1)}{6}. \text{ Hence,}$$

$$1^2 + 2^2 + 3^2 + \cdots + k^2 + (k+1)^2 = \frac{k(k+1)(2k+1)}{6} + (k+1)^2$$

$$= (k+1)\left[\frac{k(2k+1)}{6} + \frac{6(k+1)}{6}\right]$$

$$= \frac{(k+1)(2k^2+7k+6)}{6}$$

$$= \frac{(k+1)(k+2)(2k+3)}{6}.$$

Thus, P_{k+1} is true, and the proof is complete.

10 (1) P_1 is true, since $(1)^3 = \left[\dfrac{1(1+1)}{2}\right]^2 = 1$.

(2) Assume P_k is true:

$$1^3 + 2^3 + 3^3 + \cdots + k^3 = \left[\frac{k(k+1)}{2}\right]^2. \text{ Hence,}$$

$$1^3 + 2^3 + 3^3 + \cdots + k^3 + (k+1)^3 = \left[\frac{k(k+1)}{2}\right]^2 + (k+1)^3$$

$$= \frac{(k+1)^2}{2^2}[k^2 + 4(k+1)]$$

$$= \frac{(k+1)^2}{2^2}(k+2)^2$$

$$= \left[\frac{(k+1)[(k+1)+1]}{2}\right]^2.$$

Thus, P_{k+1} is true, and the proof is complete.

11 (1) P_1 is true, since $\dfrac{1}{1(1+1)} = \dfrac{1}{1+1} = \dfrac{1}{2}$.

(2) Assume P_k is true:

$$\frac{1}{1\cdot 2} + \frac{1}{2\cdot 3} + \frac{1}{3\cdot 4} + \cdots + \frac{1}{k(k+1)} = \frac{k}{k+1}. \text{ Hence,}$$

$$\frac{1}{1\cdot 2} + \frac{1}{2\cdot 3} + \frac{1}{3\cdot 4} + \cdots + \frac{1}{k(k+1)} + \frac{1}{(k+1)(k+2)} = \frac{k}{k+1} + \frac{1}{(k+1)(k+2)}$$

$$= \frac{k}{k+1} + \frac{1}{(k+1)(k+2)}$$

$$= \frac{k(k+2)+1}{(k+1)(k+2)}$$

$$= \frac{k^2+2k+1}{(k+1)(k+2)}$$

$$= \frac{k+1}{(k+1)+1}.$$

Thus, P_{k+1} is true, and the proof is complete.

$\boxed{12}$ (1) P_1 is true, since $\dfrac{1}{1(1+1)(1+2)} = \dfrac{1(1+3)}{4(1+1)(1+2)} = \dfrac{1}{6}$.

(2) Assume P_k is true:

$$\frac{1}{1\cdot2\cdot3} + \frac{1}{2\cdot3\cdot4} + \frac{1}{3\cdot4\cdot5} + \cdots + \frac{1}{k(k+1)(k+2)} = \frac{k(k+3)}{4(k+1)(k+2)}. \text{ Hence,}$$

$$\frac{1}{1\cdot2\cdot3} + \frac{1}{2\cdot3\cdot4} + \frac{1}{3\cdot4\cdot5} + \cdots + \frac{1}{k(k+1)(k+2)} + \frac{1}{(k+1)(k+2)(k+3)}$$

$$= \frac{k(k+3)}{4(k+1)(k+2)} + \frac{1}{(k+1)(k+2)(k+3)}$$

$$= \frac{k(k+3)^2 + 4}{4(k+1)(k+2)(k+3)}$$

$$= \frac{k(k^2 + 6k + 9) + 4}{4(k+1)(k+2)(k+3)}$$

$$= \frac{k^3 + 6k^2 + 9k + 4}{4(k+1)(k+2)(k+3)}$$

$$= \frac{(k+1)(k^2 + 5k + 4)}{4(k+1)(k+2)(k+3)}$$

$$= \frac{(k+1)(k+4)}{4(k+2)(k+3)}.$$

Thus, P_{k+1} is true, and the proof is complete.

$\boxed{13}$ (1) P_1 is true, since $3^1 = \frac{3}{2}(3^1 - 1) = 3$.

(2) Assume P_k is true:

$$3 + 3^2 + 3^3 + \cdots + 3^k = \tfrac{3}{2}(3^k - 1). \text{ Hence,}$$

$$3 + 3^2 + 3^3 + \cdots + 3^k + 3^{k+1} = \tfrac{3}{2}(3^k - 1) + 3^{k+1}$$

$$= \tfrac{3}{2}\cdot3^k - \tfrac{3}{2} + 3\cdot3^k$$

$$= \tfrac{9}{2}\cdot3^k - \tfrac{3}{2}$$

$$= \tfrac{3}{2}(3\cdot3^k - 1)$$

$$= \tfrac{3}{2}(3^{k+1} - 1).$$

Thus, P_{k+1} is true, and the proof is complete.

$\boxed{14}$ (1) P_1 is true, since $[2(1) - 1]^3 = (1)^2(2\cdot1^2 - 1) = 1$.

(2) Assume P_k is true:

$$1^3 + 3^3 + 5^3 + \cdots + (2k - 1)^3 = k^2(2k^2 - 1). \text{ Hence,}$$

$$1^3 + 3^3 + 5^3 + \cdots + (2k - 1)^3 + [2(k+1) - 1]^3 = k^2(2k^2 - 1) + [2(k+1) - 1]^3$$

$$= k^2(2k^2 - 1) + [2(k+1) - 1]^3$$

$$= 2k^4 - k^2 + (2k + 1)^3$$

$$= 2k^4 + 8k^3 + 11k^2 + 6k + 1$$

$$= (k+1)^2(2k^2 + 4k + 1)$$

$$= (k+1)^2[2(k+1)^2 - 1].$$

Thus, P_{k+1} is true, and the proof is complete.

15 (1) P_1 is true, since $1 < 2^1$.

    (2) Assume P_k is true: $k < 2^k$. Now $k + 1 < k + k = 2(k)$ for $k > 1$.

    From P_k, we see that $2(k) < 2(2^k) = 2^{k+1}$ and conclude that $k + 1 < 2^{k+1}$.

Thus, P_{k+1} is true, and the proof is complete.

16 (1) P_1 is true, since $1 + 2(1) \le 3^1$.

    (2) Assume P_k is true: $1 + 2k \le 3^k$.

       $1 + 2(k+1) = 2k + 3 < 6k + 3$ which is $3(1 + 2k)$. From P_k, we see that

       $3(1 + 2k) < 3(3^k) = 3^{k+1}$ and conclude that $1 + 2(k+1) \le 3^{k+1}$.

Thus, P_{k+1} is true, and the proof is complete.

17 (1) P_1 is true, since $1 < \frac{1}{8}[2(1) + 1]^2 = \frac{9}{8}$.

    (2) Assume P_k is true: $1 + 2 + 3 + \cdots + k < \frac{1}{8}(2k + 1)^2$. Hence,

$$1 + 2 + 3 + \cdots + k + (k+1) < \tfrac{1}{8}(2k+1)^2 + (k+1)$$
$$= \tfrac{1}{2}k^2 + \tfrac{3}{2}k + \tfrac{9}{8}$$
$$= \tfrac{1}{8}(4k^2 + 12k + 9)$$
$$= \tfrac{1}{8}(2k + 3)^2$$
$$= \tfrac{1}{8}[2(k+1) + 1]^2.$$

Thus, P_{k+1} is true, and the proof is complete.

18 (1) If $0 < a < b$, then $a^2 b < ab^2$ {multiply by ab} and $\frac{a^2}{b^2} < \frac{a}{b}$ {divide by b^3}.

    This is P_1: $\left(\frac{a}{b}\right)^2 < \left(\frac{a}{b}\right)^1$.

    (2) Assume P_k is true: $\left(\frac{a}{b}\right)^{k+1} < \left(\frac{a}{b}\right)^k$. Hence, $a^{k+1} b^k < a^k b^{k+1} \Rightarrow$

    $a^{k+2} b^{k+1} < a^{k+1} b^{k+2}$ {multiply by ab} $\Rightarrow \frac{a^{k+2}}{b^{k+2}} < \frac{a^{k+1}}{b^{k+1}}$ {divide by b^{2k+3}}.

    This is P_{k+1}: $\left(\frac{a}{b}\right)^{k+2} < \left(\frac{a}{b}\right)^{k+1}$.

Thus, P_{k+1} is true, and the proof is complete.

19 (1) For $n = 1$, $n^3 - n + 3 = 3$ and 3 is a factor of 3.

    (2) Assume 3 is a factor of $k^3 - k + 3$. The $(k+1)$st term is

$$(k+1)^3 - (k+1) + 3 = k^3 + 3k^2 + 2k + 3$$
$$= (k^3 - k + 3) + 3k^2 + 3k$$
$$= (k^3 - k + 3) + 3(k^2 + k).$$

By the induction hypothesis, 3 is a factor of $k^3 - k + 3$ and 3 is a factor of $3(k^2 + k)$, so 3 is a factor of the $(k+1)$st term. Thus, P_{k+1} is true, and the proof is complete.

20 (1) For $n = 1$, $n^2 + n = 2$ and 2 is a factor of 2.

(2) Assume 2 is a factor of $k^2 + k$. The $(k+1)$st term is

$$(k+1)^2 + (k+1) = k^2 + 3k + 2$$
$$= (k^2 + k) + 2k + 2$$
$$= (k^2 + k) + 2(k+1).$$

By the induction hypothesis, 2 is a factor of $k^2 + k$ and 2 is a factor of $2(k+1)$, so 2 is a factor of the $(k+1)$st term. Thus, P_{k+1} is true, and the proof is complete.

21 (1) For $n = 1$, $5^n - 1 = 4$ and 4 is a factor of 4.

(2) Assume 4 is a factor of $5^k - 1$. The $(k+1)$st term is

$$5^{k+1} - 1 = 5 \cdot 5^k - 1$$
$$= 5 \cdot 5^k - 5 + 4$$
$$= 5(5^k - 1) + 4.$$

By the induction hypothesis, 4 is a factor of $5^k - 1$ and 4 is a factor of 4, so 4 is a factor of the $(k+1)$st term. Thus, P_{k+1} is true, and the proof is complete.

22 (1) For $n = 1$, $10^{n+1} + 3 \cdot 10^n + 5 = 135$ and 9 is a factor of 135.

(2) Assume 9 is a factor of $10^{k+1} + 3 \cdot 10^k + 5$. The $(k+1)$st term is

$$10^{k+2} + 3 \cdot 10^{k+1} + 5 = 10 \cdot 10^{k+1} + 10 \cdot 3 \cdot 10^k + 5$$
$$= 10^{k+1} + 9 \cdot 10^{k+1} + 3 \cdot 10^k + 9 \cdot 3 \cdot 10^k + 5$$
$$= (10^{k+1} + 3 \cdot 10^k + 5) + 9(10^{k+1} + 3 \cdot 10^k).$$

By the induction hypothesis, 9 is a factor of $10^{k+1} + 3 \cdot 10^k + 5$ and 9 is a factor of $9(10^{k+1} + 3 \cdot 10^k)$, so 9 is a factor of the $(k+1)$st term. Thus, P_{k+1} is true and the proof is complete.

23 (1) If $a > 1$, then $a^1 = a > 1$, so P_1 is true.

(2) Assume P_k is true: $a^k > 1$.

Multiply both sides by a to obtain $a^{k+1} > a$, but since $a > 1$, we have $a^{k+1} > 1$.

Thus, P_{k+1} is true, and the proof is complete.

24 (1) For $n = 1$, $ar^{1-1} = a$ and $\dfrac{a(1-r^1)}{1-r} = a$, so P_1 is true.

(2) Assume P_k is true:

$$a + ar + ar^2 + \cdots + ar^{k-1} = \frac{a(1-r^k)}{1-r}. \text{ Hence,}$$

$$a + ar + ar^2 + \cdots + ar^{k-1} + ar^k = \frac{a(1-r^k)}{1-r} + ar^k$$

$$= a\left(\frac{1-r^k}{1-r} + \frac{r^k(1-r)}{1-r}\right)$$

(continued)

$$= a\left(\frac{1-r^k}{1-r} + \frac{r^k(1-r)}{1-r}\right) \qquad \text{(repeated)}$$

$$= a\left(\frac{1-r^k+r^k-r^{k+1}}{1-r}\right)$$

$$= \frac{a(1-r^{k+1})}{1-r}.$$

Thus, P_{k+1} is true, and the proof is complete.

$\boxed{25}$ (1) For $n = 1$, $a - b$ is a factor of $a^1 - b^1$.

(2) Assume $a - b$ is a factor of $a^k - b^k$. Following the hint for the $(k+1)$st term, $a^{k+1} - b^{k+1} = a^k \cdot a - b \cdot a^k + b \cdot a^k - b^k \cdot b = a^k(a-b) + (a^k - b^k)b$. Since $(a-b)$ is a factor of $a^k(a-b)$ and since by the induction hypothesis $a - b$ is a factor of $(a^k - b^k)$, it follows that $a - b$ is a factor of the $(k+1)$st term. Thus, P_{k+1} is true, and the proof is complete.

$\boxed{26}$ (1) For $n = 1$, $a + b$ is a factor of $a^{2(1)-1} + b^{2(1)-1} = a + b$.

(2) Assume $a + b$ is a factor of $a^{2k-1} + b^{2k-1}$. The $(k+1)$st term is
$$a^{2k+1} + b^{2k+1} = a^{2k-1} \cdot a^2 - a^{2k-1} \cdot b^2 + a^{2k-1} \cdot b^2 + b^{2k-1} \cdot b^2$$
$$= a^{2k-1}(a^2 - b^2) + b^2(a^{2k-1} + b^{2k-1}).$$

Since $(a+b)$ is a factor of $a^{2k-1}(a^2 - b^2)$ $\{a^2 - b^2 = (a+b)(a-b)\}$ and since by the induction hypothesis, $a + b$ is a factor of $b^2(a^{2k-1} + b^{2k-1})$, it follows that $a + b$ is a factor of the $(k+1)$st term. Thus, P_{k+1} is true, and the proof is complete.

Note: For Exercises 27–32 in this section and Exercises 47–48 in the Chapter Review Exercises, there are several ways to find j. Possibilities include: solve the inequality, sketch the graphs of functions representing each side, and trial and error. Trial and error may be the easiest to use.

$\boxed{27}$ For j: $n^2 \geq n + 12 \Rightarrow n^2 - n - 12 \geq 0 \Rightarrow (n-4)(n+3) \geq 0 \Rightarrow n \geq 4 \{n > 0\}$

(1) P_4 is true, since $4 + 12 \leq 4^2$.

(2) Assume P_k is true: $k + 12 \leq k^2$. Hence,
$$(k+1) + 12 = (k+12) + 1 \leq (k^2) + 1 < k^2 + 2k + 1 = (k+1)^2.$$

Thus, P_{k+1} is true, and the proof is complete.

$\boxed{28}$ For j: By trial and error, $j = 3$.

(1) P_3 is true, since $3^2 + 18 \leq 3^3$.

(2) Assume P_k is true: $k^2 + 18 \leq k^3$. Hence,
$$(k+1)^2 + 18 = (k^2 + 18) + 2k + 1$$
$$\leq (k^3) + 2k + 1 < k^3 + 3k^2 + 3k + 1 = (k+1)^3.$$

Thus, P_{k+1} is true, and the proof is complete.

29 For j: By sketching $y = 5 + \log_2 x$ and $y = x$, we see that the solution for $x > 1$

must be larger than 5. By trial and error, $j = 8$.

(1) P_8 is true, since $5 + \log_2 8 \leq 8$.

(2) Assume P_k is true: $5 + \log_2 k \leq k$. Hence,

$$5 + \log_2 (k + 1) < 5 + \log_2 (k + k)$$
$$= 5 + \log_2 2k$$
$$= 5 + \log_2 2 + \log_2 k$$
$$= (5 + \log_2 k) + 1$$
$$\leq k + 1.$$

Thus, P_{k+1} is true, and the proof is complete.

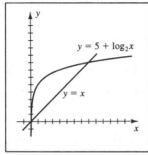

Figure 29

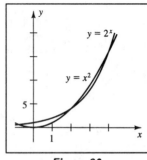

Figure 30

30 For j: By sketching $y = x^2$ and $y = 2^x$, we see that there are three intersection points, the largest being 4. Discussion Exercise 3 in Chapter 4 also dealt with this type of problem.

(1) P_4 is true, since $4^2 \leq 2^4$.

(2) Assume P_k is true: $k^2 \leq 2^k$. Hence,

$$(k + 1)^2 = k^2 + 2k + 1 = k(k + 2 + \tfrac{1}{k}) < k(k + k) = 2k^2 \leq 2 \cdot 2^k = 2^{k+1}.$$

Thus, P_{k+1} is true, and the proof is complete.

31 For j: By sketching $y = 2x + 2$ and $y = 2^x$, we see there is one positive solution.

By trial and error, $j = 3$. See *Figure 31.*

(1) P_3 is true, since $2(3) + 2 \leq 2^3$.

(2) Assume P_k is true: $2k + 2 \leq 2^k$. Hence,

$$2(k + 1) + 2 = (2k + 2) + 2 \leq 2^k + 2^k = 2 \cdot 2^k = 2^{k+1}.$$

Thus, P_{k+1} is true, and the proof is complete.

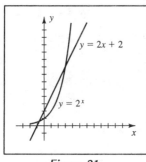

Figure 31   Figure 32

32 For j: Since $n^2 < 20$ if $n = 4$, a reasonable first guess would be $j = 5$.

By trial and error, $j = 6$.

(1) P_6 is true, since $6 \log_2 6 + 20 \le 6^2$.

(2) Assume P_k is true: $k \log_2 k + 20 \le k^2$.

$$\begin{aligned}
(k+1) \log_2 (k+1) + 20 &= k \log_2 (k+1) + \log_2 (k+1) + 20 \\
&< k \log_2 2k + \log_2 2k + 20 \\
&= k \log_2 k + k + 1 + \log_2 k + 20 \\
&\le k^2 + k + 1 + \log_2 k \\
&< k^2 + 2k + 1 = (k+1)^2.
\end{aligned}$$

Thus, P_{k+1} is true, and the proof is complete.

33 Following the hint in the text:

$$\begin{aligned}
\sum_{k=1}^{n} (k^2 + 3k + 5) &= \sum_{k=1}^{n} k^2 + 3 \sum_{k=1}^{n} k + \sum_{k=1}^{n} 5 \\
&= \frac{n(n+1)(2n+1)}{6} + 3\left[\frac{n(n+1)}{2}\right] + 5n \\
&= \frac{n(n+1)(2n+1) + 9n(n+1) + 30n}{6} \\
&= \frac{2n^3 + 12n^2 + 40n}{6} = \frac{n^3 + 6n^2 + 20n}{3}
\end{aligned}$$

34 $$\begin{aligned}
\sum_{k=1}^{n} (3k^2 - 2k + 1) &= 3 \sum_{k=1}^{n} k^2 - 2 \sum_{k=1}^{n} k + \sum_{k=1}^{n} 1 \\
&= 3\left[\frac{n(n+1)(2n+1)}{6}\right] - 2\left[\frac{n(n+1)}{2}\right] + n \\
&= \frac{2n^3 + n^2 + n}{2}
\end{aligned}$$

35 $$\begin{aligned}
\sum_{k=1}^{n} (2k - 3)^2 &= \sum_{k=1}^{n} (4k^2 - 12k + 9) \\
&= 4 \sum_{k=1}^{n} k^2 - 12 \sum_{k=1}^{n} k + \sum_{k=1}^{n} 9 \\
&= 4\left[\frac{n(n+1)(2n+1)}{6}\right] - 12\left[\frac{n(n+1)}{2}\right] + 9n \\
&= \frac{4n^3 - 12n^2 + 11n}{3}
\end{aligned}$$

36 $\sum_{k=1}^{n} (k^3 + 2k^2 - k + 4) = \sum_{k=1}^{n} k^3 + 2 \sum_{k=1}^{n} k^2 - \sum_{k=1}^{n} k + \sum_{k=1}^{n} 4$

$$= \left[\frac{n(n+1)}{2}\right]^2 + 2\left[\frac{n(n+1)(2n+1)}{6}\right] - \left[\frac{n(n+1)}{2}\right] + 4n$$

$$= \frac{3n^4 + 14n^3 + 9n^2 + 46n}{12}$$

37 (a) $n = 1 \Rightarrow a(1)^3 + b(1)^2 + c(1) = 1^2 \Rightarrow a + b + c = 1$

$n = 2 \Rightarrow a(2)^3 + b(2)^2 + c(2) = 1^2 + 2^2 \Rightarrow 8a + 4b + 2c = 5$

$n = 3 \Rightarrow a(3)^3 + b(3)^2 + c(3) = 1^2 + 2^2 + 3^2 \Rightarrow 27a + 9b + 3c = 14$

$$AX = B \Rightarrow \begin{bmatrix} 1 & 1 & 1 \\ 8 & 4 & 2 \\ 27 & 9 & 3 \end{bmatrix} \begin{bmatrix} a \\ b \\ c \end{bmatrix} = \begin{bmatrix} 1 \\ 5 \\ 14 \end{bmatrix} \Rightarrow X = A^{-1}B = \begin{bmatrix} 1/3 \\ 1/2 \\ 1/6 \end{bmatrix}.$$

(b) $a = \frac{1}{3}, b = \frac{1}{2}, c = \frac{1}{6} \Rightarrow 1^2 + 2^2 + 3^2 + \cdots + n^2 = \frac{1}{3}n^3 + \frac{1}{2}n^2 + \frac{1}{6}n = \frac{n(n+1)(2n+1)}{6}$,

which is the formula found in Exercise 9. This method does not verify the

formula for all n but only for $n = 1, 2, 3$. Mathematical induction should be

used to verify the formula for all n as in Exercise 9.

38 (a) $n = 1 \Rightarrow a(1)^4 + b(1)^3 + c(1)^2 + d(1) = 1^3 \Rightarrow a + b + c + d = 1$

$n = 2 \Rightarrow a(2)^4 + b(2)^3 + c(2)^2 + d(2) = 1^3 + 2^3 \Rightarrow 16a + 8b + 4c + 2d = 9$

$n = 3 \Rightarrow a(3)^4 + b(3)^3 + c(3)^2 + d(3) = 1^3 + 2^3 + 3^3 \Rightarrow 81a + 27b + 9c + 3d = 36$

$n = 4 \Rightarrow a(4)^4 + b(4)^3 + c(4)^2 + d(4) = 1^3 + 2^3 + 3^3 + 4^3 \Rightarrow$

$$256a + 64b + 16c + 4d = 100$$

$$AX = B \Rightarrow \begin{bmatrix} 1 & 1 & 1 & 1 \\ 16 & 8 & 4 & 2 \\ 81 & 27 & 9 & 3 \\ 256 & 64 & 16 & 4 \end{bmatrix} \begin{bmatrix} a \\ b \\ c \\ d \end{bmatrix} = \begin{bmatrix} 1 \\ 9 \\ 36 \\ 100 \end{bmatrix} \Rightarrow X = A^{-1}B = \begin{bmatrix} 1/4 \\ 1/2 \\ 1/4 \\ 0 \end{bmatrix}$$

(b) $a = \frac{1}{4}, b = \frac{1}{2}, c = \frac{1}{4}, d = 0 \Rightarrow$

$1^3 + 2^3 + 3^3 + \cdots + n^3 = \frac{1}{4}n^4 + \frac{1}{2}n^3 + \frac{1}{4}n^2 = \left[\frac{n(n+1)}{2}\right]^2$, which is the formula

found in Exercise 10. This method does not verify the formula for all n but only

for $n = 1, 2, 3, 4$. Mathematical induction should be used to verify the formula

for all n as in Exercise 10.

39 (1) For $n = 1$, $\sin(\theta + 1\pi) = \sin\theta \cos\pi + \cos\theta \sin\pi = -\sin\theta = (-1)^1\sin\theta$.

(2) Assume P_k is true: $\sin(\theta + k\pi) = (-1)^k \sin\theta$. Hence,

$$\begin{aligned}
\sin[\theta + (k+1)\pi] &= \sin[(\theta + k\pi) + \pi] \\
&= \sin(\theta + k\pi)\cos\pi + \cos(\theta + k\pi)\sin\pi \\
&= \left[(-1)^k \sin\theta\right] \cdot (-1) + \cos(\theta + k\pi) \cdot (0) \\
&= (-1)^{k+1} \sin\theta.
\end{aligned}$$

Thus, P_{k+1} is true, and the proof is complete.

40 (1) For $n = 1$, $\cos(\theta + 1\pi) = \cos\theta \cos\pi - \sin\theta \sin\pi = -\cos\theta = (-1)^1 \cos\theta$.

(2) Assume P_k is true: $\cos(\theta + k\pi) = (-1)^k \cos\theta$. Hence,

$$\begin{aligned}
\cos[\theta + (k+1)\pi] &= \cos[(\theta + k\pi) + \pi] \\
&= \cos(\theta + k\pi)\cos\pi - \sin(\theta + k\pi)\sin\pi \\
&= \left[(-1)^k \cos\theta\right] \cdot (-1) - \sin(\theta + k\pi) \cdot (0) \\
&= (-1)^{k+1} \cos\theta.
\end{aligned}$$

Thus, P_{k+1} is true, and the proof is complete.

41 (1) For $n = 1$, $\left[r(\cos\theta + i\sin\theta)\right]^1 = r^1\left[\cos(1\theta) + i\sin(1\theta)\right]$.

(2) Assume P_k is true: $\left[r(\cos\theta + i\sin\theta)\right]^k = r^k(\cos k\theta + i\sin k\theta)$. Hence,

$$\begin{aligned}
\left[r(\cos\theta + i\sin\theta)\right]^{k+1} &= \left[r(\cos\theta + i\sin\theta)\right]^k\left[r(\cos\theta + i\sin\theta)\right] \\
&= r^k\left[\cos k\theta + i\sin k\theta\right]\left[r(\cos\theta + i\sin\theta)\right] \\
&= r^{k+1}[(\cos k\theta \cos\theta - \sin k\theta \sin\theta) \\
&\qquad\qquad + i(\sin k\theta \cos\theta + \cos k\theta \sin\theta)]
\end{aligned}$$

{ Use the addition formulas for the sine and cosine. }

$$= r^{k+1}\left[\cos(k+1)\theta + i\sin(k+1)\theta\right].$$

Thus, P_{k+1} is true, and the proof is complete.

42 (1) For $n = 3$, $(n-2) \cdot 180° = 180°$, which is true for any triangle.

(2) Assume the sum of the interior angles of a polygon of k sides is $(k-2) \cdot 180°$. Now any $(k+1)$-sided polygon can be dissected into a k-sided polygon and a triangle by drawing a line from vertex (i) to vertex $(i+2)$. Its angles add up to $(k-2) \cdot 180°$ { since it is k-sided, by hypothesis } $+ 180°$ { for the triangle }, which is $(k-1) \cdot 180°$. Thus, P_{k+1} is true, and the proof is complete.

9.5 Exercises

1 $2!6! = 2 \cdot 720 = 1440$

2 $3!4! = 6 \cdot 24 = 144$

3 $7!0! = 5040 \cdot 1 = 5040$

4 $5!0! = 120 \cdot 1 = 120$

5 $\dfrac{8!}{5!} = \dfrac{8 \cdot 7 \cdot 6 \cdot 5!}{5!} = 8 \cdot 7 \cdot 6 = 336$

6 $\dfrac{6!}{3!} = 6 \cdot 5 \cdot 4 = 120$

7 $\binom{5}{5} = \frac{5!}{5!\,0!} = 1$

8 $\binom{7}{0} = \frac{7!}{0!\,7!} = 1$

9 $\binom{7}{5} = \frac{7!}{5!\,2!} = \frac{7\cdot 6}{2} = 21$

10 $\binom{8}{4} = \frac{8!}{4!\,4!} = \frac{8\cdot 7\cdot 6\cdot 5}{4\cdot 3\cdot 2} = 70$

11 $\binom{13}{4} = \frac{13!}{4!\,9!} = \frac{13\cdot 12\cdot 11\cdot 10}{4\cdot 3\cdot 2} = 715$

12 $\binom{52}{2} = \frac{52!}{2!\,50!} = \frac{52\cdot 51}{2} = 1326$

13 $\dfrac{(2n+2)!}{(2n)!} = \dfrac{(2n+2)(2n+1)(2n)!}{(2n)!} = (2n+2)(2n+1)$

14 $\dfrac{(3n+1)!}{(3n-1)!} = \dfrac{(3n+1)(3n)(3n-1)!}{(3n-1)!} = (3n+1)(3n)$

15 $(4x-y)^3 = \binom{3}{0}(4x)^3(-y)^0 + \binom{3}{1}(4x)^2(-y)^1 + \binom{3}{2}(4x)^1(-y)^2 + \binom{3}{3}(4x)^0(-y)^3$

$$= (1)(64x^3)(1) - (3)(16x^2)(y) + (3)(4x)(y^2) - (1)(1)(y^3)$$

$$= 64x^3 - 48x^2 y + 12xy^2 - y^3$$

16 $(x^2+2y)^3 = \binom{3}{0}(x^2)^3(2y)^0 + \binom{3}{1}(x^2)^2(2y)^1 + \binom{3}{2}(x^2)^1(2y)^2 + \binom{3}{3}(x^2)^0(2y)^3$

$$= (1)(x^6)(1) + (3)(x^4)(2y) + (3)(x^2)(4y^2) + (1)(1)(8y^3)$$

$$= x^6 + 6x^4 y + 12x^2 y^2 + 8y^3$$

17 $(a+b)^6 = a^6 + \binom{6}{1}a^5 b^1 + \binom{6}{2}a^4 b^2 + \binom{6}{3}a^3 b^3 + \binom{6}{4}a^2 b^4 + \binom{6}{5}a^1 b^5 + b^6 =$

$$a^6 + 6a^5 b + 15a^4 b^2 + 20a^3 b^3 + 15a^2 b^4 + 6ab^5 + b^6$$

18 $(a+b)^4 = a^4 + 4a^3 b + 6a^2 b^2 + 4ab^3 + b^4$

19 $(a-b)^7 = a^7 - 7a^6 b + 21a^5 b^2 - 35a^4 b^3 + 35a^3 b^4 - 21a^2 b^5 + 7ab^6 - b^7$

20 $(a-b)^5 = a^5 - 5a^4 b + 10a^3 b^2 - 10a^2 b^3 + 5ab^4 - b^5$

21 $(3x-5y)^4 = 81x^4 - 540x^3 y + 1350x^2 y^2 - 1500xy^3 + 625y^4$

22 $(2t-s)^5 = (2t)^5 + \binom{5}{1}(2t)^4(-s)^1 + \binom{5}{2}(2t)^3(-s)^2 + \binom{5}{3}(2t)^2(-s)^3 + \binom{5}{4}(2t)^1(-s)^4 +$

$$(-s)^5 = 32t^5 - 80t^4 s + 80t^3 s^2 - 40t^2 s^3 + 10ts^4 - s^5$$

23 $(\frac{1}{3}x + y^2)^5 = \frac{1}{243}x^5 + \frac{5}{81}x^4 y^2 + \frac{10}{27}x^3 y^4 + \frac{10}{9}x^2 y^6 + \frac{5}{3}xy^8 + y^{10}$

24 $(\frac{1}{2}c + d^3)^4 = \frac{1}{16}c^4 + \frac{1}{2}c^3 d^3 + \frac{3}{2}c^2 d^6 + 2cd^9 + d^{12}$

25 $\left(\dfrac{1}{x^2} + 3x\right)^6 = (x^{-2} + 3x)^6 =$

$$x^{-12} + 18x^{-9} + 135x^{-6} + 540x^{-3} + 1215 + 1458x^3 + 729x^6$$

26 $\left(\dfrac{1}{x^3} - 2x\right)^5 = (x^{-3} - 2x)^5 = x^{-15} - 10x^{-11} + 40x^{-7} - 80x^{-3} + 80x - 32x^5$

27 $\left(\sqrt{x} - \dfrac{1}{\sqrt{x}}\right)^5 = (x^{1/2} - x^{-1/2})^5 = x^{5/2} - 5x^{3/2} + 10x^{1/2} - 10x^{-1/2} + 5x^{-3/2} - x^{-5/2}$

28 $\left(\sqrt{x} + \dfrac{1}{\sqrt{x}}\right)^5 = (x^{1/2} + x^{-1/2})^5 = x^{5/2} + 5x^{3/2} + 10x^{1/2} + 10x^{-1/2} + 5x^{-3/2} + x^{-5/2}$

29 $(3c^{2/5} + c^{4/5})^{25}$; first three terms $= \displaystyle\sum_{k=0}^{2} \binom{25}{k}(3c^{2/5})^{25-k}(c^{4/5})^k =$

$$3^{25} c^{10} + 25\cdot 3^{24} c^{52/5} + 300\cdot 3^{23} c^{54/5}$$

30 $(x^3 + 5x^{-2})^{20}$; first three terms $= \sum_{k=0}^{2} \binom{20}{k}(x^3)^{20-k}(5x^{-2})^k =$
$$x^{60} + 100x^{55} + 4750x^{50}$$

31 $(4b^{-1} - 3b)^{15}$; last three terms $= \sum_{k=13}^{15} \binom{15}{k}(4b^{-1})^{15-k}(-3b)^k =$
$$-1680 \cdot 3^{13}b^{11} + 60 \cdot 3^{14}b^{13} - 3^{15}b^{15}$$

32 $(s - 2t^3)^{12}$; last three terms $= \sum_{k=10}^{12} \binom{12}{k}(s)^{12-k}(-2t^3)^k =$
$$67{,}584s^2 t^{30} - 24{,}576 s t^{33} + 4096 t^{36}$$

Note: For the following exercises, the general formula for the

$\underline{k\text{th term of } (a+b)^n}$ is $\binom{n}{k-1}(a)^{n-(k-1)}(b)^{k-1} = \boxed{\binom{n}{k-1}(a)^{n-k+1}(b)^{k-1}}$.

33 $\left(\dfrac{3}{c} + \dfrac{c^2}{4}\right)^7$; sixth term $= \binom{7}{5}\left(\dfrac{3}{c}\right)^2\left(\dfrac{c^2}{4}\right)^5 = 21\left(\dfrac{9}{c^2}\right)\left(\dfrac{c^{10}}{1024}\right) = \dfrac{189}{1024}c^8$

34 $(3a^2 - \sqrt{b})^9$; fifth term $= \binom{9}{4}(3a^2)^5(-\sqrt{b})^4 = 126(243a^{10})(b^2) = 30{,}618a^{10}b^2$

35 $(\frac{1}{3}u + 4v)^8$; seventh term $= \binom{8}{6}(\frac{1}{3}u)^2(4v)^6 = 28\left(\dfrac{u^2}{9}\right)(4096v^6) = \dfrac{114{,}688}{9}u^2 v^6$

36 $(3x^2 - y^3)^{10}$; fourth term $= \binom{10}{3}(3x^2)^7(-y^3)^3 = 120(3^7 x^{14})(-y^9) = -120 \cdot 3^7 x^{14} y^9$

37 $(x^{1/2} + y^{1/2})^8$; middle term $\{5\text{th term}\} = \binom{8}{4}(x^{1/2})^4(y^{1/2})^4 = 70x^2 y^2$

38 $(rs^2 + t)^7$; two middle terms $\{4\text{th and 5th terms}\} =$
$$\binom{7}{3}(rs^2)^4(t)^3 \text{ and } \binom{7}{4}(rs^2)^3(t)^4 = 35r^4 s^8 t^3 \text{ and } 35r^3 s^6 t^4$$

39 $(2y + x^2)^8$; term that contains x^{10} •

Consider only the variable x in the expansion: $(x^2)^{k-1} = x^{10} \Rightarrow 2k - 2 = 10 \Rightarrow k = 6$;
$$6\text{th term} = \binom{8}{5}(2y)^3(x^2)^5 = 448y^3 x^{10}$$

40 $(x^2 - 2y^3)^5$; term that contains y^6 •

Consider only the variable y in the expansion: $(y^3)^{k-1} = y^6 \Rightarrow 3k - 3 = 6 \Rightarrow k = 3$;
$$3\text{rd term} = \binom{5}{2}(x^2)^3(-2y^3)^2 = 40x^6 y^6$$

41 $(3b^3 - 2a^2)^4$; term that contains b^9 •

Consider only the variable b in the expansion:
$$(b^3)^{4-k+1} = b^9 \Rightarrow 15 - 3k = 9 \Rightarrow k = 2; 2\text{nd term} = \binom{4}{1}(3b^3)^3(-2a^2)^1 = -216b^9 a^2$$

42 $(\sqrt{c} + \sqrt{d})^8$; term that contains c^2 •

Consider only the variable c in the expansion:
$$(c^{1/2})^{8-k+1} = c^2 \Rightarrow \tfrac{9}{2} - \tfrac{1}{2}k = 2 \Rightarrow k = 5; 5\text{th term} = \binom{8}{4}(\sqrt{c})^4(\sqrt{d})^4 = 70c^2 d^2$$

43 $\left(3x - \dfrac{1}{4x}\right)^6$; term that does not contain x •

Consider only the variable x in the expansion:
$$x^{6-k+1}(x^{-1})^{k-1} = x^0 \Rightarrow x^{8-2k} = x^0 \Rightarrow k = 4; 4\text{th term} = \binom{6}{3}(3x)^3\left(-\dfrac{1}{4x}\right)^3 = -\dfrac{135}{16}$$

[44] $(xy - 3y^{-3})^8$; term that does not contain y • Consider only the variable y in the expansion: $y^{8-k+1}(y^{-3})^{k-1} = y^0 \Rightarrow y^{12-4k} = y^0 \Rightarrow k = 3$;

$$3\text{rd term} = \binom{8}{2}(xy)^6(-3y^{-3})^2 = 252x^6$$

[45] $\sum_{k=0}^{2}\binom{10}{k}(1)^{10-k}(0.2)^k = 1 + 2 + 1.8 = 4.8$; calculator result for $(1.2)^{10} \approx 6.19$

[46] $\sum_{k=0}^{2}\binom{4}{k}(1)^{4-k}(-0.1)^k = 1 - 0.4 + 0.06 = 0.66$; calculator result for $(0.9)^4 = 0.6561$

[47] $\dfrac{(x+h)^4 - x^4}{h} = \dfrac{(x^4 + 4x^3h + 6x^2h^2 + 4xh^3 + h^4) - x^4}{h} = \dfrac{h(4x^3 + 6x^2h + 4xh^2 + h^3)}{h} =$

$$4x^3 + 6x^2h + 4xh^2 + h^3$$

[48] $\dfrac{(x+h)^5 - x^5}{h} = \dfrac{(x^5 + 5x^4h + 10x^3h^2 + 10x^2h^3 + 5xh^4 + h^5) - x^5}{h} =$

$$\dfrac{h(5x^4 + 10x^3h + 10x^2h^2 + 5xh^3 + h^4)}{h} = 5x^4 + 10x^3h + 10x^2h^2 + 5xh^3 + h^4$$

[49] $\binom{n}{1} = \dfrac{n!}{(n-1)!\,1!} = n$ and $\binom{n}{n-1} = \dfrac{n!}{[n-(n-1)]!\,(n-1)!} = \dfrac{n!}{1!\,(n-1)!} = n$

[50] $\binom{n}{0} = \dfrac{n!}{(n-0)!\,0!} = \dfrac{n!}{n!} = 1$ and $\binom{n}{n} = \dfrac{n!}{(n-n)!\,n!} = \dfrac{n!}{0!\,n!} = 1$

9.6 Exercises

[1] $P(7, 3) = \dfrac{7!}{4!} = 7 \cdot 6 \cdot 5 = 210$

[2] $P(8, 5) = \dfrac{8!}{3!} = 8 \cdot 7 \cdot 6 \cdot 5 \cdot 4 = 6720$

[3] $P(9, 6) = \dfrac{9!}{3!} = 9 \cdot 8 \cdot 7 \cdot 6 \cdot 5 \cdot 4 = 60{,}480$

[4] $P(5, 3) = \dfrac{5!}{2!} = 5 \cdot 4 \cdot 3 = 60$

[5] $P(5, 5) = \dfrac{5!}{0!} = 5 \cdot 4 \cdot 3 \cdot 2 \cdot 1 = 120$

[6] $P(4, 4) = \dfrac{4!}{0!} = 4 \cdot 3 \cdot 2 \cdot 1 = 24$

[7] $P(6, 1) = \dfrac{6!}{5!} = 6$

[8] $P(5, 1) = \dfrac{5!}{4!} = 5$

[9] (a) $5 \cdot 4 \cdot 3 = 60$

(b) $5 \cdot 5 \cdot 5 = 125$

[10] (a) $5 \cdot 4 \cdot 3 \cdot 2 = 120$

(b) $5 \cdot 5 \cdot 5 \cdot 5 = 625$

[11] There are 4 one digit numbers; $4 \cdot 3 = 12$ two digit numbers;

$4 \cdot 3 \cdot 2 = 24$ three digit numbers; $4 \cdot 3 \cdot 2 \cdot 1 = 24$ four digit numbers.

Total is $4 + 12 + 24 + 24 = 64$.

[12] As in Exercise 11, 4; 4^2; 4^3; 4^4. Total is $4 + 16 + 64 + 256 = 340$.

[13] $P(8, 3) = \dfrac{8!}{5!} = 8 \cdot 7 \cdot 6 = 336$

[14] $P(12, 3) = \dfrac{12!}{9!} = 12 \cdot 11 \cdot 10 = 1320$

[15] By the fundamental counting principle, $4 \cdot 6 = 24$.

[16] By the fundamental counting principle, $4 \cdot 6 \cdot 3 = 72$.

[17] (a) $26 \cdot 9 \cdot 10^4 = 2{,}340{,}000$

(b) $24 \cdot 9 \cdot 10^4 = 2{,}160{,}000$

18 $6 \cdot 6 = 36$ ways (a) 2 & 1 or 1 & 2, 2 ways to equal 3

(b) 4 & 1 twice, 3 & 2 twice, 4 ways to equal 5

(c) 6 & 1 twice, 5 & 2 twice, 4 & 3 twice, 6 ways to equal 7

(d) 5 & 4 twice, 6 & 3 twice, 4 ways to equal 9

(e) 6 & 5 twice, 2 ways to equal 11

19 (a) $P(10, 6) = \frac{10!}{4!} = 10 \cdot 9 \cdot 8 \cdot 7 \cdot 6 \cdot 5 = 151,200$

(b) Boy-girl: $6 \cdot 4 \cdot 5 \cdot 3 \cdot 4 \cdot 2 = 2880$. Girl-boy: $4 \cdot 6 \cdot 3 \cdot 5 \cdot 2 \cdot 4 = 2880$.

Total $= 2880 + 2880 = 5760$

20 Picking (in order) the $\underline{\text{M}}$ath, $\underline{\text{E}}$nglish, and $\underline{\text{H}}$istory class, we obtain:

$\underline{\text{M @ 8}}$, E-9, H-11, 2, 3; E-10, H-11, 2, 3; E-1, H-11, 2, 3; E-2, H-11, 3. $\{11 \text{ ways}\}$

$\underline{\text{M @ 10}}$, E-9, H-8, 11, 2, 3; E-1, H-8, 11, 2, 3; E-2, H-8, 11, 3. $\{11 \text{ ways}\}$

$\underline{\text{M @ 11}}$, E-9, H-8, 2, 3; E-10, H-8, 2, 3; E-1, H-8, 2, 3; E-2, H-8, 3. $\{11 \text{ ways}\}$

$\underline{\text{M @ 2}}$, E-9, H-8, 11, 3; E-10, H-8, 11, 3; E-1, H-8, 11, 3. $\{9 \text{ ways}, 42 \text{ total}\}$

21 2 times itself 10 times $= 2^{10} = 1024$ **22** 5 times itself 6 times $= 5^6 = 15,625$

23 $P(8, 8) = \frac{8!}{0!} = 8! = 40,320$ **24** $P(10, 10) = \frac{10!}{0!} = 10! = 3,628,800$

25 $P(6, 3) = \frac{6!}{3!} = 6 \cdot 5 \cdot 4 = 120$

26 $P(12, 5) = \frac{12!}{7!} = 12 \cdot 11 \cdot 10 \cdot 9 \cdot 8 = 95,040$

27 (a) The number of choices for each letter are: $\underline{2} \cdot \underline{25} \cdot \underline{24} \cdot \underline{23} = 27,600$

(b) The number of choices for each letter are: $\underline{2} \cdot \underline{26} \cdot \underline{26} \cdot \underline{26} = 35,152$

28 (a) $P(24, 3) = \frac{24!}{21!} = 24 \cdot 23 \cdot 22 = 12,144$ (b) $24 \cdot 24 \cdot 24 = 13,824$

29 $9 \cdot 10^6 = 9,000,000$

30 There are 7 spots to fill. $P(7, 7) = \frac{7!}{0!} = 7! = 5040$

31 $P(4, 4) = \frac{4!}{0!} = 4! = 24$

32 Suppose the "2" is repeated. There are 4! ways to arrange 2_a, 2_b, 7, and 9.

Since 2_a, 2_b, 7, 9 and 2_b, 2_a, 7, 9 are not distinguishable permutations, we divide

4! by 2. Since there are 3 numbers to repeat, the total number of trials is $3 \cdot \frac{4!}{2} = 36$.

33 There are 3! ways to choose the couples and 2 ways for each couple to sit. $3! \cdot 2^3 = 48$

34 $P(10, 3) = \frac{10!}{7!} = 10 \cdot 9 \cdot 8 = 720$ **35** $P(10, 10) = \frac{10!}{0!} = 10! = 3,628,800$

36 (a) $52! \approx 8.07 \times 10^{67}$

(b) The aces can be arranged in 4! ways and the other 48 cards can be arranged in

48! ways. Total number of arrangements $= 4! \cdot 48! \approx 2.98 \times 10^{62}$

37 (a) There are 9 choices for the first digit, 10 for the second, 10 for the third,

and 1 for the fourth and fifth. $9 \cdot 10 \cdot 10 \cdot 1 \cdot 1 = 900$

(b) If n is even, we need to select the first $\frac{n}{2}$ digits. $9 \cdot 10^{(n/2) - 1}$

If n is odd, we need to select the first $\frac{n+1}{2}$ digits. $9 \cdot 10^{(n-1)/2}$

38 There are 10 choices for the first square and 9 choices for each successive square.

$$10 \cdot 9^5 = 590{,}490$$

39 (a) There is a horizontal asymptote of $y = 1$.

(b) $\dfrac{n! \, e^n}{n^n \sqrt{2\pi n}} \approx 1 \Rightarrow n! \approx \dfrac{n^n \sqrt{2\pi n}}{e^n}$.

Example: $50! \approx \dfrac{50^{50} \sqrt{2\pi(50)}}{e^{50}} \approx 3.0363 \times 10^{64}$.

The actual value is closer to 3.0414×10^{64}.

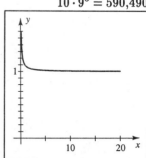

Figure 39

40 (a) Most calculators will give an error message since they can only deal with numbers the size of 10^n, where n is a 2-digit number. Looking ahead to part (b), we see that there is a 3-digit number in the exponent.

(b) $P(150, 50) = 10^r \Rightarrow r = \log P(150, 50) = \log \dfrac{150!}{(150 - 50)!} = \log \dfrac{150!}{100!} =$

$\log 150! - \log 100! \approx \left[(150 \ln 150 - 150) - (100 \ln 100 - 100)\right]/\ln 10 \approx 104.7$.

Thus, $P(150, 50) \approx 10^{104.7}$.

9.7 Exercises

1 $C(7, 3) = \dfrac{7!}{4! \, 3!} = 35$

2 $C(8, 4) = \dfrac{8!}{4! \, 4!} = 70$

3 $C(9, 8) = \dfrac{9!}{1! \, 8!} = 9$

4 $C(6, 2) = \dfrac{6!}{4! \, 2!} = 15$

5 $C(n, n - 1) = \dfrac{n!}{[n - (n - 1)]! \, (n - 1)!} = \dfrac{n!}{1! \, (n - 1)!} = n$

6 $C(n, 1) = \dfrac{n!}{(n - 1)! \, 1!} = n$

7 $C(7, 0) = \dfrac{7!}{7! \, 0!} = 1$

8 $C(5, 5) = \dfrac{5!}{5! \, 0!} = 1$

9 $\dfrac{(5 + 3 + 2 + 2)!}{5! \, 3! \, 2! \, 2!} = \dfrac{12!}{5! \, 3! \, 2! \, 2!} = 166{,}320$

10 $\dfrac{(3 + 3 + 3 + 3)!}{3! \, 3! \, 3! \, 3!} = \dfrac{12!}{(3!)^4} = 369{,}600$

11 There are 3 e's, 2 o's, and 2 k's. $\dfrac{10!}{3! \, 2! \, 2! \, 1! \, 1! \, 1!} = 151{,}200$

12 $\dfrac{4!}{2! \, 1! \, 1!} = 12$;

moon, mono, mnoo, nmoo, nomo, noom, oomn, oonm, omon, omno, onom, onmo

[13] There are $C(10, 5)$ ways to pick the first team.

   The second team is determined once the first team is selected. $C(10, 5) = 252$

[14] (a) $C(10, 6) = 210$ (b) The student needs to answer 4 of the last 8. $C(8, 4) = 70$

[15] Two points determine a unique line. $C(8, 2) = 28$

[16] Three points determine a unique triangle. $C(8, 3) = 56$

[17] There are 3! ways to order the categories. $(5! \cdot 4! \cdot 8!) \cdot 3! \doteq 696{,}729{,}600$

[18] (a) $C(12, 5) = 792$ (b) $C(2, 1) \cdot C(10, 4) = 420$

[19] Pick the center, $C(3, 1)$; two guards, $C(10, 2)$;

   two tackles from the 8 remaining linemen, $C(8, 2)$; two ends, $C(4, 2)$;

   two halfbacks, $C(6, 2)$; the quarterback, $C(3, 1)$; and the fullback, $C(4, 1)$.

$$3 \cdot C(10, 2) \cdot C(8, 2) \cdot C(4, 2) \cdot C(6, 2) \cdot 3 \cdot 4 = 4{,}082{,}400$$

[20] There would be 7! orderings if the keys were in a row.

   Since the keys are on a ring, any unique ordering can be shifted to 7 different

   positions and would be counted as only 1 ordering. $\frac{7!}{7} = 6! = 720$

[21] There are $C(12, 3)$ ways to pick the men and $C(8, 2)$ ways to pick the women.

$$C(12, 3) \cdot C(8, 2) = 6160$$

[22] If we thought of 6 positions for birth order, the girls could be selected $C(6, 3)$ ways to

   be put in those positions and the boys would fill the remaining positions.

$$C(6, 3) = 20$$

[23] We need 3 U's out of 8 moves. $C(8, 3) = 56$

[24] We need 6 U's out of 15 moves. $C(15, 6) = 5005$

[25] (a) $C(49, 6) = 13{,}983{,}816$ (b) $C(24, 6) = 134{,}596$

[26] There are $C(10, 2) = 45$ ways to pick the two faculty members to share an office.

   There are 9! ways to pick the offices. $C(10, 2) \cdot 9! = 16{,}329{,}600$

[27] Let n denote the number of players. $C(n, 2) = 45 \Rightarrow \dfrac{n!}{(n-2)!\,2!} = 45 \Rightarrow$

$$n(n-1) = 90 \Rightarrow (n-10)(n+9) = 0 \Rightarrow \{\,n > 0\,\}\ n = 10.$$

[28] (a) There are 2 answers for each question. $2^{20} = 1{,}048{,}576$

   (b) Select the 10 questions to be answered correctly. $C(20, 10) = 184{,}756$

[29] Each team must win 3 of the first 6 games for the series to be extended to a

   7th game. $C(6, 3) = 20$

[30] (a) Select 3 of the vertices to form a triangle. $C(8, 3) = 56$

   (b) Select 4 of the vertices to form a quadrilateral. $C(8, 4) = 70$

[31] They may have computed $C(31, 3)$, which is 4495.

32 Consider each condiment as either being *on* or *off*. Hence, there are 2 choices for each condiment and $2^8 = 256$ possible combinations. Alternatively, we could calculate $\sum_{k=0}^{8}\binom{8}{k}$, which is also 256.

33 (a) $S_1 = \binom{1}{1} + \binom{1}{3} + \binom{1}{5} + \cdots = 1 + 0 + 0 + \cdots = 1.$

$S_2 = \binom{2}{1} + \binom{2}{3} + \binom{2}{5} + \cdots = 2 + 0 + 0 + \cdots = 2.$

$S_3 = 3 + 1 + 0 + \cdots = 4.$ $S_4 = 4 + 4 + 0 + \cdots = 8.$

$S_5 = 16, S_6 = 32, S_7 = 64, S_8 = 128, S_9 = 256, S_{10} = 512.$

(b) It appears that $S_n = 2^{n-1}$.

34 (a) $S_1 = 1$ and $S_n = 0$ for $n = 2, 3, 4, \ldots, 10$.

(b) $S_1 = 1$ and $S_n = 0$ for $n > 1$.

35 (a) Graph the values of $C(10, 1), C(10, 2), C(10, 3), \ldots, C(10, 10)$.

(b) The maximum value of $C(10, r)$ is 252 and occurs at $r = 5$.

[0, 10] by [0, 300]   [0, 13] by [0, 2000]

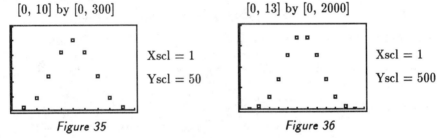

Xscl = 1   Xscl = 1

Yscl = 50   Yscl = 500

Figure 35   *Figure 36*

36 (a) Graph the values of $C(13, 1), C(13, 2), C(13, 3), \ldots, C(13, 13)$.

(b) The maximum value of $C(13, r)$ is 1716 and occurs at $r = 6, 7$.

37 (a) Graph the values of $C(19, 1), C(19, 2), C(19, 3), \ldots, C(19, 19)$.

(b) The maximum value of $C(19, r)$ is 92,378 and occurs at $r = 9, 10$.

[0, 19] by [0, 1×10^5]   [0, 20] by [0, 2×10^5]

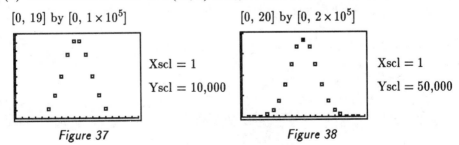

Xscl = 1   Xscl = 1

Yscl = 10,000   Yscl = 50,000

Figure 37   *Figure 38*

38 (a) Graph the values of $C(20, 1), C(20, 2), C(20, 3), \ldots, C(20, 20)$.

(b) The maximum value of $C(20, r)$ is 184,756 and occurs at $r = 10$.

9.8 Exercises

1 (a) $\frac{4}{52} = \frac{1}{13}$ (b) $\frac{4}{52} + \frac{4}{52} = \frac{8}{52} = \frac{2}{13}$ (c) $\frac{4}{52} + \frac{4}{52} + \frac{4}{52} = \frac{12}{52} = \frac{3}{13}$

2 (a) $\frac{13}{52} = \frac{1}{4}$ (b) $\frac{13}{52} + \frac{13}{52} = \frac{26}{52} = \frac{1}{2}$ (c) $\frac{13}{52} + \frac{13}{52} + \frac{13}{52} = \frac{39}{52} = \frac{3}{4}$

3 (a) $\frac{1}{6}$ (b) $\frac{1}{6}$ (c) $\frac{1}{6} + \frac{1}{6} = \frac{2}{6} = \frac{1}{3}$ 4 (a) $\frac{3}{6}$ (b) $\frac{1}{6}$ (c) $\frac{3}{6} + \frac{1}{6} = \frac{4}{6} = \frac{2}{3}$

5 $n(S) = 5 + 6 + 4 = 15$ (a) $\frac{5}{15} = \frac{1}{3}$ (b) $\frac{6}{15} = \frac{2}{5}$ (c) $\frac{5}{15} + \frac{4}{15} = \frac{9}{15} = \frac{3}{5}$

6 $n(S) = 5 + 6 + 4 = 15$ (a) $\frac{4}{15}$ (b) $\frac{6}{15} + \frac{4}{15} = \frac{10}{15} = \frac{2}{3}$ (c) $1 - \frac{6}{15} = \frac{9}{15} = \frac{3}{5}$

7 *Note:* The following table summarizes the results for the sum of two dice being tossed. Notice the symmetry about the sum of 7 in the # of ways to obtain.

Sum of two dice	2	3	4	5	6	7	8	9	10	11	12
# of ways to obtain	1	2	3	4	5	6	5	4	3	2	1

(a) $\frac{2}{36} = \frac{1}{18}$ (b) $\frac{5}{36}$ (c) $\frac{2}{36} + \frac{5}{36} = \frac{7}{36}$

8 (a) $P(10) + P(11) + P(12) = \frac{3}{36} + \frac{2}{36} + \frac{1}{36} = \frac{6}{36} = \frac{1}{6}$

(b) $P(3) + P(5) + P(7) + P(9) + P(11) = \frac{2}{36} + \frac{4}{36} + \frac{6}{36} + \frac{4}{36} + \frac{2}{36} = \frac{18}{36} = \frac{1}{2}$

9 There are 6 ways to make a sum of 5 (3 with 1, 1, 3 and 3 with 1, 2, 2). $\frac{6}{216} = \frac{1}{36}$

10 We must have a 6, not a 6, and not a 6.

There are $3(1 \cdot 5 \cdot 5) = 75$ ways this can occur. $\frac{75}{216} = \frac{25}{72}$

11 There are 3 ways to pick one tail in 3 coins. $\frac{3}{2^3} = \frac{3}{8}$

12 There are $C(4, 2)$ ways to obtain two heads from 4 coins. $\frac{C(4, 2)}{2^4} = \frac{6}{16} = \frac{3}{8}$

Note: For Exercises 13–18, there are $C(52, 5) = 2,598,960$ ways to draw 5 cards.

13 There are 13 denominations to pick from and any one of them could be combined with any one of the remaining 48 cards. $\frac{48 \cdot 13}{C(52, 5)} = \frac{1}{4165} \approx 0.00024$

14 Pick the 3 aces from 4, $C(4, 3)$, and the 2 kings from 4, $C(4, 2)$.

$$\frac{C(4, 3) \cdot C(4, 2)}{C(52, 5)} = \frac{1}{108,290} \approx 0.00000923$$

15 Pick 4 of the 13 diamonds and 1 of the 13 spades.

$$\frac{C(13, 4) \cdot C(13, 1)}{C(52, 5)} = \frac{143}{39,984} \approx 0.00358$$

16 Pick 5 of the 12 face cards. $\frac{C(12, 5)}{C(52, 5)} = \frac{33}{108,290} \approx 0.000305$

17 Pick 5 of the 13 cards in one suit. There are 4 suits. $\frac{C(13, 5) \cdot 4}{C(52, 5)} = \frac{33}{16,660} \approx 0.00198$

18 There are 4 of these hands, one in each suit. $\frac{4}{C(52, 5)} = \frac{1}{649,740} \approx 0.00000154$

19 Let E_1 be the event that the number is odd, E_2 that the number is prime.

$E_1 = \{1, 3, 5\}$ and $E_2 = \{2, 3, 5\}$.

$$P(E_1 \cup E_2) = P(E_1) + P(E_2) - P(E_1 \cap E_2) = \frac{3}{6} + \frac{3}{6} - \frac{2}{6} = \frac{4}{6} = \frac{2}{3}.$$

20 Let E_1 be the event that the card is red, E_2 that the card is a face card.

$$P(E_1 \cup E_2) = P(E_1) + P(E_2) - P(E_1 \cap E_2) = \tfrac{26}{52} + \tfrac{12}{52} - \tfrac{6}{52} = \tfrac{32}{52} = \tfrac{8}{13}.$$

21 $1 - 0.326 = 0.674.$ $(0.674)^4 \approx 0.2064$

22 $P(\text{at least } 1) = 1 - P(\text{none}) = 1 - (0.1)^2 = 0.99$

23 (a) $P(E_2) = P(2) + P(3) + P(4) = 0.10 + 0.15 + 0.20 = 0.45$

(b) $P(E_1 \cap E_2) = P(2) = 0.10$

(c) $P(E_1 \cup E_2) = P(E_1) + P(E_2) - P(E_1 \cap E_2) = 0.35 + 0.45 - 0.10 = 0.70$

(d) $P(E_2 \cup E_3') = P(E_2) + P(E_3') - P(E_2 \cap E_3').$ $E_3' = \{1, 2, 3, 5\}$ and

$$E_2 \cap E_3' = \{2, 3\} \Rightarrow P(E_2 \cup E_3') = 0.45 + 0.75 - 0.25 = 0.95.$$

24 (a) $P(E_2) = P(3) + P(4) = 0.15 + 0.20 = 0.35$

(b) $P(E_1 \cap E_2) = P(3) = 0.15$

(c) $P(E_1 \cup E_2) = P(E_1) + P(E_2) - P(E_1 \cap E_2) = 0.55 + 0.35 - 0.15 = 0.75$

(d) $P(E_2 \cup E_3') = P(E_2) + P(E_3') - P(E_2 \cap E_3').$ $E_3' = \{1, 2, 3\}$ and

$$E_2 \cap E_3' = \{3\} \Rightarrow P(E_2 \cup E_3') = 0.35 + 0.50 - 0.15 = 0.70.$$

Note: For Exercises 25–26, there are $C(60, 5) = 5{,}461{,}512$ ways to draw 5 chips.

25 (a) We want 5 blue and 0 non-blue. $\dfrac{C(20, 5) \cdot C(40, 0)}{C(60, 5)} = \dfrac{34}{11{,}977} \approx 0.0028.$

(b) $P(\text{at least 1 green}) = 1 - P(\text{no green}) =$

$$1 - \frac{C(30, 0) \cdot C(30, 5)}{C(60, 5)} = 1 - \frac{117}{4484} = \frac{4367}{4484} \approx 0.9739.$$

(c) $P(\text{at most 1 red}) = P(0 \text{ red}) + P(1 \text{ red}) =$

$$\frac{C(10, 0) \cdot C(50, 5)}{C(60, 5)} + \frac{C(10, 1) \cdot C(50, 4)}{C(60, 5)} = \frac{26{,}320}{32{,}509} \approx 0.8096.$$

26 (a) We want 4 green and 1 non-green. $\dfrac{C(30, 4) \cdot C(30, 1)}{C(60, 5)} = \dfrac{675}{4484} \approx 0.1505.$

(b) This event is the complement of part (c) in the previous exercise.

$$P(\text{at least 2 red}) = 1 - P(\text{at most 1 red}) \approx 1 - 0.8096 = 0.1904.$$

(c) $P(\text{at most 2 blue}) = P(0 \text{ blue}) + P(1 \text{ blue}) + P(2 \text{ blue}) =$

$$\frac{C(20, 0) \cdot C(40, 5)}{C(60, 5)} + \frac{C(20, 1) \cdot C(40, 4)}{C(60, 5)} + \frac{C(20, 2) \cdot C(40, 3)}{C(60, 5)} = \frac{181{,}792}{227{,}563} \approx 0.7989.$$

27 (a) $\dfrac{C(8, 8)}{2^8} = \dfrac{1}{256} \approx 0.00391$ (b) $\dfrac{C(8, 7)}{2^8} = \dfrac{1}{32} = 0.03125$

(c) $\dfrac{C(8, 6)}{2^8} = \dfrac{7}{64} = 0.109375$ (d) $\dfrac{C(8, 6) + C(8, 7) + C(8, 8)}{2^8} = \dfrac{37}{256} \approx 0.14453$

28 $\dfrac{C(8, 3) \cdot C(14, 3)}{C(22, 6)} = \dfrac{2912}{10{,}659} \approx 0.2732$

29 $1 - P(\text{no aces}) = 1 - \dfrac{C(48, 5)}{C(52, 5)} = 1 - \dfrac{35{,}673}{54{,}145} = \dfrac{18{,}472}{54{,}145} \approx 0.34116$

30 $P(\text{at least 1 heart}) = 1 - P(\text{no hearts}) =$

$$1 - \frac{C(13, 0) \cdot C(39, 5)}{C(52, 5)} = 1 - \frac{27{,}417}{123{,}760} = 1 - \frac{2109}{9520} = \frac{7411}{9520} \approx 0.7785$$

31 (a) We may use ordered pairs to represent the outcomes of the sample space S of the experiment. A representative outcome is (nine of clubs, 3). The number of outcomes in the sample space S is $n(S) = 52 \cdot 6 = 312$.

(b) For each integer k, where $2 \le k \le 6$, there are 4 ways to obtain an outcome of the form (k, k) since there are 4 suits. Because there are 5 values of k, $n(E_1) = 5 \cdot 4 = 20$. $n(E_1') = n(S) - n(E_1) = 312 - 20 = 292$.

$$P(E_1) = \frac{n(E_1)}{n(S)} = \frac{20}{312} = \frac{5}{78}.$$

(c) No, if E_2 or E_3 occurs, then the other event may occur.

Yes, the occurrence of either E_2 or E_3 has no effect on the other event.

$$P(E_2) = \frac{n(E_2)}{n(S)} = \frac{12 \cdot 6}{312} = \frac{72}{312} = \frac{3}{13}. \qquad P(E_3) = \frac{n(E_3)}{n(S)} = \frac{52 \cdot 3}{312} = \frac{156}{312} = \frac{1}{2}.$$

Since E_2 and E_3 are indep., $P(E_2 \cap E_3) = P(E_2) \cdot P(E_3) = \frac{3}{13} \cdot \frac{1}{2} = \frac{3}{26} = \frac{36}{312}$.

$P(E_2 \cup E_3) = P(E_2) + P(E_3) - P(E_2 \cap E_3) = \frac{72}{312} + \frac{156}{312} - \frac{36}{312} = \frac{192}{312} = \frac{8}{13}$.

(d) Yes, if E_1 or E_2 occurs, then the other event cannot occur. No,

the occurrence of either E_1 or E_2 influences the occurrence of the other event.

Remember, (non-empty) *mutually exclusive events* ***cannot*** *be independent events*.

Since E_1 and E_2 are mutually exclusive, $P(E_1 \cap E_2) = 0$ and

$$P(E_1 \cup E_2) = P(E_1) + P(E_2) = \frac{20}{312} + \frac{72}{312} = \frac{92}{312} = \frac{23}{78}.$$

32 (a) A representative outcome of the sample space S of the experiment is C7.

The number of outcomes in the sample space S is $n(S) = 26 \cdot 10 = 260$.

(b) The digits 1, 2, 3, 4, 5, and 6 can be matched with 3 letters each. For example, A1, K1, and U1 are the outcomes with 1 as the selected digit. The digits 7, 8, 9, and 0 can be matched with 2 letters each. Thus, $n(E_1) = 6 \cdot 3 + 4 \cdot 2 = 26$. This answer makes sense because each letter can be paired with exactly one digit.

$n(E_1') = n(S) - n(E_1) = 260 - 26 = 234.$ $\qquad P(E_1) = \dfrac{n(E_1)}{n(S)} = \dfrac{26}{260} = \dfrac{1}{10}.$

(c) No, if E_2 or E_3 occurs, then the other event may occur.

Yes, the occurrence of either E_2 or E_3 has no effect on the other event.

$$P(E_2) = \frac{n(E_2)}{n(S)} = \frac{5 \cdot 10}{260} = \frac{50}{260} = \frac{5}{26}. \qquad P(E_3) = \frac{n(E_3)}{n(S)} = \frac{26 \cdot 4}{260} = \frac{104}{260} = \frac{2}{5}.$$

Since E_2 and E_3 are indep., $P(E_2 \cap E_3) = P(E_2) \cdot P(E_3) = \frac{5}{26} \cdot \frac{2}{5} = \frac{1}{13} = \frac{20}{260}$.

$P(E_2 \cup E_3) = P(E_2) + P(E_3) - P(E_2 \cap E_3) = \frac{50}{260} + \frac{104}{260} - \frac{20}{260} = \frac{134}{260} = \frac{67}{130}$.

(d) The numerical values of the five vowels are: A-1, E-5, I-9, O-15, U-21. Since if E_2 or E_4 occurs, the other event cannot occur, the events are mutually exclusive. No, the occurrence of either E_2 or E_4 influences the occurrence of the other event. Remember, (non-empty) *mutually exclusive events* **cannot** *be independent events.* Since E_2 and E_4 are mutually exclusive, $P(E_2 \cap E_4) = 0$.

$$P(E_4) = \frac{n(E_4)}{n(S)} = \frac{13 \cdot 10}{260} = \frac{130}{260} = \frac{1}{2}. \text{ Since } E_2 \text{ and } E_4 \text{ are mutually exclusive,}$$

$$P(E_2 \cup E_4) = P(E_2) + P(E_4) = \frac{50}{260} + \frac{130}{260} = \frac{180}{260} = \frac{9}{13}.$$

33 Let k denote the sum.

$$P(k > 5) = 1 - P(k \le 5) = 1 - \left(\frac{1}{36} + \frac{2}{36} + \frac{3}{36} + \frac{4}{36}\right) = 1 - \frac{10}{36} = \frac{26}{36} = \frac{13}{18}.$$

34 There is 1 way to obtain a sum of 18 (6, 6, 6), 3 ways for a sum of 17 (6, 6, 5; 6, 5, 6; 5, 6, 6) , and 6 ways for a sum of 16 (3 with 6, 5, 5 and 3 with 6, 6, 4). Let k denote the sum.

$$P(k < 16) = 1 - P(k \ge 16) = 1 - \left(\frac{6}{216} + \frac{3}{216} + \frac{1}{216}\right) = 1 - \frac{10}{216} = \frac{206}{216} = \frac{103}{108} \approx 0.9537.$$

35 (a) $\frac{1}{2} \cdot \frac{1}{2} \cdot \frac{1}{2} \cdot \frac{1}{2} \cdot \frac{1}{2} = \frac{1}{32} = 0.03125$ (b) $1 - \frac{1}{32} = \frac{31}{32} = 0.96875$

36 $\frac{5}{20} \cdot \frac{4}{20} \cdot \frac{2}{20} = \frac{40}{8000} = \frac{1}{200} = 0.005$

37 (a) $\frac{C(4, 4)}{4!} = \frac{1}{24} \approx 0.04167$ (b) $\frac{C(4, 2)}{4!} = \frac{1}{4} = 0.25$

38 (a) There is 1 chance in 216 that all three dice show the same value and there are six different values. $6 \cdot \frac{1}{216} = \frac{6}{216} = \frac{1}{36} = 0.02\overline{7}$

(b) After the first value is chosen, the second value could be one of 5 others, and third could be one of 4 others. $\frac{P(6, 3)}{6^3} = \frac{120}{216} = \frac{5}{9} = 0.\overline{5}$

(c) Same number of dots: $6\left(\frac{1}{6^n}\right) = \frac{1}{6^{n-1}}$ for $n \ge 1$

Dots all different: $\frac{P(6, n)}{6^n}$ for $n \le 6$ and 0 for $n > 6$

39 (a) The 3, 4, or 5 on the left die would need to combine with a 4, 3, or 2 on the right die to sum to 7, but the right die only has 1, 5, or 6. The probability is 0.

(b) To obtain 8, we would need a 3 on the left die and a 5 on the right.

$$\frac{1}{3} \cdot \frac{1}{3} = \frac{1}{9} = 0.\overline{1}$$

40 There is 1 way to obtain a sum of 3, 3 ways for a sum of 4 (1, 1, 2; 1, 2, 1; 2, 1, 1), 6 ways for a sum of 5 (3 with 1, 1, 3 and 3 with 1, 2, 2), and 10 ways for a sum of 6 (3 with 1, 1, 4; 6 with 1, 2, 3; 1 with 2, 2, 2). $\frac{1}{729} + \frac{3}{729} + \frac{6}{729} + \frac{10}{729} = \frac{20}{729} \approx 0.0274$

41 (a) $P = \frac{179{,}820 + 151{,}322}{418{,}890} = \frac{331{,}142}{418{,}890} \approx 0.791$

(b) $P = \frac{418{,}890 - 84{,}475}{418{,}890} = \frac{334{,}415}{418{,}890} \approx 0.798$

42 (a) $P = \dfrac{60.4 + 18.3}{8.2 + 60.4 + 18.3} = \dfrac{78.7}{86.9} \approx 0.906$

(b) $P = \dfrac{8.2}{86.9} \approx 0.094$, or by using the complement of part (a), $1 - 0.906 = 0.094$.

43 (a) The ball must take 4 "lefts". $\frac{1}{2} \cdot \frac{1}{2} \cdot \frac{1}{2} \cdot \frac{1}{2} = \frac{1}{16} = 0.0625$

(b) We need two "lefts". $\dfrac{C(4,\,2)}{2^4} = \dfrac{6}{16} = \dfrac{3}{8} = 0.375$

44 (a) There are 18 black slots. $\frac{18}{38} = \frac{9}{19} \approx 0.4737$ (b) $\left(\frac{18}{38}\right)^2 = \frac{81}{361} \approx 0.2244$

45 For one ticket, $P(E) = \dfrac{n(E)}{n(S)} = \dfrac{C(6,\,6)}{C(54,\,6)} = \dfrac{1}{25{,}827{,}165}$.

For two tickets, $P(E) = \dfrac{2 \times 1}{25{,}827{,}165}$, or about 1 chance in 13 million.

46 $P(\text{match } 5) = \dfrac{C(6,\,5) \times C(48,\,1)}{C(54,\,6)} = \dfrac{6 \times 48}{25{,}827{,}165} = \dfrac{288}{25{,}827{,}165}$.

$P(\text{match } 4) = \dfrac{C(6,\,4) \times C(48,\,2)}{C(54,\,6)} = \dfrac{15 \times 1128}{25{,}827{,}165} = \dfrac{16{,}920}{25{,}827{,}165}$.

$P(\text{win}) = P(\text{match 4, 5, or 6}) = \dfrac{288}{25{,}827{,}165} + \dfrac{16{,}920}{25{,}827{,}165} + \dfrac{1}{25{,}827{,}165} = \dfrac{17{,}209}{25{,}827{,}165} \approx$

0.000666 (about 1 chance in 1500).

47 The probability that the first bulb is not defective is $\frac{195}{200}$ since 195 of the 200 bulbs are not defective. If the first bulb is not replaced and not defective, then there are 199 bulbs left, and 194 of them are not defective. The probability that the second bulb is not defective is then $\frac{194}{199}$. Thus, the probability that both bulbs are not defective is $\frac{195}{200} \times \frac{194}{199} = \frac{37{,}830}{39{,}800} \approx 0.9505$. The event that either light bulb is defective is the complement of the event that neither bulb is defective. The probability that the sample will be rejected is $1 - \frac{37{,}830}{39{,}800} = \frac{1970}{39{,}800} \approx 0.0495$.

48 (a) Let E_1 denote the event that the man is alive 10 years from now and E_2 that the woman is alive in 10 years. Since their life expectancies are unrelated, they are independent events. Thus, $P(E_1 \cap E_2) = P(E_1) \cdot P(E_2) = 0.74 \times 0.94 = 0.6956$.

(b) The probability that the man will be dead in 10 years is $1 - 0.74 = 0.26$ and the probability for the woman is $1 - 0.94 = 0.06$. Since their life expectancies are independent events, the probability that both of them will be dead in 10 years is $0.26 \times 0.06 = 0.0156$.

(c) Using the complement of part (b), we have $1 - 0.0156 = 0.9844$.

49 (a) $P(7 \text{ or } 11) = P(7) + P(11) = \frac{6}{36} + \frac{2}{36} = \frac{8}{36}$

(b) To win with a 4 on the first roll, we must first get a 4, and then get another 4 before a 7. The probability of getting a 4 is $\frac{3}{36}$. The probability of getting another 4 before a 7 is $\frac{3}{3+6}$ since there are 3 ways to get a 4, 6 ways to get a 7, and numbers other than 4 and 7 are immaterial.

Thus, $P(\text{winning with } 4) = \frac{3}{36} \cdot \frac{3}{3+6} = \frac{1}{36}$.

(c) Let $P(k)$ denote the probability of winning a pass line bet with the number k.

We first note that $P(4) = P(10)$, $P(5) = P(9)$, and $P(6) = P(8)$.

$P(\text{winning}) = 2 \cdot P(4) + 2 \cdot P(5) + 2 \cdot P(6) + P(7) + P(11)$

$= 2 \cdot \frac{3}{36} \cdot \frac{3}{3+6} + 2 \cdot \frac{4}{36} \cdot \frac{4}{4+6} + 2 \cdot \frac{5}{36} \cdot \frac{5}{5+6} + \frac{6}{36} + \frac{2}{36}$

$= 2 \cdot \frac{1}{36} + 2 \cdot \frac{2}{45} + 2 \cdot \frac{25}{396} + \frac{1}{6} + \frac{1}{18} = \frac{488}{990} = \frac{244}{495} \approx 0.4929$

50 Using the same notation as in Exercise 49, and the additional facts that $P(2) = P(12)$ and $P(3) = P(11)$,

$P(\text{winning}) = 2 \cdot P(2) + 2 \cdot P(3) + 2 \cdot P(4) + 2 \cdot P(5) + 2 \cdot P(6) + P(7)$

$= 2 \cdot \frac{1}{36} \cdot \frac{1}{1+6} + 2 \cdot \frac{2}{36} \cdot \frac{2}{2+6} + 2 \cdot \frac{3}{36} \cdot \frac{3}{3+6} + 2 \cdot \frac{4}{36} \cdot \frac{4}{4+6} + 2 \cdot \frac{5}{36} \cdot \frac{5}{5+6} + \frac{6}{36}$

$= \frac{2}{36}(\frac{1}{7} + \frac{4}{8} + \frac{9}{9} + \frac{16}{10} + \frac{25}{11} + 3) = \frac{1}{18} \cdot \frac{6557}{770} = \frac{6557}{13,860} \approx 0.4731$.

Note that this probability is almost 2% less than the one for the game of craps.

51 (a) $p = P((S_1 \cap S_2) \cup (S_3 \cap S_4))$

$= P(S_1 \cap S_2) + P(S_3 \cap S_4) - P((S_1 \cap S_2) \cap (S_3 \cap S_4))$

$= P(S_1) \cdot P(S_2) + P(S_3) \cdot P(S_4) - P(S_1 \cap S_2) \cdot P(S_3 \cap S_4)$

$= P(S_1) \cdot P(S_2) + P(S_3) \cdot P(S_4) - P(S_1) \cdot P(S_2) \cdot P(S_3) \cdot P(S_4)$

Let $P(S_k) = x$. Then $p = x \cdot x + x \cdot x - x \cdot x \cdot x \cdot x = -x^4 + 2x^2$.

$x = 0.9 \Rightarrow p = 0.9639$.

[-2.25, 2.25] by [-2, 1]

[0.96, 1.05] by [-0.03, 0.04]

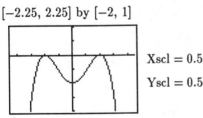

Xscl = 0.5
Yscl = 0.5

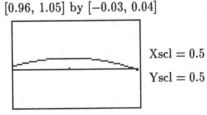

Xscl = 0.5
Yscl = 0.5

Figure 51(a)

Figure 51(b)

(b) $p = 0.99 \Rightarrow -x^4 + 2x^2 = 0.99$. The graph of $y = -x^4 + 2x^2 - 0.99$ is shown in Figure 51(a). The region near $x = 1$ is enlarged in Figure 51(b) to show that the graph is above the x-axis for some values of x. The approximate x-intercepts are ± 0.95, ± 1.05. Since $0 \le P(S_k) \le 1$, $P(S_k) = 0.95$.

52 (a) $p = P((S_1 \cup S_2) \cup (S_3 \cap S_4))$

$\qquad = P(S_1 \cup S_2) + P(S_3 \cap S_4) - P((S_1 \cup S_2) \cap (S_3 \cap S_4))$

$\qquad = P(S_1 \cup S_2) + P(S_3 \cap S_4) - P(S_1 \cup S_2) \cdot P(S_3 \cap S_4)$

Let $P(S_k) = x$. Then $P(S_1 \cup S_2) = P(S_1) + P(S_2) - P(S_1 \cap S_2) =$

$\qquad\qquad\qquad P(S_1) + P(S_2) - P(S_1) \cdot P(S_2) = x + x - x \cdot x = 2x - x^2.$

Also, $P(S_3 \cap S_4) = P(S_3) \cdot P(S_4) = x \cdot x = x^2.$

$\qquad$ Thus, $p = (2x - x^2) + x^2 - (2x - x^2)x^2 = x^4 - 2x^3 + 2x.$ $\;\; x = 0.9 \Rightarrow p = 0.9981.$

(b) $p = 0.99 \Rightarrow x^4 - 2x^3 + 2x = 0.99$. Graph $\qquad$ [−4.5, 4.5] by [−3, 3]

$y = x^4 - 2x^3 + 2x - 0.99$. The approximate

x-intercepts are -1.00 and 0.82. Since $\qquad\qquad\qquad\qquad$ Xscl = 1

$0 \le P(S_k) \le 1$, $P(S_k) = 0.82$. Note that $\qquad\qquad\qquad\qquad$ Yscl = 1

lowering the individual probability from

0.90 to approximately 0.82 *only* lowers the $\qquad\qquad$ Figure 52

system probability from 0.9981 to approximately 0.99.

53 (a) The number of ways that n people can all have a different birthday is $P(365, n)$.

The number of outcomes in the sample space is 365^n.

$$\text{Thus, } p = \frac{P(365, n)}{365^n} = \frac{365!}{365^n(365 - n)!}.$$

(b) $n = 32 \Rightarrow p = \dfrac{365!}{365^{32}\,333!} \Rightarrow \ln p = \ln \dfrac{365!}{365^{32}\,333!} =$

$\ln 365! - \ln 365^{32} - \ln 333! \approx (365 \ln 365 - 365) - (32 \ln 365) - (333 \ln 333 - 333) \approx$

$-1.45.$ Thus, $p \approx e^{-1.45} \approx 0.24.$

$\qquad$ The probability that two or more people have the same birthday is $1 - p \approx 0.76$.

54 $p = \dfrac{365!}{365^n(365 - n)!} \Rightarrow \ln p = \ln 365! - n \ln 365 - \ln(365 - n)! \Rightarrow$

$\ln p \approx (365 \ln 365 - 365) - n \ln 365 - \big[(365 - n) \ln(365 - n) - (365 - n)\big].$

To find the value of n such that $\ln p = \ln 0.5$, we graph

$\quad y = (365 \ln 365 - 365) - x \ln 365 - \big[(365 - x) \ln(365 - x) - (365 - x)\big] - \ln 0.5$

and estimate the positive x-intercept. $\qquad\qquad$ [0, 50] by [−1, 1]

From the graph, we see that this occurs at

$x \approx 22.26.$ Thus, if $n = 23$, the probability $\qquad\qquad\qquad\qquad$ Xscl = 10

of everyone having a different birthday $\qquad\qquad\qquad\qquad$ Yscl = 0.5

is less than $\frac{1}{2}$. The following (n, p) pairs

may be of interest: (30, 0.294), (40, 0.109), $\qquad\qquad$ Figure 54

(50, 0.030), (60, 0.006).

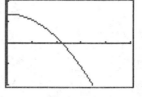

55 From Exercise 49(c), the payoff amount of \$2 has a probability of $\frac{244}{495}$.

Hence, $EV = 2 \cdot \frac{244}{495} = \frac{488}{495} \approx \$0.986$, or about \$0.99.

56 From Exercise 44(a), the payoff amount of \$2 has a probability of $\frac{18}{38}$.

Hence, $EV = 2 \cdot \frac{18}{38} = \frac{18}{19} \approx \$0.947$, or about \$0.95.

57 $EV = 1,000,000 \cdot \frac{1}{20,000,000} + 100,000 \cdot \frac{10}{20,000,000} + 10,000 \cdot \frac{100}{20,000,000} + 1000 \cdot \frac{1000}{20,000,000}$

$= \$0.20$ { less than the cost of a first class stamp }

58 $EV = 1000 \cdot \frac{1}{80} + 500 \cdot \frac{1}{80} + 300 \cdot \frac{1}{80} + 200 \cdot \frac{1}{80} + 100 \cdot 6 \cdot \frac{1}{80} = \$32.50$

Chapter 9 Review Exercises

1 $a_n = \dfrac{5n}{3 - 2n^2}$ ★ $5, -2, -1, -\frac{20}{29}; -\frac{7}{19}$

2 $a_n = (-1)^{n+1} - (0.1)^n$ ★ $0.9, -1.01, 0.999, -1.0001; 0.9999999$

3 $a_n = 1 + (-\frac{1}{2})^{n-1}$ ★ $2, \frac{1}{2}, \frac{5}{4}, \frac{7}{8}; \frac{65}{64}$

4 $a_n = \dfrac{2^n}{(n+1)(n+2)(n+3)}$ ★ $\frac{1}{12}, \frac{1}{15}, \frac{1}{15}, \frac{8}{105}; \frac{8}{45}$

5 $a_1 = 10, a_{k+1} = 1 + (1/a_k)$ ★ $10, \frac{11}{10}, \frac{21}{11}, \frac{32}{21}, \frac{53}{32}$

6 $a_1 = 2, a_{k+1} = a_k!$ ★ $2, 2, 2, 2, 2$

7 $a_1 = 9, a_{k+1} = \sqrt{a_k}$ ★ $9, 3, \sqrt{3}, \sqrt[4]{3}, \sqrt[8]{3}$

8 $a_1 = 1, a_{k+1} = (1 + a_k)^{-1}$ ★ $1, \frac{1}{2}, \frac{2}{3}, \frac{3}{5}, \frac{5}{8}$

9 $\displaystyle\sum_{k=1}^{5} (k^2 + 4) = 5 + 8 + 13 + 20 + 29 = 75$

10 $\displaystyle\sum_{k=2}^{6} \frac{2k-8}{k-1} = (-4) + (-1) + 0 + \frac{1}{2} + \frac{4}{5} = -\frac{37}{10}$

11 $\displaystyle\sum_{k=7}^{100} 10 = (100 - 7 + 1)(10) = 94(10) = 940$

12 $\displaystyle\sum_{k=1}^{4} (2^k - 10) = (-8) + (-6) + (-2) + 6 = -10$

13 $3 + 6 + 9 + 12 + 15 = \displaystyle\sum_{n=1}^{5} 3n$

14 $4 + 2 + 1 + \frac{1}{2} + \frac{1}{4} + \frac{1}{8} = \displaystyle\sum_{n=1}^{6} 4(\tfrac{1}{2})^{n-1} = \displaystyle\sum_{n=1}^{6} 2^2(2^{-1})^{n-1} = \displaystyle\sum_{n=1}^{6} 2^2 2^{1-n} = \displaystyle\sum_{n=1}^{6} 2^{3-n}$

15 $\dfrac{1}{1 \cdot 2} + \dfrac{1}{2 \cdot 3} + \dfrac{1}{3 \cdot 4} + \cdots + \dfrac{1}{99 \cdot 100} = \displaystyle\sum_{n=1}^{99} \frac{1}{n(n+1)}$

16 $\dfrac{1}{1 \cdot 2 \cdot 3} + \dfrac{1}{2 \cdot 3 \cdot 4} + \dfrac{1}{3 \cdot 4 \cdot 5} + \cdots + \dfrac{1}{98 \cdot 99 \cdot 100} = \displaystyle\sum_{n=1}^{98} \frac{1}{n(n+1)(n+2)}$

17 $\frac{1}{2} + \frac{2}{5} + \frac{3}{8} + \frac{4}{11}$. The numerators increase by 1, the denominators by 3. $\displaystyle\sum_{n=1}^{4} \frac{n}{3n-1}$

18 $\frac{1}{4} + \frac{2}{9} + \frac{3}{14} + \frac{4}{19}$. The numerators increase by 1, the denominators by 5. $\displaystyle\sum_{n=1}^{4} \frac{n}{5n-1}$

19 $100 - 95 + 90 - 85 + 80 = \displaystyle\sum_{n=1}^{5} (-1)^{n+1}(105 - 5n)$

20 $1 - \frac{1}{2} + \frac{1}{3} - \frac{1}{4} + \frac{1}{5} - \frac{1}{6} + \frac{1}{7}$. The terms have alternating signs,

the numerator is 1, and the denominators increase by 1. $\displaystyle\sum_{n=1}^{7} (-1)^{n-1}\frac{1}{n}$

21 $a_0 + a_1 x^4 + a_2 x^8 + \cdots + a_{25} x^{100} = \displaystyle\sum_{n=0}^{25} a_n x^{4n}$

22 $a_0 + a_1 x^3 + a_2 x^6 + \cdots + a_{20} x^{60} = \displaystyle\sum_{n=0}^{20} a_n x^{3n}$

23 $1 - \frac{x^2}{2} + \frac{x^4}{4} - \frac{x^6}{6} + \cdots + (-1)^n \frac{x^{2n}}{2n}$. The pattern begins with the second term

and the general term is listed. $1 + \displaystyle\sum_{k=1}^{n} (-1)^k \frac{x^{2k}}{2k}$

24 $1 + x + \frac{x^2}{2} + \frac{x^3}{3} + \cdots + \frac{x^n}{n}$.

The pattern begins with the second term and the general term is listed. $1 + \displaystyle\sum_{k=1}^{n} \frac{x^k}{k}$

25 $d = 3 - (4 + \sqrt{3}) = -1 - \sqrt{3}$; $a_{10} = (4 + \sqrt{3}) + (9)(-1 - \sqrt{3}) = -5 - 8\sqrt{3}$;

$$S_{10} = \frac{10}{2}\left[(4 + \sqrt{3}) + (-5 - 8\sqrt{3})\right] = -5 - 35\sqrt{3}.$$

26 $a_4 = a_1 + 3d \Rightarrow 9 = a_1 - 15 \Rightarrow a_1 = 24$; $S_8 = \frac{8}{2}[2(24) + (8-1)(-5)] = 52$

27 $a_5 = 5$ and $a_{13} = 77 \Rightarrow 8d = 72 \Rightarrow d = 9$;

$$a_5 = a_1 + 4d \Rightarrow 5 = a_1 + 36 \Rightarrow a_1 = -31; a_{10} = -31 + 9(9) = 50$$

28 Four arithmetic means $\Rightarrow 5d = -10 - 20 \Rightarrow d = -6$.

The terms are 20, 14, 8, 2, -4, and -10.

29 $r = \dfrac{\frac{1}{4}}{\frac{1}{8}} = 2$; $a_n = \frac{1}{8}(2)^{n-1} = 2^{n-4} \Rightarrow a_{10} = 2^6 = 64$

30 $r = \frac{-0.3}{3} = -0.1$; $a_8 = a_3 r^5 = 3(-0.1)^5 = -0.00003$

31 The geometric mean of 4 and 8 is $\sqrt{4 \cdot 8} = \sqrt{32} = 4\sqrt{2}$.

32 $a_8 = a_1 r^7 \Rightarrow 100 = a_1(-\frac{3}{2})^7 \Rightarrow a_1 = 100(-\frac{2}{3})^7 = -\frac{12{,}800}{2187}$

33 $402 = \frac{12}{2}(a_1 + 50) \Rightarrow a_1 = 17$. $a_{12} = a_1 + 11d \Rightarrow d = (50 - 17)/11 = 3$.

34 $a_5 = a_1 r^4 \Rightarrow \frac{1}{16} = a_1(\frac{3}{2})^4 \Rightarrow a_1 = \frac{1}{81}$.

$$S_5 = \frac{1}{81} \cdot \frac{1 - (\frac{3}{2})^5}{1 - \frac{3}{2}} = \frac{1}{81} \cdot \frac{1 - \frac{243}{32}}{-\frac{1}{2}} = \frac{1}{81} \cdot \frac{-\frac{211}{32}}{-\frac{1}{2}} = \frac{211}{1296}.$$

35 The sequence of terms is arithmetic. $S_{15} = \frac{15}{2}(3 + 73) = 570$.

36 The sequence of terms is arithmetic. $S_{10} = \frac{10}{2}(5.5 + 1) = 32.5$.

$\boxed{37}$ $\displaystyle\sum_{k=1}^{10} (2^k - \tfrac{1}{2}) = \sum_{k=1}^{10} 2^k - \sum_{k=1}^{10} \tfrac{1}{2} = 2 \cdot \frac{1 - 2^{10}}{1 - 2} - 10(\tfrac{1}{2}) = 2046 - 5 = 2041$

$\boxed{38}$ $\displaystyle\sum_{k=1}^{8} (\tfrac{1}{2} - 2^k) = \sum_{k=1}^{8} \tfrac{1}{2} - \sum_{k=1}^{8} 2^k = 8(\tfrac{1}{2}) - 2 \cdot \frac{1 - 2^8}{1 - 2} = 4 - 510 = -506$

$\boxed{39}$ $a_1 = 1, \; r = -\tfrac{2}{5} \Rightarrow S = \dfrac{1}{1 - (-\frac{2}{5})} = \dfrac{1}{\frac{7}{5}} = \tfrac{5}{7}.$

$\boxed{40}$ $a_1 = 0.274, \; r = 0.001 \Rightarrow S = \dfrac{0.274}{1 - 0.001} = \dfrac{274}{999}. \quad 6.\overline{274} = 6 + \dfrac{274}{999} = \dfrac{6268}{999}$

$\boxed{41}$ (1) P_1 is true, since $3(1) - 1 = \dfrac{1[3(1) + 1]}{2} = 2.$

(2) Assume P_k is true: $2 + 5 + 8 + \cdots + (3k - 1) = \dfrac{k(3k + 1)}{2}.$ Hence,

$$2 + 5 + 8 + \cdots + (3k - 1) + 3(k + 1) - 1 = \frac{k(3k + 1)}{2} + 3(k + 1) - 1$$

$$= \frac{3k^2 + k + 6k + 4}{2}$$

$$= \frac{3k^2 + 7k + 4}{2}$$

$$= \frac{(k + 1)(3k + 4)}{2}$$

$$= \frac{(k + 1)[3(k + 1) + 1]}{2}.$$

Thus, P_{k+1} is true, and the proof is complete.

$\boxed{42}$ (1) P_1 is true, since $[2(1)]^2 = \dfrac{[2(1)][2(1) + 1][1 + 1]}{3} = 4.$

(2) Assume P_k is true: $2^2 + 4^2 + 6^2 + \cdots + (2k)^2 = \dfrac{(2k)(2k + 1)(k + 1)}{3}.$ Hence,

$$2^2 + 4^2 + 6^2 + \cdots + (2k)^2 + [2(k + 1)]^2 = \frac{(2k)(2k + 1)(k + 1)}{3} + [2(k + 1)]^2$$

$$= (k + 1)\left(\frac{4k^2 + 2k}{3} + \frac{12(k + 1)}{3}\right)$$

$$= \frac{(k + 1)(4k^2 + 14k + 12)}{3}$$

$$= \frac{2(k + 1)(2k + 3)(k + 2)}{3}.$$

Thus, P_{k+1} is true, and the proof is complete.

43 (1) P_1 is true, since $\dfrac{1}{[2(1)-1][2(1)+1]} = \dfrac{1}{2(1)+1} = \dfrac{1}{3}$.

(2) Assume P_k is true:

$$\frac{1}{1\cdot 3} + \frac{1}{3\cdot 5} + \frac{1}{5\cdot 7} + \cdots + \frac{1}{(2k-1)(2k+1)} = \frac{k}{2k+1}. \text{ Hence,}$$

$$\frac{1}{1\cdot 3} + \frac{1}{3\cdot 5} + \frac{1}{5\cdot 7} + \cdots + \frac{1}{(2k-1)(2k+1)} + \frac{1}{(2k+1)(2k+3)}$$

$$= \frac{k}{2k+1} + \frac{1}{(2k+1)(2k+3)}$$

$$= \frac{k(2k+3)+1}{(2k+1)(2k+3)}$$

$$= \frac{2k^2+3k+1}{(2k+1)(2k+3)}$$

$$= \frac{(2k+1)(k+1)}{(2k+1)(2k+3)}$$

$$= \frac{k+1}{2(k+1)+1}.$$

Thus, P_{k+1} is true, and the proof is complete.

44 (1) P_1 is true, since $1(1+1) = \dfrac{(1)\,(1+1)\,(1+2)}{3} = 2$.

(2) Assume P_k is true:

$$1\cdot 2 + 2\cdot 3 + 3\cdot 4 + \cdots + k(k+1) = \frac{k(k+1)(k+2)}{3}. \text{ Hence,}$$

$$1\cdot 2 + 2\cdot 3 + 3\cdot 4 + \cdots + k(k+1) + (k+1)(k+2)$$

$$= \frac{k(k+1)(k+2)}{3} + (k+1)(k+2)$$

$$= (k+1)(k+2)\left(\frac{k}{3}+1\right)$$

$$= \frac{(k+1)(k+2)(k+3)}{3}.$$

Thus, P_{k+1} is true, and the proof is complete.

45 (1) For $n=1$, $n^3+2n = 3$ and 3 is a factor of 3.

(2) Assume 3 is a factor of k^3+2k. The $(k+1)$st term is

$$(k+1)^3 + 2(k+1) = k^3 + 3k^2 + 5k + 3$$

$$= (k^3+2k) + (3k^2+3k+3)$$

$$= (k^3+2k) + 3(k^2+k+1).$$

By the induction hypothesis, 3 is a factor of k^3+2k and 3 is a factor of $3(k^2+k+1)$, so 3 is a factor of the $(k+1)$st term. Thus, P_{k+1} is true, and the proof is complete.

46 (1) P_5 is true, since $5^2 + 3 < 2^5$.

(2) Assume P_k is true: $k^2 + 3 < 2^k$. Hence, $(k+1)^2 + 3 = k^2 + 2k + 4 =$
$$(k^2 + 3) + (k+1) < 2^k + (k+1) < 2^k + 2^k = 2 \cdot 2^k = 2^{k+1}.$$

Thus, P_{k+1} is true, and the proof is complete.

47 For j: Examining the pattern formed by letting $n = 1, 2, 3, 4$ leads us to the

conclusion that $j = 4$.

(1) P_4 is true, since $2^4 \le 4!$.

(2) Assume P_k is true: $2^k \le k!$. Hence,
$$2^{k+1} = 2 \cdot 2^k \le 2 \cdot k! < (k+1) \cdot k! = (k+1)!.$$

Thus, P_{k+1} is true, and the proof is complete.

48 For j: $10^n \le n^n \Rightarrow \left(\frac{n}{10}\right)^n \ge 1$. This is true if $\frac{n}{10} \ge 1$ or $n \ge 10$. Thus, $j = 10$.

(1) P_{10} is true, since $10^{10} \le 10^{10}$.

(2) Assume P_k is true: $10^k \le k^k$. Hence,
$$10^{k+1} = 10 \cdot 10^k \le 10 \cdot k^k < (k+1) \cdot k^k < (k+1) \cdot (k+1)^k = (k+1)^{k+1}.$$

Thus, P_{k+1} is true, and the proof is complete.

49 $(x^2 - 3y)^6 = x^{12} - 18x^{10}y + 135x^8y^2 - 540x^6y^3 + 1215x^4y^4 - 1458x^2y^5 + 729y^6$

50 $(2a + b^3)^4 = (1)(2a)^4 + (4)(2a)^3(b^3)^1 + (6)(2a)^2(b^3)^2 + (4)(2a)(b^3)^3 + (1)(b^3)^4$
$$= 16a^4 + 32a^3b^3 + 24a^2b^6 + 8ab^9 + b^{12}$$

51 $(a^{2/5} + 2a^{-3/5})^{20}$; first three terms $= a^8 + 40a^7 + 760a^6$

52 $(b^3 - \frac{1}{2}c^2)^9$; sixth term $= \binom{9}{5}(b^3)^4(-\frac{1}{2}c^2)^5 = -\frac{63}{16}b^{12}c^{10}$

53 $(4a^2 - b)^7$; term that contains a^{10} •

Consider only the variable a in the expansion:
$$(a^2)^{7-k+1} = a^{10} \Rightarrow 16 - 2k = 10 \Rightarrow k = 3; \text{ 3rd term} = \binom{7}{2}(4a^2)^5(-b)^2 = 21{,}504a^{10}b^2$$

54 $(2c^3 + 5c^{-2})^{10}$; term that does not contain $c = 52{,}500{,}000$

55 (a) $S_5 = 10 \Rightarrow 10 = \frac{5}{2}(2a_1 + 4d) \Rightarrow 4 = 2a_1 + 4d \Rightarrow 4d = 4 - 2a_1 \Rightarrow$
$$d = 1 - \tfrac{1}{2}a_1. \text{ Since } a_1 \text{ is positive, } 1 - \tfrac{1}{2}a_1 \text{ is less than 1 ft.}$$

(b) $a_1 = \frac{1}{2} \Rightarrow d = 1 - \frac{1}{2}(\frac{1}{2}) = \frac{3}{4}$.

The lengths of the other four pieces are $1\frac{1}{4}$, 2, $2\frac{3}{4}$, and $3\frac{1}{2}$ ft.

56 $n = 16 \Rightarrow a_{16} = a_1 + 15d \Rightarrow 16 = 20 + 15d \Rightarrow d = -\frac{4}{15}$.
$$S_{16} = \tfrac{16}{2}\left[2(20) + 15(-\tfrac{4}{15})\right] = 8(40 - 4) = 288 \text{ in. or 24 ft.}$$

57 If $s_1 = 1$, then $s_2 = f$, $s_3 = f^2$, ...

The sum of the s_k's is $2(1 + f + f^2 + \cdots) = 2\left(\frac{1}{1-f}\right) = \frac{2}{1-f}$.

58 $\text{Time}_{\text{total}} = \text{Time}_{\text{down}} + \text{Time}_{\text{up}}$

$$= \left[\frac{\sqrt{10}}{4} + \frac{\sqrt{10 \cdot \frac{3}{4}}}{4} + \frac{\sqrt{10 \cdot (\frac{3}{4})^2}}{4} + \cdots \right] + \left[\frac{\sqrt{10 \cdot \frac{3}{4}}}{4} + \frac{\sqrt{10 \cdot (\frac{3}{4})^2}}{4} + \cdots \right]$$

$$= \frac{\sqrt{10}}{4} + 2 \left[\frac{\sqrt{10 \cdot \frac{3}{4}}}{4} + \frac{\sqrt{10 \cdot (\frac{3}{4})^2}}{4} + \cdots \right] = \frac{\sqrt{10}}{4} + 2 \cdot \frac{\sqrt{\frac{30}{4}}/4}{1 - \sqrt{\frac{3}{4}}} = \tfrac{1}{4}\sqrt{10} + 2 \cdot \frac{\sqrt{30}/8}{1 - \frac{1}{2}\sqrt{3}}$$

$$= \tfrac{1}{4}\sqrt{10} + \frac{\sqrt{30}}{2(2 - \sqrt{3})} \cdot \frac{2 + \sqrt{3}}{2 + \sqrt{3}} = \tfrac{1}{4}\sqrt{10} + (\sqrt{30} + \tfrac{3}{2}\sqrt{10}) = \tfrac{7}{4}\sqrt{10} + \sqrt{30} \approx 11.01 \text{ sec.}$$

59 (a) $P(52, 13) \approx 3.954 \times 10^{21}$

(b) $P(13, 5) \cdot P(13, 3) \cdot P(13, 3) \cdot P(13, 2) \approx 7.094 \times 10^{13}$

60 (a) $P(6, 4) = 360$ (b) $6^4 = 1296$

61 (a) $C(12, 8) = 495$ (b) $C(9, 5) = 126$

62 $\dfrac{(6 + 5 + 4 + 2)!}{6!\,5!\,4!\,2!} = \dfrac{17!}{6!\,5!\,4!\,2!} = 85{,}765{,}680$

63 There is one way to get all heads and one way to get all tails. (a) $\frac{2}{4} = \frac{1}{2}$ (b) $\frac{2}{8} = \frac{1}{4}$

64 (a) We need 4 of the 26 cards of one color. There are 2 colors.

$$\frac{P(26, 4) \cdot 2}{P(52, 4)} = \frac{92}{833} \approx 0.1104$$

(b) We need R-B-R-B. $\dfrac{26^2 \cdot 25^2}{P(52, 4)}$ or $\dfrac{26}{52} \cdot \dfrac{26}{51} \cdot \dfrac{25}{50} \cdot \dfrac{25}{49} = \dfrac{325}{4998} \approx 0.0650$

65 (a) $\frac{1}{1000}$ (b) $\frac{10}{1000} = \frac{1}{100}$ (c) $\frac{50}{1000} = \frac{1}{20}$

66 $\dfrac{C(4, 1)}{2^4} = \dfrac{4}{16} = \dfrac{1}{4} = 0.25$

67 (a) $\dfrac{C(6, 4) + C(6, 5) + C(6, 6)}{2^6} = \dfrac{15 + 6 + 1}{64} = \dfrac{22}{64} = \dfrac{11}{32}$ (b) $1 - \dfrac{22}{64} = \dfrac{42}{64}$

68 (a) $\frac{1}{6} \cdot \frac{1}{52} = \frac{1}{312} \approx 0.0032$

(b) $\frac{1}{6} + \frac{1}{52} - \frac{1}{312} = \dfrac{52 + 6 - 1}{312} = \dfrac{57}{312} = \dfrac{19}{104} \approx 0.1827$

69 $P(O \cup F) = P(O) + P(F) - P(O \cap F) = \dfrac{1000}{5000} + \dfrac{2000}{5000} - \dfrac{0.40(2000)}{5000} = \dfrac{2200}{5000} = 0.44$

70 There are 2 ways to obtain 10 (6, 4 and 4, 6), 2 ways for 11 (6, 5 and 5, 6), 1 way for 12, 16, 20, and 24 (double 3's, 4's, 5's, and 6's). $\dfrac{2 + 2 + 1 + 1 + 1 + 1}{36} = \dfrac{8}{36} = \dfrac{2}{9} = 0.\overline{2}$

$\boxed{71}$ The two teams, A and B, can play as few as 4 games or as many as 7 games.

$P(\text{team A wins in 4 games}) = (\frac{1}{2})^4 = \frac{1}{16} = 0.0625.$

$P(\text{team A wins in 5 games})$

$= P(\text{team A wins 3 of the first 4 games } \{\text{losing 1 game}\} \text{ and then wins game 5})$

$= \binom{4}{3}(\frac{1}{2})^3 \cdot (\frac{1}{2})^1 \cdot \frac{1}{2} = \binom{4}{3}(\frac{1}{2})^5 = \frac{4}{32} = 0.125.$ In a similar fashion,

$$P(\text{team A wins in 6 games}) = \binom{5}{3}(\frac{1}{2})^6 = \frac{10}{64} = \frac{5}{32} = 0.15625$$

and $\qquad P(\text{team A wins in 7 games}) = \binom{6}{3}(\frac{1}{2})^7 = \frac{20}{128} = \frac{5}{32} = 0.15625.$

Since the probabilities for team B winning the series are the same, the expected

number of games is $4(2 \cdot \frac{1}{16}) + 5(2 \cdot \frac{4}{32}) + 6(2 \cdot \frac{5}{32}) + 7(2 \cdot \frac{5}{32}) = 5\frac{13}{16} = 5.8125.$

Chapter 9 Discussion Exercises

$\boxed{1}$ The desired sequence starts with $2n$ for $n = 1, 2, 3, 4$. To obtain the fifth term, i.e.,

a, add $\dfrac{(n-1)(n-2)(n-3)(n-4)(a-10)}{4 \cdot 3 \cdot 2 \cdot 1}$, which is 0 for $n = 1, 2, 3, 4$ and

$(a - 10)$ for $n = 5$. $a_n = 2n + \dfrac{(n-1)(n-2)(n-3)(n-4)(a-10)}{24}$

Another possibility is $a_n = \begin{cases} 2n & \text{if } 1 \le n \le 4 \\ (n-4)a & \text{if } n \ge 5 \end{cases}$

$\boxed{2}$ Examining the graphs of $y_1 = x$ and $y_2 = (\ln x)^3$, we see that $y_1 = y_2 \Rightarrow x \approx 6.4$, 93.35. For large values of x, $y_1 \boxed{\ge} y_2$. The value of j is 94.

$\boxed{3}$ (a) Following the pattern from Exercises 37–38 in Section 9.4, write

$1^4 + 2^4 + 3^4 + \cdots + n^4 = an^5 + bn^4 + cn^3 + dn^2 + en$. Then, it follows that:

$n = 1 \Rightarrow a(1)^5 + b(1)^4 + c(1)^3 + d(1)^2 + e(1) = 1^4 \Rightarrow a + b + c + d + e = 1,$

$n = 2 \Rightarrow a(2)^5 + b(2)^4 + c(2)^3 + d(2)^2 + e(2) = 1^4 + 2^4 \Rightarrow$

$$32a + 16b + 8c + 4d + 2e = 17,$$

$n = 3 \Rightarrow a(3)^5 + b(3)^4 + c(3)^3 + d(3)^2 + e(3) = 1^4 + 2^4 + 3^4 \Rightarrow$

$$243a + 81b + 27c + 9d + 3e = 98,$$

$n = 4 \Rightarrow a(4)^5 + b(4)^4 + c(4)^3 + d(4)^2 + e(4) = 1^4 + 2^4 + 3^4 + 4^4 \Rightarrow$

$$1024a + 256b + 64c + 16d + 4e = 354,$$

$n = 5 \Rightarrow a(5)^5 + b(5)^4 + c(5)^3 + d(5)^2 + e(5) = 1^4 + 2^4 + 3^4 + 4^4 + 5^4 \Rightarrow$

$$3125a + 625b + 125c + 25d + 5e = 979.$$

$$AX = B \Rightarrow \begin{bmatrix} 1 & 1 & 1 & 1 & 1 \\ 32 & 16 & 8 & 4 & 2 \\ 243 & 81 & 27 & 9 & 3 \\ 1024 & 256 & 64 & 16 & 4 \\ 3125 & 625 & 125 & 25 & 5 \end{bmatrix} \begin{bmatrix} a \\ b \\ c \\ d \\ e \end{bmatrix} = \begin{bmatrix} 1 \\ 17 \\ 98 \\ 354 \\ 979 \end{bmatrix} \Rightarrow X = A^{-1}B = \begin{bmatrix} 1/5 \\ 1/2 \\ 1/3 \\ 0 \\ -1/30 \end{bmatrix}$$

Thus, $1^4 + 2^4 + 3^4 + \cdots + n^4 = \frac{1}{5}n^5 + \frac{1}{2}n^4 + \frac{1}{3}n^3 - \frac{1}{30}n.$

This formula must be verified.

(b) Let P_n be the statement that $1^4 + 2^4 + 3^4 + \cdots + n^4 = \frac{1}{5}n^5 + \frac{1}{2}n^4 + \frac{1}{3}n^3 - \frac{1}{30}n.$

(1) $1^4 = \frac{1}{5} + \frac{1}{2} + \frac{1}{3} - \frac{1}{30} = 1$ and P_1 is true.

(2) Assume that P_k is true. We must show that P_{k+1} is true.

$P_k \Rightarrow 1^4 + 2^4 + 3^4 + \cdots + k^4 = \frac{1}{5}k^5 + \frac{1}{2}k^4 + \frac{1}{3}k^3 - \frac{1}{30}k \Rightarrow$

$1^4 + 2^4 + 3^4 + \cdots + k^4 + (k+1)^4 = \frac{1}{5}k^5 + \frac{1}{2}k^4 + \frac{1}{3}k^3 - \frac{1}{30}k + (k+1)^4 \Rightarrow$

$1^4 + 2^4 + 3^4 + \cdots + k^4 + (k+1)^4 =$

$$\frac{1}{5}k^5 + \frac{1}{2}k^4 + \frac{1}{3}k^3 - \frac{1}{30}k + (k^4 + 4k^3 + 6k^2 + 4k + 1) \Rightarrow$$

$1^4 + 2^4 + 3^4 + \cdots + k^4 + (k+1)^4 = \frac{1}{5}k^5 + \frac{3}{2}k^4 + \frac{13}{3}k^3 + 6k^2 + \frac{119}{30}k + 1.$

$P_{k+1} \Rightarrow 1^4 + 2^4 + 3^4 + \cdots + k^4 + (k+1)^4$

$= \frac{1}{5}(k+1)^5 + \frac{1}{2}(k+1)^4 + \frac{1}{3}(k+1)^3 - \frac{1}{30}(k+1)$

$= \frac{1}{5}(k^5 + 5k^4 + 10k^3 + 10k^2 + 5k + 1) + \frac{1}{2}(k^4 + 4k^3 + 6k^2 + 4k + 1) +$

$$\frac{1}{3}(k^3 + 3k^2 + 3k + 1) - \frac{1}{30}(k+1)$$

$= \frac{1}{5}k^5 + \frac{3}{2}k^4 + \frac{13}{3}k^3 + 6k^2 + \frac{119}{30}k + 1.$ Thus, the formula is true for all n.

4 (a) Following the pattern of setting the sum equal to a polynomial of degree one higher than the power in the exercise we write

$2^3 + 4^3 + 6^3 + \cdots + (2n)^3 = an^4 + bn^3 + cn^2 + dn$. Then, it follows that:

$n = 1 \Rightarrow a(1)^4 + b(1)^3 + c(1)^2 + d(1) = 2^3 \Rightarrow a + b + c + d = 8$

$n = 2 \Rightarrow a(2)^4 + b(2)^3 + c(2)^2 + d(2) = 2^3 + 4^3 \Rightarrow 16a + 8b + 4c + 2d = 72$

$n = 3 \Rightarrow a(3)^4 + b(3)^3 + c(3)^2 + d(3) = 2^3 + 4^3 + 6^3 \Rightarrow 81a + 27b + 9c + 3d = 288$

$n = 4 \Rightarrow a(4)^4 + b(4)^3 + c(4)^2 + d(4) = 2^3 + 4^3 + 6^3 + 8^3 \Rightarrow$

$$256a + 64b + 16c + 4d = 800$$

$$AX = B \Rightarrow \begin{bmatrix} 1 & 1 & 1 & 1 \\ 16 & 8 & 4 & 2 \\ 81 & 27 & 9 & 3 \\ 256 & 64 & 16 & 4 \end{bmatrix} \begin{bmatrix} a \\ b \\ c \\ d \end{bmatrix} = \begin{bmatrix} 8 \\ 72 \\ 288 \\ 800 \end{bmatrix} \Rightarrow X = A^{-1}B = \begin{bmatrix} 2 \\ 4 \\ 2 \\ 0 \end{bmatrix}$$

$a = 2$, $b = 4$, $c = 2$, $d = 0 \Rightarrow 2^3 + 4^3 + 6^3 + \cdots + (2n)^3 = 2n^4 + 4n^3 + 2n^2$.

(b) Let P_n be the statement that $2^3 + 4^3 + 6^3 + \cdots + (2n)^3 = 2n^4 + 4n^3 + 2n^2$

(1) $2^3 = 2 + 4 + 2 = 8$ and P_1 is true.

(2) Assume that P_k is true. We must show that P_{k+1} is true.

$P_k \Rightarrow 2^3 + 4^3 + 6^3 + \cdots + (2k)^3 = 2k^4 + 4k^3 + 2k^2 \Rightarrow$

$2^3 + 4^3 + 6^3 + \cdots + (2k)^3 + (2k + 2)^3 = 2k^4 + 4k^3 + 2k^2 + (2k + 2)^3 =$

$$2k^4 + 12k^3 + 26k^2 + 24k + 8$$

$P_{k+1} \Rightarrow 2^3 + 4^3 + 6^3 + \cdots + (2k)^3 + (2k + 2)^3$

$= 2(k + 1)^4 + 4(k + 1)^3 + 2(k + 1)^2$

$= 2(k^4 + 4k^3 + 6k^2 + 4k + 1) + 4(k^3 + 3k^2 + 3k + 1) + 2(k^2 + 2k + 1)$

$= 2k^4 + 12k^3 + 26k^2 + 24k + 8$. Thus, the formula is true for all n.

5 Examine the number of digits in the exponent of the value in scientific notation. The TI-82/83 can compute 69!, but not 70!, since 70! is larger than a 2-digit exponent. The TI-85/86 can compute 449!, but not 450!, since 450! is larger than a 3-digit exponent.

6 The $(k + 1)$st coefficient ($k = 0, 1, 2, \ldots, n$) of the expansion of $(a + b)^n$, namely $\binom{n}{k}$, is the same as the number of k-element subsets of an n-element set.

7 There are $8 \times 36 = 288$ contestants daily and $288 \times 30 = 8640$ contestants for the month. The probability that a contestant wins any particular prize for the daily tournament and the monthly tournament is $p_1 = \frac{1}{288}$ and $p_2 = \frac{1}{8640}$, respectively. If the game is to be fair, then the total expected value should equal the entry fee. (cont.)

$EV_1(\text{daily}) = 250p_1 + 100p_1 + 50p_1 = 400p_1.$

$EV_2(\text{month}) = 4000p_2 + 2000p_2 + 1500p_2 + 1000p_2 + 800p_2 +$

$$600p_2 + 500p_2 + 400p_2 + 300p_2 + 200p_2 +$$

$$100(40p_2) + 75(50p_2) + 50(200p_2) + 25(200p_2) = 34{,}050p_2.$$

Thus, $EV_{\text{total}} = EV_1 + EV_2$

$$= 400p_1 + 34{,}050p_2 = 400 \cdot \tfrac{1}{288} + 34{,}050 \cdot \tfrac{1}{8640} = \tfrac{46{,}050}{8640} = \tfrac{1535}{288} \approx \$5.33.$$

8   To the nearest penny with $r = 1.1008163$ (found by trial and error), we have the places 1st–10th:

$0.01:	237.37	215.63	195.89	177.95	161.65	146.85	133.40	121.18	110.08	100
$1.00:	237.00	216.00	196.00	178.00	162.00	147.00	133.00	121.00	110.00	100
$5.00:	240.00	215.00	195.00	180.00	160.00	145.00	135.00	120.00	110.00	100
$10.00:	240.00	220.00	200.00	180.00	160.00	140.00	130.00	120.00	110.00	100

If the amounts are to be realistic, the amounts may not be rounded to the *nearest* amount—i.e, \$134 may be rounded to \$140 rather than \$130.

9   Since we can have 0 to 5 toppings on a pizza, the number of ways to order one pizza

is $\displaystyle\sum_{k=0}^{5} \binom{n}{k}$. Because there are two pizzas, we have $\left[\displaystyle\sum_{k=0}^{5} \binom{n}{k} \right]^2 = 1{,}048{,}576 \Rightarrow$

$\displaystyle\sum_{k=0}^{5} \binom{n}{k} = 1024.$ By trial and error, we find that $n = 11$.

On the TI-82/83, store 11 in N and use "sum(seq(N nCr R,R,0,5,1))" to obtain 1024.

10   (a) The pattern has a 1 in the denominator, an n in the numerator, and the next terms of any row of Pascal's triangle oscillate between denominator and numerator. The signs are in pairs (two positive, two negative, etc.). The power of $\tan x$ increases one with each term. Thus,

$$\tan 5x = \frac{5 \tan x - 10 \tan^3 x + \tan^5 x}{1 - 10 \tan^2 x + 5 \tan^4 x}.$$

(b) The coefficients listed in the text are in the form 1–2–1. The next identities are:

$\cos 3x = 1 \cos^3 x \qquad\qquad -3 \cos x \sin^2 x$

$\sin 3x = \qquad\quad 3 \cos^2 x \sin x \qquad\qquad -1 \sin^3 x$

$\cos 4x = 1 \cos^4 x \qquad\qquad -6 \cos^2 x \sin^2 x \qquad\qquad\qquad +1 \sin^4 x$

$\sin 4x = \qquad\quad 4 \cos^3 x \sin x \qquad\qquad -4 \cos x \sin^3 x$

Notice the pattern of coefficients: for $\cos 3x$ and $\sin 3x$ we have 1–3–3–1; for $\cos 4x$ and $\sin 4x$ we have 1–4–6–4–1. Since these are rows in Pascal's triangle, we predict the following pattern for $\cos 5x$ and $\sin 5x$ (1–5–10–10–5–1):

$\cos 5x = 1 \cos^5 x \qquad\qquad -10 \cos^3 x \sin^2 x \qquad\qquad +5 \cos x \sin^4 x$

$\sin 5x = \qquad\quad 5 \cos^4 x \sin x \qquad\qquad -10 \cos^2 x \sin^3 x \qquad\qquad +1 \sin^5 x$

Chapter 10: Topics from Analytic Geometry

Note: Let V, F, and l denote the vertex, focus, and directrix, respectively.

[1] $8y = x^2 \Rightarrow y = \frac{1}{8}x^2 \Rightarrow p = \frac{1}{4a} = \frac{1}{4(\frac{1}{8})} = \frac{1}{\frac{1}{2}} = 2$; $V(0, 0)$; $F(0, 2)$; l: $y = -2$

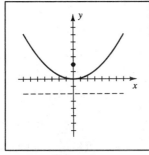

Figure 1

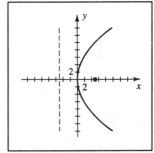

Figure 2

[2] $20x = y^2 \Rightarrow x = \frac{1}{20}y^2 \Rightarrow p = \frac{1}{4(\frac{1}{20})} = 5$; $V(0, 0)$; $F(5, 0)$; l: $x = -5$

[3] $2y^2 = -3x \Rightarrow (y - 0)^2 = -\frac{3}{2}(x - 0) \Rightarrow 4p = -\frac{3}{2} \Rightarrow p = -\frac{3}{8}$; $V(0, 0)$; $F(-\frac{3}{8}, 0)$; l: $x = \frac{3}{8}$

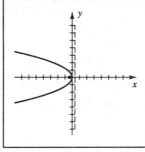

Figure 3

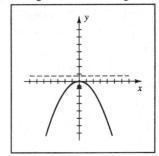

Figure 4

[4] $(x - 0)^2 = -3(y - 0) \Rightarrow 4p = -3 \Rightarrow p = -\frac{3}{4}$; $V(0, 0)$; $F(0, -\frac{3}{4})$; l: $y = \frac{3}{4}$

[5] $(x + 2)^2 = -8(y - 1) \Rightarrow 4p = -8 \Rightarrow p = -2$; $V(-2, 1)$; $F(-2, -1)$; l: $y = 3$

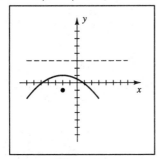

Figure 5

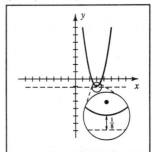

Figure 6

[6] $(x - 3)^2 = \frac{1}{2}(y + 1) \Rightarrow 4p = \frac{1}{2} \Rightarrow p = \frac{1}{8}$; $V(3, -1)$; $F(3, -\frac{7}{8})$; l: $y = -\frac{9}{8}$

7 $(y-2)^2 = \frac{1}{4}(x-3) \Rightarrow 4p = \frac{1}{4} \Rightarrow p = \frac{1}{16}$; $V(3,2)$; $F(\frac{49}{16}, 2)$; l: $x = \frac{47}{16}$

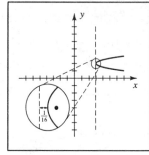

Figure 7

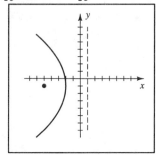

Figure 8

8 $(y+1)^2 = -12(x+2) \Rightarrow 4p = -12 \Rightarrow p = -3$; $V(-2,-1)$; $F(-5,-1)$; l: $x = 1$

9 $y = x^2 - 4x + 2 = (x^2 - 4x + \underline{4}) + 2 - \underline{4} \Rightarrow$

$$(y+2) = 1(x-2)^2 \Rightarrow 4p = 1 \Rightarrow p = \frac{1}{4};\ V(2,-2);\ F(2, -\tfrac{7}{4});\ l:\ y = -\tfrac{9}{4}$$

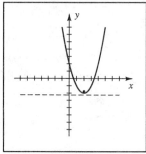

Figure 9

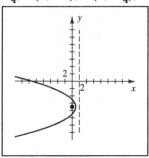

Figure 10

10 $y^2 + 14y + 4x + 45 = 0 \Rightarrow -4x = (y^2 + 14y + \underline{49}) + 45 - \underline{49} \Rightarrow$

$$-4x + 4 = (y+7)^2 \Rightarrow (y+7)^2 = -4(x-1) \Rightarrow 4p = -4 \Rightarrow p = -1;$$

$$V(1,-7);\ F(0,-7);\ l:\ x = 2$$

11 $x^2 + 20y = 10 \Rightarrow (x-0)^2 = -20(y - \frac{1}{2}) \Rightarrow 4p = -20 \Rightarrow p = -5;$

$$V(0, \tfrac{1}{2});\ F(0, -\tfrac{9}{2});\ l:\ y = \tfrac{11}{2}$$

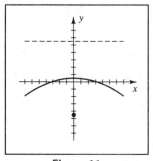

Figure 11

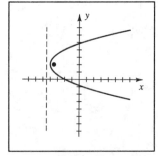

Figure 12

12 $y^2 - 4y - 2x - 4 = 0 \Rightarrow 2x = (y^2 - 4y + \underline{4}) - 4 - \underline{4} \Rightarrow$

$$2(x+4) = (y-2)^2 \Rightarrow 4p = 2 \Rightarrow p = \tfrac{1}{2};\ V(-4,2);\ F(-\tfrac{7}{2}, 2);\ l:\ x = -\tfrac{9}{2}$$

$\boxed{13}$ $V(1,\,0) \Rightarrow y^2 = 4p(x-1).$ $F(6,\,0) \Rightarrow y^2 = 4(6-1)(x-1) \Rightarrow y^2 = 20(x-1).$

$\boxed{14}$ $V(0,\,-2) \Rightarrow x^2 = 4p(y+2).$ $F(0,\,1) \Rightarrow x^2 = 4[1-(-2)](y+2) \Rightarrow x^2 = 12(y+2).$

$\boxed{15}$ $V(-2,\,3) \Rightarrow (x+2)^2 = 4p(y-3).$

$$x = 2,\, y = 2 \Rightarrow 16 = 4p(-1) \Rightarrow p = -4.\quad (x+2)^2 = -16(y-3).$$

$\boxed{16}$ $V(3,\,-2) \Rightarrow (y+2)^2 = 4p(x-3).$

$$x = 1,\, y = 0 \Rightarrow 4 = 4p(-2) \Rightarrow p = -\tfrac{1}{2}.\quad (y+2)^2 = -2(x-3).$$

$\boxed{17}$ $F(2,\,0)$ and $l\colon x = -2 \Rightarrow p = 2$ and $V(0,\,0).$ $(y-0)^2 = 4p(x-0) \Rightarrow y^2 = 8x.$

$\boxed{18}$ $F(0,\,-4)$ and $l\colon y = 4 \Rightarrow p = -4$ and $V(0,\,0).$ $(x-0)^2 = 4p(y-0) \Rightarrow x^2 = -16y.$

$\boxed{19}$ $F(6,\,4)$ and $l\colon y = -2 \Rightarrow p = 3$ and $V(6,\,1).$

$$(x-6)^2 = 4p(y-1) \Rightarrow (x-6)^2 = 12(y-1).$$

$\boxed{20}$ $F(-3,\,-2)$ and $l\colon y = 1 \Rightarrow p = -\tfrac{3}{2}$ and $V(-3,\,-\tfrac{1}{2}).$

$$(x+3)^2 = 4p(y+\tfrac{1}{2}) \Rightarrow (x+3)^2 = -6(y+\tfrac{1}{2}).$$

$\boxed{21}$ $V(3,\,-5)$ and $l\colon x = 2 \Rightarrow p = 1.$ $(y+5)^2 = 4p(x-3) \Rightarrow (y+5)^2 = 4(x-3).$

$\boxed{22}$ $V(-2,\,3)$ and $l\colon y = 5 \Rightarrow p = -2.$ $(x+2)^2 = 4p(y-3) \Rightarrow (x+2)^2 = -8(y-3).$

$\boxed{23}$ $V(-1,\,0)$ and $F(-4,\,0) \Rightarrow p = -3.$ $(y-0)^2 = 4p(x+1) \Rightarrow y^2 = -12(x+1).$

$\boxed{24}$ $V(1,\,-2)$ and $F(1,\,0) \Rightarrow p = 2.$ $(x-1)^2 = 4p(y+2) \Rightarrow (x-1)^2 = 8(y+2).$

$\boxed{25}$ The vertex at the origin and symmetric to the y-axis imply that the equation is of
the form $y = ax^2.$ Substituting $x = 2$ and $y = -3$ into that equation yields

$$-3 = a \cdot 4 \Rightarrow a = -\tfrac{3}{4}. \text{ Thus, an equation is } y = -\tfrac{3}{4}x^2, \text{ or } 3x^2 = -4y.$$

$\boxed{26}$ $y = ax^2 \Rightarrow 3 = a(6)^2 \Rightarrow a = \tfrac{1}{12}.$ $y = \tfrac{1}{12}x^2,$ or $12y = x^2.$

$\boxed{27}$ The vertex at $(-3,\,5)$ and axis parallel to the x-axis imply that the equation is of the
form $(y-5)^2 = 4p(x+3).$ Substituting $x = 5$ and $y = 9$ into that equation

yields $16 = 4p \cdot 8 \Rightarrow p = \tfrac{1}{2}.$ Thus, an equation is $(y-5)^2 = 2(x+3).$

$\boxed{28}$ $(y+2)^2 = 4p(x-3) \Rightarrow (1+2)^2 = 4p(0-3) \Rightarrow -\tfrac{9}{12} = p \Rightarrow (y+2)^2 = -3(x-3)$

$\boxed{29}$ $P(0,\,5)$ is the focus and $l\colon y = -3$ is the directrix.

The vertex V is halfway between them and is at $(0,\,1).$ $p = d(V,\,F) = 5-1 = 4.$

$$(x-h)^2 = 4p(y-k) \Rightarrow (x-0)^2 = 4(4)(y-1) \Rightarrow x^2 = 16(y-1)$$

$\boxed{30}$ $P(7,\,0)$ and $l\colon x = 1 \Rightarrow V(4,\,0).$ $p = 7-4 = 3 \Rightarrow y^2 = 4p(x-4) \Rightarrow y^2 = 12(x-4).$

$\boxed{31}$ $P(-6,\,3)$ and $l\colon x = -2 \Rightarrow V(-4,\,3).$

$$p = -6 - (-4) = -2 \Rightarrow (y-3)^2 = 4p(x+4) \Rightarrow (y-3)^2 = -8(x+4).$$

$\boxed{32}$ $P(5,\,-2)$ and $l\colon y = 4 \Rightarrow V(5,\,1).$

$$p = -2-1 = -3 \Rightarrow (x-5)^2 = 4p(y-1) \Rightarrow (x-5)^2 = -12(y-1).$$

Note: To find an equation for a lower or upper half, we need to solve for y (use $-$ or $+$ respectively). For the left or right half, solve for x (use $-$ or $+$ respectively).

33 $(y+1)^2 = x+3 \Rightarrow y+1 = \pm\sqrt{x+3} \Rightarrow y = -\sqrt{x+3}-1$

34 $(y-2)^2 = x-4 \Rightarrow y-2 = \pm\sqrt{x-4} \Rightarrow y = \sqrt{x-4}+2$

35 $(x+1)^2 = y-4 \Rightarrow x+1 = \pm\sqrt{y-4} \Rightarrow x = \sqrt{y-4}-1$

36 $(x+3)^2 = y+2 \Rightarrow x+3 = \pm\sqrt{y+2} \Rightarrow x = -\sqrt{y+2}-3$

37 The parabola has an equation of the form $y = ax^2 + bx + c$. Substituting the x and y values of $P(2, 5)$, $Q(-2, -3)$, and $R(1, 6)$ into this equation yields:

$$\begin{cases} 4a + 2b + c = 5 & P \;\; (E_1) \\ 4a - 2b + c = -3 & Q \;\; (E_2) \\ a + b + c = 6 & R \;\; (E_3) \end{cases}$$

Solving E_3 for c $\{c = 6 - a - b\}$ and substituting into E_1 and E_2 yields:

$$\begin{cases} 3a + b = -1 & (E_4) \\ 3a - 3b = -9 & (E_5) \end{cases}$$

$E_4 - E_5 \Rightarrow 4b = 8 \Rightarrow b = 2$; $a = -1$; $c = 5$. The equation is $y = -x^2 + 2x + 5$.

38 The parabola has an equation of the form $y = ax^2 + bx + c$. Substituting the x and y values of $P(3, -1)$, $Q(1, -7)$, and $R(-2, 14)$ into this equation yields:

$$\begin{cases} 9a + 3b + c = -1 & P \;\; (E_1) \\ a + b + c = -7 & Q \;\; (E_2) \\ 4a - 2b + c = 14 & R \;\; (E_3) \end{cases}$$

Solving E_2 for c $\{c = -7 - a - b\}$ and substituting into E_1 and E_3 yields:

$$\begin{cases} 8a + 2b = 6 & (E_4) \\ 3a - 3b = 21 & (E_5) \end{cases} \Rightarrow \begin{cases} 4a + b = 3 & (E_6) \\ a - b = 7 & (E_7) \end{cases}$$

$E_6 + E_7 \Rightarrow 5a = 10 \Rightarrow a = 2$; $b = -5$; $c = -4$. The equation is $y = 2x^2 - 5x - 4$.

39 The parabola has an equation of the form $x = ay^2 + by + c$. Substituting the x and y values of $P(-1, 1)$, $Q(11, -2)$, and $R(5, -1)$ into this equation yields:

$$\begin{cases} a + b + c = -1 & P \;\; (E_1) \\ 4a - 2b + c = 11 & Q \;\; (E_2) \\ a - b + c = 5 & R \;\; (E_3) \end{cases}$$

Solving E_3 for c $\{c = 5 - a + b\}$ and substituting into E_1 and E_2 yields:

$$\begin{cases} 2b = -6 & (E_4) \\ 3a - b = 6 & (E_5) \end{cases}$$

$E_4 \Rightarrow b = -3$; $a = 1$; $c = 1$. The equation is $x = y^2 - 3y + 1$.

40 The parabola has an equation of the form $x = ay^2 + by + c$. Substituting the x and y values of $P(2, 1)$, $Q(6, 2)$, and $R(12, -1)$ into this equation yields:

$$\begin{cases} a + b + c = 2 & P \;\; (E_1) \\ 4a + 2b + c = 6 & Q \;\; (E_2) \\ a - b + c = 12 & R \;\; (E_3) \end{cases}$$

(continued)

Solving E_3 for c $\{c = 12 - a + b\}$ and substituting into E_1 and E_2 yields:

$$\begin{cases} \quad\quad\; 2b = -10 \quad (E_4) \\ 3a + \;\; 3b = \;\; -6 \quad (E_5) \end{cases}$$

$E_4 \Rightarrow b = -5;\; a = 3;\; c = 4.$ The equation is $x = 3y^2 - 5y + 4.$

[41] A cross section is a parabola with $V(0,\, 0)$ and passing through $P(4,\, 1)$. We need to find the focus F. $y = ax^2 \Rightarrow 1 = a(4)^2 \Rightarrow a = \frac{1}{16}$. $p = 1/(4a) = 1/(\frac{1}{4}) = 4$.

The light will collect 4 inches from the center of the mirror.

[42] $y = ax^2 \Rightarrow 3 = a(5)^2 \Rightarrow a = \frac{3}{25}$. $p = 1/(4a) = 1/(\frac{12}{25}) = \frac{25}{12}$ ft.

[43] $y = ax^2 \Rightarrow 1 = a(\frac{3}{2})^2 \Rightarrow a = \frac{4}{9}$. $p = 1/(4a) = 1/(\frac{16}{9}) = \frac{9}{16}$ ft.

[44] $y = ax^2 \Rightarrow \frac{3}{4} = a(2)^2 \Rightarrow a = \frac{3}{16}$. $p = 1/(4a) = 1/(\frac{3}{4}) = \frac{4}{3}$ in.

[45] $a = 1/(4p) = 1/(4 \cdot 5) = \frac{1}{20}$. $y = ax^2 \; \{y = 2 \text{ ft}\} \Rightarrow 24 = \frac{1}{20}x^2 \Rightarrow x = \sqrt{480}$.

The width is twice the value of x. Width $= 2\sqrt{480} \approx 43.82$ in.

[46] $a = 1/(4p) = 1/(4 \cdot 9) = \frac{1}{36}$. $24 = \frac{1}{36}x^2 \Rightarrow x = \sqrt{864}$. Width $= 2\sqrt{864} \approx 58.79$ in.

[47] (a) Let the parabola have the equation $x^2 = 4py$.

Since the point $(r,\, h)$ is on the parabola, $r^2 = 4ph$ or $p = \dfrac{r^2}{4h}$.

(b) $p = 10$ and $h = 5 \Rightarrow r^2 = 4(10)(5) \Rightarrow r = 10\sqrt{2}$.

[48] Note that the value of p completely determines the parabola.

If $(x_1,\, y_1)$ is on the parabola, then $y_1^2 = 4p(x_1 + p) \Rightarrow 4p^2 + 4x_1 p - y_1^2 = 0 \Rightarrow$

$$p = \frac{-4x_1 \pm \sqrt{16x_1^2 + 16y_1^2}}{8} = \frac{-x_1 \pm \sqrt{x_1^2 + y_1^2}}{2}.$$

If $y_1 \neq 0$, then there are exactly two values for p and hence, exactly two parabolas.

[49] With $a = 125$ and $p = 50$, $S = \dfrac{8\pi p^2}{3}\left[\left(1 + \dfrac{a^2}{4p^2}\right)^{3/2} - 1\right] \approx 64{,}968$ ft^2.

[50] (a) From the figure we can see that the distance between Mars and the origin should be 58,000 miles. Thus, $p = 58{,}000$. $x = \frac{1}{4p}y^2 \Rightarrow x = \frac{1}{232{,}000}y^2$.

(b) Since $v = \sqrt{\dfrac{2k}{r}}$, the velocity of the satellite will be maximum when the distance r between the satellite and Mars is minimum. The minimum value of r is 58,000 miles, when the satellite is located at the vertex. First, convert r to meters. 58,000 mi $\times$ 1610 m/mi $\approx 9.34 \times 10^7$ m.

Thus, $v = \sqrt{\dfrac{2k}{r}} = \sqrt{\dfrac{2 \times 4.28 \times 10^{13}}{9.34 \times 10^7}} \approx 957$ m/sec.

(c) $y = 100{,}000 \Rightarrow x = \dfrac{100{,}000^2}{232{,}000} \approx 43{,}100.$ If the satellite is located at the point

(43,100, 100,000) and Mars is located at the point (58,000, 0), then

$r = \sqrt{(58{,}000 - 43{,}100)^2 + (100{,}000 - 0)^2} \approx 101{,}100 \text{ mi} \approx 1.63 \times 10^8 \text{ m}.$

$$\text{Thus, } v = \sqrt{\frac{2k}{r}} = \sqrt{\frac{2 \times 4.28 \times 10^{13}}{1.63 \times 10^8}} \approx 725 \text{ m/sec}.$$

51 Depending on the type of calculator or software used, we may need to solve for y in

terms of x. $x = -y^2 + 2y + 5 \Rightarrow y^2 - 2y + (x - 5) = 0.$ This is a quadratic equation

in y. Using the quadratic formula to solve for y yields

$$y = \frac{-(-2) \pm \sqrt{(-2)^2 - 4(1)(x - 5)}}{2(1)} = 1 \pm \sqrt{6 - x}.$$

[−11, 10] by [−7, 7]   [−11, 10] by [−7, 7]

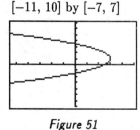

Xscl = 2

Yscl = 1

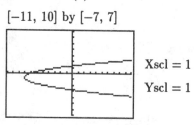

Xscl = 1

Yscl = 1

Figure 51   *Figure 52*

52 $x = 2y^2 + 3y - 7 \Rightarrow y = -\frac{3}{4} \pm \frac{1}{4}\sqrt{8x + 65}$

53 $x = y^2 + 1 \Rightarrow y = \pm\sqrt{x - 1}.$ From the graph, we can see that there are 2 points of

intersection. Their coordinates are approximately (2.08, −1.04) and (2.92, 1.38).

[−2, 4] by [−3, 3]   [−4, 4] by [−5, 3]

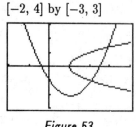

Xscl = 1

Yscl = 1

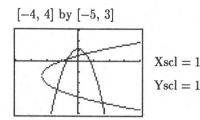

Xscl = 1

Yscl = 1

Figure 53   *Figure 54*

54 $x = 0.6y^2 + 1.7y - 1.1 \Rightarrow$

$$y = \frac{-1.7 \pm \sqrt{(1.7)^2 + 4(0.6)(x + 1.1)}}{2(0.6)} = \frac{-1.7 \pm \sqrt{2.4x + 5.53}}{1.2}.$$

From the graph, we can see that there are 4 points of intersection. Their coordinates

are approximately (−1.34,−2.69), (−0.65, 0.24), (0.49, 0.74), and (1.59, −3.97).

Note: Let C, V, F, and M denote the center, the vertices, the foci, and the endpoints of the minor axis, respectively.

1. $\dfrac{x^2}{9}+\dfrac{y^2}{4}=1$ • $c^2=9-4 \Rightarrow c=\pm\sqrt{5}$; $V(\pm 3,\, 0)$; $F(\pm\sqrt{5},\, 0)$; $M(0,\, \pm 2)$

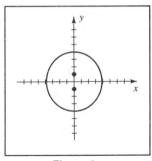

Figure 1

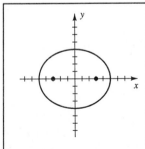

Figure 2

2. $\dfrac{x^2}{25}+\dfrac{y^2}{16}=1$ • $c^2=25-16 \Rightarrow c=\pm 3$; $V(\pm 5,\, 0)$; $F(\pm 3,\, 0)$; $M(0,\, \pm 4)$

3. $\dfrac{x^2}{15}+\dfrac{y^2}{16}=1$ • $c^2=16-15 \Rightarrow c=\pm 1$; $V(0,\, \pm 4)$; $F(0,\, \pm 1)$; $M(\pm\sqrt{15},\, 0)$

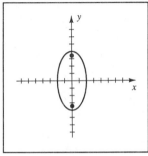

Figure 3

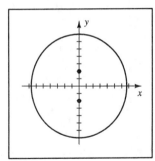

Figure 4

4. $\dfrac{x^2}{45}+\dfrac{y^2}{49}=1$ • $c^2=49-45 \Rightarrow c=\pm 2$; $V(0,\, \pm 7)$; $F(0,\, \pm 2)$; $M(\pm\sqrt{45},\, 0)$

5. $4x^2+y^2=16 \Rightarrow \dfrac{x^2}{4}+\dfrac{y^2}{16}=1$; $c^2=16-4 \Rightarrow c=\pm 2\sqrt{3}$;

$$V(0,\, \pm 4); \ F(0,\, \pm 2\sqrt{3}); \ M(\pm 2,\, 0)$$

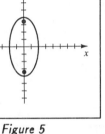

Figure 5

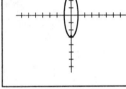

Figure 6

6. $y^2+9x^2=9 \Rightarrow \dfrac{x^2}{1}+\dfrac{y^2}{9}=1$; $c^2=9-1 \Rightarrow c=\pm 2\sqrt{2}$;

$$V(0,\, \pm 3); \ F(0,\, \pm 2\sqrt{2}); \ M(\pm 1,\, 0)$$

$\boxed{7}$ $4x^2 + 25y^2 = 1 \Rightarrow \dfrac{x^2}{\frac{1}{4}} + \dfrac{y^2}{\frac{1}{25}} = 1;\ c^2 = \frac{1}{4} - \frac{1}{25} = \frac{21}{100} \Rightarrow c = \pm\frac{1}{10}\sqrt{21};$

$$V(\pm\tfrac{1}{2},\ 0);\ F(\pm\tfrac{1}{10}\sqrt{21},\ 0);\ M(0,\ \pm\tfrac{1}{5})$$

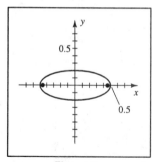

Figure 7

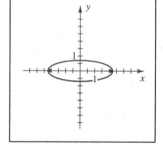

Figure 8

$\boxed{8}$ $10y^2 + x^2 = 5 \Rightarrow \dfrac{x^2}{5} + \dfrac{y^2}{\frac{1}{2}} = 1;\ c^2 = 5 - \frac{1}{2} = \frac{9}{2} \Rightarrow c = \pm\frac{3}{2}\sqrt{2};$

$$V(\pm\sqrt{5},\ 0);\ F(\pm\tfrac{3}{2}\sqrt{2},\ 0);\ M(0,\ \pm\tfrac{1}{2}\sqrt{2})$$

$\boxed{9}$ $c^2 = 16 - 9 \Rightarrow c = \pm\sqrt{7};\ C(3,\ -4);\ V(3\pm4,\ -4);\ F(3\pm\sqrt{7},\ -4);\ M(3,\ -4\pm3)$

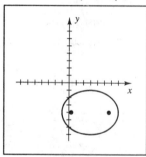

Figure 9

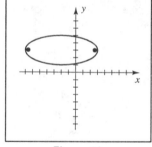

Figure 10

$\boxed{10}$ $c^2 = 25 - 4 \Rightarrow c = \pm\sqrt{21};\ C(-2,\ 3);\ V(-2\pm5,\ 3);\ F(-2\pm\sqrt{21},\ 3);\ M(-2,\ 3\pm2)$

$\boxed{11}$ $4x^2 + 9y^2 - 32x - 36y + 64 = 0 \Rightarrow$

$4(x^2 - 8x + \underline{\ 16\ }) + 9(y^2 - 4y + \underline{\ 4\ }) = -64 + \underline{\ 64\ } + \underline{\ 36\ } \Rightarrow$

$4(x - 4)^2 + 9(y - 2)^2 = 36 \Rightarrow \dfrac{(x-4)^2}{9} + \dfrac{(y-2)^2}{4} = 1;$

$$c^2 = 9 - 4 \Rightarrow c = \pm\sqrt{5};\ C(4,\ 2);\ V(4\pm3,\ 2);\ F(4\pm\sqrt{5},\ 2);\ M(4,\ 2\pm2)$$

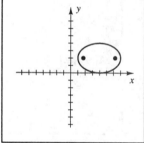

Figure 11

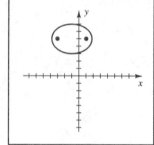

Figure 12

$\boxed{12}$ $x^2 + 2y^2 + 2x - 20y + 43 = 0 \Rightarrow$

$(x^2 + 2x + \underline{1}) + 2(y^2 - 10y + \underline{25}) = -43 + \underline{1} + \underline{50} \Rightarrow$

$(x+1)^2 + 2(y-5)^2 = 8 \Rightarrow \dfrac{(x+1)^2}{8} + \dfrac{(y-5)^2}{4} = 1;\ c^2 = 8 - 4 \Rightarrow c = \pm 2;$

$C(-1, 5);\ V(-1 \pm 2\sqrt{2},\, 5);\ F(-1 \pm 2,\, 5);\ M(-1,\, 5 \pm 2)$

$\boxed{13}$ $25x^2 + 4y^2 - 250x - 16y + 541 = 0 \Rightarrow$

$25(x^2 - 10x + \underline{25}) + 4(y^2 - 4y + \underline{4}) = -541 + \underline{625} + \underline{16} \Rightarrow$

$25(x-5)^2 + 4(y-2)^2 = 100 \Rightarrow \dfrac{(x-5)^2}{4} + \dfrac{(y-2)^2}{25} = 1;\ c^2 = 25 - 4 \Rightarrow$

$c = \pm\sqrt{21};\ C(5, 2);\ V(5,\, 2 \pm 5);\ F(5,\, 2 \pm \sqrt{21});\ M(5 \pm 2,\, 2)$

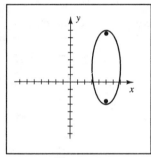

Figure 13

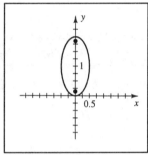

Figure 14

$\boxed{14}$ $4x^2 + y^2 = 2y \Rightarrow 4x^2 + y^2 - 2y + \underline{1} = \underline{1} \Rightarrow$

$\dfrac{x^2}{\frac{1}{4}} + \dfrac{(y-1)^2}{1} = 1;\ c^2 = 1 - \tfrac{1}{4} \Rightarrow c = \pm\tfrac{1}{2}\sqrt{3};$

$C(0, 1);\ V(0,\, 1 \pm 1);\ F(0,\, 1 \pm \tfrac{1}{2}\sqrt{3});\ M(0 \pm \tfrac{1}{2},\, 1)$

$\boxed{15}$ $a = 2$ and $b = 6 \Rightarrow \dfrac{x^2}{a^2} + \dfrac{y^2}{b^2} = 1$ is $\dfrac{x^2}{4} + \dfrac{y^2}{36} = 1.$

$\boxed{16}$ $a = 4$ and $b = 3 \Rightarrow \dfrac{x^2}{a^2} + \dfrac{y^2}{b^2} = 1$ is $\dfrac{x^2}{16} + \dfrac{y^2}{9} = 1.$

$\boxed{17}$ The center of the ellipse is $(-2, 1)$. $a = 5$ and $b = 2$ give us $\dfrac{(x+2)^2}{25} + \dfrac{(y-1)^2}{4} = 1.$

$\boxed{18}$ The center of the ellipse is $(1, -2)$. $a = 2$ and $b = 4$ give us $\dfrac{(x-1)^2}{4} + \dfrac{(y+2)^2}{16} = 1.$

$\boxed{19}$ $b^2 = 8^2 - 5^2 = 39$. An equation is $\dfrac{x^2}{64} + \dfrac{y^2}{39} = 1.$

$\boxed{20}$ $b^2 = 7^2 - 2^2 = 45$. An equation is $\dfrac{x^2}{45} + \dfrac{y^2}{49} = 1.$

$\boxed{21}$ If the length of the minor axis is 3, then $b = \tfrac{3}{2}$. An equation is $\dfrac{4x^2}{9} + \dfrac{y^2}{25} = 1.$

$\boxed{22}$ If the length of the minor axis is 2, then $b = 1$. $a^2 = 3^2 + 1^2 = 10.$

An equation is $\dfrac{x^2}{10} + \dfrac{y^2}{1} = 1.$

23 With the vertices at $(0, \pm 6)$, an equation of the ellipse is $\dfrac{x^2}{b^2} + \dfrac{y^2}{36} = 1$. Substituting

$x = 3$ and $y = 2$ and solving for b^2 yields $\dfrac{9}{b^2} + \dfrac{4}{36} = 1 \Rightarrow \dfrac{9}{b^2} = \dfrac{8}{9} \Rightarrow b^2 = \dfrac{81}{8}$.

An equation is $\dfrac{8x^2}{81} + \dfrac{y^2}{36} = 1$.

24 Substituting the x and y values for $(2, 3)$ and $(6, 1)$ into $\dfrac{x^2}{a^2} + \dfrac{y^2}{b^2} = 1$ yields the

equations $\dfrac{4}{a^2} + \dfrac{9}{b^2} = 1 \ \{E_1\}$ and $\dfrac{36}{a^2} + \dfrac{1}{b^2} = 1 \ \{E_2\}$, respectively. Solving,

$E_2 - 9E_1 \Rightarrow -\dfrac{80}{b^2} = -8 \Rightarrow b^2 = 10$ and $E_1 - 9E_2 \Rightarrow -\dfrac{320}{a^2} = -8 \Rightarrow a^2 = 40$.

An equation is $\dfrac{x^2}{40} + \dfrac{y^2}{10} = 1$.

25 With vertices $V(0, \pm 4)$, an equation of the ellipse is $\dfrac{x^2}{b^2} + \dfrac{y^2}{16} = 1$. $e = \dfrac{c}{a} = \dfrac{3}{4}$ and

$a = 4 \Rightarrow c = 3$. Thus, $b^2 = 16 - 9 = 7$. An equation is $\dfrac{x^2}{7} + \dfrac{y^2}{16} = 1$.

26 An equation of the ellipse is $\dfrac{x^2}{a^2} + \dfrac{y^2}{b^2} = 1$. $(1, 3)$ on the ellipse $\Rightarrow \dfrac{1}{a^2} + \dfrac{9}{b^2} = 1 \Rightarrow$

$b^2 = \dfrac{9a^2}{a^2 - 1}$. $e = \dfrac{c}{a} = \dfrac{1}{2} \Rightarrow c = \dfrac{1}{2}a$. $b^2 = a^2 - c^2 = a^2 - \dfrac{1}{4}a^2 = \dfrac{3}{4}a^2$.

Thus, $\dfrac{9a^2}{a^2 - 1} = \dfrac{3}{4}a^2 \Rightarrow a^2 = 13$ and $b^2 = \dfrac{39}{4}$. An equation is $\dfrac{x^2}{13} + \dfrac{4y^2}{39} = 1$.

27 $\dfrac{x^2}{2^2} + \dfrac{y^2}{(\frac{1}{3})^2} = 1 \Rightarrow \dfrac{x^2}{4} + \dfrac{y^2}{\frac{1}{9}} = 1 \Rightarrow \dfrac{x^2}{4} + 9y^2 = 1$

28 $\dfrac{x^2}{(\frac{1}{2})^2} + \dfrac{y^2}{4^2} = 1 \Rightarrow \dfrac{x^2}{\frac{1}{4}} + \dfrac{y^2}{16} = 1 \Rightarrow 4x^2 + \dfrac{y^2}{16} = 1$

29 $\dfrac{x^2}{(\frac{1}{2} \cdot 8)^2} + \dfrac{y^2}{(\frac{1}{2} \cdot 5)^2} = 1 \Rightarrow \dfrac{x^2}{16} + \dfrac{4y^2}{25} = 1$

30 $\dfrac{x^2}{(\frac{1}{2} \cdot 6)^2} + \dfrac{y^2}{(\frac{1}{2} \cdot 7)^2} = 1 \Rightarrow \dfrac{x^2}{9} + \dfrac{4y^2}{49} = 1$

31 Substituting $x = 6 - 2y$ into $x^2 + 4y^2 = 20$ yields $(6 - 2y)^2 + 4y^2 = 20 \Rightarrow$

$8y^2 - 24y + 16 = 0 \Rightarrow 8(y - 1)(y - 2) = 0 \Rightarrow y = 1, 2; \ x = 4, 2$.

The two points of intersection are $(2, 2)$ and $(4, 1)$.

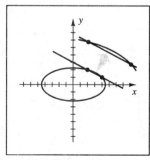

Figure 31

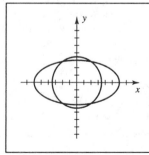

Figure 32

32 $(x^2 + 4y^2 = 36) - (x^2 + y^2 = 12) \Rightarrow 3y^2 = 24 \Rightarrow y^2 = 8; \ x^2 = 4.$

The four points of intersection are $(\pm 2, \ \pm 2\sqrt{2})$.

33 $k = 2a = 10 \Rightarrow a = 5. \quad F(3, 0)$ and $F'(-3, 0) \Rightarrow c = 3.$

$b^2 = a^2 - c^2 = 25 - 9 = 16.$ An equation is $\dfrac{x^2}{25} + \dfrac{y^2}{16} = 1.$

34 $k = 2a = 26 \Rightarrow a = 13. \quad F(12, 0)$ and $F'(-12, 0) \Rightarrow c = 12.$

$b^2 = a^2 - c^2 = 169 - 144 = 25.$ An equation is $\dfrac{x^2}{169} + \dfrac{y^2}{25} = 1.$

35 $k = 2a = 34 \Rightarrow a = 17. \quad F(0, 15)$ and $F'(0, -15) \Rightarrow c = 15.$

$b^2 = a^2 - c^2 = 289 - 225 = 64.$ An equation is $\dfrac{x^2}{64} + \dfrac{y^2}{289} = 1.$

36 $k = 2a = 20 \Rightarrow a = 10. \quad F(0, 8)$ and $F'(0, -8) \Rightarrow c = 8.$

$b^2 = a^2 - c^2 = 100 - 64 = 36.$ An equation is $\dfrac{x^2}{36} + \dfrac{y^2}{100} = 1.$

37 $y = 11\sqrt{1 - \dfrac{x^2}{49}} \Rightarrow \dfrac{y}{11} = \sqrt{1 - \dfrac{x^2}{49}} \Rightarrow \dfrac{x^2}{49} + \dfrac{y^2}{121} = 1.$ Since y is nonnegative in the

original equation, its graph is the upper half of the ellipse.

38 $y = -6\sqrt{1 - \dfrac{x^2}{25}} \Rightarrow \dfrac{y}{-6} = \sqrt{1 - \dfrac{x^2}{25}} \Rightarrow \dfrac{x^2}{25} + \dfrac{y^2}{36} = 1;$ lower half

39 $x = -\dfrac{1}{3}\sqrt{9 - y^2} \Rightarrow -3x = \sqrt{9 - y^2} \Rightarrow 9x^2 = 9 - y^2 \Rightarrow x^2 + \dfrac{y^2}{9} = 1;$ left half

40 $x = \dfrac{4}{5}\sqrt{25 - y^2} \Rightarrow \dfrac{5}{4}x = \sqrt{25 - y^2} \Rightarrow \dfrac{25}{16}x^2 = 25 - y^2 \Rightarrow \dfrac{x^2}{16} + \dfrac{y^2}{25} = 1;$ right half

41 $x = 1 + 2\sqrt{1 - \dfrac{(y+2)^2}{9}} \Rightarrow \dfrac{x-1}{2} = \sqrt{1 - \dfrac{(y+2)^2}{9}} \Rightarrow \dfrac{(x-1)^2}{4} + \dfrac{(y+2)^2}{9} = 1;$ right half

42 $x = -2 - 5\sqrt{1 - \dfrac{(y-1)^2}{16}} \Rightarrow \dfrac{x+2}{-5} = \sqrt{1 - \dfrac{(y-1)^2}{16}} \Rightarrow \dfrac{(x+2)^2}{25} + \dfrac{(y-1)^2}{16} = 1;$ left half

43 $y = 2 - 7\sqrt{1 - \dfrac{(x+1)^2}{9}} \Rightarrow \dfrac{y-2}{-7} = \sqrt{1 - \dfrac{(x+1)^2}{9}} \Rightarrow \dfrac{(x+1)^2}{9} + \dfrac{(y-2)^2}{49} = 1;$ lower half

44 $y = -1 + \sqrt{1 - \dfrac{(x-3)^2}{16}} \Rightarrow y + 1 = \sqrt{1 - \dfrac{(x-3)^2}{16}} \Rightarrow \dfrac{(x-3)^2}{16} + (y+1)^2 = 1;$

upper half

45 Model this problem as an ellipse with $V(\pm 15, 0)$ and $M(0, \pm 10)$.

Substituting $x = 6$ into $\dfrac{x^2}{15^2} + \dfrac{y^2}{10^2} = 1$ yields $\dfrac{y^2}{100} = \dfrac{189}{225} \Rightarrow y^2 = 84.$

The desired height is $\sqrt{84} = 2\sqrt{21} \approx 9.165$ ft.

46 (a) This problem can be modeled as an ellipse with $V(\pm 100, 0)$ and passing through

the point $(25, 30).$ Substituting $x = 25$ and $y = 30$ into $\dfrac{x^2}{100^2} + \dfrac{y^2}{b^2} = 1$ yields

$\dfrac{30^2}{b^2} = \dfrac{15}{16} \Rightarrow b^2 = 960.$ An equation for the ellipse is $\dfrac{x^2}{10,000} + \dfrac{y^2}{960} = 1.$

An equation for the top half of the ellipse is $y = \sqrt{960\left(1 - \dfrac{x^2}{10,000}\right)}.$

(b) The height in the middle of the bridge is $\sqrt{960} = 8\sqrt{15} \approx 31$ ft.

47 $e = \frac{c}{a} = 0.017 \Rightarrow c = 0.017a = 0.017(93,000,000) = 1,581,000.$ The maximum

and minimum distances are $a + c = 94,581,000$ mi. and $a - c = 91,419,000$ mi.

48 $e = \frac{c}{a} \Rightarrow c = ae = (\frac{1}{2} \cdot 0.774)(0.206) = (0.387)(0.206) \approx 0.080.$ As in Example 7,

the maximum and minimum distances are $a + c \approx 0.387 + 0.080 = 0.467$ AU

and $a - c \approx 0.387 - 0.080 = 0.307$ AU, respectively.

49 (a) Let c denote the distance from the center of the hemi-ellipsoid to F. Hence,

$$(\tfrac{1}{2}k)^2 + c^2 = h^2 \Rightarrow c^2 = h^2 - \tfrac{1}{4}k^2 \Rightarrow c = \sqrt{h^2 - \tfrac{1}{4}k^2}. \quad d = d(V, F) = h - c \Rightarrow$$

$$d = h - \sqrt{h^2 - \tfrac{1}{4}k^2} \text{ and } d' = d(V, F') = h + c \Rightarrow d' = h + \sqrt{h^2 - \tfrac{1}{4}k^2}.$$

(b) From part (a), $d' = h + c \Rightarrow c = d' - h = 32 - 17 = 15. \quad c = \sqrt{h^2 - \tfrac{1}{4}k^2} \Rightarrow$

$15 = \sqrt{17^2 - \tfrac{1}{4}k^2} \Rightarrow 225 = 289 - \tfrac{1}{4}k^2 \Rightarrow \tfrac{1}{4}k^2 = 64 \Rightarrow k^2 = 256 \Rightarrow k = 16$ cm.

$$d = h - c = 17 - 15 = 2 \Rightarrow F \text{ should be located 2 cm from } V.$$

50 (a) From the previous exercise, $c = \sqrt{h^2 - \tfrac{1}{4}k^2} = \sqrt{15^2 - \tfrac{1}{4}(18)^2} = 12.$

The focus F should be located $d = h - c = 15 - 12 = 3$ cm from V.

(b) The kidney stone should be located $d' = h + c = 15 + 12 = 27$ cm from V.

51 $c^2 = (\frac{1}{2} \cdot 50)^2 - 15^2 = 625 - 225 = 400 \Rightarrow c = 20.$

Their feet should be $25 - 20 = 5$ ft from the vertices.

52 Since $a = p + c$, $b^2 = a^2 - c^2 = (p + c)^2 - c^2 = p^2 + 2pc = p(p + 2c).$

Thus, the ellipse has the equation $\dfrac{[x - (p + c)]^2}{(p + c)^2} + \dfrac{y^2}{p(p + 2c)} = 1 \Rightarrow$

$$y^2 = p(p + 2c)\left[1 - \frac{(x - p - c)^2}{(p + c)^2}\right] = \frac{p(p + 2c)(2xp + 2xc - x^2)}{(p + c)^2}.$$

Consider the expression to be a rational function of c with $4px$ as the coefficient of c^2

in the numerator and 1 as the coefficient of c^2 in the denominator.

Hence, as $c \to \infty$, $y^2 \to 4px$.

53 First determine an equation of the ellipse for the orbit of Earth. $e = \frac{c}{a} \Rightarrow c = ae =$

$0.093 \times 149.6 = 13.9128.$ $b^2 = a^2 - c^2 = 149.6^2 - 13.9128^2 \Rightarrow b \approx 148.95 \approx 149.0.$

An equation for the orbit of Earth is $\dfrac{x^2}{149.6^2} + \dfrac{y^2}{149.0^2} = 1.$

Graph $Y_1 = 149\sqrt{1 - (x^2/149.6^2)}$ and $Y_2 = -Y_1.$

The sun is at $(\pm 13.9128, 0)$. Plot the point $(13.9128, 0)$ for the sun. See *Figure 53*.

[−300, 300] by [−200, 200]

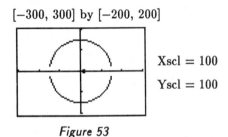

Xscl = 100

Yscl = 100

[−9000, 9000] by [−6000, 6000]

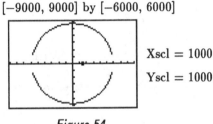

Xscl = 1000

Yscl = 1000

Figure 53   *Figure 54*

54 First determine an equation of the ellipse for the orbit of Pluto. $e = \frac{c}{a} \Rightarrow c = ae = $

$0.249 \times 5913 = 1472.337.$ $b^2 = a^2 - c^2 = 5913^2 - 1472.337^2 \Rightarrow b \approx 5726.76 \approx 5727.$

An equation for the orbit of Pluto is $\dfrac{x^2}{5913^2} + \dfrac{y^2}{5727^2} = 1.$

Graph $Y_1 = 5727\sqrt{1 - (x^2/5913^2)}$ and $Y_2 = -Y_1.$

The sun is at $(\pm 1472.337, 0).$ Plot the point $(1472.337, 0)$ for the sun.

55 $\dfrac{x^2}{2.9} + \dfrac{y^2}{2.1} = 1 \Rightarrow 2.1x^2 + 2.9y^2 = 6.09 \Rightarrow y = \pm\sqrt{\frac{1}{2.9}(6.09 - 2.1x^2)}.$

$\dfrac{x^2}{4.3} + \dfrac{(y - 2.1)^2}{4.9} = 1 \Rightarrow 4.9x^2 + 4.3(y - 2.1)^2 = 21.07 \Rightarrow$

$y = 2.1 \pm \sqrt{\frac{1}{4.3}(21.07 - 4.9x^2)}.$

From the graph, the points of intersection are approximately $(\pm 1.540, 0.618).$

[−6, 6] by [−2, 6]

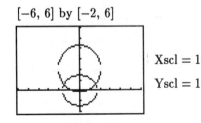

Xscl = 1

Yscl = 1

[−6, 6] by [−4, 4]

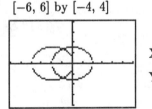

Xscl = 1

Yscl = 1

Figure 55   *Figure 56*

56 $\dfrac{x^2}{3.9} + \dfrac{y^2}{2.4} = 1 \Rightarrow 2.4x^2 + 3.9y^2 = 9.36 \Rightarrow y = \pm\sqrt{\frac{1}{3.9}(9.36 - 2.4x^2)}.$

$\dfrac{(x + 1.9)^2}{4.1} + \dfrac{y^2}{2.5} = 1 \Rightarrow 2.5(x + 1.9)^2 + 4.1y^2 = 10.25 \Rightarrow$

$y = \pm\sqrt{\frac{1}{4.1}[10.25 - 2.5(x + 1.9)^2]}.$

From the graph, the points of intersection are approximately $(-0.905, \pm 1.377).$

[57] $\dfrac{(x+0.1)^2}{1.7}+\dfrac{y^2}{0.9}=1 \Rightarrow y=\pm\sqrt{0.9[1-(x+0.1)^2/1.7]}.$

$\dfrac{x^2}{0.9}+\dfrac{(y-0.25)^2}{1.8}=1 \Rightarrow y=0.25\pm\sqrt{1.8(1-x^2/0.9)}.$

From the graph, the points of intersection are approximately

$(-0.88,\,0.76),\,(-0.48,-0.91),\,(0.58,-0.81),$ and $(0.92,\,0.59).$

$[-3,\,3]$ by $[-2,\,2]$ $[-4.5,\,4.5]$ by $[-3,\,3]$

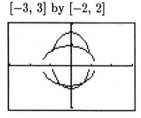
Xscl = 1
Yscl = 1

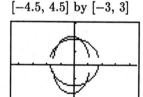
Xscl = 1
Yscl = 1

Figure 57   Figure 58

[58] $\dfrac{x^2}{3.1}+\dfrac{(y-0.2)^2}{2.8}=1 \Rightarrow y=0.2\pm\sqrt{2.8(1-x^2/3.1)}.$

$\dfrac{(x+0.23)^2}{1.8}+\dfrac{y^2}{4.2}=1 \Rightarrow y=\pm\sqrt{4.2[1-(x+0.23)^2/1.8]}.$

From the graph, the points of intersection are approximately

$(-1.49,\,-0.68),\,(-1.19,\,1.44),\,(0.36,\,1.84),$ and $(0.82,\,-1.28).$

10.3 Exercises

Note: Let C, V, F, and W denote the center, the vertices, the foci, and the endpoints of the conjugate axis, respectively.

[1] $\dfrac{x^2}{9}-\dfrac{y^2}{4}=1 \quad \bullet \quad c^2=9+4 \Rightarrow c=\pm\sqrt{13};$

$V(\pm 3,\,0);\; F(\pm\sqrt{13},\,0);\; W(0,\,\pm 2);\; y=\pm\tfrac{2}{3}x$

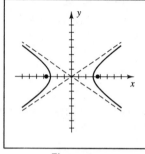

Figure 1

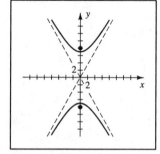

Figure 2

[2] $\dfrac{y^2}{49}-\dfrac{x^2}{16}=1 \quad \bullet \quad c^2=49+16 \Rightarrow c=\pm\sqrt{65};$

$V(0,\,\pm 7);\; F(0,\,\pm\sqrt{65});\; W(\pm 4,\,0);\; y=\pm\tfrac{7}{4}x$

3 $\frac{y^2}{9} - \frac{x^2}{4} = 1$ • $c^2 = 9 + 4 \Rightarrow c = \pm\sqrt{13}$;

$V(0, \pm 3)$; $F(0, \pm\sqrt{13})$; $W(\pm 2, 0)$; $y = \pm\frac{3}{2}x$

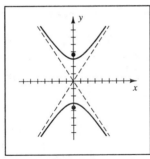

Figure 3

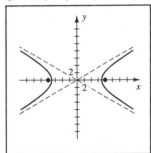

Figure 4

4 $\frac{x^2}{49} - \frac{y^2}{16} = 1$ • $c^2 = 49 + 16 \Rightarrow c = \pm\sqrt{65}$;

$V(\pm 7, 0)$; $F(\pm\sqrt{65}, 0)$; $W(0, \pm 4)$; $y = \pm\frac{4}{7}x$

5 $x^2 - \frac{y^2}{24} = 1$ • $c^2 = 1 + 24 \Rightarrow c = \pm 5$;

$V(\pm 1, 0)$; $F(\pm 5, 0)$; $W(0, \pm\sqrt{24})$; $y = \pm\sqrt{24}x$

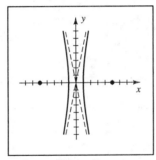

Figure 5

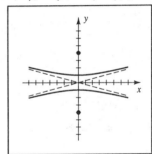

Figure 6

6 $y^2 - \frac{x^2}{15} = 1$ • $c^2 = 1 + 15 \Rightarrow c = \pm 4$;

$V(0, \pm 1)$; $F(0, \pm 4)$; $W(\pm\sqrt{15}, 0)$; $y = \pm(1/\sqrt{15})x$

7 $y^2 - 4x^2 = 16 \Rightarrow \frac{y^2}{16} - \frac{x^2}{4} = 1$; $c^2 = 16 + 4 \Rightarrow c = \pm 2\sqrt{5}$;

$V(0, \pm 4)$; $F(0, \pm 2\sqrt{5})$; $W(\pm 2, 0)$; $y = \pm 2x$

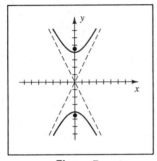

Figure 7

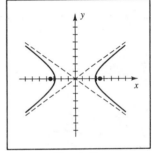

Figure 8

8 $x^2 - 2y^2 = 8 \Rightarrow \frac{x^2}{8} - \frac{y^2}{4} = 1$; $c^2 = 8 + 4 \Rightarrow c = \pm 2\sqrt{3}$;

$V(\pm 2\sqrt{2}, 0)$; $F(\pm 2\sqrt{3}, 0)$; $W(0, \pm 2)$; $y = \pm\frac{1}{2}\sqrt{2}\,x$

9 $16x^2 - 36y^2 = 1 \Rightarrow \dfrac{x^2}{\frac{1}{16}} - \dfrac{y^2}{\frac{1}{36}} = 1;\ c^2 = \frac{1}{16} + \frac{1}{36} \Rightarrow c = \pm\frac{1}{12}\sqrt{13};$

$$V(\pm\tfrac{1}{4},\, 0);\ F(\pm\tfrac{1}{12}\sqrt{13},\, 0);\ W(0,\ \pm\tfrac{1}{6});\ y = \pm\tfrac{2}{3}x$$

Note that the branches of the hyperbola almost coincide with the asymptotes.

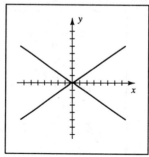

Figure 9

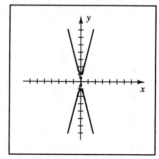

Figure 10

10 $y^2 - 16x^2 = 1 \Rightarrow \dfrac{y^2}{1} - \dfrac{x^2}{\frac{1}{16}} = 1;\ c^2 = 1 + \frac{1}{16} \Rightarrow c = \pm\frac{1}{4}\sqrt{17};$

$$V(0,\ \pm 1);\ F(0,\ \pm\tfrac{1}{4}\sqrt{17});\ W(\pm\tfrac{1}{4},\, 0);\ y = \pm 4x$$

11 $\dfrac{(y+2)^2}{9} - \dfrac{(x+2)^2}{4} = 1;\ c^2 = 9 + 4 \Rightarrow c = \pm\sqrt{13}; \qquad\qquad C(-2,\, -2);$

$$V(-2,\, -2\pm 3);\ F(-2,\, -2\pm\sqrt{13});\ W(-2\pm 2,\, -2);\ (y+2) = \pm\tfrac{3}{2}(x+2)$$

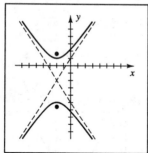

Figure 11

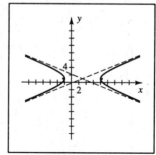

Figure 12

12 $\dfrac{(x-3)^2}{25} - \dfrac{(y-1)^2}{4} = 1;\ c^2 = 25 + 4 \Rightarrow c = \pm\sqrt{29};$

$$C(3,\, 1);\ V(3\pm 5,\, 1);\ F(3\pm\sqrt{29},\, 1);\ W(3,\, 1\pm 2);\ (y-1) = \pm\tfrac{2}{5}(x-3)$$

$\boxed{13}$ $144x^2 - 25y^2 + 864x - 100y - 2404 = 0 \Rightarrow$

$144(x^2 + 6x + \underline{\ 9\ }) - 25(y^2 + 4y + \underline{\ 4\ }) = 2404 + \underline{\ 1296\ } - \underline{\ 100\ } \Rightarrow$

$144(x+3)^2 - 25(y+2)^2 = 3600 \Rightarrow \dfrac{(x+3)^2}{25} - \dfrac{(y+2)^2}{144} = 1; \ c^2 = 25 + 144 \Rightarrow c = \pm 13;$

$C(-3, -2); \ V(-3 \pm 5, -2); \ F(-3 \pm 13, -2); \ W(-3, -2 \pm 12); \ (y+2) = \pm \frac{12}{5}(x+3)$

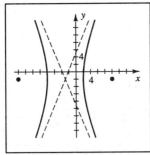

Figure 13

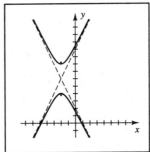

Figure 14

$\boxed{14}$ $y^2 - 4x^2 - 12y - 16x + 16 = 0 \Rightarrow$

$(y^2 - 12y + \underline{\ 36\ }) - 4(x^2 + 4x + \underline{\ 4\ }) = -16 + \underline{\ 36\ } - \underline{\ 16\ } \Rightarrow$

$(y-6)^2 - 4(x+2)^2 = 4 \Rightarrow \dfrac{(y-6)^2}{4} - \dfrac{(x+2)^2}{1} = 1; \ c^2 = 4 + 1 \Rightarrow c = \pm \sqrt{5};$

$C(-2, 6); \ V(-2, 6 \pm 2); \ F(-2, 6 \pm \sqrt{5}); \ W(-2 \pm 1, 6); \ (y-6) = \pm 2(x+2)$

$\boxed{15}$ $4y^2 - x^2 + 40y - 4x + 60 = 0 \Rightarrow$

$4(y^2 + 10y + \underline{\ 25\ }) - 1(x^2 + 4x + \underline{\ 4\ }) = -60 + \underline{\ 100\ } - \underline{\ 4\ } \Rightarrow$

$4(y+5)^2 - (x+2)^2 = 36 \Rightarrow \dfrac{(y+5)^2}{9} - \dfrac{(x+2)^2}{36} = 1;$

$c^2 = 9 + 36 \Rightarrow c = \pm 3\sqrt{5};$ $\qquad\qquad\qquad C(-2, -5);$

$V(-2, -5 \pm 3); \ F(-2, -5 \pm 3\sqrt{5}); \ W(-2 \pm 6, -5); \ (y+5) = \pm \frac{1}{2}(x+2)$

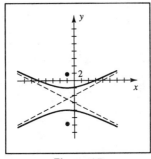

Figure 15

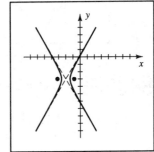

Figure 16

$\boxed{16}$ $25x^2 - 9y^2 + 100x - 54y + 10 = 0 \Rightarrow$

$25(x^2 + 4x + \underline{\ 4\ }) - 9(y^2 + 6y + \underline{\ 9\ }) = -10 + \underline{\ 100\ } - \underline{\ 81\ } \Rightarrow$

$25(x+2)^2 - 9(y+3)^2 = 9 \Rightarrow \dfrac{(x+2)^2}{\frac{9}{25}} - \dfrac{(y+3)^2}{1} = 1;$

$c^2 = \frac{9}{25} + 1 \Rightarrow c = \pm \frac{1}{5}\sqrt{34};$ $\qquad\qquad\qquad C(-2, -3);$

$V(-2 \pm \frac{3}{5}, -3); \ F(-2 \pm \frac{1}{5}\sqrt{34}, -3); \ W(-2, -3 \pm 1); \ (y+3) = \pm \frac{5}{3}(x+2)$

17 $a = 3$ and $c = 5 \Rightarrow b^2 = c^2 - a^2 = 16.$ $\frac{x^2}{a^2} - \frac{y^2}{b^2} = 1$ is then $\frac{x^2}{9} - \frac{y^2}{16} = 1.$

18 $a = 4$ and $c = 6 \Rightarrow b^2 = c^2 - a^2 = 20.$ $\frac{y^2}{a^2} - \frac{x^2}{b^2} = 1$ is then $\frac{y^2}{16} - \frac{x^2}{20} = 1.$

19 The center of the hyperbola is $(-2, -3)$.

$$a = 1 \text{ and } c = 2 \Rightarrow b^2 = 2^2 - 1^2 = 3 \text{ and an equation is } (y + 3)^2 - \frac{(x+2)^2}{3} = 1.$$

20 The center of the hyperbola is $(1, 2)$.

$$a = 1 \text{ and } c = 3 \Rightarrow b^2 = 3^2 - 1^2 = 8 \text{ and an equation is } (x - 1)^2 - \frac{(y-2)^2}{8} = 1.$$

21 $F(0, \pm 4)$ and $V(0, \pm 1) \Rightarrow W(\pm\sqrt{15}, 0)$. An equation is $\frac{y^2}{1} - \frac{x^2}{15} = 1.$

22 $F(\pm 8, 0)$ and $V(\pm 5, 0) \Rightarrow W(0, \pm\sqrt{39})$. An equation is $\frac{x^2}{25} - \frac{y^2}{39} = 1.$

23 $F(\pm 5, 0)$ and $V(\pm 3, 0) \Rightarrow W(0, \pm 4)$. An equation is $\frac{x^2}{9} - \frac{y^2}{16} = 1.$

24 $F(0, \pm 3)$ and $V(0, \pm 2) \Rightarrow W(\pm\sqrt{5}, 0)$. An equation is $\frac{y^2}{4} - \frac{x^2}{5} = 1.$

25 Conjugate axis of length 4 and $F(0, \pm 5) \Rightarrow W(\pm 2, 0)$ and $V(0, \pm\sqrt{21})$.

$$\text{An equation is } \frac{y^2}{21} - \frac{x^2}{4} = 1.$$

26 An equation of a hyperbola with vertices at $(\pm 4, 0)$ is $\frac{x^2}{16} - \frac{y^2}{b^2} = 1$. Substituting

$$x = 8 \text{ and } y = 2 \text{ yields } 4 - \frac{4}{b^2} = 1 \Rightarrow b^2 = \frac{4}{3}. \text{ An equation is } \frac{x^2}{16} - \frac{3y^2}{4} = 1.$$

27 Asymptote equations of $y = \pm 2x$ and $V(\pm 3, 0) \Rightarrow W(0, \pm 6)$.

$$\text{An equation is } \frac{x^2}{9} - \frac{y^2}{36} = 1.$$

28 Let the y value of V equal a and the x value of W equal b.

Now $a = \frac{1}{3}b$ { from the asymptote equation } and $a^2 + b^2 = 10^2$ { from the foci } $\Rightarrow$

$$(\tfrac{1}{3}b)^2 + b^2 = 10^2 \Rightarrow \tfrac{10}{9}b^2 = 100 \Rightarrow b^2 = 90 \text{ and } a^2 = 10. \text{ An equation is } \frac{y^2}{10} - \frac{x^2}{90} = 1.$$

29 $a = 5$, $b = 2(5) = 10$. $\frac{x^2}{5^2} - \frac{y^2}{10^2} = 1 \Rightarrow \frac{x^2}{25} - \frac{y^2}{100} = 1.$

30 $a = 2$, $2 = \frac{1}{4}(b) \Rightarrow b = 8$. $\frac{y^2}{2^2} - \frac{x^2}{8^2} = 1 \Rightarrow \frac{y^2}{4} - \frac{x^2}{64} = 1.$

31 $\frac{y^2}{(\frac{1}{2} \cdot 10)^2} - \frac{x^2}{(\frac{1}{2} \cdot 14)^2} = 1 \Rightarrow \frac{y^2}{25} - \frac{x^2}{49} = 1.$

32 $\frac{x^2}{(\frac{1}{2} \cdot 6)^2} - \frac{y^2}{(\frac{1}{2} \cdot 2)^2} = 1 \Rightarrow \frac{x^2}{9} - \frac{y^2}{1} = 1.$

$\boxed{33}$ Substituting $y = x + 4$ into $y^2 - 4x^2 = 16$ yields $(x + 4)^2 - 4x^2 = 16 \Rightarrow$

$3x^2 - 8x = 0 \Rightarrow x(3x - 8) = 0 \Rightarrow x = 0, \frac{8}{3}$ and $y = 4, \frac{20}{3}$.

The two points of intersection are $(0, 4)$ and $\left(\frac{8}{3}, \frac{20}{3}\right)$.

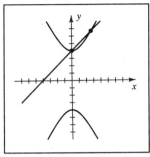

Figure 33

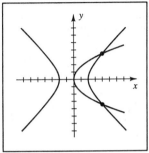

Figure 34

$\boxed{34}$ Adding the two equations yields $x^2 - 3x = 4 \Rightarrow x^2 - 3x - 4 = 0 \Rightarrow$

$(x - 4)(x + 1) = 0 \Rightarrow x = 4, -1$. Substituting these values in the second equation,

we find that for $x = 4$, $y = \pm 2\sqrt{3}$, and for $x = -1$, there are no real solutions for y.

The two points of intersection are $(4, \pm 2\sqrt{3})$.

$\boxed{35}$ $k = 2a = 24 \Rightarrow a = 12$. $F(13, 0)$ and $F'(-13, 0) \Rightarrow c = 13$.

$b^2 = c^2 - a^2 = 169 - 144 = 25$. An equation is $\dfrac{x^2}{144} - \dfrac{y^2}{25} = 1$.

$\boxed{36}$ $k = 2a = 8 \Rightarrow a = 4$. $F(5, 0)$ and $F'(-5, 0) \Rightarrow c = 5$.

$b^2 = c^2 - a^2 = 25 - 16 = 9$. An equation is $\dfrac{x^2}{16} - \dfrac{y^2}{9} = 1$.

$\boxed{37}$ $k = 2a = 16 \Rightarrow a = 8$. $F(0, 10)$ and $F'(0, -10) \Rightarrow c = 10$.

$b^2 = c^2 - a^2 = 100 - 64 = 36$. An equation is $\dfrac{y^2}{64} - \dfrac{x^2}{36} = 1$.

$\boxed{38}$ $k = 2a = 30 \Rightarrow a = 15$. $F(0, 17)$ and $F'(0, -17) \Rightarrow c = 17$.

$b^2 = c^2 - a^2 = 289 - 225 = 64$. An equation is $\dfrac{y^2}{225} - \dfrac{x^2}{64} = 1$.

$\boxed{39}$ $x = \frac{5}{4}\sqrt{y^2 + 16} \Rightarrow \frac{4}{5}x = \sqrt{y^2 + 16} \Rightarrow \frac{16}{25}x^2 = y^2 + 16 \Rightarrow \frac{16}{25}x^2 - y^2 = 16 \Rightarrow \dfrac{x^2}{25} - \dfrac{y^2}{16} = 1$.

Since x is positive in the original equation,

its graph is the right branch of the hyperbola.

$\boxed{40}$ $x = -\frac{5}{4}\sqrt{y^2 + 16} \Rightarrow -\frac{4}{5}x = \sqrt{y^2 + 16} \Rightarrow \frac{16}{25}x^2 = y^2 + 16 \Rightarrow \dfrac{x^2}{25} - \dfrac{y^2}{16} = 1$; left branch

$\boxed{41}$ $y = \frac{3}{7}\sqrt{x^2 + 49} \Rightarrow \frac{7}{3}y = \sqrt{x^2 + 49} \Rightarrow \frac{49}{9}y^2 = x^2 + 49 \Rightarrow \dfrac{y^2}{9} - \dfrac{x^2}{49} = 1$; upper branch

$\boxed{42}$ $y = -\frac{3}{7}\sqrt{x^2 + 49} \Rightarrow -\frac{7}{3}y = \sqrt{x^2 + 49} \Rightarrow \frac{49}{9}y^2 = x^2 + 49 \Rightarrow \dfrac{y^2}{9} - \dfrac{x^2}{49} = 1$; lower branch

$\boxed{43}$ $y = -\frac{9}{4}\sqrt{x^2 - 16} \Rightarrow -\frac{4}{9}y = \sqrt{x^2 - 16} \Rightarrow \frac{16}{81}y^2 = x^2 - 16 \Rightarrow \dfrac{x^2}{16} - \dfrac{y^2}{81} = 1$;

lower halves of the branches

44 $y = \frac{9}{4}\sqrt{x^2 - 16} \Rightarrow \frac{4}{9}y = \sqrt{x^2 - 16} \Rightarrow \frac{16}{81}y^2 = x^2 - 16 \Rightarrow \frac{x^2}{16} - \frac{y^2}{81} = 1$;

upper halves of the branches

45 $x = -\frac{2}{3}\sqrt{y^2 - 36} \Rightarrow -\frac{3}{2}x = \sqrt{y^2 - 36} \Rightarrow \frac{9}{4}x^2 = y^2 - 36 \Rightarrow \frac{y^2}{36} - \frac{x^2}{16} = 1$;

left halves of the branches

46 $x = \frac{2}{3}\sqrt{y^2 - 36} \Rightarrow \frac{3}{2}x = \sqrt{y^2 - 36} \Rightarrow \frac{9}{4}x^2 = y^2 - 36 \Rightarrow \frac{y^2}{36} - \frac{x^2}{16} = 1$;

right halves of the branches

47 Their equations are $\frac{x^2}{25} - \frac{y^2}{9} = 1$ and $\frac{x^2}{25} - \frac{y^2}{9} = -1$,

or, equivalently, $\frac{y^2}{9} - \frac{x^2}{25} = 1$.

Conjugate hyperbolas have the same asymptotes
and exchange transverse and conjugate axes.

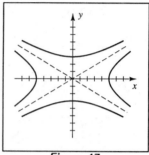

Figure 47

48 The center is $C(h, k)$ with $W(h, k \pm b)$. An equation is $\frac{(x-h)^2}{a^2} - \frac{(y-k)^2}{b^2} = 1$.

49 The path is a hyperbola with $V(\pm 3, 0)$ and $W(0, \pm\frac{3}{2})$.

An equation is $\frac{x^2}{(3)^2} - \frac{y^2}{(\frac{3}{2})^2} = 1$ or equivalently, $x^2 - 4y^2 = 9$.

If only the right branch is considered, then $x = \sqrt{9 + 4y^2}$ is an equation of the path.

50 Let A and P be the points $(3, 0)$ and (x, y), respectively.

$S = [d(A, P)]^2 = (x - 3)^2 + (y - 0)^2 = x^2 - 6x + 9 + y^2 =$

$x^2 - 6x + 9 + (\frac{1}{2}x^2 + 4)$ {from $2y^2 - x^2 = 8$} $= \frac{3}{2}x^2 - 6x + 13$.

Since S is a quadratic function, its minimum occurs at $x = -\frac{b}{2a} = -\frac{-6}{2(\frac{3}{2})} = 2$.

If $x = 2$, $S = 7$, and the plane comes within $\sqrt{7}$ miles of A.

51 Set up a coordinate system like Example 6. Then, $d_1 - d_2 = 2a = 160 \Rightarrow a = 80$.

$b^2 = c^2 - a^2 = 100^2 - 80^2 \Rightarrow b = 60$. The equation of the hyperbola with focus

A, passing through the coordinates of the ship at $P(x, y)$ is $\frac{x^2}{80^2} - \frac{y^2}{60^2} = 1$. Now,

$y = 100 \Rightarrow x = \frac{80}{3}\sqrt{34}$. The ship's coordinates are $(\frac{80}{3}\sqrt{34}, 100) \approx (155.5, 100)$.

52 By the reflective property of parabolic mirrors (see pages 687–688) parallel rays
striking the parabolic mirror will be reflected toward F_1. By the reflective property
of hyperbolic mirrors (see page 714), these rays will be reflected toward the exterior
focus of the hyperbolic mirror, which is located below the parabolic mirror in the
figure.

53 $\dfrac{(y-0.1)^2}{1.6} - \dfrac{(x+0.2)^2}{0.5} = 1 \Rightarrow 0.5(y-0.1)^2 - 1.6(x+0.2)^2 = 0.8 \Rightarrow$

$$y = 0.1 \pm \sqrt{1.6 + 3.2(x+0.2)^2}.$$

$\dfrac{(y-0.5)^2}{2.7} - \dfrac{(x-0.1)^2}{5.3} = 1 \Rightarrow 5.3(y-0.5)^2 - 2.7(x-0.1)^2 = 14.31 \Rightarrow$

$$y = 0.5 \pm \sqrt{\tfrac{1}{5.3}[14.31 + 2.7(x-0.1)^2]}.$$

From the graph,

the point of intersection in the first quadrant is approximately $(0.741, 2.206)$.

$[-15, 15]$ by $[-10, 10]$

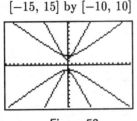

Xscl $= 1$

Yscl $= 1$

Figure 53

$[-4.5, 4.5]$ by $[-3, 3]$

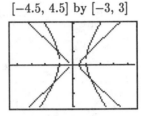

Xscl $= 1$

Yscl $= 1$

Figure 54

54 $\dfrac{(x-0.1)^2}{0.12} - \dfrac{y^2}{0.1} = 1 \Rightarrow 0.1(x-0.1)^2 - 0.12y^2 = 0.012 \Rightarrow$

$$y = \pm \sqrt{\tfrac{1}{0.12}[0.1(x-0.1)^2 - 0.012]}.$$

$\dfrac{x^2}{0.9} - \dfrac{(y-0.3)^2}{2.1} = 1 \Rightarrow 2.1x^2 - 0.9(y-0.3)^2 = 1.89 \Rightarrow$

$$y = 0.3 \pm \sqrt{\tfrac{1}{0.9}[2.1x^2 - 1.89]}.$$

From the graph,

the point of intersection in the first quadrant is approximately $(0.994, 0.752)$.

55 $\dfrac{(x-0.3)^2}{1.3} - \dfrac{y^2}{2.7} = 1 \Rightarrow y = \pm \sqrt{2.7[-1 + (x-0.3)^2/1.3]}.$

$\dfrac{y^2}{2.8} - \dfrac{(x-0.2)^2}{1.2} = 1 \Rightarrow y = \pm \sqrt{2.8[1 + (x-0.2)^2/1.2]}.$

The two graphs nearly intersect in the second and fourth quadrants,

but there are no points of intersection.

$[-15, 15]$ by $[-10, 10]$

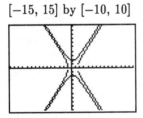

Xscl $= 2$

Yscl $= 2$

Figure 55

$[-25, 25]$ by $[-25, 25]$

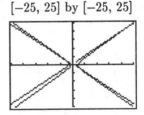

Xscl $= 5$

Yscl $= 5$

Figure 56

56 $\dfrac{(x+0.2)^2}{1.75} - \dfrac{(y-0.5)^2}{1.6} = 1 \Rightarrow y = 0.5 \pm \sqrt{1.6[-1 + (x+0.2)^2/1.75]}.$

$\dfrac{(x-0.6)^2}{2.2} - \dfrac{(y+0.4)^2}{2.35} = 1 \Rightarrow y = -0.4 \pm \sqrt{2.35[-1 + (x-0.6)^2/2.2]}.$

From the graph, we can see that there are 2 points of intersection.

One is in the first quadrant, near the point $(23, 23)$,

and the other is in the fourth quadrant, near the point $(3, -2)$.

$\boxed{57}$ (a) The comet's path is hyperbolic with $a^2 = 26 \times 10^{14}$ and $b^2 = 18 \times 10^{14}$.

$c^2 = a^2 + b^2 = 26 \times 10^{14} + 18 \times 10^{14} = 44 \times 10^{14} \Rightarrow c \approx 6.63 \times 10^7$.

The coordinates of the sun are approximately $(6.63 \times 10^7, 0)$.

(b) The minimum distance between the comet and the sun will be

$$c - a = \sqrt{44 \times 10^{14}} - \sqrt{26 \times 10^{14}} = 1.53 \times 10^7 \text{ mi.}$$

Since r must be in meters, 1.53×10^7 mi $\times 1610$ m/mi $\approx 2.47 \times 10^{10}$ m. At this

distance, v must be greater than $\sqrt{\frac{2k}{r}} \approx \sqrt{\frac{2(1.325 \times 10^{20})}{2.47 \times 10^{10}}} \approx 103{,}600$ m/sec.

10.4 Exercises

$\boxed{1}$ $x = t - 2 \Rightarrow t = x + 2$. $y = 2t + 3 = 2(x + 2) + 3 = 2x + 7$.

As t varies from 0 to 5, (x, y) varies from $(-2, 3)$ to $(3, 13)$.

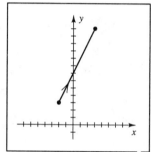

Figure 1

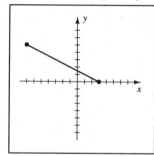

Figure 2

$\boxed{2}$ $y = 1 + t \Rightarrow t = y - 1$. $x = 1 - 2t = 1 - 2(y - 1) = -2y + 3$.

As t varies from -1 to 4, (x, y) varies from $(3, 0)$ to $(-7, 5)$.

$\boxed{3}$ $x = t^2 + 1 \Rightarrow t^2 = x - 1$. $y = t^2 - 1 = x - 2$. As t varies from -2 to 2,

(x, y) varies from $(5, 3)$ to $(1, -1)$ {when $t = 0$} and back to $(5, 3)$.

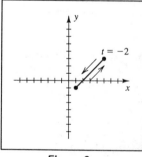

Figure 3

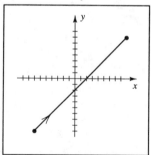

Figure 4

$\boxed{4}$ $x = t^3 + 1 \Rightarrow t^3 = x - 1$. $y = t^3 - 1 = x - 2$.

As t varies from -2 to 2, (x, y) varies from $(-7, -9)$ to $(9, 7)$.

5 $y = 2t + 3 \Rightarrow t = \frac{1}{2}(y - 3)$. $x = 4\left[\frac{1}{2}(y - 3)\right]^2 - 5 \Rightarrow (y - 3)^2 = x + 5$.

This is a parabola with vertex at $(-5, 3)$.

Since t takes on all real values, so does y, and the curve C is the entire parabola.

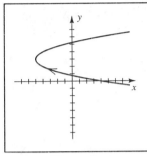

Figure 5

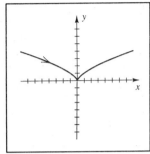

Figure 6

6 $x = t^3 \Rightarrow t = \sqrt[3]{x}$. $y = t^2 = x^{2/3}$. x takes on all real values.

7 $y = e^{-2t} = (e^t)^{-2} = x^{-2} = 1/x^2$.

As t varies from $-\infty$ to ∞, x varies from 0 to ∞, excluding 0.

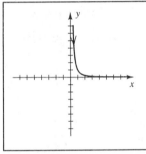

Figure 7

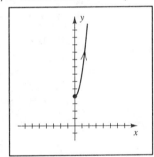

Figure 8

8 $x = \sqrt{t} \Rightarrow t = x^2$. $y = 3t + 4 = 3x^2 + 4$. As t varies from 0 to ∞,

x varies from 0 to ∞ and the graph is the right half of the parabola.

9 $x = 2\sin t$ and $y = 3\cos t \Rightarrow \frac{x}{2} = \sin t$ and $\frac{y}{3} = \cos t \Rightarrow$

$\frac{x^2}{4} + \frac{y^2}{9} = \sin^2 t + \cos^2 t = 1$. As t varies from 0 to 2π,

(x, y) traces the ellipse from $(0, 3)$ in a clockwise direction back to $(0, 3)$.

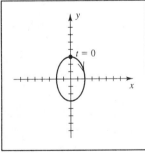

Figure 9

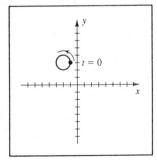

Figure 10

10 $x = \cos t - 2$ and $y = \sin t + 3 \Rightarrow x + 2 = \cos t$ and $y - 3 = \sin t \Rightarrow$ (continued)

$(x + 2)^2 + (y - 3)^2 = \cos^2 t + \sin^2 t = 1$. As t varies from 0 to 2π,

    (x, y) traces the circle from $(-1, 3)$ in a counterclockwise direction back to $(-1, 3)$.

11 $x = \sec t$ and $y = \tan t \Rightarrow x^2 - y^2 = \sec^2 t - \tan^2 t = 1$.

    As t varies from $-\frac{\pi}{2}$ to $\frac{\pi}{2}$, (x, y) traces the right branch of the hyperbola along the

                asymptote $y = -x$ to $(1, 0)$ and then along the asymptote $y = x$.

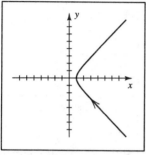

Figure 11

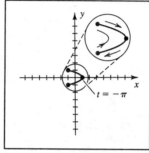

Figure 12

12 $x = \cos 2t = 1 - 2\sin^2 t = 1 - 2y^2$. As t varies from $-\pi$ to π,

    (x, y) varies from $(1, 0)$ {the vertex} down to $(-1, -1)$ {when $t = -\frac{\pi}{2}$}, back to

    the vertex when $t = 0$, up to $(-1, 1)$ {when $t = \frac{\pi}{2}$}, and finally back to the vertex.

13 $y = 2\ln t = \ln t^2$ {since $t > 0$} $= \ln x$.

                As t varies from 0 to ∞, so does x, and y varies from $-\infty$ to ∞.

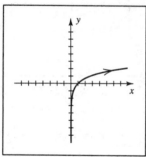

Figure 13

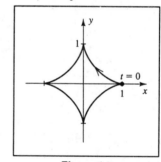

Figure 14

14 $x = \cos^3 t$ and $y = \sin^3 t \Rightarrow x^{2/3} = \cos^2 t$ and $y^{2/3} = \sin^2 t \Rightarrow x^{2/3} + y^{2/3} = 1$ or

    $y = \pm(1 - x^{2/3})^{3/2}$. As t varies from 0 to 2π,

    (x, y) traces the astroid from $(1, 0)$ in a counterclockwise direction back to $(1, 0)$.

$\boxed{15}$ $y = \csc t = \dfrac{1}{\sin t} = \dfrac{1}{x}$.

As t varies from 0 to $\frac{\pi}{2}$, (x, y) varies asymptotically from the positive y-axis to $(1, 1)$.

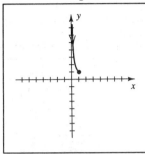

Figure 15

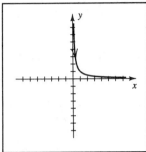

Figure 16

$\boxed{16}$ $y = e^{-t} = (e^t)^{-1} = x^{-1} = \dfrac{1}{x}$.   As t varies from $-\infty$ to ∞,

(x, y) varies asymptotically from the positive y-axis to the positive x-axis.

$\boxed{17}$ $x = t$ and $y = \sqrt{t^2 - 1} \Rightarrow y = \sqrt{x^2 - 1} \Rightarrow x^2 - y^2 = 1$.

Since y is nonnegative, the graph is the top half of both branches of the hyperbola.

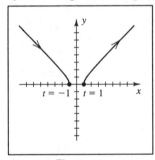

Figure 17

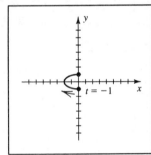

Figure 18

$\boxed{18}$ $y = t$ and $x = -2\sqrt{1 - t^2} \Rightarrow x = -2\sqrt{1 - y^2} \Rightarrow x^2 = 4 - 4y^2 \Rightarrow x^2 + 4y^2 = 4$.

As t varies from -1 to 1, (x, y) traces the ellipse from $(0, -1)$ to $(0, 1)$.

$\boxed{19}$ $x = t$ and $y = \sqrt{t^2 - 2t + 1} \Rightarrow y = \sqrt{x^2 - 2x + 1} = \sqrt{(x - 1)^2} = |x - 1|$.

As t varies from 0 to 4, (x, y) traces $y = |x - 1|$ from $(0, 1)$ to $(4, 3)$.

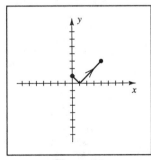

Figure 19

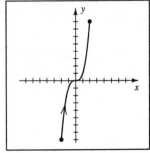

Figure 20

$\boxed{20}$ $y = 8t^3 = (2t)^3 = x^3$. As t varies from -1 to 1, (x, y) varies from $(-2, -8)$ to $(2, 8)$.

21 $x = (t+1)^3 \Rightarrow t = x^{1/3} - 1.$ $y = (t+2)^2 = (x^{1/3} + 1)^2.$

As t varies from 0 to 2, (x, y) varies from $(1, 4)$ to $(27, 16)$.

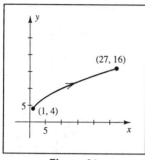

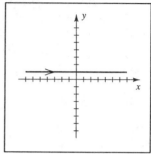

Figure 21   *Figure 22*

22 As t varies from $-\frac{\pi}{2}$ to $\frac{\pi}{2}$, x varies from $-\infty$ to ∞.

y is always 1 so we have the graph of $y = 1$.

23 All of the curves are a portion of the parabola $x = y^2$.

C_1: $x = t^2 = y^2$. y takes on all real values and we have the entire parabola.

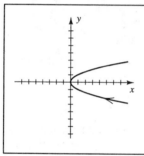

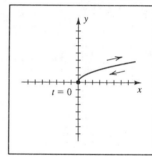

Figure 23 (C_1)   *Figure 23 (C_2)*

C_2: $x = t^4 = (t^2)^2 = y^2$. C_2 is only the top half since $y = t^2$ is nonnegative.

As t varies from $-\infty$ to ∞, the top portion is traced twice.

C_3: $x = \sin^2 t = (\sin t)^2 = y^2$. C_3 is the portion of the curve from $(1, -1)$ to $(1, 1)$.

The point $(1, 1)$ is reached at $t = \frac{\pi}{2} + 2\pi n$ and the point $(1, -1)$ when

$$t = \frac{3\pi}{2} + 2\pi n.$$

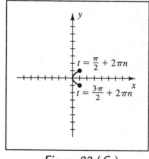

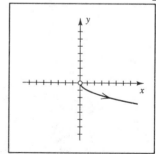

Figure 23 (C_3)   *Figure 23 (C_4)*

C_4: $x = e^{2t} = (e^t)^2 = (-e^t)^2 = y^2$. C_4 is the bottom half of the parabola since y

is negative. As t approaches $-\infty$, the parabola approaches the origin.

24 All of the curves are a portion of the line $x + y = 1$.

C_1: $x + y = t + (1 - t) = 1$. C_1 is the entire line since x takes on all real values.

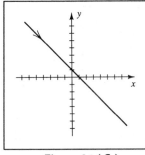

Figure 24 (C_1)

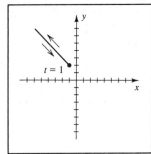

Figure 24 (C_2)

C_2: $x + y = (1 - t^2) + t^2 = 1$. C_2 is the portion of the line where $y \geq 0$ since $y = t^2$.

C_3: $x + y = \cos^2 t + \sin^2 t = 1$. C_3 is only the portion from $(0, 1)$ to $(1, 0)$

since $\sin^2 t$ and $\cos^2 t$ are bounded by 0 and 1.

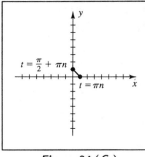

Figure 24 (C_3)

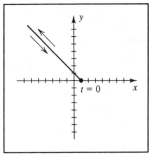

Figure 24 (C_4)

C_4: $x + y = (\ln t - t) + (1 + t - \ln t) = 1$. C_4 is defined when $t > 0$.

When $t = 1$, $(x, y) = (-1, 2)$. As t approaches 0 or ∞, x approaches $-\infty$.

25 In each part, the motion is on the unit circle since $x^2 + y^2 = 1$.

(a) $P(x, y)$ moves from $(1, 0)$ counterclockwise to $(-1, 0)$.

(b) $P(x, y)$ moves from $(0, 1)$ clockwise to $(0, -1)$.

(c) $P(x, y)$ moves from $(-1, 0)$ clockwise to $(1, 0)$.

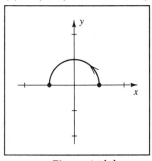

Figure 25(a)

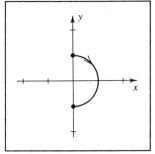

Figure 25(b)

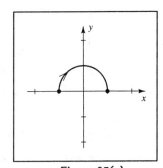

Figure 25(c)

26 In each part, the motion is on a line since $x + y = 1$.

   (a) $P(x, y)$ moves from $(0, 1)$ to $(1, 0)$.

   (b) $P(x, y)$ moves from $(1, 0)$ to $(0, 1)$.

   (c) $P(x, y)$ moves from $(1, 0)$ to $(0, 1)$ twice in each direction.

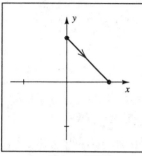
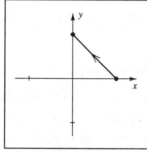
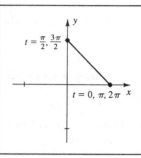

    Figure 26(a)   *Figure 26(b)*   *Figure 26(c)*

27 $x = a \cos t + h$ and $y = b \sin t + k \Rightarrow \frac{x-h}{a} = \cos t$ and $\frac{y-k}{b} = \sin t \Rightarrow$

$\frac{(x-h)^2}{a^2} + \frac{(y-k)^2}{b^2} = \cos^2 t + \sin^2 t = 1$. This is the equation of an ellipse with

        center (h, k) and semiaxes of lengths a and b (axes of lengths $2a$ and $2b$).

28 $x = a \sec t + h$, $y = b \tan t + k \Rightarrow \frac{x-h}{a} = \sec t$, $\frac{y-k}{b} = \tan t \Rightarrow$

$\frac{(x-h)^2}{a^2} - \frac{(y-k)^2}{b^2} = \sec^2 t - \tan^2 t = 1$. This is an equation of a hyperbola with

center (h, k), vertices $V(h \pm a, k)$ and $W(h, k \pm b)$. The transverse axis has length

$2a$ and the conjugate axis has length $2b$. The right branch corresponds to

$$-\tfrac{\pi}{2} < t < \tfrac{\pi}{2} \text{ and the left branch corresponds to } \tfrac{\pi}{2} < t < \tfrac{3\pi}{2}.$$

29 Some choices for parts (a) and (b) are given—there are an infinite number of choices.

   (a) (1) $x = t$, $y = t^2$; $t \in \mathbb{R}$

       (2) $x = \tan t$, $y = \tan^2 t$; $-\tfrac{\pi}{2} < t < \tfrac{\pi}{2}$

       (3) $x = t^3$, $y = t^6$; $t \in \mathbb{R}$

   (b) (1) $x = e^t$, $y = e^{2t}$; $t \in \mathbb{R}$ (only gives $x > 0$)

       (2) $x = \sin t$, $y = \sin^2 t$; $t \in \mathbb{R}$ (only gives $-1 \le x \le 1$)

       (3) $x = \tan^{-1} t$, $y = (\tan^{-1} t)^2$; $t \in \mathbb{R}$ (only gives $-\tfrac{\pi}{2} < x < \tfrac{\pi}{2}$)

30 (a) (1) $x = t$, $y = \ln t$; $t > 0$

       (2) $x = e^t$, $y = t$; $t \in \mathbb{R}$

       (3) $x = t^2$, $y = 2 \ln t$; $t > 0$

   (b) (1) $x = \sec t$, $y = \ln \sec t$; $-\tfrac{\pi}{2} < t < \tfrac{\pi}{2}$ (only gives $x \ge 1$)

       (2) $x = \sin t$, $y = \ln \sin t$; $0 < t < \pi$ (only gives $0 < x \le 1$)

       (3) $x = \tan^{-1} t$, $y = \ln \tan^{-1} t$; $t > 0$ (only gives $0 < x < \tfrac{\pi}{2}$)

31 (a) $x = a \sin \omega t$ and $y = b \cos \omega t \Rightarrow \frac{x}{a} = \sin \omega t$ and $\frac{y}{b} = \cos \omega t \Rightarrow \frac{x^2}{a^2} + \frac{y^2}{b^2} = 1$.

The figure is an ellipse with center $(0, 0)$ and axes of lengths $2a$ and $2b$.

(b) $f(t + p) = a \sin[\omega_1(t + p)] = a \sin[\omega_1 t + \omega_1 p] = a \sin[\omega_1 t + 2\pi n] =$

$$a \sin \omega_1 t = f(t).$$

$g(t + p) = b \cos[\omega_2(t + p)] = b \cos[\omega_2 t + \frac{\omega_2}{\omega_1} 2\pi n] = b \cos[\omega_2 t + \frac{m}{n} 2\pi n] =$

$$b \cos[\omega_2 t + 2\pi m] = b \cos \omega_2 t = g(t).$$

Since f and g are periodic with period p,

the curve retraces itself every p units of time.

32 Since $x = 2 \sin 3t$ has period $\frac{2\pi}{3}$ and $y = 3 \sin(1.5t)$ has period $\frac{4\pi}{3}$,

the curve will repeat itself every $\frac{4\pi}{3}$ units of time.

33 (a) Let $x = 3 \sin(240\pi t)$ and $y = 4 \sin(240\pi t)$ for $0 \le t \le 0.01$.

(b) From the graph, $y_{\text{int}} = 0$ and $y_{\text{max}} = 4$.

Thus, the phase difference is $\phi = \sin^{-1} \frac{y_{\text{int}}}{y_{\text{max}}} = \sin^{-1} \frac{0}{4} = 0°$.

[−9, 9] by [−6, 6]

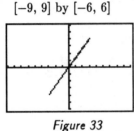

Figure 33

[−9, 9] by [−6, 6]

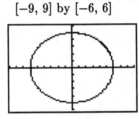

Xscl = 1

Yscl = 1

Xscl = 1

Yscl = 1

Figure 34

34 (a) Let $x = 6 \sin(120\pi t)$ and $y = 5 \cos(120\pi t)$ for $0 \le t \le 0.02$.

(b) From the graph, $y_{\text{int}} = 5$ and $y_{\text{max}} = 5$.

Thus, the phase difference is $\phi = \sin^{-1} \frac{y_{\text{int}}}{y_{\text{max}}} = \sin^{-1} \frac{5}{5} = 90°$.

Note: $5 \cos(120\pi t) = 5 \sin(120\pi t + \pi/2)$

35 (a) Let $x = 80 \sin(60\pi t)$ and $y = 70 \cos(60\pi t - \pi/3)$ for $0 \le t \le 0.035$.

(b) See *Figure 35*. From the graph, $y_{\text{int}} = 35$ and $y_{\text{max}} = 70$.

Thus, the phase difference is $\phi = \sin^{-1} \frac{y_{\text{int}}}{y_{\text{max}}} = \sin^{-1} \frac{35}{70} = 30°$.

Note: Tstep must be sufficiently small to obtain the maximum of 70 on the graph. $70 \cos(60\pi t - \pi/3) = 70 \sin(60\pi t + \pi/6)$

[−120, 120] by [−80, 80]

[−300, 300] by [−200, 200]

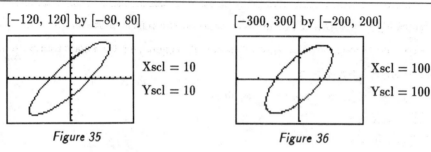

Xscl = 10

Yscl = 10

Xscl = 100

Yscl = 100

Figure 35

Figure 36

36 (a) Let $x = 163 \sin(120\pi t)$ and $y = 163 \sin(120\pi t + \pi/4)$ for $0 \le t \le 0.02$.

(b) From the graph, $y_{\text{int}} \approx 115.26$ and $y_{\text{max}} = 163$.

Thus, the phase difference is $\phi = \sin^{-1}\dfrac{y_{\text{int}}}{y_{\text{max}}} = \sin^{-1}\dfrac{115}{163} \approx 45°$.

37 $x(t) = \sin(6\pi t)$, $y(t) = \cos(5\pi t)$ for $0 \le t \le 2$

[−1, 1] by [−1, 1]

[−1, 1] by [−1, 1]

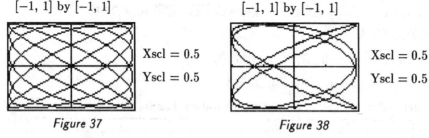

Xscl = 0.5

Yscl = 0.5

Xscl = 0.5

Yscl = 0.5

Figure 37

Figure 38

38 $x(t) = \sin(4t)$, $y(t) = \sin(3t + \pi/6)$ for $0 \le t \le 6.5$

39 Let $\theta = \angle FDP$ and $\alpha = \angle GDP = \angle EDP$. Then $\angle ODG = \left(\frac{\pi}{2} - t\right)$ and

$\alpha = \theta - \left(\frac{\pi}{2} - t\right) = \theta + t - \frac{\pi}{2}$. Arcs AF and PF are equal in length since each is

the distance rolled. Thus, $at = b\theta$, or $\theta = \left(\frac{a}{b}\right)t$ and $\alpha = \dfrac{a+b}{b}t - \dfrac{\pi}{2}$.

Note that $\cos \alpha = \sin\left(\dfrac{a+b}{b}t\right)$ and $\sin \alpha = -\cos\left(\dfrac{a+b}{b}t\right)$.

For the location of the points as illustrated, the coordinates of P are:

$$x = d(O, G) + d(G, B) = d(O, G) + d(E, P) \quad = (a+b)\cos t + b\sin\alpha$$
$$= (a+b)\cos t - b\cos\left(\dfrac{a+b}{b}t\right)$$
$$y = d(B, P) = d(G, D) - d(D, E) = (a+b)\sin t - b\cos\alpha$$
$$= (a+b)\sin t - b\sin\left(\dfrac{a+b}{b}t\right)$$

It can be verified that these equations are valid for all locations of the points.

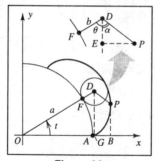

Figure 39

40 See *Figures 40(a) & 40(b)*. The line from O to C, the center of the smaller circle, must also pass through B, the common point of tangency as the smaller circle rolls inside the larger. Note that:

(1) $t = \alpha$ by the properties of parallel lines

(2) $\overline{OB} = \overline{OA} = a$

(3) $\overline{CB} = \overline{CP} = b$

(4) $\overline{OC} = \overline{OB} - \overline{CB} = a - b$

(5) $\angle CPD = \beta$ by the properties of parallel lines

(6) $\angle BCP = \alpha + \beta = t + \beta$

(7) in $\triangle OCE$, $\overline{OE} = \overline{OC} \cos t$ and $\overline{EC} = \overline{OC} \sin t$

(8) in $\triangle DCP$, $\overline{DP} = \overline{CP} \cos \angle CPD$ and $\overline{DC} = \overline{CP} \sin \angle CPD$

(9) $\overline{DP} = \overline{EF}$

(10) in the smaller circle, $\overset{\frown}{BP} = b(\angle BCP)$

(11) in the larger circle, $\overset{\frown}{BA} = a(\angle BOA)$

(12) since $\overset{\frown}{BP} = \overset{\frown}{BA}$ (each is the distance rolled), $b(\angle BCP) = at \Rightarrow \angle BCP = \frac{a}{b}t$

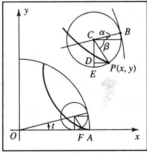

Figure 40(a)

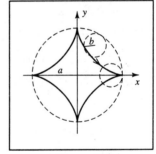

Figure 40(b)

Now, $x = \overline{OE} + \overline{EF}$

$\qquad = \overline{OC} \cos t + \overline{CP} \cos \angle CPD$

$\qquad = (a - b) \cos t + b \cos \beta$

$\qquad = (a - b) \cos t + b \cos (\angle BCP - \alpha)$

$\qquad = (a - b) \cos t + b \cos \left(\frac{a}{b}t - t\right)$

$\qquad = (a - b) \cos t + b \cos \left(\frac{a - b}{b}t\right).$

Similarly, $y = \overline{EC} - \overline{DC}$

$\qquad = \overline{OC} \sin t - \overline{CP} \sin \angle CPD$

$\qquad = (a - b) \sin t - b \sin \beta$

$\qquad = (a - b) \sin t - b \sin (\angle BCP - \alpha)$

$\qquad = (a - b) \sin t - b \sin \left(\frac{a}{b}t - t\right)$

$\qquad = (a - b) \sin t - b \sin \left(\frac{a - b}{b}\right).$

(continued)

If $b = \frac{1}{4}a$, then $x = (a - \frac{1}{4}a)\cos t + \frac{1}{4}a \cos\left(\dfrac{a - \frac{1}{4}a}{\frac{1}{4}a}t\right)$

$$= \tfrac{3}{4}a \cos t + \tfrac{1}{4}a \cos 3t = \tfrac{3}{4}a \cos t + \tfrac{1}{4}a\left(4\cos^3 t - 3\cos t\right) = a \cos^3 t.$$

Also, $y = (a - \frac{1}{4}a)\sin t - \frac{1}{4}a \sin\left(\dfrac{a - \frac{1}{4}a}{\frac{1}{4}a}t\right)$

$$= \tfrac{3}{4}a \sin t - \tfrac{1}{4}a \sin 3t = \tfrac{3}{4}a \sin t - \tfrac{1}{4}a\left(3\sin t - 4\sin^3 t\right) = a \sin^3 t.$$

The identities used for $\cos 3t$ and $\sin 3t$ can be derived by applying the addition,

double angle, and fundamental identities.

$\boxed{41}$ $b = \frac{1}{3}a \Rightarrow a = 3b$. Substituting into the equations from Exercise 39 yields:

$$x = (3b + b)\cos t - b \cos\left(\frac{3b + b}{b}t\right) = 4b \cos t - b \cos 4t$$

$$y = (3b + b)\sin t - b \sin\left(\frac{3b + b}{b}t\right) = 4b \sin t - b \sin 4t$$

As an aid in graphing, to determine where the path of the smaller circle will intersect the path of the larger circle (for the original starting point of intersection at $A(a, 0)$), we can solve $x^2 + y^2 = a^2$ for t.

$$x^2 + y^2 = 16b^2 \cos^2 t - 8b^2 \cos t \cos 4t + b^2 \cos^2 4t +$$

$$16b^2 \sin^2 t - 8b^2 \sin t \sin 4t + b^2 \sin^2 4t$$

$$= 17b^2 - 8b^2 \left(\cos t \cos 4t + \sin t \sin 4t\right)$$

$$= 17b^2 - 8b^2 \left[\cos\left(t - 4t\right)\right] = 17b^2 - 8b^2 \cos 3t.$$

Thus, $x^2 + y^2 = a^2 \Rightarrow 17b^2 - 8b^2 \cos 3t = a^2 = 9b^2 \Rightarrow 8b^2 = 8b^2 \cos 3t \Rightarrow$

$1 = \cos 3t \Rightarrow 3t = 2\pi n \Rightarrow t = \frac{2\pi}{3}n$.

It follows that the intersection points are at $t = \frac{2\pi}{3}, \frac{4\pi}{3},$ and 2π.

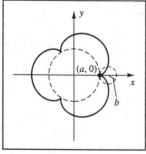

Figure 41

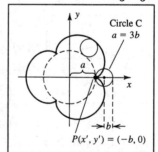

Figure 42

42 Let $C'(h, k)$ be the center of the circle C (in *Figure 42*) and $a = 3b$. Its coordinates are always $x = 4b \cos t$ and $y = 4b \sin t$ since it can be thought of as being on a circle of radius $4b$. Since the equations given in Exercise 41 are for a point P relative to the origin, we can see that the coordinates of P relative to C' are $P(x', y') = P(-b \cos 4t, -b \sin 4t)$. At the starting point A, the coordinates of P relative to C' are $(-b, 0)$. Each time P has these relative coordinates, it will have made one revolution. Setting the coordinates equal to each other and solving for t we have:

$-b \cos 4t = -b \Rightarrow \cos 4t = 1 \Rightarrow 4t = 2\pi n \Rightarrow t = \frac{\pi}{2}n$ and also

$-b \sin 4t = 0 \Rightarrow \sin 4t = 0 \Rightarrow 4t = \pi n \Rightarrow t = \frac{\pi}{4}n$. These results

indicate that C will make one revolution every $\frac{\pi}{2}$ units, or 4 revolutions in 2π units.

43 Change to "Par" from "Func" under $\boxed{\text{MODE}}$. Make the assignments $3(\sin T)\hat{\ }5$ to X_{1T}, $3(\cos T)\hat{\ }5$ to Y_{1T}, 0 to Tmin, 2π to Tmax, and $\pi/30$ to Tstep. Algebraically, we   have $x = 3 \sin^5 t$ and $y = 3 \cos^5 t \Rightarrow \frac{x}{3} = \sin^5 t$ and $\frac{y}{3} = \cos^5 t \Rightarrow$ $(\frac{x}{3})^{2/5} + (\frac{y}{3})^{2/5} = \sin^2 t + \cos^2 t = 1$. The graph traces an astroid.

$[-6, 6]$ by $[-4, 4]$ $[-15, 15]$ by $[-10, 10]$

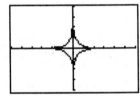
Xscl = 1
Yscl = 1

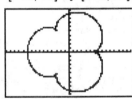
Xscl = 1
Yscl = 1

Figure 43   *Figure 44*

44 The graph traces an epicycloid. See Exercise 39 with $a = 6$ and $b = 2$.

45 The graph traces a curtate cycloid.

$[-30, 30]$ by $[-20, 20]$ $[-15, 15]$ by $[-10, 10]$

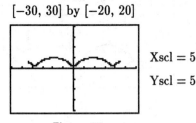
Xscl = 5
Yscl = 5

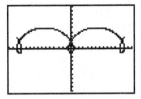
Xscl = 1
Yscl = 1

Figure 45   *Figure 46*

46 The graph traces a prolate cycloid.

47 The figure is a mask with a mouth, nose, and eyes. This graph may be obtained with a graphing utility that has the capability to graph 5 sets of parametric equations.

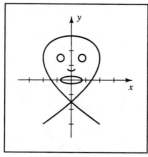

Figure 47

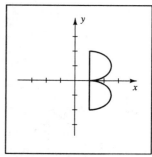

Figure 48

48 C_1: $x = \frac{3}{2}\cos t + 1$ and $y = \sin t - 1 \Rightarrow \frac{2}{3}(x-1) = \cos t$ and $(y+1) = \sin t \Rightarrow$

$\dfrac{(x-1)^2}{\frac{9}{4}} + (y+1)^2 = 1$.   This curve is part of an ellipse with center $(1, -1)$ and

endpoints $(1, -2)$ and $(1, 0)$. Similarly, C_2 is part of an ellipse with center $(1, 1)$ and endpoints $(1, 0)$ and $(1, 2)$. C_3 is a vertical line, $x = 1$, with endpoints $(1, -2)$ and $(1, 2)$. The figure is the letter B.

49 C_1 is the line $y = 3x$ from $(0, 0)$ to $(1, 3)$.   For C_2, $x - 1 = \tan t$ and

$1 - \frac{1}{3}y = \tan t \Rightarrow x - 1 = 1 - \frac{1}{3}y \Rightarrow y = -3x + 6$. This line is sketched from $(1, 3)$ to

$(2, 0)$. C_3 is the horizontal line $y = \frac{3}{2}$ from $(\frac{1}{2}, \frac{3}{2})$ to $(\frac{3}{2}, \frac{3}{2})$. The figure is the letter A.

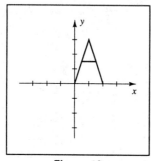

Figure 49

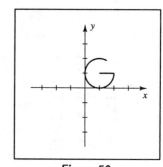

Figure 50

50 C_1 is the circle $(x-1)^2 + (y-1)^2 = 1$ from $(\frac{3}{2}, 1 + \frac{1}{2}\sqrt{3})$ to $(2, 1)$. C_2 is the horizontal line $y = 1$ from $(1, 1)$ to $(2, 1)$. The figure is the letter G.

10.5 Exercises

Note: For the following exercises, the substitutions $x = r\cos\theta$, $y = r\sin\theta$, $r^2 = x^2 + y^2$, and $\tan\theta = \frac{y}{x}$ are used without mention. The numbers listed on each line of the r-θ chart correspond to the numbers labeled on the figures.

$\boxed{1}$ $r = 5 \Rightarrow r^2 = 25 \Rightarrow x^2 + y^2 = 25$, a circle centered at the origin with radius 5.

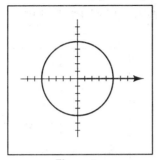

Figure 1

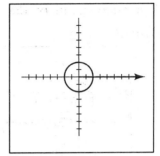

Figure 2

$\boxed{2}$ $r = -2 \Rightarrow r^2 = 4 \Rightarrow x^2 + y^2 = 4$, a circle centered at the origin with radius 2.

$\boxed{3}$ $\theta = -\frac{\pi}{6}$ and $r \in \mathbb{R}$. The line is $y = (\tan \theta)\, x$, or $y = -\frac{1}{3}\sqrt{3}\, x$.

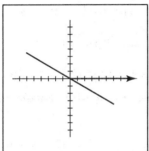

Figure 3

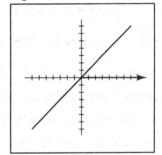

Figure 4

$\boxed{4}$ $\theta = \frac{\pi}{4}$ and $r \in \mathbb{R}$. The line is $y = (\tan \theta)\, x$, or $y = x$.

$\boxed{5}$ $r = 3 \cos \theta \Rightarrow r^2 = 3r \cos \theta \Rightarrow x^2 + y^2 = 3x \Rightarrow$
$(x^2 - 3x + \frac{9}{4}) + y^2 = \frac{9}{4} \Rightarrow (x - \frac{3}{2})^2 + y^2 = \frac{9}{4}.$

Variation of θ			Variation of r	
1)	0	$\rightarrow \frac{\pi}{2}$	$3 \rightarrow$	0
2)	$\frac{\pi}{2}$	$\rightarrow \pi$	$0 \rightarrow$	-3

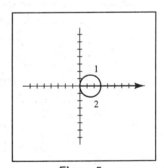

Figure 5

$\boxed{6}$ $r = -2 \sin \theta \Rightarrow r^2 = -2r \sin \theta \Rightarrow x^2 + y^2 = -2y \Rightarrow$
$x^2 + y^2 + 2y + \underline{1} = \underline{1} \Rightarrow x^2 + (y + 1)^2 = 1.$

Variation of θ			Variation of r	
1)	0	$\rightarrow \frac{\pi}{2}$	$0 \rightarrow$	-2
2)	$\frac{\pi}{2}$	$\rightarrow \pi$	$-2 \rightarrow$	0

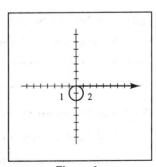

Figure 6

7 $r = 4\cos\theta + 2\sin\theta \Rightarrow r^2 = 4r\cos\theta + 2r\sin\theta \Rightarrow$

$x^2 + y^2 = 4x + 2y \Rightarrow$

$x^2 - 4x + \underline{4} + y^2 - 2y + \underline{1} = \underline{4} + \underline{1} \Rightarrow$

$(x-2)^2 + (y-1)^2 = 5.$

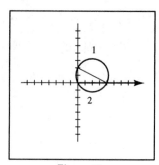

Variation of θ	Variation of r
1) $0 \quad \to \quad \frac{\pi}{2}$	$4 \to \quad 2$
2) $\frac{\pi}{2} \quad \to \quad \pi$	$2 \to \quad -4$

Figure 7

8 $r = 6\cos\theta - 2\sin\theta \Rightarrow r^2 = 6r\cos\theta - 2r\sin\theta \Rightarrow$

$x^2 + y^2 = 6x - 2y \Rightarrow$

$x^2 - 6x + \underline{9} + y^2 + 2y + \underline{1} = \underline{9} + \underline{1} \Rightarrow$

$(x-3)^2 + (y+1)^2 = 10.$

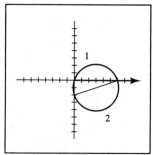

Variation of θ	Variation of r
1) $0 \quad \to \quad \frac{\pi}{2}$	$6 \to \quad -2$
2) $\frac{\pi}{2} \quad \to \quad \pi$	$-2 \to \quad -6$

Figure 8

9 $r = 4(1 - \sin\theta)$ is a cardioid since the coefficient of $\sin\theta$ has the same magnitude as the constant term. We next find the pole values by solving the equation $r = 0$.

$0 = 4(1 - \sin\theta) \Rightarrow \sin\theta = 1 \Rightarrow \theta = \frac{\pi}{2} + 2\pi n.$

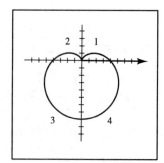

Variation of θ	Variation of r
1) $0 \quad \to \quad \frac{\pi}{2}$	$4 \to \quad 0$
2) $\frac{\pi}{2} \quad \to \quad \pi$	$0 \to \quad 4$
3) $\pi \quad \to \quad \frac{3\pi}{2}$	$4 \to \quad 8$
4) $\frac{3\pi}{2} \quad \to \quad 2\pi$	$8 \to \quad 4$

Figure 9

10 $r = 3(1 + \cos\theta)$ is a cardioid.

$0 = 3(1 + \cos\theta) \Rightarrow \cos\theta = -1 \Rightarrow \theta = \pi + 2\pi n.$

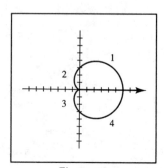

Variation of θ	Variation of r
1) $0 \quad \to \quad \frac{\pi}{2}$	$6 \to \quad 3$
2) $\frac{\pi}{2} \quad \to \quad \pi$	$3 \to \quad 0$
3) $\pi \quad \to \quad \frac{3\pi}{2}$	$0 \to \quad 3$
4) $\frac{3\pi}{2} \quad \to \quad 2\pi$	$3 \to \quad 6$

Figure 10

$\boxed{11}$ $r = -6(1 + \cos\theta)$ is a cardioid.

$0 = -6(1 + \cos\theta) \Rightarrow \cos\theta = -1 \Rightarrow \theta = \pi + 2\pi n.$

Variation of θ		Variation of r	
1)	$0 \rightarrow \frac{\pi}{2}$	$-12 \rightarrow$	-6
2)	$\frac{\pi}{2} \rightarrow \pi$	$-6 \rightarrow$	0
3)	$\pi \rightarrow \frac{3\pi}{2}$	$0 \rightarrow$	-6
4)	$\frac{3\pi}{2} \rightarrow 2\pi$	$-6 \rightarrow$	-12

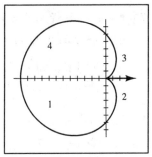

Figure 11

$\boxed{12}$ $r = 2(1 + \sin\theta)$ is a cardioid.

$0 = 2(1 + \sin\theta) \Rightarrow \sin\theta = -1 \Rightarrow \theta = \frac{3\pi}{2} + 2\pi n.$

Variation of θ		Variation of r	
1)	$0 \rightarrow \frac{\pi}{2}$	$2 \rightarrow$	4
2)	$\frac{\pi}{2} \rightarrow \pi$	$4 \rightarrow$	2
3)	$\pi \rightarrow \frac{3\pi}{2}$	$2 \rightarrow$	0
4)	$\frac{3\pi}{2} \rightarrow 2\pi$	$0 \rightarrow$	2

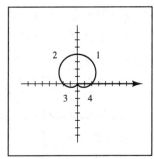

Figure 12

$\boxed{13}$ $r = 2 + 4\sin\theta$ is a limaçon with a loop since the constant term has a smaller magnitude than the coefficient of $\sin\theta$.
$0 = 2 + 4\sin\theta \Rightarrow \sin\theta = -\frac{1}{2} \Rightarrow \theta = \frac{7\pi}{6} + 2\pi n, \frac{11\pi}{6} + 2\pi n.$
We use the pole values as well as the quadrantal angles to set up the r-θ variation chart.

Variation of θ		Variation of r	
1)	$0 \rightarrow \frac{\pi}{2}$	$2 \rightarrow$	6
2)	$\frac{\pi}{2} \rightarrow \pi$	$6 \rightarrow$	2
3)	$\pi \rightarrow \frac{7\pi}{6}$	$2 \rightarrow$	0
4)	$\frac{7\pi}{6} \rightarrow \frac{3\pi}{2}$	$0 \rightarrow$	-2
5)	$\frac{3\pi}{2} \rightarrow \frac{11\pi}{6}$	$-2 \rightarrow$	0
6)	$\frac{11\pi}{6} \rightarrow 2\pi$	$0 \rightarrow$	2

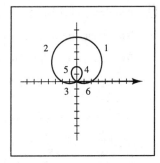

Figure 13

14 $r = 1 + 2\cos\theta$ is a limaçon with a loop.

$0 = 1 + 2\cos\theta \Rightarrow \cos\theta = -\frac{1}{2} \Rightarrow \theta = \frac{2\pi}{3} + 2\pi n, \frac{4\pi}{3} + 2\pi n.$

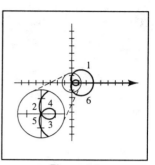

	Variation of θ		Variation of r	
1)	0	$\to \frac{\pi}{2}$	$3 \to$	1
2)	$\frac{\pi}{2}$	$\to \frac{2\pi}{3}$	$1 \to$	0
3)	$\frac{2\pi}{3}$	$\to \pi$	$0 \to$	-1
4)	π	$\to \frac{4\pi}{3}$	$-1 \to$	0
5)	$\frac{4\pi}{3}$	$\to \frac{3\pi}{2}$	$0 \to$	1
6)	$\frac{3\pi}{2}$	$\to 2\pi$	$1 \to$	3

Figure 14

15 $r = \sqrt{3} - 2\sin\theta$ is a limaçon with a loop. $0 = \sqrt{3} - 2\sin\theta \Rightarrow \sin\theta = \sqrt{3}/2 \Rightarrow$

$\theta = \frac{\pi}{3} + 2\pi n, \frac{2\pi}{3} + 2\pi n.$ Let $a = \sqrt{3} - 2 \approx -0.27$ and $b = \sqrt{3} + 2 \approx 3.73.$

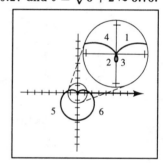

	Variation of θ		Variation of r	
1)	0	$\to \frac{\pi}{3}$	$\sqrt{3} \to$	0
2)	$\frac{\pi}{3}$	$\to \frac{\pi}{2}$	$0 \to$	a
3)	$\frac{\pi}{2}$	$\to \frac{2\pi}{3}$	$a \to$	0
4)	$\frac{2\pi}{3}$	$\to \pi$	$0 \to$	$\sqrt{3}$
5)	π	$\to \frac{3\pi}{2}$	$\sqrt{3} \to$	b
6)	$\frac{3\pi}{2}$	$\to 2\pi$	$b \to$	$\sqrt{3}$

Figure 15

16 $r = 2\sqrt{3} - 4\cos\theta$ is a limaçon with a loop. $0 = 2\sqrt{3} - 4\cos\theta \Rightarrow \cos\theta = \sqrt{3}/2 \Rightarrow$

$\theta = \frac{\pi}{6} + 2\pi n, \frac{11\pi}{6} + 2\pi n.$ Let $a = 2\sqrt{3} - 4 \approx -0.54$ and $b = 2\sqrt{3} + 4 \approx 7.46.$

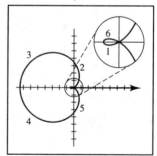

	Variation of θ		Variation of r	
1)	0	$\to \frac{\pi}{6}$	$a \to$	0
2)	$\frac{\pi}{6}$	$\to \frac{\pi}{2}$	$0 \to$	$2\sqrt{3}$
3)	$\frac{\pi}{2}$	$\to \pi$	$2\sqrt{3} \to$	b
4)	π	$\to \frac{3\pi}{2}$	$b \to$	$2\sqrt{3}$
5)	$\frac{3\pi}{2}$	$\to \frac{11\pi}{6}$	$2\sqrt{3} \to$	0
6)	$\frac{11\pi}{6}$	$\to 2\pi$	$0 \to$	a

Figure 16

$\boxed{17}$ $r = 2 - \cos\theta$ ●

$0 = 2 - \cos\theta \Rightarrow \cos\theta = 2 \Rightarrow$ no pole values.

Variation of θ			Variation of r	
1)	0	$\rightarrow$ $\frac{\pi}{2}$	$1 \rightarrow$	2
2)	$\frac{\pi}{2}$	$\rightarrow$ π	$2 \rightarrow$	3
3)	π	$\rightarrow$ $\frac{3\pi}{2}$	$3 \rightarrow$	2
4)	$\frac{3\pi}{2}$	$\rightarrow$ 2π	$2 \rightarrow$	1

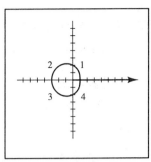

Figure 17

$\boxed{18}$ $r = 5 + 3\sin\theta$ ●

$0 = 5 + 3\sin\theta \Rightarrow \sin\theta = -\frac{5}{3} \Rightarrow$ no pole values.

Variation of θ			Variation of r	
1)	0	$\rightarrow$ $\frac{\pi}{2}$	$5 \rightarrow$	8
2)	$\frac{\pi}{2}$	$\rightarrow$ π	$8 \rightarrow$	5
3)	π	$\rightarrow$ $\frac{3\pi}{2}$	$5 \rightarrow$	2
4)	$\frac{3\pi}{2}$	$\rightarrow$ 2π	$2 \rightarrow$	5

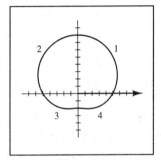

Figure 18

$\boxed{19}$ $r = 4\csc\theta \Rightarrow r\sin\theta = 4 \Rightarrow y = 4$. r is undefined at $\theta = \pi n$.

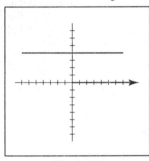

Figure 19

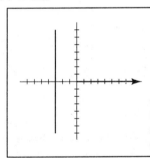

Figure 20

$\boxed{20}$ $r = -3\sec\theta \Rightarrow r\cos\theta = -3 \Rightarrow x = -3$. r is undefined at $\theta = \frac{\pi}{2} + \pi n$.

$\boxed{21}$ $r = 8\cos 3\theta$ is a 3-leafed rose since 3 is odd.

$0 = 8\cos 3\theta \Rightarrow \cos 3\theta = 0 \Rightarrow 3\theta = \frac{\pi}{2} + \pi n \Rightarrow \theta = \frac{\pi}{6} + \frac{\pi}{3}n$.

Variation of θ			Variation of r	
1)	0	$\rightarrow$ $\frac{\pi}{6}$	$8 \rightarrow$	0
2)	$\frac{\pi}{6}$	$\rightarrow$ $\frac{\pi}{3}$	$0 \rightarrow$	-8
3)	$\frac{\pi}{3}$	$\rightarrow$ $\frac{\pi}{2}$	$-8 \rightarrow$	0
4)	$\frac{\pi}{2}$	$\rightarrow$ $\frac{2\pi}{3}$	$0 \rightarrow$	8
5)	$\frac{2\pi}{3}$	$\rightarrow$ $\frac{5\pi}{6}$	$8 \rightarrow$	0
6)	$\frac{5\pi}{6}$	$\rightarrow$ π	$0 \rightarrow$	-8

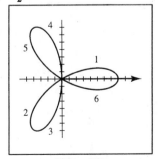

Figure 21

22 $r = 2\sin 4\theta$ is an 8-leafed rose since 4 is even. $0 = 2\sin 4\theta \Rightarrow \sin 4\theta = 0 \Rightarrow$
$4\theta = \pi n \Rightarrow \theta = \frac{\pi}{4}n$. Steps 9 through 16 follow a similar pattern to steps 1 through
8 and are labeled in the correct order.

Variation of θ			Variation of r		
1)	0	$\rightarrow \frac{\pi}{8}$		$0 \rightarrow$	2
2)	$\frac{\pi}{8}$	$\rightarrow \frac{\pi}{4}$		$2 \rightarrow$	0
3)	$\frac{\pi}{4}$	$\rightarrow \frac{3\pi}{8}$		$0 \rightarrow$	-2
4)	$\frac{3\pi}{8}$	$\rightarrow \frac{\pi}{2}$		$-2 \rightarrow$	0
5)	$\frac{\pi}{2}$	$\rightarrow \frac{5\pi}{8}$		$0 \rightarrow$	2
6)	$\frac{5\pi}{8}$	$\rightarrow \frac{3\pi}{4}$		$2 \rightarrow$	0
7)	$\frac{3\pi}{4}$	$\rightarrow \frac{7\pi}{8}$		$0 \rightarrow$	-2
8)	$\frac{7\pi}{8}$	$\rightarrow \pi$		$-2 \rightarrow$	0

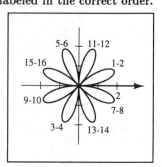

Figure 22

23 $r = 3\sin 2\theta$ is a 4-leafed rose. $0 = 3\sin 2\theta \Rightarrow \sin 2\theta = 0 \Rightarrow 2\theta = \pi n \Rightarrow \theta = \frac{\pi}{2}n$.

Variation of θ			Variation of r		
1)	0	$\rightarrow \frac{\pi}{4}$		$0 \rightarrow$	3
2)	$\frac{\pi}{4}$	$\rightarrow \frac{\pi}{2}$		$3 \rightarrow$	0
3)	$\frac{\pi}{2}$	$\rightarrow \frac{3\pi}{4}$		$0 \rightarrow$	-3
4)	$\frac{3\pi}{4}$	$\rightarrow \pi$		$-3 \rightarrow$	0
5)	π	$\rightarrow \frac{5\pi}{4}$		$0 \rightarrow$	3
6)	$\frac{5\pi}{4}$	$\rightarrow \frac{3\pi}{2}$		$3 \rightarrow$	0
7)	$\frac{3\pi}{2}$	$\rightarrow \frac{7\pi}{4}$		$0 \rightarrow$	-3
8)	$\frac{7\pi}{4}$	$\rightarrow 2\pi$		$-3 \rightarrow$	0

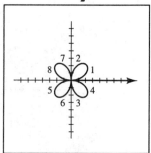

Figure 23

24 $r = 8\cos 5\theta$ is a 5-leafed rose.

$$0 = 8\cos 5\theta \Rightarrow \cos 5\theta = 0 \Rightarrow 5\theta = \frac{\pi}{2} + \pi n \Rightarrow \theta = \frac{\pi}{10} + \frac{\pi}{5}n.$$

Variation of θ			Variation of r		
1)	0	$\rightarrow \frac{\pi}{10}$		$8 \rightarrow$	0
2)	$\frac{\pi}{10}$	$\rightarrow \frac{2\pi}{10}$		$0 \rightarrow$	-8
3)	$\frac{2\pi}{10}$	$\rightarrow \frac{3\pi}{10}$		$-8 \rightarrow$	0
4)	$\frac{3\pi}{10}$	$\rightarrow \frac{4\pi}{10}$		$0 \rightarrow$	8
5)	$\frac{4\pi}{10}$	$\rightarrow \frac{5\pi}{10}$		$8 \rightarrow$	0
6)	$\frac{5\pi}{10}$	$\rightarrow \frac{6\pi}{10}$		$0 \rightarrow$	-8
7)	$\frac{6\pi}{10}$	$\rightarrow \frac{7\pi}{10}$		$-8 \rightarrow$	0
8)	$\frac{7\pi}{10}$	$\rightarrow \frac{8\pi}{10}$		$0 \rightarrow$	8
9)	$\frac{8\pi}{10}$	$\rightarrow \frac{9\pi}{10}$		$8 \rightarrow$	0
10)	$\frac{9\pi}{10}$	$\rightarrow \pi$		$0 \rightarrow$	-8

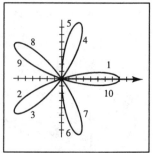

Figure 24

25 $r^2 = 4\cos 2\theta$ (lemniscate) •

$0 = 4\cos 2\theta \Rightarrow \cos 2\theta = 0 \Rightarrow 2\theta = \frac{\pi}{2} + \pi n \Rightarrow \theta = \frac{\pi}{4} + \frac{\pi}{2}n.$

	Variation of θ			Variation of r	
1)	0	$\rightarrow$	$\frac{\pi}{4}$	$\pm 2 \rightarrow$	0
2)	$\frac{\pi}{4}$	$\rightarrow$	$\frac{\pi}{2}$	undefined	
3)	$\frac{\pi}{2}$	$\rightarrow$	$\frac{3\pi}{4}$	undefined	
4)	$\frac{3\pi}{4}$	$\rightarrow$	π	$0 \rightarrow$	± 2

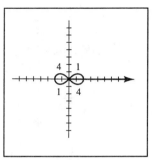

Figure 25

26 $r^2 = -16\sin 2\theta$ •

$0 = -16\sin 2\theta \Rightarrow \sin 2\theta = 0 \Rightarrow 2\theta = \pi n \Rightarrow \theta = \frac{\pi}{2}n.$

	Variation of θ			Variation of r	
1)	0	$\rightarrow$	$\frac{\pi}{4}$	undefined	
2)	$\frac{\pi}{4}$	$\rightarrow$	$\frac{\pi}{2}$	undefined	
3)	$\frac{\pi}{2}$	$\rightarrow$	$\frac{3\pi}{4}$	$0 \rightarrow$	± 4
4)	$\frac{3\pi}{4}$	$\rightarrow$	π	$\pm 4 \rightarrow$	0

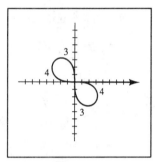

Figure 26

27 $r = 2^\theta$, $\theta \geq 0$ (spiral) •

	Variation of θ			Variation of r	
1)	0	$\rightarrow$	$\frac{\pi}{2}$	1	$\rightarrow$	2.97
2)	$\frac{\pi}{2}$	$\rightarrow$	π	2.97	$\rightarrow$	8.82
3)	π	$\rightarrow$	$\frac{3\pi}{2}$	8.82	$\rightarrow$	26.22
4)	$\frac{3\pi}{2}$	$\rightarrow$	2π	22.62	$\rightarrow$	77.88

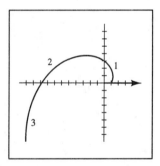

Figure 27

28 The values in the table are listed to emphasize the exponential growth. Note that $e^{2\theta} = (e^2)^\theta$.

	Variation of θ			Variation of r	
1)	0	$\rightarrow$	$\frac{\pi}{2}$	1	$\rightarrow$	23.14
2)	$\frac{\pi}{2}$	$\rightarrow$	π	23.14	$\rightarrow$	535
3)	π	$\rightarrow$	$\frac{3\pi}{2}$	535	$\rightarrow$	$12,392$
4)	$\frac{3\pi}{2}$	$\rightarrow$	2π	$12,392$	$\rightarrow$	$286,751$

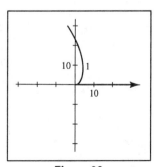

Figure 28

29 $r = 2\theta$, $\theta \geq 0$ •

Variation of θ			Variation of r		
1)	0	$\rightarrow \frac{\pi}{2}$	0	$\rightarrow$	π
2)	$\frac{\pi}{2}$	$\rightarrow \pi$	π	$\rightarrow$	2π
3)	π	$\rightarrow \frac{3\pi}{2}$	2π	$\rightarrow$	3π

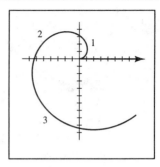

Figure 29

30 $r\theta = 1$, $\theta > 0$ (spiral) •

$r\theta = 1 \Rightarrow r = 1/\theta$. r is undefined at $\theta = 0$.

Variation of θ			Variation of r		
1)	0	$\rightarrow \frac{\pi}{2}$	$+\infty$	$\rightarrow$	0.64
2)	$\frac{\pi}{2}$	$\rightarrow \pi$	0.64	$\rightarrow$	0.32
3)	π	$\rightarrow \frac{3\pi}{2}$	0.32	$\rightarrow$	0.21
4)	$\frac{3\pi}{2}$	$\rightarrow 2\pi$	0.21	$\rightarrow$	0.16

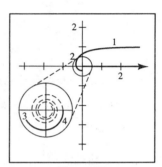

Figure 30

31 $r = 6\sin^2\left(\frac{\theta}{2}\right) = 6\left(\frac{1 - \cos\theta}{2}\right) = 3(1 - \cos\theta)$ is a cardioid.

$0 = 3(1 - \cos\theta) \Rightarrow \cos\theta = 1 \Rightarrow \theta = 2\pi n$.

Variation of θ			Variation of r	
1)	0	$\rightarrow \frac{\pi}{2}$	$0 \rightarrow$	3
2)	$\frac{\pi}{2}$	$\rightarrow \pi$	$3 \rightarrow$	6
3)	π	$\rightarrow \frac{3\pi}{2}$	$6 \rightarrow$	3
4)	$\frac{3\pi}{2}$	$\rightarrow 2\pi$	$3 \rightarrow$	0

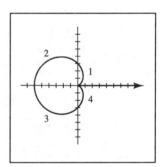

Figure 31

32 $r = -4\cos^2\left(\frac{\theta}{2}\right) = -4\left(\frac{1 + \cos\theta}{2}\right) = -2(1 + \cos\theta)$ is a

cardioid. $0 = -2(1 + \cos\theta) \Rightarrow \cos\theta = -1 \Rightarrow \theta = \pi + 2\pi n$.

Variation of θ			Variation of r	
1)	0	$\rightarrow \frac{\pi}{2}$	$-4 \rightarrow$	-2
2)	$\frac{\pi}{2}$	$\rightarrow \pi$	$-2 \rightarrow$	0
3)	π	$\rightarrow \frac{3\pi}{2}$	$0 \rightarrow$	-2
4)	$\frac{3\pi}{2}$	$\rightarrow 2\pi$	$-2 \rightarrow$	-4

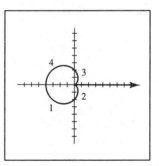

Figure 32

33 Note that $r = 2\sec\theta$ is equivalent to $x = 2$. If $0 < \theta < \frac{\pi}{2}$ or $\frac{3\pi}{2} < \theta < 2\pi$, then $\sec\theta > 0$ and the graph of $r = 2 + 2\sec\theta$ is to the right of $x = 2$. If $\frac{\pi}{2} < \theta < \frac{3\pi}{2}$, $\sec\theta < 0$ and $r = 2 + 2\sec\theta$ is to the left of $x = 2$. r is undefined at $\theta = \frac{\pi}{2} + \pi n$.

$0 = 2 + 2\sec\theta \Rightarrow \sec\theta = -1 \Rightarrow \theta = \pi + 2\pi n$.

Variation of θ			Variation of r	
1)	0	$\rightarrow$ $\frac{\pi}{2}$	$4 \rightarrow$	∞
2)	$\frac{\pi}{2}$	$\rightarrow$ π	$-\infty \rightarrow$	0
3)	π	$\rightarrow$ $\frac{3\pi}{2}$	$0 \rightarrow$	$-\infty$
4)	$\frac{3\pi}{2}$	$\rightarrow$ 2π	$\infty \rightarrow$	4

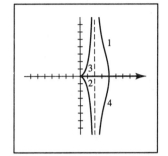

Figure 33

34 Note that $r = -\csc\theta$ is equivalent to $y = -1$. If $0 < \theta < \pi$, then $\csc\theta > 0$ and the graph of $r = 1 - \csc\theta$ is above $y = -1$. If $\pi < \theta < 2\pi$, $\csc\theta < 0$ and $r = 1 - \csc\theta$ is below $y = -1$. r is undefined at $\theta = \pi n$. $0 = 1 - \csc\theta \Rightarrow \csc\theta = 1 \Rightarrow \theta = \frac{\pi}{2} + 2\pi n$.

Variation of θ			Variation of r	
1)	0	$\rightarrow$ $\frac{\pi}{2}$	$-\infty \rightarrow$	0
2)	$\frac{\pi}{2}$	$\rightarrow$ π	$0 \rightarrow$	$-\infty$
3)	π	$\rightarrow$ $\frac{3\pi}{2}$	$\infty \rightarrow$	2
4)	$\frac{3\pi}{2}$	$\rightarrow$ 2π	$2 \rightarrow$	∞

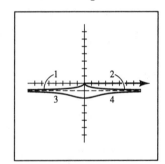

Figure 34

35 (a) $x = r\cos\theta = 3\cos\frac{\pi}{4} = 3\left(\frac{\sqrt{2}}{2}\right) = \frac{3}{2}\sqrt{2}$. $y = r\sin\theta = 3\sin\frac{\pi}{4} = 3\left(\frac{\sqrt{2}}{2}\right) = \frac{3}{2}\sqrt{2}$.

(b) $x = -1\cos\frac{2\pi}{3} = -1(-\frac{1}{2}) = \frac{1}{2}$. $y = -1\sin\frac{2\pi}{3} = -1\left(\frac{\sqrt{3}}{2}\right) = -\frac{1}{2}\sqrt{3}$.

36 (a) $x = 5\cos\frac{5\pi}{6} = 5\left(-\frac{\sqrt{3}}{2}\right) = -\frac{5}{2}\sqrt{3}$. $y = 5\sin\frac{5\pi}{6} = 5(\frac{1}{2}) = \frac{5}{2}$.

(b) $x = -6\cos\frac{7\pi}{3} = -6(\frac{1}{2}) = -3$. $y = -6\sin\frac{7\pi}{3} = -6\left(\frac{\sqrt{3}}{2}\right) = -3\sqrt{3}$.

37 (a) $x = 8\cos\left(-\frac{2\pi}{3}\right) = 8(-\frac{1}{2}) = -4$. $y = 8\sin\left(-\frac{2\pi}{3}\right) = 8\left(-\frac{\sqrt{3}}{2}\right) = -4\sqrt{3}$.

(b) $x = -3\cos\frac{5\pi}{3} = -3(\frac{1}{2}) = -\frac{3}{2}$. $y = -3\sin\frac{5\pi}{3} = -3\left(-\frac{\sqrt{3}}{2}\right) = \frac{3}{2}\sqrt{3}$.

38 (a) $x = 4\cos\left(-\frac{\pi}{4}\right) = 4\left(\frac{\sqrt{2}}{2}\right) = 2\sqrt{2}$. $y = 4\sin\left(-\frac{\pi}{4}\right) = 4\left(-\frac{\sqrt{2}}{2}\right) = -2\sqrt{2}$.

(b) $x = -2\cos\frac{7\pi}{6} = -2\left(-\frac{\sqrt{3}}{2}\right) = \sqrt{3}$. $y = -2\sin\frac{7\pi}{6} = -2(-\frac{1}{2}) = 1$.

39 Let $\theta = \arctan\frac{3}{4}$. $x = 6\cos\theta = 6(\frac{4}{5}) = \frac{24}{5}$. $y = 6\sin\theta = 6(\frac{3}{5}) = \frac{18}{5}$.

40 Let $\theta = \arccos(-\frac{1}{3})$. $x = 10\cos\theta = 10(-\frac{1}{3}) = -\frac{10}{3}$.

$$y = 10\sin\theta = 10\left(\frac{\sqrt{8}}{3}\right) = \frac{10}{3}\sqrt{8} = \frac{20}{3}\sqrt{2}.$$

41 (a) $r^2 = x^2 + y^2 = (-1)^2 + (1)^2 = 2 \Rightarrow r = \sqrt{2}$.

$$\tan\theta = \frac{y}{x} = \frac{1}{-1} = -1 \Rightarrow \theta = \frac{3\pi}{4} \,\{\theta \text{ in QII}\}.$$

(b) $r^2 = (-2\sqrt{3})^2 + (-2)^2 = 16 \Rightarrow r = 4$. $\tan\theta = \frac{-2}{-2\sqrt{3}} = \frac{1}{\sqrt{3}} \Rightarrow \theta = \frac{7\pi}{6} \,\{\theta \text{ in QIII}\}.$

42 (a) $r^2 = (3\sqrt{3})^2 + 3^2 = 36 \Rightarrow r = 6$. $\tan\theta = \frac{3}{3\sqrt{3}} = \frac{1}{\sqrt{3}} \Rightarrow \theta = \frac{\pi}{6} \,\{\theta \text{ in QI}\}.$

(b) $r^2 = 2^2 + (-2)^2 = 8 \Rightarrow r = 2\sqrt{2}$. $\tan\theta = \frac{-2}{2} = -1 \Rightarrow \theta = \frac{7\pi}{4} \,\{\theta \text{ in QIV}\}.$

43 (a) $r^2 = 7^2 + (-7\sqrt{3})^2 = 196 \Rightarrow r = 14$.

$$\tan\theta = \frac{-7\sqrt{3}}{7} = -\sqrt{3} \Rightarrow \theta = \frac{5\pi}{3} \,\{\theta \text{ in QIV}\}.$$

(b) $r^2 = 5^2 + 5^2 = 50 \Rightarrow r = 5\sqrt{2}$. $\tan\theta = \frac{5}{5} = 1 \Rightarrow \theta = \frac{\pi}{4} \,\{\theta \text{ in QI}\}.$

44 (a) $r^2 = (-2\sqrt{2})^2 + (-2\sqrt{2})^2 = 16 \Rightarrow r = 4$.

$$\tan\theta = \frac{-2\sqrt{2}}{-2\sqrt{2}} = 1 \Rightarrow \theta = \frac{5\pi}{4} \,\{\theta \text{ in QIII}\}.$$

(b) $r^2 = (-4)^2 + (4\sqrt{3})^2 = 64 \Rightarrow r = 8$. $\tan\theta = \frac{4\sqrt{3}}{-4} = -\sqrt{3} \Rightarrow \theta = \frac{2\pi}{3} \,\{\theta \text{ in QII}\}.$

45 Choices (a) $(3, 7\pi/3)$, (c) $(-3, 4\pi/3)$, and (e) $(-3, -2\pi/3)$ represent

the same point as $(3, \pi/3)$.

46 Choices (b) $(4, 7\pi/2)$, (d) $(4, -5\pi/2)$, (e) $(-4, -3\pi/2)$, and (f) $(-4, \pi/2)$ represent

the same point as $(4, -\pi/2)$.

47 $x = -3 \Rightarrow r\cos\theta = -3 \Rightarrow r = \frac{-3}{\cos\theta} \Rightarrow r = -3\sec\theta$

48 $y = 2 \Rightarrow r\sin\theta = 2 \Rightarrow r = \frac{2}{\sin\theta} \Rightarrow r = 2\csc\theta$

49 $x^2 + y^2 = 16 \Rightarrow r^2 = 16 \Rightarrow r = \pm 4$ {both are circles with radius 4}.

50 $x^2 = 8y \Rightarrow r^2\cos^2\theta = 8r\sin\theta \Rightarrow r = \frac{8r\sin\theta}{r\cos^2\theta} = 8 \cdot \frac{\sin\theta}{\cos\theta} \cdot \frac{1}{\cos\theta} = 8\tan\theta\sec\theta.$

51 $2y = -x \Rightarrow \frac{y}{x} = -\frac{1}{2} \Rightarrow \tan\theta = -\frac{1}{2} \Rightarrow \theta = \tan^{-1}(-\frac{1}{2})$

52 $y = 6x \Rightarrow \frac{y}{x} = 6 \Rightarrow \tan\theta = 6 \Rightarrow \theta = \tan^{-1}6 \,\{\approx 1.41 \text{ or } 80.54°\}$

53 $y^2 - x^2 = 4 \Rightarrow r^2\sin^2\theta - r^2\cos^2\theta = 4 \Rightarrow -r^2(\cos^2\theta - \sin^2\theta) = 4 \Rightarrow$

$$-r^2\cos 2\theta = 4 \Rightarrow r^2 = \frac{-4}{\cos 2\theta} \Rightarrow r^2 = -4\sec 2\theta$$

54 $xy = 8 \Rightarrow (r\cos\theta)(r\sin\theta) = 8 \Rightarrow r^2(\frac{1}{2})(2\sin\theta\cos\theta) = 8 \Rightarrow r^2\sin 2\theta = 16 \Rightarrow$

$$r^2 = \frac{16}{\sin 2\theta} \Rightarrow r^2 = 16\csc 2\theta$$

55 $(x-1)^2 + y^2 = 1 \Rightarrow x^2 - 2x + 1 + y^2 = 1 \Rightarrow x^2 + y^2 = 2x \Rightarrow$

$$r^2 = 2r\cos\theta \Rightarrow r = 2\cos\theta$$

$\boxed{56}$ $(x+2)^2 + (y-3)^2 = 13 \Rightarrow x^2 + 4x + 4 + y^2 - 6y + 9 = 13 \Rightarrow$

$$x^2 + y^2 = 6y - 4x \Rightarrow r^2 = 6r\sin\theta - 4r\cos\theta \Rightarrow r = 6\sin\theta - 4\cos\theta$$

$\boxed{57}$ $r\cos\theta = 5 \Rightarrow x = 5.$

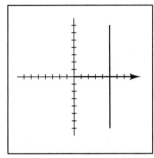

Figure 57

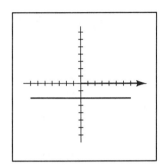

Figure 58

$\boxed{58}$ $r\sin\theta = -2 \Rightarrow y = -2.$

$\boxed{59}$ $r - 6\sin\theta = 0 \Rightarrow r^2 = 6r\sin\theta \Rightarrow x^2 + y^2 = 6y \Rightarrow x^2 + y^2 - 6y + \underline{9} = \underline{9} \Rightarrow$

$$x^2 + (y-3)^2 = 9.$$

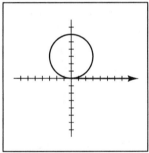

Figure 59

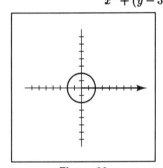

Figure 60

$\boxed{60}$ $r = 2 \Rightarrow r^2 = 4 \Rightarrow x^2 + y^2 = 4.$

$\boxed{61}$ $\theta = \frac{\pi}{4} \Rightarrow \tan\theta = \tan\frac{\pi}{4} \Rightarrow \frac{y}{x} = 1 \Rightarrow y = x.$

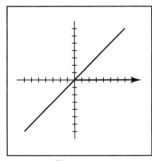

Figure 61

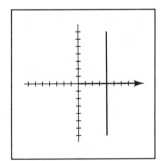

Figure 62

$\boxed{62}$ $r = 4\sec\theta \Rightarrow r\cos\theta = 4 \Rightarrow x = 4.$ θ is undefined at $\frac{\pi}{2} + \pi n.$

63 $r^2(4\sin^2\theta - 9\cos^2\theta) = 36 \Rightarrow 4r^2\sin^2\theta - 9r^2\cos^2\theta = 36 \Rightarrow$

$$4y^2 - 9x^2 = 36 \Rightarrow \frac{y^2}{9} - \frac{x^2}{4} = 1.$$

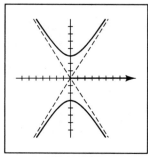

Figure 63

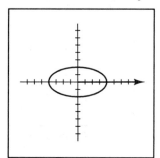

Figure 64

64 $r^2(\cos^2\theta + 4\sin^2\theta) = 16 \Rightarrow r^2\cos^2\theta + 4r^2\sin^2\theta = 16 \Rightarrow$

$$x^2 + 4y^2 = 16 \Rightarrow \frac{x^2}{16} + \frac{y^2}{4} = 1.$$

65 $r^2\cos 2\theta = 1 \Rightarrow r^2(\cos^2\theta - \sin^2\theta) = 1 \Rightarrow r^2\cos^2\theta - r^2\sin^2\theta = 1 \Rightarrow x^2 - y^2 = 1.$

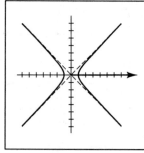

Figure 65

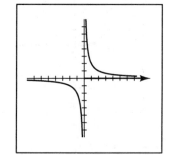

Figure 66

66 $r^2\sin 2\theta = 4 \Rightarrow r^2(2\sin\theta\,\cos\theta) = 4 \Rightarrow (r\sin\theta)(r\cos\theta) = 2 \Rightarrow xy = 2.$

67 $r(\sin\theta - 2\cos\theta) = 6 \Rightarrow r\sin\theta - 2r\cos\theta = 6 \Rightarrow y - 2x = 6.$

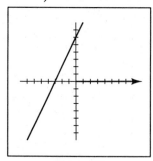

Figure 67

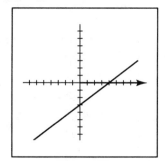

Figure 68

68 $r(3\cos\theta - 4\sin\theta) = 12 \Rightarrow 3r\cos\theta - 4r\sin\theta = 12 \Rightarrow 3x - 4y = 12.$

69 $r(\sin\theta + r\cos^2\theta) = 1 \Rightarrow r\sin\theta + r^2\cos^2\theta = 1 \Rightarrow y + x^2 = 1,$ or $y = -x^2 + 1.$

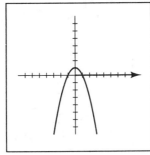

Figure 69

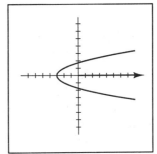

Figure 70

70 $r(r\sin^2\theta - \cos\theta) = 3 \Rightarrow r^2\sin^2\theta - r\cos\theta = 3 \Rightarrow y^2 - x = 3 \Rightarrow x = y^2 - 3.$

71 $r = 8\sin\theta - 2\cos\theta \Rightarrow r^2 = 8r\sin\theta - 2r\cos\theta \Rightarrow x^2 + y^2 = 8y - 2x \Rightarrow$

$$x^2 + 2x + \underline{1} + y^2 - 8y + \underline{16} = \underline{1} + \underline{16} \Rightarrow (x+1)^2 + (y-4)^2 = 17.$$

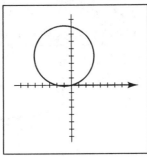

Figure 71

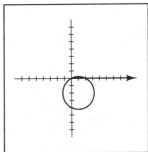

Figure 72

72 $r = 2\cos\theta - 4\sin\theta \Rightarrow r^2 = 2r\cos\theta - 4r\sin\theta \Rightarrow x^2 + y^2 = 2x - 4y \Rightarrow$

$$x^2 - 2x + \underline{1} + y^2 + 4y + \underline{4} = \underline{1} + \underline{4} \Rightarrow (x-1)^2 + (y+2)^2 = 5.$$

73 $r = \tan\theta \Rightarrow r^2 = \tan^2\theta \Rightarrow x^2 + y^2 = \dfrac{y^2}{x^2} \Rightarrow x^4 + x^2 y^2 = y^2 \Rightarrow$

$$y^2 - x^2 y^2 = x^4 \Rightarrow y^2(1 - x^2) = x^4 \Rightarrow y^2 = \frac{x^4}{1 - x^2}$$

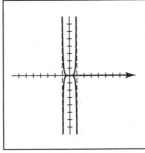

Figure 73

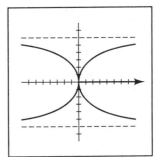

Figure 74

74 $r = 6\cot\theta \Rightarrow r^2 = 36\cot^2\theta \Rightarrow x^2 + y^2 = 36\left(\dfrac{x^2}{y^2}\right) \Rightarrow x^2 y^2 + y^4 = 36x^2 \Rightarrow$

$$36x^2 - x^2 y^2 = y^4 \Rightarrow x^2(36 - y^2) = y^4 \Rightarrow x^2 = \frac{y^4}{36 - y^2}$$

75 Let $P_1(r_1, \theta_1)$ and $P_2(r_2, \theta_2)$ be points in an $r\theta$-plane.

Let $a = r_1$, $b = r_2$, $c = d(P_1, P_2)$, and $\gamma = \theta_2 - \theta_1$.

Substituting into the law of cosines,

$c^2 = a^2 + b^2 - 2ab \cos\gamma$, gives us the formula.

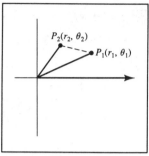

Figure 75

76 (a) $r = a \sin\theta \Rightarrow r^2 = ar \sin\theta \Rightarrow x^2 + y^2 - ay = 0 \Rightarrow$

$$x^2 + y^2 - ay + \tfrac{1}{4}a^2 = \tfrac{1}{4}a^2 \Rightarrow x^2 + (y - \tfrac{1}{2}a)^2 = \tfrac{1}{4}a^2. \quad C(0, \tfrac{1}{2}a); \; r = \tfrac{1}{2}\,|\,a\,|$$

(b) $r = b \cos\theta \Rightarrow r^2 = br \cos\theta \Rightarrow x^2 + y^2 - bx = 0 \Rightarrow$

$$x^2 + y^2 - bx + \tfrac{1}{4}b^2 = \tfrac{1}{4}b^2 \Rightarrow (x - \tfrac{1}{2}b)^2 + y^2 = \tfrac{1}{4}b^2. \quad C(\tfrac{1}{2}b, 0); \; r = \tfrac{1}{2}\,|\,b\,|$$

(c) $r = a \sin\theta + b \cos\theta \Rightarrow r^2 = ar \sin\theta + br \cos\theta \Rightarrow x^2 - bx + y^2 - ay = 0 \Rightarrow$

$$(x - \tfrac{1}{2}b)^2 + (y - \tfrac{1}{2}a)^2 = \tfrac{1}{4}b^2 + \tfrac{1}{4}a^2. \quad C(\tfrac{1}{2}b, \tfrac{1}{2}a); \; r = \tfrac{1}{2}\sqrt{b^2 + a^2}$$

77 (a) $I = \tfrac{1}{2}I_0[1 + \cos(\pi \sin\theta)] \Rightarrow r = 2.5[1 + \cos(\pi \sin\theta)]$ for $\theta \in [0, 2\pi]$.

(b) The signal is maximum in an east–west direction and minimum in a north–south
direction.

[−9, 9] by [−6, 6]   [−9, 9] by [−6, 6]

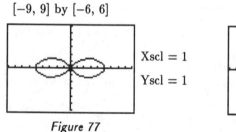
    Xscl = 1

    Yscl = 1

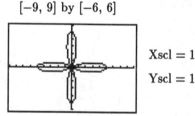
    Xscl = 1

    Yscl = 1

Figure 77   *Figure 78*

78 (a) $I = \tfrac{1}{2}I_0[1 + \cos(\pi \sin 2\theta)] \Rightarrow r = 2.5[1 + \cos(\pi \sin 2\theta)]$ for $\theta \in [0, 2\pi]$.

(b) The signal is maximum in the east, west, north, and south directions. It is
minimum in northwest, southeast, northeast, and southwest directions.

79 Change to "Pol" mode under ⟦ MODE ⟧, assign $2(\sin\theta)^2(\tan\theta)^2$ to r1 under ⟦ Y = ⟧,
and $-\pi/3$ to θmin, $\pi/3$ to θmax, and 0.04 to θstep under ⟦ WINDOW ⟧. The graph is
symmetric with respect to the polar axis.

[−9, 9] by [−6, 6]   [−9, 9] by [−6, 6]

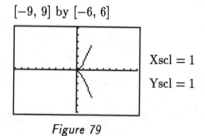
    Xscl = 1

    Yscl = 1

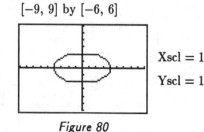
    Xscl = 1

    Yscl = 1

Figure 79   *Figure 80*

80 Assign $4/(1 + (\sin\theta)^2)$ to r1, 0 to θmin, 2π to θmax, and $\pi/30$ to θstep. The graph is symmetric with respect to the polar axis, the line $\theta = \frac{\pi}{2}$, and the pole.

81 Assign $8\cos(3\theta)$ to r1, $4 - 2.5\cos\theta$ to r2, 0 to θmin, 2π to θmax, and $\pi/30$ to θstep. From the graph, there are six points of intersection. The approximate polar coordinates are $(1.75, \pm 0.45)$, $(4.49, \pm 1.77)$, and $(5.76, \pm 2.35)$.

[−12, 12] by [−9, 9]   [−3, 3] by [−2, 2]

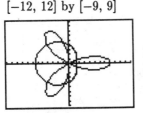
Xscl = 1
Yscl = 1

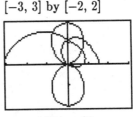
Xscl = 1
Yscl = 1

Figure 81   *Figure 82*

82 Assign $2(\sin\theta)^2$ to r1, $0.75(\theta + (\cos\theta)^2)$ to r2, $-\pi$ to θmin, π to θmax, and $\pi/30$ to θstep. Be sure to plot r2 for both positive and negative values of θ. From the graph, there are five points of intersection. The approximate polar coordinates are $(0, 0)$, $(0.32, -0.41)$, $(0.96, 0.77)$, $(1.39, 0.99)$, and $(1.64, 2.01)$.

10.6 Exercises

Note: (1) For the ellipse, the major axis is vertical if the denominator contains $\sin\theta$, horizontal if the denominator contains $\cos\theta$.

(2) For the hyperbola, the transverse axis is vertical if the denominator contains $\sin\theta$, horizontal if the denominator contains $\cos\theta$. The focus at the pole is called F and V is the vertex associated with (or closest to) F. $d(V, F)$ denotes the distance from the vertex to the focus. The foci are not asked for in the directions, but are listed.

(3) For the parabola, the directrix is on the right, left, top, or bottom of the focus depending on the term "+cos", "−cos", "+sin", or "−sin", respectively, appearing in the denominator.

$\boxed{1}$ Divide the numerator and denominator by the constant term in the denominator, i.e.,

6. $r = \dfrac{12}{6 + 2\sin\theta} = \dfrac{2}{1 + \frac{1}{3}\sin\theta} \Rightarrow e = \frac{1}{3} < 1$, ellipse. From the preceding note,

we see that the denominator has $\sin\theta$ and we have vertices at $\theta = \frac{\pi}{2}$ and $\frac{3\pi}{2}$.

$$V(\tfrac{3}{2}, \tfrac{\pi}{2}) \text{ and } V'(3, \tfrac{3\pi}{2}). \quad d(V, F) = \tfrac{3}{2} \Rightarrow F' = (\tfrac{3}{2}, \tfrac{3\pi}{2}).$$

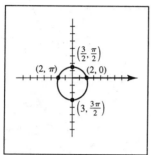

Figure 1

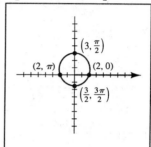

Figure 2

$\boxed{2}$ $r = \dfrac{12}{6 - 2\sin\theta} = \dfrac{2}{1 - \frac{1}{3}\sin\theta} \Rightarrow e = \frac{1}{3} < 1$, ellipse.

$$V(\tfrac{3}{2}, \tfrac{3\pi}{2}) \text{ and } V'(3, \tfrac{\pi}{2}). \quad d(V, F) = \tfrac{3}{2} \Rightarrow F' = (\tfrac{3}{2}, \tfrac{\pi}{2}).$$

$\boxed{3}$ $r = \dfrac{12}{2 - 6\cos\theta} = \dfrac{6}{1 - 3\cos\theta} \Rightarrow e = 3 > 1$, hyperbola.

$$V(\tfrac{3}{2}, \pi) \text{ and } V'(-3, 0). \quad d(V, F) = \tfrac{3}{2} \Rightarrow F' = (-\tfrac{9}{2}, 0).$$

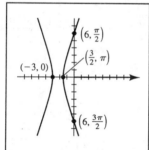

Figure 3

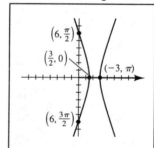

Figure 4

$\boxed{4}$ $r = \dfrac{12}{2 + 6\cos\theta} = \dfrac{6}{1 + 3\cos\theta} \Rightarrow e = 3 > 1$, hyperbola.

$$V(\tfrac{3}{2}, 0) \text{ and } V'(-3, \pi). \quad d(V, F) = \tfrac{3}{2} \Rightarrow F' = (-\tfrac{9}{2}, \pi).$$

$\boxed{5}$ $r = \dfrac{3}{2 + 2\cos\theta} = \dfrac{\frac{3}{2}}{1 + 1\cos\theta} \Rightarrow e = 1$, parabola. Note that the expression is

undefined in the $\theta = \pi$ direction. The vertex is in the $\theta = 0$ direction, $V(\frac{3}{4}, 0)$.

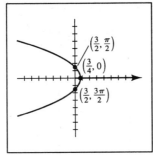

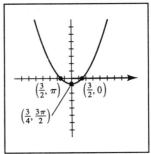

Figure 5   *Figure 6*

$\boxed{6}$ $r = \dfrac{3}{2 - 2\sin\theta} = \dfrac{\frac{3}{2}}{1 - 1\sin\theta} \Rightarrow e = 1$, parabola.

The vertex is in the $\theta = \frac{3\pi}{2}$ direction, $V(\frac{3}{4}, \frac{3\pi}{2})$.

$\boxed{7}$ $r = \dfrac{4}{\cos\theta - 2} = \dfrac{-2}{1 - \frac{1}{2}\cos\theta} \Rightarrow e = \frac{1}{2} < 1$, ellipse.

$V(-\frac{4}{3}, \pi)$ and $V'(-4, 0)$. $d(V, F) = \frac{4}{3} \Rightarrow F' = (-\frac{8}{3}, 0)$

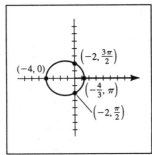

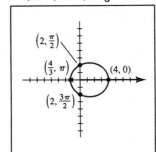

Figure 7   *Figure 8*

$\boxed{8}$ $r = \dfrac{4\sec\theta}{2\sec\theta - 1} \cdot \dfrac{\cos\theta}{\cos\theta} = \dfrac{4}{2 - 1\cos\theta} = \dfrac{2}{1 - \frac{1}{2}\cos\theta} \Rightarrow e = \frac{1}{2} < 1$, ellipse.

$V(\frac{4}{3}, \pi)$ and $V'(4, 0)$. $d(V, F) = \frac{4}{3} \Rightarrow F' = (\frac{8}{3}, 0)$.

Since the original equation is undefined when $\sec\theta$ is undefined,

the points $(2, \frac{\pi}{2})$ and $(2, \frac{3\pi}{2})$ are excluded from the graph.

⑨ $r = \dfrac{6\csc\theta}{2\csc\theta + 3} \cdot \dfrac{\sin\theta}{\sin\theta} = \dfrac{6}{2 + 3\sin\theta} = \dfrac{3}{1 + \frac{3}{2}\sin\theta} \Rightarrow e = \frac{3}{2} > 1$, hyperbola.

$V(\frac{6}{5}, \frac{\pi}{2})$ and $V'(-6, \frac{3\pi}{2})$. $d(V, F) = \frac{6}{5} \Rightarrow F' = (-\frac{36}{5}, \frac{3\pi}{2})$.

Since the original equation is undefined when $\csc\theta$ is undefined,

the points $(3, 0)$ and $(3, \pi)$ are excluded from the graph.

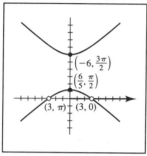

Figure 9

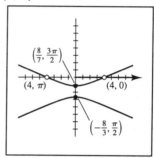

Figure 10

⑩ $r = \dfrac{8\csc\theta}{2\csc\theta - 5} \cdot \dfrac{\sin\theta}{\sin\theta} = \dfrac{8}{2 - 5\sin\theta} = \dfrac{4}{1 - \frac{5}{2}\sin\theta} \Rightarrow e = \frac{5}{2} > 1$, hyperbola.

$V(\frac{8}{7}, \frac{3\pi}{2})$ and $V'(-\frac{8}{3}, \frac{\pi}{2})$. $d(V, F) = \frac{8}{7} \Rightarrow F' = (-\frac{80}{21}, \frac{\pi}{2})$.

Since the original equation is undefined when $\csc\theta$ is undefined,

the points $(4, 0)$ and $(4, \pi)$ are excluded from the graph.

⑪ $r = \dfrac{4\csc\theta}{1 + \csc\theta} \cdot \dfrac{\sin\theta}{\sin\theta} = \dfrac{4}{1 + 1\sin\theta} \Rightarrow e = 1$, parabola. The vertex is in the $\theta = \frac{\pi}{2}$

direction, $V(2, \frac{\pi}{2})$. Since the original equation is undefined when $\csc\theta$ is undefined,

the points $(4, 0)$ and $(4, \pi)$ are excluded from the graph.

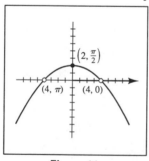

Figure 11

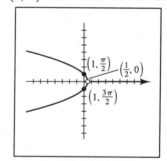

Figure 12

⑫ $r = \csc\theta\,(\csc\theta - \cot\theta) = \dfrac{1}{\sin\theta}\left(\dfrac{1 - \cos\theta}{\sin\theta}\right) = \dfrac{1 - \cos\theta}{1 - \cos^2\theta} = \dfrac{1}{1 + 1\cos\theta} \Rightarrow e = 1$,

parabola. The vertex is in the $\theta = 0$ direction, $V(\frac{1}{2}, 0)$. Since the original equation

is undefined when $\csc\theta$ is undefined, the point $(\frac{1}{2}, 0)$ is excluded from the graph.

Note: For the following exercises, the substitutions

$x = r \cos\theta$, $y = r \sin\theta$, and $r^2 = x^2 + y^2$ are made without mention.

13 $r = \dfrac{12}{6 + 2\sin\theta} \Rightarrow 6r + 2y = 12 \Rightarrow 3r = 6 - y \Rightarrow 9r^2 = 36 - 12y + y^2 \Rightarrow$

$$9x^2 + 8y^2 + 12y - 36 = 0$$

14 $r = \dfrac{12}{6 - 2\sin\theta} \Rightarrow 6r - 2y = 12 \Rightarrow 3r = y + 6 \Rightarrow 9r^2 = y^2 + 12y + 36 \Rightarrow$

$$9x^2 + 8y^2 - 12y - 36 = 0$$

15 $r = \dfrac{12}{2 - 6\cos\theta} \Rightarrow 2r - 6x = 12 \Rightarrow r = 3x + 6 \Rightarrow r^2 = 9x^2 + 36x + 36 \Rightarrow$

$$8x^2 - y^2 + 36x + 36 = 0$$

16 $r = \dfrac{12}{2 + 6\cos\theta} \Rightarrow 2r + 6x = 12 \Rightarrow r = 6 - 3x \Rightarrow r^2 = 36 - 36x + 9x^2 \Rightarrow$

$$8x^2 - y^2 - 36x + 36 = 0$$

17 $r = \dfrac{3}{2 + 2\cos\theta} \Rightarrow 2r + 2x = 3 \Rightarrow 2r = 3 - 2x \Rightarrow 4r^2 = 4x^2 - 12x + 9 \Rightarrow$

$$4y^2 + 12x - 9 = 0$$

18 $r = \dfrac{3}{2 - 2\sin\theta} \Rightarrow 2r - 2y = 3 \Rightarrow 2r = 2y + 3 \Rightarrow 4r^2 = 4y^2 + 12y + 9 \Rightarrow$

$$4x^2 - 12y - 9 = 0$$

19 $r = \dfrac{4}{\cos\theta - 2} \Rightarrow x - 2r = 4 \Rightarrow x - 4 = 2r \Rightarrow x^2 - 8x + 16 = 4r^2 \Rightarrow$

$$3x^2 + 4y^2 + 8x - 16 = 0$$

20 $r = \dfrac{4\sec\theta}{2\sec\theta - 1} \cdot \dfrac{\cos\theta}{\cos\theta} = \dfrac{4}{2 - 1\cos\theta} \Rightarrow 2r - x = 4 \Rightarrow 2r = x + 4 \Rightarrow$

$4r^2 = x^2 + 8x + 16 \Rightarrow 3x^2 + 4y^2 - 8x - 16 = 0.$

r is undefined when $\theta = \frac{\pi}{2}$ or $\frac{3\pi}{2}$. For the rectangular equation, these points

correspond to $x = 0$ (or $r\cos\theta = 0$). Substituting $x = 0$ into the above rectangular

equation yields $4y^2 = 16$, or $y = \pm 2$. $\therefore$ <u>exclude</u> $(0, \pm 2)$

21 $r = \dfrac{6\csc\theta}{2\csc\theta + 3} \cdot \dfrac{\sin\theta}{\sin\theta} = \dfrac{6}{2 + 3\sin\theta} \Rightarrow 2r + 3y = 6 \Rightarrow 2r = 6 - 3y \Rightarrow$

$4r^2 = 36 - 36y + 9y^2 \Rightarrow 4x^2 - 5y^2 + 36y - 36 = 0.$

r is undefined when $\theta = 0$ or π. For the rectangular equation, these points

correspond to $y = 0$ (or $r\sin\theta = 0$). Substituting $y = 0$ into the above rectangular

equation yields $4x^2 = 36$, or $x = \pm 3$. $\therefore$ <u>exclude</u> $(\pm 3, 0)$

22 $r = \dfrac{8\csc\theta}{2\csc\theta - 5} \cdot \dfrac{\sin\theta}{\sin\theta} = \dfrac{8}{2 - 5\sin\theta} \Rightarrow 2r - 5y = 8 \Rightarrow 2r = 5y + 8 \Rightarrow$

$4r^2 = 25y^2 + 80y + 64 \Rightarrow 4x^2 - 21y^2 - 80y - 64 = 0.$

r is undefined when $\theta = 0$ or π. For the rectangular equation, these points

correspond to $y = 0$ (or $r\sin\theta = 0$). Substituting $y = 0$ into the above rectangular

equation yields $4x^2 = 64$, or $x = \pm 4$. $\therefore$ <u>exclude</u> $(\pm 4, 0)$

$\boxed{23}$ $r = \dfrac{4\csc\theta}{1+\csc\theta} \cdot \dfrac{\sin\theta}{\sin\theta} = \dfrac{4}{1+1\sin\theta} \Rightarrow r + y = 4 \Rightarrow r = 4 - y \Rightarrow$

$r^2 = y^2 - 8y + 16 \Rightarrow x^2 + 8y - 16 = 0.$ r is undefined when $\theta = 0$ or π.

For the rectangular equation, these points correspond to $y = 0$ (or $r\sin\theta = 0$).

Substituting $y = 0$ into the above rectangular equation yields $x^2 = 16$, or $x = \pm 4$.

$\therefore$ exclude $(\pm 4, 0)$

$\boxed{24}$ $r = \csc\theta(\csc\theta - \cot\theta) = \dfrac{1}{\sin\theta}\left(\dfrac{1-\cos\theta}{\sin\theta}\right) = \dfrac{1-\cos\theta}{1-\cos^2\theta} = \dfrac{1}{1+\cos\theta} \Rightarrow$

$r + x = 1 \Rightarrow r = 1 - x \Rightarrow r^2 = 1 - 2x + x^2 \Rightarrow y^2 + 2x - 1 = 0.$

r is undefined when $\theta = 0$ or π. For the rectangular equation, this point corresponds

to $y = 0$ (or $r\sin\theta = 0$). Substituting $y = 0$ into the above rectangular equation

yields $2x - 1 = 0$, or $x = \frac{1}{2}$. $\therefore$ exclude $(\frac{1}{2}, 0)$

$\boxed{25}$ $r = 2\sec\theta \Rightarrow r\cos\theta = 2 \Rightarrow x = 2.$ Thus, $d = 2$ and since the directrix is on the

right of the focus at the pole, we use "$+\cos\theta$". $r = \dfrac{2(\frac{1}{3})}{1+\frac{1}{3}\cos\theta} \cdot \dfrac{3}{3} = \dfrac{2}{3+\cos\theta}.$

$\boxed{26}$ $r\cos\theta = 5 \Rightarrow x = 5 \Rightarrow d = 5$ and use "$+\cos\theta$". $r = \dfrac{5(1)}{1+1\cos\theta} = \dfrac{5}{1+\cos\theta}.$

$\boxed{27}$ $r\cos\theta = -3 \Rightarrow x = -3.$ Thus, $d = 3$ and since the directrix is on the left of the

focus at the pole, we use "$-\cos\theta$". $r = \dfrac{3(\frac{4}{3})}{1-\frac{4}{3}\cos\theta} \cdot \dfrac{3}{3} = \dfrac{12}{3-4\cos\theta}.$

$\boxed{28}$ $r = -4\sec\theta \Rightarrow r\cos\theta = -4 \Rightarrow x = -4 \Rightarrow d = 4$ and use "$-\cos\theta$".

$$r = \dfrac{4(3)}{1-3\cos\theta} = \dfrac{12}{1-3\cos\theta}.$$

$\boxed{29}$ $r\sin\theta = -2 \Rightarrow y = -2.$ Thus, $d = 2$ and since the directrix is under the focus at

the pole, we use "$-\sin\theta$". $r = \dfrac{2(1)}{1-1\sin\theta} = \dfrac{2}{1-\sin\theta}.$

$\boxed{30}$ $r = -3\csc\theta \Rightarrow r\sin\theta = -3 \Rightarrow y = -3 \Rightarrow d = 3$ and use "$-\sin\theta$".

$$r = \dfrac{3(4)}{1-4\sin\theta} = \dfrac{12}{1-4\sin\theta}.$$

$\boxed{31}$ $r = 4\csc\theta \Rightarrow r\sin\theta = 4 \Rightarrow y = 4.$ Thus, $d = 4$ and since the directrix is above

the focus at the pole, we use "$+\sin\theta$". $r = \dfrac{4(\frac{2}{5})}{1+\frac{2}{5}\sin\theta} \cdot \dfrac{5}{5} = \dfrac{8}{5+2\sin\theta}.$

$\boxed{32}$ $r\sin\theta = 5 \Rightarrow y = 5 \Rightarrow d = 5$ and use "$+\sin\theta$". $r = \dfrac{5(\frac{3}{4})}{1+\frac{3}{4}\sin\theta} \cdot \dfrac{4}{4} = \dfrac{15}{4+3\sin\theta}.$

$\boxed{33}$ For a parabola, $e = 1$. The vertex is 4 units on top of the focus at the pole so

$d = 2(4)$ and we should use "$+\sin\theta$" in the denominator. $r = \dfrac{8}{1+\sin\theta}$

$\boxed{34}$ For a parabola, $e = 1$. The vertex is 5 units to the right of the focus at the pole so

$d = 2(5)$ and we should use "$+\cos\theta$" in the denominator. $r = \dfrac{10}{1+\cos\theta}$

35 (a) See *Figure 35.* $e = \frac{c}{a} = \frac{d(C, F)}{d(C, V)} = \frac{3}{4}.$

(b) Since the vertex is under the focus at the pole, use "$-\sin\theta$".

$$r = \frac{d\left(\frac{3}{4}\right)}{1 - \frac{3}{4}\sin\theta} \text{ and } r = 1 \text{ when } \theta = \frac{3\pi}{2} \Rightarrow 1 = \frac{d\left(\frac{3}{4}\right)}{1 - \frac{3}{4}(-1)} \Rightarrow 1 = \frac{\frac{3}{4}d}{\frac{7}{4}} \Rightarrow$$

$$d = \frac{7}{3}. \text{ Thus, } r = \frac{\left(\frac{7}{3}\right)\left(\frac{3}{4}\right)}{1 - \frac{3}{4}\sin\theta} \cdot \frac{4}{4} = \frac{7}{4 - 3\sin\theta}. \quad \left\{\frac{x^2}{7} + \frac{(y-3)^2}{16} = 1\right\}$$

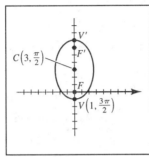

Figure 35

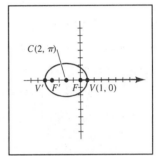

Figure 36

36 (a) See *Figure 36.* $e = \frac{c}{a} = \frac{d(C, F)}{d(C, V)} = \frac{2}{3}.$

(b) Since the vertex is to the right of the focus at the pole, use "$+\cos\theta$".

$$r = \frac{d\left(\frac{2}{3}\right)}{1 + \frac{2}{3}\cos\theta} \text{ and } r = 1 \text{ when } \theta = 0 \Rightarrow 1 = \frac{d\left(\frac{2}{3}\right)}{1 + \frac{2}{3}(1)} \Rightarrow 1 = \frac{\frac{2}{3}d}{\frac{5}{3}} \Rightarrow d = \frac{5}{2}.$$

$$\text{Thus, } r = \frac{\left(\frac{5}{2}\right)\left(\frac{2}{3}\right)}{1 + \frac{2}{3}\cos\theta} \cdot \frac{3}{3} = \frac{5}{3 + 2\cos\theta}. \quad \left\{\frac{(x+2)^2}{9} + \frac{y^2}{5} = 1\right\}$$

37 (a) Let V and C denote the vertex closest to the sun and the center of the ellipse, respectively. Let s denote the distance from V to the directrix to the left of V.

$d(O, V) = d(C, V) - d(C, O) = a - c = a - ea = a(1 - e).$

Also, by the first theorem in §10.6, $\dfrac{d(O, V)}{s} = e \Rightarrow s = \dfrac{d(O, V)}{e} = \dfrac{a(1-e)}{e}.$

Now, $d = s + d(O, V) = \dfrac{a(1-e)}{e} + a(1-e) = \dfrac{a(1-e^2)}{e}$ and $de = a(1 - e^2).$

Thus, the equation of the orbit is $r = \dfrac{(1 - e^2)a}{1 - e\cos\theta}.$

(b) The minimum distance occurs when $\theta = \pi$. $r_{\text{per}} = \dfrac{(1 - e^2)a}{1 - e(-1)} = a(1 - e).$

The maximum distance occurs when $\theta = 0$. $r_{\text{aph}} = \dfrac{(1 - e^2)a}{1 - e(1)} = a(1 + e).$

[38] $r = \dfrac{(1-e^2)a}{1-e\cos\theta} = \dfrac{(1+e)[(1-e)a]}{1-e\cos\theta} = \dfrac{(1+0.249)(29.62)}{1-0.249\cos\theta}$ { since $r_{per} = a(1-e)$ }

$\approx \dfrac{37.00}{1-0.249\cos\theta}$ is an equation of Pluto's orbit.

$$r_{aph} = a(1+e) = \left(\dfrac{r_{per}}{1-e}\right)(1+e) = \left(\dfrac{29.62}{1-0.249}\right)(1+0.249) \approx 49.26 \text{ AU.}$$

[39] (a) Since $e = 0.9673 < 1$, the orbit of Halley's Comet is elliptical.

(b) The polar equation for the orbit of Saturn is $r = \dfrac{9.006(1+0.056)}{1-0.056\cos\theta}$.

The polar equation for Halley's comet is $r = \dfrac{0.5871(1+0.9673)}{1-0.9673\cos\theta}$.

[−36, 36] by [−24, 24]   [−18, 18] by [−12, 12]

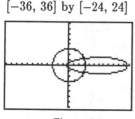 Xscl = 3   Yscl = 3   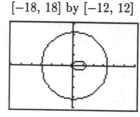 Xscl = 3   Yscl = 3

Figure 39   Figure 40

[40] (a) Since $e = 0.8499 < 1$, the orbit of Encke's Comet is elliptical.

(b) The polar equation for Encke's comet is $r = \dfrac{0.3317(1+0.8499)}{1-0.8499\cos\theta}$.

[41] (a) Since $e = 1.003 > 1$, the orbit of Comet 1959 III is hyperbolic.

(b) The polar equation for Comet 1959 III is $r = \dfrac{1.251(1+1.003)}{1-1.003\cos\theta}$.

[−18, 18] by [−12, 12]   [−18, 18] by [−12, 12]

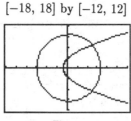 Xscl = 3   Yscl = 3   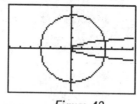 Xscl = 3   Yscl = 3

Figure 41   Figure 42

[42] (a) Since $e = 1.000$, the orbit of Comet 1973.99 is parabolic.

(b) The polar equation for Comet 1973.99 is $r = \dfrac{0.142(1+1.000)}{1-1.000\cos\theta}$.

Chapter 10 Review Exercises

Note: Let the notation be the same as in §10.1–10.6.

$\boxed{1}$ $y^2 = 64x \Rightarrow x = \frac{1}{64}y^2 \Rightarrow a = \frac{1}{64}.$ $p = \frac{1}{4(\frac{1}{64})} = 16.$ $V(0, 0);$ $F(16, 0);$ $l: x = -16$

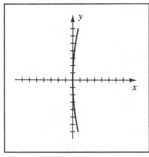

Figure 1

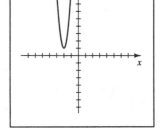

Figure 2

$\boxed{2}$ $y = 8x^2 + 32x + 33 \Rightarrow a = 8.$ $p = \frac{1}{4(8)} = \frac{1}{32}.$ $V(-2, 1);$ $F(-2, \frac{33}{32});$ $l: y = \frac{31}{32}$

$\boxed{3}$ $9y^2 = 144 - 16x^2 \Rightarrow \frac{x^2}{9} + \frac{y^2}{16} = 1;$ $c^2 = 16 - 9 \Rightarrow c = \pm\sqrt{7};$

$$V(0, \pm 4); F(0, \pm\sqrt{7}); M(\pm 3, 0)$$

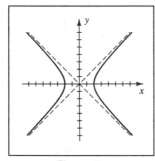

Figure 3

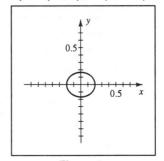

Figure 4

$\boxed{4}$ $9y^2 = 144 + 16x^2 \Rightarrow \frac{y^2}{16} - \frac{x^2}{9} = 1;$ $c^2 = 16 + 9 \Rightarrow c = \pm 5;$

$$V(0, \pm 4); F(0, \pm 5); W(\pm 3, 0); y = \pm\tfrac{4}{3}x$$

$\boxed{5}$ $x^2 - y^2 - 4 = 0 \Rightarrow \frac{x^2}{4} - \frac{y^2}{4} = 1;$ $c^2 = 4 + 4 \Rightarrow c = \pm 2\sqrt{2};$

$$V(\pm 2, 0); F(\pm 2\sqrt{2}, 0); W(0, \pm 2); y = \pm x$$

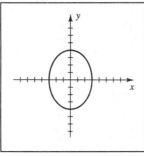

Figure 5

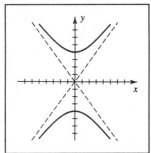

Figure 6

$\boxed{6}$ $\frac{x^2}{\frac{1}{25}} + \frac{y^2}{\frac{1}{36}} = 1;$ $c^2 = \frac{1}{25} - \frac{1}{36} \Rightarrow c = \pm\frac{1}{30}\sqrt{11};$ $V(\pm\frac{1}{5}, 0);$ $F(\pm\frac{1}{30}\sqrt{11}, 0);$ $M(0, \pm\frac{1}{6})$

$\boxed{7}$ $25y = 100 - x^2 \Rightarrow y = 4 - \frac{1}{25}x^2 \Rightarrow a = -\frac{1}{25}.$ $p = \dfrac{1}{4(-\frac{1}{25})} = -\frac{25}{4}.$

$$V(0,\, 4);\; F\left(0,\, -\tfrac{9}{4}\right);\; l{:}\, y = \tfrac{41}{4}$$

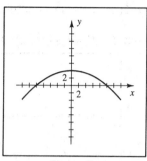

Figure 7

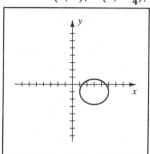

Figure 8

$\boxed{8}$ $3x^2 + 4y^2 - 18x + 8y + 19 = 0 \Rightarrow$

$3(x^2 - 6x + \underline{\;9\;}) + 4(y^2 + 2y + \underline{\;1\;}) = -19 + \underline{\;27\;} + \underline{\;4\;} \Rightarrow$

$3(x-3)^2 + 4(y+1)^2 = 12 \Rightarrow \dfrac{(x-3)^2}{4} + \dfrac{(y+1)^2}{3} = 1;$

$c^2 = 4 - 3 \Rightarrow c = \pm 1;\; C(3,\, -1);\; V(3 \pm 2,\, -1);\; F(3 \pm 1,\, -1);\; M(3,\, -1 \pm \sqrt{3})$

$\boxed{9}$ $x^2 - 9y^2 + 8x + 90y - 210 = 0 \Rightarrow$

$(x^2 + 8x + \underline{\;16\;}) - 9(y^2 - 10y + \underline{\;25\;}) = 210 + \underline{\;16\;} - \underline{\;225\;} \Rightarrow$

$(x+4)^2 - 9(y-5)^2 = 1 \Rightarrow \dfrac{(x+4)^2}{1} - \dfrac{(y-5)^2}{\frac{1}{9}} = 1;\; c^2 = 1 + \tfrac{1}{9} \Rightarrow c = \pm \tfrac{1}{3}\sqrt{10};$

$$C(-4,\, 5);\; V(-4 \pm 1,\, 5);\; F\left(-4 \pm \tfrac{1}{3}\sqrt{10},\, 5\right);\; W\left(-4,\, 5 \pm \tfrac{1}{3}\right);\; (y-5) = \pm \tfrac{1}{3}(x+4)$$

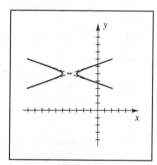

Figure 9

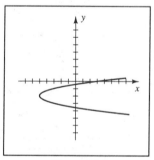

Figure 10

$\boxed{10}$ $x = 2y^2 + 8y + 3 \Rightarrow a = 2.$ $p = \dfrac{1}{4(2)} = \tfrac{1}{8}.$ $V(-5,\, -2);\; F\left(-\tfrac{39}{8},\, -2\right);\; l{:}\, x = -\tfrac{41}{8}$

11. $4x^2 + 9y^2 + 24x - 36y + 36 = 0 \Rightarrow$

$4(x^2 + 6x + \underline{9}) + 9(y^2 - 4y + \underline{4}) = -36 + \underline{36} + \underline{36} \Rightarrow$

$4(x+3)^2 + 9(y-2)^2 = 36 \Rightarrow \dfrac{(x+3)^2}{9} + \dfrac{(y-2)^2}{4} = 1; \; c^2 = 9 - 4 \Rightarrow c = \pm\sqrt{5};$

$C(-3, 2); \; V(-3 \pm 3, 2); \; F(-3 \pm \sqrt{5}, 2); \; M(-3, 2 \pm 2)$

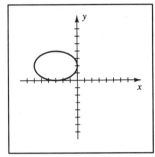

Figure 11

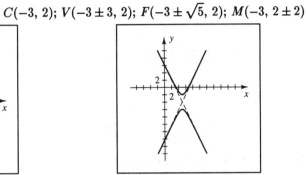

Figure 12

12. $4x^2 - y^2 - 40x - 8y + 88 = 0 \Rightarrow$

$4(x^2 - 10x + \underline{25}) - (y^2 + 8y + \underline{16}) = -88 + \underline{100} - \underline{16} \Rightarrow$

$4(x-5)^2 - (y+4)^2 = -4 \Rightarrow \dfrac{(y+4)^2}{4} - \dfrac{(x-5)^2}{1} = 1; \; c^2 = 4 + 1 \Rightarrow c = \pm\sqrt{5};$

$C(5, -4); \; V(5, -4 \pm 2); \; F(5, -4 \pm \sqrt{5}); \; W(5 \pm 1, -4); \; (y+4) = \pm 2(x-5)$

13. $y^2 - 8x + 8y + 32 = 0 \Rightarrow x = \frac{1}{8}y^2 + y + 4 \Rightarrow a = \frac{1}{8}. \; p = \dfrac{1}{4(\frac{1}{8})} = 2.$

$V(2, -4); \; F(4, -4); \; l: x = 0$

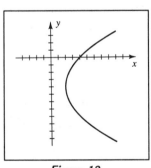

Figure 13

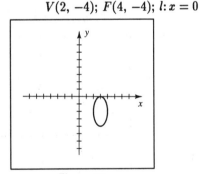

Figure 14

14. $4x^2 + y^2 - 24x + 4y + 36 = 0 \Rightarrow$

$4(x^2 - 6x + \underline{9}) + (y^2 + 4y + \underline{4}) = -36 + \underline{36} + \underline{4} \Rightarrow$

$4(x-3)^2 + (y+2)^2 = 4 \Rightarrow \dfrac{(x-3)^2}{1} + \dfrac{(y+2)^2}{4} = 1; \; c^2 = 4 - 1 \Rightarrow c = \pm\sqrt{3};$

$C(3, -2); \; V(3, -2 \pm 2); \; F(3, -2 \pm \sqrt{3}); \; M(3 \pm 1, -2)$

15 $x^2 - 9y^2 + 8x + 7 = 0 \Rightarrow$

$(x^2 + 8x + \underline{16}) - 9(y^2) = -7 + \underline{16} \Rightarrow (x+4)^2 - 9(y^2) = 9 \Rightarrow$

$\dfrac{(x+4)^2}{9} - \dfrac{y^2}{1} = 1; \ c^2 = 9 + 1 \Rightarrow c = \pm\sqrt{10};$

$C(-4, 0); \ V(-4 \pm 3, 0); \ F(-4 \pm \sqrt{10}, 0); \ W(-4, 0 \pm 1); \ y = \pm\frac{1}{3}(x + 4)$

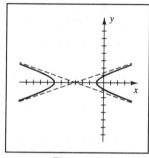

Figure 15

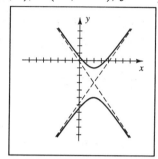

Figure 16

16 $y^2 - 2x^2 + 6y + 8x - 3 = 0 \Rightarrow$

$(y^2 + 6y + \underline{9}) - 2(x^2 - 4x + \underline{4}) = 3 + \underline{9} - \underline{8} \Rightarrow$

$(y+3)^2 - 2(x-2)^2 = 4 \Rightarrow \dfrac{(y+3)^2}{4} - \dfrac{(x-2)^2}{2} = 1; \ c^2 = 4 + 2 \Rightarrow c = \pm\sqrt{6};$

$C(2, -3); \ V(2, -3 \pm 2); \ F(2, -3 \pm \sqrt{6}); \ W(2 \pm \sqrt{2}, -3); \ (y + 3) = \pm\sqrt{2}(x - 2)$

17 The vertex is $V(-7, k)$. $y = a(x + 10)(x + 4)$ and $x = 0, y = 80 \Rightarrow$

$80 = a(10)(4) \Rightarrow a = 2$. $x = -7 \Rightarrow y = 2(3)(-3) = -18$. Hence, $y = 2(x + 7)^2 - 18$.

18 The vertex is $V(-4, k)$. $y = a(x + 11)(x - 3)$ and $x = 2, y = 39 \Rightarrow$

$39 = a(13)(-1) \Rightarrow a = -3$. $x = -4 \Rightarrow y = -3(7)(-7) = 147$.

Hence, $y = -3(x + 4)^2 + 147$.

19 An equation is $\dfrac{y^2}{7^2} - \dfrac{x^2}{3^2} = 1$ or $\dfrac{y^2}{49} - \dfrac{x^2}{9} = 1$.

20 $F(-4, 0)$ and $l : x = 4 \Rightarrow p = -4$ and $V(0, 0)$.

An equation is $(y - 0)^2 = \big[4(-4)\big](x - 0)$, or $y^2 = -16x$.

21 $F(0, -10)$ and $l : y = 10 \Rightarrow p = -10$ and $V(0, 0)$.

An equation is $(x - 0)^2 = \big[4(-10)\big](y - 0)$, or $x^2 = -40y$.

22 The general equation of a parabola that is symmetric to the x-axis and has its vertex at the origin is $x = ay^2$. Substituting $x = 5$ and $y = -1$ into that equation yields

$a = 5$. An equation is $x = 5y^2$.

23 $V(0, \pm 10)$ and $F(0, \pm 5) \Rightarrow b^2 = 10^2 - 5^2 = 75$.

An equation is $\dfrac{x^2}{75} + \dfrac{y^2}{10^2} = 1$ or $\dfrac{x^2}{75} + \dfrac{y^2}{100} = 1$.

24 $F(\pm 10, 0)$ and $V(\pm 5, 0) \Rightarrow b^2 = 10^2 - 5^2 = 75$.

An equation is $\dfrac{x^2}{5^2} - \dfrac{y^2}{75} = 1$ or $\dfrac{x^2}{25} - \dfrac{y^2}{75} = 1$.

[25] Asymptote equations of $y = \pm 9x$ and $V(0, \pm 6) \Rightarrow b = \frac{6}{9} = \frac{2}{3}$.

$$\text{An equation is } \frac{y^2}{6^2} - \frac{x^2}{\left(\frac{2}{3}\right)^2} = 1 \text{ or } \frac{y^2}{36} - \frac{x^2}{\frac{4}{9}} = 1.$$

[26] $F(\pm 2, 0) \Rightarrow c^2 = 4$. Now $\frac{x^2}{a^2} + \frac{y^2}{b^2} = 1$ can be written as $\frac{x^2}{a^2} + \frac{y^2}{a^2 - 4} = 1$ since

$b^2 = a^2 - c^2$. Substituting $x = 2$ and $y = \sqrt{2}$ into that equation yields

$\frac{4}{a^2} + \frac{2}{a^2 - 4} = 1 \Rightarrow 4a^2 - 16 + 2a^2 = a^4 - 4a^2 \Rightarrow a^4 - 10a^2 + 16 = 0 \Rightarrow$

$(a^2 - 2)(a^2 - 8) = 0 \Rightarrow a^2 = 2, 8$. Since $a > c$, a^2 must be 8 and b^2 is equal to 4.

$$\text{An equation is } \frac{x^2}{8} + \frac{y^2}{4} = 1.$$

[27] $M(\pm 5, 0) \Rightarrow b = 5$. $e = \frac{c}{a} = \frac{\sqrt{a^2 - b^2}}{a} = \frac{\sqrt{a^2 - 25}}{a} = \frac{2}{3} \Rightarrow \frac{2}{3}a = \sqrt{a^2 - 25} \Rightarrow$

$$\frac{4}{9}a^2 = a^2 - 25 \Rightarrow \frac{5}{9}a^2 = 25 \Rightarrow a^2 = 45. \text{ An equation is } \frac{x^2}{25} + \frac{y^2}{45} = 1.$$

[28] $F(\pm 12, 0) \Rightarrow c = 12$. $e = \frac{c}{a} = \frac{12}{a} = \frac{3}{4} \Rightarrow a = 16$.

$$b^2 = a^2 - c^2 = 16^2 - 12^2 = 112. \text{ An equation is } \frac{x^2}{256} + \frac{y^2}{112} = 1.$$

[29] (a) Substituting $x = 2$ and $y = -3$ in $Ax^2 + 2y^2 = 4 \Rightarrow A = -\frac{7}{2}$.

(b) The equation is $-\frac{7}{2}x^2 + 2y^2 = 4$ or $\frac{y^2}{2} - \frac{7x^2}{8} = 1$, a hyperbola.

[30] The vertex of the square in the first quadrant has coordinates (x, x).

Since it is on the ellipse, $\frac{x^2}{a^2} + \frac{y^2}{b^2} = 1 \Rightarrow b^2x^2 + a^2x^2 = a^2b^2 \Rightarrow x^2 = \frac{a^2b^2}{a^2 + b^2}$.

$$x^2 \text{ is } \frac{1}{4} \text{ of the area of the square, hence } A = \frac{4a^2b^2}{a^2 + b^2}.$$

[31] The focus is a distance of $p = 1/(4a) = 1/(4 \cdot \frac{1}{8}) = 2$ units from the origin.

$$\text{The equation of the circle is } x^2 + (y - 2)^2 = 2^2 = 4.$$

[32] $y = \frac{1}{64}\omega^2 x^2 + k \Rightarrow x^2 = \frac{64}{\omega^2}(y - k) \Rightarrow 4p = \frac{64}{\omega^2} \Rightarrow p = \frac{16}{\omega^2} = 2 \Rightarrow$

$$\omega = 2\sqrt{2} \text{ rad/sec} \approx 0.45 \text{ rev/sec}.$$

$\boxed{33}$ $y = t - 1 \Rightarrow t = y + 1$. $x = 3 + 4t = 3 + 4(y + 1) = 4y + 7$.

As t varies from -2 to 2, (x, y) varies from $(-5, -3)$ to $(11, 1)$.

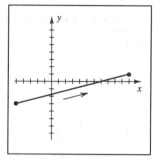

Figure 33

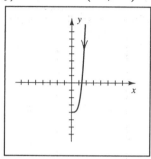

Figure 34

$\boxed{34}$ $x = \sqrt{-t} \Rightarrow t = -x^2$. $y = t^2 - 4 = x^4 - 4$. As t varies from $-\infty$ to 0,

x varies from ∞ to 0 and the graph is the right half of the quartic.

$\boxed{35}$ $x = \cos^2 t - 2 \Rightarrow x + 2 = \cos^2 t$; $y = \sin t + 1 \Rightarrow (y - 1)^2 = \sin^2 t$.

$\sin^2 t + \cos^2 t = 1 = x + 2 + (y - 1)^2 \Rightarrow (y - 1)^2 = -(x + 1)$. This is a parabola with

vertex at $(-1, 1)$ and opening to the left. $t = 0$ corresponds to the vertex and as t

varies from 0 to 2π, the point (x, y) moves to $(-2, 2)$ at $t = \frac{\pi}{2}$, back to the vertex at

$t = \pi$, down to $(-2, 0)$ at $t = \frac{3\pi}{2}$, and finishes at the vertex at $t = 2\pi$.

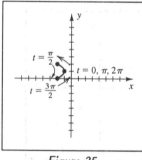

Figure 35

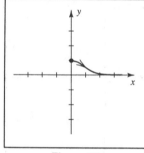

Figure 36

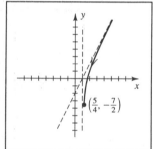

Figure 37

$\boxed{36}$ $x = \sqrt{t} \Rightarrow x^2 = t$ and $y = 2^{-x^2}$. The graph is a bell-shaped curve with a

maximum point at $t = 0$, or $(0, 1)$. As t increases, x increases, and y gets close to 0.

$\boxed{37}$ $x = \frac{1}{t} + 1 \Rightarrow t = \frac{1}{x - 1}$ and $y = 2(x - 1) - \left(\frac{1}{x - 1}\right) = \frac{2(x^2 - 2x + 1) - 1}{x - 1} =$

$\frac{2x^2 - 4x + 1}{x - 1}$; This is a rational function with a vertical asymptote at $x = 1$ and an

oblique asymptote of $y = 2x - 2$. The graph has a minimum point at $\left(\frac{5}{4}, -\frac{7}{2}\right)$ when

$t = 4$ and then approaches the oblique asymptote as t approaches 0. See *Figure 37*.

38 All of the curves are a portion of the circle $x^2 + y^2 = 16$.

C_1: $y = \sqrt{16 - t^2} = \sqrt{16 - x^2}$.

Since $y = \sqrt{16 - t^2}$, y must be nonnegative and we have the top half of the circle.

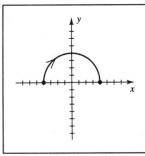

Figure 38 (C_1)

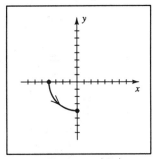

Figure 38 (C_2)

C_2: $x = -\sqrt{16 - t} = -\sqrt{16 - (-\sqrt{t})^2} = -\sqrt{16 - y^2}$.

This is the left half of the circle. Since $y = -\sqrt{t}$, y can only be nonpositive.

Hence we have only the third quadrant portion of the circle.

C_3: $x = 4\cos t$, $y = 4\sin t \Rightarrow \frac{x}{4} = \cos t$, $\frac{y}{4} = \sin t \Rightarrow \frac{x^2}{16} = \cos^2 t$, $\frac{y^2}{16} = \sin^2 t \Rightarrow$

$\frac{x^2}{16} + \frac{y^2}{16} = \cos^2 t + \sin^2 t = 1 \Rightarrow x^2 + y^2 = 16$. This is the entire circle.

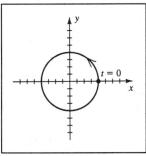

Figure 38 (C_3)

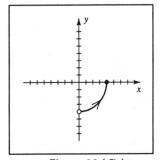

Figure 38 (C_4)

C_4: $y = -\sqrt{16 - e^{2t}} = -\sqrt{16 - (e^t)^2} = -\sqrt{16 - x^2}$.

This is the bottom half of the circle. Since e^t is positive, x takes on all positive real values. Note that $(0, -4)$ is <u>not</u> included on the graph since $x \neq 0$.

39 $x = r\cos\theta = 5\cos\frac{7\pi}{4} = 5\left(\frac{\sqrt{2}}{2}\right) = \frac{5}{2}\sqrt{2}$. $y = r\sin\theta = 5\sin\frac{7\pi}{4} = 5\left(-\frac{\sqrt{2}}{2}\right) = -\frac{5}{2}\sqrt{2}$.

40 $r^2 = x^2 + y^2 = (2\sqrt{3})^2 + (-2)^2 = 16 \Rightarrow r = 4$.

$\tan\theta = \frac{y}{x} = \frac{-2}{2\sqrt{3}} = -\frac{1}{\sqrt{3}} \Rightarrow \theta = \frac{11\pi}{6}$ {θ in QIV }.

$\boxed{41}$ $r = -4\sin\theta \Rightarrow r^2 = -4r\sin\theta \Rightarrow x^2 + y^2 = -4y \Rightarrow$

$$x^2 + y^2 + 4y + \underline{4} = \underline{4} \Rightarrow x^2 + (y+2)^2 = 4.$$

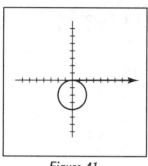

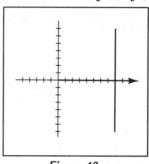

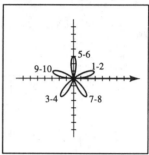

Figure 41   *Figure 42*   *Figure 43*

$\boxed{42}$ $r = 8\sec\theta \Rightarrow r\cos\theta = 8 \Rightarrow x = 8.$

$\boxed{43}$ $r = 3\sin 5\theta$ is a 5-leafed rose. $0 = 3\sin 5\theta \Rightarrow \sin 5\theta = 0 \Rightarrow 5\theta = \pi n \Rightarrow \theta = \frac{\pi}{5}n.$

The numbers 1–10 correspond to θ ranging from 0 to π in $\frac{\pi}{10}$ increments.

$\boxed{44}$ $r = 6 - 3\cos\theta$ •

$0 = 6 - 3\cos\theta \Rightarrow \cos\theta = 2 \Rightarrow$ no pole values.

Variation of θ			Variation of r		
1)	0	$\to$	$\frac{\pi}{2}$	3 $\to$	6
2)	$\frac{\pi}{2}$	$\to$	π	6 $\to$	9
3)	π	$\to$	$\frac{3\pi}{2}$	9 $\to$	6
4)	$\frac{3\pi}{2}$	$\to$	2π	6 $\to$	3

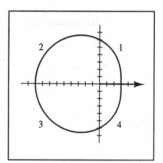

Figure 44

$\boxed{45}$ $r = 3 - 3\sin\theta$ is a cardioid since the coefficient of $\sin\theta$ has the same magnitude as the constant term.

$0 = 3 - 3\sin\theta \Rightarrow \sin\theta = 1 \Rightarrow \theta = \frac{\pi}{2} + 2\pi n.$

Variation of θ			Variation of r		
1)	0	$\to$	$\frac{\pi}{2}$	3 $\to$	0
2)	$\frac{\pi}{2}$	$\to$	π	0 $\to$	3
3)	π	$\to$	$\frac{3\pi}{2}$	3 $\to$	6
4)	$\frac{3\pi}{2}$	$\to$	2π	6 $\to$	3

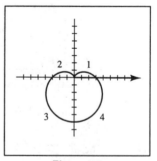

Figure 45

46 $r = 2 + 4\cos\theta$ is a limaçon with a loop.

$0 = 2 + 4\cos\theta \Rightarrow \cos\theta = -\frac{1}{2} \Rightarrow \theta = \frac{2\pi}{3} + 2\pi n, \frac{4\pi}{3} + 2\pi n.$

Variation of θ			Variation of r	
1)	0	$\rightarrow$ $\frac{\pi}{2}$	$6 \rightarrow$	2
2)	$\frac{\pi}{2}$	$\rightarrow$ $\frac{2\pi}{3}$	$2 \rightarrow$	0
3)	$\frac{2\pi}{3}$	$\rightarrow$ π	$0 \rightarrow$	-2
4)	π	$\rightarrow$ $\frac{4\pi}{3}$	$-2 \rightarrow$	0
5)	$\frac{4\pi}{3}$	$\rightarrow$ $\frac{3\pi}{2}$	$0 \rightarrow$	2
6)	$\frac{3\pi}{2}$	$\rightarrow$ 2π	$2 \rightarrow$	6

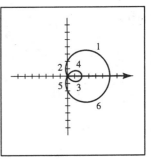

Figure 46

47 $r^2 = 9\sin 2\theta$ •

$0 = 9\sin 2\theta \Rightarrow \sin 2\theta = 0 \Rightarrow 2\theta = \pi n \Rightarrow \theta = \frac{\pi}{2}n.$

Variation of θ			Variation of r	
1)	0	$\rightarrow$ $\frac{\pi}{4}$	$0 \rightarrow$	± 3
2)	$\frac{\pi}{4}$	$\rightarrow$ $\frac{\pi}{2}$	$\pm 3 \rightarrow$	0
3)	$\frac{\pi}{2}$	$\rightarrow$ $\frac{3\pi}{4}$	undefined	
4)	$\frac{3\pi}{4}$	$\rightarrow$ π	undefined	

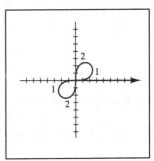

Figure 47

48 $2r = \theta \Rightarrow r = \frac{1}{2}\theta.$ Positive values of θ yield the "counterclockwise spiral" while the "clockwise spiral" is obtained from the negative values of θ.

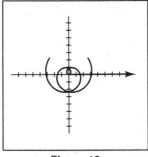

Figure 48

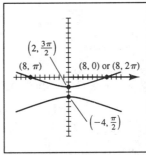

Figure 49

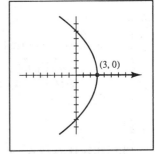

Figure 50

49 $r = \dfrac{8}{1 - 3\sin\theta} \Rightarrow e = 3 > 1$, hyperbola. See §10.6 for more details on this problem.

$$V(2, \tfrac{3\pi}{2}) \text{ and } V'(-4, \tfrac{\pi}{2}). \quad d(V, F) = 2 \Rightarrow F'(-6, \tfrac{\pi}{2}).$$

50 $r = 6 - r\cos\theta \Rightarrow r + r\cos\theta = 6 \Rightarrow r(1 + \cos\theta) = 6 \Rightarrow r = \dfrac{6}{1 + 1\cos\theta} \Rightarrow$

$e = 1$, parabola. The vertex is in the $\theta = 0$ direction, $V(3, 0)$.

$\boxed{51}$ $r = \dfrac{6}{3 + 2\cos\theta} = \dfrac{2}{1 + \frac{2}{3}\cos\theta} \Rightarrow e = \frac{2}{3} < 1$, ellipse.

$V(\frac{6}{5}, 0)$ and $V'(6, \pi)$. $d(V, F) = \frac{6}{5} \Rightarrow F' = (\frac{24}{5}, \pi)$.

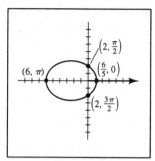

Figure 51

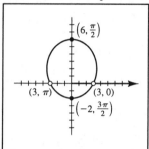

Figure 52

$\boxed{52}$ $r = \dfrac{-6\csc\theta}{1 - 2\csc\theta} \cdot \dfrac{-\sin\theta}{-\sin\theta} = \dfrac{6}{2 - \sin\theta} = \dfrac{3}{1 - \frac{1}{2}\sin\theta} \Rightarrow e = \frac{1}{2} < 1$, ellipse.

$V(2, \frac{3\pi}{2})$ and $V'(6, \frac{\pi}{2})$. $d(V, F) = 2 \Rightarrow F' = (4, \frac{\pi}{2})$.

Since the original equation is undefined when $\csc\theta$ is undefined,

the points $(3, 0)$ and $(3, \pi)$ are excluded from the graph.

$\boxed{53}$ $y^2 = 4x \Rightarrow r^2 \sin^2\theta = 4r\cos\theta \Rightarrow r = \dfrac{4r\cos\theta}{r\sin^2\theta} = 4 \cdot \dfrac{\cos\theta}{\sin\theta} \cdot \dfrac{1}{\sin\theta} \Rightarrow r = 4\cot\theta\,\csc\theta$.

$\boxed{54}$ $x^2 + y^2 - 3x + 4y = 0 \Rightarrow r^2 - 3r\cos\theta + 4r\sin\theta = 0 \Rightarrow$

$$r - 3\cos\theta + 4\sin\theta = 0 \Rightarrow r = 3\cos\theta - 4\sin\theta.$$

$\boxed{55}$ $2x - 3y = 8 \Rightarrow 2r\cos\theta - 3r\sin\theta = 8 \Rightarrow r(2\cos\theta - 3\sin\theta) = 8$.

$\boxed{56}$ $x^2 + y^2 = 2xy \Rightarrow r^2 = 2r^2\cos\theta\sin\theta \Rightarrow 1 = 2\sin\theta\cos\theta \Rightarrow \sin 2\theta = 1 \Rightarrow$

$$2\theta = \tfrac{\pi}{2} + 2\pi n \Rightarrow \theta = \tfrac{\pi}{4}, \tfrac{5\pi}{4} \text{ on } [0, 2\pi), \text{ which are the same lines.}$$

In rectangular coordinates: $x^2 + y^2 = 2xy \Rightarrow x^2 - 2xy + y^2 = 0 \Rightarrow$

$$(x - y)^2 = 0 \Rightarrow x - y = 0, \text{ or } y = x.$$

$\boxed{57}$ $r^2 = \tan\theta \Rightarrow x^2 + y^2 = \dfrac{y}{x} \Rightarrow x^3 + xy^2 = y$.

$\boxed{58}$ $r = 2\cos\theta + 3\sin\theta \Rightarrow r^2 = 2r\cos\theta + 3r\sin\theta \Rightarrow x^2 + y^2 = 2x + 3y$.

$\boxed{59}$ $r^2 = 4\sin 2\theta \Rightarrow r^2 = 4(2\sin\theta\cos\theta) \Rightarrow r^2 = 8\sin\theta\cos\theta \Rightarrow$

$$r^2 \cdot r^2 = 8(r\sin\theta)(r\cos\theta) \Rightarrow (x^2 + y^2)^2 = 8xy.$$

$\boxed{60}$ $\theta = \sqrt{3} \Rightarrow \tan^{-1}(\frac{y}{x}) = \sqrt{3} \Rightarrow \frac{y}{x} = \tan\sqrt{3} \Rightarrow y = (\tan\sqrt{3})x$.

Note that $\tan\sqrt{3} \approx -6.15$. This is a line through the origin making an angle of

approximately $99.24°$ with the positive x-axis. The line is <u>not</u> $y = \frac{\pi}{3}x$.

$\boxed{61}$ $r = 5\sec\theta + 3r\sec\theta \Rightarrow r\cos\theta = 5 + 3r \Rightarrow x - 5 = 3r \Rightarrow x^2 - 10x + 25 = 9r^2 \Rightarrow$

$$x^2 - 10x + 25 = 9x^2 + 9y^2 \Rightarrow 8x^2 + 9y^2 + 10x - 25 = 0$$

$\boxed{62}$ $r^2\sin\theta = 6\csc\theta + r\cot\theta \Rightarrow$

$$r^2\sin^2\theta = 6 + r\cos\theta \text{ \{multiply by } \sin\theta \text{ to get } r^2\sin^2\theta\} \Rightarrow y^2 = 6 + x$$

Chapter 10 Discussion Exercises

1. For $y = ax^2$, the horizontal line through the focus is $y = p$. Since $a = 1/(4p)$, we have $p = (1/(4p))x^2 \Rightarrow x^2 = 4p^2 \Rightarrow x = 2|p|$. Doubling this value for the width gives us $w = 4|p|$.

2. The circle goes through both foci and all four vertices of the auxiliary rectangle.

3. Refer to Figure 14 and the derivation on text page 693.

4. Refer to Figure 25 and the derivation on text page 706.

5. $P(x, y)$ is a distance of $(2 + d)$ from $(0, 0)$ and a distance of d from $(4, 0)$. The difference of these distances is $(2 + d) - d = 2$, a <u>positive constant</u>. By the definition of a hyperbola, $P(x, y)$ lies on the right branch of the hyperbola with foci $(0, 0)$ and $(4, 0)$. The center of the hyperbola is halfway between the foci, i.e., $(2, 0)$. The vertex is halfway from $(2, 0)$ to $(4, 0)$ since the distance from the circle to P equals the distance from P to $(4, 0)$.

Thus, the vertex is $(3, 0)$ and $a = 1$.

$b^2 = c^2 - a^2 = 2^2 - 1^2 = 3$ and

an equation of the right branch of the hyperbola is

$\dfrac{(x-2)^2}{1} - \dfrac{y^2}{3} = 1$, $x \geq 3$ or $x = 2 + \sqrt{1 + \dfrac{y^2}{3}}$.

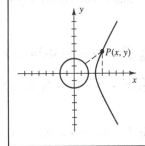

Figure 5

6. The graph of $r = f(\theta - \alpha)$ is the graph of $r = f(\theta)$ rotated counterclockwise through an angle α, whereas the graph $r = f(\theta + \alpha)$ is rotated clockwise.

7. **n even:** There are $2n$ leaves, each having a leaf angle of $(180/n)°$. There is no open space between the leaves.

n odd: There are n leaves, each having a leaf angle of $(180/n)°$. There is $180°$ of open space—each space is $(180/n)°$, equispaced between the leaves. If $n = 4k - 1$, where k is a natural number, there is a leaf centered on the $\theta = 3\pi/2$ axis; and if $n = 4k + 1$, there is a leaf centered on the $\theta = \pi/2$ axis.

For $r = \sin n\theta$, the pole values start at $0°$ and occur every $(180/n)°$. For $r = \cos n\theta$, the pole values start at $(90/n)°$ and occur every $(180/n)°$.